Teacher's
Edition

Heath

GENERAL
MATHEMATICS

David W. Lowry
Earl G. Ockenga
Walter E. Rucker

D.C. Heath and Company
Lexington, Massachusetts Toronto

CONTENTS

General Mathematics students are given an incentive to learn mathematics.

When students are interested in the material being presented, they are more actively involved and learn more.

HEATH GENERAL MATHEMATICS uses lesson settings and situations that are familiar and motivational to students. These settings help students see a connection between the mathematics taught in the classroom and the mathematics used in everyday life.

Computational skills are taught in the context of real situations.

When computational skills are taught in context, students see a need to learn the skill and are more willing to complete the practice required for mastery.

Skills taught in isolation seem irrelevant and uninteresting.

The lesson theme
- *provides a motivational setting that holds the students' attention.*
- *gets students involved with data taken from everyday experiences.*
- *includes such things as newspaper articles, charts, tables, advertisements, menus, price lists, and photographs.*

The first few questions help get students started.

The HERE'S HOW box provides
- *step-by-step examples worked out the same way teachers do on the chalkboard.*
- *an easy reference for students who need reteaching later in the year.*

The follow-up questions
- *extend the HERE'S HOW instruction.*
- *provide additional examples when appropriate.*

Subtracting fractions with common denominators

You won first prize at a sports-car rally.

BEFORE RALLY   AFTER RALLY

1. Fuel check! What fraction of a tank did you have before the rally?

2. Fuel check! What fraction of a tank did you have after the rally?

3. Would you add or subtract to compute what fraction of a tank you used?

Here's how *to subtract fractions with a common denominator.*

$$\frac{3}{4} - \frac{1}{4} = ?$$

Subtract the numerators and use the common denominator.

$$\frac{3}{4} - \frac{1}{4} = \frac{2}{4}$$
$$= \frac{1}{2}$$

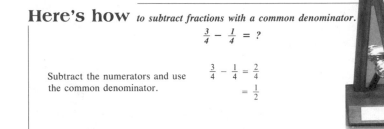

4. Look at the *Here's how.* What fraction of a tank did you use on the rally?

5. Check these examples. Give each difference in simplest form.

a. $\frac{7}{8} - \frac{3}{8} = \frac{4}{8}$ b. $\frac{5}{12} - \frac{1}{12} = \frac{4}{12}$ c. $\frac{5}{2} - \frac{2}{2} = \frac{3}{2}$

       $= ?$ $= ?$ $= ?$

164 *Chapter 7*

RAL MATHEMATICS

Problem-solving skills and strategies are developed through the use of realistic problems.

Every Problem Solving lesson focuses on real applications of mathematics. The lessons feature **computer applications, mathematics on the job, consumer mathematics,** *and other life skills. In addition to the Problem Solving lessons, every two-page lesson in the text has problem-solving exercises.*

The Teacher's Edition is a comprehensive resource that is easily accessible.

A wide variety of suggestions for each lesson are provided in the extended margins of the Teacher's Edition. Teaching suggestions include the use of Visual Aids and Worksheets.

EXERCISES

Subtract. Write the difference in simplest form.
Here are scrambled answers for the next row of exercises: $\frac{5}{6}$ $\frac{1}{4}$ $\frac{1}{6}$ $\frac{1}{2}$ 0 $\frac{2}{5}$

6. $\frac{3}{5} - \frac{1}{5}$ 7. $\frac{2}{4} - \frac{1}{4}$ 8. $\frac{6}{6} - \frac{1}{6}$ 9. $\frac{4}{6} - \frac{3}{6}$ 10. $\frac{5}{8} - \frac{1}{8}$ 11. $\frac{3}{8} - \frac{3}{8}$

12. $\frac{5}{8} - \frac{3}{8}$ 13. $\frac{5}{9} - \frac{0}{9}$ 14. $\frac{5}{4} - \frac{1}{4}$ 15. $\frac{7}{6} - \frac{3}{6}$ 16. $\frac{5}{6} - \frac{1}{6}$ 17. $\frac{6}{4} - \frac{2}{4}$

18. $\frac{3}{5} - \frac{0}{5}$ 19. $\frac{11}{8} - \frac{5}{8}$ 20. $\frac{5}{9} - \frac{2}{9}$ 21. $\frac{12}{8} - \frac{6}{8}$ 22. $\frac{11}{4} - \frac{3}{4}$ 23. $\frac{7}{4} - \frac{4}{4}$

24. $\frac{9}{4} - \frac{3}{4}$ 25. $\frac{5}{8} - \frac{4}{8}$ 26. $\frac{8}{6} - \frac{2}{6}$ 27. $\frac{5}{3} - \frac{2}{3}$ 28. $\frac{7}{6} - \frac{2}{6}$ 29. $\frac{10}{9} - \frac{4}{9}$

30. $\frac{12}{4} - \frac{3}{4}$ 31. $\frac{7}{8} - \frac{3}{8}$ 32. $\frac{13}{4} - \frac{3}{4}$ 33. $\frac{10}{8} - \frac{2}{8}$ 34. $\frac{9}{6} - \frac{6}{6}$ 35. $\frac{10}{4} - \frac{2}{4}$

36. $\frac{2}{3} - \frac{2}{3}$ 37. $\frac{7}{4} - \frac{3}{4}$ 38. $\frac{8}{9} - \frac{3}{9}$ 39. $\frac{4}{5} - \frac{2}{5}$ 40. $\frac{9}{8} - \frac{3}{8}$ 41. $\frac{13}{7} - \frac{8}{7}$

42. $\frac{12}{10} - \frac{7}{10}$ 43. $\frac{7}{8} - \frac{4}{8}$ 44. $\frac{6}{4} - \frac{2}{4}$ 45. $\frac{5}{6} - \frac{5}{6}$ 46. $\frac{6}{5} - \frac{3}{5}$ 47. $\frac{5}{6} - \frac{3}{6}$

Solve. Look at the top of page 164.

48. How many miles had your car been driven before the rally?

49. How many miles had your car been driven after the rally?

50. How many miles was the rally? *Hint: Use your answers to problems 48 and 49.*

51. If you used 7.8 gallons of gasoline on the rally, how many miles did you average per gallon? Round the answer to the nearest tenth.

Where are they? Making a sketch

52. Study the clues to find out how far Carol and Joe are from the checkpoint at Clara's Corner. *Hint: Make a sketch.*
Clues:
- They left Bruskville and drove 18.6 miles east to Clara's Corner.
- They turned right on Highway 26 and drove 13.9 miles to the second checkpoint at Harold's Hollow.
- They drove 6.4 miles beyond Harold's Hollow.
- They turned around and started back for Clara's Corner. They drove 10.4 miles toward Clara's Corner.

Adding and Subtracting Fractions and Mixed Numbers **165**

The EXERCISES include
- *scrambled answers that help students get started.*
- *sufficient practice for every ability level.*
- *problem-solving exercises that relate to the lesson setting.*

The lesson challenge
- *appears at the end of every lesson.*
- *provides practice of problem-solving skills learned earlier.*
- *includes many consumer mathematics problems.*

STUDENT-TEXT RESOURCES

SKILL MAINTENANCE—PROBLEM SOLVING

After three or four lessons, students have an opportunity to practice skills learned previously and learn new problem-solving skills.

The Problem Solving lessons feature realistic problems that emphasize everyday applications, mathematics on the job, consumer mathematics, and computer applications.

Cumulative Skill Practice

Give the product. *(page 68)*

1. 8.23 × 10
2. 8.23 × 100
3. 8.23 × 1000
4. 45 × 1000
5. 45 × 10
6. 45 × 100
7. 0.004 × 10
8. 0.004 × 100
9. 0.004 × 1000
10. 9.1 × 1000
11. 9.1 × 10
12. 9.1 × 100

Give the quotient. *(page 92)*

13. 789.5 ÷ 10
14. 789.5 ÷ 100
15. 789.5 ÷ 1000
16. 297 ÷ 100
17. 297 ÷ 10
18. 297 ÷ 1000
19. 7.1 ÷ 100
20. 7.1 ÷ 10
21. 7.1 ÷ 1000
22. 9 ÷ 10
23. 9 ÷ 100
24. 9 ÷ 1000

Change to a decimal rounded to the nearest hundredth. *(page 146)*

25. $\frac{1}{3}$ 26. $\frac{1}{6}$ 27. $\frac{1}{8}$ 28. $\frac{1}{12}$ 29. $\frac{5}{6}$ 30. $\frac{3}{8}$ 31. $\frac{7}{9}$

32. $\frac{5}{12}$ 33. $\frac{11}{12}$ 34. $\frac{2}{3}$ 35. $\frac{1}{16}$ 36. $\frac{7}{8}$ 37. $\frac{9}{16}$ 38. $\frac{1}{11}$

39. $\frac{5}{3}$ 40. $\frac{7}{6}$ 41. $\frac{5}{8}$ 42. $\frac{16}{9}$ 43. $\frac{4}{3}$ 44. $\frac{11}{8}$ 45. $\frac{13}{7}$

Give the sum in simplest form. *(page 160)*

46. $2\frac{1}{2}$ 47. 5   48. $1\frac{1}{4}$ 49. $2\frac{1}{3}$ 50. $3\frac{5}{8}$ 51. $4\frac{2}{3}$
    $+3$ $+2\frac{2}{3}$ $+2\frac{1}{4}$ $+1\frac{1}{3}$ $+\frac{1}{4}$ $+3\frac{1}{5}$

52. $5\frac{1}{2}$ 53. $6\frac{2}{3}$ 54. $5\frac{5}{8}$ 55. $7\frac{5}{6}$ 56. $9\frac{3}{4}$ 57. $6\frac{1}{4}$
    $+4\frac{1}{3}$ $+3\frac{1}{2}$ $+1\frac{1}{4}$ $+7\frac{2}{3}$ $+8\frac{2}{3}$ $+3\frac{1}{2}$

Give the product in simplest form. *(page 182)*

58. $3 \times 1\frac{1}{3}$
59. $2 \times 2\frac{1}{2}$
60. $1\frac{3}{4} \times 4$
61. $3\frac{1}{3} \times 3$
62. $1\frac{1}{3} \times 1\frac{1}{2}$
63. $2\frac{1}{2} \times 2\frac{1}{3}$
64. $3\frac{1}{2} \times 2\frac{1}{4}$
65. $3\frac{1}{3} \times 2\frac{1}{2}$
66. $1\frac{1}{6} \times 2\frac{3}{4}$
67. $3\frac{1}{2} \times 1\frac{1}{4}$
68. $1\frac{2}{3} \times 2\frac{1}{2}$
69. $4\frac{1}{2} \times 2\frac{1}{3}$

368 *Chapter 16*

Problem solving
YOU'RE THE PIZZA MAKER!

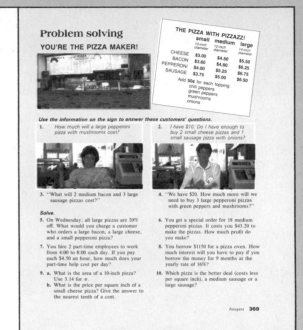

THE PIZZA WITH PIZZAZZ!			
	small 10-inch diameter	medium 12-inch diameter	large 14-inch diameter
CHEESE	$3.00	$4.50	$5.50
BACON	$3.60	$4.80	$6.25
PEPPERONI	$4.00	$5.25	$6.75
SAUSAGE	$3.75	$5.00	$6.50

Add 50¢ for each topping:
chili peppers
green peppers
mushrooms
onions

Use the information on the sign to answer these customers' questions.

1. How much will a large pepperoni pizza with mushrooms cost?

2. I have $10. Do I have enough to buy 2 small cheese pizzas and 1 small sausage pizza with onions?

3. "What will 2 medium bacon and 3 large sausage pizzas cost?"

4. "We have $20. How much more will we need to buy 3 large pepperoni pizzas with green peppers and mushrooms?"

Solve.

5. On Wednesday, all large pizzas are 20% off. What would you charge a customer who orders a large bacon, a large cheese, and a small pepperoni pizza?

6. You get a special order for 18 medium pepperoni pizzas. It costs you $43.20 to make the pizzas. How much profit do you make?

7. You hire 2 part-time employees to work from 4:00 to 8:00 each day. If you pay each $4.50 an hour, how much does your part-time help cost per day?

8. You borrow $1150 for a pizza oven. How much interest will you have to pay if you borrow the money for 9 months at the yearly rate of 16%?

9. a. What is the area of a 10-inch pizza? Use 3.14 for π.
   b. What is the price per square inch of a small cheese pizza? Give the answer to the nearest tenth of a cent.

10. Which pizza is the better deal (costs less per square inch), a medium sausage or a large sausage?

Integers **369**

CHAPTER WRAP-UP

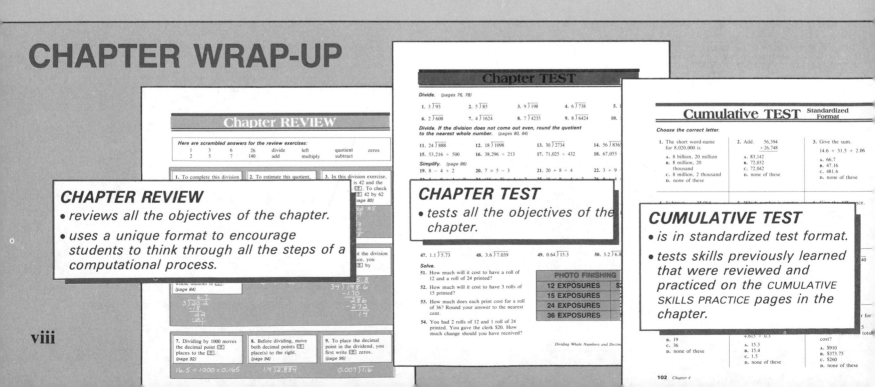

Chapter REVIEW

Here are scrambled answers for the review exercises:

| 1 | 3 | 6 | 26 | divide | left | quotient | zeros |
| 2 | 5 | 7 | 140 | add | multiply | subtract | |

1. To complete this division,
2. To estimate this quotient,
3. In this division exercise, ...is 42 and the ...☐. To check ...☐ 42 by 62 *(page 80)*

...R5

...t the division ...place, you ...☐ by

...5.8
34)198.6
−170
286
−272
14

3)...

7. Dividing by 1000 moves the decimal point ☐ places to the ☐. *(page 92)*
$16.5 \div 1000 = 0.0165$

8. Before dividing, move both decimal points ☐ place(s) to the right. *(page 94)*
1.4)2.884

9. To place the decimal point in the dividend, you first write ☐ zeros. *(page 96)*
0.007)1.6

CHAPTER REVIEW
- reviews all the objectives of the chapter.
- uses a unique format to encourage students to think through all the steps of a computational process.

Chapter TEST

Divide. *(pages 76, 78)*

1. 3)93
2. 5)85
3. 9)198
4. 6)714
5.
6. 2)608
7. 4)1624
8. 7)4235
9. 6)6424
10.

Divide. If the division does not come out even, round the quotient to the nearest whole number. *(pages 80, 84)*

11. 24)888
12. 18)1098
13. 30)2734
14. 56)8365
15. 53,216 ÷ 500
16. 38,296 ÷ 213
17. 71,025 ÷ 432
18. 67,055

Simplify. *(page 86)*

19. 8 − 4 ÷ 2
20. 7 × 5 − 3
21. 20 + 8 ÷ 4
22. 3 + 9

47. 1.1)5.73
48. 3.6)7.039
49. 0.64)15.3
50. 3.2)6.8

Solve.

51. How much will it cost to have a roll of 12 and a roll of 24 printed?
52. How much will it cost to have 3 rolls of 15 printed?
53. How much does each print cost for a roll of 36? Round your answer to the nearest cent.
54. You had 2 rolls of 12 and 1 roll of 24 printed. You gave the clerk $20. How much change should you have received?

PHOTO FINISHING	
12 EXPOSURES	
15 EXPOSURES	
24 EXPOSURES	
36 EXPOSURES	

Dividing Whole Numbers and Decimals

CHAPTER TEST
- tests all the objectives of the chapter.

Cumulative TEST — Standardized Format

Choose the correct letter.

1. The short word-name for 8,020,000 is
   A. 8 billion, 20 million
   B. 8 million, 20 thousand
   C. 8 million, 2 thousand
   D. none of these

2. Add.   56,394
        +26,748
   A. 83,142
   B. 72,032
   C. 72,042
   D. none of these

3. Give the sum.
   14.6 + 31.5 + 2.06
   A. 66.7
   B. 47.16
   C. 481.6
   D. none of these

...Subtract.   35,064
...Which number is greater...
...Give the difference...

B. 19
C. 36
D. none of these

A. 15.3
B. 15.4
C. 1.5
D. none of these

4.613 ÷ 0.3

...cost?
A. $910
B. $373.75
C. $260
D. none of these

102 *Chapter 4*

CUMULATIVE TEST
- is in standardized test format.
- tests skills previously learned that were reviewed and practiced on the CUMULATIVE SKILLS PRACTICE pages in the chapter.

There are many resources in the student text to help you meet the requirements of your school's curriculum.

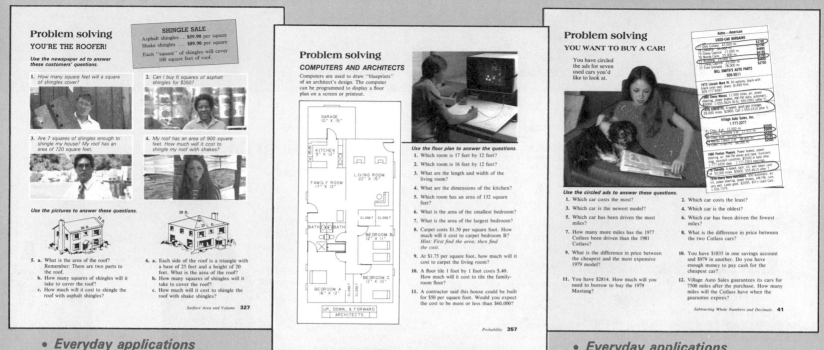

Problem solving
YOU'RE THE ROOFER!

SHINGLE SALE
Asphalt shingles ... $59.90 per square
Shake shingles ... $89.90 per square
Each "square" of shingles will cover 100 square feet of roof.

Use the newspaper ad to answer these customers' questions.

1. How many square feet will a square of shingles cover?
2. Can I buy 6 squares of asphalt shingles for $350?
3. Are 7 squares of shingles enough to shingle my house? My roof has an area of 720 square feet.
4. My roof has an area of 900 square feet. How much will it cost to shingle my roof with shakes?

Use the pictures to answer these questions.

5. a. What is the area of the roof? Remember: There are two parts to the roof.
   b. How many squares of shingles will it take to cover the roof?
   c. How much will it cost to shingle the roof with asphalt shingles?
6. a. Each side of the roof is a triangle with a base of 25 feet and a height of 20 feet. What is the area of the roof?
   b. How many squares of shingles will it take to cover the roof?
   c. How much will it cost to shingle the roof with shake shingles?

Surface Area and Volume **327**

Problem solving
COMPUTERS AND ARCHITECTS

Computers are used to draw "blueprints" of an architect's design. The computer can be programmed to display a floor plan on a screen or printout.

Use the floor plan to answer the questions.

1. Which room is 17 feet by 12 feet?
2. Which room is 16 feet by 12 feet?
3. What are the length and width of the living room?
4. What are the dimensions of the kitchen?
5. Which room has an area of 132 square feet?
6. What is the area of the smallest bedroom?
7. What is the area of the largest bedroom?
8. Carpet costs $1.50 per square foot. How much will it cost to carpet bedroom B? *Hint: First find the area; then find the cost.*
9. At $1.75 per square foot, how much will it cost to carpet the living room?
10. A floor tile 1 foot by 1 foot costs $.49. How much will it cost to tile the family-room floor?
11. A contractor said this house could be built for $50 per square foot. Would you expect the cost to be more or less than $60,000?

Probability **357**

Problem solving
YOU WANT TO BUY A CAR!

You have circled the ads for seven used cars you'd like to look at.

Use the circled ads to answer these questions.

1. Which car costs the most?
2. Which car costs the least?
3. Which car is the newest model?
4. Which car is the oldest?
5. Which car has been driven the most miles?
6. Which car has been driven the fewest miles?
7. How many more miles has the 1977 Cutlass been driven than the 1981 Cutlass?
8. What is the difference in price between the two Cutlass cars?
9. What is the difference in price between the cheapest and the most expensive 1979 model?
10. You have $1835 in one savings account and $979 in another. Do you have enough money to pay cash for the cheapest car?
11. You have $2814. How much will you need to borrow to buy the 1979 Mustang?
12. Village Auto Sales guarantees its cars for 7500 miles after the purchase. How many miles will the Cutlass have when the guarantee expires?

Subtracting Whole Numbers and Decimals **41**

- *Everyday applications*
- *Mathematics on the job*

- *Computer application*

- *Everyday applications*
- *Consumer mathematics*

END-OF-BOOK RESOURCES

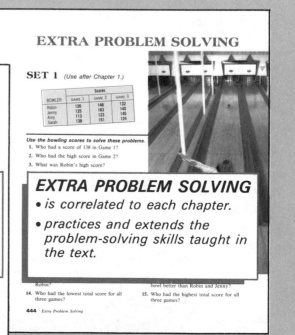

SKILL TEST

	SKILL	TEST ITEMS				EXTRA PRACTICE
1	Adding whole numbers *page 6*	78 +35	396 +672	56 37 +92	406 328 78 +281	*page 412*
2	Adding whole numbers *page 8*	7549 + 4261 496 + 3081 + 2566		80,665 + 24,364 26,245 + 6518 + 276		*page 412*
3	Rounding whole numbers	Round to the nearest ten. 63 125 682 598				*page 413*

page 24
8.04 + 7 + 9.6   0.483 + 1.56 + 4.4

| 7 | Comparing whole numbers *page 32* | < or >? 743 ⬚ 734 42,382 ⬚ 42,328 | | 3321 ⬚ 3400 599,999 ⬚ 600,000 | | *page 415* |
| 8 | Subtracting whole numbers *page 34* | 89 −37 | 90 −41 | 763 −280 | 846 −198 | *page 415* |

404 *Skill Test*

SKILL TEST
- tests the 64 major computational skills taught in the text.
- is referenced to EXTRA PRACTICE.

EXTRA PRACTICE
SKILL 1 *(Use after page 6.)*
Add.

Here's how
Add ones and regroup.
96
284
+163
3

Add tens and regroup.
1
96
284
+163

1. 84 +15	2. 50 +38	3. 63 +28	4. 65 +27
5. 29 +48	6. 47 +27	7. 68 +68	8. 93 +49
9. 356 + 82	10. 483 + 56	11. 297 +240	12. 839 +374

...are in the same place.

245
92
+3916

Add.
245
92
+3916

5. 34,006 + 8825
6. 4721 + 76,082
7. 12,500 + 38,926
8. 38,842 + 27,111
9. 493 + 3493 + 977
10. 8218 + 739 + 1005
11. 182 + 4200 + 3628
12. 7467 + 941 + 604
13. 593 + 444 + 1660
14. 2741 + 8009 + 476
15. 4850 + 1188 + 2055
16. 1748 + 2966 + 1826
17. 54,388 + 2112 + 599
18. 4368 + 829 + 12,477
19. 20,006 + 2704 + 1822
20. 2864 + 31,000 + 8002

EXTRA PRACTICE
- includes 64 practice sets correlated to the SKILL TEST.
- provides HERE'S HOW examples to reteach and/or review the skill.

EXTRA PROBLEM SOLVING

SET 1 *(Use after Chapter 1.)*

BOWLER	GAME 1	GAME 2	GAME 3
Robin	126	146	132
Jenny	125	163	140
Amy	113	123	145
Sarah	138	151	124

Use the bowling scores to solve these problems.
1. Who had a score of 138 in Game 1?
2. Who had the high score in Game 2?
3. What was Robin's high score?

...Robin?
...bowl better than Robin and Jenny?
14. Who had the lowest total score for all three games?
15. Who had the highest total score for all three games?

444 *Extra Problem Solving*

EXTRA PROBLEM SOLVING
- is correlated to each chapter.
- practices and extends the problem-solving skills taught in the text.

TEACHING SUPPORT

CHALKBOARD QUIZ
on previous lesson
Subtract.
1. 0.64 − 0.38   0.26
2. 15.85 − 3.41   12.44
3. 83.61 − 7.31   76.3
4. 6.1 − 3.7   2.4
5. 60.02 − 4.16   55.86

LESSON OBJECTIVES
To subtract decimals (with a different number of decimal places)
To estimate differences when subtracting decimals

PROBLEM-SOLVING SKILLS
Finding information in a display
Using a guess-and-check strategy

STARTING THE LESSON
If a digital watch that shows tenths or hundredths of seconds is available, have volunteers follow the contest rules and estimate 30 seconds. Record their times on the chalkboard to determine who came closest to guessing how long 30 seconds is.

HERE'S HOW NOTE
Use **Visual Aid 3** (lined notebook paper) to assist the students in aligning the digits.

30 − 24.29 = ?

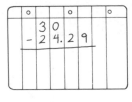

More on subtracting decimals

HOW LONG IS 30 SECONDS?

Cal and Barb had a contest to see who could come closer to guessing how long 30 seconds is. Their stopwatches show the results.

CONTEST RULES
- Use a stopwatch.
- Push the Start button.
- Don't look at the display.
- When you think 30 seconds have passed, push the Stop button.
- The person whose guess is closer to 30 seconds wins.

1. Read the stopwatches. Whose guess was off by 5.67 seconds?
2. What time is shown on Barb's stopwatch? 24.29 sec
3. Which two numbers would you use to compute how far off Barb's guess was? 30 and 24.29

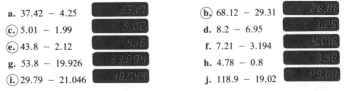

Cal's guess

Barb's guess

Here's how *to subtract decimals.*   30 − 24.29 = ?

Line up the decimal points. Write in the 0's.	Regroup.	Subtract.
30.00 −24.29	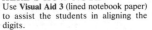 −24.29	 −24.29 ——— 5.71

To estimate the difference, first round to the nearest second and then subtract:

30 − 24 = 6

4. Look at the *Here's how*. Whose guess was off by 5.71 seconds? Who won the contest, Cal or Barb?   Barb's, Cal

EXERCISES

5. Four of the calculator answers are wrong. Find them by estimating.

a. 37.42 − 4.25   33.17
b. 68.12 − 29.31   28.81
c. 5.01 − 1.99   9.02
d. 8.2 − 6.95   1.25
e. 43.8 − 2.12   4.16
f. 7.21 − 3.194   4.016
g. 53.8 − 19.926   33.874
h. 4.78 − 0.8   3.98
i. 29.79 − 21.046   18.744
j. 118.9 − 19.02   99.88

46

The TEACHER'S EDITION *includes annotated student pages and comprehensive teaching suggestions.*

Here is a typical lesson from the TEACHER'S EDITION.

Subtract. *Here are scrambled answers for the next row of exercises:* 1.055 9.42 5.21 3.84 0.69 13.02

| 6. | 8.63
−3.42
5.21 | 7. | 9.76
−0.34
9.42 | 8. | 24.1
−11.08
13.02 | 9. | 6.3
−5.245
1.055 | 10. | 3.29
−2.6
0.69 | 11. | 6.14
−2.3
3.84 |

| 12. | 3.74
−2.5
1.24 | 13. | 7.3
−0.74
6.56 | 14. | 7.86
−1.59
6.27 | 15. | 6.83
−2.7
4.13 | 16. | 8.7
−6.25
2.45 | 17. | 9.61
−2.9
6.71 |

| 18. | 9.6
−2.64
6.96 | 19. | 28.31
−24.7
3.61 | 20. | 17.0
− 8.95
8.05 | 21. | 3.781
−0.97
2.811 | 22. | 7.52
−4.083
3.437 | 23. | 8.312
−2.77
5.542 |

| 24. | $4
−2.98
$1.02 | 25. | $5
−1.47
$3.53 | 26. | $10
− 5.78
$4.22 | 27. | $24
−16.43
$7.57 | 28. | $16
−11.29
$4.71 | 29. | $6
−3.11
$2.89 |

30. 6 − 2.7   6.0 / −2.7 / 3.3   31. 8 − 4.2 3.8   32. 12.94 − 8.53 4.41

33. 16.4 − 5 11.4   34. 15.1 − 12.8 2.3   35. 23.4 − 2.89 20.51

36. 9.5 − 6 3.5   37. 14.5 − 12.8 1.7   38. 7 − 6.52 0.48

39. 9.72 − 0.865 8.855   40. 7.4 − 5.125 2.275   41. 123.7 − 101.4 22.3

42. 12.935 − 4.6 8.335   43. 9.323 − 1.747 7.576   44. 5.2 − 2.456 2.744

45. 25 − 8.2 16.8   46. 100 − 44.75 55.25   47. 75.25 − 16 59.25

Solve.

48. What is the difference in price between a $37 digital watch and a $29.85 alarm watch? $7.15

49. You have $17.50. How much more money do you need in order to buy a $29.95 video-game watch? $12.45

50. A customer paid for a $32.99 calculator watch with a $50 bill. How much change should she get? $17.01

51. You are the clerk. How much change should you give a customer who paid for a $27.97 stopwatch and a $24.95 alarm watch with a $100 bill? $47.08

Key it in!
Find a way to push each marked key once to get the answer.

52. 5 − 3.8 =

53. 3.5 − 2 =

54. 9 − 6.7 =

Subtracting Whole Numbers and Decimals **47**

EXTRA PRACTICE
Page 418   Skill 13

PRACTICE WORKSHEET
Copymaster S173 or Duplicating Master S173

WORKSHEET 21
(Use after page 47.)

RIDDLE TIME
What did one green tomato say to the other green tomato?

To find the answer:
1. Subtract.
2. Write the letter over its matching number in the DECODER.

1. 8 − 3.4 4.6 E	2. 13.84 − 8.5 5.34 C	3. 17.3 − 6 11.3 E
4. 33.6 − 3.89 29.71 H	5. 8 − 7.52 0.48 I	6. 8.65 − 0.676 7.974 K
7. 8.3 − 6.236 2.064 L	8. 132.7 − 102.8 29.9 L	9. 13.946 − 5.8 8.146 P
10. 5.2 − 3.679 1.521 R	11. 31 − 9.6 21.4 T	12. 100 − 56.83 43.17 U
13. 91.26 − 19 62.26 V	14. 3.781 − 0.97 2.811 W	15. 8.7 − 6.25 2.45 E

DECODER
W I L L   W E   E V E R
2.811 0.48 2.064 29.9   2.811 11.3   4.6 62.26 11.3 1.521
K E T C H U P ?
7.974 2.45 21.4 5.34 29.71 43.17 8.146

S173   *Subtracting decimals*

CHALKBOARD CHALLENGE
Find the largest number on page 47.
Find the smallest number.
Subtract your two numbers.
Did you get a difference of 123.36?

123.7, 0.34, Yes

47

This practice is in the student's text.

The reduced facsimile of the WORKSHEET *designed for use with this lesson helps you decide whether to assign it to any of your students. Answers are overprinted for your convenience.*

(This WORKSHEET *uses a Decoder format with a riddle. See page xii for examples of other formats.)*

Use this CHALKBOARD CHALLENGE *to extend the lesson for your more able students.*

Sometimes a LIFE SKILL PROJECT *appears in this space.*

SUPPLEMENTARY RESOURCES

TESTS

- **Chapter Tests**

  Forms A and B for each chapter.

  Each test is two pages.

- **Four quarterly tests and a Final Test**

Available as copymasters and duplicating masters

WORKSHEETS

Worksheets are available for every lesson in the student text.

Available as copymasters, duplicating masters, and workbooks

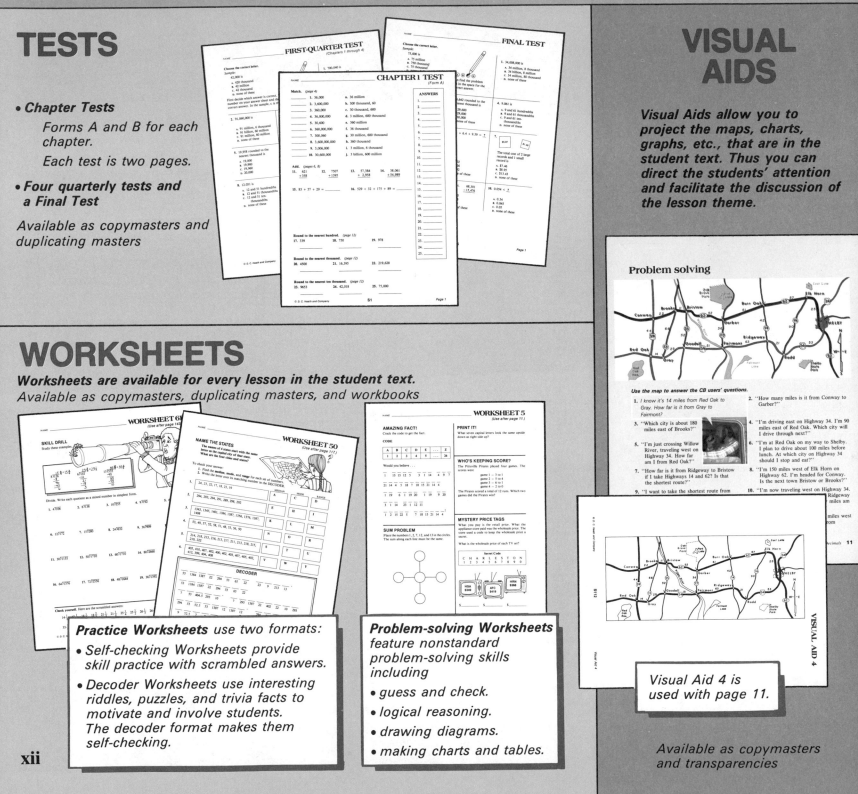

Practice Worksheets use two formats:
- **Self-checking Worksheets** provide skill practice with scrambled answers.
- **Decoder Worksheets** use interesting riddles, puzzles, and trivia facts to motivate and involve students. The decoder format makes them self-checking.

Problem-solving Worksheets feature nonstandard problem-solving skills including
- guess and check.
- logical reasoning.
- drawing diagrams.
- making charts and tables.

VISUAL AIDS

Visual Aids allow you to project the maps, charts, graphs, etc., that are in the student text. Thus you can direct the students' attention and facilitate the discussion of the lesson theme.

Visual Aid 4 is used with page 11.

Available as copymasters and transparencies

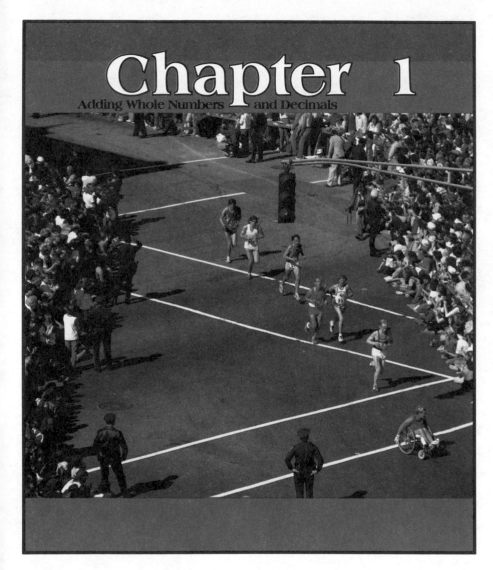

Chapter 1
Adding Whole Numbers and Decimals

CHAPTER 1
Adding Whole Numbers and Decimals

LESSON OBJECTIVES
To read standard numerals less than 1 billion (*pages 2–3*)
To write standard numerals (through the billions) in words
  (*pages 4–5*)
To add whole numbers (addends less than 1000) (*pages 6–7*)
To add whole numbers (addends up to 5 digits) (*pages 8–9*)
To round whole numbers (*pages 12–13*)
To estimate sums (*pages 14–15*)
To read decimals (*pages 16–17*)
To round decimals (*pages 20–21*)
To add decimals (addends having the same number of decimal
  places) (*pages 22–23*)
To add decimals (addends not having the same number of decimal
  places) (*pages 24–25*)

PROBLEM-SOLVING SKILLS
Reading a chart (*pages 2, 4, 6, 8, 21–22, 25*)
Using logical reasoning (*pages 3, 9*)
Using road-mileage signs (*page 7*)
Reading a map (*page 11*)
Following instructions (*page 13*)
Finding information in an ad (*pages 14–15*)
Using a guess-and-check strategy (*pages 14–15, 23*)
Interpreting information (*page 17*)
Reading a sign (*page 19*)
Solving problems involving more than one step (*page 19*)
Selecting information from a newspaper article (*page 24*)
Using computer-displayed information (*page 27*)

RESOURCES
- **VISUAL AIDS**
  Movie chart from page 2 (*Visual Aid 1, Copymaster S109*)
  Chart from page 4; blank place-value chart (*Visual Aid 2,
    Copymaster S110*)
  Notebook paper (*Visual Aid 3, Copymaster S111*)
  Map from page 11 (*Visual Aid 4, Copymaster S112*)
  Car from page 12; list of car's special features (*Visual Aid 5,
    Copymaster S113*)
  Place-value chart for decimals (*Visual Aid 6, Copymaster S114*)
- **WORKSHEETS 1–13** (*Copymasters S153–S165 or Duplicating
    Masters S153–S165*)

LESSON OBJECTIVE
To read standard numerals less than 1 billion

PROBLEM-SOLVING SKILLS
Reading a chart
Using logical reasoning

STARTING THE LESSON
Write these movie titles on the chalkboard:

    E.T.
    Star Wars
    Star Trek

Before the students open their books, take a survey. Ask them to guess which of these movies cost the most to produce. (*Star Trek*) Record the guesses on the chalkboard. Then say: "Open your book to page 2. Use the chart at the top of the page to check your guess."

Go over the *Here's how*. The chart on page 2 is also on **Visual Aid 1**. Use the chart to discuss questions 1–7.

EXERCISE NOTE
Exercises 8–15 require logical reasoning. Some students may benefit from the following: "Look at exercise 8. List all the movies that fit the first clue. (*Star Wars, Close Encounters*) Cross out the movie that does not fit the second clue." (*Star Wars, ~~Close Encounters~~*)

Reading standard numerals

BOX OFFICE CHAMPS	COST OF PRODUCTION *	EARNINGS FROM RENTALS *
E.T., 1982	$10,001,096	$195,063,412
Star Wars, 1977	13,100,056	193,138,000
The Empire Strikes Back, 1980	21,002,500	134,209,000
Superman, 1978	35,001,098	82,500,000
Close Encounters of the Third Kind, 1977	21,040,600	77,000,000
Star Trek, 1979	42,998,700	56,000,000
2001: A Space Odyssey, 1968	10,499,056	24,100,000
Planet of the Apes, 1968	5,800,021	15,000,000
Journey to the Center of the Earth, 1959	3,400,144	4,777,000

Figures are approximate and are for exercise use only. Actual figures may differ.

Here's how *to read large numbers.*

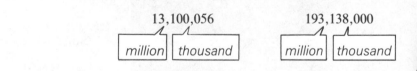

13,100,056   193,138,000

million | thousand   million | thousand

Star Wars cost 13 million, 100 thousand, 56 dollars to produce. The film earned 193 million, 138 thousand dollars.

1. Which film cost 10 million, 1 thousand, 96 dollars to produce?
    E.T.

2. Which film earned 24 million, 100 thousand dollars?
    2001: A Space Odyssey

3. *Star Wars* was released in 1977. Which film was released in 1978?
    Superman

4. Which films earned more than 100 million dollars?
    The Empire Strikes Back, Star Wars, E.T.

5. Which films cost less than 10 million dollars to produce?
    Planet of the Apes, Journey to the Center of the Earth

6. Which film earned about 134 million dollars?
    The Empire Strikes Back

7. Which film earned about 110 million dollars more than it cost?
    The Empire Strikes Back

EXERCISES

Study the clues. Use the chart on page 2 to name the movie.

8. Clues:
- This movie was released in 1977.
- It earned more than 100 million dollars.

Star Wars

9. Clues:
- This movie earned less than 90 million dollars.
- It was released in 1977.

Close Encounters of the Third Kind

10. Clues:
- This movie cost less than 10 million dollars to produce.
- It earned more than 10 million dollars.

Planet of the Apes

11. Clues:
- This movie earned more than 100 million dollars.
- It cost more than 20 million dollars to produce.

The Empire Strikes Back

12. Clues:
- This movie earned less than 70 million dollars.
- It was released before 1979.
- It cost more than 10 million dollars to produce.

2001: A Space Odyssey

13. Clues:
- This movie was released after 1977.
- It cost more than 30 million dollars to produce.
- It earned less than 60 million dollars.

Star Trek

14. Clues:
- This movie cost less than 15 million dollars to produce.
- It was released in 1968.
- It earned less than 20 million dollars.

Planet of the Apes

15. Clues:
- This movie earned less than 80 million dollars.
- It cost more than 20 million dollars to produce.
- It was released after 1978.

Star Trek

Show time **Reading an ad**

Use the ad to answer the questions.

16. What movie is showing at Cinema 2?
Superman

17. What time is the first showing of *E.T.*?
2:15

18. Sonya went to see *E.T.* She arrived at the theater at 3:10. How long did she wait for the next movie to begin?
1 hour 20 minutes

19. You live 15 minutes from Cinema 2. What time should you leave home to get to the theater 5 minutes before the start of the last showing? 9:10

LITTLETOWN CINEMA

E.T. THE EXTRA-TERRESTRIAL [PG]
2:15, 4:30 7:15, 9:30
CINEMA 1

SUPERMAN THE MOVIE [PG]
1:45, 4:15 7:00, 9:30
CINEMA 2

LIFE-SKILL PROJECT
Reading a newspaper ad
Have the students use newspaper movie-ads to make up problems similar to exercises 16–19.

* *Worksheets are also available as workbooks.*

LESSON OBJECTIVE
To write standard numerals (through
the billions) in words

PROBLEM-SOLVING SKILL
Reading a chart

STARTING THE LESSON
Before the students open their books,
have them guess how long it would take
to slice 2,400,000,000 slices of cheese,
slicing one slice per second, 24 hours
per day. Have the students write their
guesses. Record the high and low
guesses. Then say: "Open your book
to page 4. Read the first paragraph. What
answer does the book give?" (More
than 75 years)

The chart on page 4 is also on **Visual
Aid 2**. Use the chart to discuss exercises
1–8 and the *Here's how*.

Visual Aid 2 also provides you with
a blank place-value chart. Use this chart
to show more examples of writing standard numerals.

EXERCISE NOTE
Exercises 30 and 34 require the students
to write 4-digit numbers. Remind the
students that it is not necessary to use
a comma when writing a 4-digit number.

Answers for page 5.
9. 47 thousand, 258
10. 16 thousand, 234
11. 776 thousand, 39
12. 14 thousand, 732
13. 520 thousand, 66
14. 177 thousand, 406
15. 6 million, 835 thousand, 270
16. 93 million, 427 thousand, 600
17. 74 million, 50
18. 75 million
19. 60 million, 600 thousand, 600
20. 275 million, 675 thousand, 834
21. 14 billion, 360 million, 220 thousand
22. 842 billion
23. 5 billion, 600 thousand

4

Writing standard numerals in words

A famous fast-food chain served
2,400,000,000 slices of cheese
last year. If you sliced one
piece of cheese per second,
24 hours per day, it would
take you more than
75 years to slice
this much cheese.

Jack's fast food FACTS

FOOD SERVED LAST YEAR

	BILLIONS	MILLIONS	THOUSANDS	
Slices of cheese	2	400	000	000
Pounds of fish		46	205	500
Pounds of potatoes		542	840	000
Eggs		378	210	400

1. How many pounds of potatoes did the fast-food chain serve last year? 542,840,000

2. How many pounds of fish were served? 46,205,500

3. How many eggs were served? 378,210,400

Here's how *to write the standard numeral 46,205,500 in words.*

Short word-name: 46 million, 205 thousand, 500
Long word-name: forty-six million, two hundred five thousand, five hundred

4. Write the short word-name for the number of eggs the fast-food chain served.
378 million, 210 thousand, 400
5. Write the long word-name for the number of eggs served.
three hundred seventy-eight million, two hundred ten thousand, four hundred
6. Write the short word-name for the number of slices of cheese served.
2 billion, 400 million
7. Write the long word-name for the number of slices of cheese served.
two billion, four hundred million
8. Write the long word-name for the number of pounds of potatoes served.
five hundred forty-two million, eight hundred forty thousand

EXERCISES

Write the short word-name. *Hint: Study the* Here's how.

9. 47,258

10. 16,234

11. 776,039

12. 14,732

13. 520,066

14. 177,406

15. 6,835,270

16. 93,427,600

17. 74,000,050

18. 75,000,000

19. 60,600,600

20. 275,675,834

21. 14,360,220,000

22. 842,000,000,000

23. 5,000,600,000

Write the standard numeral.

24. 225 thousand, 16   225,016

25. 14 million   14,000,000

26. 14 thousand, 616
14,616

27. 543 billion   543,000,000,000

28. 8 million, 800 thousand   8,800,000

29. 999 thousand, 50
999,050

30. six thousand two hundred four   6204

31. fifty-nine thousand, eight hundred
59,800

32. four million, three hundred eleven thousand, one hundred thirty-seven
4,311,137

33. twenty-one million, sixty-three thousand, three hundred
21,063,300

Write each short word-name as a standard numeral.

34. A fast-food chain serves **860 million** ounces of orange juice yearly. This is enough juice to fill **1 thousand 200** home-size swimming pools.
860,000,000; 1200

35. The same fast-food chain has served a total of **40 billion** hamburgers. This is enough hamburgers to make a stack **473 thousand, 500** miles high.
40,000,000,000; 473,500

The check is in the mail!   Writing checks

This check was mailed to the winner of Jack's Pot-of-Gold Sweepstakes. The amount of the check is written as a standard numeral and in words.

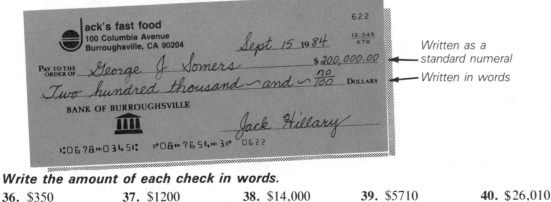

Written as a standard numeral

Written in words

Write the amount of each check in words.

36. $350

37. $1200

38. $14,000

39. $5710

40. $26,010

41. $12,900

42. $9999

43. $48,600

44. $125,800

45. $132,002

LIFE-SKILL PROJECT

Using library resources
Have the students use a book of world records to find the amount of the largest check ever written. Challenge the students to write the amount of the check in words. (This information can be found in the *Guinness Book of World Records*.)

Two billion, forty-six million, seven hundred thousand dollars

More answers for page 5.
36. three hundred fifty
37. one thousand two hundred
38. fourteen thousand
39. five thousand seven hundred ten
40. twenty-six thousand, ten
41. twelve thousand, nine hundred
42. nine thousand nine hundred ninety-nine
43. forty-eight thousand, six hundred
44. one hundred twenty-five thousand, eight hundred
45. one hundred thirty-two thousand, two

LESSON OBJECTIVE
To add whole numbers (addends less than 1000)

PROBLEM-SOLVING SKILLS
Reading a chart
Using road-mileage signs

STARTING THE LESSON
Sketch these shapes on the chalkboard:

Ask the students to identify the road sign suggested by each shape. Find out how many students correctly identified each sign.

EXERCISE NOTES
Scrambled answers for exercises 5–10 are given. Have the students use them to check their work.

Some students may benefit from using a drawing to solve problems 59–62.

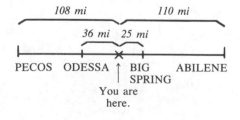

108 mi   110 mi

36 mi 25 mi

PECOS   ODESSA ↑ BIG   ABILENE
                 SPRING
              You are
              here.

Adding whole numbers

Do you know these road signs? Two hundred people in each of three age groups were surveyed. This chart shows the number of people who identified each sign.

Age	Sign A	Sign B	Sign C
Under 10	93	16	65
10 to 15	172	73	115
16 and over	197	157	183

1. How many of the people 10 to 15 years old knew that Sign B was a yield sign? 73

2. How many of the people 16 and over knew that Sign C was a railroad-crossing sign? 183

3. Which three numbers would you add to find out how many of the people surveyed knew that Sign A was a stop sign? 93, 172, and 197

SIGNS OF THE TIMES

Here's how *to add whole numbers.* $93 + 172 + 197 = ?$

Line up the digits vertically.	Add ones. Regroup.	Add tens. Regroup.	Add hundreds.
93 172 +197	93 172 +197 ‾‾2 *Look for the sums of 10.*	$\overset{2}{9}3$ 172 +197 ‾‾62	$\overset{1}{9}3$ $\overset{1}{1}72$ +197 ‾‾462

The answer is called the **sum.**

4. Look at the *Here's how.* How many of the people could identify a stop sign? 462

EXERCISES

Add. Here are scrambled answers for the next row of exercises: 94   131   101   71   87   77

5.	6.	7.	8.	9.	10.
72 +15 ‾‾87	54 +23 ‾‾77	69 +25 ‾‾94	94 + 7 ‾‾101	55 +76 ‾‾131	62 + 9 ‾‾71

11. 247 +462 709	**12.** 156 +348 504	**13.** 436 + 86 522	**14.** 593 + 28 621	**15.** 297 +886 1183	**16.** 623 +152 775
17. 57 38 + 13 108	**18.** 68 83 + 3 154	**19.** 883 96 +741 1720	**20.** 382 759 + 58 1199	**21.** 426 18 + 4 448	**22.** 215 24 + 9 248
23. 526 28 104 + 71 729	**24.** 79 41 9 + 17 146	**25.** 142 85 98 +444 769	**26.** 59 7 123 + 83 272	**27.** 164 646 88 + 3 901	**28.** 24 117 15 + 4 160
29. 68 13 428 + 7 516	**30.** 304 45 221 + 38 608	**31.** 723 372 86 +197 1378	**32.** 65 267 5 + 43 380	**33.** 597 64 563 +314 1538	**34.** 615 71 386 +714 1786

35. 231 + 316 547 **36.** 623 + 192 815 **37.** 154 + 480 634 **38.** 263 + 259 522

39. 176 + 87 263 **40.** 81 + 253 334 **41.** 253 + 57 310 **42.** 945 + 46 991

43. 236 + 61 + 9 306 **44.** 81 + 914 + 39 1034 **45.** 7 + 38 + 214 259 **46.** 876 + 28 + 4 908

47. 47 + 567 + 8 622 **48.** 104 + 54 + 86 244 **49.** 92 + 7 + 163 262 **50.** 721 + 86 + 2 809

51. 68 + 219 + 6 293 **52.** 301 + 98 + 24 423 **53.** 68 + 9 + 252 329 **54.** 321 + 96 + 9 426

Solve. Use the survey information on page 6.

55. How many of the people surveyed identified the railroad-crossing sign? 363

56. How many people identified the yield sign? 246

57. How many people 10 or over identified the stop sign? 369

58. How many people under 16 identified the railroad-crossing sign? 180

On the road again   Reading road signs

59. How many miles is it from Abilene to Odessa? 146

60. How far is it from Big Spring to Pecos? 133 miles

61. When you are at Big Spring, how far are you from Odessa? 61 miles

62. Which city is 218 miles from Pecos? Abilene

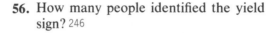

PRACTICE WORKSHEET
Copymaster S155 or Duplicating Master S155

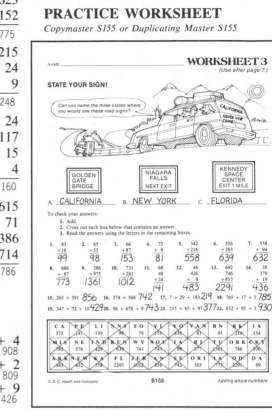

LIFE-SKILL PROJECT
Researching information

Have the students make a color sketch of each of these road signs: No Passing Zone, Do Not Enter, Hospital, and No U Turn. (This information may be found through observation, in driver's education texts, or in publications obtained from the Department of Motor Vehicles or local automobile travel clubs.)

LESSON OBJECTIVE

To add whole numbers (addends up to 5 digits)

PROBLEM-SOLVING SKILLS

Reading a chart

Using logical reasoning

STARTING THE LESSON

Before the students open their books, ask them what sport each of these Hall of Fame players played.

    Hank Aaron (Baseball)
    Jim Brown (Football)
    Bill Russell (Basketball)
    Frank Gifford (Football)

Then say: "Look at the chart on page 8. Which Hall of Fame football player gained more yards rushing, Jim Brown or Frank Gifford?" (Jim Brown)

HERE'S HOW NOTE

Use lined notebook paper to assist the students in aligning the digits. You may wish to use **Visual Aid 3** to demonstrate this.

$$27{,}345 + 802 + 6718 = ?$$

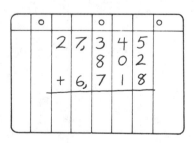

Adding larger numbers

TOTAL YARDS GAINED		
NFL HALL OF FAME PLAYER	YARDS RUSHING	YARDS PASS-RECEIVING
Jim Brown	12,312	2,499
Frank Gifford	3,069	5,434
Lenny Moore	5,174	6,039
Gale Sayers	4,957	1,309
Jim Taylor	8,597	225

1. Which Hall of Fame player gained the most yards rushing? Jim Brown

2. Who had the most pass-receiving yards? Lenny Moore

3. What two numbers would you add to compute Jim Brown's total rushing and pass-receiving yardage? 12,312 and 2,499

Here's how *to add large numbers.*

$$12{,}312 + 2499 = ?$$

Line up the digits that are in the same place and add.

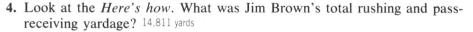

4. Look at the *Here's how*. What was Jim Brown's total rushing and pass-receiving yardage? 14,811 yards

5. Did Lenny Moore gain as many total yards as Jim Brown? No

EXERCISES

Add. *Here are scrambled answers for the next row of exercises:*
12,316 8054 12,824 6673 5152

6. 6375 + 298 = 6673	**7.** 4378 + 774 = 5152	**8.** 9856 + 2968 = 12,824	**9.** 7409 + 4907 = 12,316	**10.** 6395 + 1659 = 8054
11. 46,342 + 7,955 = 54,297	**12.** 62,237 + 8,073 = 70,310	**13.** 53,087 + 26,941 = 80,028	**14.** 34,668 + 62,951 = 97,619	**15.** 92,876 + 38,846 = 131,722
16. 7234 + 186 + 2145 = 9565	**17.** 483 + 2964 + 192 = 3639	**18.** 9263 + 4063 + 812 = 14,138	**19.** 12,610 + 8,715 + 24,025 = 45,350	**20.** 37,096 + 492 + 15,405 = 52,993
21. \$2.78 + 3.18 + 6.92 = \$12.88	**22.** \$6.99 + 2.08 + 9.36 = \$18.43	**23.** \$71.24 + 9.76 + 43.08 = \$124.08	**24.** \$28.09 + 75.34 + 38.68 = \$142.11	**25.** \$34.76 + 52.64 + 93.28 = \$180.68

26. 24,198 + 9473 33,671
27. 543 + 1087 1630
28. 19 + 9478 9497
29. 7809 + 43,000 50,809
30. 38,624 + 1134 39,758
31. 356 + 2093 2449
32. 1275 + 619 + 4235 6129
33. 723 + 4263 + 82 5068
34. 9261 + 2324 + 185 11,770
35. 256 + 1102 + 981 2339
36. 6421 + 840 + 19 7280
37. 618 + 5423 + 6 6047
38. 14,726 + 8214 + 385 23,325
39. 24,426 + 902 + 6128 31,456
40. 83,280 + 4726 + 754 88,760
41. 25,002 + 312 + 1666 26,980
42. 72,016 + 354 + 14 72,384
43. 68,203 + 4204 + 8 72,415

Solve. Use the chart on page 8.

44. What was Gale Sayers' total rushing and pass-receiving yardage? 6266 yards

45. Which player had a total rushing and pass-receiving yardage of 11,213 yards? Lenny Moore

46. What was the total rushing yardage of Jim Brown and Jim Taylor? 20,909 yards

47. What was the total pass-receiving yardage of the five players? 15,506 yards

Who wore this helmet? Logical reasoning

48. Study the clues. Use the chart on page 8 to name the player.
Clues:
- This player gained more than 5000 yards pass-receiving.
- This player gained less than 5000 yards rushing. Frank Gifford

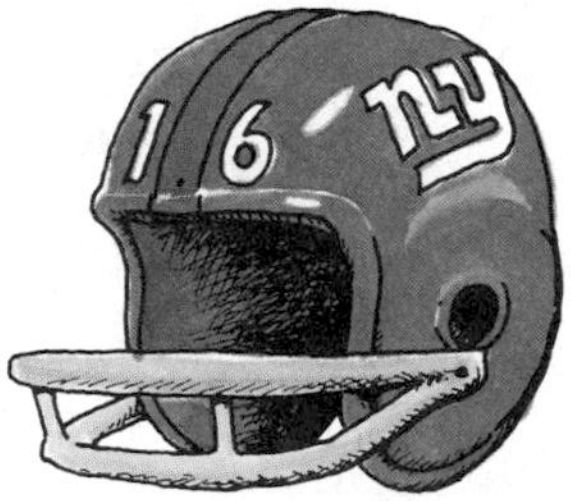

EXTRA PRACTICE
Page 412 Skill 2

PRACTICE WORKSHEET
Copymaster S156 or Duplicating Master S156

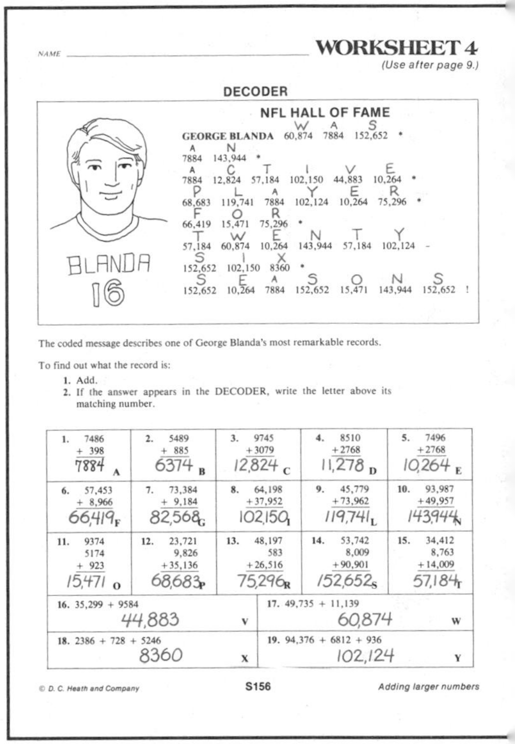
NAME ______ **WORKSHEET 4**
(Use after page 9.)

DECODER

NFL HALL OF FAME

BLANDA 16

GEORGE BLANDA W 60,874 A 7884 S 152,652 •
A 7884 N 143,944 •
A 7884 C 12,824 T 57,184 I 102,150 V 44,883 E 10,264 •
P 68,683 L 119,741 A 7884 Y 102,124 E 10,264 R 75,296 •
F 66,419 O 15,471 R 75,296 •
T 57,184 W 60,874 E 10,264 N 143,944 T 57,184 Y 102,124 -
S 152,652 I 102,150 X 8360 •
S 152,652 E 10,264 A 7884 S 152,652 O 15,471 N 143,944 S 152,652 !

The coded message describes one of George Blanda's most remarkable records.

To find out what the record is:
1. Add.
2. If the answer appears in the DECODER, write the letter above its matching number.

1. 7486 + 398 = 7884 A	**2.** 5489 + 885 = 6374 B	**3.** 9745 + 3079 = 12,824 C	**4.** 8510 + 2768 = 11,278 D	**5.** 7496 + 2768 = 10,264 E
6. 57,453 + 8,966 = 66,419 F	**7.** 73,384 + 9,184 = 82,568 G	**8.** 64,198 + 37,952 = 102,150 I	**9.** 45,779 + 73,962 = 119,741 L	**10.** 93,987 + 49,957 = 143,944 N
11. 9374 + 5174 + 923 = 15,471 O	**12.** 23,721 + 9,826 + 35,136 = 68,683 P	**13.** 48,197 + 583 + 26,516 = 75,296 R	**14.** 53,742 + 8,009 + 90,901 = 152,652 S	**15.** 34,412 + 8,763 + 14,009 = 57,184 T
16. 35,299 + 9584 = 44,883 V		**17.** 49,735 + 11,139 = 60,874 W		
18. 2386 + 728 + 5246 = 8360 X		**19.** 94,376 + 6812 + 936 = 102,124 Y		

© D. C. Heath and Company S156 *Adding larger numbers*

CHALKBOARD CHALLENGE
Find the missing digits.

1. 2 [9] + [3] 4 = 6 3

2. 3 [3] 2 + 1 8 [0] = [5] 1 2

3. 2 [3] 4 + 3 9 [5] + 1 4 2 = [7] 7 1

SKILLS REVIEWED
Writing standard numerals in words
Adding whole numbers

PROBLEM-SOLVING SKILL
Reading a map

STARTING THE LESSON
Cumulative Skill Practice
Write these six answers on the chalkboard:

92 thousand, 57
96 million, 20
51,967
82
576
839

Challenge the students to an answer hunt by saying: "Look for the six even-numbered exercises on page 10 that have these answers. You have five minutes to find as many of the exercises as you can." (Exercises 6, 12, 24, 32, 42, and 54) Do not expect any one student to find all six answers.

EXERCISE NOTE
Cumulative Skill Practice
The page number in parentheses indicates the page on which the skill was first introduced.

STARTING THE LESSON
Problem Solving
The map on page 11 is also on **Visual Aid 4**. Help the students read the map by asking questions like these:
• Which cities on Highway 62 are east of Burr Oak? (Elk Horn and Shelby)
• How many miles is it from Fairmont to Ridgeway? (63 miles)
• Which city is about 60 miles west of Burr Oak? (Garber)

10

Cumulative Skill Practice

Write the short word-name. *(page 4)*
Hint: Think about where the commas go.

1. 35198   2. 4354   3. 12326   4. 36402
5. 443031   6. 92057   7. 180043   8. 200001
9. 45823926   10. 15481320   11. 82148099   12. 96000020
13. 1426005   14. 63128   15. 42000261   16. 86100000

Write the standard numeral. *(page 4)*

17. 347 thousand, 172   347,172
18. 18 million   18,000,000
19. 62 billion   62,000,000,000
20. 19 million, 418 thousand   19,418,000
21. 219 million, 76 thousand   219,076,000
22. 7 million, 3 thousand, 4   7,003,004
23. six hundred thirty-seven thousand, two hundred sixteen   637,216
24. fifty-one thousand, nine hundred sixty-seven   51,967
25. eighteen million, one hundred sixteen thousand   18,116,000
26. four hundred twenty-three thousand, fourteen   423,014
27. three billion, one hundred ten   3,000,000,110

Add. *(page 6)*

28. 83 +92 = 175	29. 69 +23 = 92	30. 78 +65 = 143	31. 82 +49 = 131	32. 53 +29 = 82	33. 24 +19 = 43
34. 964 +673 = 1637	35. 857 + 95 = 952	36. 107 +682 = 789	37. 47 +90 = 137	38. 232 +563 = 795	39. 302 +191 = 493
40. 683 +457 = 1140	41. 992 +193 = 1185	42. 426 +150 = 576	43. 962 +193 = 1155	44. 700 +538 = 1238	45. 542 +619 = 1161
46. 36 29 +18 = 83	47. 35 74 +81 = 190	48. 56 18 +66 = 140	49. 54 29 +93 = 176	50. 71 71 +39 = 181	51. 88 88 +88 = 264
52. 267 384 37 +115 = 803	53. 628 35 275 + 56 = 994	54. 57 629 38 +115 = 839	55. 342 708 56 + 86 = 1192	56. 628 52 395 +544 = 1619	57. 291 35 426 +184 = 936

Problem solving

Use the map to answer the CB users' questions.

1. *I know it's 14 miles from Red Oak to Gray. How far is it from Gray to Fairmont?* 80 miles

2. "How many miles is it from Conway to Garber?" 85

3. "Which city is about 180 miles east of Brooks?" Elk Horn

4. "I'm driving east on Highway 34. I'm 90 miles east of Red Oak. Which city will I drive through next?" Fairmont

5. "I'm just crossing Willow River, traveling west on Highway 34. How far am I from Red Oak?" 94 miles

6. "I'm at Red Oak on my way to Shelby. I plan to drive about 100 miles before lunch. At which city on Highway 34 should I stop and eat?" Fairmont

7. "How far is it from Ridgeway to Bristow if I take Highways 14 and 62? Is that the shortest route?" 155 miles, No

8. "I'm 150 miles west of Elk Horn on Highway 62. I'm headed for Conway. Is the next town Bristow or Brooks?" Bristow

9. "I want to take the shortest route from Elk Horn to Fairmont. What highways should I take?" 62 and 77

10. "I'm now traveling west on Highway 34. I just passed a sign that says Ridgeway is 15 miles ahead. How many miles am I from Goodell?" 129

11. "I'm 16 miles south of Bristow, going north on Highway 25. How far am I from Burr Oak?" 129 miles

12. "I'm at Grant's Truckstop, 40 miles west of Burr Oak. How far am I from Shelby?" 122 miles

EXTRA PROBLEM SOLVING
Page 444   Odd exercises

PROBLEM-SOLVING WORKSHEET
Copymaster S157 or Duplicating Master S157

NAME _____

WORKSHEET 5
(Use after page 11.)

AMAZING FACT!
Crack the code to get the fact.

CODE

A	B	C	D	E	...	Z
1	2	3	4	5	...	26

Would you believe . . .

A MOLE CAN DIG
1 13 15 12 5 3 1 14 4 9 7

UNDERGROUND
21 14 4 5 18 7 18 15 21 14 4

AS FAST AS IT
1 19 6 1 19 20 1 19 9 20

CAN WALK
3 1 14 23 1 11 4

ABOVE GROUND,
1 2 15 22 5 7 18 15 21 14 4

SUM PROBLEM
Place the numbers 1, 2, 7, 12, and 13 in the circles. The sum along each line must be the same.

⑬
Answers may vary.
⑫ — ⑦ — ②
①

PRINT IT!
What seven capital letters look the same upside down as right side up?

H, I, N, O, S, X, Z

WHO'S KEEPING SCORE?
The Pittsville Pirates played four games. The scores were

game 1 — 3 to 1
game 2 — 5 to 4
game 3 — 6 to 1
game 4 — 2 to 0

The Pirates scored a total of 12 runs. Which two games did the Pirates win?

Games 2 and 3

MYSTERY PRICE TAGS
What you pay is the retail price. What the appliance store paid was the wholesale price. The store used a code to keep the wholesale price a secret.

What is the wholesale price of each TV set?

Secret Code
C H A R L E S T O N
1 2 3 4 5 6 7 8 9 0

HSA $349   ATC $419   HRN $368

$ 273 $ 381 $ 240

© D. C. Heath and Company   **S157**   Problem solving

CHALKBOARD CHALLENGE
Look on page 10. Find the largest number less than 500. Find the smallest number greater than 500. Add. Did you get a sum of 995?

457, 538, Yes

Answers for page 10.
1. 35 thousand, 198
2. 4 thousand, 354
3. 12 thousand, 326
4. 36 thousand, 402
5. 443 thousand, 31
6. 92 thousand, 57
7. 180 thousand, 43
8. 200 thousand, 1
9. 45 million, 623 thousand, 926
10. 15 million, 481 thousand, 320
11. 82 million, 148 thousand, 99
12. 96 million, 20
13. 1 million, 426 thousand, 5
14. 63 thousand, 128
15. 42 million, 261
16. 86 million, 100 thousand

11

LESSON OBJECTIVE
To round whole numbers

PROBLEM-SOLVING SKILL
Following instructions

STARTING THE LESSON
Have the students guess the price of the car pictured at the top of page 12. (This car is also shown on **Visual Aid 5**.) Tell the students that this car is "loaded" with special features such as a 5-liter engine, automatic transmission, tilt steering wheel, removable hatch roof, AM/FM radio with front and rear speakers, custom air-conditioning, dual exhaust system, hand-rubbed lacquer paint, and a security system. Have the students write their guesses. Then list the guesses on the chalkboard and determine whose guess was closest to the exact price, $19,574.

***HERE'S HOW* NOTE**
You may wish to present these additional examples before assigning the exercises.

Round to the nearest ten.
  3 (0) 197 (200) 6998 (7000)
Round to the nearest hundred.
  43 (0) 4985 (5000) 12,999 (13,000)

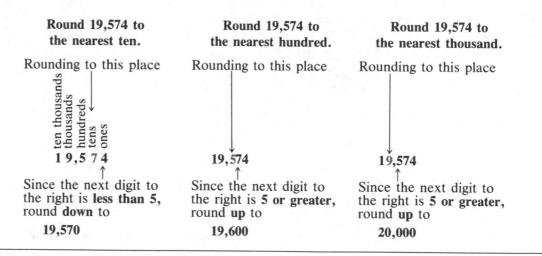

EAST MEADOW MALL
GRAND OPENING
GUESS THE PRICE!
WIN THE CAR!

My guess is $_____.
Name_____
Address_____
City_____State____Zip____
Winner does not have to be present.

1. Carlos guessed $19,500. Joan guessed $19,600. The exact price of the sports car is $19,574. Whose guess was nearer the exact price? Joan's

2. Is $19,570 or $19,580 nearer the exact price? $19,570

Rounded numbers are often used in place of exact numbers.

Here's how *to round a whole number.*

Round 19,574 to the nearest ten.	Round 19,574 to the nearest hundred.	Round 19,574 to the nearest thousand.
Rounding to this place	Rounding to this place	Rounding to this place
1 9,5 7 4 (ten thousands, thousands, hundreds, tens, ones)	19,574	19,574
Since the next digit to the right is **less than 5**, round **down** to	Since the next digit to the right is **5 or greater**, round **up** to	Since the next digit to the right is **5 or greater**, round **up** to
19,570	**19,600**	**20,000**

3. Look at the *Here's how*. In 19,574, which digit is in the ten thousands place? Is the next digit to the right 5 or greater? Yes

4. Round 19,574 to the nearest ten thousand. 20,000

EXERCISES

Round to the nearest ten.

5. 73 *70* **6.** 65 *70* **7.** 6 *10* **8.** 497 *500* **9.** 521 *520*

10. 3 *0* **11.** 2653 *2650* **12.** 4708 *4710* **13.** 6222 *6220* **14.** 6803 *6800*

Round to the nearest hundred.

15. 378 *400* **16.** 450 *500* **17.** 99 *100* **18.** 3692 *3700* **19.** 4987 *5000*

20. 2509 *2500* **21.** 5621 *5600* **22.** 7770 *7800* **23.** 9050 *9100* **24.** 3021 *3000*

25. 16,405 *16,400* **26.** 25,980 *26,000* **27.** 41,912 *41,900* **28.** 53,950 *54,000* **29.** 6092 *6100*

Round to the nearest thousand.

30. 5732 *6000* **31.** 8026 *8000* **32.** 741 *1000* **33.** 8500 *9000* **34.** 203 *0*

35. 26,332 *26,000* **36.** 41,582 *42,000* **37.** 64,398 *64,000* **38.** 50,225 *50,000* **39.** 15,432 *15,000*

40. 236,479 *236,000* **41.** 183,500 *184,000* **42.** 379,199 *379,000* **43.** 829,602 *830,000* **44.** 699,999 *700,000*

Round to the nearest ten thousand.

45. 37,168 *40,000* **46.** 42,600 *40,000* **47.** 63,911 *60,000* **48.** 9830 *10,000* **49.** 17,302 *20,000*

50. 58,502 *60,000* **51.** 47,300 *50,000* **52.** 62,499 *60,000* **53.** 92,888 *90,000* **54.** 65,898 *70,000*

55. 239,100 *240,000* **56.** 468,492 *470,000* **57.** 623,619 *620,000* **58.** 745,000 *750,000* **59.** 99,999 *100,000*

Round.

60. During the first day of the grand opening at East Meadow, **13,721** shoppers entered the Guess the Sports-Car Price contest. Round the number to the nearest hundred. *13,700*

61. A total of **173,517** shoppers entered the sports-car contest. Round the number to the nearest thousand. *174,000*

Changing times

62. In 1921, you could buy this Model T for about $400. In an antique-car auction in 1982, this car sold for $⬚.

To find ⬚, write a *6* in the tens place, a *9* in the hundreds place, a *4* in the ones place, and a *5* in the thousands place. *5964*

63. If the buyer at the auction used hundred-dollar bills to pay for the car, how many bills did he use? (*Hint: the buyer got back some bills in change.*) *60*

PRACTICE WORKSHEET
Copymaster S158 or Duplicating Master S158

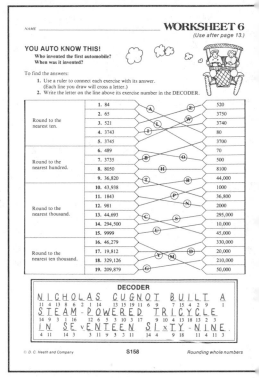

LIFE-SKILL PROJECT
Researching information

Have the students use a book of world records to find the greatest price paid for a used car. Challenge them to write the price in words. (This information can be found in the *Guinness Book of World Records*.)

four hundred twenty-one thousand, forty dollars

LESSON OBJECTIVE
To estimate sums

PROBLEM-SOLVING SKILLS
Finding information in an ad
Using a guess-and-check strategy

STARTING THE LESSON
Play 'What are the facts?' Have the students study the sale ad on page 14 for 30 seconds and then close their books. Challenge the students to answer these questions from memory:

- What four items are on sale? (Camera, TV, radio, and calculator)
- What is the most expensive item? (Camera)
- Which item costs about $20? (Calculator)
- Which item costs about $100? (TV or Radio)
- Are the items in a summer, fall, or winter sale catalog? (Fall)

EXERCISE NOTE
Exercises 44–55 involve rounding and mental arithmetic. Some students may need to use a guess-and-check approach.

Estimating sums

1. Which item costs about $300? Camera

2. Which item costs about $90? Radio

3. Which two prices would you round to estimate the total cost of the camera and the personal radio? $329 and $87

Here's how *to estimate sums.*

Round to the nearest ten dollars.

Ray
$329 → 330
$87 →+ 90
$420

Round to the nearest hundred dollars.

Cindy
$329 → 300
$87 →+100
$400

4. What is the actual total cost of the camera and the personal radio? $416

5. Look at the *Here's how.* Whose estimate was closer to the actual total cost, Ray's or Cindy's? Ray's

6. Use Ray's method. Which two items cost about $110? Radio and calculator

7. Use Cindy's method. Which two items cost about $200? Radio and TV

EXERCISES

Which estimate would Cindy give? *Hint: Study the* Here's how.

8. $325 + $479   a. $600   (b.) $800   c. $1000

9. $281 + $94 + $319   (a.) $700   b. $1000   c. $1300

10. $631 + $477 + $819   a. $1300   b. $1600   (c.) $1900

Which estimate would Ray give?

11. $789 + $42   a. $810   (b.) $830   c. $850

12. $37 + $86 + $129   a. $230   (b.) $260   c. $290

13. $29 + $43 + $68   (a.) $140   b. $170   c. $200

Estimate each sum by rounding to the nearest hundred dollars.

14.
$428 → $400
+ 583 → + 600
$1000

15.
$685
+ 519
$1200

16.
$867
+ 109
$1000

17.
$929
+ 409
$1300

18.
$789
+ 239
$1000

19.
$581 → $600
302 → 300
+ 18 → + 0
$900

20.
$106
18
+ 289
$400

21.
$ 22
599
+ 372
$1000

22.
$928
82
+ 614
$1600

23.
$871
28
+ 79
$1000

Estimate each sum by rounding to the nearest ten.

24. 281 + 78   360
25. 329 + 19   350
26. 49 + 53   100
27. 39 + 43 + 19   100
28. 27 + 86 + 39   160
29. 78 + 23 + 49   150
30. 96 + 32 + 12   140
31. 448 + 89 + 72   610
32. 24 + 81 + 16   120
33. 305 + 17 + 29   360
34. 28 + 486 + 5   530
35. 16 + 24 + 111   150
36. 98 + 14 + 29   140
37. 15 + 82 + 199   300
38. 254 + 60 + 1   310
39. 14 + 86 + 999   1100
40. 69 + 35 + 42   150
41. 38 + 246 + 10   300
42. 521 + 62 + 15   600
43. 87 + 6 + 981   1080

Jewelry juggle Estimating costs

Use your estimation skills. Which two items cost about

44. $500?   45. $1100?   46. $300?

47. $110?   48. $700?   49. $900?

Which three items cost about

50. $700?   51. $500?   52. $300?

53. $1200?   54. $800?   55. $1300?

WALKER'S GRAND OPENING SALE

14K Gold Chain $209
Quartz Watch $415
Emerald Ring $88
Diamond Pendant $679
Silver Charm $19

East Meadow Mall

NAME _____ **WORKSHEET 7**
(Use after page 15.)

SKILL DRILL

Estimate each sum by rounding to the nearest hundred dollars.

1.
$429 → $400
+ 79 → + 100
$500

2.
$273 → $300
+ 129 → + 100
$400

3.
$809 → $800
+ 333 → + 300
$1100

4.
$726 → $700
+ 133 → + 100
$800

5.
$816 → $800
89 → 100
+ 359 → + 400
$1300

6.
$903 → $900
619 → 600
+ 306 → + 300
$1800

7.
$393 → $400
416 → 400
+ 909 → + 900
$1700

8.
$891 → $900
23 → 0
+ 89 → + 100
$1000

Estimate each sum by rounding to the nearest ten dollars.

9.
$319 → $320
+ 89 → + 90
$410

10.
$463 → $460
+ 219 → + 220
$680

11.
$708 → $710
+ 434 → + 430
$1140

12.
$516 → $520
+ 142 → + 140
$660

13.
$629 → $630
78 → 80
+ 513 → + 510
$1220

14.
$103 → $100
809 → 810
+ 718 → + 720
$1630

15.
$113 → $110
8 → 10
+ 21 → + 20
$140

16.
$ 4 → $ 0
17 → 20
+ 103 → + 100
120

17. $415 + $389 $810
18. $381 + $411 + $95 $890
19. $741 + $583 + $915 $2240
20. $32 + $585 + $472 $1090
21. $828 + $93 + $513 $1430
22. $19 + $609 + $759 $1390

Check yourself. Here are the scrambled answers:
$120 $140 $400 $410 $500 $660 $680 $800 $810
$890 $1000 $1090 $1100 $1140 $1220 $1300 $1390 $1430
$1630 $1700 $1800 $2240

© D. C. Heath and Company   S159   *Estimating sums*

LIFE-SKILL PROJECT

Using a catalog
Have a contest. The winner is the person who finds 3 items in a catalog that come closest to costing a total of $100.

Answers for page 15.
44. watch, ring
45. watch, pendant
46. chain, ring
47. ring, charm
48. pendant, charm
49. chain, pendant
50. chain, watch, ring
51. watch, ring, charm
52. chain, ring, charm
53. watch, ring, pendant
54. ring, pendant, charm
55. chain, watch, pendant

LESSON OBJECTIVE
To read decimals

PROBLEM-SOLVING SKILL
Interpreting information

STARTING THE LESSON
Write this statement on the chalkboard:

A downhill skier, going 30 miles per hour, can travel 50 feet in 1136 seconds.

Have the students decide where to place the decimal point in the number 1136 so that the statement makes sense. (1.136 seconds)

HERE'S HOW **NOTE**
Use **Visual Aid 6** or draw a place-value chart on the chalkboard to reinforce the idea of decimal place-value.

Answers for page 17.
25. 3 and 5 tenths
26. 12 and 35 hundredths
27. 125 thousandths
28. 17 and 3 thousandths
29. 9 and 2 hundredths
30. 25 thousandths
31. 14 and 9 tenths
32. 3 and 75 ten-thousandths
33. 634 ten-thousandths
34. 253 and 61 hundredths
35. 72 and 6 thousandths
36. 594 ten-thousandths
37. 631 and 74 hundredths
38. 3 and 1005 ten-thousandths
39. 875 thousandths
40. 3968 and 4 tenths
41. 860 and 2 tenths
42. 9002 and 11 hundredths
43. 63 and 4 ten-thousandths
44. 4005 ten-thousandths
45. 4216 and 9 tenths

Reading decimals

The decimal shows the time (in seconds) that it took the skier to complete her first downhill run.

SPLIT SECONDS!

5 Tens 7 Ones . 6 Tenths 8 Hundredths

1. In what place is the digit 6? tenths

2. In what place is the last digit? hundredths

Here's how *to read decimals.*

Her first run took **57 and 68 hundredths** seconds. Notice that the decimal point is read as "and" and the place of the last digit is read last.

Here are some more examples of how to read decimals:

STANDARD NUMERAL	SHORT WORD-NAME
0.8	8 tenths
6.3	6 and 3 tenths
5.0 9	5 and 9 hundredths
8.4 6 3	8 and 463 thousandths
4 2.3 2 6 5	42 and 3265 ten-thousandths

(place-value labels: tens, ones, tenths, hundredths, thousandths, ten-thousandths)

3. Look at the *Here's how*. To read 57.68, you say "57 and 68 [?]." hundredths

4. To read 8.463, you say "8 and 463 [?]." thousandths

EXERCISES

In what place is the last digit?

5. 16.3 `tenths`

6. 0.357 thousandths **7.** 6.25 hundredths **8.** 0.4216 ten-thousandths **9.** 2.069 thousandths

10. 16.38 hundredths **11.** 26.9 tenths **12.** 0.0371 ten-thousandths **13.** 19.6421 ten-thousandths **14.** 58.4 tenths

15. 13.005 thousandths **16.** 24.57 hundredths **17.** 8.0007 ten-thousandths **18.** 220.68 hundredths **19.** 126.9 tenths

20. 8.594 thousandths **21.** 1206.74 hundredths **22.** 1.7241 ten-thousandths **23.** 0.003 thousandths **24.** 468.2 tenths

Write the short word-name.

25. 3.5 `3 and 5 tenths`

26. 12.35 **27.** 0.125 **28.** 17.003 **29.** 9.02

30. 0.025 **31.** 14.9 **32.** 3.0075 **33.** 0.0634 **34.** 253.61

35. 72.006 **36.** 0.0594 **37.** 631.74 **38.** 3.1005 **39.** 0.875

40. 3968.4 **41.** 860.2 **42.** 9002.11 **43.** 63.0004 **44.** 0.4005

45. 4216.9 **46.** 421.69 **47.** 42.169 **48.** 4.2169 **49.** 0.0062

Write the standard numeral.

50. 2 thousandths `0.002`

52. 12 and 3 hundredths 12.03

54. 34 and 32 hundredths 34.32

56. 452 thousandths 0.452

58. 9 and 75 thousandths 9.075

60. 4275 ten-thousandths 0.4275

51. 25 and 4 tenths 25.4

53. 2 thousandths 0.002

55. 164 and 58 hundredths 164.58

57. 27 and 148 thousandths 27.148

59. 8 and 6 thousandths 8.006

61. 20 and 840 ten-thousandths 20.0840

Speed records

Here are my fastest speeds.

Bill Gomez
Bicycling — miles per hour 23.2
Skateboarding 13.8
Rollerskating 18.1

Copy the numeral and place a decimal point so that the statement makes sense. Hint: Use Bill's chart.

62. The world speed record for a skateboard is **718** miles per hour. 71.8

63. The world speed record for a bicycle is **140525** miles per hour. 140.525

64. Top speed for roller skates is **2578** miles per hour. 25.78

REVIEW PRACTICE
Adding whole numbers
Page 412   Skill 2

PRACTICE WORKSHEET
Copymaster S160 or Duplicating Master S160

NAME _____   **WORKSHEET 8**
(Use after page 17.)

OLYMPIC FACT

Catherine Breyton of France held a world's speed record for women skiers.

What was Catherine Breyton's speed in miles per hour?

To find the answer:
1. Write the standard numeral.
2. Cross out each box below that contains an answer.
3. Read the answer to the riddle using the letters in the remaining boxes.

1.	4 thousandths	0.004		11.	4 hundredths	0.04
2.	17 and 5 tenths	17.5		12.	17 and 5 thousandths	17.005
3.	24 and 3 hundredths	24.03		13.	24 and 3 tenths	24.3
4.	7 thousandths	0.007		14.	7 hundredths	0.07
5.	57 and 51 hundredths	57.51		15.	57 and 51 thousandths	57.051
6.	278 and 69 hundredths	278.69		16.	278 and 69 thousandths	278.069
7.	578 thousandths	0.578		17.	578 ten-thousandths	0.0578
8.	35 and 256 thousandths	35.256		18.	35 and 256 ten-thousandths	35.0256
9.	8 and 69 thousandths	8.069		19.	8 and 69 hundredths	8.69
10.	4275 ten-thousandths	0.4275		20.	4 and 275 thousandths	4.275

F 0.4275	O 17.05	U 57.51	8.69	N 27.869	K 0.007	E 5.7051
0.07	H 0.004	G 5.78	U 8.069	80.69	I 4.275	17.005
N 14.275	24.3	0.4	35.0256	R 2.43	278.069	42.75
T 35.256	D 86.9	E 57.051	0.7	H 17.5	0.243	H 0.578
R 427.5	74.01	E 8.0069	278.69	W 0.04	O 1.75	U 0.0578

Answer: ONE HUNDRED THREE _____ miles per hour

© D. C. Heath and Company   **S160**   *Reading decimals*

LIFE-SKILL PROJECT
Using a newspaper
Have the students choose a page from a newspaper and circle every decimal they find. The student who finds the most decimals wins.

More answers for page 17.
46. 421 and 69 hundredths
47. 42 and 169 thousandths
48. 4 and 2169 ten-thousandths
49. 62 ten-thousandths

SKILLS REVIEWED
Adding whole numbers
Rounding whole numbers
Reading decimals

PROBLEM-SOLVING SKILLS
Reading a sign
Solving problems involving more than
  one step

STARTING THE LESSON
Cumulative Skill Practice
Challenge the students to an estimation
hunt by saying, ''Pick the exercise that
has the largest sum in the first row of
exercises.'' (Exercise 5) Then have the
students pick the exercise with the
largest sum in the second, third, and
fourth rows of exercises. (Exercises 9,
12, and 19)

STARTING THE LESSON
Problem Solving
Have the students use the ticket price
information to answer questions like
these:
• How much would you charge a 20-
  year-old to ride the slide? ($2.25)
• Can a teenager ride the slide for $1?
  (No)
• Is $5 enough money to buy 2 adult
  tickets and 1 child's ticket? (No)

Cumulative Skill Practice

Add. *(pages 6, 8)*

1.	7406 +1629 9035	2.	2917 +2579 5496	3.	824 +5081 5905	4.	1056 +3780 4836	5.	3643 +8561 12,204
6.	53,246 + 2,107 55,353	7.	38,529 + 4,266 42,795	8.	17,329 +54,600 71,929	9.	51,083 +74,291 125,374	10.	38,294 +27,461 65,755
11.	83,174 +29,356 112,530	12.	71,892 +71,892 143,784	13.	56,093 + 8,714 64,807	14.	30,005 + 6,999 37,004	15.	43,770 +29,846 73,616
16.	76,391 +28,477 104,868	17.	63,085 +25,473 88,558	18.	69,377 +44,293 113,670	19.	58,296 +87,742 146,038	20.	64,888 +59,999 124,887

21. 76 + 82 + 53 211
22. 374 + 29 + 659 1062
23. 572 + 153 + 604 1329
24. 3982 + 427 + 965 5374
25. 428 + 3461 + 2009 5898
26. 4721 + 3066 + 5814 13,601
27. 52,140 + 89 + 2417 54,646
28. 17 + 2573 + 43,880 46,470
29. 889 + 14 + 72,354 73,257
30. 68,613 + 19,216 + 526 88,355
31. 909 + 7326 + 27 8262
32. 3068 + 402 + 25,162 28,632

Round to the nearest ten. *(page 12)*

33. 62 60	34. 85 90	35. 151 150	36. 438 440	37. 395 400	38. 982 980
39. 216 220	40. 302 300	41. 461 460	42. 285 290	43. 373 370	44. 795 800
45. 5675 5680	46. 3502 3500	47. 6296 6300	48. 8743 8740	49. 9608 9610	50. 6304 6300
51. 3438 3440	52. 5164 5160	53. 8750 8750	54. 2309 2310	55. 6791 6790	56. 9997 10,000

Write the standard numeral. *(page 16)*

57. 9 tenths 0.9
58. 6 hundredths 0.06
59. 4 thousandths 0.004
60. 15 hundredths 0.15
61. 36 thousandths 0.036
62. 147 thousandths 0.147
63. 6 and 3 tenths 6.3
64. 22 and 81 hundredths 22.81
65. 40 and 5 hundredths 40.05
66. 36 and 235 ten-thousandths 36.0235
67. 28 and 16 thousandths 28.016
68. 9 and 1374 ten-thousandths 9.1374
69. 45 and 4653 ten-thousandths 45.4653
70. 38 and 491 ten-thousandths 38.0491

Problem solving

You have a summer job at the Lincoln Woods Mountain Slide. You sell tickets and work in the gift shop.

RIDE THE SLIDE!	TICKET PRICES
	Adult (18 and over) . . . $2.25
	Student (12 to 18) $1.50
	Child (under 12) $1.00

Use the chart to answer these customers' questions.

1. *How much will 2 adult tickets cost?* $4.50

2. *How much for 2 adult tickets and 1 child's ticket?* $5.50

3. *5 students and 1 adult, please. How much do I owe you?* $9.75

4. "I have $5.00. Can I buy tickets for 2 adults and 1 child?" *Hint: Use your answer to problem 2.* No

5. "Is $10.00 enough money to buy 1 adult ticket and 5 student tickets?" Yes

6. "My sister has $4.75 and I have $3.50."
   a. "How much do we have altogether?" $8.25
   b. "Do we have enough money to buy 5 student tickets?" Yes

7. a. "What is the total cost of 1 student ticket and 1 child's ticket?" $2.50
   b. "My father decided not to ride. Can we trade his adult ticket for 1 student ticket and 1 child's ticket?" No

Solve.

8. Your ticket sales for today were 350 children's, 249 students', and 123 adults'.
   a. How many tickets did you sell in all? 722
   b. Yesterday you sold a total of 738 tickets. Did you sell at least that many tickets today? No

9. Bumper-sticker sales for today were 24 *LINCOLN WOODS*, 72 *ZIPPER*, and 63 *MOUNTAIN SLIDE*.
   a. Which bumper sticker had the highest number of sales? Zipper
   b. What were the combined sales of the *ZIPPER* and the *MOUNTAIN SLIDE*? 135 bumper stickers

---

PROBLEM-SOLVING WORKSHEET
Copymaster S161 or Duplicating Master S161

NAME _____   **WORKSHEET 9**
(Use after page 19.)

SCRAMBLED MATH
Unscramble the letters to get the answer.
ETN plus HIEGT plus REHTE equals 21
TEN EIGHT THREE

WHO IS IT?
Bubba scored more points than O'Brien. O'Brien scored fewer points than Gus. Tony scored more points than Bubba, but fewer points than Gus.
Who scored the most points? Gus

OFF AND ON
You switched off a light. Then you switched it 15 more times. Then you switched it 13 more times. Was the light on or off when you stopped?
Off

LOOSE CHANGE
There is 55¢ in the purse. What 4 coins are in the purse?
quarter
dime
dime
dime

BOWLING SCORES

Name	FIRST GAME	SECOND GAME	THIRD GAME
Rick	118	101	158
Carrie	159	112	137
Jody	97	121	89
Eric	167	116	127

Which bowler had the lowest total score for all three games? Jody

NUMBER IT!
How many times would you use the digit 9 to number the pages of a 100-page book? *Hint: The answer is more than 18.* 20

Which two bowlers had about the same total score for all three games? Carrie and Eric

© D. C. Heath and Company   S161   Problem solving

LIFE-SKILL PROJECT
Researching information
Have the students guess which four states in the United States have mountain peaks higher than 14,000 feet. Have the students use an almanac to check their guesses.

Alaska, California, Colorado, and Washington

CHALKBOARD QUIZ
on previous lesson

Solve. Use the ticket prices on page 19.
1. How much will 1 adult and 3 student tickets cost? $6.75
2. Is $7.50 enough money for 1 child's and 3 adult tickets? No

LESSON OBJECTIVE
To round decimals

PROBLEM-SOLVING SKILL
Selecting data from a chart

STARTING THE LESSON
Play 'What are the facts?' Have the students look at the picture on page 20, read the paragraph at the top of the page, and then close their books. Challenge the students to answer these questions from memory:
• Who holds the land speed record for women? (Kitty O'Neil)
• Did she average more or less than 500 miles per hour? (More)
• Did her car have more or less than 50,000 horsepower? (Less)
• How many wheels were on her rocket-powered car? (3)

HERE'S HOW NOTE
Use **Visual Aid 6** or draw a place-value chart on the chalkboard to reinforce the idea of rounding decimals.

Rounding decimals

Kitty O'Neil holds the land speed record for women. Driving her 48,000-horsepower rocket-powered car, she averaged 512.715 miles per hour. It took her over 5 miles just to stop!

1. What was O'Neil's average speed?
512.715 miles per hour

Here's how *to round a decimal.*

Rounding to this place
512.715

*Since the next digit to the right is **5 or greater**, round **up** to **513**.*

Rounded to the nearest whole number, 512.715 is **513**.

Rounding to this place
512.715

*Since the next digit to the right is **less than 5**, round **down** to **512.7**.*

Rounded to the nearest tenth, 512.715 is **512.7**.

Rounding to this place
512.715

*Since the next digit to the right is **5 or greater**, round **up** to **512.72**.*

Rounded to the nearest hundredth, 512.715 is **512.72**.

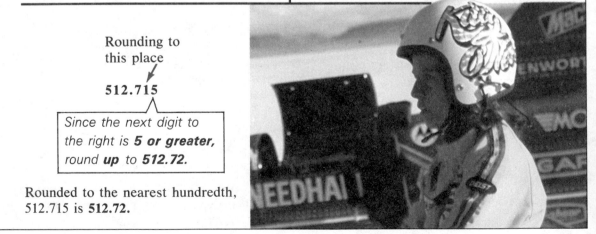

2. Was O'Neil's speed closer to 512 miles per hour or 513 miles per hour? 513

EXERCISES

Round to the nearest whole number.

3. 15.7 *16*   **4.** 47.2 *47*   **5.** 0.25 *0*   **6.** 35.34 *35*   **7.** 0.95 *1*

8. 52.19 *52*   **9.** 28.928 *29*   **10.** 69.523 *70*   **11.** 421.073 *421*   **12.** 99.786 *100*

13. 215.07 *215*   **14.** 429.562 *430*   **15.** 0.895 *1*   **16.** 76.0125 *76*   **17.** 25.21 *25*

18. 97.612 *98*   **19.** 10.72 *11*   **20.** 172.26 *172*   **21.** 51.347 *51*   **22.** 0.86 *1*

Round to the nearest tenth.

23. 1.62 *1.6*   **24.** 28.108 *28.1*   **25.** 7.28 *7.3*   **26.** 0.552 *0.6*   **27.** 7.342 *7.3*

28. 2.460 *2.5*   **29.** 69.169 *69.2*   **30.** 31.03 *31.0*   **31.** 9.381 *9.4*   **32.** 8.1106 *8.1*

33. 705.49 *705.5*   **34.** 913.91 *913.9*   **35.** 0.056 *0.1*   **36.** 43.012 *43.0*   **37.** 53.299 *53.3*

38. 4.295 *4.3*   **39.** 0.123 *0.1*   **40.** 72.575 *72.6*   **41.** 2.107 *2.1*   **42.** 41.0086 *41.0*

Round to the nearest hundredth.

43. 18.216 *18.22*   **44.** 38.107 *38.11*   **45.** 2.543 *2.54*   **46.** 61.625 *61.63*   **47.** 84.612 *84.61*

48. 83.581 *83.58*   **49.** 4.2029 *4.20*   **50.** 0.0254 *0.03*   **51.** 8.3815 *8.38*   **52.** 0.013 *0.01*

53. 6.3522 *6.35*   **54.** 0.005 *0.01*   **55.** 16.949 *16.95*   **56.** 234.789 *234.79*   **57.** 13.023 *13.02*

58. 2.1685 *2.17*   **59.** 12.825 *12.83*   **60.** 5.201 *5.20*   **61.** 398.166 *398.17*   **62.** 4.117 *4.12*

Round to the nearest dollar.

63. $7.77 *$8*   **64.** $14.48 *$14*   **65.** $234.61 *$235*   **66.** $67.52 *$68*   **67.** $24.87 *$25*

68. $35.92 *$36*   **69.** $35.50 *$36*   **70.** $129.79 *$130*   **71.** $99.89 *$100*   **72.** $3.02 *$3*

73. $179.79 *$180*   **74.** $42.49 *$42*   **75.** $2.55 *$3*   **76.** $34.09 *$34*   **77.** $48.91 *$49*

You're a reporter   Using a chart

Use the chart. Complete the story.

78. On August __?__ , __?__ , *5, 63*
(date) (year)

_____?_____ in the _____?_____
(driver's name) (car's name)

set a new one-mile speed record
of about 410 miles per hour.
Breedlove, Spirit of America

79. On October __?__ , __?__ , *27, 64*
(date) (year)

_____?_____ in the _____?_____
(driver's name) (car's name)

set a new record of nearly 540 miles
per hour. *Arfons, Green Monster*

One-Mile Speed Records			
DATE	DRIVER	CAR	MPH
9/3/35	Campbell	Bluebird Special	301.13
9/16/38	Eyston	Thunderbolt 1	357.5
9/16/47	Cobb	Railton-Mobil	394.2
8/5/63	Breedlove	Spirit of America	407.45
10/27/64	Arfons	Green Monster	536.71
11/15/65	Breedlove	Spirit of America	600.601
10/23/70	Gabelich	Blue Flame	622.407

EXTRA PRACTICE
Page 413   Skill 4

PRACTICE WORKSHEET
Copymaster S162 or Duplicating Master S162

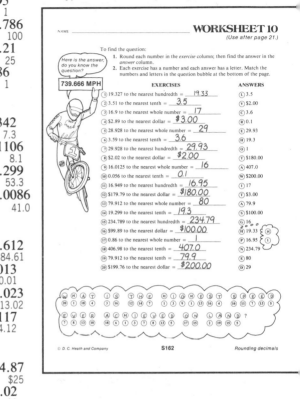

CHALKBOARD CHALLENGE
Find the number on page 21 that fits
the clues.

Clues:
• It is less than 400.
• Rounded to the nearest hundred, it
is 200.
• Rounded to the nearest ten, it is 220.

215.07 (exercise 13)

LESSON OBJECTIVE
To add decimals (addends having the same number of decimal places)

PROBLEM-SOLVING SKILLS
Selecting information from a chart
Using a guess-and-check strategy

STARTING THE LESSON
On the chalkboard write these statements:

In 1964, the Beatles recorded "A Hard Day's Night." The 247-minute song sold over 1000000 copies.

Tell the students one of the numbers is missing a decimal point. Have them decide where to place the decimal point so that the statement makes sense. (2.47)

EXERCISE NOTE
Encourage the students to use a guess-and-check strategy for exercises 56–58. The thinking for exercise 56 might be as follows:

34.6 + 20 = 54.6 → too small
42.6 + 30 = 72.6 → too big
43.6 + 20 = 63.6 → perfect

Adding decimals

You are a disc jockey! You have a request to play some songs from the soundtracks of old Beatles movies. The list below shows some of the songs you plan to play.

SONG	PLAYING TIME (IN MINUTES)
A Hard Day's Night	2.47
I Am the Walrus	4.57
And I Love Her	2.45
Help!	2.28
Yellow Submarine	2.62
Let It Be	4.02
Ticket to Ride	3.10
The Long and Winding Road	3.60

1. How many minutes will it take to play *A Hard Day's Night*?   2.47

2. How many minutes will it take to play *I Am the Walrus*?   4.57

3. Would you add or subtract to find the number of minutes needed to play both songs?   Add

Here's how *to add decimals.*   2.47 + 4.57 = ?

Line up the decimal points.	Add hundredths and regroup.	Add tenths and regroup.	Add ones.
2.47 +4.57	2.47 +4.57 --- 4	2.47 +4.57 --- .04	2.47 +4.57 --- 7.04

4. Study the *Here's how*. How long will it take you to play both songs?   7.04 minutes

EXERCISES

Add. Here are scrambled answers for the next row of exercises:
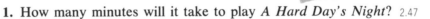
19.6   9.1   13.4   8.7   10.7   10.4

5. 6.3 +2.4 8.7	6. 8.5 +0.6 9.1	7. 9.8 +9.8 19.6	8. 8.6 +4.8 13.4	9. 6.5 +3.9 10.4	10. 7.2 +3.5 10.7

11.	5.26 +3.42 8.68	12.	6.74 +3.19 9.93	13.	8.65 +4.93 13.58	14.	5.99 +0.86 6.85	15.	2.48 +0.06 2.54	16.	7.91 +3.14 11.05

11.   5.26   +3.42 = 8.68
12.   6.74   +3.19 = 9.93
13.   8.65   +4.93 = 13.58
14.   5.99   +0.86 = 6.85
15.   2.48   +0.06 = 2.54
16.   7.91   +3.14 = 11.05

17.   52.83   + 1.95 = 54.78
18.   73.47   + 8.61 = 82.08
19.   5.09   +34.84 = 39.93
20.   641.1   + 74.9 = 716.0
21.   63.84   + 9.66 = 73.50
22.   2.43   +1.11 = 3.54

23.   5.6   3.9   +8.4 = 17.9
24.   9.4   5.9   +4.3 = 19.6
25.   42.6   55.7   +62.8 = 161.1
26.   8.96   3.74   +5.09 = 17.79
27.   81.6   5.9   +17.4 = 104.9
28.   87.2   1.3   +15.2 = 103.7

29.   3.8   2.6   0.7   +1.5 = 8.6
30.   2.93   1.06   5.11   +4.04 = 13.14
31.   23.5   8.6   13.4   + 9.7 = 55.2
32.   23.48   9.57   14.22   + 3.08 = 50.35
33.   15.60   21.47   5.92   +11.05 = 54.04
34.   24.13   3.40   15.91   + 2.03 = 45.47

35. 5.8 + 2.9   8.7
36. 9.4 + 3.7   13.1
37. 12.0 + 7.5   19.5
38. 19.8 + 6.5   26.3
39. 4.32 + 1.65   5.97
40. 0.83 + 9.07   9.90
41. 6.93 + 1.86   8.79
42. 81.3 + 26.5   107.8
43. 9.4 + 3.8   13.2
44. 1.16 + 3.28 + 5.36   9.80
45. 4.07 + 0.35 + 1.68   6.10
46. 2.06 + 3.18 + 6.95   12.19
47. 16.3 + 0.8 + 5.7   22.8
48. 3.99 + 0.87 + 5.77   10.63
49. 2.74 + 3.95 + 6.05   12.74

Solve. Refer to the list on page 22.

50. How many minutes will it take you to play *A Hard Day's Night* and *Help!*?   4.75

51. How many minutes will it take you to play the two shortest songs on the list?   4.73

52. You play *And I Love Her*, read a 0.75-minute commercial, then play *Yellow Submarine*. How much program time do you use?   5.82 minutes

53. You have 10 minutes left in your show. Do you have time to play *Let It Be*, *Ticket to Ride*, and *The Long and Winding Road*?   No

54. How many minutes will be needed to play the two longest songs on the list?   8.59

55. Which four songs can you play in less than 10 minutes?   *A Hard Day's Night, And I Love Her, Help!, Yellow Submarine*

Key it in!

Find a way to push each marked key once to get the answer.

Answers will vary.

Sample answers:

56. 63.6   20.6 + 43 =

57. 360.8   359 + 1.8 =

58. 38.4   13.4 + 25 =

PRACTICE WORKSHEET
Copymaster S163 or Duplicating Master S163

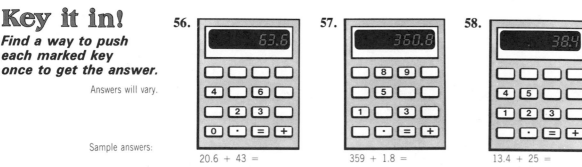

NAME _____   **WORKSHEET 11**   *(Use after page 23.)*

SKILL DRILL
Add.

1. 7.86 + 3.79 = 11.65
2. 57.6 + 68.9 = 126.5
3. 5.74 + 0.38 = 6.12
4. 0.933 + 0.256 = 1.189
5. 93.4 + 25.9 = 119.3
6. 36.82 + 5.93 = 42.75
7. 759.2 + 88.8 = 848.0
8. 3.784 + 0.916 = 4.700
9. 59.38 + 2.57 = 61.95
10. 629.4 + 57.8 = 687.2
11. 25.1 + 38.4 + 59.2 + 16.5 = 139.2
12. 5.93 + 8.26 + 7.61 + 4.58 = 26.38
13. 0.963 + 0.178 + 0.420 + 0.560 = 2.121
14. 2.341 + 7.158 + 4.250 + 3.680 = 17.429
15. 71.35 + 20.06 + 58.01 + 39.49 = 188.91
16. 6.9 + 13.8 + 0.5 = 21.2
17. 28.3 + 2.6 + 1.7 = 32.6
18. 11.9 + 6.4 + 2.1 = 20.4
19. 28.7 + 5.4 + 12.6 = 46.7
20. 3.21 + 2.76 + 14.05 = 20.02
21. 0.72 + 8.96 + 10.22 = 19.90
22. 6.27 + 10.91 + 42.25 = 59.43
23. 7.39 + 42.06 + 1.65 = 51.10
24. 0.29 + 1.63 + 12.42 = 14.34

Check yourself. Here are the scrambled answers:
1.189   2.121   4.700   6.12   11.65   14.34   17.429   19.90   20.02   20.4   21.2
26.38   32.6   42.75   46.7   51.10   59.43   61.95   119.3   126.5   139.2   188.91
687.2   848.0

© D. C. Heath and Company   **S163**   *Adding decimals*

CHALKBOARD CHALLENGE
Find the missing digits.

1.   ☐2☐ . 7
  + 1 . ☐4☐
  4 . 1

2.   ☐6☐ 3 . 7
  + 1 4 . 5
  7 8 . ☐2☐

3.   2 ☐4☐ . 1
  3 . ☐6☐
  + 5 7 . 2
  ☐8☐ 4 . 9

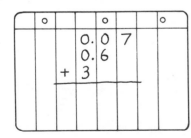

More on adding decimals

MULTIMILLION–DOLLAR DEAL

Rolling Hills, KY Unicorn Acres, the largest local horse farm, made two near-record sales at yesterday's thoroughbred auction. Western Dancer was sold for $2.835 million, and Miss Smoothy went for $1.39 million.

Western Dancer and his new owner, Alice Logan of Saratoga, NY.

1. Read the newspaper report. What was Western Dancer's sale price? $2.835 million

2. What was Miss Smoothy's sale price? $1.39 million

3. Would you add or subtract to find the amount of the total sale in millions of dollars? Add

Here's how *to add decimals.* $2.835 + 1.39 = ?$

Line up the decimal points.	Add.
2.835 +1.39	2.835 +1.39 ———— 4.225

To estimate the sum, I first round each number to the nearest whole number and then add. 3 + 1 = 4. So the total sale price was about $4 million.

4. Look at the *Here's how*. Would $4 million be a good estimate? Yes

EXERCISES

5. Three of the calculator answers are wrong. Find them by estimating.

a. 58.07 + 9.784   `67.854`

b. 29.799 + 21.042   `50.841`

c. 8.0654 + 2.8152   `10.8806`

d. 34.968 + 12.141   `69.109`

e. 63.597 + 8.295   `71.892`

f. 6.9537 + 4.8806   `11.8343`

g. 43.952 + 14.231   `58.183`

h. 7.693 + 8.444   `161.35`

i. 53.809 + 20.298   `94.109`

j. 5.3975 + 0.7055   `6.103`

First estimate the sum and then add.

6.
$$18.33$$
$$+\ 9.40$$
27.73

7.
$$19.783$$
$$+15.95$$
35.733

8.
$$26.3$$
$$+24.0$$
50.3

9.
$$17$$
$$+\ 8.56$$
25.56

10.
$$16.33$$
$$+38.994$$
55.324

11.
$$\$4.32$$
$$+\ 3.18$$
$7.50

12.
$$\$7$$
$$+\ 4.35$$
$11.35

13.
$$\$12.52$$
$$+\ \ \ 9$$
$21.52

14.
$$\$18.06$$
$$+\ \ 7.29$$
$25.35

15.
$$\$23.56$$
$$+\ 17$$
$40.56

16.
$$\$32.21$$
$$+\ 19$$
$51.21

17.
$$\$25$$
$$+\ \ 3.98$$
$28.98

18.
$$\$52.06$$
$$+\ \ 8.35$$
$60.41

19.
$$\$46.53$$
$$+\ \ 9.00$$
$55.53

20.
$$\$8.57$$
$$+\ 2$$
$10.57

21.
$$3.329$$
$$+6.437$$
9.766

22.
$$9.509$$
$$+7.388$$
16.897

23.
$$7.4206$$
$$+0.7835$$
8.2041

24.
$$9.684$$
$$+6.70$$
16.384

25.
$$16.942$$
$$+\ 9.77$$
26.712

26.
$$5.96$$
$$+8.842$$
14.802

27.
$$16.543$$
$$+\ 8.92$$
25.463

28.
$$8.04$$
$$+2.973$$
11.013

29.
$$16.295$$
$$+12.03$$
28.325

30.
$$6.4928$$
$$+9.653$$
16.1458

31.
$$5.6$$
$$3.84$$
$$+2.9$$
12.34

32.
$$5.72$$
$$3.6$$
$$+2.89$$
12.21

33.
$$8$$
$$2.74$$
$$+3.6$$
14.34

34.
$$8.07$$
$$4$$
$$+3.99$$
16.06

35.
$$7.4$$
$$3.75$$
$$+16$$
27.15

36. 3.18 + 4   7.18

37. 5 + 2.63   7.63

38. 1.8 + 9.38   11.18

39. 7.04 + 2.9   9.94

40. 8.62 + 5   13.62

41. 7 + 4.6   11.6

42. 4.16 + 0.379   4.539

43. 27.6 + 9.28   36.88

44. 7.88 + 0.594   8.474

45. 3.21 + 0.853   4.063

46. 0.174 + 6.76   6.934

47. 3.0683 + 1.925   4.9933

48. 5.8 + 2.42 + 6.3   14.52

49. 19.4 + 31.6 + 8.74   59.74

50. 52 + 3.6 + 1.8   57.4

51. 2.5 + 17 + 0.8   20.3

52. 30 + 2.9 + 0.541   33.441

53. 2.6 + 4 + 0.75   7.35

54. 0.06 + 0.4 + 2   2.46

55. 0.8 + 0.36 + 0.04   1.20

56. 12 + 1.2 + 0.372   13.572

57. 5.36 + 0.1 + 0.4   5.86

58. 9 + 3.2 + 0.15   12.35

59. 6 + 7.2 + 9.184   22.384

And the winner is . . .

Reading a chart

60. Which horse won $1.98 million? Kelso

61. Which horse won $1.46 million? Buckpasser

62. Which horse won $1.75 million? Round Table

63. Which horse won about $2.4 million? Spectacular Bid

64. Which horse won $1.18 million more than Seattle Slew? Spectacular Bid

Thoroughbred Racing—Money Winners	
HORSE	TOTAL WINNINGS
Spectacular Bid	$2,390,000
Kelso	1,980,000
Forego	1,940,000
Round Table	1,750,000
Buckpasser	1,460,000
Seattle Slew	1,210,000

PRACTICE WORKSHEET

Copymaster S164 or Duplicating Master S164

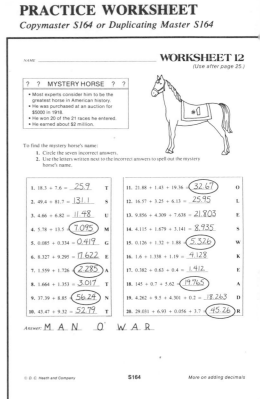

NAME _____

WORKSHEET 12
(Use after page 25.)

? ? MYSTERY HORSE ? ?

- Most experts consider him to be the greatest horse in American history.
- He was purchased at an auction for $5000 in 1918.
- He won 20 of the 21 races he entered.
- He earned about $2 million.

To find the mystery horse's name:
1. Circle the seven incorrect answers.
2. Use the letters written next to the incorrect answers to spell out the mystery horse's name.

1. 18.3 + 7.6 = 25.9   T
2. 49.4 + 81.7 = 131.1   S
3. 4.66 + 6.82 = 11.48   U
4. 5.78 + 13.5 = (7.095)   M
5. 0.085 + 0.334 = 0.419   G
6. 8.327 + 9.295 = 17.622   E
7. 1.559 + 1.726 = (2.285)   A
8. 1.664 + 1.353 = 3.017   T
9. 37.39 + 8.85 = (56.24)   N
10. 43.47 + 9.32 = 52.79   T

11. 21.88 + 1.43 + 19.36 = (32.67)   O
12. 16.57 + 3.25 + 6.13 = 25.95   L
13. 9.856 + 4.309 + 7.638 = 21.803   E
14. 4.115 + 1.679 + 3.141 = 8.935   S
15. 0.126 + 1.32 + 1.88 = (5.326)   W
16. 1.6 + 1.338 + 1.19 = 4.128   K
17. 0.382 + 0.63 + 0.4 = 1.412   E
18. 145 + 0.7 + 5.62 = (19.765)   A
19. 4.262 + 9.5 + 4.301 + 0.2 = 18.263   D
20. 29.031 + 6.93 + 0.056 + 3.7 = (45.26)   R

Answer: M A N   O'   W A R

  S164   *More on adding decimals*

LIFE-SKILL PROJECT

Researching information

Have the students use a book of world records to find the name and dollar value of the most valuable horse. Challenge the students to write the dollar value of the horse in words. (This information can be found in the *Guinness Book of World Records*.)

Conquistador Cielo; thirty-six million, four hundred thousand dollars

SKILLS REVIEWED
Rounding decimals
Adding decimals

PROBLEM-SOLVING SKILL
Using computer-displayed information

STARTING THE LESSON
Cumulative Skill Practice
Write these four answers on the
chalkboard:

18.3
4.53
7.82
62.35

Challenge the students to an answer
hunt by saying: "Look for the four even-
numbered exercises on page 26 that have
these answers. You have four minutes
to find as many of the exercises as you
can." (Exercises 8, 26, 38, and 62)

STARTING THE LESSON
Problem Solving
Have the students look at the display
screens to decide whether each of these
statements is true or false.

• To make a payment, you push the
white key in the bottom row. (True)
• To make a deposit, you push the white
key in the top row. (False)
• If you want to make a withdrawal,
you must type in an amount that is
a multiple of $10.00. (True)

Cumulative Skill Practice

Round to the nearest tenth.   *(page 20)*

1. 0.42 0.4 | **2.** 8.55 8.6 | **3.** 6.69 6.7 | **4.** 13.42 13.4 | **5.** 50.98 51.0
6. 2.436 2.4 | **7.** 8.761 8.8 | **8.** 18.250 18.3 | **9.** 27.342 27.3 | **10.** 71.062 71.1
11. 3.8214 3.8 | **12.** 6.3500 6.4 | **13.** 9.6175 9.6 | **14.** 14.0924 14.1 | **15.** 26.9341 26.9

Round to the nearest hundredth.   *(page 20)*

16. 2.726 2.73 | **17.** 4.634 4.63 | **18.** 4.205 4.21 | **19.** 2.371 2.37 | **20.** 8.082 8.08
21. 1.0314 1.03 | **22.** 7.2936 7.29 | **23.** 5.1171 5.12 | **24.** 9.0853 9.09 | **25.** 6.6152 6.62
26. 4.5347 4.53 | **27.** 6.0821 6.08 | **28.** 3.6349 3.63 | **29.** 8.5981 8.60 | **30.** 2.7436 2.74

Add.   *(page 22)*

| **31.** 8.1 +2.3 = 10.4 | **32.** 6.7 +2.8 = 9.5 | **33.** 5.9 +5.9 = 11.8 | **34.** 7.4 +6.8 = 14.2 | **35.** 4.8 +3.6 = 8.4 | **36.** 6.2 +9.1 = 15.3 |

| **37.** 4.72 +3.61 = 8.33 | **38.** 5.08 +2.74 = 7.82 | **39.** 3.96 +0.84 = 4.80 | **40.** 9.72 +1.99 = 11.71 | **41.** 3.86 +0.44 = 4.30 | **42.** 4.02 +1.77 = 5.79 |

| **43.** 53.6 +29.4 = 83.0 | **44.** 7.38 +2.97 = 10.35 | **45.** 5.33 +0.46 = 5.79 | **46.** 9.74 +2.38 = 12.12 | **47.** 5.75 +5.75 = 11.50 | **48.** 6.03 +6.03 = 12.06 |

| **49.** 5.6 2.9 +3.4 = 11.9 | **50.** 6.82 3.74 +2.96 = 13.52 | **51.** 15.4 38.3 +29.7 = 83.4 | **52.** 8.72 6.91 +4.75 = 20.38 | **53.** 5.93 8.41 +1.09 = 15.43 | **54.** 5.91 2.33 +1.09 = 9.33 |

Give the sum.   *(page 24)*

55. 2.1 + 3.46 5.56 | **56.** 5.78 + 2.92 8.70 | **57.** 8.14 + 35.6 43.74
58. 2.74 + 0.635 3.375 | **59.** 0.182 + 7.853 8.035 | **60.** 4.0831 + 2.619 6.7021
61. 6.2 + 3.14 + 7.4 16.74 | **62.** 15.8 + 42.6 + 3.95 62.35 | **63.** 36 + 5.4 + 2.9 44.3
64. 7.5 + 18 + 0.6 26.1 | **65.** 50 + 4.7 + 0.184 54.884 | **66.** 7.7 + 6 + 0.92 14.62
67. 0.05 + 0.8 + 6 6.85 | **68.** 0.1 + 0.73 + 0.05 0.88 | **69.** 15 + 1.5 + 0.15 16.65
70. 5 + 2.3 + 6.4 13.7 | **71.** 5.9 + 2.7 + 5.4 14.0 | **72.** 18 + 6.7 + 3.4 28.1
73. 9.23 + 6.04 + 5.8 21.07 | **74.** 16 + 3.74 + 19 38.74 | **75.** 22.8 + 3.5 + 31 57.3
76. 0.03 + 2 + 2.1 4.13 | **77.** 6.3841 + 2.9871 + 4.0035 13.3747 | **78.** 6.281 + 3.091 + 15.26 24.632

Problem solving
COMPUTERS IN BANKING

Many banks have computers to operate machines that can be used by customers 24 hours a day. Customers can use these "24-hour tellers" to deposit and withdraw money, make payments, and check account balances. The customer follows directions that appear on the screen. The computer makes the transaction and prints a record of it.

When Justine inserts her card and enters her personal identification number, this message appears on the screen.

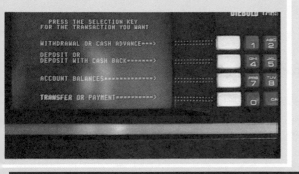

When she wants to make a withdrawal, this message appears.

PROBLEM-SOLVING
WORKSHEET
Copymaster S165 or Duplicating Master S165

NAME _____   **WORKSHEET 13**
(Use after page 27.)

HAVE YOU HEARD THIS ONE?
Crack the code to get the answer.

CODE					
A	**B**	**C**	**D**	**...**	**Z**
1+1	2+2	3+3	4+4		26+26

Riddle: What do you get when you cross a parrot with a tiger?
Answer:

I D O N T K N O W
18   8 30 28 40   22 28 30 46
B U T W H E N I T
4 42 40   46 16 10 28   18 40
T A L K S   Y O U
40 2 24 22 38   50 30 42
H A D B E T T E R
16 2 8   4 10 40 40 10 36
L I S T E N !
24 18 38 40 10 28

IT ALL ADDS UP
What is the smallest whole number you can add to 637 and get all 5's in the answer?

4918

MISSING DIGITS
Fill in the missing digits.

```
      5 2 7
      2 7 6
   +  4 4 5
    1 2 4 8
```

HAPPY BIRTHDAY
Jeff's birthday was the day before yesterday. The day after tomorrow is Saturday. On what day was Jeff's birthday?

Tuesday

MONEY PROBLEM
You have these coins:

What different amounts could you pay?

1 ¢	5 ¢	6 ¢
10 ¢	11 ¢	15 ¢
16 ¢	25 ¢	26 ¢
30 ¢	31 ¢	35 ¢
36 ¢	40 ¢	41 ¢

AGE PROBLEM
Susan, Shelly, Shirley, and Sandra are sisters. Sally is younger than Susan. Shirley is older than Susan. Sandra is younger than Sally.

Who is the oldest? Shirley
Who is the youngest? Sandra

© D. C. Heath and Company   S165   Problem solving

Solve.

1. If Justine needs $27, she has to withdraw $30. How much would she withdraw if she needs
   a. $18.57? $20 **b.** $69.50? $70 **c.** $31.95? $40
   d. $185.99? $190 **e.** $5.92? $10 **f.** $299.30? $300

2. Justine requests her account balances. They are:

   Savings $695.43
   Checking $381.35

   What is her total balance? $1076.78

3. In October Justine made these deposits to her checking account:

   October 5 $78.00
   October 14 $89.00
   October 20 $65.00
   October 31 $83.00

   a. What was the amount of her largest deposit in October? $89.00
   b. Did Justine deposit more than $350 in October? No

4. Justine made these withdrawals from her savings account in October:

   October 17 $20.00
   October 23 $60.00
   October 29 $90.00

   a. What was the amount of her smallest withdrawal? $20.00
   b. Did she withdraw less than $200 in October? Yes

LIFE-SKILL PROJECT
Estimating sums

Have the students estimate which two decimals in exercises 1–15 on page 26 have a sum of about

   1. 45.2   18.250 + 26.9341
   2. 85.2   14.0924 + 71.062
   3. 60.6   9.6175 + 50.98
   4. 6.3   2.436 + 3.8214
   5. 10.0   0.42 + 9.6175

If calculators are available, have the students use a calculator to see whether they made the correct choices.

CHAPTER 1 TEST
(Form A)

NAME _____

Match. *(page 4)*

f	1. 36,000	a.	36 million
d	2. 3,600,000	b.	300 thousand, 60
h	3. 360,000	c.	30 thousand, 600
a	4. 36,000,000	d.	3 million, 600 thousand
c	5. 30,600	e.	360 million
e	6. 360,000,000	f.	36 thousand
b	7. 300,060	g.	30 million, 600 thousand
j	8. 3,600,000,000	h.	360 thousand
i	9. 3,006,000	i.	3 million, 6 thousand
g	10. 30,600,000	j.	3 billion, 600 million

ANSWERS
1. f
2. d
3. h
4. a
5. c
6. e
7. b
8. j
9. i
10. g

Add. *(pages 6, 8)*

11. 621	12. 7507	13. 57,384	14. 38,061
+358	+1395	+ 2,958	+54,989
979	8902	60,342	93,050

15. 83 + 57 + 29 = 169   16. 529 + 32 + 175 + 89 = 825

11. 979
12. 8902
13. 60,342
14. 93,050
15. 169
16. 825
17. 300
18. 800
19. 1000
20. 5000
21. 16,000
22. 220,000
23. 10,000
24. 40,000
25. 80,000

Round to the nearest hundred. *(page 12)*

17. 339   300   18. 750   800   19. 978   1000

Round to the nearest thousand. *(page 12)*

20. 4500   5000   21. 16,395   16,000   22. 219,628   220,000

Round to the nearest ten thousand. *(page 12)*

23. 9653   10,000   24. 42,018   40,000   25. 75,000   80,000

© D. C. Heath and Company   S1   Page 1

CHAPTER 1 TEST
(Form A)

NAME _____

Match. *(page 16)*

d	26. 5.307	a.	53 and 7 tenths
f	27. 50.37	b.	53 and 7 thousandths
a	28. 53.7	c.	50 and 370 thousandths
g	29. 5.37	d.	5 and 307 thousandths
b	30. 53.007	e.	53 and 7 hundredths
j	31. 50.037	f.	50 and 37 hundredths
e	32. 53.07	g.	5 and 37 hundredths
c	33. 50.370	h.	53 and 70 hundredths
h	34. 53.70	i.	5 and 37 thousandths
i	35. 5.037	j.	50 and 37 thousandths
k	36. 5.73	k.	5 and 73 hundredths

ANSWERS
26. d
27. f
28. a
29. g
30. b
31. j
32. e
33. c
34. h
35. i
36. k
37. 6.4
38. 2.0
39. 6.0
40. 42.36
41. 9.09
42. 6.40
43. 5.8
44. 20.81
45. 12.040
46. 9.635
47. 11.63
48. 32.085
49. $3.70
50. Yes

Round to the nearest tenth. *(page 20)*

37. 6.35   6.4   38. 2.049   2.0   39. 5.97   6.0

Round to the nearest hundredth. *(page 20)*

40. 42.362   42.36   41. 9.085   9.09   42. 6.397   6.40

Add. *(pages 22, 24)*

43. 3.7	44. 16.94	45. 9.387	46. 5.77
+2.1	+ 3.87	+2.653	+3.865
5.8	20.81	12.040	9.635

47. 2.04 + 3.6 + 5.99 = 11.63   48. 17.28 + 6.065 + 8.74 = 32.085

Solve.

49. What is the total cost of a bowl of chili, a beef burger, and a hot chocolate? $3.70

50. You have $3.00. Can you buy a bowl of vegetable soup and 2 hot chocolates? Yes

SOUP AND SANDWICH	
Vegetable Soup	$ .95
Chili	1.40
Split Pea Soup	1.25
Beef Burger	1.75
Grilled Cheese	1.35
Hot Dog	1.20
Milk	.45
Orange Juice	.75
Hot Chocolate	.55

© D. C. Heath and Company   S2   Page 2

Chapter REVIEW

Here are scrambled answers for the review exercises:

4	13	billion	greater	hundredths	sum	thousand
8	80	decimal	hundreds	million	tenths	thousandths

1. million, thousand

1. The short word-name for this number is 2 [?], 74 [?]. *(page 4)*

2,074,000

2. billion

2. The long word-name for this number is two [?], six million, fifty-four thousand. *(page 4)*

2,006,054,000

3. sum, hundreds

3. The answer to an addition exercise is called the [?]. To complete this addition exercise, add the digits in the [?] place. *(page 6)*

328
+154
82

4. greater, 4

4. To round this number to the nearest hundred, first look at the digit in the tens place. Since it is [?] than 5, round the hundreds digit up to [?]. *(page 12)*

16,382

5. 80

5. To estimate this sum, round each amount to the nearest ten dollars. The estimated sum is [?] dollars. *(page 14)*

$54
+32

6. thousandths

6. The short word-name for this number is 24 and 86 [?]. *(page 16)*

24.086

7. tenths, 8

7. To round this number to the nearest whole number, you would first look at the digit in the [?] place. Since it is less than 5, you would round the number to [?]. *(page 20)*

8.247

8. hundredths

8. To do this addition exercise, first add the digits in the [?] place. *(page 22)*

5.78
+2.95

9. 13, decimal

9. Round each number to the nearest whole number and estimate the sum. The estimate is [?]. To find the sum, line up the [?] points and add. *(page 24)*

2.94 + 10.2 = ?

25. 5 and 9 tenths **26.** 38 and 6 hundredths **27.** 9 and 274 thousandths
28. 63 thousandths **29.** 7 and 865 ten-thousandths **30.** 6 and 803 thousandths

Chapter TEST

Write the short word-name. *(page 4)*
1. 25,340
25 thousand, 340
2. 836,000
836 thousand
3. 19,046,000
19 million, 46 thousand
4. 25,000,260
25 million, 260
5. 6,330,000,000
6 billion, 330 million

Write the standard numeral. *(page 4)*
6. 9 thousand 420 9420
7. 63 million, 75 thousand, 436 63,075,436
8. five hundred nine thousand
509,000
9. sixteen million, eighty-three thousand 16,083,000

Add. *(pages 6, 8)*
10. 52
$+36$
88
11. 349
$+142$
491
12. 396
$+158$
554
13. 6381
$+2974$
9355
14. 26,352
$+ 8,968$
35,320
15. 79,368
$+14,973$
94,341

16. 74 + 39 + 98 211
17. 25 + 82 + 9 116
18. 236 + 95 + 381 + 74 786

Round to the nearest hundred. *(page 12)*
19. 634 600
20. 850 900
21. 961 1000
22. 13,439 13,400
23. 42,956 43,000
24. 908
900

Write the short word-name. *(page 16)*
25. 5.9
26. 38.06
27. 9.274
28. 0.063
29. 7.0865
30. 6.803

Write the standard numeral. *(page 16)*
31. 26 and 43 hundredths
26.43
32. 8 and 61 thousandths
8.061
33. 60 and 52 ten-thousandths
60.0052

Round to the nearest tenth. *(page 20)*
34. 6.38 6.4
35. 15.43 15.4
36. 9.75 9.8
37. 8.064 8.1
38. 6.98 7.0
39. 8.87
8.9

Add. *(pages 22, 24)*
40. 8.4
$+2.3$
10.7
41. 15.9
$+ 8.7$
24.6
42. 6.09
$+2.954$
9.044
43. 15.936
$+ 8.742$
24.678
44. 3.750
$+8.6$
12.350
45. 6.36
$+1.2$
7.56

46. 8.3 + 2.9 11.2
47. 2.7 + 3.45 6.15
48. 6.01 + 8.213 14.223
49. 3.06 + 2.784 + 5.39
11.234

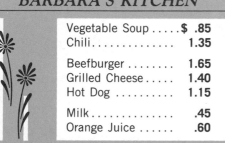

BARBARA'S KITCHEN

Vegetable Soup	$ .85
Chili	1.35
Beefburger	1.65
Grilled Cheese	1.40
Hot Dog	1.15
Milk	.45
Orange Juice	.60

Solve.
50. How much for a beefburger and milk?
$2.10
51. What is the total cost of a bowl of chili, a grilled cheese sandwich, and orange juice?
$3.35
52. You have $3.00. Can you buy 2 hot dogs and an orange juice? Yes

---

NAME _____ **CHAPTER 1 TEST**
(Form B)

Match. *(page 4)*

b	1. 4,700,000	a. 47 thousand		ANSWERS
f	2. 47,000,000	b. 4 million, 700 thousand		1. b
a	3. 47,000	c. 400 thousand, 70		2. f
d	4. 40,700	d. 40 thousand, 700		3. a
g	5. 470,000	e. 4 billion, 700 million		4. d
e	6. 4,700,000,000	f. 47 million		5. g
i	7. 470,000,000	g. 470 thousand		6. e
j	8. 40,700,000	h. 4 million, 7 thousand		7. i
c	9. 400,070	i. 470 million		8. j
h	10. 4,007,000	j. 40 million, 700 thousand		9. c
				10. h

Add. *(pages 6, 8)*

11. 326
$+521$
847
12. 6394
$+2367$
8761
13. 84,295
$+ 6,927$
91,222
14. 48,395
$+26,708$
75,103

15. 74 + 66 + 38 = 178
16. 474 + 23 + 7 + 76 = 580

ANSWERS (cont.)
11. 847
12. 8761
13. 91,222
14. 75,103
15. 178
16. 580
17. 400
18. 700
19. 1000
20. 7000
21. 27,000
22. 160,000
23. 10,000
24. 30,000
25. 90,000

Round to the nearest hundred. *(page 12)*
17. 426 400
18. 650 700
19. 961 1000

Round to the nearest thousand. *(page 12)*
20. 6500 7000
21. 27,056 27,000
22. 159,744 160,000

Round to the nearest ten thousand. *(page 12)*
23. 9531 10,000
24. 34,388 30,000
25. 85,000 90,000

© D. C. Heath and Company   S3   Page 1

NAME _____ **CHAPTER 1 TEST**
(Form B)

Match. *(page 16)*

d	26. 4.206	a. 40 and 26 hundredths
a	27. 40.26	b. 42 and 6 thousandths
e	28. 42.6	c. 42 and 6 hundredths
g	29. 4.26	d. 4 and 206 thousandths
b	30. 42.006	e. 42 and 6 tenths
h	31. 40.026	f. 42 and 60 hundredths
c	32. 42.06	g. 4 and 26 hundredths
j	33. 40.260	h. 40 and 26 thousandths
f	34. 42.60	i. 4 and 26 thousandths
i	35. 4.026	j. 4 and 260 thousandths
k	36. 4.62	k. 4 and 62 hundredths

ANSWERS
26. d
27. a
28. e
29. g
30. b
31. h
32. c
33. j
34. f
35. i
36. k
37. 8.3
38. 9.0
39. 7.0
40. 67.51
41. 7.17
42. 3.50
43. 9.7
44. 21.60
45. 15.211
46. 10.411
47. 14.39
48. 26.107
49. $3.20
50. No

Round to the nearest tenth. *(page 20)*
37. 8.25 8.3
38. 9.038 9.0
39. 6.98 7.0

Round to the nearest hundredth. *(page 20)*
40. 67.514 67.51
41. 7.165 7.17
42. 3.496 3.50

Add. *(pages 22, 24)*
43. 4.4
$+5.3$
9.7
44. 15.83
$+ 5.77$
21.60
45. 6.519
$+8.692$
15.211
46. 8.66
$+1.751$
10.411

47. 5.02 + 2.5 + 6.87 = 14.39
48. 15.32 + 4.057 + 6.73 = 26.107

Solve.

SOUP AND SANDWICH	
Vegetable Soup	$ .95
Chili	1.40
Split Pea Soup	1.25
Beef Burger	1.75
Grilled Cheese	1.35
Hot Dog	1.20
Milk	.45
Orange Juice	.75
Hot Chocolate	.55

49. What is the total cost of a bowl of split pea soup, a hot dog, and an orange juice? $3.20

50. You have $4.00. Can you buy 2 bowls of chili and a grilled cheese? No

© D. C. Heath and Company   S4   Page 2

Use Copymaster S336 to provide the students with an answer sheet in standardized test format.

Answers for Cumulative Test, Chapter 1

1. Ⓐ Ⓑ Ⓒ ●	2. Ⓐ Ⓑ ● Ⓓ	3. Ⓐ ● Ⓒ Ⓓ
4. ● Ⓑ Ⓒ Ⓓ	5. Ⓐ Ⓑ ● Ⓓ	6. Ⓐ Ⓑ ● Ⓓ
7. ● Ⓑ Ⓒ Ⓓ	8. Ⓐ Ⓑ ● Ⓓ	9. Ⓐ Ⓑ ● Ⓓ
10. ● Ⓑ Ⓒ Ⓓ	11. Ⓐ Ⓑ Ⓒ ●	12. Ⓐ ● Ⓒ Ⓓ

The table below correlates test items with student text pages.

Test Item	Page(s) Taught	Skill Practice
1	4	p. 10, exercises 1–16
2	4	p. 10, exercises 17–27
3	4	p. 10, exercises 17–27
4	6	p. 10, exercises 28–57
5	6, 8	p. 18, exercises 1–32
6	12	p. 18, exercises 33–56
7	16	p. 18, exercises 57–70
8	20	p. 26, exercises 1–15
9	20	p. 26, exercises 16–30
10	22	p. 26, exercises 31–54
11	24	p. 26, exercises 55–78
12	22	

Cumulative TEST Standardized Format

Choose the correct letter.

1. The short word-name for 5,060,000 is

A. 5 million, 600 thousand
B. 5 million, 6 thousand
c. 5 billion, 60 million
Ⓓ none of these

2. The standard numeral for five billion, twenty-five million is

A. 5,025,000
B. 5,000,025,000
Ⓒ 5,025,000,000
D. none of these

3. The standard numeral for thirty-two million is

A. 32,000
Ⓑ 32,000,000
c. 32,000,000,000
D. none of these

4. Add.   563
             291
          + 87

Ⓐ 941
B. 931
c. 741
D. none of these

5. Give the sum.

327 + 84 + 219

A. 1386
B. 610
Ⓒ 630
D. none of these

6. 2895 rounded to the nearest ten is

A. 3000
B. 2890
Ⓒ 2900
D. none of these

7. The standard numeral for 15 and 34 thousandths is

Ⓐ 15.034
B. 15.34
c. 15.0034
D. none of these

8. 36.952 rounded to the nearest tenth is

A. 36.9
B. 36.95
Ⓒ 37.0
D. none of these

9. 54.0349 rounded to the nearest hundredth is

A. 54.035
B. 54.04
Ⓒ 54.03
D. none of these

10. Add.   3.82
                2.09
             + 6.57

Ⓐ 12.48
B. 11.38
c. 11.48
D. none of these

11. Give the sum.

36.3 + 8.09 + 5.96

A. 17.68
B. 39.25
c. 49.35
Ⓓ none of these

12. What is the total price of 2 adult tickets and 1 child's ticket?

LITTLETOWN CINEMA 1 ADULT $3.25   LITTLETOWN CINEMA 1 CHILD $1.50

A. $6.25   Ⓑ $8.00
c. $4.75   D. none of these

CHAPTER 2
Subtracting Whole Numbers and Decimals

LESSON OBJECTIVES
To compare whole numbers (*pages 32–33*)
To subtract 2- and 3-digit numbers (*pages 34–35*)
To estimate differences (*pages 36–37*)
To subtract 3- and 4-digit numbers (*pages 36–37*)
To subtract across zeros (*pages 36–37*)
To subtract larger numbers (up to 6 digits) (*pages 38–39*)
To check subtraction by addition (*pages 38–39*)
To compare decimals (*pages 42–43*)
To subtract decimals (with the same number of decimal places) (*pages 44–45*)
To subtract decimals (with a different number of decimal places) (*pages 46–47*)
To estimate differences when subtracting decimals (*pages 46–47*)

PROBLEM-SOLVING SKILLS
Reading a chart (*pages 33–34, 42–45*)
Using logical reasoning (*pages 33, 39, 45*)
Choosing the correct operation (*pages 34, 36, 39, 41, 44, 49*)
Finding information in a display (*pages 36–37, 46, 49*)
Using a guess-and-check strategy (*pages 37, 47*)
Finding information in a table (*pages 38–39*)
Reading a newspaper ad (*page 41*)

RESOURCES
- **VISUAL AIDS**
  Newspaper ad from page 41 (*Visual Aid 7, Copymaster S115*)
  Notebook paper (*Visual Aid 3, Copymaster S111*)
  Computer display from page 49 (*Visual Aid 8, Copymaster S116*)
- **WORKSHEETS 14–22** (*Copymasters A166–S174 or Duplicating Masters S166–S174*)

LESSON OBJECTIVE
To compare whole numbers

PROBLEM-SOLVING SKILLS
Reading a chart
Using logical reasoning

STARTING THE LESSON
Play 'What are the facts?' Have the students study the two paragraphs on page 32 for 30 seconds and then close their books. Challenge the students to answer these questions:
- What were the names of the two balloons? (*High Rise, Explorer*)
- In what event did the balloons compete? (*Cross-country event*)
- How far did *High Rise* float? (8206 meters)
- How far did *Explorer* float? (8098 meters)
- Which balloon floated the greater distance? (*High Rise*)

Have the students open their books and look at the *Here's how* to check their answers to the last question.

HERE'S HOW NOTE
Remind the students that the smaller end of the symbols < and > always "points to" the smaller number.

Comparing whole numbers

Hot-air balloonists compete in several events. In the cross-country event, the balloon that floats farthest during a specified time wins the event.

High Rise floated 8206 meters, and *Explorer* floated 8098 meters. To determine the winner, the balloonists compared the two numbers.

Here's how *to compare whole numbers.*   *8206* ● *8098*

To compare two whole numbers, start at the left and compare the digits that are in the same place.

Step 1.

8206 ● 8098

| same |

Step 2.

8206 ● 8098

| 2 is greater than 0. |

Step 3.

So, 8206 > 8098.
Read > as "is greater than."

---

1. Look at the *Here's how*. Which balloon won (floated the greater distance)? High Rise

Study these examples.

Example A.

| 2 is less than 5. |

So, 3628 < 3659.
Read < as "is less than."

Example B.

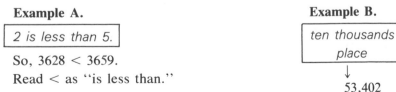

| ten thousands place | | No digit here! |

53,402   >   6348

2. Look at Example B. Are the digits 5 and 6 in the same place? No

EXERCISES

Less than (<) or greater than (>)?

3. 783 ● 784   <
4. 593 ● 590   >
5. 856 ● 1200   <
6. 1342 ● 819   >

7. 3621 ● 3514   >
8. 5834 ● 5741   >
9. 9834 ● 9843   <
10. 6519 ● 6514   >

11. 68,352 ● 68,411   <
12. 39,436 ● 39,400   >
13. 88,361 ● 89,000   <

14. 29,361 ● 30,362   <
15. 86,000 ● 85,999   >
16. 74,399 ● 74,000   >

17. 634,298 ● 624,298   >
18. 714,362 ● 714,459   <
19. 597,821 ● 609,375   <

20. 560,000 ● 559,000   >
21. 900,000 ● 879,694   >
22. 89,999 ● 900,000   <

Solve.

23. The results of the spot-landing event are shown in the table. The winner is the balloon that lands closest to a certain spot.

   a. Which balloon came in first (landed closest to the spot)? Free Spirit

   b. Which balloon came in last? Easy Floater

   c. List the balloons in order of finish, from first to last. Free Spirit, High Flier, America, Up and Away, Big Apple, Easy Floater

24. Remember that the winner of the cross-country event is the balloon that floats the farthest.

   a. Which balloon came in first? Up and Away

   b. Which balloon came in last? Big Apple

   c. List the balloons in order of finish, from first to last. Up and Away, America, Easy Floater, Free Spirit, High Flier, Big Apple

SPOT-LANDING EVENT	
NAME OF BALLOON	METERS LANDED FROM SPOT
America	834
Big Apple	929
Easy Floater	938
Free Spirit	763
High Flier	771
Up and Away	840

CROSS-COUNTRY EVENT	
NAME OF BALLOON	METERS TRAVELED
America	12,642
Big Apple	10,837
Easy Floater	11,134
Free Spirit	11,099
High Flier	10,909
Up and Away	12,800

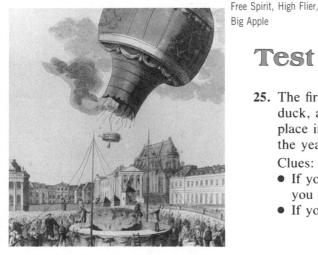

Test pilots wanted

25. The first "test pilots" on a hot-air balloon were a duck, a rooster, and a sheep. The historic flight took place in the year [?]. Study these clues to find the year. 1783

Clues:
- If you round the year to the nearest ten, you get 1780.
- If you add the digits of the year, you get 19.

EXTRA PRACTICE
Page 415   Skill 7

PRACTICE WORKSHEET
Copymaster S166 or Duplicating Master S166

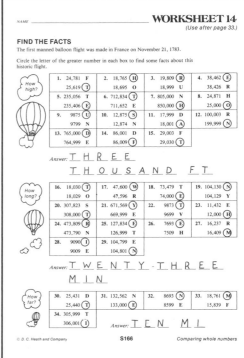

WORKSHEET 14
(Use after page 33.)

FIND THE FACTS
The first manned balloon flight was made in France on November 21, 1783.

Circle the letter of the greater number in each box to find some facts about this historic flight.

Answer: T H R E E   T H O U S A N D   F T

Answer: T W E N T Y - T H R E E   M I N

Answer: T E N   M I

© D. C. Heath and Company   S166   Comparing whole numbers

CHALKBOARD CHALLENGE
How many different 4-digit numbers can you build using these four digits?

 24

How many of the numbers are greater than 5000? 12

LESSON OBJECTIVES
To subtract 2- and 3-digit numbers

PROBLEM-SOLVING SKILLS
Reading a chart
Choosing the correct operation

STARTING THE LESSON
Write these listening times on the chalkboard:

Less than 1 hour
1 hour
2 hours
3 hours
4 hours
More than 4 hours

Before the students open their books, take a class survey. Ask the students to guess how long most people listen to the radio each day. Record their guesses on the chalkboard. Have the students compare their results with the data in the chart on page 34.

EXERCISE NOTE
Many students may assume that problems 45–48 will all require subtraction. Remind the students to read each problem carefully before solving it.

Subtracting 2- and 3-digit numbers

WHAT WOULD YOU SAY?

Twelve hundred people were asked how long they listened to the radio each day. Here are the results of the survey:

LISTENING TIME	NUMBER OF PEOPLE
Less than 1 hour	240
1 hour	456
2 hours	252
3 hours	96
4 hours	84
More than 4 hours	72

1. How many people listened 2 hours a day? 252

2. How many listened 3 hours? 96

3. Would you add or subtract to find how many more people listened 2 hours than listened 3 hours? Subtract

Here's how *to subtract whole numbers.*   *252 − 96 = ?*

Line up the digits that are in the same place.	Regroup. Subtract ones.	Regroup. Subtract tens.	Subtract hundreds.
252 − 96	⁴ 2 5̸ 2 − 96 ‾‾6	¹ ¹⁴ 2̸ 5̸ 2 − 96 ‾‾56	¹ ¹⁴ 2̸ 5̸ 2 − 96 ‾‾156

The answer is called the **difference.**

4. Look at the *Here's how.* How many more people listened 2 hours than listened 3 hours? 156

EXERCISES

Subtract. *Here are scrambled answers
for the next row of exercises:* 26 13 15 21 27 54

5. 56 −35 21	**6.** 68 −42 26	**7.** 42 −15 27	**8.** 73 −58 15	**9.** 90 −77 13	**10.** 81 −27 54
11. 256 − 28 228	**12.** 341 − 50 291	**13.** 722 − 65 657	**14.** 429 − 84 345	**15.** 536 − 98 438	**16.** 828 − 19 809
17. 429 −116 313	**18.** 638 −229 409	**19.** 514 −152 362	**20.** 923 −347 576	**21.** 752 −294 458	**22.** 541 −329 212
23. 361 −183 178	**24.** 511 −256 255	**25.** 837 −389 448	**26.** 640 −462 178	**27.** 438 −249 189	**28.** 827 −143 684

29. 93 − 21 72   **30.** 53 − 17 36   **31.** 60 − 28 32   **32.** 72 − 56 16

33. 243 − 30 213   **34.** 351 − 26 325   **35.** 633 − 59 574   **36.** 835 − 76 759

37. 598 − 375 223   **38.** 547 − 229 318   **39.** 743 − 256 487   **40.** 921 − 538 383

41. 418 − 179 239   **42.** 320 − 183 137   **43.** 635 − 379 256   **44.** 523 − 244 279

Solve. *Use the survey information on page 34.*

45. How many more people listened 1 hour
than listened 2 hours? 204

46. How many more people listened 1 hour
than listened less than 1 hour? 216

47. How many people listened 1 hour or
less than 1 hour? 696

48. How many people listened 3 hours or
more? 252

You're a program director Reading a schedule

Program Schedule

Show *What's Happening?*

Time *3:00 P.M. − 3:30 P.M.*

1. Record #43
2. Commercial 3:18
3. Record #65 .... 0:45
4. Guest interview 4:10
5. Commercial 9:40
6. Record #19 .... 0:25
7. .... 3:07
8.

49. What is the name of the show?
    What's Happening?

50. How many minutes long is the
show? 30

51. The schedule shows that the
first record will take 3 minutes
and 18 seconds to play. Study
the schedule. How much more
time must you fill to complete
the show? *Hint: 1 minute = 60
seconds.* 8 minutes 35 seconds

EXTRA PRACTICE
Page 415   Skill 8

PRACTICE WORKSHEET
Copymaster S167 or Duplicating Master S167

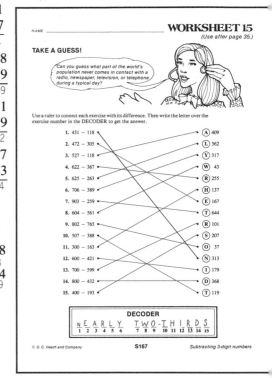

LIFE-SKILL PROJECT
Researching information
Have the students use a book of world
records to find the number of hours of
the longest continuous radio broadcast.
(This information can be found in the
Guinness Book of World Records.)

373 hours 35 minutes, by Bruce "Spanky" Smith of
KCRJ-FM Radio, Arizona

LESSON OBJECTIVES

To subtract 3- and 4-digit numbers
To subtract across zeros

PROBLEM-SOLVING SKILLS

Finding information in a display
Choosing the correct operation
Using a guess-and-check strategy

STARTING THE LESSON

Write these inventions and dates on the chalkboard:

Phonograph	1877
Radio	1875
Telephone	1894

Before the students open their books, ask them to try matching each item with its date of invention. Then have them check their guesses with the information at the top of the page.

Subtracting 3- and 4-digit numbers

Here are some things that you probably use each day. Notice that each was invented before the beginning of the 20th century (the year 1901).

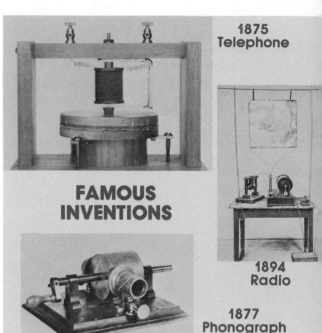

1875 Telephone

1894 Radio

1877 Phonograph

FAMOUS INVENTIONS

1. Which was invented first? second? third? Telephone, phonograph, radio

2. Was the telephone invented before or after the beginning of the 20th century? Before

3. Would you add or subtract to find how many years before the beginning of the 20th century the telephone was invented? Subtract

Here's how *to subtract whole numbers.* 1901 − 1875 = ?

To estimate the difference, first round each number to the nearest ten and then subtract. 1900 − 1880 = 20

Line up the digits that are in the same place.	No tens! Regroup 1 hundred for 10 tens.	Regroup 1 ten for 10 ones.	Subtract.
1 9 0 1 −1 8 7 5	1 $\overset{8}{9}$ 0 1 −1 8 7 5	1 $\overset{8}{9}$ $\overset{9}{0}$ 1 −1 8 7 5	1 $\overset{8}{9}$ $\overset{9}{0}$ 1 −1 8 7 5 26

4. Look at the *Here's how*. Was 20 a good estimate? Yes

5. How many years before the beginning of the 20th century was the telephone invented? 26

EXERCISES

6. Three of the calculator answers are wrong. Find them by estimating.

a. 281 − 259 `22` b. 329 − 197 `132` c. 578 − 383 `295`

d. 600 − 511 `89` e. 902 − 750 `252` f. 800 − 311 `489`

g. 1249 − 993 `256` h. 1680 − 1275 `305` i. 2000 − 1309 `691`

First estimate the difference. Then subtract.

7. 802
    −238
    564

8. 305
    −157
    148

9. 901
    −396
    505

10. 704
    −429
    275

11. 806
    −638
    168

12. 861
    −249
    612

13. 976
    −238
    738

14. 579
    −243
    336

15. 701
    −455
    246

16. 800
    −627
    173

17. 506
    −329
    177

18. 209
    −124
    85

19. 1883
    − 351
    1532

20. 1980
    − 635
    1345

21. 1704
    − 658
    1046

22. 1700
    − 453
    1247

23. 1603
    − 496
    1107

24. 3302
    − 861
    2441

25. $35.00
    −13.94
    $21.06

26. $29.00
    −16.82
    $12.18

27. $23.02
    −13.44
    $ 9.58

28. $42.00
    −29.37
    $12.63

29. $96.00
    −47.01
    $48.99

30. $98.02
    −12.99
    $85.03

31. 796 − 313 483

32. 804 − 375 429

33. 900 − 493 407

34. 800 − 366 434

35. 756 − 403 353

36. 601 − 574 27

37. 1976 − 533 1443

38. 2834 − 685 2149

39. 5603 − 4384 1219

40. 5600 − 2916 2684

41. 9000 − 3817 5183

42. 7000 − 5034 1966

43. $37.00 − $20.59 $16.41

44. $80.03 − $57.97 $22.06

45. $60.00 − $38.92 $21.08

Solve. Use the dates on page 36.

46. How many years after the invention of the telephone was the radio invented? 19

47. How many years before the beginning of the 20th century was the phonograph invented? 24

48. The telescope was invented 288 years before the radio. What year was that? 1606

49. The pendulum clock was invented 221 years before the telephone. What year was that? 1654

50. The airplane was invented 26 years after the phonograph. What year was that? 1903

51. The thermometer was invented 7 years before the beginning of the 17th century. What year was that? 1594

Key it in!

Find a way to push each marked key once to get the answer.

52. 87 − 51 =
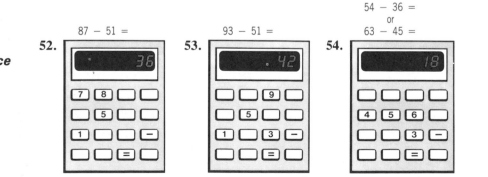

53. 93 − 51 =

54. 54 − 36 =
    or
    63 − 45 =

EXTRA PRACTICE
Page 416   Skill 9

PRACTICE WORKSHEET
Copymaster S168 or Duplicating Master S168

CHALKBOARD CHALLENGE
Find the missing digits.

1. 7 [8]
    −[2] 5
    5 3

2. 3 [6] 4
    − 2 5 [3]
    [1] 1 1

3. [8] 6 4
    − 6 3 [5]
    2 [2] 9

LESSON OBJECTIVES
To subtract larger numbers (up to 6 digits)
To check subtraction by addition

PROBLEM-SOLVING SKILLS
Finding information in a table
Choosing the correct operation
Using logical reasoning

STARTING THE LESSON
Play 'What are the facts?' Have the students study the opening paragraph at the top of the page for 30 seconds. Then tell them to close their books and challenge them to answer these questions from memory:
- What National League record did Pete Rose set? (Lifetime hits)
- Were there more or less than 60,000 fans in attendance? (More)
- In what stadium was the record set? (Veterans Stadium)

Subtracting larger numbers

IT HAPPENED IN VETERANS STADIUM!

On August 10, 1981, Pete Rose became the National League's leader in lifetime hits. Rose hit number 3631 before an over-capacity crowd of 60,561 fans.

SEATING CAPACITIES OF SOME MAJOR LEAGUE STADIUMS		
TEAM	STADIUM	SEATING CAPACITY
Braves	Atlanta Stadium	52,744
Orioles	Memorial Stadium	52,137
Cubs	Wrigley Field	37,741
Tigers	Tiger Stadium	54,220
Astros	Astrodome	45,000
Dodgers	Dodger Stadium	56,000
Yankees	Yankee Stadium	73,205
Phillies	Veterans Stadium	56,581
Rangers	Arlington Stadium	40,078

1. How many people attended the game when Pete Rose set a new record for lifetime hits? 60,561

2. What is the seating capacity of Veterans Stadium? 56,581

3. What two numbers would you use to find the number of fans that could not be seated? 60,561 and 56,581

Here's how *to subtract.*

$$60,561 - 56,581 = ?$$

Subtract.	Regroup and subtract.	Regroup twice.	Subtract.
60,561 −56,581 ————— 0	60,5̸61 −56,581 ————— 80	60,5̸61 −56,581 ————— 80	60,5̸61 −56,581 ————— 3,980

> First round each number to the nearest thousand and then estimate the difference:
> 61,000 − 57,000 = 4000

4. Look at the *Here's how*. Was 4000 a good estimate? Yes

5. How many fans could not be seated? 3980

Here's how *to check the difference by addition.*

```
    60,561  ←
  − 56,581
  ────────
     3,980  ──→  3,980      It checks!
                + 56,581
                ────────
                  60,561  ──
```

EXERCISES

6. Three of the calculator answers are wrong. Find them by estimating.

a. 935 − 426   `509`   **b.** 883 − 201   `682`   **c.** 618 − 225   `393`

d. 1813 − 637   `1176`   **e.** 2490 − 678   `1812`   **f.** 3331 − 846   `2485`

g. 5823 − 1995   `.4828`   **h.** 4993 − 3481   `2512`   **i.** 3603 − 1587   `1016`

First estimate the difference. Then subtract.

7. 7383 − 5906 1477	**8.** 3826 − 1039 2787	**9.** 5287 − 3240 2047	**10.** 8002 − 3495 4507	**11.** 6081 − 2943 3138
12. 5960 − 2880 3080	**13.** 7020 − 1930 5090	**14.** 9220 − 7900 1320	**15.** 8007 − 3241 4766	**16.** 8063 − 1297 6766
17. 35,110 − 8,790 26,320	**18.** 40,230 − 7,320 32,910	**19.** 53,984 − 6,216 47,768	**20.** 47,832 − 9,949 37,883	**21.** 86,142 − 1,986 84,156

Subtract. Then check by addition.

22. 19,354 − 16,258 3096	**23.** 36,093 − 24,720 11,373	**24.** 68,391 − 26,493 41,898	**25.** 94,003 − 62,875 31,128	**26.** 36,902 − 12,118 24,784
27. 359,061 − 52,839 306,222	**28.** 365,291 − 64,775 300,516	**29.** 903,461 − 386,229 517,232	**30.** 806,000 − 542,600 263,400	**31.** 603,010 − 225,311 377,699

Solve. Use the table on page 38.

32. How many more seats does Yankee Stadium have than the Astrodome? 28,205

34. Which stadium has 15,003 more seats than Wrigley Field? Atlanta Stadium

33. How many more seats does Dodger Stadium have than Tiger Stadium? 1780

35. List the nine stadiums from greatest seating capacity to least capacity.

Won by one!

36. Study the clues to find which team won.
Clues:
- After 7 complete innings, the Dodgers were leading the Pirates 5 to 3.
- Both teams scored after the 7th inning.
- The game went extra innings.
- A total of 11 runs was scored. Dodgers

PRACTICE WORKSHEET

Copymaster S169 or Duplicating Master S169

NAME _____   **WORKSHEET 17**
(Use after page 39.)

SKILL DRILL
Study these examples.

5 6̶2̶84 − 1473 4811	7 4 8̶0̶,065 − 17,244 62,821	3 1 2 1 4̶1̶7̶,0̶2̶6̶ − 181,419 233,607

Subtract.

1. 6871 −2652 4219	2. 8131 −2041 6090	3. 9331 −8217 1114	4. 8300 −6295 2005
5. 6000 −2836 3164	6. 5012 −1378 3634	7. 5006 −3561 1445	8. 3509 −1254 2255
9. 8000 −7483 517	10. 9603 −4538 5065	11. 8291 −2714 5577	12. 8706 −1291 7415
13. 17,465 −11,269 6196	14. 47,184 −29,729 17,455	15. 59,495 −38,999 20,496	16. 93,003 −56,875 36,128
17. 80,000 −62,416 17,584	18. 76,216 −15,432 60,784	19. 82,763 −71,652 11,111	20. 87,065 −26,038 61,027
21. 468,051 − 56,847 411,204	22. 574,298 − 52,186 522,112	23. 813,724 −761,615 52,109	24. 800,000 −709,050 90,950

Check yourself. Here are the scrambled answers:
517 1114 1445 2005 2255 3164 3634 4219 5065 5577 6090
6196 7415 11,111 17,455 17,584 20,496 36,128 52,109 60,784
61,027 90,950 411,204 522,112

© D. C. Heath and Company   **S169**   *Subtracting larger numbers*

CHALKBOARD CHALLENGE

Copy and complete this Magic Square so that the sums of the numbers along each row, column, and diagonal are the same.

23	28	21
22	24	26
27	20	25

Answers for page 39.
35. Yankee Stadium
Veterans Stadium
Dodger Stadium
Tiger Stadium
Atlanta Stadium
Memorial Stadium
Astrodome
Arlington Stadium
Wrigley Field

SKILLS REVIEWED
Writing standard numerals in words
Adding whole numbers
Rounding whole numbers and decimals

PROBLEM-SOLVING SKILLS
Reading a newspaper ad
Choosing the correct operation

STARTING THE LESSON
Cumulative Skill Practice
Write these five answers on the chalkboard:

    63 thousand, 201
    31,000,286
    58,360
    700
    7.4

Challenge the students to an answer hunt by saying, "Look for the five even-numbered exercises on page 40 that have these answers. You have five minutes to find as many of the exercises as you can." (Exercises 4, 22, 30, 44, and 62)

STARTING THE LESSON
Problem Solving
The ad at the top of page 41 is also on **Visual Aid 7**. Use the ad and ask questions like these:
- What is the price of the '81 Cutlass? ($5895)
- Is $4500 enough money to buy the '79 Malibu? (No)
- How many miles has the '79 Mustang been driven? (25,000)

Answers for page 40.
1. 46 thousand, 220
2. 9 thousand, 337
3. 11 thousand, 835
4. 63 thousand, 201
5. 186 thousand, 743
6. 237 thousand, 105
7. 864 thousand, 319

Cumulative Skill Practice

Write the short word-name. *(page 4)*

1. 46220
2. 9337
3. 11835
4. 63201
5. 186743
6. 237105
7. 864319
8. 145623
9. 6723804
10. 5657129
11. 29000673
12. 1000235

Write the standard numeral. *(page 4)*

13. 246 thousand, 659
    246,659
14. 34 million
    34,000,000
15. 57 billion
    57,000,000,000
16. 28 million, 213 thousand
    28,213,000
17. 5 million, 18 thousand
    5,018,000
18. 4 million, 24 thousand, 73
    4,024,073
19. five hundred forty-seven thousand, three hundred ninety-five
    547,395
20. sixty-two thousand, two hundred fifty
    62,250
21. thirty-one million, two hundred eighty-six thousand
    31,286,000
22. thirty-one million, two hundred eighty-six
    31,000,286
23. seventeen million, sixty-three thousand, ninety
    17,063,090

Add. *(page 8)*

24. 5384 + 297 = 5681	25. 4627 + 309 = 4936	26. 6714 + 888 = 7602	27. 5376 + 2944 = 8320	28. 2846 + 5907 = 8753	29. 6302 + 1984 = 8286
30. 52,374 + 5,986 = 58,360	31. 92,335 + 4,618 = 96,953	32. 27,584 + 27,584 = 55,168	33. 57,319 + 65,007 = 122,326	34. 52,916 + 38,155 = 91,071	35. 71,209 + 36,142 = 107,351
36. 328 + 296 + 54 = 678	37. 927 + 58 + 629 = 1614	38. 3942 + 567 + 8314 = 12,823	39. 2715 + 6130 + 852 = 9697	40. 593 + 2577 + 4255 = 7425	41. 623 + 1586 + 29 = 2238

Round to the nearest hundred. *(page 12)*

42. 567 → 600	43. 824 → 800	44. 650 → 700	45. 471 → 500	46. 35 → 0	47. 98 → 100
48. 3607 → 3600	49. 6532 → 6500	50. 8880 → 8900	51. 9050 → 9100	52. 3982 → 4000	53. 1924 → 1900

Round to the nearest tenth. *(page 20)*

54. 3.53 → 3.5	55. 24.305 → 24.3	56. 9.67 → 9.7	57. 0.884 → 0.9	58. 1.750 → 1.8	59. 3.215 → 3.2
60. 52.04 → 52.0	61. 8.96 → 9.0	62. 7.390 → 7.4	63. 0.064 → 0.1	64. 27.95 → 28.0	65. 9.013 → 9.0

Problem solving

YOU WANT TO BUY A CAR!

You have circled the ads for seven used cars you'd like to look at.

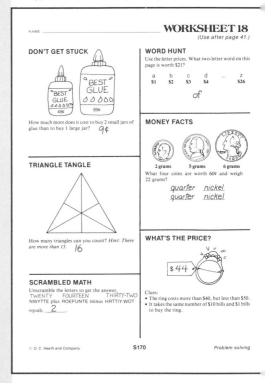

Autos—American

USED-CAR BARGAINS

77 Olds Cutlass 47,000 mi	$3795
78 Chevette 34,000 mi	$2195
79 Chevy Caprice 17,000 mi	$4895
78 Monte Carlo 25,000 mi	$4195
79 Mustang 25,000 mi	$4195
77 Chevy Caprice 25,000 mi	$4450
77 Ford Granada 78,000 mi	$2750

BILL SMITH'S AUTO PARTS
555-5511

1972 Lincoln Mark IV. All options, black with black vinyl roof, sharp. $1495 firm. 309-777-9397.

1980 Chevy Monza. 11,500 miles, air, power steering, power brakes, AM-FM radio, automatic, $5000. 1-555-3624 (8-5), 555-2991 (after 5).

1978 CHEVETTE. 4-speed, good gas mileage, 39,000 miles. $2800. Call 1-555-2310 after 5.

Village Auto Sales, Inc.
1-777-2277

81 Chev. 4-dr 12,000 mi	$5595
81 Cutlass Supreme 2-dr 17,311 mi	$5895
80 Chev. 4-dr 52,000 mi	$4795
79 Malibu Classic 2-dr 38,000 mi	$4795
76 Chev. ½-ton PU 58,000 mi	$2500

1980 Pontiac Phoenix. Power brakes, power steering, air, AM-FM stereo and tape. Excellent mpg, excellent condition. $5500 or best offer. 1-777-4456 days. 1-777-2303 evenings.

79 Chevette. 4-speed, tach, tilt, well taken care of. 50,000 miles. $3600. 555-4615 after 7.

1976 Chevy Nova Hatchback. 350 automatic, air, tilt, power steering, power brakes, AM-FM, runs very well. Looks good. $2095. Bill's Used Cars. 1-555-7379.

Use the circled ads to answer these questions.

1. Which car costs the most?
   81 Cutlass Supreme

2. Which car costs the least?
   1978 Chevette

3. Which car is the newest model?
   81 Cutlass Supreme

4. Which car is the oldest?
   77 Olds Cutlass

5. Which car has been driven the most miles? 79 Chevette

6. Which car has been driven the fewest miles? 1980 Chevy Monza

7. How many more miles has the 1977 Cutlass been driven than the 1981 Cutlass? 29,689

8. What is the difference in price between the two Cutlass cars? $2100

9. What is the difference in price between the cheapest and the most expensive 1979 model? $1195

10. You have $1835 in one savings account and $979 in another. Do you have enough money to pay cash for the cheapest car? Yes

11. You have $2814. How much will you need to borrow to buy the 1979 Mustang? $1381

12. Village Auto Sales guarantees its cars for 7500 miles after the purchase. How many miles will the Cutlass have when the guarantee expires? 24,811

Subtracting Whole Numbers and Decimals **41**

EXTRA PROBLEM SOLVING
Page 445   Odd exercises

PROBLEM-SOLVING WORKSHEET
Copymaster S170 or Duplicating Master S170

NAME _____

WORKSHEET 18
(Use after page 41.)

DON'T GET STUCK

BEST GLUE 49¢
BEST GLUE 89¢

How much more does it cost to buy 2 small jars of glue than to buy 1 large jar? 9¢

WORD HUNT
Use the letter prices. What two-letter word on this page is worth $21?

a	b	c	d	...	z
$1	$2	$3	$4		$26

of

TRIANGLE TANGLE

How many triangles can you count? *Hint: There are more than 15.* 16

SCRAMBLED MATH
Unscramble the letters to get the answer.
TWENTY FOURTEEN THIRTY-TWO
NWYTTE plus ROEFUNTE minus HRTTIY-WOT
equals 2

MONEY FACTS

2 grams   5 grams   6 grams

What four coins are worth 60¢ and weigh 22 grams?

quarter nickel
quarter nickel

WHAT'S THE PRICE?

$44

Clues:
• The ring costs more than $40, but less than $50.
• It takes the same number of $10 bills and $1 bills to buy the ring.

© D. C. Heath and Company   S170   Problem solving

LIFE-SKILL PROJECT
Reading newspaper ads
Have the students use a used-car ad to find the difference in price between the most-expensive and the least-expensive 1980 model advertised.

More answers for page 40.
8. 145 thousand, 623
9. 6 million, 723 thousand, 804
10. 5 million, 657 thousand, 129
11. 29 million, 673
12. 1 million, 235

41

LESSON OBJECTIVE
To compare decimals

PROBLEM-SOLVING SKILL
Reading a chart

STARTING THE LESSON
Ask the students if they can identify the four common objects in the close-up photos at the top of the page. Have them write their answers. Challenge them to identify all four photos in less than 60 seconds. (Rubber bands, strawberry, crayon tip, broom)

EXERCISE NOTE
Some students may find it helpful to annex zeros when comparing some of the numbers in exercises 11–41.

Comparing decimals

Can you recognize the four common objects in these close-up photos?

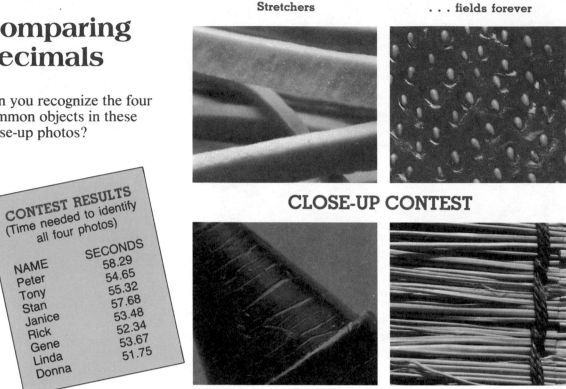

Stretchers   . . . fields forever

CLOSE-UP CONTEST

Draw, Pardner!   Solve this for a clean sweep

CONTEST RESULTS
(Time needed to identify all four photos)

NAME	SECONDS
Peter	58.29
Tony	54.65
Stan	55.32
Janice	57.68
Rick	53.48
Gene	52.34
Linda	53.67
Donna	51.75

Reprinted from GAMES Magazine (515 Madison Avenue, New York, N.Y. 10022). Copyright

1. Who recognized all four close-up photos in 53.67 seconds? Linda

2. Who had a time of 53.48 seconds? Rick

3. Which two numbers would you compare to decide whether Rick or Linda had the better (shorter) time? 53.48 and 53.67

Here's how *to compare decimals.*   **53.48 ● 53.67**

Start at the left and compare digits that are in the same place.

Step 1.   53.48 ● 53.67 | same |

Step 2.   53.48 ● 53.67 | 4 is less than 6. |

Step 3.   53.48 < 53.67

---

4. Look at the *Here's how*. Who had the better time, Linda or Rick? Rick

5. Check each example. Have the decimals been compared correctly?

   a. 52.34 ● 51.68 | 2 is greater than 1. |
       52.34 > 51.68   Yes

   b. 54.60 ● 54.65 | It helps to fill in a zero. |
       54.6   < 54.65
             Yes

EXERCISES

Less than (<) or greater than (>)?

6. 0.4 ● 0.5
   <

7. 0.07 ● 0.06
   >

8. 0.009 ● 0.008
   >

9. 14.3 ● 14.1
   >

10. 6.75 ● 6.57
    >

11. 0.27 ● 0.2
    >

12. 0.005 ● 0.03
    <

13. 0.1 ● 0.02
    >

14. 8.23 ● 8.32
    <

15. 31.69 ● 31.7
    <

16. 2.1 ● 1.98
    >

17. 5.352 ● 53.52
    <

18. 0.725 ● 1.1
    <

19. 1.07 ● 1.007
    >

20. 0.815 ● 0.82
    <

21. 33.86 ● 33.87
    <

22. 0.34 ● 0.43
    <

23. 6.215 ● 62.16
    <

24. 23.78 ● 21.88
    >

25. 1.1 ● 1.08
    >

26. 782.1 ● 783
    <

27. 18.02 ● 18.003
    >

28. 53.06 ● 53.2
    <

29. 0.333 ● 0.332
    >

30. 3.504 ● 3.54
    <

31. 52.8 ● 8.29
    >

32. 0.021 ● 0.12
    <

33. 6.72 ● 6.75
    <

34. 6.153 ● 6.2
    <

35. 2.61 ● 2.58
    >

36. 0.04 ● 0.006
    >

37. 7.017 ● 7.005
    >

38. 3.53 ● 3.55
    <

39. 13.7 ● 13.69
    >

40. 38.06 ● 38.7
    <

41. 0.914 ● 0.92
    <

Solve. Use the chart on page 42.

42. Which girl recognized the four close-up photos in less than 52 seconds? Donna

43. Which boys took more than 55 seconds? Peter, Stan

44. Who had the shorter time, Tony or Gene? Gene

45. Who had the longer time, Rick or Janice? Janice

46. Who had the better combined time, Tony and Linda or Janice and Gene? Tony and Linda

47. a. List the times in order from best (shortest) to worst (longest).
    b. Who came in first? Donna
    c. Who came in last? Peter

    a. 51.75, 52.34, 53.48, 53.67, 54.65, 55.32, 57.68, 58.29

More close-ups

Use the word clues to name these close-ups.

48.
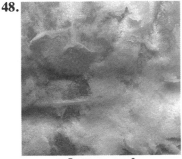
Lost appeal
Orange peel

49.

Ears to you!
Cotton swab

50.

Rubber soul
Sole of running shoe

EXTRA PRACTICE
Page 417   Skill 11

PRACTICE WORKSHEET
Copymaster S171 or Duplicating Master S171

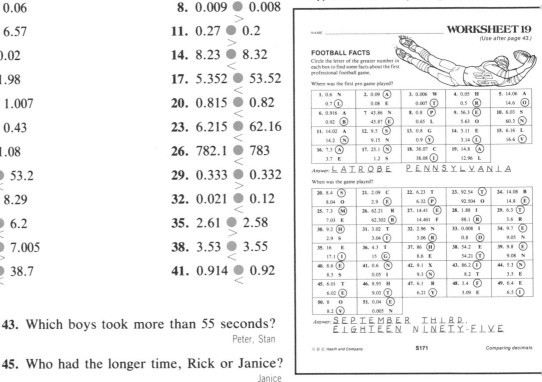

CHALKBOARD CHALLENGE
Write the numbers *1, 2, 3, 4, 5, 6, 7,* and *8* in the circles so that no two consecutive numbers are connected by a line. (Consecutive numbers have a difference of 1.)

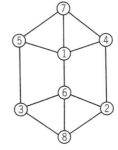

Answers may vary.

CHALKBOARD QUIZ
on previous lesson

< or > ?

1. 0.6 ● 0.7   <
2. 0.35 ● 0.3   >
3. 1.05 ● 1.005   >
4. 2.302 ● 2.32   <
5. 36.08 ● 36.6   <

LESSON OBJECTIVE

To subtract decimals (with the same number of decimal places)

PROBLEM-SOLVING SKILLS

Reading a chart
Choosing the correct operation
Using logical reasoning

STARTING THE LESSON

Write these dates and market values on the chalkboard:

Date	Market Value
1900 nickel	$2.90
1920 nickel	$1.75
1940 nickel	$1.25
1950 nickel	$0.20

Before the students open their books, have them try matching each of the nickels to its market value. Tell them to check their guesses with the chart at the top of page 44.

Subtracting decimals

1890   1900   1910

1920   1930   1940   1950

NICKELS (1890–1950)		
DATE	MILLIONS MINTED	MARKET VALUE
1890	16.1	$8.80
1900	27.2	2.90
1910	30.0	2.00
1920	63.4	1.25
1930	23.8	0.75
1940	176.1	0.20
1950	10.2	1.75

1. A coin dealer will pay you $8.80 for one of these nickels. Which nickel is it? 1890

2. Which nickel has a market value of $1.25? 1920

3. How many million nickels were minted in 1920? in 1930? 63.4, 23.8

4. Would you add or subtract to find how many more millions of nickels were minted in 1920 than in 1930? Subtract

Here's how *to subtract decimals.*   *63.4 − 23.8 = ?*

Line up the decimal points.

```
  6 3 . 4
- 2 3 . 8
```

Regroup and subtract.

```
    2
  6 3̶ .¹4
- 2 3 . 8
      . 6
```

Regroup and subtract.

```
  5¹2
  6̶ 3̶ .¹4
- 2 3 . 8
  3 9 . 6
```

5. Look at the *Here's how.* How many more millions of nickels were minted in 1920 than in 1930? 39.6

EXERCISES

Subtract.
Here are scrambled answers for the next row of exercises: *6.54   7.15   26.4   21.7   34.7   37.1*

6.
```
  49.6
-12.5
```
37.1

7.
```
  7.42
-0.27
```
7.15

8.
```
 42.6
- 7.9
```
34.7

9.
```
 9.18
-2.64
```
6.54

10.
```
 75.3
-48.9
```
26.4

11.
```
 43.5
-21.8
```
21.7

12.	0.31 -0.18 0.13	13.	80.2 -38.9 41.3	14.	6.19 -2.74 3.45	15.	5.91 -0.26 5.65	16.	72.9 $-\ 8.7$ 64.2	17.	8.42 -3.54 4.88
18.	0.74 -0.68 0.06	19.	646.5 $-\ 89.3$ 557.2	20.	6.75 -2.41 4.34	21.	87.3 $-\ 1.6$ 85.7	22.	93.71 $-\ 8.41$ 85.30	23.	104.5 $-\ 25.6$ 78.9
24.	$52.40 -12.75 $39.65	25.	$7.29 -5.36 $1.93	26.	$7.38 $-\ .88$ $6.50	27.	$110.60 $-\ 85.20$ $25.40	28.	$47.35 -39.88 $7.47	29.	$87.65 $-\ 4.82$ $82.83

30. 70.2 − 6.1 64.1   31. 16.3 − 5.7 10.6   32. 80.06 − 5.14 74.92   33. 55.06 − 2.14 52.92

34. 59.4 − 23.7 35.7   35. 23.16 − 4.10 19.06   36. 75.4 − 44.6 30.8   37. 35.2 − 8.4 26.8

38. 60.49 − 33.71 26.78   39. 63.3 − 9.6 53.7   40. 70.02 − 4.16 65.86   41. 63.14 − 7.21 55.93

42. 0.35 − 0.22 0.13   43. 7.89 − 0.97 6.92   44. 115.4 − 53.4 62   45. 86.3 − 42.3 44

46. 9.4 − 2.9 6.5   47. 345.8 − 258.4 87.4   48. 8.04 − 0.56 7.48   49. 3.42 − 2.91 0.51

50. 8.74 − 2.06 6.68   51. 5.03 − 2.78 2.25   52. 5.0 − 2.6 2.4   53. 6.1 − 3.7 2.4

54. 51.0 − 29.4 21.6   55. 2.00 − 1.46 0.54   56. 18.00 − 6.93 11.07   57. 7.00 − 1.92 5.08

Solve. Use the chart on page 44.

58. How many million nickels were minted in
   a. 1890? 16.1
   b. 1900? 27.2
   c. 1950? 10.2

59. The number of nickels minted in 1890 written as a whole number is 16,100,000. Write the number of nickels minted in the other years as whole numbers.

60. How many more nickels were minted in 1940 than in 1930? Give the answer as a whole number. 152,300,000

61. How much more is the market value of a 1900 nickel than the market value of a 1920 nickel? $1.65

62. What is the total market value of a 1910, a 1940, and a 1950 nickel? $3.95

63. Why do you think a 1950 nickel has a greater market value than a 1930 nickel? Fewer were minted.

Nickel mysteries

Study the clue. Use the pictures of the coins and the chart on page 44.

64. What date is on each nickel?
   a.   b.

   Clue:
   ● The total market value of both nickels is $4.15.
   a. 1920   b. 1900

65. What date is on each nickel?
   a.   b.

   Clue:
   ● 40.2 million of these nickels were minted altogether.
   a. 1950   b. 1910

Subtracting Whole Numbers and Decimals **45**

PRACTICE WORKSHEET
Copymaster S172 or Duplicating Master S172

NAME _____ WORKSHEET 20
(Use after page 45.)

FLIP IT OVER
This type of nickel is usually called a "buffalo" nickel. Whose portrait is on the other side?

Use a ruler to connect each exercise with its difference. Then write the letter over the exercise number in the DECODER to get the answer.

1. 69.9 − 5.9   (M) 84.82
2. 58.7 − 23.4   (A) 16.4
3. 23.2 − 6.8   (C) 84.92
4. 91.07 − 6.25   (I) 64.6
5. 31.25 − 3.18   (A) 0.13
6. 86.5 − 55.7   (A) 64
7. 74.4 − 9.8   (R) 30.8
8. 91.17 − 6.25   (D) 87.4
9. 0.46 − 0.33   (N) 35.3
10. 7.78 − 0.86   (E) 28.07
11. 226.5 − 53.5   (I) 8.48
12. 8.6 − 3.9   (I) 173
13. 456.9 − 369.5   (N) 4.7
14. 9.15 − 0.67   (N) 6.92
15. 0.29 − 0.23   (N) 41.6
16. 91.3 − 49.7   (A) 0.06

DECODER

A	N		A	M	E	R	I	C	A	N
1	2		3	4	5	6	7	8	9	10
I	N	D	I	A	N					
11	12	13	14	15	16					

© D. C. Heath and Company   S172   *Subtracting decimals*

LIFE-SKILL PROJECT
Researching information
Have the students use a book of world records to find the highest price paid for a coin collection. (This information can be found in the *Guinness Book of World Records*.)

$7,300,000

Answer for page 45.

59.	1900	27,200,000
	1910	30,000,000
	1920	63,400,000
	1930	23,800,000
	1940	176,100,000
	1950	10,200,000

45

LESSON OBJECTIVES

To subtract decimals (with a different number of decimal places)
To estimate differences when subtracting decimals

PROBLEM-SOLVING SKILLS

Finding information in a display
Using a guess-and-check strategy

STARTING THE LESSON

If a digital watch that shows tenths or hundredths of seconds is available, have volunteers follow the contest rules and estimate 30 seconds. Record their times on the chalkboard to determine who came closest to guessing how long 30 seconds is.

HERE'S HOW NOTE

Use **Visual Aid 3** (lined notebook paper) to assist the students in aligning the digits.

30 − 24.29 = ?

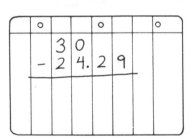

More on subtracting decimals

HOW LONG IS 30 SECONDS?

Cal and Barb had a contest to see who could come closer to guessing how long 30 seconds is. Their stopwatches show the results.

1. Read the stopwatches. Whose guess was off by 5.67 seconds? Cal's

2. What time is shown on Barb's stopwatch? 24.29 sec

3. Which two numbers would you use to compute how far off Barb's guess was? 30 and 24.29

CONTEST RULES

- Use a stopwatch.
- Push the Start button.
- Don't look at the display.
- When you think 30 seconds have passed, push the Stop button.
- The person whose guess is closer to 30 seconds wins.

Cal's guess

00'00" L
00'35"67

Barb's guess

00'00"
00'24"29

Here's how *to subtract decimals.* $30 - 24.29 = ?$

Line up the decimal points. Write in the 0's.	Regroup.	Subtract.
30.00 −24.29	29 9 30.00 −24.29	29 9 30.00 −24.29 5.71

To estimate the difference, first round to the nearest second and then subtract:

$30 - 24 = 6$

4. Look at the *Here's how*. Whose guess was off by 5.71 seconds? Who won the contest, Cal or Barb?   Barb's, Cal

EXERCISES

5. Four of the calculator answers are wrong. Find them by estimating.

a. 37.42 − 4.25   `33.17`

c. 5.01 − 1.99   `9.02`

e. 43.8 − 2.12   `4.16`

g. 53.8 − 19.926   `33.874`

i. 29.79 − 21.046   `18.744`

b. 68.12 − 29.31   `28.81`

d. 8.2 − 6.95   `1.25`

f. 7.21 − 3.194   `4.016`

h. 4.78 − 0.8   `3.98`

j. 118.9 − 19.02   `99.88`

Subtract. *Here are scrambled answers for the next row of exercises:* 1.055 9.42 5.21 3.84 0.69 13.02

6.	8.63	7.	9.76	8.	24.1	9.	6.3	10.	3.29	11.	6.14
	−3.42		−0.34		−11.08		−5.245		−2.6		−2.3
	5.21		9.42		13.02		1.055		0.69		3.84

12.	3.74	13.	7.3	14.	7.86	15.	6.83	16.	8.7	17.	9.61
	−2.5		−0.74		−1.59		−2.7		−6.25		−2.9
	1.24		6.56		6.27		4.13		2.45		6.71

18.	9.6	19.	28.31	20.	17.0	21.	3.781	22.	7.52	23.	8.312
	−2.64		−24.7		−8.95		−0.97		−4.083		−2.77
	6.96		3.61		8.05		2.811		3.437		5.542

24.	$4	25.	$5	26.	$10	27.	$24	28.	$16	29.	$6
	−2.98		−1.47		−5.78		−16.43		−11.29		−3.11
	$1.02		$3.53		$4.22		$7.57		$4.71		$2.89

30. 6 − 2.7   6.0 −2.7   3.3
31. 8 − 4.2   3.8
32. 12.94 − 8.53   4.41
33. 16.4 − 5   11.4
34. 15.1 − 12.8   2.3
35. 23.4 − 2.89   20.51
36. 9.5 − 6   3.5
37. 14.5 − 12.8   1.7
38. 7 − 6.52   0.48
39. 9.72 − 0.865   8.855
40. 7.4 − 5.125   2.275
41. 123.7 − 101.4   22.3
42. 12.935 − 4.6   8.335
43. 9.323 − 1.747   7.576
44. 5.2 − 2.456   2.744
45. 25 − 8.2   16.8
46. 100 − 44.75   55.25
47. 75.25 − 16   59.25

Solve.

48. What is the difference in price between a $37 digital watch and a $29.85 alarm watch? $7.15

49. You have $17.50. How much more money do you need in order to buy a $29.95 video-game watch? $12.45

50. A customer paid for a $32.99 calculator watch with a $50 bill. How much change should she get? $17.01

51. You are the clerk. How much change should you give a customer who paid for a $27.97 stopwatch and a $24.95 alarm watch with a $100 bill? $47.08

Key it in!

Find a way to push each marked key once to get the answer.

5 − 3.8 =

3.5 − 2 =

9 − 6.7 =

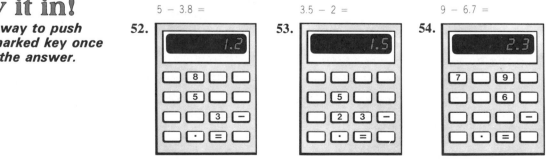

52. [calculator display: 1.2] keys: 8, 5, 3, −, ., =
53. [calculator display: 1.5] keys: 5, 2, 3, −, ., =
54. [calculator display: 2.3] keys: 7, 9, 6, −, ., =

PRACTICE WORKSHEET
Copymaster S173 or Duplicating Master S173

NAME _____   **WORKSHEET 21**
(Use after page 47.)

RIDDLE TIME
What did one green tomato say to the other green tomato?

To find the answer:
1. Subtract.
2. Write the letter over its matching number in the DECODER.

1. 8 − 3.4	2. 13.84 − 8.5	3. 17.3 − 6
4.6	5.34	11.3
E	C	E
4. 33.6 − 3.89	5. 8 − 7.52	6. 8.65 − 0.676
29.71	0.48	7.974
H	I	K
7. 8.3 − 6.236	8. 132.7 − 102.8	9. 13.946 − 5.8
2.064	29.9	8.146
L	L	P
10. 5.2 − 3.679	11. 31 − 9.6	12. 100 − 56.83
1.521	21.4	43.17
R	T	U
13. 81.26 − 19	14. 3.781 − 0.97	15. 8.7 − 6.25
62.26	2.811	2.45
V	W	E

DECODER
W I L L   W E   E V E R
2.811 0.48 2.064 29.9   2.811 11.3   4.6 62.26 11.3 1.521
K E T C H U P ?
7.974 2.45 21.4 5.34 29.71 43.17 8.146

© D. C. Heath and Company   **S173**   *Subtracting decimals*

CHALKBOARD CHALLENGE
Find the largest number on page 47. Find the smallest number. Subtract your two numbers. Did you get a difference of 123.36?

123.7, 0.34, Yes

47

SKILLS REVIEWED
Adding decimals
Comparing whole numbers and decimals
Subtracting whole numbers and
  decimals

PROBLEM-SOLVING SKILLS
Finding information on a display
Choosing the correct operation

STARTING THE LESSON
Cumulative Skill Practice
Challenge the students to an estimation
hunt by saying, "Pick the largest sum
in the first row of exercises." (Exercise
3) Then have the students pick the largest sum in the second, third, and fourth
rows of exercises. (Exercises 4, 9,
and 12)

STARTING THE LESSON
Problem Solving
The computer display at the top of page
49 is also on **Visual Aid 8**. Have the
students use the computer display to
answer questions like these:
• What time does Flight 65 arrive from
  Atlanta? (9:35)
• Which flight is arriving at Gate 2?
  (Flight 303)
• Which flight is scheduled to depart
  55 minutes after it arrives? (Flight 110)

Cumulative Skill Practice

Give the sum. *(page 24)*

1. $7.6 + 0.82 + 5.3$ 13.72
2. $3.74 + 2.9 + 65.9$ 72.54
3. $39.82 + 52 + 96.5$ 188.3
4. $84.8 + 7.463 + 73.29$ 165.553
5. $7.564 + 7.3 + 68.83$ 83.694
6. $70.2 + 58.61 + 3.56$ 132
7. $52.14 + 0.89 + 24$ 77.03
8. $1.7 + 25.73 + 43.83$ 71.26
9. $88.9 + 14 + 72.35$ 175.25
10. $68.6 + 19.21 + 52.6$ 140.41
11. $90.9 + 73.26 + 25$ 189.16
12. $30.68 + 4.02 + 251.6$ 2

Less than (<) or greater than (>)? *(page 32)*

13. 593 ● 594   <
14. 786 ● 768   >
15. 599 ● 600   <
16. 895 ● 885   >
17. 960 ● 1000   <
18. 1501 ● 999   >
19. 3431 ● 3318   >
20. 2815 ● 3815   <
21. 29,361 ● 29,400   <
22. 40,000 ● 38,652   >
23. 55,399 ● 54,000   >
24. 4106 ● 4214   <

Subtract. *(page 36)*

25.	26.	27.	28.	29.	30.
567	863	802	901	600	459
−239	−299	−574	−732	−371	−368
328	564	228	169	229	91

31.	32.	33.	34.	35.	36.
2634	7972	3174	2063	3105	4986
−256	−388	−570	−1421	−1638	−2897
2378	7584	2604	642	1467	2089

37.	38.	39.	40.	41.	42.
6017	5203	3800	4000	5000	7001
−2842	−195	−695	−928	−1639	−3542
3175	5008	3105	3072	3361	3459

Less than (<) or greater than (>)? *(page 42)*

43. 0.008 ● 0.007   >
44. 3.57 ● 3.75   <
45. 0.005 ● 0.03   <
46. 2.01 ● 2.1   <
47. 3.1 ● 2.97   >
48. 0.615 ● 0.62   <
49. 4.215 ● 42.15   <
50. 3.82 ● 3.62   >
51. 1.1 ● 1.07   >
52. 621.7 ● 622   <
53. 0.031 ● 0.13   <
54. 73.9 ● 7.39   >

Give the difference. *(pages 44, 46)*

55. $53.4 − 29.6$ 23.8
56. $30.6 − 15.8$ 14.8
57. $9.00 − 5.74$ 3.26
58. $25.41 − 3.02$ 22
59. $8.6 − 3.5$ 5.1
60. $10.18 − 9.54$ 0.64
61. $20.34 − 15.95$ 4.39
62. $41.08 − 23.6$ 17
63. $26 − 13.5$ 12.5
64. $20 − 6.34$ 13.66
65. $9.8 − 6.99$ 2.81
66. $14.32 − 4.08$ 10.
67. $42.1 − 3.84$ 38.26
68. $9.6 − 3.74$ 5.86
69. $12 − 3.52$ 8.48
70. $83 − 52.06$ 30.9

Problem solving

COMPUTERS AT THE AIRPORT

You're an airline agent. You use computers to write tickets, make reservations, assign seats, check luggage, and provide arrival and departure information.

─── ARRIVALS ───

FLIGHT	CITY	TIME	GATE
303	BOSTON	9:05	2
110	LOS ANGELES	9:20	8
65	ATLANTA	9:35	14
220	PHILADELPHIA	9:40	20

─── DEPARTURES ───

FLIGHT	CITY	TIME	GATE
303	DENVER	9:45	2
615	DALLAS	10:10	15
110	NEW YORK	10:15	8
45	SEATTLE	10:20	12

Use the computer screen to answer these customers' questions.

1. *What time does Flight 615 leave for Dallas?* 10:10 *From which gate?* 15

2. *Which flight is arriving at 9:35? Which city is it coming from?* 65, Atlanta

3. *My sister is arriving at 9:40 from Philadelphia. At which gate should I meet her?* 20

4. "My friend is arriving on Flight 65 and departing on Flight 45. Will he have more than a half hour between flights?" Yes

5. "My travel agent said you start assigning seats 45 minutes before each flight leaves. Will you be assigning seats for Flight 110 at 9:00?" No

Solve.

6. A first-class ticket from Atlanta to Chicago is $201. Coach fare is $32 less. What is the price of a coach ticket? $169

7. Airfare from Los Angeles to Chicago is $372. How much would 2 tickets cost? $744

8. A 727 jet liner carries 135 passengers. Your computer shows 123 coach reservations and 18 first-class reservations. Has the flight been overbooked? Yes ("Overbooked" means there are more reservations than seats.)

9. A DC 9 has 139 passenger seats. The flight attendant counted 27 empty seats. Your computer shows you have assigned seats to 129 passengers. Are all the passengers on board? No

Subtracting Whole Numbers and Decimals **49**

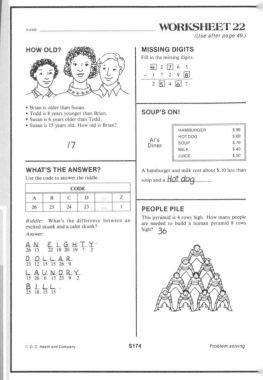
LIFE-SKILL PROJECT
Using library resources
Have the students use an almanac to find which airport in the United States has the most takeoffs and landings.

Chicago O'Hare

49

< or > ? *(page 32)*

1. 936 ⓒ 940   2. 699 ⓒ 700   3. 543 ⓒ 534
4. 1023 ⓢ 865   5. 2074 ⓒ 2007   6. 3000 ⓢ 2994
7. 5173 ⓒ 51,370   8. 56,344 ⓢ 65,340   9. 83,219 ⓒ 79,465
10. 320,000 ⓒ 332,000   11. 500,000 ⓢ 469,538   12. 699,999 ⓒ 900,000

Subtract. *(pages 34, 36, 38)*

13. 78 −21 **57**	14. 61 −37 **24**	15. 521 −307 **214**	16. 825 −278 **547**
17. 901 −526 **375**	18. 1700 −356 **1344**	19. 18,841 −6,876 **11,965**	20. 46,807 −12,559 **34,248**

21. 526 − 318 = **208**   22. 904 − 666 = **238**

23. 800 − 729 = **71**   24. 3764 − 529 = **3235**

25. 5004 − 1375 = **3629**

ANSWERS
1. **<**
2. **<**
3. **>**
4. **>**
5. **>**
6. **>**
7. **<**
8. **<**
9. **>**
10. **<**
11. **>**
12. **<**
13. **57**
14. **24**
15. **214**
16. **547**
17. **375**
18. **1344**
19. **11,965**
20. **34,248**
21. **208**
22. **238**
23. **71**
24. **3235**
25. **3629**

S5   *Page 1*

< or > ? *(page 42)*

26. 0.4 ⓒ 0.5   27. 0.38 ⓢ 0.35   28. 0.08 ⓒ 0.7
29. 0.53 ⓒ 0.35   30. 6.0 ⓢ 5.99   31. 2.1 ⓒ 2.02
32. 32.58 ⓢ 23.5   33. 2.614 ⓒ 2.637   34. 0.065 ⓒ 0.56

Subtract. *(pages 44, 46)*

35. 36.8 −21.4 **15.4**	36. 53.1 −20.7 **32.4**	37. 6.11 −4.82 **1.29**	38. 80.4 −37.6 **42.8**
39. 73.4 −12.25 **61.15**	40. 5.3 −2.38 **2.92**	41. 2.651 −0.84 **1.811**	42. 6.33 −2.091 **4.239**

43. 43.4 − 29.6 = **13.8**   44. 5.04 − 1.66 = **3.38**

45. 8 − 6.4 = **1.6**   46. 11.5 − 3.625 = **7.875**

Solve.

47. What is the total cost of a photo album and a package of cassette tapes? **$3.99**

48. How much do you save on a package of flashbulbs if you use the coupon? **$.30**

49. How much do you save if you buy a package of cassette tapes and a photo album on sale? **$1.19**

50. You had $5. You bought a package of cassette tapes and a photo album. How much money did you have then? **$1.01**

ANSWERS
26. **<**
27. **>**
28. **<**
29. **>**
30. **>**
31. **>**
32. **>**
33. **<**
34. **<**
35. **15.4**
36. **32.4**
37. **1.29**
38. **42.8**
39. **61.15**
40. **2.92**
41. **1.811**
42. **4239**
43. **13.8**
44. **3.38**
45. **1.6**
46. **7.875**
47. **$3.99**
48. **$.30**
49. **$1.19**
50. **$1.01**

S6   *Page 2*

Chapter REVIEW

Here are scrambled answers for the review exercises:

2	add	digits	same
10	decimal	less	zero
900	difference	regroup	

1. same, less   **2.** regroup, difference   **3.** 900

1. To compare two whole numbers, start at the left and compare digits that are in the [?] place. The symbol < is read as "is [?] than." *(page 32)*

264 ● 486
264 < 486

2. To do this subtraction exercise, first [?] 1 ten for 10 ones and then subtract ones. The answer to a subtraction exercise is called the [?]. *(page 34)*

324
− 75

3. To estimate this difference, you can round each number to the nearest hundred. The estimate would be [?]. *(page 36)*

1602 − 695

4. 10   **5.** add   **6.** digits

4. The next step in this subtraction exercise is to regroup 1 hundred for [?] tens. *(page 36)*

4
8̸10̸ 4 6
− 3 9 4
2

5. To check this difference, [?] 1719 and 895. *(page 38)*

2614
− 895
1719

6. To compare these two numbers, start at the left and compare [?] that are in the same place. *(page 42)*

48.67 ● 48.52

7. decimal   **8.** zero   **9.** 2

7. To do this subtraction exercise, first line up the [?] points. *(page 44)*

6.29 − 0.58

8. To do this subtraction exercise, first write a [?] after 8.3 and then subtract. *(page 46)*

8.3
− 2.57

9. To estimate this difference, you can round each number to the nearest whole number. The estimate would be [?]. *(page 46)*

4.18 − 2.09

Chapter TEST

Less than (<) or greater than (>)? (page 32)

1. 843 ● 840 >
2. 799 ● 800 <
3. 653 ● 635 >
4. 900 ● 3482 <
5. 2836 ● 2851 <
6. 5396 ● 684 >
7. 6999 ● 700 >
8. 248 ● 1419 <
9. 39,426 ● 39,420 >
10. 172,299 ● 71,109 >
11. 48,746 ● 58,764 <
12. 68,342 ● 68,411 <

Subtract. (pages 34, 36, 38)

13. 87
    −23
    64

14. 76
    −39
    37

15. 421
    −156
    265

16. 604
    −275
    329

17. 703
    −214
    489

18. 800
    −158
    642

19. 9008
   −3721
   5287

20. 1503
   − 829
   674

21. 16,800
   − 3,562
   13,238

22. 35,216
   −21,628
   13,588

23. 61,100
   −13,251
   47,849

24. 25,112
   −11,004
   14,108

25. 724 − 98 626
26. 803 − 229 574
27. 3921 − 766 3155
28. 32,407 − 8,959 23,448

Less than (<) or greater than (>)? (page 42)

29. 0.8 ● 0.9 <
30. 0.05 ● 0.4 <
31. 5.1 ● 4.99 >
32. 6.3 ● 2.77 >
33. 1.1 ● 1.06 >
34. 18.3 ● 18.26 >
35. 0.034 ● 0.43 <
36. 0.011 ● 0.22 <

Subtract. (pages 44, 46)

37. 37.3
    −15.1
    22.2

38. 8.03
    −2.94
    5.09

39. 15.23
    − 4.7
    10.53

40. 7.51
    −3.467
    4.043

41. 8.12
    −3.345
    4.775

42. 6.31
    −2.7
    3.61

43. 16.4 − 8.7 7.7
44. 50.25 − 12.89 37.36
45. 7.51 − 3.861 3.649
46. 21 − 13.66 7.34

Solve.

47. What is the total cost of a baseball shirt and a package of notebook paper? $3.78

48. How much do you save on a package of batteries if you use the coupon? $.50

49. You had $5. You bought two packages of batteries using a coupon. How much money did you have then? $2.42

200 SHEETS FILLER PAPER
Wide or Narrow Ruled
79¢ SALE
Reg 1.29

Coupon
BATTERIES
Pack of 2
AA alkaline
Limit 2 packs
without coupon 1.79
1 29

BASEBALL SHIRT
Polyester & Cotton
SAVE 1.00
Reg. 3.99
2 99 SALE

Use Copymaster S336 to provide the students with an answer sheet in standardized test format.

Answers for Cumulative Test, Chapters 1–2

1. ⬤ⒷⒸⒹ	2. ⒶⒷ⬤Ⓓ	3. ⒶⒷ⬤Ⓓ
4. ⬤ⒷⒸⓄ	5. Ⓐ⬤ⒸⒹ	6. ⒶⒷ⬤Ⓓ
7. ⬤ⒷⒸⒹ	8. Ⓐ⬤ⒸⒹ	9. ⒶⒷⒸ⬤
10. ⒶⒷ⬤Ⓓ	11. Ⓐ⬤ⒸⒹ	12. ⒶⒷ⬤Ⓓ

The table below correlates test items with student text pages.

Test Item	Page(s) Taught	Skill Practice
1	4	p. 40, exercises 1–12
2	4	p. 40, exercises 13–23
3	8	p. 40, exercises 24–41
4	12	p. 40, exercises 42–53
5	20	p. 40, exercises 54–65
6	24	p. 48, exercises 1–12
7	32	p. 48, exercises 13–24
8	36	p. 48, exercises 25–42
9	42	p. 48, exercises 43–54
10	44, 46	p. 48, exercises 55–70
11	22	
12	46	

Cumulative TEST Standardized Format

Choose the correct letter.

1. The short word-name for 6,034,000 is

  A. 6 million, 34 thousand
  B. 6 billion, 34 million
  C. 6 billion, 34 thousand
  D. none of these

2. The standard numeral for two billion, fifty thousand is

  A. 2,050,000
  B. 2,050,000,000
  C. 2,000,050,000
  D. none of these

3. Add.   4435
            796
         +2074

  A. 6195
  B. 7205
  C. 7305
  D. none of these

4. 6984 rounded to the nearest hundred is

  A. 7000
  B. 6980
  C. 6990
  D. none of these

5. 36.0572 rounded to the nearest tenth is

  A. 36.06
  B. 36.1
  C. 36.05
  D. none of these

6. Give the sum.
$42.5 + 3.18 + 6.8$

  A. 41.48
  B. 14.23
  C. 52.48
  D. none of these

7. Which number is less than 43,057?

  A. 42,978
  B. 43,507
  C. 43,100
  D. none of these

8. Subtract.   1304
                 − 295

  A. 1019
  B. 1009
  C. 1191
  D. none of these

9. Which number is greater than 0.54?

  A. 0.45
  B. 0.5
  C. 0.055
  D. none of these

10. Give the difference.
$42.8 − 3.56$

  A. 0.72
  B. 39.36
  C. 39.24
  D. none of these

11. Record album: $5.79
Single record: $1.35

What will 1 album and 2 single records cost?

  A. $12.93
  B. $8.49
  C. $7.14
  D. none of these

12. Record Album: $5.79
Single record: $1.35

You had $10. You bought 1 album and 1 single. How much money did you have left?

  A. $4.21
  B. $8.65
  C. $2.86
  D. none of these

Chapter 3
Multiplying — Whole Numbers and Decimals

CHAPTER 3
Multiplying Whole Numbers and Decimals

LESSON OBJECTIVES
To multiply by multiples of 10, 100, or 1000   (*pages 54–55*)
To multiply by a 1-digit number   (*pages 56–57*)
To estimate products   (*pages 56–57*)
To multiply by a 2-digit number   (*pages 58–59*)
To multiply by a 3-digit number   (*pages 60–61*)
To multiply decimals   (*pages 64–65*)
To estimate products of decimals   (*pages 64–65*)
To simplify expressions   (*pages 66–67*)
To multiply decimals by 10, 100, or 1000   (*pages 68–69*)

PROBLEM-SOLVING SKILLS
Reading a chart   (*pages 55, 61*)
Using logical reasoning   (*pages 57, 65*)
Reading a newspaper ad   (*pages 58–59*)
Using a guess-and-check strategy   (*pages 59, 71*)
Finding information in a display   (*pages 60, 66*)
Choosing the correct operation   (*pages 61, 63, 67, 71*)
Finding information in an ad   (*page 63*)
Recognizing when needed information is missing   (*page 63*)
Finding information in a table   (*pages 64, 68*)
Solving a multi-step problem   (*pages 65, 67*)
Checking answers   (*page 69*)
Using information on a menu and cash-register display
   (*page 71*)

RESOURCES
- **VISUAL AIDS**
  Notebook paper   (*Visual Aid 3, Copymaster S111*)
  Sale ad from page 63   (*Visual Aid 9, Copymaster S116*)
- **WORKSHEETS 23–31**   (*Copymasters S175–S183 or Duplicating
  Masters S175–S183*)

STARTING THE LESSON
Have the students number from *1* to *12* on scratch paper. Tell them you will read a multiplication fact and they are to write the product. Explain that you will read each fact only twice.

1. 5×8 (40)   **2.** 4×9 (36)
3. 7×7 (49)   **4.** 8×9 (72)
5. 6×8 (48)   **6.** 5×9 (45)
7. 6×9 (54)   **8.** 8×8 (64)
9. 9×9 (81)   **10.** 9×7 (63)
11. 7×8 (56)   **12.** 8×5 (40)

Have the students correct their own papers as you give the answers.

Before students open their books, ask them which is worth more money, a bill with Hamilton's portrait on it, a bill with Cleveland's portrait, or a bill with Franklin's portrait. Then have them open their books and find the answer at the top of page 54.

EXERCISE NOTE
Use several of exercises 1–44 as oral exercises before making a written assignment. Have the students verbalize the method they used to mentally compute the products.

Multiplying by multiples of 10, 100, or 1000

FRANKLIN, HAMILTON, OR CLEVELAND?

Which is worth more money, 6 Hamiltons, 4 Franklins, or 3 Clevelands? *Hint: Hamilton is on the $10 bill, Franklin is on the $100 bill, and Cleveland is on the $1000 bill.*   3 Clevelands

To answer the question, you will need to multiply by 10, 100, and 1000.

Here's how *to multiply by multiples of 10, 100, or 1000.*

$6 \times 10 = ?$	$4 \times 100 = ?$	$3 \times 1000 = ?$
To multiply a whole number by 10, multiply by 1 and write 1 zero.	To multiply a whole number by 100, multiply by 1 and write 2 zeros.	To multiply a whole number by 1000, multiply by 1 and write 3 zeros.
$6 \times 10 = 60$	$4 \times 100 = 400$	$3 \times 1000 = 3000$
Six Hamiltons are worth $60.	Four Franklins are worth $400.	Three Clevelands are worth $3000.

Study these examples.

a.
$$\begin{array}{r} 20 \\ \times 30 \\ \hline 600 \end{array}$$
Use basic facts.
Multiply 2×3.
Write 2 zeros.

b.
$$\begin{array}{r} 500 \\ \times 70 \\ \hline 35,000 \end{array}$$
Multiply 7×5.
Write 3 zeros.

EXERCISES

Multiply. *Here are scrambled answers for the next row of exercises:*   *800*   *12,000*   *120*   *6000*

1. 12 × 10   120
2. 20 × 40   800
3. 60 × 100   6000
4. 60 × 200   12,000

5. 83 × 10   830
6. 9 × 1000   9000
7. 44 × 10   440
8. 60 × 40   2400

9. 81 × 10   810
10. 30 × 300   9000
11. 50 × 30   1500
12. 60 × 400   24,000

13. 3 × 70   210
14. 9 × 200   1800
15. 70 × 60   4200
16. 4 × 200   800

17. 8 × 3000   24,000
18. 50 × 70   3500
19. 23 × 100   2300
20. 8 × 2000   16,000

21. 20 × 4   80
22. 800 × 3   2400
23. 70 × 40   2800
24. 500 × 3   1500

25. 900 × 20   18,000
26. 10 × 30   300
27. 100 × 40   4000
28. 8000 × 2   16,000

29. 70 × 70   4900
30. 5000 × 50   250,000
31. 80 × 100   8000
32. 70 × 100   7000

33. 70 × 1000   70,000
34. 60 × 1000   60,000
35. 300 × 100   30,000
36. 5000 × 90   450,000

37. 400 × 80   32,000
38. 1000 × 600   600,000
39. 900 × 100   90,000
40. 600 × 800   480,000

41. 80 × 1000   80,000
42. 600 × 10   6,000
43. 700 × 100   70,000
44. 300 × 10   3000

Use the money facts. How much money would you have if you had

45. 14 Hamiltons? $140
46. 40 Jeffersons? $80

47. 23 Franklins? $2300
48. 60 Lincolns? $300

49. 7 Grants? $350
50. 9 Jacksons? $180

51. 10 Washingtons and 5 Jacksons? $110
52. 20 Jeffersons and 3 Grants? $190

MONEY FACTS

BILL	PORTRAIT
$1	Washington
$2	Jefferson
$5	Lincoln
$10	Hamilton
$20	Jackson
$50	Grant
$100	Franklin

You're the bank teller!

Answer these questions.

53. *Are 9 Hamiltons the same amount of money as 90 Washingtons?*   Yes

54. "Are 8 Grants the same amount of money as 80 Lincolns?"   Yes

55. "Are 7 Jacksons and 30 Jeffersons equal to 3 Franklins?"   No

56. "Would you give me 50 Hamiltons, 20 Jacksons, and 60 Grants for 15 Franklins? Why or why not?"   No. $3900 is more than $1500.

PRACTICE WORKSHEET

Copymaster S175 or Duplicating Master S175

NAME _____

WORKSHEET 23
(Use after page 55.)

A BILLION DOLLARS
How high would a stack of a billion $1 bills be?

Multiply. Then use the DECODER to get the answer.

DECODER

24,000	40,000	2400	1200	6000	10,000	16,000	800	45,000	12,000
I	B	S	K	E	A	M	C	D	N
1600	1500	4000	4800	8000	4500	28,000	2800	120,000	600
G	V	O	T	H	F	W	L	U	Y

1. 200 × 50 = 10,000 A
2. 30 × 80 = 2400 S
3. 800 × 6 = 4800 T
4. 1000 × 10 = 10,000 A
5. 400 × 2 = 800 C
6. 60 × 20 = 1200 K
7. 200 × 20 = 4000 O
8. 90 × 50 = 4500 F
9. 2400 × 2 = 4800 T
10. 80 × 100 = 8000 H
11. 30 × 200 = 6000 E
12. 400 × 40 = 16,000 M
13. 700 × 40 = 28,000 W
14. 50 × 80 = 4000 O
15. 300 × 400 = 120,000 U
16. 14 × 200 = 2800 L
17. 5000 × 9 = 45,000 D
18. 200 × 200 = 40,000 B
19. 20 × 300 = 6000 E
20. 60 × 40 = 2400 S
21. 60 × 100 = 6000 E
22. 30 × 50 = 1500 V
23. 10 × 600 = 6000 E
24. 600 × 20 = 12,000 N
25. 60 × 80 = 4800 T
26. 20 × 30 = 600 Y
27. 80 × 200 = 16,000 M
28. 400 × 60 = 24,000 I
29. 70 × 40 = 2800 L
30. 200 × 30 = 6000 E
31. 24 × 100 = 2400 S
32. 40 × 200 = 8000 H
33. 30 × 800 = 24,000 I
34. 40 × 40 = 1600 G
35. 80 × 100 = 8000 H

© D. C. Heath and Company   S175   Multiplying by multiples of 10, 100, and 1000

LIFE-SKILL PROJECT

Researching information
Have the students find out how many times the digit *1* or the word *one* appears on the front and back of a dollar bill.

16 or more

LESSON OBJECTIVES
To multiply by a 1-digit number
To estimate products

PROBLEM-SOLVING SKILL
Using logical reasoning

STARTING THE LESSON
Draw these boxes on the chalkboard:

Before the students open their books, have them place the digits *7, 8, 9,* and *0* in the boxes in the way that they think would give the largest possible answer. Then have them look at page 56 and compare their results with the results of the two students shown.

Answers for page 57.
Estimates for exercises 5-54.
(Estimates may vary.)
5. 80 **6.** 480 **7.** 450 **8.** 450 **9.** 240
10. 320 **11.** 350 **12.** 210 **13.** 490 **14.** 540
15. 360 **16.** 150 **17.** 5400 **18.** 4800
19. 4500 **20.** 1800 **21.** 4800 **22.** 1600
23. 2000 **24.** 4900 **25.** 5600 **26.** 2500
27. 1800 **28.** 2100 **29.** $96 **30.** $66
31. $102 **32.** $387 **33.** $236 **34.** $120

56

Multiplying by a 1-digit number

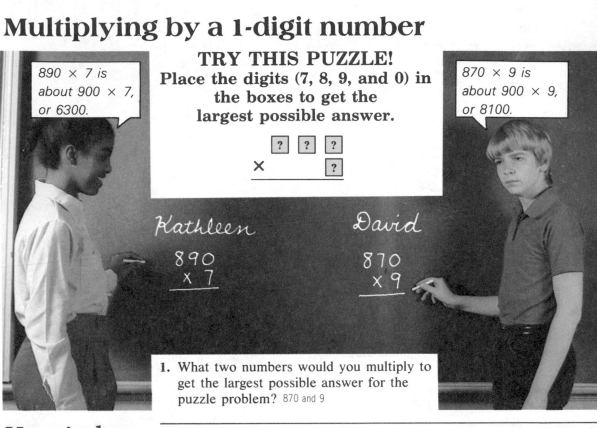

TRY THIS PUZZLE!
Place the digits (7, 8, 9, and 0) in the boxes to get the largest possible answer.

890×7 is about 900×7, or 6300.

870×9 is about 900×9, or 8100.

Kathleen
890
× 7

David
870
× 9

1. What two numbers would you multiply to get the largest possible answer for the puzzle problem? 870 and 9

Here's how *to multiply by a 1-digit number.* $870 \times 9 = ?$

Multiply ones.	Multiply tens and regroup.	Multiply hundreds and add.
870 × 9 —— 0	6 870 × 9 —— 30	6 870 × 9 —— 7830

The numbers that are multiplied are called **factors.**
The answer is called the **product.**

2. Look at the *Here's how.* Was David's estimate near the actual product?

3. Check each example. Is the estimate near the product? Yes

a.
$890 \times 7 = ?$
Estimate.
$900 \times 7 = 6300$

6
890
× 7
——
6230
Yes

b.
$790 \times 8 = ?$
Estimate.
$800 \times 8 = 6400$

7
790
× 8
——
6320
Yes

EXERCISES

4. Four of these calculator answers are wrong. Find them by estimating.

(a.) 89 × 9 `641`   **b.** 398 × 2 `796`

c. 71 × 5 `355`   **d.** 602 × 4 `2408`

(e.) 62 × 7 `334`   **f.** 707 × 9 `6363`

g. 59 × 6 `354`   **h.** 207 × 8 `1656`

(i.) 78 × 6 `358`   **(j.)** 198 × 4 `592`

First estimate the product. Then multiply.

5. 19	**6.** 81	**7.** 53	**8.** 87	**9.** 32	**10.** 44
× 4	× 6	× 9	× 5	× 8	× 8
76	486	477	435	256	352

11. 46	**12.** 71	**13.** 68	**14.** 90	**15.** 89	**16.** 29
× 7	× 3	× 7	× 6	× 4	× 5
322	213	476	540	356	145

17. 612	**18.** 797	**19.** 921	**20.** 584	**21.** 604	**22.** 201
× 9	× 6	× 5	× 3	× 8	× 8
5508	4782	4605	1752	4832	1608

23. 504	**24.** 685	**25.** 732	**26.** 493	**27.** 893	**28.** 691
× 4	× 7	× 8	× 5	× 2	× 3
2016	4795	5856	2465	1786	2073

29. $12.02	**30.** $21.93	**31.** $16.88	**32.** $43.07	**33.** $58.87	**34.** $23.81
× 8	× 3	× 6	× 9	× 4	× 5
$96.16	$65.79	$101.28	$387.63	$235.48	$119.05

35. 63 × 7 441   **36.** 88 × 4 352   **37.** 47 × 9 423   **38.** 31 × 6 186

39. 252 × 9 2268   **40.** 319 × 5 1595   **41.** 571 × 6 3426   **42.** 487 × 8 3896

43. 1023 × 5 5115   **44.** 4216 × 4 16,864   **45.** 3924 × 6 23,544   **46.** 4879 × 3 14,637

47. 2106 × 7 14,742   **48.** 8135 × 9 73,215   **49.** 2147 × 2 4294   **50.** 6627 × 8 53,016

51. 7265 × 9 65,385   **52.** 2140 × 5 10,700   **53.** 8108 × 6 48,648   **54.** 5479 × 3 16,437

Missing digits

Copy; then fill in the missing digits.

55.
```
    4 [?] 8
  ×       4
 [?] 9 1 [?]
   1      2
```

56.
```
  5     4
 [?] 0 [?]
 ×       6
 [?] 0 2 [?]
  3      4
```

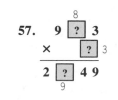

57.
```
      8
  9 [?] 3
 ×    [?] 3
 2 [?] 4 9
      9
```

Multiplying Whole Numbers and Decimals **57**

PRACTICE WORKSHEET
Copymaster S176 or Duplicating Master S176

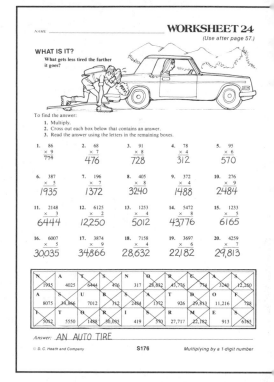

WORKSHEET 24
(Use after page 57.)

WHAT IS IT?
What gets less tired the farther it goes?

To find the answer:
1. Multiply.
2. Cross out each box below that contains an answer.
3. Read the answer using the letters in the remaining boxes.

1. 86 × 9	2. 68 × 7	3. 91 × 8	4. 78 × 4	5. 95 × 6
774	476	728	312	570

6. 387 × 5	7. 196 × 7	8. 405 × 8	9. 372 × 4	10. 276 × 9
1935	1372	3240	1488	2484

11. 2148 × 3	12. 6125 × 2	13. 1253 × 4	14. 5472 × 8	15. 1233 × 5
6444	12,250	5012	43,776	6165

16. 6007 × 5	17. 3874 × 9	18. 7158 × 4	19. 3697 × 6	20. 4259 × 7
30,035	34,866	28,632	22,182	29,813

Answer: AN AUTO TIRE

© D. C. Heath and Company   S176   Multiplying by a 1-digit number

CHALKBOARD CHALLENGE
What's the missing number?

```
START                              END
 [6] —(× 8)—(+ 2)—(× ?)—(− 20)—[80]
                      2
```

More answers for page 57.
35. 420 **36.** 360 **37.** 450 **38.** 180 **39.** 2700
40. 1500 **41.** 3600 **42.** 4000 **43.** 5000
44. 16,000 **45.** 24,000 **46.** 15,000 **47.** 14,000
48. 72,000 **49.** 4000 **50.** 56,000 **51.** 63,000
52. 10,000 **53.** 48,000 **54.** 15,000

LESSON OBJECTIVE
To multiply by a 2-digit number

PROBLEM-SOLVING SKILLS
Reading a newspaper ad
Using a guess-and-check strategy

STARTING THE LESSON
Play 'What are the facts?' Have the students study the want ad and the photo at the top of page 58 for 30 seconds. Then have them close their books and challenge them to answer these questions from memory:
• To be a rodeo clown, how old must you be? (18)
• How much per hour does the job pay? ($12)
• If you took the job, would you work more or less than 30 hours per week? (Less)

EXERCISE NOTE
Encourage the students to use a guess-and-check-strategy for exercises 43–45. The thinking for exercise 43 might be as follows:

$$27 \times 9 = 243 \rightarrow \text{too big}$$
$$29 \times 7 = 203 \rightarrow \text{perfect}$$

Multiplying by a 2-digit number

WANTED:
RODEO CLOWN

Must be 18 or older
Earn $12/hour
Work 26 hours/week

1. Which operation would you use to find how many dollars a rodeo clown is paid per week? Multiplication

Here's how *to multiply by a 2-digit number.*   *26 × 12 = ?*

Line up the digits.

Multiply by 2.	Multiply by 10.	Add.
26	26	26
× 12	× 12	× 12
52	52	52
	260	260
		312

2. Look at the *Here's how*. How much money is a rodeo clown paid per week? $312 Would you take the job for that much money?

3. Check each example. Is the answer correct?

a. 473
    × 54
    1892
  23650
  25,542 Yes

b. 4936
    × 63
    14808
  296160
  310,968 Yes

c. 7254
    × 89
    65286
  58032
  645,606 Yes

EXERCISES

Multiply. *Here are scrambled answers for the next row of exercises:* 2576 2655 1980 1242 2176 1610

4. 68 × 32 ——— 2176	5. 59 × 45 ——— 2655	6. 46 × 56 ——— 2576	7. 70 × 23 ——— 1610	8. 33 × 60 ——— 1980	9. 27 × 46 ——— 1242
10. 631 × 20 ——— 12,620	11. 168 × 52 ——— 8736	12. 246 × 19 ——— 4674	13. 604 × 31 ——— 18,724	14. 120 × 20 ——— 2400	15. 403 × 15 ——— 6045
16. 146 × 32 ——— 4672	17. 487 × 51 ——— 24,837	18. 268 × 25 ——— 6700	19. 452 × 46 ——— 20,792	20. 283 × 49 ——— 13,867	21. 765 × 43 ——— 32,895
22. 864 × 65 ——— 56,160	23. 398 × 56 ——— 22,288	24. 577 × 48 ——— 27,696	25. 903 × 52 ——— 46,956	26. 685 × 63 ——— 43,155	27. 492 × 53 ——— 26,076
28. 2413 × 41 ——— 98,933	29. 2804 × 34 ——— 95,336	30. 6533 × 95 ——— 620,635	31. 1897 × 57 ——— 108,129	32. 4294 × 83 ——— 356,402	33. 2319 × 24 ——— 55,656
34. $1.56 × 33 ——— $51.48	35. $4.08 × 17 ——— $69.36	36. $18.06 × 22 ——— $397.32	37. $71.24 × 95 ——— $6767.80	38. $38.65 × 79 ——— $3053.35	39. $42.08 × 44 ——— $1851.52

Solve. *Use the classified-ad information to tell which job each person is thinking about.*

40. "If I took that job, I'd earn $48 a day." *Photographer*

41. "I would earn $440 a week doing that job." *Water-tower painter*

42. "If I took that job, I would earn $75 in three days." *Dishwasher*

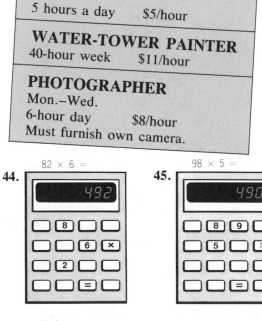

DISHWASHER
Mon.–Sat.
5 hours a day $5/hour

WATER-TOWER PAINTER
40-hour week $11/hour

PHOTOGRAPHER
Mon.–Wed.
6-hour day $8/hour
Must furnish own camera.

Key it in!

Find a way to push each marked key once to get the answer.

43. 29 × 7 =   [203] keys: 7, 9, ×, 2

44. 82 × 6 =   [492] keys: 8, 6, ×, 2

45. 98 × 5 =   [490] keys: 8, 9, 5, ×

EXTRA PRACTICE
Page 419   Skill 16

PRACTICE WORKSHEET
Copymaster S177 or Duplicating Master S177

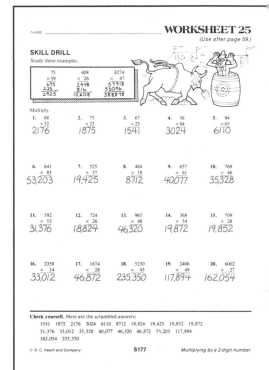

NAME _____

WORKSHEET 25
(Use after page 59.)

SKILL DRILL
Study these examples.

75 × 39 ——— 675 2.25 ——— 2.925	408 × 26 ——— 2448 816 ——— 10,608	8274 × 47 ——— 57,918 33096 ——— 388,878

Multiply.

1. 68 ×32 2176	2. 75 ×25 1875	3. 67 ×23 1541	4. 36 ×84 3024	5. 94 ×65 6110
6. 641 × 83 53,203	7. 525 × 37 19,425	8. 484 × 18 8712	9. 657 × 61 40,077	10. 768 × 46 35,328
11. 592 × 53 31,376	12. 724 × 26 18,824	13. 965 × 48 46,320	14. 368 × 54 19,872	15. 709 × 28 19,852
16. 2358 × 14 33,012	17. 1674 × 28 46,872	18. 5230 × 45 235,350	19. 2406 × 49 117,894	20. 6002 × 27 162,054

Check yourself. Here are the scrambled answers:
1541   1875   2176   3024   6110   8712   18,824   19,425   19,852   19,872
31,376   33,012   35,328   40,077   46,320   46,872   53,203   117,894
162,054   235,350

© D. C. Heath and Company   S177   *Multiplying by a 2-digit number*

LIFE-SKILL PROJECT
Researching information
Have the students use a book of world records to find who holds the record for the longest industrial career in one job. (This information can be found in the *Guinness Book of World Records*.)

Miss Polly Gadsby worked 86 years wrapping elastic for the same company.

LESSON OBJECTIVE
To multiply by a 3-digit number

PROBLEM-SOLVING SKILLS
Finding information in a display
Reading a chart
Choosing the correct operation

STARTING THE LESSON
Play 'What are the facts?' Allow the students 30 seconds to study the information at the top of page 60. Then have the students close their books and answer these questions from memory:
• How many buttons are in a box? (144)
• Are there more or less than 200 boxes of buttons in stock? (More)
• How many buttons are being ordered by Concert Tours, Inc.? (36,000)

HERE'S HOW NOTE
Use **Visual Aid 3** (lined notebook paper) to assist the students in aligning the partial products.

246 × 144 = ?

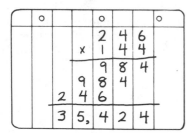

Multiplying larger numbers

You're a Shipping Clerk!

You have 246 boxes of assorted buttons. There are 144 buttons in each box.

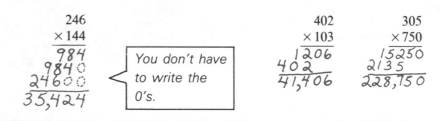

SEND 36000 ASSORTED BUTTONS STOP
MUST RECEIVE BY FRIDAY STOP
SHIP TO CONCERT TOURS INC STOP

1. How many buttons are in a box? 144

2. How many boxes do you have in stock? 246

3. What two numbers would you multiply to find out whether you have enough buttons to fill the order? 144 and 246

Here's how *to multiply 3-digit numbers.*   *246 × 144 = ?*

Start each product directly below the digit you are multiplying by.

```
   246
 × 144
 ─────
   984
  9840
 24600
 ─────
 35,424
```

You don't have to write the 0's.

Other examples:

```
   402
 × 103
 ─────
  1206
 402
 ─────
 41,406
```

```
   305
 × 750
 ─────
 15250
 2135
 ─────
 228,750
```

4. Look at the *Here's how*. Do you have enough buttons to fill the order? No

5. Check each example. Is the answer correct?

a.
```
   372
 × 132
 ─────
   744
 1116
 372
 ─────
 49,104   Yes
```

b.
```
   301
 × 506
 ─────
  1806
 1505
 ─────
 152,306   Yes
```

c.
```
   807
 × 490
 ─────
 72630
 3228
 ─────
 395,430   Yes
```

EXERCISES.

Multiply. Here are scrambled answers
for the next row of exercises: 122,990 81,315 81,432 52,204 146,784 124,982

6. 348 ×234 ___ 81,432	7. 695 ×117 ___ 81,315	8. 834 ×176 ___ 146,784	9. 502 ×245 ___ 122,990	10. 506 ×247 ___ 124,982	11. 421 ×124 ___ 52,204

12. 523 ×402 ___ 210,246	13. 938 ×136 ___ 127,568	14. 734 ×274 ___ 201,116	15. 608 ×403 ___ 245,024	16. 909 ×123 ___ 111,807	17. 707 ×246 ___ 173,922

18. 1839 × 256 ___ 470,784	19. 1265 × 329 ___ 416,185	20. 2576 × 395 ___ 1,017,520	21. 8152 × 406 ___ 3,309,712	22. 6805 × 203 ___ 1,381,415	23. 7304 × 155 ___ 1,132,120

24. 1652 × 330 ___ 545,160	25. 3728 × 250 ___ 932,000	26. 9162 × 407 ___ 3,728,934	27. 8610 × 720 ___ 6,199,200	28. 1785 × 909 ___ 1,622,565	29. 8042 × 105 ___ 844,410

30. $65.23 × 200 ___ $130.46	31. $13.75 × 400 ___ $5500	32. $17.06 × 600 ___ $10,236	33. $86.10 × 500 ___ $43,050	34. $75.69 × 300 ___ $22,707	35. $42.30 × 200 ___ $8460

36. 546 × 324 176,904

37. 603 × 425 256,275

38. 582 × 515 299,730

39. 497 × 305 151,585

40. 1252 × 213 266,676

41. 8260 × 206 1,701,560

42. 1175 × 225 264,375

43. 1063 × 215 228,545

44. 8606 × 400 3,442,400

45. 7625 × 900 6,862,500

46. 5403 × 700 3,782,100

47. 9302 × 200 1,860,400

EXTRA PRACTICE
Page 420   Skill 17

PRACTICE WORKSHEET
Copymaster S178 or Duplicating Master S178

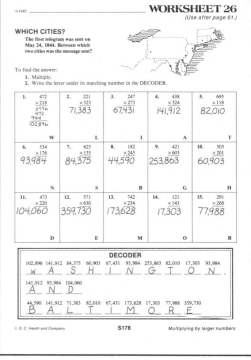

WHICH CITIES?
The first telegram was sent on May 24, 1844. Between which two cities was the message sent?

To find the answer:
1. Multiply.
2. Write the letter under its matching number in the DECODER.

WORKSHEET 26 (Use after page 61.)

1. 472 ×218 _ 3776 472 _ 102,896 W	2. 221 ×323 71,383 L	3. 247 ×273 67,431 I	4. 438 ×324 141,912 A	5. 695 ×118 82,010 T
6. 534 ×176 93,984 N	7. 625 ×135 84,375 S	8. 182 ×245 44,590 B	9. 421 ×603 253,863 G	10. 303 ×201 60,903 H
11. 473 ×220 104,060 D	12. 571 ×630 359,730 E	13. 742 ×234 173,628 M	14. 121 ×143 17,303 O	15. 291 ×268 77,988 R

DECODER

102,896 141,912 84,375 60,903 67,431 93,984 253,863 82,010 17,303 93,984
W A S H I N G T O N .

141,912 93,984 104,060
A N D

44,590 141,912 71,383 67,431 173,628 17,303 77,988 359,730
B A L T I M O R E .

© D. C. Heath and Company   S178   Multiplying by larger numbers

---

Solve. Use the price list.

Button Prices	
NUMBER	COST
1	$ .60
2	$1.20
3	$1.80
6	$3.60
9	$5.40

48. How many buttons can you buy for $1.20? 2

49. What is the cost of 6 buttons? $3.60

50. How many buttons can you buy for $5.40? 9

51. What is the cost of 10 buttons? $6.00

52. You gave the clerk a $10 bill for 9 buttons. How much change should you receive? $4.60

CHALKBOARD CHALLENGE
Where would four darts land to score 51?

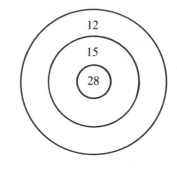

15 + 12 + 12 + 12

Make the change

53. Carlo made a $1.43 purchase. He gave the clerk $2. What 5 coins did he get in change? 2 pennies, 1 nickel, and 2 quarters

54. Sandy made an $8.79 purchase. She gave the clerk $10.04. What coin and bill did Sandy receive as change?
A quarter and a dollar bill

Multiplying Whole Numbers and Decimals **61**

SKILLS REVIEWED
Adding whole numbers and decimals
Rounding whole numbers and decimals
Writing standard numerals (decimals)

PROBLEM-SOLVING SKILLS
Finding information in an ad
Recognizing when needed information is missing
Choosing the correct operation

STARTING THE LESSON
Cumulative Skill Practice
Write these five answers on the chalkboard:

    962
    8100
    8.32
    9.38
    35.21

Challenge students to an answer hunt by saying, "Look for the five even-numbered exercises on page 62 that have these answers. You have five minutes to find as many of the exercises as you can." (Exercises 8, 26, 34, 46, and 54)

STARTING THE LESSON
Problem Solving
The sale ad at the top of page 63 is also on **Visual Aid 9**. Use the ad to ask questions like these:
- How much does a roll of 110 film cost? ($1.49)
- How many exposures are on a roll of 126 film? (20)
- Which size enlargement costs $.99? (5 × 7)
- How many color prints can you get for $.55? (3)

62

Cumulative Skill Practice

Add. *(page 6)*

1. 395 + 21 = 416	2. 267 + 38 = 305	3. 409 + 126 = 535	4. 536 + 342 = 878	5. 658 + 591 = 1249	6. 796 + 384 = 1180
7. 246 138 + 52 = 436	8. 506 74 + 382 = 962	9. 921 274 + 136 = 1331	10. 729 635 + 347 = 1711	11. 911 555 + 426 = 1892	12. 687 42 + 394 = 1123
13. 462 329 83 + 114 = 988	14. 632 95 377 + 216 = 1320	15. 536 291 432 + 51 = 1310	16. 329 416 238 + 627 = 1610	17. 513 753 916 + 742 = 2924	18. 457 365 21 + 914 = 1757

Round to the nearest hundred. *(page 12)*

19. 478 500
20. 609 600
21. 746 700
22. 250 300
23. 963 1000
24. 2748 2700
25. 3290 3300
26. 8062 8100
27. 5555 5600
28. 6350 6400

Write the standard numeral. *(page 16)*

29. 6 tenths 0.6
30. 29 hundredths 0.29
31. 7 hundredths 0.07
32. 15 thousandths 0.015
33. 3 and 9 tenths 3.9
34. 8 and 32 hundredths 8.32
35. 15 and 4 hundredths 15.04
36. 7 and 26 thousandths 7.026
37. 9 and 3 thousandths 9.003
38. 24 and 396 ten-thousandths 24.0396

Round to the nearest hundredth. *(page 20)*

39. 0.296 0.30
40. 0.275 0.28
41. 3.6081 3.61
42. 4.002 4.00
43. 2.7450 2.75
44. 3.4382 3.44
45. 8.297 8.30
46. 9.3841 9.38
47. 7.5004 7.50
48. 6.8296 6.83

Give the sum. *(page 24)*

49. 3.28 + 0.56 3.84
50. 4.381 + 2.743 7.124
51. 15.829 + 6.542 22.371
52. 9.1 + 3.06 12.16
53. 17.2 + 23.4 40.6
54. 26.71 + 8.5 35.21
55. 6 + 3.7 + 2.94 12.64
56. 0.18 + 1.6 + 3 4.78
57. 52.5 + 6.21 + 7 65.71
58. 0.06 + 2.432 + 1.5 3.992
59. 7.5 + 6.37 + 0.057 13.927
60. 6.91 + 4.283 + 9.71 20.903
61. 2.4 + 1.65 + 4 8.05
62. 25.5 + 1.26 + 10 36.76
63. 8.1 + 16 + 0.3 24.4

Problem solving

You are a sales clerk at the Quick Print Photo Shop. The shop is running a sale on film and photo finishing.

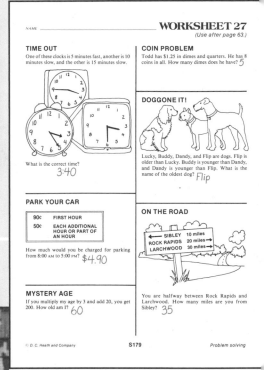

Big Holiday Sale!

FILM SHOP Color Film			PHOTO FINISHING Color Prints	
SIZE	EXPOSURES	PRICE		
135	36	$3.00	Any negative	25¢
135	20	$2.15	Each additional print	15¢
126	20	$2.05	5 x 7 enlargement	99¢
110	12	$1.49	8 x 10 enlargement	$2.59

What questions would you have to ask each customer before you could complete the sale?

1. *I'd like a print of this negative for each person in my family.*

2. *I'd like a roll of size 135 film for my camera.*

3. *My mother wants an enlargement of this picture of Niagara Falls. How much will it cost?*

4. "I have $15. Can I buy 6 rolls of film for my camera?" What size film do you need? How many exposures would you like?

5. "I'd like to have a 5 x 7 enlargement made from each of these negatives. How much will they cost?" How many negatives do you have?

Solve. Use the sale prices.

6. Garret had $7.50. He bought a roll of 20-exposure size 135 film. How much money did he have left? $5.35

7. Jenny bought a roll of film. She got $7.95 change from a $10 bill. What size film did she buy? 126

8. Mrs. Fisher bought 2 rolls of film. She spent $5.15. How many pictures will she be able to take? 56

9. How much more does an 8 x 10 enlargement cost than a 5 x 7 enlargement? $1.60

10. How many pictures will a customer be able to take if she buys 3 rolls of 36-exposure size 135 film? 108

11. Mr. Wilson wants 5 negatives made into color prints. How much will they cost? $1.25

Multiplying Whole Numbers and Decimals **63**

EXTRA PROBLEM SOLVING
Page 446   Odd exercises

PROBLEM-SOLVING WORKSHEET
Copymaster S179 or Duplicating Master S179

NAME _____

WORKSHEET 27
(Use after page 63.)

TIME OUT
One of these clocks is 5 minutes fast, another is 10 minutes slow, and the other is 15 minutes slow.

What is the correct time? 3:40

COIN PROBLEM
Todd has $1.25 in dimes and quarters. He has 8 coins in all. How many dimes does he have? 5

DOGGONE IT!
Lucky, Buddy, Dandy, and Flip are dogs. Flip is older than Lucky. Buddy is younger than Dandy, and Dandy is younger than Flip. What is the name of the oldest dog? Flip

PARK YOUR CAR

| 90¢ | FIRST HOUR |
| 50¢ | EACH ADDITIONAL HOUR OR PART OF AN HOUR |

How much would you be charged for parking from 8:00 AM to 5:00 PM? $4.90

ON THE ROAD

SIBLEY 10 miles
ROCK RAPIDS 20 miles
LARCHWOOD 30 miles

You are halfway between Rock Rapids and Larchwood. How many miles are you from Sibley? 35

MYSTERY AGE
If you multiply my age by 3 and add 20, you get 200. How old am I? 60

© D. C. Heath and Company   S179   Problem solving

CHALKBOARD CHALLENGE
A customer traded some dollar bills for the same number of dimes as quarters. How many dollars did the customer have? *Hint: The customer had about $20.*

21 (60 dimes and 60 quarters)

Answers for page 63.
1. How many people are there in your family?
2. Would you like 36 or 20 exposures?
3. What size enlargement would you like?

63

Multiplying decimals

DID YOU KNOW . . . The height that you can jump depends on the force of gravity. Since the force of gravity varies from planet to planet, you would jump different heights on different planets.

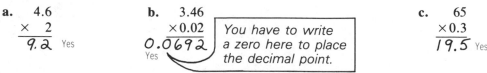

PLANET	HIGH-JUMP FACTOR
Earth	1.00
Mercury	3.57
Venus	1.16
Mars	2.63
Jupiter	0.38
Saturn	0.83
Uranus	1.09
Neptune	0.91
Pluto	1.43

1. What is the high-jump factor for the planet Mercury? 3.57

2. Suppose that you high-jumped 1.63 m (meters) on the planet Earth. You could multiply 1.63 by the high-jump factor of Venus to find how high the jump would have been on Venus. What two numbers would you multiply to find how many meters you would have jumped on Venus? 1.63 and 1.16

Here's how *to multiply decimals.* $1.63 \times 1.16 = ?$

To estimate the product, round each decimal to the nearest whole number and multiply. $2 \times 1 = 2$

Multiply as whole numbers.

1.63
×1.16
978
163
163
18908

Count the digits to the right of the decimal points.

1.63
×1.16 ☐4
978
163
163
18908

Count off the same number of digits in the product.

1.63
×1.16
978
163
163
1.8908

3. Look at the *Here's how.* How high would you have jumped on Venus? 1.8908 meters
Was 2 meters a good estimate? Yes

4. Check each example. Is the answer correct?

a.   4.6
    × 2
    9.2   Yes

b.   3.46
    ×0.02
    0.0692   Yes

You have to write a zero here to place the decimal point.

c.   65
    ×0.3
    19.5   Yes

EXERCISES

Multiply. *Here are scrambled answers for the next row of exercises:*   0.0231   11.97   2.914   2.635   26.22   4.8

5.	6.	7.	8.	9.	10.
3.8 ×6.9 = 26.22	5.7 ×2.1 = 11.97	2.4 × 2 = 4.8	0.31 × 9.4 = 2.914	2.31 ×0.01 = 0.0231	4.25 ×0.62 = 2.635

11.	12.	13.	14.	15.	16.
1.8 × 56 = 100.8	7.4 × 10 = 74	0.05 × 0.7 = 0.035	0.85 × 16 = 13.6	0.44 × 6.6 = 2.904	321 × 8.4 = 2696.4

17.	18.	19.	20.	21.	22.
3.28 × 3.5 = 11.48	7.46 × 6.1 = 45.506	5.26 × 4.2 = 22.092	0.06 ×0.44 = 0.0264	8.52 ×0.65 = 5.538	4.16 ×0.06 = 0.2496

23.	24.	25.	26.	27.	28.
$7.52 × 89 = $669.28	$5.47 × 33 = $180.51	$2.83 × 17 = $48.11	$7.53 × 62 = $466.86	$3.91 × 53 = $207.23	$8.74 × 21 = $183.54

29. 5.7 × 0.42   2.394

30. 3.5 × 0.57   1.995

31. 0.29 × 0.05   0.0145

32. 2.4 × 0.6   1.44

33. 39 × 6.3   245.7

34. 0.51 × 8.2   4.182

35. 65 × 0.39   25.35

36. 77 × 1.4   107.8

37. 368 × 2.7   993.6

38. 4.06 × 10   40.6

39. 0.08 × 0.4   0.032

40. 0.25 × 0.3   0.075

41. 5.83 × 0.95   5.5385

42. 0.01 × 0.5   0.005

43. 79.5 × 0.36   28.62

44. 4.62 × 9.5   43.89

Solve. Use the table on page 64.

45. If you high-jumped 1.63 meters on Earth, how high would you have jumped on Pluto? 2.3309 meters

46. If you high-jumped 1.56 meters on Earth, how high would you have jumped on Mercury? Round the answer to the nearest hundredth of a meter. 5.57 meters

47. On which planet would you jump the lowest? the highest? Jupiter, Mercury

48. On which planets would you jump higher than on the planet Earth? On which planets would you jump lower?

49. Suppose that you could jump 1.54 meters on Earth. How much higher could you jump on Uranus than on Neptune?
0.2772 meter

50. Solve problem 49 in another way.
1.54 × (1.09 − 0.91)

Moon meet

51. Study the clues to determine the high-jump factor for the moon. 5.88

Clues:
- There are two places to the right of the decimal point.
- If you round it to the nearest tenth, you get 5.9.
- It has two digits that are the same.
- The sum of the digits is odd.

PRACTICE WORKSHEET
Copymaster S180 or Duplicating Master S180

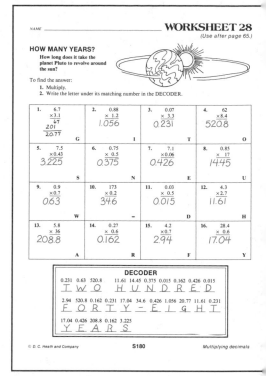

LIFE-SKILL PROJECT
Using library resources

Ask the students which planet, with an orbit speed of over 100,000 miles per hour, is the fastest planet. (This information can be found in the *Guinness Book of World Records*.)

Mercury

Answer for page 65.
48. higher—Mercury, Venus, Mars, Uranus, Pluto
    lower—Jupiter, Saturn, Neptune

Simplifying expressions

You are a mail-order clerk for the Wee Forest Folk Gift Shop. Your job is to compute the total cost of the gifts you pack and ship.

Travelin' Bear $39.89

$29.79 Graduate Owl

Wee Forest Folk Gifts

Office Mouse $24.79

1. What is the cost of an Office Mouse? $24.79
2. What is the cost of a Graduate Owl? $29.79
3. To find the total cost of 3 Graduate Owls and an Office Mouse, you would first multiply 3 times [?] and then add $24.79. $29.79

Here's how *to simplify the expression (3 × $29.79) + $24.79.*

If you estimate before you calculate, you will know whether your answer makes sense.

Estimate this way:
(3 × 30) + 25 = ?
90 + 25 = 115

Remember to work inside the grouping symbols first.

(3 × $29.79) + $24.79 = ?

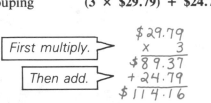

First multiply.
$29.79
×   3
$89.37

Then add.
+ 24.79
$114.16

4. Look at the *Here's how*. What is the total cost of 3 Graduate Owls and an Office Mouse? Was the estimate near the answer? $114.16, Yes

5. Check each example. Which answer cannot be correct? b
   Hint: Estimate by rounding each decimal to the nearest whole number.

   | 80 | − | (25 | + | 30) |

   a. 79.78 − (24.79 + 29.79) = 25.20

   | (30 | + | 40) | × 4 |

   b. (29.79 + 39.89) × 4 = 73.68

EXERCISES

6. Two of these calculator answers are wrong. Find them by estimating.
Hint: Remember to work inside the grouping symbols first.

$$(82 + 60) - 10$$

a. $(82.3 + 59.7) - 9.8$ — `132.2`

c. $29.7 + (19.8 \times 3)$ — `198.5`

e. $(59.2 - 10.9) + 21.8$ — `70.1`

g. $(3.1 + 5.8) \times 2.1$ — `18.69`

$$9 - (6 + 2)$$

b. $9.3 - (6.2 + 1.9)$ — `1.2`

d. $(24.8 + 35.3) + 40.1$ — `100.2`

f. $20 - (5.8 \times 2.1)$ — `51.06`

h. $3.1 + (5.8 \times 2.1)$ — `15.28`

Simplify. Here are scrambled answers for the next row of exercises: **2.2 12.4 74.4**

7. $5.2 + (2.4 \times 3)$ 12.4

8. $10 - (4.6 + 3.2)$ 2.2

9. $9.3 \times (4.8 + 3.2)$ 74.4

10. $(15 \times 0.6) + 3.25$ 12.25

11. $(0.3 \times 4) + 1.45$ 2.65

12. $6 - (3.5 + 2.5)$ 0

13. $(4.8 - 3.5) \times 5$ 6.5

14. $(2.8 + 4.2) + 5.9$ 12.9

15. $2.4 + (2.65 \times 4)$ 13

16. $14.6 + (9.2 - 3.1)$ 20.7

17. $35 - (3.6 \times 8)$ 6.2

18. $(3.4 \times 6) - 8.2$ 12.2

19. $(9.15 + 6.45) - 12$ 3.6

20. $(9.1 \times 2) + 4.6$ 22.8

21. $8 - (1.5 \times 3)$ 3.5

22. $1.45 + (2.15 \times 3)$ 7.9

23. $(7.7 + 5.2) - 6$ 6.9

24. $15 - (2.5 \times 4)$ 5

25. $(7.2 + 8.4) - 5.9$ 9.7

26. $2.8 + (6 \times 5.4)$ 35.2

27. $(6 \times 2.5) - 7$ 8

28. $8.5 - (4.4 + 1.8)$ 2.3

29. $(7.5 \times 4) - 12$ 18

30. $22.25 - (5.25 \times 3)$ 6.5

You decide!

Use the prices on page 66. Decide whether expression A, B, C, or D would be used to solve the problem. Then solve the problem.

31. What's the total cost for an Office Mouse and 3 Travelin' Bears? D, $144.46

Expression A: $39.89 + (3 \times $24.79)$
Expression B: $100 - (3 \times $29.79)$
Expression C: $(3 \times $39.89) - $100
Expression D: $24.79 + (3 \times $39.89)$

32. What is the total cost for a Travelin' Bear and 3 Office Mice? A, $114.26

33. A customer paid for 3 Graduate Owls with a $100 bill. How much change should the customer receive? B, $10.63

34. How much more money would a customer need in order to buy 3 Travelin' Bears if the customer had a $100 gift certificate? C, $19.67

EXTRA PRACTICE
Page 421   Skill 19

PRACTICE WORKSHEET
Copymaster S181 or Duplicating Master S181

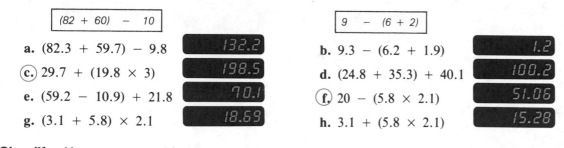

WORKSHEET 29
(Use after page 67.)

NAME _____

CHECKING ANSWERS
Eight of Andy's answers are wrong.
Find and correct the eight incorrect answers.

QUIZ   Andy Gilbert

1. $7.45 + 6.9 =$ __14.35__
2. $3.5 + 9.81 =$ __13.31__
3. $25.62 - 23.43 =$ __2.19__
4. $28.65 + 15.06 =$ (79.71) 43.71
5. $8.8 - 0.34 =$ __8.46__
6. $15.6 + 3.32 =$ __18.92__
7. $19.09 - 10.8 =$ (18.01) 8.29
8. $36.4 + 5.97 =$ __42.37__
9. $7.15 \times 1.9 =$ __13.585__
10. $20.6 \times 2.1 =$ (24.72) 43.26
11. $10.1 \times 2.9 =$ (9.29) 29.29
12. $9.8 \times 6.1 =$ __59.78__
13. $(6.1 + 3.8) \times 4 =$ __39.6__
14. $9.7 + (20 \times 3) =$ __69.7__
15. $(7.4 \times 2) - 10 =$ (13.8) 4.8
16. $8.1 \times (4.8 + 5.1) =$ __80.19__
17. $6.3 + (3.9 \times 2) =$ __14.1__
18. $30 - (14.8 + 5.3) =$ (2.1) 9.9
19. $7.3 - (5.2 + 0.9) =$ __1.2__
20. $(8.4 - 3.3) \times 9.1 =$ __46.41__
21. $(7.1 \times 2) - 12 =$ (22.2) 2.2
22. $(47.2 - 7) \times 3 =$ __120.6__
23. $9.89 + (7 \times 1.99) =$ (31.87) 13.87
24. $(4 \times 0.99) + 20 =$ __23.96__

© D. C. Heath and Company   S181   *Simplifying expressions*

CHALKBOARD CHALLENGE

Put in parentheses to make the equation true.
1. $3 \times (6 + 4) = 30$
2. $(6 + 2) \times 3 - 4 = 20$
3. $(5 - 4) \times 6 + 4 = 10$

LESSON OBJECTIVE
To multiply decimals by 10, 100, or 1000

PROBLEM-SOLVING SKILLS
Finding information in a table
Checking answers

STARTING THE LESSON
Before the students open their books, take a class survey. Ask the students to guess how many pounds of paper products the average person throws away each day. Record the high and low guesses on the chalkboard. Then say, "Open your book to page 68. Look at the top of the page. What answer does the book give?"   (2.48)

EXERCISE NOTE
Use several of exercises 4–55 as oral exercises before making a written assignment. Have the students verbalize the method they use to mentally compute the products.

Multiplying decimals by 10, 100, or 1000

Average Person's Trash	
TYPE	POUNDS PER DAY
Paper	2.48
Glass	0.54
Aluminum	0.51
Other metal	0.09

1. How many pounds of paper products does the average person throw away each day? 2.48

2. What two numbers would you multiply to find how many pounds of paper products the average person throws away in 10 days? 100 days? 1000 days?
2.48 and 10; 2.48 and 100; 2.48 and 1000

Here's how *to multiply by 10, 100, or 1000.*

When you multiply a number by 10, 100, or 1000, the product is greater than the number.

2.48 × 10 = ?

Multiplying by 10 moves the decimal point 1 place to the right.

$$\begin{array}{r} 2.48 \\ \times\ 10 \\ \hline 24.80 \end{array}$$

2.48 × 100 = ?

Multiplying by 100 moves the decimal point 2 places.

2.48 × 1000 = ?

Multiplying by 1000 moves the decimal point 3 places.

2.48 × 10 = 24.8   2.48 × 100 = 248.   2.48 × 1000 = 2480.

3. Look at the *Here's how*. How many pounds of paper products does the average person throw away in 10 days? 100 days? 1000 days? 24.8; 248; 2480

EXERCISES

Give the product. Here are scrambled answers for the next two rows of exercises: 53,600 680 42 420 536 5360 4.2 6800

4. 4.2 × 10   42
5. 42 × 10   420
6. 0.42 × 10   4.2
7. 5.36 × 100   536

8. 536 × 100   53,600
9. 5.36 × 1000   5360
10. 6.8 × 1000   6800
11. 0.68 × 1000   680

12. 68 × 1000   68,000
13. 0.396 × 1000   396
14. 3.96 × 10   39.6
15. 3.96 × 100   396

16. 3.96×1000 _3960_

17. 15.3×10 _153_

18. 15.3×100 _1530_

19. 15.3×1000 _15,300_

20. 4900×10 _49,000_

21. 4900×100 _490,000_

22. 4900×1000 _4,900,000_

23. 490×100 _49,000_

24. 38×10 _380_

25. 38×100 _3800_

26. 38×1000 _38,000_

27. 380×100 _38,000_

28. 0.67×1000 _670_

29. 0.67×100 _67_

30. 0.67×10 _6.7_

31. 6.7×1000 _6700_

32. 0.08×1000 _80_

33. 0.08×100 _8_

34. 0.08×10 _0.8_

35. 0.8×10 _8_

36. 142×10 _1420_

37. 142×1000 _142,000_

38. 142×100 _14,200_

39. 1.42×100 _142_

40. 346×100 _34,600_

41. 346×10 _3460_

42. 346×1000 _346,000_

43. 34.6×1000 _34,600_

44. 7.46×1000 _7460_

45. 7.46×10 _74.6_

46. 7.46×100 _746_

47. 746×100 _74,600_

48. 0.006×100 _0.6_

49. 0.006×1000 _6_

50. 0.006×10 _0.06_

51. 0.06×10 _0.6_

52. 6.088×1000 _6088_

53. 6.088×100 _608.8_

54. 6.088×10 _60.88_

55. 60.88×10 _608.8_

Solve. Use the table on page 68. Assume that your trash is the average amount.

56. How many pounds of glass would you throw away in 10 days? _5.4_

57. How many pounds of aluminum would you throw away in 100 days? _51_

58. What is the total number of pounds of trash that you throw away each day? _3.62_

59. How many pounds of non-paper trash would you throw away in 100 days? _114_

60. Suppose you save glass instead of throwing it away. How many pounds would you save for recycling in 100 days? _54_

61. How many pounds of aluminum would you save for the recycling center in 100 days? _51_

62. The recycling center pays $.02 a pound for paper products. How much would you earn if you sold 100 days' worth of paper products? _$4.96_

63. The price for recycled aluminum is $.15 per pound. How much would you earn if you recycled 100 days' worth of aluminum? _$7.65_

Check the products

64. Find and correct the two wrong answers.

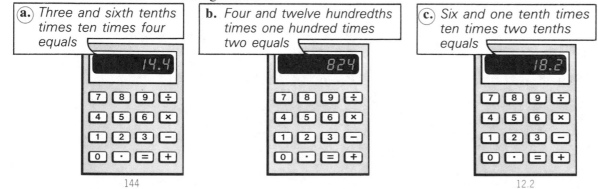

a. *Three and sixth tenths times ten times four equals* `14.4` → 144

b. *Four and twelve hundredths times one hundred times two equals* `824`

c. *Six and one tenth times ten times two tenths equals* `18.2` → 12.2

PRACTICE WORKSHEET
Copymaster S182 or Duplicating Master S182

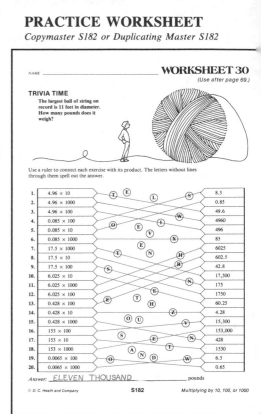

NAME _____

WORKSHEET 30
(Use after page 69.)

TRIVIA TIME

The largest ball of string on record is 11 feet in diameter. How many pounds does it weigh?

Use a ruler to connect each exercise with its product. The letters without lines through them spell out the answer.

1.	4.96×10	8.5
2.	4.96×1000	0.85
3.	4.96×100	49.6
4.	0.085×100	4960
5.	0.085×10	496
6.	0.085×1000	85
7.	17.5×1000	6025
8.	17.5×10	602.5
9.	17.5×100	42.8
10.	6.025×10	17,500
11.	6.025×1000	175
12.	6.025×100	1750
13.	0.428×100	60.25
14.	0.428×10	4.28
15.	0.428×1000	15,300
16.	153×100	153,000
17.	153×10	428
18.	153×1000	1530
19.	0.0065×100	6.5
20.	0.0065×1000	0.65

Answer: _ELEVEN THOUSAND_ pounds

© D. C. Heath and Company   **S182**   *Multiplying by 10, 100, or 1000*

LIFE-SKILL PROJECT
Collecting data

Have the students collect all the newspapers delivered to their homes for one week. Then have them weigh them and figure out how many pounds of newspaper are delivered to their homes in a year.

SKILLS REVIEWED

Subtracting whole numbers and decimals

Comparing decimals

Multiplying whole numbers and decimals

Simplifying expressions

PROBLEM-SOLVING SKILLS

Using information on a menu and a cash-register display

Choosing the correct operation

Using a guess-and-check strategy

STARTING THE LESSON

Cumulative Skill Practice

Challenge the students to an estimation hunt by saying, "Pick the largest difference in the first row of exercises." (Exercise 6) Then have students pick the largest difference in the second and third row of exercises. (Exercise 10 and exercise 16)

STARTING THE LESSON

Problem Solving

Have the students use the menu and cash-register display to answer questions like these:

- How much does a chef salad cost? ($2.85)
- What would the total be if you pushed the milk, tuna, and total keys? ($2.65)
- Which 2 items on the menu cost a total of $3.80? (Ham and tossed green salad)

EXERCISE NOTE

Problem Solving

Encourage the students to use a guess-and-check strategy to solve problems 5 and 6.

70

Cumulative Skill Practice

Subtract. *(page 36)*

1. 3897 − 142 = 3755	2. 6351 − 248 = 6103	3. 7293 − 1526 = 5767	4. 8374 − 2987 = 5387	5. 5328 − 1479 = 3849	6. 9742 − 2836 = 6906
7. 2384 − 1527 = 857	8. 6635 − 558 = 6077	9. 4981 − 3465 = 1516	10. 9310 − 2852 = 6458	11. 7611 − 3629 = 3982	12. 4280 − 1066 = 3214
13. 6034 − 351 = 5683	14. 5901 − 529 = 5372	15. 4077 − 1384 = 2693	16. 8300 − 564 = 7736	17. 6700 − 1387 = 5313	18. 3040 − 1264 = 1776

Less than (<) or greater than (>)? *(page 42)*

19. 0.6 > 0.5   20. 0.03 < 0.04   21. 12.8 > 12.7

22. 0.1 > 0.03   23. 3.05 > 3.005   24. 2.6 > 2.599

25. 4.206 < 4.26   26. 1 > 0.99   27. 0.034 < 0.34

Give the difference. *(page 46)*

28. 74.3 − 38.5 35.8   29. 26.3 − 14.9 11.4   30. 6.00 − 3.81 2.19

31. 9.4 − 3.8 5.6   32. 20.15 − 6.83 13.32   33. 48.06 − 3.57 44.49

34. 29 − 15.8 13.2   35. 30 − 7.42 22.58   36. 6.3 − 5.88 0.42

Multiply. *(page 60)*

37. 223 ×115 = 25,645	38. 402 ×321 = 129,042	39. 336 ×152 = 51,072	40. 538 ×226 = 121,588	41. 629 ×427 = 268,583	42. 745 ×281 = 209,345
43. 592 ×206 = 121,952	44. 380 ×305 = 115,900	45. 635 ×530 = 336,550	46. 706 ×290 = 204,740	47. 832 ×308 = 256,256	48. 434 ×267 = 115,878

Give the product. *(page 64)*

49. 3.2 × 0.8 2.56   50. 4.6 × 0.31 1.426   51. 0.55 × 0.4 0.22

52. 28 × 1.4 39.2   53. 0.56 × 8.3 4.648   54. 4.21 × 1.3 5.473

55. 6.54 × 18 117.72   56. 26.8 × 7.3 195.64   57. 46.3 × 0.84 38.892

Simplify. *(page 66)*

58. 3.5 + (2.1 × 4) 11.9   59. 26 − (8.3 + 2.6) 15.1   60. (8.3 − 6) + 2.6 4.9

61. (9.4 × 0.5) − 1.4 3.3   62. (7.2 − 3.81) × 5 16.95   63. 4.6 + (4.2 × 3) 17.2

64. (5.4 + 3.86) × 2 18.52   65. 5.4 + (3.86 × 2) 13.12   66. (7.5 − 4.1) × 0.7 2.3

Problem solving

COMPUTERIZED CASH REGISTERS

Many cafeterias use computerized cash registers. The computer is programmed to calculate and display the total cost when the cashier keys in an order. When the cashier keys in the amount rendered (the amount the customer uses to pay), the computer will calculate the amount of change.

MENU

DINNERS	
BAKED HAM	$3.25
ROAST BEEF	2.75
FRIED CHICKEN	2.50
TUNA PLATE	2.25
SALADS	
TOSSED GREEN	.55
FRUIT	.65
CHEF	2.85
DRINKS	
MILK	.40
JUICE	.80
COFFEE OR TEA	.30

Use the information on the menu and the cash register to answer these questions.

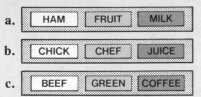

1. *My last customer ordered a dinner and a salad. What keys did I push?* Chick, Fruit

2. *He paid with a $5 bill. I gave him 4 coins and a bill for change. What were the coins?* 3 quarters and 1 dime

```
TOTAL              3.15
HAM   FRUIT  MILK        ( )
CHICK CHEF   JUICE  7 8 9
BEEF  GREEN  COFFEE 4 5 6
TUNA  *      TEA    1 2 3
TOTAL RENDER CHANGE 0 + .
```

3. What total does the computer display when these keys are pushed?

a. HAM FRUIT MILK

b. CHICK CHEF JUICE

c. BEEF GREEN COFFEE

4. What coins and bills would you use to make change for these purchases? (Assume each customer paid with a $10 bill. Use the fewest coins possible.)

a. TOTAL   6.90

b. TOTAL   3.80

c. TOTAL   3.55

5. Each of these customers bought a dinner, a salad, and a drink. What did each customer order?

a. TOTAL   5.90

b. TOTAL   3.20

c. TOTAL   4.10

6. Each of these customers bought two items and paid with a $5 bill. What did each customer buy?

a. CHANGE   2.45

b. CHANGE   .95

c. CHANGE   .25

Multiplying Whole Numbers and Decimals **71**

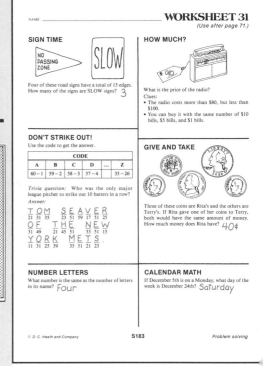
LIFE-SKILL PROJECT
Researching information
Have the students find out how clerks give change. Have them use the clerk's method to tell the coins given as change for a dollar for each of these purchases:

$.57   3 pennies, 1 dime, 1 nickel, 1 quarter
$.19   1 penny, 1 nickel, 3 quarters
$.36   4 pennies, 1 dime, 2 quarters
$.34   1 penny, 1 nickel, 1 dime, 2 quarters
$.83   2 pennies, 1 nickel, 1 dime

Note: Answers will vary if half dollars are used.

Answers for Page 71.
3. **a.** $4.30 **b.** $6.15 **c.** $3.60
4. **a.** 1 dime, 3 $1 bills
   b. 2 dimes, 1 $1 bill, 1 $5 bill
   c. 2 dimes, 1 quarter, 1 $1 bill, 1 $5 bill
5. **a.** roast beef, chef salad, coffee or tea
   b. tuna plate, fruit salad, coffee or tea; or tuna plate, green salad, milk
   c. roast beef, green salad, juice; or ham, green salad, coffee
6. **a.** tuna and coffee or tea
   b. ham and juice
   c. chicken and tuna

71

CHAPTER 3 TEST (Form A)

NAME _____

Multiply. *(page 54)*

1. $8 \times 10 =$ __80__
2. $6 \times 100 =$ __600__
3. $5 \times 1000 =$ __5000__
4. $30 \times 20 =$ __600__
5. $60 \times 70 =$ __4200__
6. $400 \times 50 =$ __20,000__
7. $80 \times 300 =$ __24,000__
8. $300 \times 500 =$ __150,000__
9. $700 \times 700 =$ __490,000__

Multiply. *(pages 56, 58, 60)*

10. $61 \times 5 = $ __305__
11. $86 \times 7 =$ __602__
12. $574 \times 4 =$ __2296__
13. $47 \times 20 =$ __940__
14. $82 \times 49 =$ __4018__
15. $375 \times 62 =$ __23,250__
16. $228 \times 163 =$ __37,164__
17. $544 \times 309 =$ __168,096__

Multiply. *(page 64)*

18. $4.2 \times 2 =$ __8.4__
19. $5.7 \times 0.4 =$ __2.28__
20. $1.03 \times 0.06 =$ __0.0618__
21. $9.4 \times 2.8 =$ __26.32__
22. $7.33 \times 8.5 =$ __62.305__
23. $229 \times 6.4 =$ __1465.6__
24. $5.94 \times 0.96 =$ __5.7024__
25. $6.04 \times 7.1 =$ __42.884__

ANSWERS
1. 80
2. 600
3. 5000
4. 600
5. 4200
6. 20,000
7. 24,000
8. 150,000
9. 490,000
10. 305
11. 602
12. 2296
13. 940
14. 4018
15. 23,250
16. 37,164
17. 168,096
18. 8.4
19. 2.28
20. 0.0618
21. 26.32
22. 62.305
23. 1465.6
24. 5.7024
25. 42.884

© D. C. Heath and Company   S9   Page 1

CHAPTER 3 TEST (Form A)

NAME _____

Simplify. *(page 66)*

26. $2.1 + (3.2 \times 2) =$ __8.5__
27. $12 - (4.7 + 3.5) =$ __3.8__
28. $6.8 \times (5.4 + 3.6) =$ __61.2__
29. $10 - (2.4 \times 3) =$ __2.8__
30. $(12.7 - 5.7) \times 4 =$ __28__
31. $16.4 - (9.8 - 3.5) =$ __10.1__
32. $(8.64 - 2.7) + 3.04 =$ __8.98__
33. $7.7 + (2.6 \times 2.6) =$ __14.46__
34. $(8.25 \times 1.5) + 6.53 =$ __18.905__
35. $8.25 \times (1.5 + 6.53) =$ __66.2475__

Multiply. *(page 68)*

36. $18.4 \times 10 =$ __184__
37. $3.25 \times 100 =$ __325__
38. $7.425 \times 1000 =$ __7425__
39. $54.7 \times 100 =$ __5470__
40. $35.6 \times 10 =$ __356__
41. $3.04 \times 1000 =$ __3040__
42. $8.6 \times 1000 =$ __8600__
43. $0.5 \times 100 =$ __50__
44. $0.09 \times 10 =$ __0.9__
45. $0.67 \times 1000 =$ __670__

Solve.

46. What is the total price of 1 pound of Irish Blarney and 1 pound of cheddar? __$6.68__

47. How much will 2.5 pounds of Swiss cost? __$8.00__

48. How much will 1.7 pounds of Long Horn cost? Round the answer to the nearest cent. __$5.93__

49. You had $8. You bought 2 pounds of cheddar. How much did you have then? __$2.24__

50. You have $4.35. You want to buy 1.6 pounds of Irish Blarney. How much more money do you need? __$1.73__

Cheese Shop
Imports from Wisconsin to Switzerland. The finest quality, the best variety!

Irish Blarney Cheese ... $3.80
Cheddar $2.18
Long Horn $3.49
Swiss $3.20

ANSWERS
26. 8.5
27. 3.8
28. 61.2
29. 2.8
30. 28
31. 10.1
32. 8.98
33. 14.46
34. 18.905
35. 66.2475
36. 184
37. 325
38. 7425
39. 5470
40. 356
41. 3040
42. 8600
43. 50
44. 0.9
45. 670
46. $6.68
47. $8.00
48. $5.93
49. $2.24
50. $1.73

© D. C. Heath and Company   S10   Page 2

Copymasters S9 and S10 or Duplicating Masters S9 and S10

Chapter REVIEW

Here are scrambled answers for the review exercises:

3	5	12	add	right	zeros
4	7	80	product	whole	

1. 4   2. 5. product   3. 7

1. To do this multiplication exercise, you can multiply 3×5 and write [?] zeros. *(page 54)*

300×500

2. To estimate this product, you could multiply 400 by [?]. The answer to a multiplication exercise is called the [?]. *(page 56)*

391×5

3. To complete this multiplication exercise, you would multiply 3 by 8 and then add [?]. *(page 56)*

$$\begin{array}{r} 7 \\ 391 \\ \times\ 8 \\ \hline 28 \end{array}$$

4. 80   5. zeros   6. 12

4. To find this product, you would multiply 97 by 6 and 97 by [?] and then add. *(page 58)*

$$\begin{array}{r} 97 \\ \times 86 \\ \hline \end{array}$$

5. To do this multiplication exercise, you don't have to write the 3 [?]. *(page 60)*

$$\begin{array}{r} 342 \\ \times 127 \\ \hline 2394 \\ 6840 \\ 34200 \\ \hline 43,434 \end{array}$$

6. To estimate this product, you could round each decimal to the nearest whole number. The estimate would be [?]. *(page 64)*

1.95×6.1

7. whole. 3   8. add   9. right

7. To find this product, you would multiply as if the factors were [?] numbers and count off [?] digits to put the decimal point in the product. *(page 64)*

$$\begin{array}{r} 1.95 \\ \times 6.1 \\ \hline \end{array}$$

8. To simplify this expression, you would first [?] and then subtract. *(page 66)*

$12.4 - (4.6 + 3.05)$

9. Multiplying a decimal by 1000 moves the decimal point 3 places to the [?]. *(page 68)*

$6.2 \times 1000 = 6200$

72 Chapter 3

Chapter TEST

Multiply. *(pages 54, 56)*

1. 6×10 60   **2.** 9×100 900   **3.** 8×1000 8000   **4.** 30×30 900   **5.** 23×100 2300

6. 60×40 2400   **7.** 18×100 1800   **8.** 30×500 15,000   **9.** 700×800 560,000   **10.** 5000×90 450,000

11. 32×3 96   **12.** 76×8 608   **13.** 256×5 1280   **14.** 3906×6 23,436   **15.** 487×8 3896

Multiply. *(pages 58, 60)*

16.	**17.**	**18.**	**19.**	**20.**	**21.**
24	78	139	420	268	685
×12	×27	×35	×64	×25	×63
288	2106	4865	26,880	6700	43,155

22.	**23.**	**24.**	**25.**	**26.**	**27.**
326	439	3561	4298	6533	1806
×153	×540	×209	×753	×95	×22
49,878	237,060	744,249	3,236,394	620,635	39,732

Multiply. *(page 64)*

28.	**29.**	**30.**	**31.**	**32.**	**33.**
3.4	6.3	0.84	53.7	0.06	3.28
×1.5	×1.4	×0.6	×4.6	×0.44	×3.5
5.1	8.82	0.504	247.02	0.0264	11.48

34. 0.39×2.8 1.092   **35.** 0.12×6 0.72   **36.** 9.44×1.05 9.912   **37.** 82.1×0.7 57.47

Simplify. *(page 66)*

38. $2.41 + (0.04 \times 0.2)$ 2.418   **39.** $(31.5 - 4.6) + 8.9$ 35.8   **40.** $(5.7 + 3.2) \times 4.6$ 40.94

41. $10.42 - (8.63 - 2.48)$ 4.27   **42.** $(60 - 5.4) \times 5.6$ 305.76   **43.** $4 - (1.63 \times 1.5)$ 1.555

Multiply. *(page 68)*

44. 27×10 270   **45.** 3.49×10 34.9   **46.** 5.4×100 540   **47.** 0.67×1000 670

48. 0.08×100 8   **49.** 15.6×1000 15,600   **50.** 0.04×1000 40   **51.** 2.0312×100 203.12

Solve.

52. What is the total price of 1 pound of macaroni salad and 1 pound of Bar-B-Q beef ribs? $3.97

53. How much will 1.5 pounds of honey-cured ham cost? $6.72

54. How much will 2.25 pounds of cheddar cheese cost? Round the answer to the nearest cent. $6.50

55. What is the total price of 1.5 pounds of beef ribs and 1.75 pounds of ham? $12.31

DAVID'S DELI

Fresh and Creamy
Macaroni Salad . . . . ^{pound} **99¢**

Fresh Sliced
Honey-cured Ham . . . . ^{pound} **$4⁴⁸**

Bar-B-Q Beef Ribs . . . . ^{pound} **$2⁹⁸**

Fresh Sliced
Cheddar Cheese . . . . ^{pound} **$2⁸⁹**

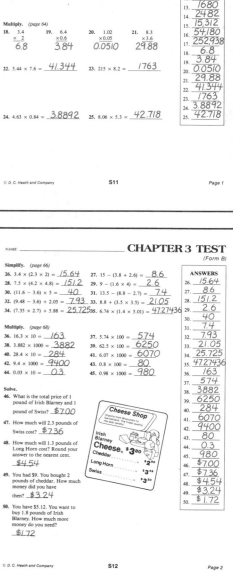

Use Copymaster S336 to provide the students with an answer sheet in standardized test format.

Answers for Cumulative Test, Chapters 1–3

1. Ⓐ Ⓑ Ⓒ Ⓓ	2. Ⓐ Ⓑ Ⓒ Ⓓ	3. Ⓐ Ⓑ Ⓒ Ⓓ
4. Ⓐ Ⓑ Ⓒ Ⓓ	5. Ⓐ Ⓑ Ⓒ Ⓓ	6. Ⓐ Ⓑ Ⓒ Ⓓ
7. Ⓐ Ⓑ Ⓒ Ⓓ	8. Ⓐ Ⓑ Ⓒ Ⓓ	9. Ⓐ Ⓑ Ⓒ Ⓓ
10. Ⓐ Ⓑ Ⓒ Ⓓ	11. Ⓐ Ⓑ Ⓒ Ⓓ	12. Ⓐ Ⓑ Ⓒ Ⓓ

The table below correlates test items with student text pages.

Test Item	Page Taught	Skill Practice
1	6	p. 62, exercises 1–18
2	12	p. 62, exercises 19–28
3	16	p. 62, exercises 29–38
4	20	p. 62, exercises 39–48
5	24	p. 62, exercises 49–63
6	36	p. 70, exercises 1–18
7	42	p. 70, exercises 19–27
8	46	p. 70, exercises 28–36
9	60	p. 70, exercises 37–48
10	64	p. 70, exercises 49–57
11	66	p. 70, exercises 58–66
12	46	

Cumulative TEST Standardized Format

Choose the correct letter.

1. Add.
$$\begin{array}{r} 326 \\ 435 \\ 284 \\ +175 \\ \hline \end{array}$$
- **A.** 1220
- **B.** 1000
- **C.** 1200
- **D.** none of these

2. 4950 rounded to the nearest hundred is
- **A.** 4950
- **B.** 4900
- **C.** 5000
- **D.** none of these

3. The standard numeral for 3 and 48 thousandths is
- **A.** 3.48
- **B.** 3.0048
- **C.** 3.048
- **D.** none of these

4. 8.954 rounded to the nearest hundredth is
- **A.** 9.0
- **B.** 8.95
- **C.** 8.75
- **D.** none of these

5. Give the sum.
$$31.4 + 3.89 + 4$$
- **A.** 39.29
- **B.** 38.29
- **C.** 70.7
- **D.** none of these

6. Subtract.
$$\begin{array}{r} 4600 \\ -235 \\ \hline \end{array}$$
- **A.** 4375
- **B.** 4365
- **C.** 4435
- **D.** none of these

7. Which number is less than 0.89?
- **A.** 0.98
- **B.** 0.089
- **C.** 1
- **D.** none of these

8. Give the difference.
$$35.2 - 1.84$$
- **A.** 16.8
- **B.** 33.44
- **C.** 33.36
- **D.** none of these

9. Multiply.
$$\begin{array}{r} 374 \\ \times 106 \\ \hline \end{array}$$
- **A.** 39,644
- **B.** 5984
- **C.** 5564
- **D.** none of these

10. Give the product.
$$6.25 \times 1.8$$
- **A.** 112.50
- **B.** 1125.0
- **C.** 5.625
- **D.** none of these

11. Simplify.
$$26.3 - (4.6 \times 3.8)$$
- **A.** 35.12
- **B.** 8.82
- **C.** 82.46
- **D.** none of these

12. You're on a 10-mile hike. You hike 2.5 miles during the first hour. How many miles do you have left to hike?
- **A.** 7.5
- **B.** 6.5
- **C.** 4.5
- **D.** none of these

CHAPTER 4
Dividing Whole Numbers and Decimals

LESSON OBJECTIVES
To divide by a 1-digit number (with a 3-digit dividend) (*pages 76–77*)

To divide by a 1-digit number (with 4-digit dividends and zeros in the quotient) (*pages 78–79*)

To divide by a 2-digit number (*pages 80–81*)

To check division (*pages 80–81*)

To divide by a 3-digit number (*pages 84–85*)

To round quotients to the nearest whole number (*pages 84–85*)

To apply the rules for order of operations in simplifying expressions (*pages 86–87*)

To write mathematical expressions (*pages 86–87*)

To divide a decimal by a whole number (*pages 88–89*)

To divide by 10, 100, or 1000 (*pages 92–93*)

To divide a decimal by a decimal (*pages 94–97*)

To write a remainder as a decimal (*pages 96–97*)

PROBLEM-SOLVING SKILLS
Finding information in a newspaper article (*pages 76, 94*)

Choosing the correct operation (*pages 76–77, 79, 83, 85, 88–89, 91, 93, 95, 97*)

Solving a multi-step problem (*pages 77, 91*)

Selecting information from an ad (*pages 78–79*)

Selecting data from a table (*pages 80–81*)

Using a guess-and-check strategy (*page 81*)

Reading a mileage chart (*page 83*)

Finding information in a display (*pages 84–85, 93*)

Selecting data from a chart (*pages 88–89, 96*)

Following instructions (*page 93*)

Selecting data from a drawing (*page 96*)

Making a drawing (*page 97*)

Finding information on a computer printout (*page 99*)

RESOURCES
- **VISUAL AIDS**
  Notebook paper (*Visual Aid 3, Copymaster S111*)

  Mileage chart from page 83 (*Visual Aid 10, Copymaster S117*)

  Contest information from page 84 (*Visual Aid 11, Copymaster S117*)

  Banker's statement from page 92 (*Visual Aid 12, Copymaster S118*)

  Chart and drawing from page 96 (*Visual Aid 13, Copymaster S118*)
- **WORKSHEETS 32–43** (*Copymasters S184–S195 or Duplicating Masters S184–S195*)

LESSON OBJECTIVE
To divide by a 1-digit number (with a 3-digit dividend)

PROBLEM-SOLVING SKILLS
Finding information in a newspaper article
Choosing the correct operation
Solving a multi-step problem

STARTING THE LESSON
Have the students number from *1* to *12* on scratch paper. Tell them you will read a division fact and they are to write the quotient. Explain that you will read each fact only twice.

1. 42 ÷ 6 (7)   **2.** 54 ÷ 9 (6)
3. 45 ÷ 9 (5)   **4.** 72 ÷ 8 (9)
5. 56 ÷ 7 (8)   **6.** 49 ÷ 7 (7)
7. 81 ÷ 9 (9)   **8.** 63 ÷ 7 (9)
9. 48 ÷ 6 (8)   **10.** 40 ÷ 5 (8)
11. 36 ÷ 6 (6)   **12.** 24 ÷ 3 (8)

Have the students check their own papers as you give the answers. Next, play 'What are the facts?' Allow the students one minute to study the article at the top of page 76. Then have the students close their books and decide whether these statements are true or false:
- One hundred four cyclists raised $1456. (True)
- The cyclists were raising money for the Cancer Fund Drive. (False)
- Eight members of the Touring Club rode a total of 384 miles. (True)

Dividing by a 1-digit number

BIKE-FOR-BUCKS SUCCESSFUL!

One hundred four local cyclists raised a total of $1456 for this year's Heart Fund Drive. According to John Weaver, this year's organizer, 53 cyclists each rode more than 20 miles and the 8 members of the Touring Club rode a total of 384 miles.

1. How many members of the Touring Club rode a total of 384 miles? 8

2. What two numbers would you use to compute the average number of miles ridden by the Touring Club members? 384 and 8

3. Would you multiply or divide to compute the average? Divide

Here's how *to divide by a 1-digit number.*   *384 ÷ 8 = ?*

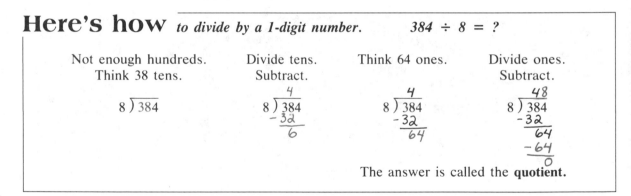

Not enough hundreds. Think 38 tens.

$$8\overline{)384}$$

Divide tens. Subtract.

$$\begin{array}{r} 4 \\ 8\overline{)384} \\ -32 \\ \hline 6 \end{array}$$

Think 64 ones.

$$\begin{array}{r} 4 \\ 8\overline{)384} \\ -32 \\ \hline 64 \end{array}$$

Divide ones. Subtract.

$$\begin{array}{r} 48 \\ 8\overline{)384} \\ -32 \\ \hline 64 \\ -64 \\ \hline 0 \end{array}$$

The answer is called the **quotient.**

4. Look at the *Here's how*. What was the average distance ridden by the Touring Club members? 48 miles

EXERCISES
Divide. *Here are scrambled answers for the next row of exercises:* 22 21 24 14 13 29

5. $2\overline{)48}$ (24)   **6.** $3\overline{)39}$ (13)   **7.** $4\overline{)56}$ (14)   **8.** $3\overline{)63}$ (21)   **9.** $4\overline{)88}$ (22)   **10.** $2\overline{)58}$ (29)

11. $2\overline{)38}$ (19)   **12.** $2\overline{)86}$ (43)   **13.** $5\overline{)75}$ (15)   **14.** $6\overline{)96}$ (16)   **15.** $2\overline{)66}$ (33)   **16.** $3\overline{)72}$ (24)

17. $8\overline{)96}$ **12**   18. $4\overline{)92}$ **23**   19. $7\overline{)91}$ **13**   20. $2\overline{)96}$ **48**   21. $4\overline{)60}$ **15**   22. $5\overline{)65}$ **13**

23. $3\overline{)81}$ **27**   24. $5\overline{)85}$ **17**   25. $4\overline{)72}$ **18**   26. $2\overline{)84}$ **42**   27. $6\overline{)72}$ **12**   28. $4\overline{)96}$ **24**

29. $7\overline{)84}$ **12**   30. $9\overline{)99}$ **11**   31. $5\overline{)70}$ **14**   32. $3\overline{)75}$ **25**   33. $5\overline{)90}$ **18**   34. $7\overline{)77}$ **11**

35. $2\overline{)426}$ **213**   36. $4\overline{)484}$ **121**   37. $3\overline{)693}$ **231**   38. $5\overline{)555}$ **111**   39. $4\overline{)848}$ **212**   40. $6\overline{)456}$ **76**

41. $3\overline{)537}$ **179**   42. $6\overline{)738}$ **123**   43. $3\overline{)432}$ **144**   44. $7\overline{)994}$ **142**   45. $3\overline{)735}$ **245**   46. $8\overline{)432}$ **54**

47. $2\overline{)536}$ **268**   48. $9\overline{)396}$ **44**   49. $6\overline{)438}$ **73**   50. $8\overline{)752}$ **94**   51. $4\overline{)636}$ **159**   52. $2\overline{)348}$ **174**

53. $7\overline{)658}$ **94**   54. $5\overline{)735}$ **147**   55. $5\overline{)360}$ **72**   56. $4\overline{)676}$ **169**   57. $2\overline{)174}$ **87**   58. $9\overline{)531}$ **59**

59. $8\overline{)656}$ **82**   60. $9\overline{)846}$ **94**   61. $5\overline{)235}$ **47**   62. $7\overline{)595}$ **85**   63. $6\overline{)858}$ **143**   64. $4\overline{)932}$ **233**

65. $4\overline{)792}$ **198**   66. $7\overline{)434}$ **62**   67. $9\overline{)621}$ **69**   68. $6\overline{)534}$ **89**   69. $8\overline{)792}$ **99**   70. $5\overline{)965}$ **193**

71. 84 ÷ 6 **14**   72. 60 ÷ 5 **12**   73. 84 ÷ 3 **28**   74. 78 ÷ 6 **13**   75. 896 ÷ 8 **112**

76. 267 ÷ 3 **89**   77. 216 ÷ 9 **24**   78. 725 ÷ 5 **145**   79. 896 ÷ 7 **128**   80. 844 ÷ 4 **211**

81. 732 ÷ 6 **122**   82. 592 ÷ 8 **74**   83. 684 ÷ 9 **76**   84. 679 ÷ 7 **97**   85. 745 ÷ 5 **149**

Solve.

86. One cyclist had 4 pledges. They were $.60, $.85, $1.25, and $.55 per mile. What was her total pledge per mile? **$3.25**

87. The best time for a 68-mile course was 4 hours. How many miles per hour did the cyclist average? **17**

88. One cyclist had a total pledge of $3.17 per mile. He rode 53 miles. How much money did he raise? **$168.01**

89. One Touring Club member had a total pledge of $3.35 per mile and another had a total pledge of $2.92 per mile. They both rode 56 miles. What was the difference in the amounts they raised? **$24.08**

An awesome average!

90. In 1973, Dr. Allan Abbot set a speed record for a bicycle. He rode behind a special windshield mounted on a car. Over a 1-mile course he averaged ? miles per hour.

To find ?, write the number that has
8 ones	3 tens
7 hundredths	6 tenths
4 thousandths	1 hundred

138.674

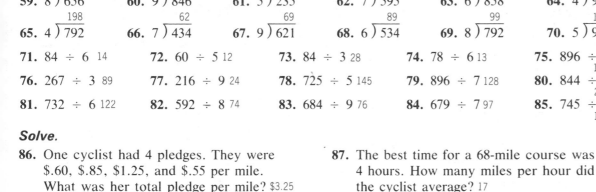

LESSON OBJECTIVES
To divide by a 1-digit number (with a 4-digit dividend and zeros in the quotient)
To estimate quotients

PROBLEM-SOLVING SKILLS
Selecting information from an ad
Choosing the correct operation

STARTING THE LESSON
Play 'What are the facts?' Have the students study the ad at the top of page 78 for 30 seconds. Then have them close their books and answer these questions from memory:
• What is the ad selling?
  (Home computer)
• How much down payment is needed?
  (No down payment)
• Do you have more or less than 4 months to pay? (Less)

HERE'S HOW NOTE
Use **Visual Aid 3** (lined notebook paper) to assist the students in aligning the digits.

615 ÷ 3 = ?

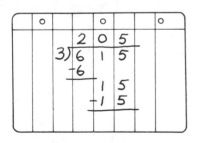

More on dividing by a 1-digit number

*"... BUY A HOME COMPUTER.
PAY NO MONEY DOWN.
PAY $615 IN THREE EQUAL
MONTHLY PAYMENTS ..."*

1. Read the radio commercial. What is the price of the home computer? $615

2. How many monthly payments would you have to make? 3

3. To compute how many dollars you would pay each month, you would divide 615 by what number? 3

Here's how *to divide by a 1-digit number.* $615 \div 3 = ?$.

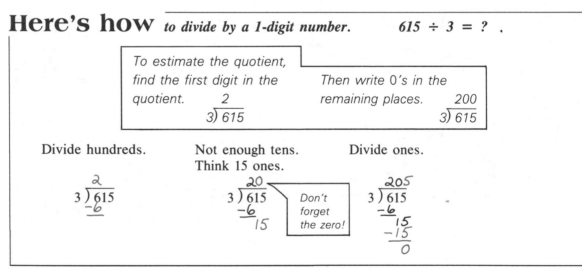

4. Look at the *Here's how*. Is $200 a good estimate for the monthly payment? Yes

5. How much is the monthly payment? $205

6. Find the missing quotient. Use an estimate to check your answer.

a. $\begin{array}{r} 907 \\ 4\overline{)3628} \\ -36 \\ \hline 28 \\ -28 \\ \hline 0 \end{array}$

b. $\begin{array}{r} 420 \\ 6\overline{)2520} \\ -24 \\ \hline 12 \\ -12 \\ \hline 0 \end{array}$

EXERCISES

7. Three of the calculator answers are wrong. Find them by estimating.

a. 3) 6243   `2081`

b. 4) 832   `208`

c. 5) 1020   `24` ⊘

d. 6) 6456   `176` ⊘

e. 9) 873   `97`

f. 4) 1624   `46` ⊘

g. 7) 2961   `423`

h. 8) 5608   `701`

i. 6) 3792   `632`

Divide. *Here are scrambled answers*
for the next row of exercises: 31 2077 412 405 302

8. 5) 2025 → 405

9. 8) 248 → 31

10. 7) 2884 → 412

11. 6) 1812 → 302

12. 4) 8308 → 2077

13. 3) 597 → 199

14. 7) 217 → 31

15. 9) 450 → 50

16. 5) 355 → 71

17. 6) 2934 → 489

18. 2) 4132 → 2066

19. 6) 3672 → 612

20. 9) 6390 → 710

21. 7) 5621 → 803

22. 3) 525 → 175

23. 4) 732 → 183

24. 6) 240 → 40

25. 5) 2965 → 593

26. 7) 4263 → 609

27. 9) 207 → 23

28. 5) 405 → 81

29. 8) 744 → 93

30. 3) 3648 → 1216

31. 6) 1266 → 211

32. 5) 365 → 73

33. 782 ÷ 2   391

34. 592 ÷ 4   148

35. 480 ÷ 3   160

36. 1248 ÷ 6   208

37. 830 ÷ 5   166

38. 945 ÷ 9   105

39. 1640 ÷ 2   820

40. 405 ÷ 5   81

41. 450 ÷ 9   50

42. 1896 ÷ 4   474

Solve. Use the information in the ad.

43. What was the regular price of the radio? $79.99

44. How much would you save if you bought the radio on sale? $11.99

45. After you made the first monthly payment, how much would you have left to pay on the radio? $51

RADIO SALE
Was $79⁹⁹
Now $68⁰⁰
No money down!   4 monthly payments

Which statement is correct?

Disc jockeys play your favorite records, present the news, and read commercials.

46. The air time for the commercials a D.J. reads costs $480 per minute. Which statement is correct?

a. A 30-second commercial costs $240.

b. A 30-second commercial costs $300.

EXTRA PRACTICE
Page 422   Skill 22

PRACTICE WORKSHEET
Copymaster S185 or Duplicating Master S185

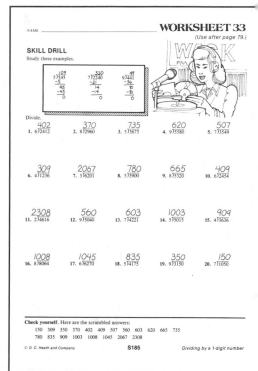

LIFE-SKILL PROJECT
Researching information
Have the students use a book of world records to find the highest price ever paid for a single page of advertising. (This information can be found in the *Guinness Book of World Records*.)

$199,040

Dividing by a 2-digit number

You can predict your adult height by first multiplying your present height (in inches) by 100 and then dividing the answer by the growth factor found in the table.

1. On his 12th birthday, John was 57 inches tall. To predict his adult height, you would first multiply 57 by what number? 100

2. Which number in the table is the growth factor for John? 82

3. To predict John's adult height, you would divide what number by 82? 5700

HOW TALL WILL YOU BE?

| | | Growth Factor | |
Age (in years)		Girl	Boy
12		91	82
13		95	86
14		98	90
15		99	94
16		100	97

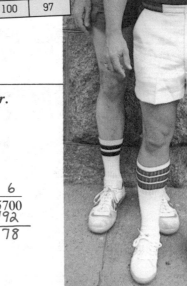

Here's how *to divide by a 2-digit number.*

$$5700 \div 82 = ?$$

Step 1. Think about dividing 57 by 8. So, try 7.

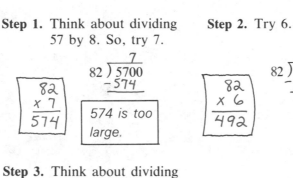

```
        7
    82 ) 5700
       - 574
```

82
× 7
─────
574

574 is too large.

Step 2. Try 6.

```
        6
    82 ) 5700
       - 492
         78
```

82
× 6
─────
492

Step 3. Think about dividing 78 by 8. Try 9.

```
        69 R42
    82 ) 5700
       - 492
         780
       - 738
          42
```

82
× 9
─────
738

Notice that the division did not come out even. The **quotient** is 69 and the **remainder** is 42.

Here's how to check the division.

```
      69    ← quotient
    × 82
    ─────
     138
    552
    ─────
    5658
   +  42   ← remainder
   ─────
    5700
```

4. Look at the *Here's how*. John's adult height would be between 69 and [?] inches. 70

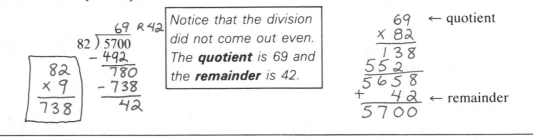

EXERCISES

Divide and check.

5. $\overset{31}{43 \overline{)1333}}$ 6. $\overset{26 \text{ R}11}{51 \overline{)1337}}$ 7. $\overset{47 \text{ R}22}{34 \overline{)1620}}$ 8. $\overset{28 \text{ R}10}{60 \overline{)1690}}$ 9. $\overset{26}{63 \overline{)1638}}$

10. $\overset{33 \text{ R}30}{81 \overline{)2703}}$ 11. $\overset{74}{38 \overline{)2812}}$ 12. $\overset{60 \text{ R}40}{41 \overline{)2500}}$ 13. $\overset{54}{54 \overline{)2916}}$ 14. $\overset{38 \text{ R}61}{73 \overline{)2835}}$

15. $\overset{57 \text{ R}61}{66 \overline{)3823}}$ 16. $\overset{40 \text{ R}20}{92 \overline{)3700}}$ 17. $\overset{38 \text{ R}52}{83 \overline{)3206}}$ 18. $\overset{48}{71 \overline{)3408}}$ 19. $\overset{79 \text{ R}8}{46 \overline{)3642}}$

Divide. Here are scrambled answers for the next row of exercises: 24 R37   36   25   44 R25   26

20. $\overset{25}{63 \overline{)1575}}$ 21. $\overset{24 \text{ R}37}{56 \overline{)1381}}$ 22. $\overset{44 \text{ R}25}{92 \overline{)4073}}$ 23. $\overset{26}{58 \overline{)1508}}$ 24. $\overset{36}{78 \overline{)2808}}$

25. $\overset{450}{12 \overline{)5400}}$ 26. $\overset{109 \text{ R}12}{39 \overline{)4263}}$ 27. $\overset{41 \text{ R}31}{53 \overline{)2204}}$ 28. $\overset{21 \text{ R}42}{61 \overline{)1323}}$ 29. $\overset{81 \text{ R}23}{57 \overline{)4640}}$

30. $\overset{1287 \text{ R}47}{58 \overline{)74,693}}$ 31. $\overset{680 \text{ R}21}{94 \overline{)63,941}}$ 32. $\overset{202 \text{ R}69}{78 \overline{)15,825}}$ 33. $\overset{1787 \text{ R}7}{42 \overline{)75,061}}$ 34. $\overset{535 \text{ R}21}{44 \overline{)23,561}}$

35. $1596 \div 38$ 42   36. $2974 \div 24$ 123 R22   37. $2624 \div 82$ 32   38. $3806 \div 17$ 223 R15

39. $50,000 \div 72$ 694 R32   40. $89,216 \div 82$ 1088   41. $53,819 \div 25$ 2152 R19   42. $74,281 \div 31$ 2396 R5

Solve. Use the table on page 80.

43. A 13-year-old girl is 60 inches tall. Her adult height (in inches) should be between which two whole numbers?
63 and 64

44. A 15-year-old boy is 64 inches tall. His adult height (in inches) should be between which two whole numbers?
68 and 69

45. a. What is your height to the nearest inch? Answers will vary.
   b. What is your growth factor? Answers will vary.

46. Your adult height (in inches) should be between what two whole numbers?
Answers will vary.

47. At what age do girls usually attain their adult height? 16

48. Do boys usually attain their adult height earlier or later than girls? Later

49. Who should be the taller adult, a 12-year-old girl who is 56 inches tall or a 13-year-old girl who is 58 inches tall?
The 12-year-old

50. Who should be the taller adult, a 15-year-old girl who is 66 inches tall or a 15-year-old boy who is 65 inches tall?
The boy

Key it in!

Find a way to push each marked key once to get the answer.

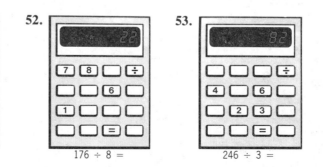

51. $128 \div 4 =$ 52. $176 \div 8 =$ 53. $246 \div 3 =$

PRACTICE WORKSHEET
Copymaster S186 or Duplicating Master S186

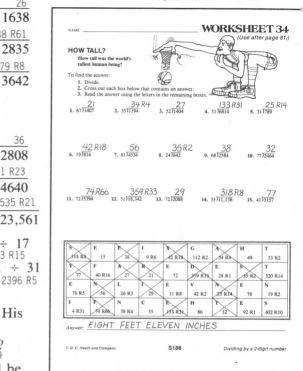

CHALKBOARD CHALLENGE

If an adult is 6 feet (72 inches) tall, about how tall was he at age 14?

65 inches, or 5 feet 5 inches

SKILLS REVIEWED
Writing standard numerals in words
Adding whole numbers and decimals

PROBLEM-SOLVING SKILLS
Reading a mileage chart
Choosing the correct operation

STARTING THE LESSON
Cumulative Skill Practice
Write these four answers on the chalkboard:

64 thousand, 83
5 million, 643 thousand, 88
109,350
52.71

Challenge the students to an answer hunt by saying, "Look for the four even-numbered exercises on page 82 that have these answers. You have four minutes to find as many of the exercises as you can." (Exercises 6, 14, 28, and 56)

STARTING THE LESSON
Problem Solving
The mileage chart at the top of page 83 is also on **Visual Aid 10**. Have the students use the mileage chart to answer questions like these:

• How many miles is it from Baltimore to Denver? (1621)
• How far is it from Houston to Cleveland? (1273 miles)
• Which city is 2786 miles from Los Angeles? (New York)

Answers for page 82.
1. 26 thousand, 338
2. 9 thousand, 57
3. 36 thousand, 401
4. 23 thousand, 104
5. 419 thousand, 853
6. 64 thousand, 83
7. 250 thousand, 36
8. 100 thousand, 3
9. 9 million, 961 thousand, 240

Write the short word-name. *(page 4)*

1. 26338
2. 9057
3. 36401
4. 23104
5. 419853
6. 64083
7. 250036
8. 100003
9. 9961240
10. 344082129
11. 31650000
12. 261418
13. 68000125
14. 5643088
15. 83000000
16. 10000000

Add. *(page 8)*

17.	18.	19.	20.	21.
6217	8107	5628	7436	3054
+ 435	+ 399	+ 529	+ 289	+ 729
6652	8506	6157	7725	3783

22.	23.	24.	25.	26.
58,237	36,051	44,729	6,508	1,994
+ 3,916	+ 5,471	+ 3,821	+19,261	+37,306
62,153	41,522	48,550	25,769	39,300

27.	28.	29.	30.	31.
21,345	85,841	11,295	38,451	93,816
+18,466	+23,509	+27,832	+56,009	+26,957
39,811	109,350	39,127	94,460	120,773

32.	33.	34.	35.	36.
$9.25	$7.63	$5.94	$8.32	$5.99
.63	1.25	3.29	4.73	5.99
+ .25	+ .18	+ 1.36	+ 5.19	+ 6.14
$10.13	$9.06	$10.59	$18.24	$18.12

37.	38.	39.	40.	41.
$21.32	$16.53	$12.34	$47.35	$56.00
18.56	6.74	12.34	62.00	37.52
+ 9.27	+ 29.07	+ 12.34	+ 73.65	+ 83.36
$49.15	$52.34	$37.02	$183.00	$176.88

Give the sum. *(page 24)*

42. 8.3 + 2.6 10.9
43. 5.74 + 3.96 9.7
44. 0.82 + 1.74 2.56
45. 3.521 + 2.806 6.327
46. 4.333 + 9.074 13.407
47. 12.02 + 9.08 21.1
48. 6 + 3.4 9.4
49. 8.2 + 9 17.2
50. 15 + 7.68 22.68
51. 2.6 + 3 + 8.04 13.64
52. 5 + 6.71 + 3.0 14.71
53. 0.83 + 2.7 + 6 9.53
54. 0.92 + 2.7 + 8.6 12.22
55. 9.34 + 21.6 + 9.8 40.74
56. 15.21 + 16 + 21.5 52.71
57. 3.471 + 2.05 + 6.4 11.921
58. 4.21 + 3 + 7.813 15.023
59. 6.2 + 3.816 + 7.55 17.566
60. 8.64 + 2.009 + 7.5 18.149
61. 3.004 + 0.06 + 0.5 3.564
62. 8.32 + 6.1 + 0.008 14.428
63. 4 + 2.38 + 9.6 15.98
64. 5.07 + 2.452 + 8.1 15.622
65. 3.96 + 2.74 + 5.3 12

Problem solving

Use the chart to answer these truckers' questions.

1. I know it's 802 miles from New York to Chicago. How far is it from New York to Denver? 1771 miles

2. How far is it from New York to Los Angeles? 2786 miles

3. "I first drive from Chicago to Denver and then from Denver to Los Angeles. What is the total mileage?" 2055

4. "What is the total mileage of a Houston–Denver–Los Angeles run?" 2078

5. "How much farther is Cleveland from Baltimore than from Chicago?" 8 miles

6. "I have driven the first 195 miles of a Houston–Cleveland run. How much farther do I have to go?" 1078 miles

7. "I am 380 miles from Chicago on a Baltimore–Chicago run. How many miles have I driven?" 288

8. "I leave Cleveland and plan to drive 55 miles per hour. Will I be in Baltimore in 7 hours?" Yes

9. "I want to drive from Chicago to Baltimore in less than 10 hours. Can I do it by traveling at 50 miles per hour?" No

10. "I leave Chicago at 8:00 A.M. and plan to drive 50 miles per hour on a run to Cleveland. Will I reach Cleveland by 3:00 P.M.?" Yes

11. "My truck holds 100 gallons of diesel fuel. If it averages 4.5 miles per gallon, can I drive from Denver to Cleveland without stopping for fuel?" No

12. "My truck gets about 5 miles per gallon of diesel fuel. How many gallons of fuel will I need to get from Chicago to Cleveland?" 67

MILEAGE CHART	Baltimore	Chicago	Cleveland	Denver	Houston	Los Angeles	New York
Baltimore		668	343	1621	1412	2636	196
Chicago	668		335	996	1067	2054	802
Cleveland	343	335		1321	1273	2367	473
Denver	1621	996	1321		1019	1538	1771
Houston	1412	1067	1273	1019		1608	1608
Los Angeles	2636	2054	2367	1059	1538		2786
New York	196	802	473	1771	1608	2786	

Dividing Whole Numbers and Decimals **83**

EXTRA PROBLEM SOLVING
Page 447   Odd exercises

PROBLEM-SOLVING WORKSHEET

Copymaster S187 or Duplicating Master S187

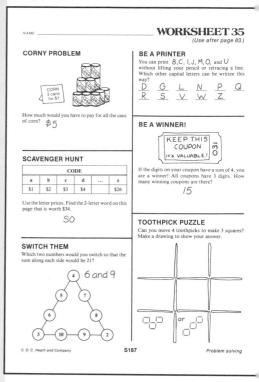

NAME _____   **WORKSHEET 35**
(Use after page 83.)

CORNY PROBLEM

CORN 3 cans for $1

How much would you have to pay for all the cans of corn? $5

BE A PRINTER
You can print B, C, I, J, M, O, and U without lifting your pencil or retracing a line. Which other capital letters can be written this way?

D G L N P Q
R S V W Z

SCAVENGER HUNT

	CODE				
a	b	c	d	...	z
$1	$2	$3	$4		$26

Use the letter prices. Find the 2-letter word on this page that is worth $34. SO

BE A WINNER!

KEEP THIS COUPON It's VALUABLE! 031

If the digits on your coupon have a sum of 4, you are a winner! All coupons have 3 digits. How many winning coupons are there? 15

TOOTHPICK PUZZLE
Can you move 4 toothpicks to make 3 squares? Make a drawing to show your answer.

SWITCH THEM
Which two numbers would you switch so that the sum along each side would be 21?

6 and 9

© D. C. Heath and Company   S187   Problem solving

LIFE-SKILL PROJECT

Researching information

Have the students find how many miles more it is from Chicago to Los Angeles by truck than by airplane. (The highway distance can be obtained from the mileage chart on page 83. Air distances can be found in an atlas or almanac.)

About 300 miles

More answers for page 82.
10. 344 million, 82 thousand, 129
11. 31 million, 650 thousand
12. 261 thousand, 418
13. 68 million, 125
14. 5 million, 643 thousand, 88
15. 83 million
16. 10 million

LESSON OBJECTIVES
To divide by a 3-digit number
To round quotients to the nearest whole number

PROBLEM-SOLVING SKILLS
Finding information in a display
Choosing the correct operation

STARTING THE LESSON
Carry-the-Cash Contest information at the top of the page is also on **Visual Aid 11.** Have the students use the information on page 84 to guess the weight of the $100,000 bag. Record the high and low guesses on the chalkboard. Discuss exercises 1–4 and the *Here's how* to determine the actual weight of the $100,000 bag.

***HERE'S HOW* NOTE**
Stress Step 4, in which a zero is annexed in order to continue the division process.

Dividing by a 3-digit number

Suppose that an eccentric millionaire asked you to enter this contest.

CARRY-THE-CASH CONTEST

1. Before touching any of the bags, choose a bag of money.
2. If you can carry the bag of money for 1 mile without resting, the money is yours.

Note: Each bag contains only $1 bills.

WHICH WOULD YOU CHOOSE?

1. How many $1 bills are in the largest bag? 100,000

2. The weight of 454 $1 bills is one pound. Suppose that you choose the $100,000 bag. To find the number of pounds that you would have to carry you would divide 100,000 by [?]. 454

Here's how *to divide by a 3-digit number.* $100,000 \div 454 = ?$

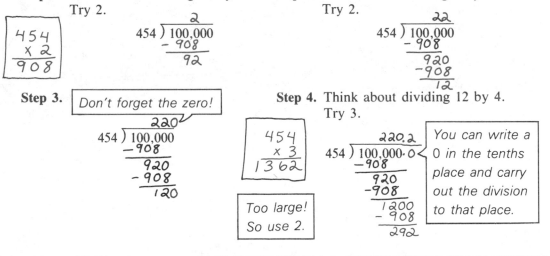

3. Look at the *Here's how.* How many pounds would the $100,000 weigh? Round the answer to the nearest whole pound. 220

4. Could you have carried the $100,000 for a mile? No

EXERCISES

Divide. Use the multiplication facts.

215 × 0 0	215 × 1 215	215 × 2 430	215 × 3 645	215 × 4 860	215 × 5 1075	215 × 6 1290	215 × 7 1505	215 × 8 1720	215 × 9 1935

5. 215) 6880   *32*

6. 215) 21,070   *98*

7. 215) 17,845   *83*

8. 215) 13,115   *61*

9. 215) 88,365   *411*

10. 215) 69,660   *324*

11. 215) 114,165   *531*

12. 215) 175,010   *814*

13. 215) 91,160   *424*

14. 215) 159,745   *743*

15. 215) 189,630   *882*

16. 215) 444,620   *2068*

First carry out the division to the tenths place.
Then round the quotient to the nearest whole number.
Here are scrambled answers for the next row of exercises: 139 82 43 101

17. 7) 299   *42.7* 43

18. 9) 741   *82.3* 82

19. 6) 604   *100.6* 101

20. 4) 555   *138.7* 139

21. 3) 811   *270.3* 270

22. 8) 507   *63.3* 63

23. 2) 731   *365.5* 366

24. 9) 847   *94.1* 94

25. 8) 3421   *427.6* 428

26. 6) 6539   *1089.8* 1090

27. 7) 9603   *1371.8* 1372

28. 5) 5702   *1140.4* 1140

29. 12) 593   *49.4* 49

30. 15) 974   *64.9* 65

31. 18) 800   *44.4* 44

32. 16) 777   *48.5* 49

33. 23) 5012   *217.9* 218

34. 35) 2906   *83.0* 83

35. 40) 3582   *89.5* 90

36. 56) 4711   *84.1* 84

37. 123) 53,061   *431.3* 431

38. 130) 29,438   *226.4* 226

39. 146) 42,111   *288.4* 288

40. 193) 70,629   *365.9* 366

41. 625) 139,528   *223.2* 223

42. 834) 374,200   *448.6* 449

43. 935) 561,348   *600.3* 600

44. 753) 829,005   *1100.9* 1101

Solve. Use the information on page 84.

45. How many pounds would the $60,000 bag weigh? Round the answer to the nearest whole number. 132

46. How many pounds would the $25,000 bag weigh? Round the answer to the nearest whole number. 55

47. Suppose that you could carry 48 pounds for 1 mile. How many $1 bills would that be? 21,792

Million-dollar weigh-in

48. How much would 1 million dollars in $100 bills weigh? Round the answer to the nearest whole number. 22 pounds

49. Could you carry 1 million dollars in $100 bills? Answers may vary.

EXTRA PRACTICE
Page 423   Skill 24

PRACTICE WORKSHEET
Copymaster S188 or Duplicating Master S188

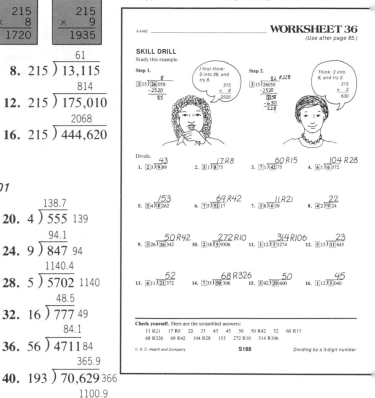

CHALKBOARD CHALLENGE
Find the missing digits.

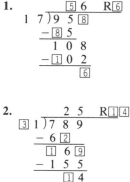

Dividing Whole Numbers and Decimals **85**

LESSON OBJECTIVES
To apply the rules for order of operations in simplifying expressions
To write mathematical expressions

PROBLEM-SOLVING SKILL
Finding information in a store coupon

STARTING THE LESSON
Write this expression on the chalkboard:

$$36 + 2 \times 24$$

Have the students determine the value of the expression. List the various student answers on the chalkboard. Next to each answer, write the number of students who got that answer. Have the students open their books. Discuss exercises 1–5 and the *Here's how*. Go back to the list on the chalkboard to determine how many students got the correct answer.

Order of operations

David, Carla, and Jane take pictures for their school's yearbook. In checking the film supply, David found a roll of 36 and 2 rolls of 24. Here is how he wrote the number of pictures that they could take:

NOTES

$36 + 2 \times 24$

1. When Carla saw the note, she claimed that they could take 912 pictures. How did she get 912?   She added 36 and 2, and then multiplied by 24.

2. When Jane saw the note, she claimed that they could take 84 pictures. How did she get 84?   She multiplied 2 and 24, and then added 36.

3. They got different answers because they did the operations in different orders. Who added first and then multiplied?   Carla

4. Which operation did Jane do first?   Multiplication

Here's how *to simplify expressions having more than one kind of operation.*

So that an expression has only one value, we use these rules for the **order of operations:**

Rule 1. First do the operations within the grouping symbols.

Rule 2. Next, work from left to right doing any multiplication and division.

Rule 3. Last, work from left to right doing any addition and subtraction.

5. Study the rules. Who was right, Carla or Jane?   Jane

EXERCISES

Simplify each expression.
Hint: The order of operations is shown by the numbered arrows.

6. $\overset{1}{8} \div \overset{2}{4} \times 2$ 4

7. $\overset{1}{10} - \overset{2}{6} + 3$ 7

8. $\overset{2}{7} + \overset{1}{3} \times \overset{3}{8} - 4$ 27

9. $\overset{1}{4} \times \overset{3}{2} + 20 \overset{2}{\div} 2$ 18

10. $5 + (\overset{3}{6} + \overset{1}{2}) \overset{2}{\div} 4$ 7

11. $(\overset{1}{7} + 6) \times \overset{2}{2} - \overset{3}{10}$ 16

12. $20 \div 5 - 1$ 3

13. $5 \times 6 - 3$ 27

14. $18 \times 3 \div 3$ 18

15. $50 - 10 - 4$ 36

16. $20 + 16 \div 4$ 24

17. $16 + 8 \div 4$ 18

18. $36 \div 9 \times 2$ 8

19. $43 + 17 - 20$ 40

20. $23 - 9 + 6$ 20

21. $(96 + 24) \div 6$ 20

22. $72 \times (8 - 2)$ 432

23. $16 \times (15 - 5)$ 160

24. $24 + 8 \div 4 + 4$ 30

25. $(24 + 8) \div 4 + 4$ 12

26. $24 + 8 \div (4 + 4)$ 25

27. $18 + 12 \times 6 - 1$ 89

28. $(18 + 12) \times 6 - 1$ 179

29. $18 + 12 \times (6 - 1)$ 78

30. $15 \times 3 + 5 \times 3$ 60

31. $(15 + 5) \times 3$ 60

32. $15 \times (3 + 5) \times 3$ 360

33. $24 - (14 + 4) \div 2$ 15

34. $24 - 14 + 4 \div 2$ 12

35. $(24 - 14) + 4 \div 2$ 12

36. $36 \div (2 + 4) \times 4 - 2$ 22

37. $36 \div 2 + 4 \times 4 - 2$ 32

38. $36 \div 2 + 4 \times (4 - 2)$ 26

Write an expression for the number of pictures that can be taken with

39. 3 rolls of 24.   3 × 24

40. 5 rolls of 36 and 12 on another roll.   5 × 36 + 12

41. 4 rolls of 24 with 7 pictures already taken on one of the rolls.   4 × 24 − 7

42. 2 rolls of 24 and 3 rolls of 36.   2 × 24 + 3 × 36

Clip 'n' save

43. Two of these statements are false. Which two are they?

a. With this coupon you can buy 6 rolls of film and get 2 rolls free.

b. This coupon is good on the third Monday in March.

c. The regular price for 4 rolls of film is $15.96.

d. With this coupon you get 4 rolls of film for less than $10.

STORE COUPON

BUY 3 rolls of film and get 1 roll FREE.

COLOR FILM FOR PRINTS

Heathcofilm Inc.   36 exp.

Reg. **$3.99** a roll

Limit: 1 free roll per coupon
Coupon expires March 22.

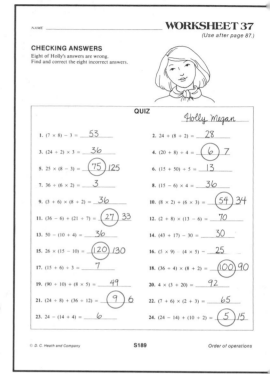
CHALKBOARD CHALLENGE
Look for the pattern.
Find the missing numbers.

$(1 \times 8) + 1 = 9$

$(12 \times 8) + 2 = 98$

$(123 \times 8) + 3 = 987$

$\cdot$
$\cdot$
$\cdot$

$(? \times ?) + ? = 9{,}876{,}543$

1,234,567; 8; 7

CHALKBOARD QUIZ
on previous lesson

Simplify each expression.
1. $6 + 3 \times 5$ 21
2. $30 \div 6 - 1$ 4
3. $4 + (5 + 3) \div 2$ 8
4. $16 + 8 \div 2$ 20
5. $10 + 6 \times (3 + 2)$ 40

LESSON OBJECTIVE
To divide a decimal by a whole number

PROBLEM-SOLVING SKILLS
Selecting data from a chart
Choosing the correct operation

STARTING THE LESSON
Have groups of students conduct the experiment described on page 88. You will need a stopwatch. Some students may have stopwatches on their wristwatches. If not, you might try to borrow one from the physical education department. On the chalkboard, record the total reaction time (in seconds) and the number of students in each group. Discuss exercises 1–5 and the *Here's how*. Then have the students look at the information on the chalkboard and compute the average reaction time for each of their groups.

Dividing a decimal by a whole number

HOW FAST CAN YOU REACT?

Here is how some students answered the question. First they formed a circle by grasping hands. Then with their eyes closed, they "passed a hand squeeze" around the circle as quickly as possible. Their teacher timed how long it took for the squeeze to go around the circle.

1. How many students were in Experiment 1? 24

2. How long did it take the hand squeeze to go around the circle (the Total Reaction Time)? 10.32 seconds

3. For Experiment 1, what would you do to compute the average reaction time per student? Divide 10.32 by 24.

Here's how *to divide a decimal by a whole number.* $10.32 \div 24 = ?$

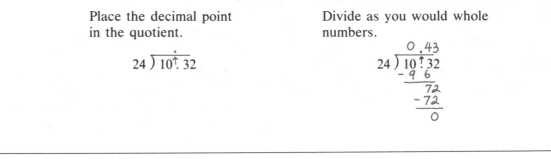

Place the decimal point in the quotient.

$$24 \overline{) 10\overset{.}{}32}$$

Divide as you would whole numbers.

$$
\begin{array}{r}
0.43 \\
24 \overline{) 10.32} \\
-9\ 6 \\
\hline
72 \\
-72 \\
\hline
0
\end{array}
$$

4. Look at the *Here's How*. What is the average reaction time for Experiment 1? 0.43 second

5. Study these examples. Round each quotient to the nearest hundredth.

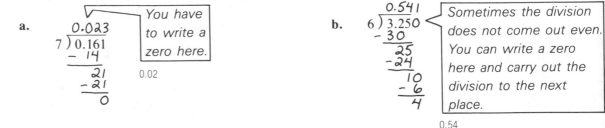

a.
$$
\begin{array}{r}
0.023 \\
7 \overline{) 0.161} \\
-14 \\
\hline
21 \\
-21 \\
\hline
0
\end{array}
$$
You have to write a zero here.   0.02

b.
$$
\begin{array}{r}
0.541 \\
6 \overline{) 3.250} \\
-30 \\
\hline
25 \\
-24 \\
\hline
10 \\
-6 \\
\hline
4
\end{array}
$$
Sometimes the division does not come out even. You can write a zero here and carry out the division to the next place.   0.54

EXERCISES

Divide. *Here are scrambled answers for the next row of exercises:* **6.5   0.94   1.76   0.346**

$$\textbf{6.}\ 8\overline{)14.08}\quad 1.76$$
$$\textbf{7.}\ 12\overline{)11.28}\quad 0.94$$
$$\textbf{8.}\ 6\overline{)2.076}\quad 0.346$$
$$\textbf{9.}\ 25\overline{)162.5}\quad 6.5$$

$$\textbf{10.}\ 34\overline{)0.714}\quad 0.021$$
$$\textbf{11.}\ 41\overline{)108.65}\quad 2.65$$
$$\textbf{12.}\ 7\overline{)2.492}\quad 0.356$$
$$\textbf{13.}\ 53\overline{)331.25}\quad 6.25$$

$$\textbf{14.}\ 78\overline{)\$82.68}\quad \$1.06$$
$$\textbf{15.}\ 81\overline{)\$286.74}\quad \$3.54$$
$$\textbf{16.}\ 66\overline{)\$162.36}\quad \$2.46$$
$$\textbf{17.}\ 35\overline{)\$368.55}\quad \$10.53$$

$$\textbf{18.}\ 90\overline{)367.20}\quad 4.08$$
$$\textbf{19.}\ 9\overline{)165.33}\quad 18.37$$
$$\textbf{20.}\ 87\overline{)3036.3}\quad 34.9$$
$$\textbf{21.}\ 8\overline{)821.6}\quad 102.7$$

First carry out the division to the thousandths place. Then round the quotient to the nearest hundredth.

$$\textbf{22.}\ 7\overline{)4.100}\quad \frac{0.585}{}\approx 0.59$$
$$\begin{array}{r} -35 \\ \hline 60 \\ -56 \\ \hline 40 \\ -35 \\ \hline 5 \end{array}$$

$$\textbf{23.}\ 12\overline{)8}\quad 0.67$$
$$\textbf{24.}\ 18\overline{)42.16}\quad 2.34$$
$$\textbf{25.}\ 64\overline{)38.45}\quad 0.60$$

$$\textbf{26.}\ 11\overline{)6}\quad 0.55$$
$$\textbf{27.}\ 62\overline{)74.08}\quad 1.19$$
$$\textbf{28.}\ 23\overline{)4.278}\quad 0.19$$

29. 56.92 ÷ 25 2.28
30. 7.34 ÷ 14 0.52
31. 3.64 ÷ 90 0.04

32. 0.891 ÷ 8 0.11
33. 7.53 ÷ 38 0.,20
34. 2.96 ÷ 26 0.11

35. 4.82 ÷ 68 0.07
36. 3.11 ÷ 42 0.07
37. 89.1 ÷ 94 0.95

38. 3.8 ÷ 9 0.42
39. 4.64 ÷ 12 0.39
40. 8.42 ÷ 15 0.56

41. 9.25 ÷ 13 0.71
42. 8.42 ÷ 15 0.56
43. 9.9 ÷ 24 0.41

Solve. Use the experiments on page 88.

44. What was the average reaction time for Experiment 2? Round the answer to the nearest hundredth of a second. 0.46 sec

45. What was the average reaction time for Experiment 3? Round the answer to the nearest hundredth of a second. 0.40 sec

46. In which experiment was the reaction time the fastest? Experiment 3

47. What was the difference between the fastest and slowest average reaction times? Work with times rounded to the nearest hundredth of a second. 0.06 sec

Muscle messages

48. Impulses from your brain control the muscles in all parts of your body. Certain impulses can travel through your body at the rate of 300 feet per second. Change the rate to miles per hour by multiplying by 3600 and dividing the answer by 5280. About 204.55 miles per hour

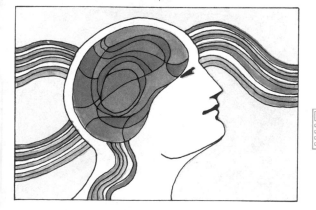

PRACTICE WORKSHEET
Copymaster S190 or Duplicating Master S190

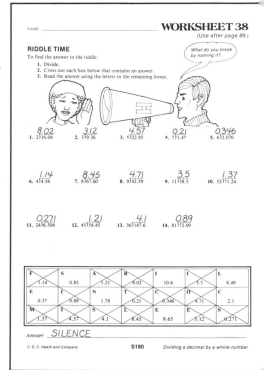

NAME _____ **WORKSHEET 38**
(Use after page 89.)

RIDDLE TIME
To find the answer to the riddle:
1. Divide.
2. Cross out each box below that contains an answer.
3. Read the answer using the letters in the remaining boxes.

What do you break by naming it?

8.02	3.12	4.57	0.21	0.346
1. 2)16.04	2. 3)9.36	3. 5)22.85	4. 7)1.47	5. 6)2.076

1.14	8.45	4.71	3.5	1.37
6. 4)4.56	7. 8)67.60	8. 9)42.39	9. 11)38.5	10. 52)71.24

0.271	1.21	4.1	0.89
11. 24)6.504	12. 45)54.45	13. 36)147.6	14. 81)72.09

F 1.14	S 0.83	A 1.21	R 8.01	I 10.6	I 3.5	L 8.49
E 0.37	N 0.89	T 1.78	C 0.21	O 4.71	C 2.1
M 1.37	I 4.57	S 4.1	L 8.45	E 9.65	E 3.12	S 0.271

Answer: SILENCE

© D. C. Heath and Company   **S190**   *Dividing a decimal by a whole number*

CHALKBOARD CHALLENGE
Place the digits *0, 1, 2, 3, 4,* and *5* in the boxes so that the quotient will be 4.45.

$$\overset{4\ .\ 4\ 5}{\boxed{1}\,\boxed{2}\,)\,\boxed{5}\,\boxed{3}\,.\,\boxed{4}\,\boxed{0}}$$

CHALKBOARD QUIZ
on previous lesson
Divide.
1. $43.8 \div 6$ 7.3
2. $13.95 \div 9$ 1.55
3. $2.480 \div 20$ 0.124
4. $165.33 \div 9$ 18.37
5. $22 \div 5$ 4.4

SKILLS REVIEWED
Subtracting whole numbers and
decimals
Comparing decimals
Multiplying whole numbers

PROBLEM-SOLVING SKILLS
Choosing the correct operation
Solving a two-step problem

STARTING THE LESSON
Cumulative Skill Practice
Challenge the students to an estimation hunt by saying, "Pick the largest difference in the first row of exercises." (Exercise 4) Then have the students pick the largest difference in the second and third rows of exercises. (Exercises 7 and 11)

STARTING THE LESSON
Problem Solving
Direct the students' attention to the comments at the top of page 91. Ask the students whose calculations should be used to compute these:

$(457 \times 4) + 825$ (Matt and Anne's)
$(150 - 125) \div 5$ (Susan and David's)
$20 - (5.75 \times 3)$ (Matt and Susan's)

Cumulative Skill Practice

Subtract.   *(page 38)*

1. 4897 −2235 = 2662	2. 6271 −5004 = 1267	3. 7829 −374 = 7455	4. 9652 −836 = 8816	5. 5834 −1297 = 4537
6. 3902 −1755 = 2147	7. 7301 −879 = 6422	8. 5026 −3477 = 1549	9. 6085 −392 = 5693	10. 5004 −1679 = 3325
11. 86,294 −7,381 = 78,913	12. 72,855 −6,974 = 65,881	13. 68,302 −9,756 = 58,546	14. 29,001 −17,362 = 11,639	15. 30,047 −18,492 = 11,555

Less than (<) or greater than (>)?   *(page 42)*

16. $0.5 < 0.6$ 17. $0.08 > 0.07$ 18. $0.008 > 0.007$
19. $16.1 > 16.0$ 20. $7.86 > 7.68$ 21. $0.38 > 0.3$
22. $42.79 < 42.8$ 23. $3.1 > 2.97$ 24. $6.347 < 63.4$
25. $0.852 < 1.2$ 26. $1.3 > 1.03$ 27. $529.6 < 530$
28. $14.006 < 14.06$ 29. $73.02 > 72.03$ 30. $0.021 < 0.21$

Give the difference.   *(page 46)*

31. $5.9 - 3.6$ 2.3   32. $8.42 - 3.76$ 4.66   33. $5.02 - 3.44$ 1.58
34. $72.3 - 2.59$ 69.71   35. $29.7 - 15.92$ 13.78   36. $74.36 - 2.1$ 72.26
37. $26.083 - 7.461$ 18.622   38. $74.4 - 3.88$ 70.52   39. $65.0 - 42.5$ 22.5
40. $12 - 3.7$ 8.3   41. $52 - 9.64$ 42.36   42. $29.4 - 2.94$ 26.46
43. $56.7 - 8.821$ 47.879   44. $37.4 - 18$ 19.4   45. $45.6 - 2.735$ 42.865

Multiply.   *(page 60)*

46. 538 ×132 = 71,016	47. 603 ×115 = 69,345	48. 492 ×236 = 116,112	49. 871 ×382 = 332,722	50. 729 ×533 = 388,557	51. 821 ×364 = 298,844
52. 666 ×240 = 159,840	53. 434 ×320 = 138,880	54. 921 ×402 = 370,242	55. 399 ×306 = 122,094	56. 671 ×580 = 389,180	57. 214 ×200 = 42,800
58. 738 ×426 = 314,388	59. 521 ×180 = 93,780	60. 426 ×253 = 107,778	61. 903 ×116 = 104,748	62. 800 ×204 = 163,200	63. 900 ×305 = 274,500

90

Problem solving

| This calculator only does addition. | This one only does subtraction. | Multiplication is the only operation this one will do. | Division only on this one. |

ANNE SUSAN MATT DAVID

Whose calculator solved it? Name the two people who worked together to solve each problem.

1. Names — Matt ? — Anne ?

My friend delivers 35 papers 6 days a week. She also delivers 48 Sunday papers. How many papers does she deliver each week?

Answer: _258 papers_

2. Names — Susan ? — David ?

We bought some $3 records. We gave the cashier $20 and got $8 in change. How many records did we buy?

Answer: _4 records_

3. Names — Anne ? — David ?

My friend and I earned $27.50 yesterday and $15.40 today. We shared the money equally. How much money did I get?

Answer: _$21.45_

4. Names — Matt ? — Susan ?

I bought 4 frozen pizzas at $2.90 each. How much change should I get from a $20 bill?

Answer: _$8.40_

Name the two people who should work together to solve each problem. Then solve each problem.

5. Names — Matt ? — Anne ?

After 5 friends each ate 4 tacos, there were 3 tacos left. How many tacos were there to start with?

Answer: _? 23_

6. Names — Susan ? — David ?

I bought 5 hockey tickets. I gave the cashier $20 and got $2.50 in change. What was the price of each ticket?

Answer: _? $3.50_

7. Names — Anne ? — David ?

At my school, 106 girls and 92 boys signed up to play volleyball. A total of 18 teams were formed. How many players were on each team?

Answer: _? 11_

8. Names — Matt ? — Anne ?

We bought a 14.5-pound watermelon at $.08 per pound and a $2.98 bag of oranges. What was the total cost?

Answer: _? $4.14_

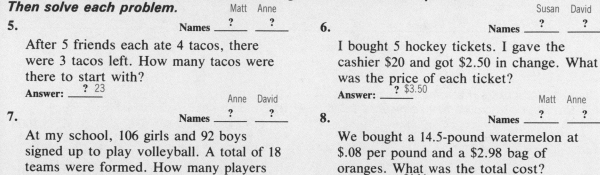

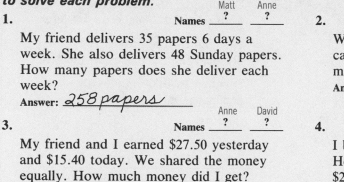

Dividing Whole Numbers and Decimals **91**

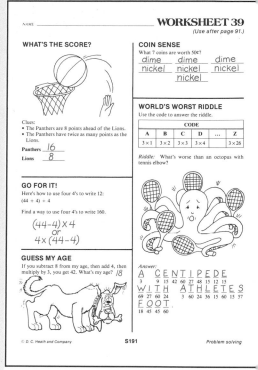

EXTRA PROBLEM SOLVING

Page 447   Even exercises

PROBLEM-SOLVING WORKSHEET

Copymaster S191 or Duplicating Master S191

WORKSHEET 39
(Use after page 91.)

NAME _____

WHAT'S THE SCORE?

Clues:
- The Panthers are 8 points ahead of the Lions.
- The Panthers have twice as many points as the Lions.

Panthers _16_
Lions _8_

COIN SENSE

What 7 coins are worth 50¢?

dime   dime   dime
nickel   nickel   nickel
nickel

WORLD'S WORST RIDDLE

Use the code to answer the riddle.

CODE

A	B	C	D	...	Z
3×1	3×2	3×3	3×4		3×26

Riddle: What's worse than an octopus with tennis elbow?

Answer:
A CENTIPEDE
3 9 15 42 60 27 48 15 12 15
WITH ATHLETES
69 27 60 24   3 60 24 36 15 60 15 57
FOOT
18 45 45 60

GO FOR IT!

Here's how to use four 4's to write 12:
(44 + 4) ÷ 4

Find a way to use four 4's to write 160.

(44−4) × 4
or
4 × (44−4)

GUESS MY AGE

If you subtract 8 from my age, then add 4, then multiply by 3, you get 42. What's my age? _18_

© D. C. Heath and Company   S191   *Problem solving*

CHALKBOARD CHALLENGE

Suppose the 5 key does not work on your calculator. Tell how you might use your broken calculator to do these multiplication problems.

1. 375 × 34   (374 × 34) + 34
2. 52 × 47   (42 × 47) + (10 × 47)

Answers will vary.

LESSON OBJECTIVE
To divide by 10, 100, or 1000

PROBLEM-SOLVING SKILLS
Selecting information from a display
Choosing the correct operation
Following instructions

STARTING THE LESSON
The comment from the banker at the top of page 92 is also on **Visual Aid 12.** Use the banker's comment. Tell the students that the banker can fill in the missing numbers in five seconds. Have the students determine how fast they can do it. Have them describe the method they use to get the missing numbers.

EXERCISE NOTE
Point out to the students that division by 10, 100, or 1000 should always be done mentally rather than by the division algorithm. Thus, for exercises 1–60 they only need to record the quotients on their papers.

Dividing by 10, 100, or 1000

The banker can fill in these missing numbers in 5 seconds. How fast can you do it?

> 800
> 8000 $1 bills equals ? $10 bills, ? $100 bills, or ? $1000 bills.
> 80   8

The banker knows that if you divide a number by 10, 100, or 1000, the quotient is less than the number. So, she moves the decimal point to the left.

Here's how *to divide by 10, 100, or 1000.*

$8000 \div 10 = 800.0$ or 800 Dividing by 10 moves the decimal point 1 place to the left.

$8000 \div 100 = 80.00$ or 80 Dividing by 100 moves the decimal point 2 places to the left.

$8000 \div 1000 = 8.000$ or 8 Dividing by 1000 moves the decimal point 3 places to the left.

Other examples:
Dividing by

10	$23.25 \div 10 = 2.325$
100	$6.1 \div 100 = 0.061$
1000	$9.75 \div 1000 = 0.00975$

> Some zeros had to be written before the decimal point could be placed in the quotient

EXERCISES

Divide. *Here are scrambled answers for the next two rows of exercises:* 0.536 6.7 0.067 3.62 36.2 5.36 0.0536 0.67

1. $36.2 \div 10$ 3.62
2. $362 \div 10$ 36.2
3. $53.6 \div 100$ 0.536
4. $53.6 \div 1000$

5. $536 \div 100$ 5.36
6. $67 \div 1000$ 0.067
7. $6700 \div 1000$ 6.7
8. $67 \div 100$ 0.6

9. $712.2 \div 10$ 71.22
10. $712.2 \div 100$ 7.122
11. $712.2 \div 1000$ 0.7122
12. $71.22 \div 10$ 7

13. $18.6 \div 1000$ 0.0186
14. $18.6 \div 100$ 0.186
15. $18.6 \div 10$ 1.86
16. $0.186 \div 10$ 0

17. $60 \div 10$ 6
18. $60 \div 100$ 0.6
19. $60 \div 1000$ 0.06
20. $600 \div 10$ 60

21. $14.32 \div 10$ 1.432
22. $14.32 \div 100$ 0.1432
23. $14.32 \div 1000$ 0.01432
24. $143.2 \div 100$ 1.432

25. $486 \div 1000$ 0.486
26. $486 \div 100$ 4.86
27. $486 \div 10$ 48.6
28. $4.86 \div 10$ 0.486

29. $421.9 \div 1000$ 0.4219
30. $421.9 \div 100$ 4.219
31. $421.9 \div 10$ 42.19
32. $42.19 \div 1000$ 0.04219

33. $242 \div 10$ 24.2
34. $242 \div 1000$ 0.242
35. $242 \div 100$ 2.42
36. $24.2 \div 1000$ 0.0242

37. $81.5 \div 100$ 0.815
38. $81.5 \div 10$ 8.15
39. $81.5 \div 1000$ 0.0815
40. $815 \div 10$ 81.5

41. $7 \div 1000$ 0.007
42. $7 \div 10$ 0.7
43. $7 \div 100$ 0.07
44. $70 \div 100$ 0.7

45. $9.3 \div 100$ 0.093
46. $9.3 \div 1000$ 0.0093
47. $9.3 \div 10$ 0.93
48. $93 \div 1000$ 0.093

49. $2.03 \div 10$ 0.203
50. $2.03 \div 1000$ 0.00203
51. $2.03 \div 100$ 0.0203
52. $20.3 \div 10$ 2.03

53. $765 \div 1000$ 0.765
54. $765 \div 10$ 76.5
55. $765 \div 100$ 7.65
56. $76.5 \div 10$ 7.65

57. $0.6 \div 100$ 0.006
58. $0.6 \div 1000$ 0.0006
59. $0.6 \div 10$ 0.06
60. $60 \div 1000$ 0.06

Solve. Use the money facts.

61. What is the height of $50,000 in
    a. $10 bills?   20 inches
    b. $100 bills?   2 inches
    c. $1000 bills?   0.2 inches
    d. $1 bills?   200 inch

62. What is the weight of $50,000 in
    a. $10 bills?   11 pounds
    b. $100 bills?   1.1 pounds
    c. $1000 bills?   0.11 pounds
    d. $1 bills?   110 pound

> **MONEY FACTS**
>
> $50,000 in $10 bills is 20 inches high.
>
> $50,000 in $10 bills weighs 11 pounds.

Make your money stretch

63. **a.** Suppose you have 1 million dollars in $1 bills. If you laid the bills end-to-end, how many miles of money would you have? To find the number of miles, write a   97.85
      5 in the hundredths place
      7 in the ones place
      8 in the tenths place
      9 in the tens place

    b. Suppose that you have 1 billion dollars in $1 bills. If you laid the bills end-to-end, how many miles of money would you have? *Hints: 1000 million is 1 billion. Use your answer from part a.*   97,850

EXTRA PRACTICE
Page 425   Skill 27

PRACTICE WORKSHEET
Copymaster S192 or Duplicating Master S192

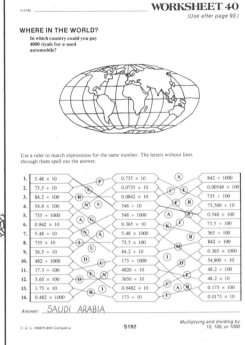

CHALKBOARD CHALLENGE
Find the missing numbers.

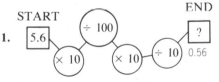

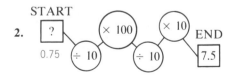

LESSON OBJECTIVE
To divide a decimal by a decimal

PROBLEM-SOLVING SKILLS
Finding information in a newspaper article
Choosing the correct operation

STARTING THE LESSON
Play 'What are the facts?' Have the students study the article at the top of page 94 for 60 seconds. Then tell the students to close their books and decide whether these statements are true or false:

- Skip Gilligan's attempt at setting an onion-peeling record ended after 3.5 minutes. (True)
- He peeled more than 30 pounds of onions. (True)
- He was forced to stop due to sore fingers. (False)
- Skip is a 28-year-old construction worker. (False)

HERE'S HOW NOTE
After discussing exercises 1–5, it may be helpful to have several of exercises 6–57 demonstrated at the chalkboard before the students begin their independent work.

Dividing a decimal by a decimal

ONION TEARS

Skip Gilligan's attempt at setting a new onion-peeling record ended in tears. After 3.5 minutes and 31.5 pounds of peeled onions, Gilligan was forced to stop due to eye discomfort. With tears in his eyes, the 28-year-old cafeteria worker said he would be back for another shot at the record.

1. Read the newspaper article. How many pounds of onions did Gilligan peel in 3.5 minutes? 31.5

2. To compute how many pounds of onions he peeled per minute, you would divide 31.5 by what number? 3.5

Here's how *to divide a decimal by a decimal.* $31.5 \div 3.5 = ?$

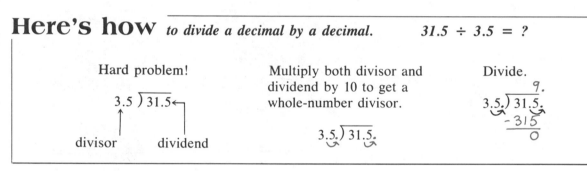

3. Look at the *Here's how*. To get a whole-number divisor, both decimal points were moved ☐? place(s) to the right. one

4. How many pounds of onions did Gilligan peel per minute? 9

5. Check these examples. Are the answers correct? Yes

a. $8.32 \div 0.32$

b. $0.9856 \div 0.004$

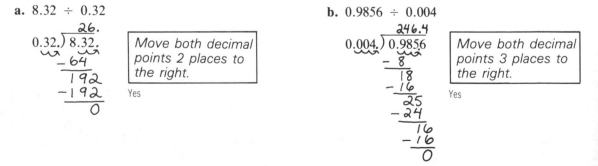

EXERCISES

Divide. Here are scrambled answers for the next row of exercises: 3.6   6.8   6.5   38

6. $0.2\overline{)1.36}$ 6.8

7. $0.5\overline{)3.25}$ 6.5

8. $0.4\overline{)1.44}$ 3.6

9. $0.02\overline{)0.76}$ 38

10. $0.07\overline{)4.62}$ 66

11. $0.02\overline{)2.12}$ 106

12. $0.005\overline{)0.515}$ 103

13. $0.007\overline{)7.280}$ 1040

14. $0.6\overline{)1.5}$ 2.5

15. $0.8\overline{)2.56}$ 3.2

16. $0.03\overline{)1.26}$ 42

17. $0.005\overline{)0.485}$ 97

18. $0.2\overline{)5.46}$ 27.3

19. $4.5\overline{)22.5}$ 5

20. $0.05\overline{)0.075}$ 1.5

21. $0.08\overline{)1.016}$ 12.7

22. $0.4\overline{)2.488}$ 6.22

23. $0.3\overline{)0.06}$ 0.2

24. $0.05\overline{)0.75}$ 15

25. $0.008\overline{)0.512}$ 64

26. $1.2\overline{)31.2}$ 26

27. $0.15\overline{)0.57}$ 3.8

28. $3.4\overline{)3.57}$ 1.05

29. $0.26\overline{)0.884}$ 3.4

30. $7.4\overline{)40.7}$ 5.5

31. $5.9\overline{)21.24}$ 3.6

32. $0.81\overline{)49.41}$ 61

33. $0.94\overline{)10.528}$ 11.2

34. $9.3\overline{)6.045}$ 0.65

35. $0.66\overline{)0.3366}$ 0.51

36. $5.2\overline{)21.164}$ 4.07

37. $0.48\overline{)1.5216}$ 3.17

38. $4.5 \div 0.3$ 15

39. $12.6 \div 0.2$ 63

40. $56.84 \div 0.7$ 81.2

41. $4.32 \div 0.4$ 10.8

42. $1.684 \div 0.02$ 84.2

43. $0.7085 \div 0.05$ 14.17

44. $0.1128 \div 0.08$ 1.41

45. $0.567 \div 0.09$ 6.3

46. $0.341 \div 0.11$ 3.1

47. $1.875 \div 0.25$ 7.5

48. $26.22 \div 5.7$ 4.6

49. $23.24 \div 2.8$ 8.3

50. $4.14 \div 1.8$ 2.3

51. $8.4 \div 2.1$ 4

52. $1.56 \div 0.12$ 13

53. $1.260 \div 0.12$ 10.5

54. $43.2 \div 0.24$ 180

55. $0.522 \div 0.036$ 14.5

56. $1.6254 \div 3.01$ 0.54

57. $43.594 \div 0.71$ 61.4

Solve.

58. Calvin set out to break the onion-peeling record. He peeled 12.6 pounds in 1.5 minutes. Did he peel more or less than 9 pounds per minute? *Hint: Divide to get the answer.* Less

59. In 1979, a team of 57 men pushed a baby carriage 345.25 miles in 24 hours. How many miles did they average per hour? Round the answer to the nearest hundredth of a mile. 14.39

60. Fourteen students leapfrogged for 148 hours at the average rate of 3.75 miles per hour. How many miles did they leapfrog? 555

61. The record for treading water is 80 hours. How many minutes is that? 4800

Just for the record

62. In 1981, Norman Johnson sliced a 12-inch cucumber into 22 slices per inch. It took him 19.11 seconds. What was his average time per slice? Round the answer to the nearest hundredth. 0.07 second per slice

Dividing Whole Numbers and Decimals **95**

EXTRA PRACTICE
Page 425   Skill 28

PRACTICE WORKSHEET
Copymaster S193 or Duplicating Master S193

NAME _____ **WORKSHEET 41**
(Use after page 95.)

SKILL DRILL
Study these examples.

Divide.

1. $0.5\overline{)2.65}$ 5.3
2. $0.08\overline{)0.376}$ 4.7
3. $0.3\overline{)92.7}$ 309
4. $0.07\overline{)0.91}$ 13

5. $0.04\overline{)13.20}$ 330
6. $0.003\overline{)1.701}$ 567
7. $0.09\overline{)0.0378}$ 0.42
8. $0.08\overline{)0.136}$ 1.7

9. $3.3\overline{)1.40}$ 0.4
10. $0.31\overline{)0.0961}$ 0.31
11. $2.2\overline{)70.62}$ 32.1
12. $0.42\overline{)0.294}$ 0.7

13. $5.6\overline{)21.28}$ 3.8
14. $0.12\overline{)0.228}$ 1.9
15. $0.25\overline{)6.25}$ 25
16. $3.3\overline{)2.541}$ 0.77

Check yourself. Here are the scrambled answers:
0.31   0.4   0.42   0.7   0.77   1.7   1.9   3.8   4.7   5.3   13   25   32.1
309   330   567

© D. C. Heath and Company   **S193**   *Dividing a decimal by a decimal*

CHALKBOARD CHALLENGE
Use the digits. Fill in the boxes to get the answer.

1. 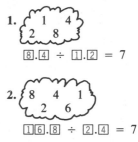 1   4   2   8

$$\boxed{8}.\boxed{4} \div \boxed{1}.\boxed{2} = 7$$

2. 8   4   1   2   6

$$\boxed{1}\boxed{6}.\boxed{8} \div \boxed{2}.\boxed{4} = 7$$

95

CHALKBOARD QUIZ
on previous lesson

Divide.
1. 6.25 ÷ 0.5   12.5
2. 0.84 ÷ 0.02   42
3. 0.423 ÷ 0.003   141
4. 2.4 ÷ 1.2   2
5. 1.68 ÷ 21   0.08

LESSON OBJECTIVES
To divide a decimal by a decimal
To write a remainder as a decimal

PROBLEM-SOLVING SKILLS
Finding information in a chart and a drawing
Choosing the correct operation
Making a drawing

STARTING THE LESSON
The chart and drawing at the top of page 96 are also on **Visual Aid 13**. Use the chart and drawing and ask questions like these before discussing exercises 1–5.
• What is this type of race called? (BMX race)
• On this track, is the distance from start to finish more or less than half a mile? (Less)
• Did the two BMX riders complete the race in more or less than half a minute? (More)

HERE'S HOW NOTE
After discussing exercises 1–5, you may wish to use several of exercises 6–37 as chalkboard examples before the students begin their independent work.

More on dividing a decimal by a decimal

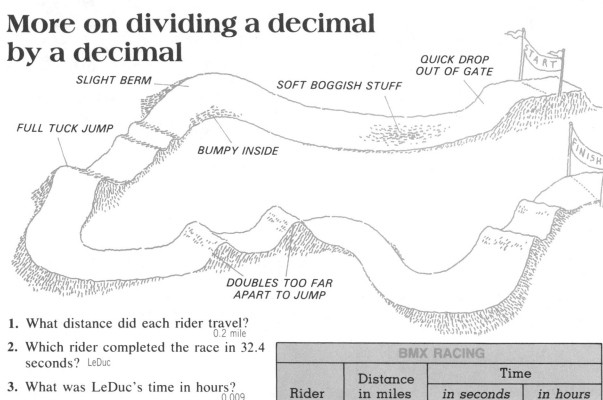

1. What distance did each rider travel?
    0.2 mile
2. Which rider completed the race in 32.4 seconds? LeDuc
3. What was LeDuc's time in hours?
    0.009
4. To compute LeDuc's average speed in miles per hour, you would divide 0.2 (miles traveled) by what number?
    0.009

Rider	Distance in miles	Time in seconds	Time in hours
		in seconds	*in hours*
LeDuc	0.2	32.4	0.009
Elliott	0.2	39.6	0.011

BMX RACING

Here's how *to divide a decimal by a decimal.*
$$0.2 \div 0.009 = ?$$

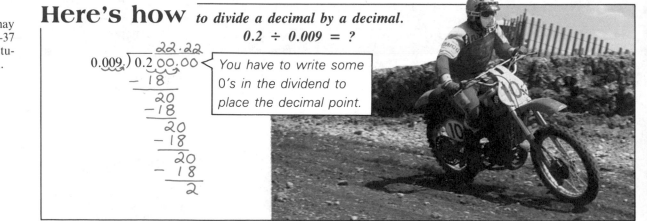

You have to write some 0's in the dividend to place the decimal point.

5. Look at the *Here's how*. Notice that the division will never come out even. What is LeDuc's average speed rounded to the nearest tenth? 22.2 miles per hour

EXERCISES

Divide. *Hint: You will need to write some zeros.*
Here are scrambled answers for the next row of exercises: 5.5   5   7.2   7.5

6. $0.5 \overline{)3.6}$ — 7.2

7. $0.2 \overline{)1.1}$ — 5.5

8. $0.06 \overline{)0.3}$ — 5

9. $0.4 \overline{)3}$ — 7.5

10. $0.8 \overline{)56}$ — 70

11. $0.4 \overline{)1.4}$ — 3.5

12. $0.02 \overline{)7}$ — 350

13. $0.005 \overline{)0.047}$ — 9.4

14. $0.2 \overline{).01}$ — 0.05

15. $0.4 \overline{)0.26}$ — 0.65

16. $0.08 \overline{)1.24}$ — 15.5

17. $0.006 \overline{)0.285}$ — 47.5

18. $1.2 \overline{)4.2}$ — 3.5

19. $2.5 \overline{)0.55}$ — 0.22

20. $3.1 \overline{)124}$ — 40

21. $4.2 \overline{)6.3}$ — 1.5

Divide. Round each quotient to the nearest tenth.
Here are scrambled answers for the next row of exercises: 0.4   2.3   0.2   4.7

22. $0.3 \overline{)1.4}$ — 4.7

23. $0.6 \overline{)0.14}$ — 0.2

24. $1.4 \overline{)0.528}$ — 0.4

25. $2.2 \overline{)4.98}$ — 2.3

26. $2.5 \overline{)6.1}$ — 2.4

27. $3.1 \overline{)7.5}$ — 2.4

28. $0.06 \overline{)0.5}$ — 8.3

29. $1.2 \overline{)0.54}$ — 0.5

30. $7.5 \overline{)62.91}$ — 8.4

31. $3.9 \overline{)7.503}$ — 1.9

32. $2.6 \overline{)7.4}$ — 2.8

33. $0.31 \overline{)0.09}$ — 0.3

34. $12.1 \overline{)156.3}$ — 12.9

35. $1.84 \overline{)192.6}$ — 104.7

36. $23.5 \overline{)6.843}$ — 0.3

37. $3.41 \overline{)18.5}$ — 5.4

Solve. Refer to the chart and drawing on page 96.

38. Was Elliott's average speed more or less than 20 miles per hour? *Hint: Divide to answer the question.*   Less

39. How many seconds faster did LeDuc ride the 0.2-mile track than Elliott?   7.2

40. From the starting line to the full tuck jump is 0.09 mile. How far is it from the full tuck jump to the finish line?   0.11 mile

41. LeDuc's riding time from start to the full tuck jump was 14.7 seconds. How many seconds did it take LeDuc to ride from the full tuck jump to the finish line?   17.7 seconds

Who's ahead?

As the winner crosses the finish line,
Cherie is 4 feet ahead of Eric.
Kenny is 2 feet behind Justin.
Eric is 6 feet ahead of Kenny.

42. Who is the winner?   Cherie

43. Who is last?   Kenny

44. How many feet separate the first and last racers?   10

Draw a picture like this one. It will help you solve the problems.

PRACTICE WORKSHEET
Copymaster S194 or Duplicating Master S194

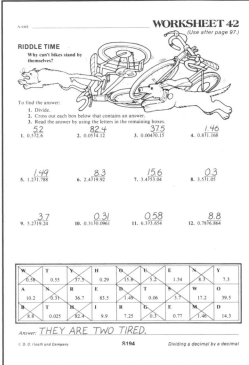

WORKSHEET 42
(Use after page 97.)

RIDDLE TIME
Why can't bikes stand by themselves?

To find the answer:
1. Divide.
2. Cross out each box below that contains an answer.
3. Read the answer by using the letters in the remaining boxes.

1. $0.5 \overline{)2.6}$ — 52
2. $0.05 \overline{)4.12}$ — 82.4
3. $0.004 \overline{)0.15}$ — 37.5
4. $0.8 \overline{)1.168}$ — 1.46

5. $1.2 \overline{)1.788}$ — 1.49
6. $2.4 \overline{)19.92}$ — 8.3
7. $3.4 \overline{)53.04}$ — 15.6
8. $3.5 \overline{)1.05}$ — 0.3

9. $5.2 \overline{)19.24}$ — 3.7
10. $0.31 \overline{)0.0961}$ — 0.31
11. $6.3 \overline{)3.654}$ — 0.58
12. $0.78 \overline{)6.864}$ — 8.8

W	T	Y	H	O	U	E	N	Y
0.58	0.55	37.5	0.29	15.6	5.2	1.54	8.3	7.3
A	N	R	E	D	T	S	W	O
10.2	0.31	36.7	83.5	1.49	0.06	3.7	17.2	39.5
B	T	H	I	R	G	E	M	D
8.8	0.025	82.4	9.9	7.25	0.3	0.77	1.46	14.3

Answer: THEY ARE TWO TIRED.

© D. C. Heath and Company   S194   Dividing a decimal by a decimal

LIFE-SKILL PROJECT

Collecting data
Have the students time how long it takes them to walk (taking normal steps) a distance of 30 feet. Have them compute their walking speed in feet per second. Challenge them to also compute their speed in miles per hour.

SKILLS REVIEWED
Multiplying decimals
Dividing whole numbers and decimals
Simplifying expressions

PROBLEM-SOLVING SKILL
Finding information on a computer printout

STARTING THE LESSON
Cumulative Skill Practice
Challenge the students to an estimation hunt by saying, ''Pick the largest product in the first row of exercises.'' (Exercise 3) Then have the students use their estimation skills to pick the largest product in the second, third, fourth, fifth, and sixth rows of exercises. (Exercises 7, 12, 13, 18, and 23)

STARTING THE LESSON
Problem Solving
Write this student identification number on the chalkboard:

185-72-335

Tell the students that part of the ID number contains a student's month, day of month, and year of birth. Challenge them to figure out the student's year of birth. (1972) Then tell them to read the top of page 99 to find out how to break the code to find the student's birthday.

Cumulative Skill Practice

Give the product. *(page 64)*

1. 2.6 × 0.9 2.34
2. 3.98 × 0.6 2.388
3. 27.5 × 0.8 22
4. 2.9 × 0.7 2.03

5. 6.2 × 0.59 3.658
6. 0.38 × 1.5 0.57
7. 36 × 0.42 15.12
8. 3.1 × 0.2 0.62

9. 206 × 4.3 885.8
10. 8.36 × 19 158.84
11. 0.35 × 50 17.5
12. 14.6 × 82 1197.2

13. 8.32 × 5.6 46.592
14. 7.42 × 3.9 28.938
15. 5.66 × 0.41 2.3206
16. 3.12 × 4.15 12.948

17. 4.63 × 2.06 9.5378
18. 3.05 × 71 216.55
19. 6.09 × 5.51 33.5559
20. 6.2 × 1.93 11.966

21. 3.2 × 2.81 8.992
22. 4.5 × 30 135
23. 6.41 × 62 397.42
24. 9.8 × 1.34 13.132

Divide. If the division does not come out even, round the quotient to the nearest whole number. *(pages 80, 84)*

25. $24\overline{)864}$ 36
26. $24\overline{)2328}$ 97
27. $24\overline{)2160}$ 90
28. $24\overline{)2472}$ 103
29. $24\overline{)5016}$ 209

30. $28\overline{)1932}$ 69
31. $39\overline{)3042}$ 78
32. $15\overline{)1470}$ 98
33. $62\overline{)1426}$ 23
34. $17\overline{)1003}$ 59

35. $12\overline{)10,446}$ 871
36. $56\overline{)69,454}$ 1240
37. $36\overline{)20,882}$ 580
38. $41\overline{)35,867}$ 875
39. $48\overline{)31,200}$ 650

40. $117\overline{)72,594}$ 620
41. $117\overline{)70,551}$ 603
42. $117\overline{)24,687}$ 211
43. $400\overline{)14,400}$ 36
44. $504\overline{)16,128}$ 32

45. $221\overline{)21,658}$ 98
46. $221\overline{)67,184}$ 304
47. $221\overline{)35,426}$ 160
48. $109\overline{)34,989}$ 321
49. $109\overline{)98,142}$ 900

Simplify. *(page 86)*

50. 24 ÷ 4 + 2 8
51. 30 − 5 + 7 32
52. 8 × 4 − 1 31

53. 36 ÷ 6 ÷ 3 2
54. 14 × 5 ÷ 5 14
55. 18 + 8 ÷ 2 22

56. (25 + 25) ÷ 10 5
57. 16 × (7 − 3) 64
58. 20 × (10 − 4) 120

59. 36 + 12 ÷ 4 + 2 41
60. (36 + 12) ÷ 4 + 2 14
61. 36 + 12 ÷ (4 + 2) 38

62. 32 × 8 − 8 + 4 252
63. 32 × (8 − 8) + 4 4
64. 32 × 8 − (8 + 4) 244

Give the quotient. Round the quotient to the nearest tenth. *(pages 94, 96)*

65. 16.4 ÷ 0.6 27.3
66. 3.74 ÷ 0.2 18.7
67. 9.05 ÷ 0.05 181

68. 28.7 ÷ 0.3 95.7
69. 4.38 ÷ 0.04 109.5
70. 8.4 ÷ 0.08 105

71. 6.15 ÷ 1.2 5.1
72. 2.038 ÷ 2.4 0.8
73. 4.06 ÷ 0.25 16.2

74. 12.063 ÷ 0.33 36.6
75. 5.008 ÷ 0.61 8.2
76. 6.42 ÷ 6.2 1.0

77. 5.38 ÷ 5.04 1.1
78. 2.971 ÷ 3.7 0.8
79. 23.4 ÷ 8.07 2.9

Problem solving

COMPUTERS IN SCHOOLS

Schools use computers to store student data. In the Franklin School District, a computer assigns each student an identification number.

Look at Carol's identification number. The middle two digits of the number tell Carol's year of birth. The last three digits tell her birthday.

To find her birthday, divide the last 3-digit number by 31. The whole number in the quotient is her month of birth, and the remainder is the day of the month.

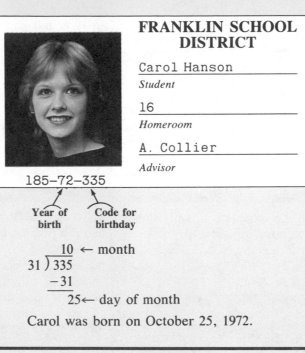

FRANKLIN SCHOOL DISTRICT

Carol Hanson
Student

16
Homeroom

A. Collier
Advisor

185–72–335

Year of birth | Code for birthday

$$\begin{array}{r} 10 \leftarrow \text{month} \\ 31\overline{)335} \\ -31 \\ \hline 25 \leftarrow \text{day of month} \end{array}$$

Carol was born on October 25, 1972.

Use the information on the computer printout to answer these questions.

1. *My name is Chris Harris. What is my date of birth?*

July 22, 1974

NAME	I.D. NUMBER	HOME ROOM	ADVISOR
Hanson, Carol	185-72-335	16	Collier
Harris, Chris	204-74-239	16	Vandegrift
Holmes, Brian	133-73-133	29	Collier
Holway, Amy	218-74-326	34	Vandegrift
Hull, Jack	199-73-185	34	Haver
Hurst, Mary	306-75-223	16	Collier
Heinbrough, Karen	156-76-121	16	Haver
Hernandez, Ralph	254-73-144	29	Collier
Hirai, George	314-76-289	34	Vandegrift

2. Give the birthday for each student.

  a. Amy Holway   October 16, 1974
  b. Mary Hurst   July 6, 1975
  c. Jack Hull   May 30, 1973

3. Mr. Haver's birthday is March 28. Which student on the list has the same birthday as Mr. Haver?   Karen Heinbrough

4. Who is the youngest student on the list?
George Hirai

5. How many students on the list have birthdays during the school year?   7

Solve.

6. Brian Ogel was born on March 25, 1976. What are the last 5 digits of his student ID number?   76-118

7. Suppose you registered in the Franklin School District. What would be the last 5 digits of your student ID number?
Answers will vary.

Dividing Whole Numbers and Decimals **99**

REVIEW PRACTICE
Rounding decimals
Page 413   Skill 4

PROBLEM-SOLVING WORKSHEET
Copymaster S195 or Duplicating Master S195

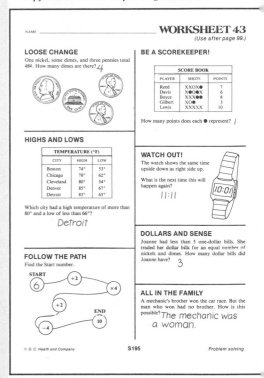

NAME _____ **WORKSHEET 43**
(Use after page 99.)

LOOSE CHANGE
One nickel, some dimes, and three pennies total 48¢. How many dimes are there? 4

BE A SCOREKEEPER!

SCORE BOOK		
PLAYER	SHOTS	POINTS
Reed	XXOX●	7
Davis	X●O●X	6
Boyce	XXX●●	8
Gilbert	XO●	3
Lewis	XXXXX	10

How many points does each ● represent? 1

HIGHS AND LOWS

TEMPERATURE (°F)		
CITY	HIGH	LOW
Boston	74°	53°
Chicago	78°	62°
Cleveland	80°	54°
Denver	85°	67°
Detroit	83°	65°

Which city had a high temperature of more than 80° and a low of less than 66°?
Detroit

WATCH OUT!
The watch shows the same time upside down as right side up.
What is the next time this will happen again?
11:11

FOLLOW THE PATH
Find the Start number.

START 6 → +2 → ×4 → +2 → -4 → END 10

DOLLARS AND SENSE
Joanne had less than 5 one-dollar bills. She traded her dollar bills for an equal number of nickels and dimes. How many dollar bills did Joanne have? 3

ALL IN THE FAMILY
A mechanic's brother won the car race. But the man who won had no brother. How is this possible? The mechanic was a woman.

© D. C. Heath and Company   S195   *Problem solving*

LIFE-SKILL PROJECT
Researching information
Have the students use an almanac to find which two presidents of the United States had their birthdays on the same day and month.

Warren Harding and James Polk both had a November 2 birthday.

CHAPTER 4 TEST
(Form A)

Divide. (pages 76, 78)

1. 3)96 = 32
2. 6)72 = 12
3. 4)756 = 189

4. 7)469 = 67
5. 5)515 = 103
6. 8)6416 = 802

Divide. If the division does not come out even, round the quotient to the nearest whole number. (pages 80, 84)

7. 25)1150 = 46
8. 42)2142 = 51
9. 68)3540 = 52

10. 120)3857 = 32
11. 271)60,075 = 222
12. 652)538,265 = 826

Simplify. (page 86)

13. 32 ÷ 8 + 8 = 12
14. 6 + 3 × 5 = 21
15. 12 × (10 − 4) = 72
16. (18 − 3) × 2 = 30
17. 7 × 8 + 3 × 8 = 80
18. (5 + 7) ÷ 3 + 1 = 5
19. 24 ÷ (4 + 4) × 3 − 1 = 8

Divide. Round the quotient to the nearest hundredth. (page 88)

20. 6 ÷ 9 = 0.67
21. 11 ÷ 6 = 1.83
22. 17.44 ÷ 3 = 5.81
23. 9.061 ÷ 7 = 1.29
24. 6.01 ÷ 35 = 0.17
25. 81.6 ÷ 29 = 2.81

ANSWERS
1. 32
2. 12
3. 189
4. 67
5. 103
6. 802
7. 46
8. 51
9. 52
10. 32
11. 222
12. 826
13. 12
14. 21
15. 72
16. 30
17. 80
18. 5
19. 8
20. 0.67
21. 1.83
22. 5.81
23. 1.29
24. 0.17
25. 2.81

CHAPTER 4 TEST
(Form A)

Divide. (page 92)

26. 325 ÷ 10 = 32.5
27. 432 ÷ 1000 = 0.432
28. 482.5 ÷ 100 = 4.825
29. 56.8 ÷ 10 = 5.68
30. 24 ÷ 1000 = 0.024
31. 7 ÷ 10 = 0.7
32. 3.4 ÷ 1000 = 0.0034
33. 2.59 ÷ 1000 = 0.00259
34. 6.15 ÷ 100 = 0.0615
35. 56.4 ÷ 1000 = 0.0564

Divide. (page 94)

36. 0.2)4.38 = 21.9
37. 0.05)0.275 = 5.5
38. 0.008)1.376 = 172
39. 0.25)4.75 = 19
40. 6.4)24.768 = 3.87
41. 0.037)0.08029 = 2.17

Divide. Round the quotient to the nearest tenth. (page 96)

42. 0.4)2.27 = 5.7
43. 0.06)1.3 = 21.7
44. 0.003)7.4 = 2466.7
45. 0.38)15.3 = 40.3
46. 4.9)0.91 = 0.2
47. 1.75)4.771 = 2.7

Solve.

48. How much more do 12 bumper stickers cost than 6 bumper stickers? $2.80

49. You bought 12 bumper stickers. How much did each bumper sticker cost? $.50

50. Your friend bought 18 bumper stickers. How much did he pay for each bumper sticker? Round the answer to the nearest cent. $.44

BUMPER-STICKER SALE!

Choose any 6	$3.20
Choose any 12	$6.00
Choose any 18	$8.00
Choose any 24	$9.50

ANSWERS
26. 32.5
27. 0.432
28. 4.825
29. 5.68
30. 0.024
31. 0.7
32. 0.0034
33. 0.00259
34. 0.0615
35. 0.0564
36. 21.9
37. 5.5
38. 172
39. 19
40. 3.87
41. 2.17
42. 5.7
43. 21.7
44. 2466.7
45. 40.3
46. 0.2
47. 2.7
48. $2.80
49. $.50
50. $.44

Chapter REVIEW

Here are scrambled answers for the review exercises:

1	3	6	26	divide	left	quotient	zeros
2	5	7	140	add	multiply	subtract	

1. 6, quotient

2. zeros, 26

3. 5, multiply, add

1. To complete this division exercise, divide 24 by ? . The answer is called the ? . *(page 76)*

$$6)\overline{324}$$
$$-30$$
$$\overline{24}$$

2. To estimate this quotient, find the first digit in the quotient and write ? in the remaining places. To find the first digit of this quotient, think about dividing ? by 6. *(pages 78, 80)*

$$62)\overline{2609}$$

3. In this division exercise, the quotient is 42 and the remainder is ? . To check the division, ? 42 by 62 and ? 5. *(page 80)*

$$62)\overline{2609} \quad 42\ R5$$
$$-248$$
$$\overline{129}$$
$$-124$$
$$\overline{5}$$

4. 7

5. divide, subtract

6. 140

4. A zero was written in the tenths place and the division was carried out to that place. The quotient rounded to the nearest whole number is ? . *(page 84)*

$$3)\overline{22.0} \quad 7.3$$
$$-21$$
$$\overline{18}$$
$$-9$$
$$\overline{1}$$

5. To simplify this expression, first ? and then ? . *(page 86)*

$$6 - 4 \div 2$$

6. To carry out the division to the next place, you would divide ? by 34. *(page 88)*

$$34)\overline{198.6} \quad 5.8$$
$$-170$$
$$\overline{286}$$
$$-272$$
$$\overline{14}$$

7. 3, left

8. 1

9. 2

7. Dividing by 1000 moves the decimal point ? places to the ? . *(page 92)*

$$16.5 \div 1000 = 0.165$$

8. Before dividing, move both decimal points ? place(s) to the right. *(page 94)*

$$1.4)\overline{2.884}$$

9. To place the decimal point in the dividend, you first write ? zeros. *(page 96)*

$$0.007)\overline{1.6}$$

Divide. *(pages 76, 78)*

1. $3\overline{)93}$ = 31
2. $5\overline{)85}$ = 17
3. $9\overline{)198}$ = 22
4. $6\overline{)738}$ = 123
5. $8\overline{)816}$ = 102

6. $2\overline{)608}$ = 304
7. $4\overline{)1624}$ = 406
8. $7\overline{)4235}$ = 605
9. $8\overline{)6424}$ = 803
10. $5\overline{)4195}$ = 839

Divide. If the division does not come out even, round the quotient to the nearest whole number. *(pages 80, 84)*

11. $24\overline{)888}$ = 37
12. $18\overline{)1098}$ = 61
13. $30\overline{)2734}$ = 91
14. $56\overline{)8365}$ = 149

15. $53{,}216 \div 500$ 106
16. $38{,}296 \div 213$ 180
17. $71{,}025 \div 432$ 164
18. $67{,}055 \div 621$ 108

Simplify. *(page 86)*

19. $8 - 4 + 2$ 6
20. $7 \times 5 - 3$ 32
21. $20 + 8 \div 4$ 22
22. $3 + 9 \div 3$ 6

23. $5 + 8 \div 4 + 9$ 16
24. $(16 + 8) \div 4 + 2$ 8
25. $16 + 8 \div 4 + 2$ 20
26. $8 + 4 \times 2 - 1$ 15

Divide. *(pages 88, 92)*

27. $19.2 \div 8$ 2.4
28. $118.4 \div 4$ 29.6
29. $109.62 \div 9$ 12.18
30. $6.45 \div 5$ 1.29

31. $558.7 \div 37$ 15.1
32. $99.84 \div 48$ 2.08
33. $1483.2 \div 72$ 20.6
34. $205.44 \div 32$ 6.42

35. $364 \div 10$ 36.4
36. $528 \div 100$ 5.28
37. $327 \div 1000$ 0.327
38. $326 \div 100$ 3.26

39. $123.9 \div 100$ 1.239
40. $682.3 \div 10$ 68.23
41. $529.64 \div 100$ 5.2964
42. $65.2 \div 100$ 0.652

Divide. Round each quotient to the nearest tenth. *(pages 94, 96)*

43. $0.5\overline{)4.8}$ = 9.6
44. $0.6\overline{)31.26}$ = 52.1
45. $0.9\overline{)4.32}$ = 4.8
46. $1.6\overline{)35}$ = 21.9

47. $1.1\overline{)5.73}$ = 5.2
48. $3.6\overline{)7.039}$ = 2.0
49. $0.64\overline{)15.3}$ = 23.9
50. $3.2\overline{)6.84}$ = 2.1

Solve.

51. How much will it cost to have a roll of 12 and a roll of 24 printed? $6.10

52. How much will it cost to have 3 rolls of 15 printed? $8.16

53. How much does each print cost for a roll of 36? Round your answer to the nearest cent. $.14

54. You had 2 rolls of 12 and 1 roll of 24 printed. You gave the clerk $20. How much change should you have received? $11.51

PHOTO FINISHING	
12 EXPOSURES	$2.39
15 EXPOSURES	2.72
24 EXPOSURES	3.71
36 EXPOSURES	5.03

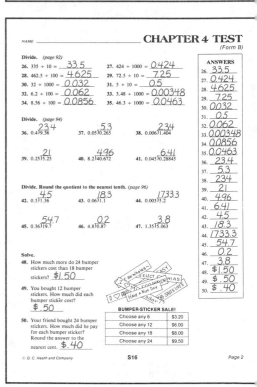

CUMULATIVE TEST
(*Chapters 1–4*)

Use Copymaster S336 to provide the students with an answer sheet in standardized test format.

Answers for Cumulative Test, Chapters 1–4

1. Ⓐ ●ⒸⒹ   2. ●ⒷⒸⒹ   3. ⒶⒷⒸ●
4. Ⓐ●ⒸⒹ   5. ●ⒷⒸⒹ   6. ⒶⒷ●Ⓓ
7. Ⓐ●ⒸⒹ   8. ⒶⒷ●Ⓓ   9. ●ⒷⒸⒹ
10. ⒶⒷⒸ●   11. Ⓐ●ⒸⒹ   12. ●ⒷⒸⒹ

The table below correlates test items with student text pages.

Test Item	Page(s) Taught	Skill Practice
1	4	p. 82, exercises 1–16
2	8	p. 82, exercises 17–41
3	24	p. 82, exercises 42–65
4	38	p. 90, exercises 1–15
5	42	p. 90, exercises 16–30
6	46	p. 90, exercises 31–45
7	60	p. 90, exercises 46–63
8	64	p. 98, exercises 1–24
9	80, 84	p. 98, exercises 25–49
10	86	p. 98, exercises 50–64
11	94, 96	p. 98, exercises 65–79
12	64	

102

Cumulative TEST — Standardized Format

Choose the correct letter.

1. The short word-name for 8,020,000 is

A. 8 billion, 20 million
B. 8 million, 20 thousand
C. 8 million, 2 thousand
D. none of these

2. Add.   56,394
           + 26,748

A. 83,142
B. 72,032
C. 72,042
D. none of these

3. Give the sum.

14.6 + 31.5 + 2.06

A. 66.7
B. 47.16
C. 481.6
D. none of these

4. Subtract.   35,064
              − 13,297

A. 22,233
B. 21,767
C. 22,767
D. none of these

5. Which number is greater than 0.06?

A. 0.5
B. 0.04
C. 0.059
D. none of these

6. Give the difference.

424.7 − 38.46

A. 40.1
B. 382.36
C. 386.24
D. none of these

7. Multiply.   629
               × 240

A. 15,096
B. 150,960
C. 149,660
D. none of these

8. Give the product.

3.62 × 1.7

A. 5.774
B. 61.54
C. 6.154
D. none of these

9. Divide. $68\overline{)7140}$

A. 105
B. 15
C. 106
D. none of these

10. Simplify.

20 − 8 ÷ 4 × 2

A. 6
B. 19
C. 36
D. none of these

11. Give the quotient rounded to the nearest tenth.

4.615 ÷ 0.3

A. 15.3
B. 15.4
C. 1.5
D. none of these

12. You can buy a car for $325 down and 12 payments of $48.75 each. What is the total cost?

A. $910
B. $373.75
C. $260
D. none of these

FIRST-QUARTER TEST

The first-quarter test shown on these two pages is in standardized format so that the students can become accustomed to taking standardized tests.

NAME _____ **FIRST-QUARTER TEST**
(Chapters 1 through 4)

Choose the correct letter.
Sample:
42,000 is
A. 420 thousand
B. 42 million
C. 42 thousand
D. none of these

(A) (B) (C) (D)

First decide which answer is correct. Then find the problem number on your answer sheet and darken in the space for the correct answer. In the sample, c is the correct answer.

1. 700,040 is
A. 7 million, 40
B. 700 thousand, 40
C. 7 billion, 40
D. none of these

2. 91,060,000 is
A. 91 million, 6 thousand
B. 91 billion, 60 million
C. 91 million, 60 million
D. none of these

3. Add.   53,237
         + 18,965
A. 72,202
B. 61,192
C. 62,192
D. none of these

4. 527 rounded to the nearest hundred is
A. 500
B. 520
C. 530
D. 600

5. 19,958 rounded to the nearest thousand is
A. 19,000
B. 19,900
C. 19,960
D. 20,000

6. 35,000 rounded to the nearest ten thousand is
A. 30,000
B. 35,000
C. 36,000
D. 40,000

7. 6.08 is
A. 6 and 8 tenths
B. 6 and 8 hundredths
C. 6 and 8 thousandths
D. none of these

8. 12.051 is
A. 12 and 51 hundredths
B. 12 and 51 thousandths
C. 12 and 51 ten-thousandths
D. none of these

9. 4.45 rounded to the nearest tenth is
A. 4.5
B. 4.4
C. 4.0
D. none of these

10. 6.395 rounded to the nearest hundredth is
A. 6.4
B. 6.39
C. 6.40
D. none of these

© D. C. Heath and Company   S69   Page 1

NAME _____ **FIRST-QUARTER TEST**
(Chapters 1 through 4)

Choose the correct letter.

11. 12.942 + 8.377 = ?
A. 21.319
B. 20.219
C. 20.319
D. none of these

12. 2.09 + 5.1 + 7.83 = ?
A. 10.43
B. 14.92
C. 15.02
D. none of these

13. [$2.75 ONE ADULT] [$1.25 ONE CHILD]
The total cost of one adult ticket and one child's ticket is
A. $2.50
B. $3.75
C. $5.50
D. none of these

14. [$2.75 ONE ADULT] [$1.25 ONE CHILD]
The total cost of two adult tickets and one child's ticket is
A. $5.50
B. $5.25
C. $6.75
D. none of these

15. 2816 < ?
A. 2544
B. 2810
C. 2717
D. 2861

16. 583,096 > ?
A. 584,096
B. 583,960
C. 583,906
D. 583,069

17. Subtract.   24,216
              − 9,378
A. 15,162
B. 33,594
C. 14,838
D. none of these

18. Subtract.   32,205
              −17,476
A. 14,739
B. 14,729
C. 14,839
D. none of these

19. 3.1 > ?
A. 3.2
B. 3.10
C. 3.01
D. none of these

20. 0.076 < ?
A. 0.76
B. 0.067
C. 0.07
D. none of these

21. 6.03 − 4.55 = ?
A. 2.52
B. 1.48
C. 1.58
D. none of these

22. 52 − 4.9 = ?
A. 3.1
B. 48.9
C. 47.1
D. none of these

23. 26.3 − 1.527 = ?
A. 24.773
B. 24.827
C. 24.783
D. none of these

24. Blue jeans that regularly cost $24.35 are on sale for $17.79. How much do you save if you buy a pair on sale?
A. $13.44
B. $6.56
C. $7.66
D. none of these

25. You had $20. You bought 2 shirts for $8.79 each. How much money did you have then?
A. $3.58
B. $11.21
C. $2.42
D. none of these

© D. C. Heath and Company   S70   Page 2

NAME _____ **FIRST-QUARTER TEST**
(Chapters 1 through 4)

Choose the correct letter.

26. 18 × 100 = ?
A. 18
B. 180
C. 1800
D. none of these

27. 200 × 30 = ?
A. 600
B. 6000
C. 60,000
D. none of these

28. Multiply.   537
              × 8
A. 4296
B. 4046
C. 4096
D. none of these

29. Multiply.   342
              × 37
A. 11,444
B. 3420
C. 12,554
D. none of these

30. Multiply.   621
              × 308
A. 191,168
B. 23,598
C. 191,268
D. none of these

31. 4.6 × 1.7 = ?
A. 78.2
B. 7.82
C. 7.42
D. none of these

32. 1.02 × 0.02 = ?
A. 0.0204
B. 0.204
C. 2.04
D. none of these

33. 4.5 + (3.2 × 0.6) = ?
A. 0.462
B. 23.7
C. 6.42
D. 8.3

34. 16 − (6.64 × 1.03) = ?
A. 10.8392
B. 9.1608
C. 9.6408
D. 10.9592

35. 7.75 × 100 = ?
A. 775
B. 77.5
C. 0.775
D. 0.0775

36. 9.06 × 1000 = ?
A. 90.6
B. 906
C. 9060
D. 90,600

37. [APPLES $.65 per lb]
How much will 2.4 pounds of apples cost?
A. $15.60
B. $1.44
C. $1.56
D. none of these

38. [APPLES $.65 per lb] [ORANGES $.84 per lb]
What is the total price of 1.8 pounds of apples and 2.5 pounds of oranges?
A. $3.27
B. $3.14
C. $2.75
D. none of these

39. Divide.   6)642
A. 17
B. 107
C. 108
D. none of these

40. Divide.   63)2150
A. 34 R63
B. 43 R8
C. 34 R8
D. none of these

© D. C. Heath and Company   S71   Page 3

NAME _____ **FIRST-QUARTER TEST**
(Chapters 1 through 4)

Choose the correct letter.

41. Round the quotient to the nearest whole number.
234)59,637
A. 255
B. 254
C. 253
D. none of these

42. 5 + 3 × 6 = ?
A. 29
B. 23
C. 48
D. none of these

43. 6 × 6 + 4 + 2 = ?
A. 20
B. 30
C. 38
D. none of these

44. Round the quotient to the nearest hundredth.
4.037 ÷ 13 = ?
A. 0.31
B. 0.32
C. 0.30
D. none of these

45. 478 ÷ 10 = ?
A. 4780
B. 4.78
C. 47.8
D. none of these

46. 5.6 ÷ 1000 = ?
A. 0.056
B. 0.56
C. 0.0056
D. none of these

47. 0.745 ÷ 0.05 = ?
A. 14.9
B. 1.49
C. 149
D. none of these

48. Round the quotient to the nearest tenth.
16.3 ÷ 0.29 = ?
A. 5.6
B. 56.2
C. 562.0
D. none of these

49. You bought 12 identical posters for $16.68. How much did each poster cost?
A. $1.39
B. $1.69
C. $200.16
D. none of these

50. You had $10. You bought 7 identical postcards. Then you had $7.27. How much did each postcard cost?
A. $1.04
B. $1.43
C. $.39
D. none of these

© D. C. Heath and Company   S72   Page 4

102A

Use Copymaster S92 or Duplicating Master S92 to provide the students with an answer sheet in standardized test format.

Copymaster S106 has a quick-score answer key for the first-quarter test.

Answer Sheet for **QUARTERLY TESTS**
_____-Quarter Test (Chapters __—__)

NAME _____
DATE _____
SCORE _____

page 1

1. Ⓐ Ⓑ Ⓒ Ⓓ
2. Ⓐ Ⓑ Ⓒ Ⓓ   3. Ⓐ Ⓑ Ⓒ Ⓓ   4. Ⓐ Ⓑ Ⓒ Ⓓ
5. Ⓐ Ⓑ Ⓒ Ⓓ   6. Ⓐ Ⓑ Ⓒ Ⓓ   7. Ⓐ Ⓑ Ⓒ Ⓓ
8. Ⓐ Ⓑ Ⓒ Ⓓ   9. Ⓐ Ⓑ Ⓒ Ⓓ   10. Ⓐ Ⓑ Ⓒ Ⓓ

page 2

11. Ⓐ Ⓑ Ⓒ Ⓓ   12. Ⓐ Ⓑ Ⓒ Ⓓ   13. Ⓐ Ⓑ Ⓒ Ⓓ
14. Ⓐ Ⓑ Ⓒ Ⓓ   15. Ⓐ Ⓑ Ⓒ Ⓓ   16. Ⓐ Ⓑ Ⓒ Ⓓ
17. Ⓐ Ⓑ Ⓒ Ⓓ   18. Ⓐ Ⓑ Ⓒ Ⓓ   19. Ⓐ Ⓑ Ⓒ Ⓓ
20. Ⓐ Ⓑ Ⓒ Ⓓ   21. Ⓐ Ⓑ Ⓒ Ⓓ   22. Ⓐ Ⓑ Ⓒ Ⓓ
23. Ⓐ Ⓑ Ⓒ Ⓓ   24. Ⓐ Ⓑ Ⓒ Ⓓ   25. Ⓐ Ⓑ Ⓒ Ⓓ

page 3

26. Ⓐ Ⓑ Ⓒ Ⓓ   27. Ⓐ Ⓑ Ⓒ Ⓓ   28. Ⓐ Ⓑ Ⓒ Ⓓ
29. Ⓐ Ⓑ Ⓒ Ⓓ   30. Ⓐ Ⓑ Ⓒ Ⓓ   31. Ⓐ Ⓑ Ⓒ Ⓓ
32. Ⓐ Ⓑ Ⓒ Ⓓ   33. Ⓐ Ⓑ Ⓒ Ⓓ   34. Ⓐ Ⓑ Ⓒ Ⓓ
35. Ⓐ Ⓑ Ⓒ Ⓓ   36. Ⓐ Ⓑ Ⓒ Ⓓ   37. Ⓐ Ⓑ Ⓒ Ⓓ
38. Ⓐ Ⓑ Ⓒ Ⓓ   39. Ⓐ Ⓑ Ⓒ Ⓓ   40. Ⓐ Ⓑ Ⓒ Ⓓ

page 4

41. Ⓐ Ⓑ Ⓒ Ⓓ   42. Ⓐ Ⓑ Ⓒ Ⓓ   43. Ⓐ Ⓑ Ⓒ Ⓓ
44. Ⓐ Ⓑ Ⓒ Ⓓ   45. Ⓐ Ⓑ Ⓒ Ⓓ   46. Ⓐ Ⓑ Ⓒ Ⓓ
47. Ⓐ Ⓑ Ⓒ Ⓓ   48. Ⓐ Ⓑ Ⓒ Ⓓ   49. Ⓐ Ⓑ Ⓒ Ⓓ
50. Ⓐ Ⓑ Ⓒ Ⓓ

© D. C. Heath and Company   **S92**   Answer sheet—Quarterly Tests

Quick-Score Answer Key for **FIRST-QUARTER TEST** (Chapters 1–4)

Quick-Score Answer Key for **SECOND-QUARTER TEST** (Chapters 5–8)

© D. C. Heath and Company   **S106**   Answer key—Quarterly Tests

The table below correlates test items with student text pages.

Test Item	Text Page	Test Item	Text Page	Test Item	Text Page	Test Item	Text Page
1	p. 4	14	p. 22	27	p. 54	40	p. 80
2	p. 4	15	p. 32	28	p. 56	41	p. 84
3	p. 8	16	p. 32	29	p. 58	42	p. 86
4	p. 12	17	p. 38	30	p. 60	43	p. 86
5	p. 12	18	p. 38	31	p. 64	44	p. 88
6	p. 12	19	p. 42	32	p. 64	45	p. 92
7	p. 16	20	p. 42	33	p. 66	46	p. 92
8	p. 16	21	p. 44	34	p. 66	47	p. 94
9	p. 20	22	p. 46	35	p. 68	48	p. 96
10	p. 20	23	p. 46	36	p. 68	49	p. 91
11	p. 22	24	p. 44	37	p. 64	50	p. 91
12	p. 24	25	p. 46	38	p. 64		
13	p. 22	26	p. 54	39	p. 78		

102B

CHAPTER 5
Graphs and Statistics

LESSON OBJECTIVES
To read data from frequency tables   (*pages 104–105*)
To make a frequency table from a set of data   (*pages 104–105*)
To read data from bar graphs   (*pages 106–107*)
To read data from line graphs   (*pages 108–109*)
To read data from circle graphs and picture graphs
   (*pages 110–111*)
To compute the mean of a set of data   (*pages 114–115*)
To compute the range, mode, and median of a set of data
   (*pages 116–117*)
To interpret bar graphs, circle graphs, picture graphs, and line
   graphs   (*pages 118–119*)
To construct circle, bar, and picture graphs   (*pages 118–119*)

PROBLEM-SOLVING SKILLS
Reading and interpreting a table   (*pages 104–105*)
Organizing and tabulating data   (*page 105*)
Reading and interpreting bar graphs   (*pages 106–107*)
Reading and interpreting line graphs   (*pages 108–109*)
Reading and interpreting circle graphs and picture graphs
   (*pages 110–111*)
Using a graph to solve a problem   (*page 113*)
Choosing the correct operation   (*pages 113, 115*)
Reading a chart   (*pages 114–115*)
Using logical reasoning   (*page 115*)
Reading and interpreting a chart   (*pages 116–117*)
Reading and interpreting graphs   (*pages 118–119, 121*)

RESOURCES
- **VISUAL AIDS**
  Quiz from page 104 and blank frequency table   (*Visual Aid 14,
    Copymaster S119*)
  Bar graph from page 106   (*Visual Aid 15, Copymaster S120*)
  Line graph from page 108   (*Visual Aid 16, Copymaster S121*)
  Line graph from page 109   (*Visual Aid 17, Copymaster S122*)
  Line graph from page 113   (*Visual Aid 18, Copymaster S123*)
  Graphs from pages 118 and 119   (*Visual Aid 19, Copymaster
    S124*)
- **WORKSHEETS 44–52**   (*Copymasters S196–S204 or Duplicating
    Masters S196–S204*)

LESSON OBJECTIVES
To read data from frequency tables
To make a frequency table from a set of data

PROBLEM-SOLVING SKILLS
Reading and interpreting a table
Organizing and tabulating data

STARTING THE LESSON
The National Road-Sign Quiz and blank frequency table from page 104 are also on **Visual Aid 14**. Have the students take the National Road-Sign Quiz. Correct and save their quiz papers. After discussing questions 1–7, use the students' papers to make a frequency table of their scores. Then have the students answer questions 3–7 from the information on their own frequency table.

Organizing data

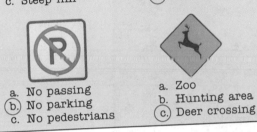

National Road-Sign Quiz
Choose the correct answer.

a. Slippery when wet
b. Road curves
c. Steep hill

a. Housing
b. Youth hostel
c. Hospital

a. No passing
b. No parking
c. No pedestrians

a. Zoo
b. Hunting area
c. Deer crossing

A group of students took the road-sign quiz. Their scores are listed on this card.

NAME	SCORE	NAME	SCORE
B. Barrett	3	H. Lee	1
M. Cataldo	4	B. Lynch	3
A. Collier	3	P. Perez	4
C. DeBold	4	A. Riccio	3
J. Dombrowski	2	A. Sargent	2
D. Dori	4	R. Smith	1
J. Goldman	2	G. Summers	3
V. Hawkins	3	J. Vandegrift	3
A. Jacobson	1	S. Vlahach	4
K. Kennedy	2	C. Werner	0

1. Look at the score card. How many students had a score of 4? 5

2. How many students had a score of 3? 7

To help answer questions like these, you can make a frequency table.

Answer for page 105.

19.

Age	Number of Occurrences	
	Tally	Frequency
14	IIII II	7
15	IIII IIII I	11
15½	I	1
16	IIII IIII IIII IIII IIII IIII	30
16½	I	1
18	I	1

Here's how *to organize the data (quiz scores) in a frequency table.*

A tally mark shows each time a score occurred. The frequency column shows the total number of times each score occurred.

Frequency Table for Quiz Scores		
	NUMBER OF TIMES SCORE OCCURRED	
SCORE	TALLY	FREQUENCY
4	IIII	5
3	IIII II	7
2	IIII	4
1	III	3
0	I	1

3. How many students had a score less than 4? 15

4. How many had a score greater than 2? 12

5. What was the highest score? lowest score? 4, 0

6. Which score occurred most often? least often? 3, 0

7. How many students took the quiz? 20

EXERCISES

Use the frequency tables to answer the questions.

8. What was the highest score on the engine-repair exam? 15

9. Which score occurred most often? 13

10. How many students scored 13 or less? 20

11. How many students took the exam? 27

12. What was the difference between the highest and lowest scores? 5

13. A score of 14 or better is an A. How many students received an A? 7

14. How many families in the survey have 3 cars? 7

15. How many families have 2 or more cars? 25

16. How many families have at least 1 car? 47

17. What is the most common number of cars per family? 1

18. How many families were in the survey? 50

Frequency Table for Engine-Repair Exam Scores		
	NUMBER OF OCCURRENCES	
SCORE	**TALLY**	**FREQUENCY**
15					3
14						4
13	HHT HHT ||	12
12	HHT		6
11		0
10				2

Frequency Table for Cars per Family		
CARS PER FAMILY	**NUMBER OF FAMILIES**	
	TALLY	**FREQUENCY**
4				2
3	HHT ||	7
2	HHT HHT HHT		16
1	HHT HHT HHT HHT ||	22
0					3

Try it yourself! Organizing information

19. Make a frequency table for the driver's-license information on the map.

20. In how many states can you obtain a driver's license before age 16? 19

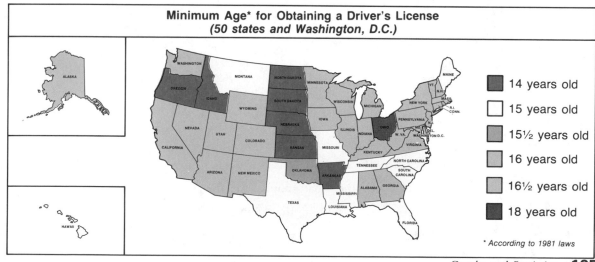

Minimum Age* for Obtaining a Driver's License
(50 states and Washington, D.C.)

- ■ 14 years old
- □ 15 years old
- ▨ 15½ years old
- ▥ 16 years old
- ▧ 16½ years old
- ■ 18 years old

* According to 1981 laws

Graphs and Statistics **105**

REVIEW PRACTICE
Adding decimals
Page 414   Skill 5

PRACTICE WORKSHEET
Copymaster S196 or Duplicating Master S196

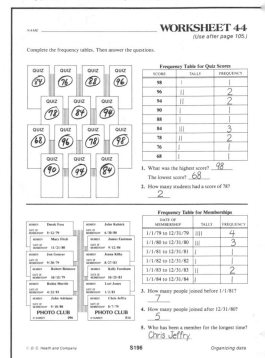

WORKSHEET 44
(Use after page 105.)

Complete the frequency tables. Then answer the questions.

Frequency Table for Quiz Scores

SCORE	TALLY	FREQUENCY
98			1
96				2
94				2
90			1
88			1
84					3
78				2
76			1
68			1

1. What was the highest score? 98
   The lowest score? 68
2. How many students had a score of 78? 2

Frequency Table for Memberships

DATE OF MEMBERSHIP	TALLY	FREQUENCY
1/1/79 to 12/31/79	||||	4
1/1/80 to 12/31/80	|||	3
1/1/81 to 12/31/81			1
1/1/82 to 12/31/82			1
1/1/83 to 12/31/83	||	2
1/1/84 to 12/31/84			1

3. How many people joined before 1/1/81? 7
4. How many people joined after 12/31/80? 5
5. Who has been a member for the longest time? Chris Jeffry

© D. C. Heath and Company   S196   Organizing data

LIFE-SKILL PROJECT
Collecting data
Have the students take a survey of teenagers to find the kind of car they like best. Then have them make a frequency chart to show their findings.

106

Solve. Use the frequency tables on page 105.

1. How many students scored 12 or more on the engine-repair exam? 25

2. How many families in the survey have 3 or more cars? 9

3. How many families have at least 2 cars? 25

LESSON OBJECTIVE
To read data from bar graphs

PROBLEM-SOLVING SKILL
Reading and interpreting bar graphs

STARTING THE LESSON
Use the pictures of characters on page 106 to take a survey of the students to see how many of the characters they can name. Then discuss questions 1–7 using the bar graph. The bar graph is also on **Visual Aid 15.**

Using bar graphs

Fifty people took part in a TV trivia survey. In Part 1 of the survey, each person was asked to name these situation comedy characters.

WHO ARE THESE CHARACTERS?

The results of Part 1 of the survey are shown in this **bar graph.**

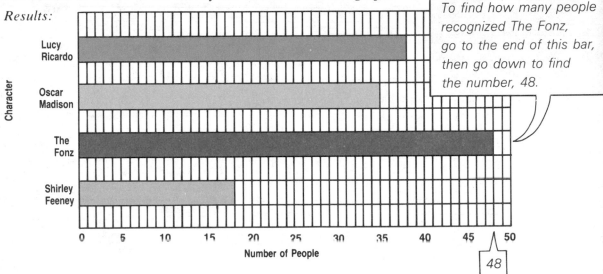

To find how many people recognized The Fonz, go to the end of this bar, then go down to find the number, 48.

1. Read the bar graph. How many people recognized The Fonz? 48

2. How many recognized Shirley Feeney? 18

3. How many knew Oscar Madison? 35

4. How many knew Lucy Ricardo? 38

5. Which character was recognized by the most people? the fewest people? The Fonz, Shirley Feeney

6. How many more people recognized The Fonz than Shirley Feeney? 30

7. How many of the 50 people surveyed did not recognize Oscar Madison? 15

EXERCISES

Use the bar graphs to answer the questions.

In Part 2 of the survey, each person was asked to name the TV show in which the character appeared.

8. How many people knew that Shirley appeared in *Laverne and Shirley*? 32

9. How many knew that Oscar appeared in *The Odd Couple*? 25

10. How many more people knew the name of the TV show The Fonz appeared in than knew the TV show Oscar appeared in? 22

Results:

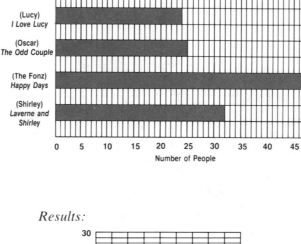

In Part 3 each person was asked to name the actor or actress that played the character.

11. Which actor or actress was identified by the most people? the fewest people?
    Henry Winkler, Cindy Williams

12. How many people identified Lucille Ball? 15

13. How many people identified Jack Klugman? 7

14. How many more people identified Henry Winkler than identified Cindy Williams? 22

Results:

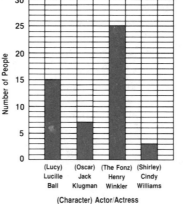

You're the reporter

Use the bar graph. Complete the story.

15. The price of a movie ticket in [?] was $1.50. A movie ticket in 1980 cost [?].
    1975, $2

16. Between 1975 and [?], the price of a ticket increased $1.00, from $1.50 to [?].
    1983, $2.50

17. In 1975, 4 tickets cost [?]. The cost of [?] tickets in 1980 was $10.00. $6, 5

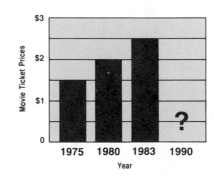

REVIEW PRACTICE
Adding decimals
Page 414   Skill 6

PRACTICE WORKSHEET
Copymaster S197 or Duplicating Master S197

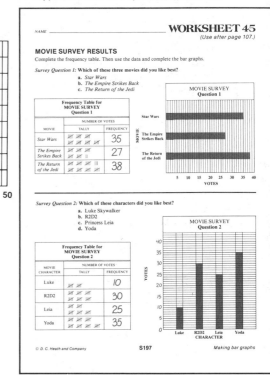

LIFE-SKILL PROJECT

Collecting and presenting data
Have the students take a survey of teenagers to find the kind of music they like best.

MUSIC	TALLY
Popular	
Rock	
Country	
Jazz	
Classical	
Other	

Then have them show their findings on a bar graph.

LESSON OBJECTIVE
To read data from line graphs

PROBLEM-SOLVING SKILL
Reading and interpreting line graphs

STARTING THE LESSON
Play 'What are the facts?' Have the students study the newspaper article and line graph on page 108 for one minute. Then have them close their books and decide whether these statements are true or false:
- Zella was this year's Mason County Grand Champion lamb. (True)
- Zella is 7 months old and weighs 50 pounds. (False)
- The line graph shows Zella's weight increase. (True)
- When Zella was 1 month old, she weighed 14 pounds. (True)
- Zella won a red ribbon for her owner, Julie Eastman. (False)

EXERCISE NOTE
The line graphs on pages 108 and 109 are also on **Visual Aids 16 and 17.** You might wish to use these visual aids when discussing exercises 1–13.

Using line graphs

Livestock that are raised to be shown at fairs receive special care and attention. Feed is controlled and growth is measured monthly. The **line graph** shows Zella's weight increase.

Zella's growth graph

Each space between lines stands for 2 pounds.

ZELLA WINS THE BLUE!
LANCASTER, N.H. This year's Grand Champion Lamb is Zella. Zella is 7 months old and weighs 70 pounds.

This year's Mason County Grand Champion Lamb with her owner, Julie Eastman.

To find Zella's weight when she was 1 month old, look up along the 1-month line, then look left to find her weight, 14 pounds.

1. Read the line graph. How much did Zella weigh at
   a. 4 months? 44 lb   b. 5 months? 58 lb   c. 7 months? 70 lb

2. How old was Zella when she weighed
   a. 20 pounds? 2 mo   b. 31 pounds? 3 mo   c. 66 pounds? 6 mo

3. How many pounds did Zella gain during the first two months? 12

4. How much more did Zella weigh at 3 months than she did at 1 month? 17 lb

5. When did Zella gain more, in the third month or in the sixth month? Third

6. During which 3-month period did Zella gain the most weight?
   Between the 2nd and 5th months

EXERCISES

***Use the line graphs to answer
the questions.***

7. What was the fair attendance at
   a. 10 A.M.? 600   **b.** noon? 800
   c. 6 P.M.? 1800   **d.** 10 P.M.? 2700

8. What was the approximate time when the
   attendance reached
   a. 1200 people? 2 P.M.   **b.** 1800 people? 6 P.M.
   c. 2500 people? 8 P.M.   **d.** 2700 people? 10 P.M.

9. Fair officials predicted that 3000 people
   would be in attendance opening day,
   September 1. How far off was their
   prediction? 200 people

10. Workers at the booth worked 4-hour
    shifts. The first shift took in $150. How
    much did the second shift take in? $250

11. How much money did the Lancaster
    Booster Club take in between 8 P.M. and
    midnight? $300

12. The shift Carmen worked took in $500.
    What time did she get off work? 8 P.M.

13. The Booster Club charged $5 for each
    hat. About how many hats did the club
    sell on September 1? 240

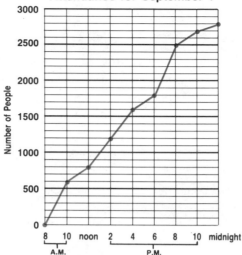

Mason County Fair
Attendance for September 1

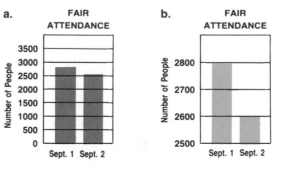

Lancaster Booster Club
Hat Sales Booth
Receipts for September 1

Don't be fooled! Interpreting data

14. Each bar graph compares attendance at
    the Mason County Fair. One of the two
    graphs has been drawn to mislead
    people. Which graph is misleading? How
    is it misleading? b
    The scale begins at 2500. Therefore it appears that many more
    people attended the fair on Sept. 1 than on Sept. 2.

a. FAIR ATTENDANCE

b. FAIR ATTENDANCE

REVIEW PRACTICE
Comparing whole numbers
Page 415   Skill 7

PRACTICE WORKSHEET
Copymaster S198 or Duplicating Master S198

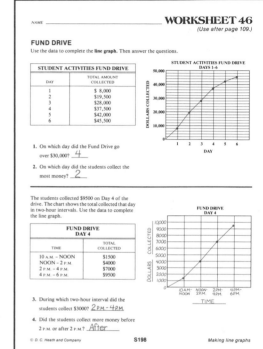

LIFE-SKILL PROJECT
Collecting and presenting data
Have the students make a line graph
that will show the daily high temperatures in the community for a week.

CHALKBOARD QUIZ
on previous lesson

Solve. Use the line graphs on page 109.
1. What was the fair attendance at 4 P.M.? 1600 people
2. What was the approximate time when the attendance reached 800 people? Noon
3. How much money did the Lancaster Booster Club take in between 4 P.M. and midnight? $800

LESSON OBJECTIVE
To read data from circle graphs and picture graphs

PROBLEM-SOLVING SKILL
Reading and interpreting circle graphs and picture graphs

STARTING THE LESSON
Write these states on the chalkboard:
Connecticut
Illinois
Iowa
New Jersey
Rhode Island

Before the students open their books, take an opinion poll. Ask them which of these five states they think has the most expensive farmland. Make a frequency table of their answers. Then have the students compare their results with the graphs on page 110.

Answer for page 111.
20.

Yearly Consumption of Fruit by the Average American	
TYPE	NUMBER OF POUNDS
Fresh	🍓🍓🍓🍓🍓🍓🍓🍓🍓🍓🍓🍓🍓🍓🍓🍓🍓🍓🍓🍓🍓🍓
Canned	🍓🍓🍓🍓🍓🍓🍓🍓
Frozen	🍓🍓🍓🍓
Dried	🍓

Each 🍓 represents 4 pounds.

110

Reading circle graphs and picture graphs

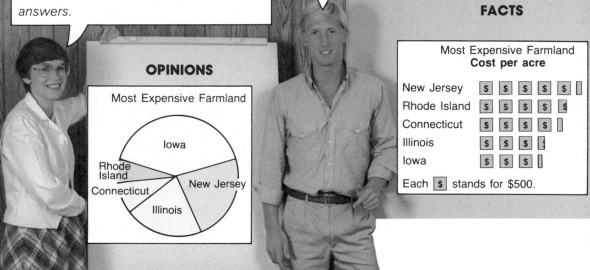

*I took an opinion poll of 172 people. I asked people which of these five states they thought had the most expensive farmland. This **circle graph** shows their answers.*

*I collected the facts. This **picture graph** shows the actual price of farmland in these states.*

Use the circle graph to answer these questions.

1. Which state was picked by the most people? Iowa

2. Which state was picked by the fewest people? Rhode Island

3. Did more people pick Illinois than picked Connecticut? Yes

4. Did more people pick New Jersey than picked Iowa? No

Use the picture graph to answer these questions.

5. Which state has the most expensive farmland? New Jersey

6. Which state's farmland averages about $1800 an acre? About $2700 an acre? Illinois, New Jersey

7. How many $ would be used to show $1500-an-acre farmland? 3

8. How many $ would be used to show $1250-an-acre farmland? $2\frac{1}{2}$

9. Does Connecticut's farmland average more or less than $2000 an acre? More

10. Which state's farmland costs about $500 per acre more than Connecticut's? New Jersey

EXERCISES

Use the circle graph to answer the questions.

11. How many people thought Alaska had the least expensive farmland? 86

12. Which state was picked by 42 people? Wyoming

13. Which state was picked by the fewest people? Nevada

14. Which two states were picked by a total of 128 people? Alaska, Wyoming

15. Which three states were picked by a total of 75 people? New Mexico, Arizona, Wyoming

Use the picture graph to answer the questions.

16. Which state's farmland costs about
  a. $109 per acre? Alaska
  b. $191 per acre? Nevada
  c. $195 per acre? Arizona
  d. $146 per acre? Wyoming

17. Which state's farmland costs about $90 per acre more than Alaska's? Arizona

18. Does New Mexico's farmland cost more or less than $150 per acre? More

19. How many $ would be used to show $260-per-acre land? 13

Make a picture graph

20. Use the information in the chart to make a picture graph. You may choose any symbol to represent pounds of fruit. Draw one symbol for each 4 pounds. Be sure to label your graph.

Least Expensive Farmland According to an Opinion Poll

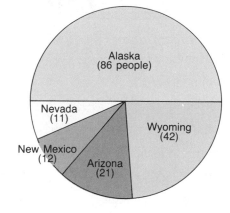

Alaska (86 people)
Nevada (11)
New Mexico (12)
Arizona (21)
Wyoming (42)

Least Expensive Farmland (based on U.S. Census Bureau averages)

Alaska	$ $ $ $ $ $
Wyoming	$ $ $ $ $ $ $ $ ◖
New Mexico	$ $ $ $ $ $ $ $ ◖
Nevada	$ $ $ $ $ $ $ $ $ $ ◖
Arizona	$ $ $ $ $ $ $ $ $ $ $ ◖

Each $ stands for $20 per acre.

Yearly Consumption of Fruit by the Average American

TYPE	NUMBER OF POUNDS
Fresh	80
Canned	36
Frozen	12
Dried	4

REVIEW PRACTICE
Subtracting whole numbers
Page 415   Skill 8

PRACTICE WORKSHEET
Copymaster S199 or Duplicating Master S199

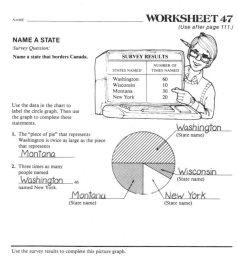

WORKSHEET 47
(Use after page 111.)

NAME A STATE
Survey Question:
Name a state that borders Canada.

SURVEY RESULTS

STATES NAMED	NUMBER OF TIMES NAMED
Washington	60
Wisconsin	10
Montana	30
New York	20

Use the data in the chart to label the circle graph. Then use the graph to complete these statements.

1. The "piece of pie" that represents Washington is twice as large as the piece that represents __Montana__.

2. Three times as many people named __Washington__ as named New York.

Washington (State name)
Wisconsin (State name)
Montana (State name)
New York (State name)

Use the survey results to complete this picture graph.

SURVEY RESULTS

Washington	☺☺☺☺☺☺☺☺☺☺☺☺
Wisconsin	☺☺
Montana	☺☺☺☺☺☺
New York	☺☺☺☺

3. Each ☺ represents __5__ people.

© D. C. Heath and Company   S199   *Making circle graphs and picture graphs*

LIFE-SKILL PROJECT
Researching information
Have the students use a book of world records to find the cost per square foot of the most expensive land in the world. (This information can be found in the *Guinness Book of World Records*.)

A parcel of land in Kowloon, Hong Kong, was sold for $5569 per square foot.

Solve. Use the circle graph and picture graph on page 111.

1. How many people thought Wyoming had the least expensive farmland? 42

2. Which two states were picked by a total of 33 people?
New Mexico and Arizona

3. Which state's farmland costs about $80 per acre more than Alaska's? Nevada's

SKILLS REVIEWED
Writing standard numerals (whole numbers and decimals)
Rounding whole numbers and decimals
Adding decimals
Subtracting decimals

PROBLEM-SOLVING SKILLS
Using a graph to solve a problem
Choosing the correct operation

STARTING THE LESSON
Cumulative Skill Practice
Write these six answers on the chalkboard:

3,375,000	0.07
540,000	3.61
15.235	41.81

Challenge the students to an answer hunt by saying, "Look for the six even-numbered exercises on page 112 that have these answers. You have five minutes to find as many of the exercises as you can." (Exercises 6, 26, 34, 42, 50, and 62)

STARTING THE LESSON
Problem Solving
The line graph on page 113 is also on **Visual Aid 18**. Have the students read the introductory paragraph on page 113 and then use the graph to answer questions like these:

• What is the title of the graph? (Total Miles Traveled)
• How many miles is it from Houston to San Antonio? (200)
• On which day did Andy and Sarah travel 400 miles? (3rd day)

112

Cumulative Skill Practice

Write the standard numeral. *(page 4)*

1. 26 thousand, 429   26,429
2. 18 thousand, 92   18,092
3. 238 thousand, 164   238,164
4. 37 million   37,000,000
5. 259 million   259,000,000
6. 3 million, 375 thousand   3,375,000
7. 38 million, 61   38,000,061
8. 9 billion   9,000,000,000
9. 7 billion, 293 million   7,293,000,000
10. two hundred twenty-five thousand, four hundred seven   225,407
11. sixty thousand, ninety-one   60,091
12. thirty-three million, eight hundred seventy-three thousand   33,873,000
13. five million, thirty thousand, two hundred eight   5,030,208
14. six billion, one hundred ninety three million, four hundred thousand   6,193,400,000

Round to the nearest ten thousand. *(page 12)*

15. 28,192   30,000
16. 56,700   60,000
17. 74,825   70,000
18. 59,600   60,000
19. 76,501   80,000
20. 48,400   50,000
21. 74,391   70,000
22. 93,866   90,000
23. 356,200   360,000
24. 635,000   640,000
25. 824,999   820,000
26. 544,099   540,000

Write the standard numeral. *(page 16)*

27. 5 hundredths   0.05
28. 36 thousandths   0.036
29. 12 and 5 tenths   12.5
30. 59 and 74 hundredths   59.74
31. 74 and 18 thousandths   74.018
32. 3951 ten-thousandths   0.3951
33. 8 and 7 ten-thousandths   8.0007
34. 15 and 235 thousandths   15.235
35. 41 and 72 ten-thousandths   41.0072

Round to the nearest hundredth. *(page 20)*

36. 8.316   8.32
37. 22.207   22.21
38. 8.530   8.53
39. 60.845   60.85
40. 74.573   74.57
41. 6.3048   6.30
42. 0.0659   0.07
43. 5.3625   5.36
44. 9.3511   9.35
45. 0.005   0.01
46. 13.949   13.95
47. 372.678   372.68

Give the sum. *(page 24)*

48. 7.4 + 2.2   9.6
49. 6.83 + 2.59   9.42
50. 0.73 + 2.88   3.61
51. 2.793 + 3.899   6.692
52. 5.466 + 1.805   7.271
53. 18.05 + 8.03   26.08
54. 0.84 + 5.96 + 7.6   14.4
55. 56.4 + 1.82 + 6.6   64.82
56. 7 + 3.85 + 6.8   17.65

Give the difference. *(page 46)*

57. 7.8 − 3.1   4.7
58. 9.63 − 2.08   7.55
59. 8.03 − 6.55   1.48
60. 54.5 − 4.56   49.94
61. 32.6 − 19.38   13.22
62. 45.61 − 3.8   41.81
63. 22 − 5.9   16.1
64. 9 − 0.748   8.252
65. 6.1 − 3.045   3.055

Problem solving

Andy and Sarah Wallace have just completed a 5-day motorcycle trip. They started in Dallas, rode to Houston, and spent the night with friends. They spent the next three nights in San Antonio, Lubbock, and Amarillo, and returned to Dallas on the fifth day.

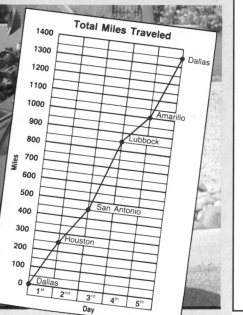

Sarah made the line graph using the information from their log book. Use the graph to answer these questions.

1. The log book says they were in San Antonio the second night. How many miles is it from Dallas to San Antonio? 450

2. How many miles is it from San Antonio to Lubbock? 400

3. How far is it from Lubbock to Amarillo? 150 miles

4. On which day did they travel 150 miles? 4th

5. On which day did they travel the most miles? How many miles did they travel that day? 3rd, 400

6. The log book shows that they traveled 4 hours on the second day. How many miles per hour did they average the second day? 50 mph

7. During which day did their trip mileage reach a total of 1000 miles? 4th

8. They were between what two cities when their trip was half over? *Hint: Divide the total distance by 2 and use the graph.* San Antonio and Lubbock

9. One day they drove 10 hours and averaged 40 miles per hour. They were between what cities? San Antonio and Lubbock

10. Could they have completed the trip in 4 days if they had driven 50 miles per hour for 6 hours each day? No

Graphs and Statistics **113**

EXTRA PROBLEM SOLVING
Page 448   Odd exercises

PROBLEM-SOLVING WORKSHEET
Copymaster S200 or Duplicating Master S200

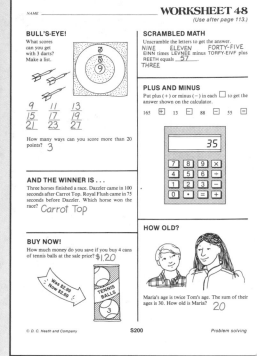

LIFE-SKILL PROJECT
Estimating sums

Have the students estimate which two decimals in exercises 36–47 on page 112 have a sum of about

1. 447.3   74.573 + 372.678
2. 20.3   6.3048 + 13.949
3. 96.8   74.573 + 22.207
4. 70.2   60.845 + 9.3511

If calculators are available, have the students use them to see whether they made the correct choices.

Analyzing data—finding the mean

Nine students in a psychology class conducted an experiment on hand-eye coordination. Each student was asked to stack 50 pennies as quickly as possible.

The results are shown in the chart.

1. What was Dan Holway's time? 43.3 seconds
2. Who stacked the coins in 44.2 seconds? Judy Conrey
3. Who had the shortest time? the longest time? Polly Smith, Charlie Allen
4. The average of a set of numbers is called the **mean.** Whose time do you think is closer to the mean time, Ed Dorr's or Polly Smith's? Ed Dorr's

STUDENT	TIME (SECONDS)
Dan Holway	43.3
Julia Belmore	38.2
Charlie Allen	56.1
Ed Dorr	45.4
Judy Conrey	44.2
Tracy McDonald	45.2
Polly Smith	37.1
José Rivera	52.8
Angelo Robinson	46.3

Here's how *to find the mean.*

Find the sum of the times.

```
  43.3
  38.2
  56.1
  45.4
  44.2
  45.2
  37.1
  52.8
+ 46.3
──────
 408.6
```

Divide the sum by the number of students.

```
        45.4
   9) 408.6
      -36
      ────
       48
      -45
      ────
       36
      -36
      ────
        0
```

The mean time is 45.4 seconds.

5. Look at the *Here's how*. Who had a time that was the same as the mean time? Ed Dorr

6. Which students had a time longer than the mean time? Charlie Allen, José Rivera, Angelo Robinson

7. Which students had a time shorter than the mean time? Dan Holway, Julia Belmore, Judy Conrey, Tracy McDonald, Polly Smith

EXERCISES

Find the mean. Round each answer to the nearest tenth.
Here are scrambled answers for the next two rows of exercises: 182.6   32.3   9.8   264.6

8. 12   4   14   9   9.8

9. 35   39   27   28   32.3

10. 195   176   183   178   181   182.6

11. 253   276   248   281   265   264.6

12. 361   375   392   386   379   378.6

13. 432   481   467   429   450   451.8

14. 18.6   19.4   21.6   19.9

15. 13.5   14.8   14.2   14.2

16. 29.6   32.7   31.9   28.7   30.7

17. 46.8   48.9   43.7   41.2   45.2

18. 112.2   114.7   116.3   114.4

19. 129.6   128.7   126.3   128.2

20. 18   28   16   32   14   26   10   20.6

21. 15   21   18   24   31   27   19   22.1

22. 28   31   19   42   37   16   12   26.4

23. 19   29   17   33   15   27   11   21.6

Use the chart on page 114 to answer the questions.

24. Who stacked the coins in a shorter time, Ed Dorr or Julia Belmore? Julia Belmore

25. Which student had a time that was 1.2 seconds less than the mean time? Judy Conrey

26. Who stacked the coins 2.1 seconds faster than Ed Dorr? Dan Holway

27. Who stacked the coins 1.1 seconds slower than Tracy McDonald? Angelo Robinson

Tee time! Analyzing data

To qualify for the finals in the Heavy Hitters Golf Ball Driving Contest, golfers must have a mean distance of 205 yards on 4 drives.

GOLFER	LENGTH OF DRIVE (YARDS)			
	1	2	3	4
Ann	195	210	200	?
Jan	205	195	200	?
Nan	198	205	218	?

Use the clues to name each golfer.

28. *I hit my fourth drive 215 yards and I just barely made the finals!* Ann

29. *I made the finals with a fourth drive of 200 yards.* Nan

30. *I never made the finals.* Jan

Hint: To make the finals, what must the four drives total?

REVIEW PRACTICE
Subtracting whole numbers
Page 416   Skill 9

PRACTICE WORKSHEET
Copymaster S201 or Duplicating Master S201

WORKSHEET 49
(Use after page 115.)

NAME _____

PRESIDENTIAL TRIVIA
Do you know the middle names of these presidents?

- John F. Kennedy (JFK)
- Lyndon B. Johnson (LBJ)
- Dwight D. Eisenhower (IKE)
- Franklin D. Roosevelt (FDR)

To find the middle names:
Find the *mean* of each set of numbers.
Then use the DECODER to get the answer.

1. 14, 6, 16, 12	2. 472, 486, 493, 497, 480	3. 223.3, 225.8, 227.4
12 A	485.6 D	225.5
4. 39, 42, 34, 53, 48, 27, 23	**5.** 230.7, 239.8, 237.5	**6.** 32.8, 34.4, 39.7, 41.5
38 I	236 N	37.1 R
7. 506, 493, 498, 502, 501	**8.** 18, 23, 27, 32, 19, 21, 30, 36, 29, 32, 23, 19, 16	**9.** 197, 178, 185, 182, 183
500 T	25 Z	185 B
10. 29.7, 30.5, 31.3	**11.** 29, 39, 37, 43, 25, 37, 21	**12.** 24.6, 25.9, 25.4
30.5 E	33 G	25.3 L
13. 29, 32, 29, 39, 41, 38, 30	**14.** 118.2, 123.8, 131.6, 126.4	**15.** 49.6, 45.3, 45.1, 48.4
34 O	125 S	47.1 V

DECODER

1. F I T Z G E R A L D (JFK)
   225.5 38 500 25 33 30.5 37.1 12 25.3 485.6
2. B A I N E S (LBJ)
   185 12 38 236 30.5 125
3. D A V I D (IKE)
   485.6 12 47.1 38 485.6
4. D E L A N O (FDR)
   485.6 30.5 25.3 12 236 34

© D. C. Heath and Company   S201   Finding the mean

LIFE-SKILL PROJECT
Collecting data
Have each student try the coin-stacking contest described on page 114. Each coin must be flat on a table to start and must be picked up (not slid off the edge). Compile the data for the entire class, and have the students use a calculator to find the mean.

LESSON OBJECTIVE
To compute the range, mode, and median of a set of data

PROBLEM-SOLVING SKILL
Reading and interpreting a chart

STARTING THE LESSON
Have the students take the Famous-Faces Quiz at the top of page 116. Correct and score their papers. After discussing exercises 1–3, have the students find the median, mode, and range of their Famous-Faces Quiz scores.

Analyzing data—finding the median, mode, and range

FAMOUS-FACES QUIZ Whose famous face is in the picture?

Cartoonist
(*10 points*)
a. Johnny Hart
b. Walt Disney
c. Charles Schulz

Tennis player
(*8 points*)
a. Tracy Austin
b. Chris Evert-Lloyd
c. Pam Shriver

U.S. President
(*5 points*)
a. Harry Truman
b. John F. Kennedy
c. Abraham Lincoln

Singer
(*7 points*)
a. Juice Newton
b. Barbra Streisand
c. Donna Summer

Fifteen high school students took the Famous-Faces Quiz. Their scores are shown in the chart.

NAME	SCORE	NAME	SCORE	NAME	SCORE
T. Coyle	5	A. Milan	20	C. Sanford	13
L. Cummings	13	M. Olsen	18	A. Travers	17
F. Epstein	15	K. Panetta	7	L. Vita	5
J. Kenney	12	J. Perry	13	K. Wong	23
J. Lubell	15	J. Quiroga	22	M. Young	25

1. What would be your score if you knew the cartoonist and the singer? 17

2. What is the lowest score shown on the chart? the highest score? 5, 25

Here's how *to find the median, the mode, and the range of a collection of data.*

Rank the numbers from least to greatest.

The **median** is the score in the middle.

The **mode** is the number that appears most often.

The **range** is the difference between the largest number and the smallest number.

5
5
7
12
13
13
13
15
15
15
17
18
20
22
23
25

*13 appears most often, so the **mode** is 13.*

*There are 7 scores above this 15 and 7 scores below it. So 15 is the **median.***

$$\begin{array}{r} 25 \\ -\ 5 \\ \hline 20 \end{array}$$

*The **range** is 20.*

3. Look at the *Here's how*. What are the median, the mode, and the range of the Famous-Faces Quiz scores? Median 15, mode 13, range 20

EXERCISES

Find the median.

4. 13, 12, 11, 6, 7, 12, 9   11

6. 14, 7, 12, 7, 7, 10, 13   10

8. 183, 182, 183, 180, 187, 182   182.5

10. 1243, 1245, 1301, 1248, 1256, 1276, 1287, 1308, 1299   1276

5. 12, 9, 8, 14, 10, 11   10.5

Hint: Average the two middle numbers, 10 and 11.

7. 13, 14, 9, 11, 13, 10, 9   11

9. 12, 15, 13, 19, 13, 15, 13   13

11. 6797, 6785, 6897, 6579, 6057, 6896, 6570, 6075, 6597, 6895, 6579, 6719, 6852   6719

Find the mode and range. (It is possible for a list to have more than one mode.)

12. 5, 7, 9, 7, 5, 9, 7   7,4

14. 20, 27, 22, 23, 21, 24, 22   22, 7

16. 16, 19, 21, 16, 18, 19, 23   16, 19; 7

18. 104, 108, 103, 106, 103, 107, 101, 103, 108, 104, 100, 110   103, 10

13. 11, 15, 12, 15, 10, 14, 15   15,5

15. 66, 82, 69, 73, 68, 66, 76, 66   66, 16

17. 43, 39, 47, 43, 48, 41, 38, 43   43, 10

19. 506, 511, 508, 503, 500, 503, 505, 508, 505, 503, 514, 501, 505, 509   503, 505; 14

Solve. Refer to the data on page 116.

20. Whose scores were greater than the median?   A. Milan, M. Olsen, J. Quiroga, K. Wong, A. Travers, M. Young

22. What is the mean rounded to the nearest tenth?   14.9

21. Did any student know all four famous people?   No

23. Is the mean greater than or less than the median?   Less than

You're the reporter   Math on the job

Copy and complete the chart. Then complete the story.

Larry Bird's 7-Game Point Production				
TEAM	FG	FT	TOTAL POINTS	
Knicks	10	8	?	28
Nets	12	6	?	30
76ers	9	11	?	29
Bucks	14	6	?	34
Pacers	8	3	?	19
Bulls	10	8	?	28
Lakers	7	7	?	21
FG	Field Goal—2 points each			
FT	Free Throw—1 point each			

24. Larry Bird of the Boston Celtics averaged [?] points per game for these seven games.   27

25. His lowest scoring effort during the seven games was against the [?], when he only scored [?] points.   Pacers, 19

26. On his best scoring night he scored [?] points above his mean score for the seven games.   7

REVIEW PRACTICE
Subtracting whole numbers
Page 416   Skill 10

PRACTICE WORKSHEET
Copymaster S202 or Duplicating Master S202

NAME _____

WORKSHEET 50
(Use after page 117.)

NAME THE STATES
The names of 4 states start with the same letter as the capital city of that state. What are the four cities and states?

To check your answer:
1. Find the **median**, **mode**, and **range** for each set of numbers.
2. Write the letter over its matching number in the DECODER.

		MEDIAN	MODE	RANGE
1.	24, 23, 22, 17, 18, 23, 19	A 22	C 23	D 7
2.	294, 293, 294, 291, 289, 298, 292	E 293	H 294	I 9
3.	1343, 1345, 1401, 1384, 1387, 1356, 1376, 1387, 1408	K 1384	L 1387	M 65
4.	53, 49, 57, 52, 58, 51, 48, 53, 56, 50	N 52.5	O 53	R 10
5.	214, 218, 213, 216, 213, 217, 211, 213, 218, 215, 210, 222	S 214.5	T 213	U 12
6.	405, 410, 407, 402, 400, 402, 403, 407, 405, 402, 412, 399, 404, 408	V 404.5	W 402	Y 13

DECODER

O K L A H O M A   C I T Y .
53 1384 1387 22 294 53 65 22   23 9 213 13
O K L A H O M A
53 1384 1387 22 294 53 65 22
D O V E R .   D E L A W A R E
53 404.5 293 10   7 293 1387 22 402 22 10 293
H O N O L U L U .   H A W A I I
294 53 52.5 53 1387 12 1387 12   294 22 402 9 9
I N D I A N A P O L I S .
9 52.5 7 9 22 52.5 22   402 53 53 1387 9 214.5
I N D I A N A
9 52.5 7 9 22 52.5 22

© D.C. Heath and Company   S202   Finding the median, mode, and range

LIFE-SKILL PROJECT
Collecting and analyzing data
Have the students collect data on the number of absences in their class for a week. Have them find the median, mode, and range of their data.

LESSON OBJECTIVES
To interpret bar graphs, circle graphs, picture graphs, and line graphs
To construct circle, bar, and picture graphs

PROBLEM-SOLVING SKILL
Finding information from graphs

STARTING THE LESSON
Write these five bumper-sticker slogans on the chalkboard:

DRAGON POWER!
Big Green Machine
Hayden High is #1
MEAN AND GREEN
Go for it, Dragons!

Before the students open their books, tell them that the Hayden High School Band sold these five bumper stickers to raise money for new uniforms. Have the students guess which bumper sticker sold the most. Then have them turn to page 118 to check their guesses.

EXERCISE NOTE
The graphs on pages 118 and 119 are also on **Visual Aid 19**. You may wish to use the visual aid when discussing exercises 1–11.

Presenting data—constructing graphs

The Haydon High School Band sold bumper stickers to raise money for new uniforms. Five different bumper stickers were offered. The table shows the distribution of the first 100 bumper stickers sold.

Frequency Table for Bumper-Sticker Sales   (First 100)

Bumper sticker	Number sold	
	TALLY	FREQUENCY
DRAGON POWER!	||||| ||||| ||||| ||||| ||||| ||||| ||||| |||||	40
Big Green Machine	||||| ||||| ||||| |||||	20
Haydon High is #1	|||||	5
MEAN AND GREEN	||||| |||||	10
Go for it, Dragons	||||| ||||| ||||| ||||| |||||	25

Answer these questions to see how you would fill in the missing information on the graphs.

Look at the bar graph and the frequency table.

1. What bumper sticker does the longest bar represent?
   Dragon Power

2. What number is represented by H? A? B? J?
   35, 0, 5, 45

3. The shortest bar represents what bumper sticker?
   Haydon High is # 1

4. What bumper sticker is represented by a? b? c? d? e?
   Dragon Power; Big Green Machine; Haydon High is # 1; Mean and Green; Go for it, Dragons

Look at the circle graph and the frequency table.

5. What number does each color represent?
   Green, 40; Blue, 25; Yellow, 10; Red, 5; Orange, 20

6. The blue sector represents sales of which bumper sticker?   Go for it, Dragons

7. Which graph do you think allows you to compare the sales more accurately? Bar graph

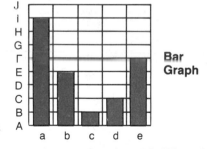

Bar Graph

BUMPER-STICKER SALES (First 100)

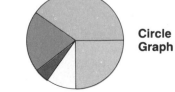

Circle Graph

EXERCISES

Solve.

8. Look at the sales chart and the picture graph.
   a. How many  were used to show the first week's sales? 10
   b. What does each  represent? $15

9. Look at the sales chart and the line graph.
   a. Sales for the first week were $150. What number is represented by C? A? L? $150, $50, $600
   b. The total sales goal was $500. Did the band reach this goal? Yes

10. Look at both graphs. Which one do you think shows total sales better? Why?
    Line graph. Less counting is involved.

11. Which of the two graphs do you think looks more interesting? Why?
    Answers will vary.

Join the band

12. The Haydon High School Band has 66 members. Complete the frequency table and make a bar or picture graph showing the distribution of instruments in the band.

INSTRUMENT	TALLY	FREQUENCY
Baritone	||	?
Bassoon	||	?
Clarinet	HHT HHT HHT	?
Flute	HHT HHT	?
French horn	||||	?
Oboe	||	?
Percussion	HHT		?
Piccolo			?
Saxophone	HHT	?
Trombone	HHT	?
Trumpet	HHT HHT ||	?
Tuba	||	?

SALES— FIRST 4 WEEKS

Sales Chart

Week	Sales
1	$150
2	$185
3	$135
4	$ 70

Line Graph

TOTAL SALES

Picture Graph

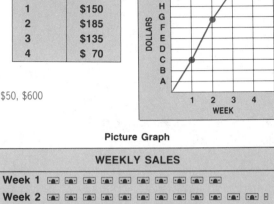

WEEKLY SALES

Week 1
Week 2
Week 3
Week 4

Graphs and Statistics **119**

REVIEW PRACTICE
Comparing decimals
Page 417   Skill 11

PRACTICE WORKSHEET
Copymaster S203 or Duplicating Master S203

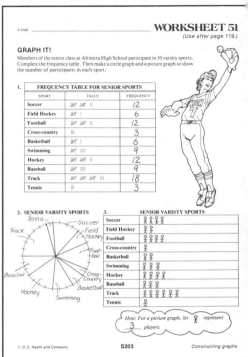

NAME _____   **WORKSHEET 51**
(Use after page 119.)

GRAPH IT!
Members of the senior class at Altimira High School participate in 10 varsity sports. Complete the frequency table. Then make a circle graph and a picture graph to show the number of participants in each sport.

1.

FREQUENCY TABLE FOR SENIOR SPORTS		
SPORT	TALLY	FREQUENCY
Soccer	HHT HHT ||	12
Field Hockey	HHT		6
Football	HHT HHT ||	12
Cross-country	|||	3
Basketball	HHT		6
Swimming	HHT ||||	9
Hockey	HHT HHT ||	12
Baseball	HHT ||||	9
Track	HHT HHT HHT |||	18
Tennis	|||	3

2. SENIOR VARSITY SPORTS

3. SENIOR VARSITY SPORTS

Soccer	
Field Hockey	
Football	
Cross-country	
Basketball	
Swimming	
Hockey	
Baseball	
Track	
Tennis	

Hint: For a picture graph, let ☺ represent 3 players.

© D. C. Heath and Company   S203   Constructing graphs

LIFE-SKILL PROJECT
Constructing bar graphs
Have the students find an example of a line graph or circle graph in a newspaper or magazine. Have them show the same information in a bar graph.

Answer for page 119.

12.

Haydon High School Band	
Baritone	♩
Bassoon	♩
Clarinet	♩♩♩♩♩♩♩
Flute	♩♩♩♩♩
French Horn	♩♩
Oboe	♩
Percussion	♩♩♩
Piccolo	•
Saxophone	♩♩♩
Trombone	♩♩♩
Trumpet	♩♩♩♩♩♩
Tuba	♩

Each ♩ represents 2 players.

119

SKILLS REVIEWED
Multiplying decimals
Multiplying and dividing by 10, 100, or 1000
Dividing decimals
Computing the mean

PROBLEM-SOLVING SKILL
Reading and interpreting graphs

STARTING THE LESSON
Cumulative Skill Practice
Challenge the students to an estimation hunt by saying, "Pick the smallest product in the first row of exercises." (Exercise 1) Then have the students pick the smallest product in the second, third, fourth, and fifth rows of exercises. (Exercises 5, 9, 12, and 15)

STARTING THE LESSON
Problem Solving
Discuss the computer graphics on page 121. Use questions such as "What is the title of the circle graph? What data are shown on the vertical scale of the bar graph? How many students are enrolled in the fine-arts activities for the current year?"

Cumulative Skill Practice

Give the product.   *(page 64)*

1. 3.4×0.8 2.72
2. 5.61×0.9 5.049
3. 32.4×0.4 12.96
4. 8.4×0.44 3.696
5. 0.47×0.16 0.0752
6. 36×0.52 18.72
7. 305×5.8 1769
8. 9.63×17 163.71
9. 0.33×40 13.2
10. 7.41×6.5 48.165
11. 8.53×2.6 22.178
12. 0.05×0.29 0.0145
13. 3.51×2.08 7.3008
14. 4.07×71 288.97
15. 0.02×1.03 0.0206

Give the product.   *(page 68)*

16. 18.4×10 184
17. 18.4×100 1840
18. 18.4×1000 18,400
19. 39×10 390
20. 39×100 3900
21. 39×1000 39,000
22. 2.07×100 207
23. 2.07×1000 2070
24. 2.07×10 20.7
25. 0.007×10 0.07
26. 0.007×1000 7
27. 0.007×100 0.7
28. 16.49×100 1649
29. 16.49×1000 16,490
30. 16.49×10 164.9

Give the quotient.   *(page 92)*

31. $234 \div 10$ 23.4
32. $234 \div 100$ 2.34
33. $234 \div 1000$ 0.234
34. $36.4 \div 10$ 3.64
35. $36.4 \div 100$ 0.364
36. $36.4 \div 1000$ 0.0364
37. $8 \div 100$ 0.08
38. $8 \div 10$ 0.8
39. $8 \div 1000$ 0.008
40. $83.07 \div 1000$ 0.08307
41. $83.07 \div 10$ 8.307
42. $83.07 \div 100$ 0.8307
43. $9.73 \div 100$ 0.0973
44. $9.73 \div 1000$ 0.00973
45. $9.73 \div 10$ 0.973

Give the quotient rounded to the nearest tenth.   *(pages 94, 96)*

46. $13.5 \div 0.6$ 22.5
47. $2.81 \div 0.3$ 9.4
48. $5.08 \div 0.05$ 101.6
49. $35.7 \div 0.3$ 119
50. $2.76 \div 0.04$ 69
51. $6.3 \div 0.03$ 210
52. $6.34 \div 1.4$ 4.5
53. $2.059 \div 2.5$ 0.8
54. $5.07 \div 0.12$ 42.3
55. $15.082 \div 0.33$ 45.7
56. $4.006 \div 0.52$ 7.7
57. $4.21 \div 4.1$ 1.0
58. $7.49 \div 5.11$ 1.5
59. $3.716 \div 2.9$ 1.3
60. $38.2 \div 6.05$ 6.3

Find the mean.   *(page 114)*

61. 124, 117, 131 124
62. 243, 257, 232 244
63. 706, 599, 639 648
64. 18, 27, 15, 24 21
65. 58, 40, 63, 46 51.75
66. 163, 174, 150, 157 161
67. 16, 23, 15, 20, 18 18.4
68. 43, 81, 49, 58, 74 61
69. 93, 85, 90, 93, 87 89.6

Problem solving

USING COMPUTER GRAPHICS

Lori Adriano is the Fine Arts Coordinator for Lincoln High School. She uses a personal computer to store data about students who participate in school-sponsored fine-arts activities. A special **software** package helped her produce these graphs.

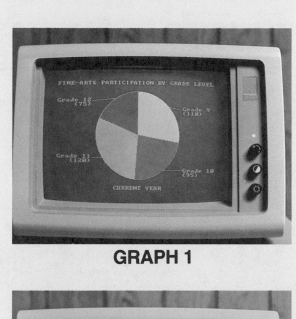

GRAPH 1

GRAPH 2

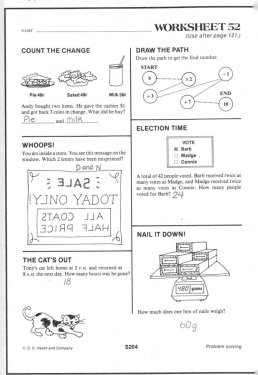

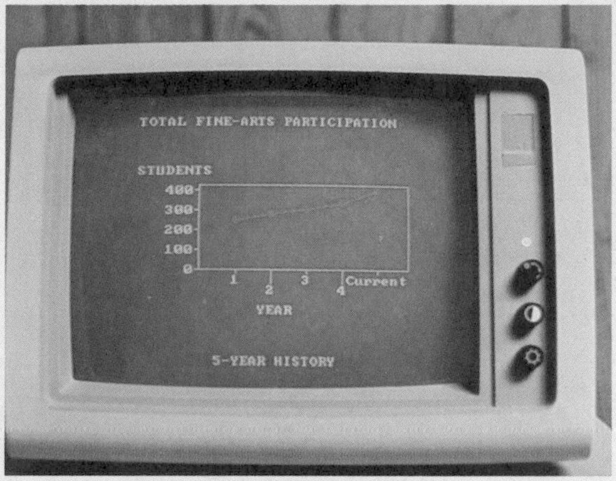

Decide which graph or graphs Ms. Adriano could use to answer the question. Then write a reasonable answer.

1. Parent: "Which fine-arts activity is the most popular?"   Graph 2, Band

2. School Board Member: "Are the school's fine-arts activities as popular with seniors as they are with freshmen?" Graph 1, No

3. Taxpayer: "How many students are enrolled in fine-arts activities anyway?" Graph 1 or 3, 400

4. Parent: "Is participation in fine-arts activities increasing or decreasing?" Graph 3, Increasing

5. School Board Member: "Our costs have gone up nearly 25% over the past 5 years. How do you account for this?"
   Graph 3, Student participation has been increasing over the past 5 years.

6. Taxpayer: "I read in the paper that 50 players tried out for football this year. Why doesn't the school do more for non-athletes?" Graph 2 or 3, Four hundred students participate in the fine-arts program. They participate in band, chorus, drama, music, and other activities.

Graphs and Statistics **121**

EXTRA PROBLEM SOLVING
Page 448   Even exercises

PROBLEM-SOLVING WORKSHEET
Copymaster S204 or Duplicating Master S204

NAME _____   **WORKSHEET 52**
(Use after page 121.)

COUNT THE CHANGE

Pie 46¢   Salad 49¢   Milk 38¢

Andy bought two items. He gave the cashier $1 and got back 3 coins in change. What did he buy?
Pie   and   milk

WHOOPS!
You are inside a store. You see this message on the window. Which 2 letters have been misprinted?   D and N

꒐SALE꒐
YADOT ꒐YJNO
ꓕꓥꓵꓳꓛ ꓡꓡꓯ
ꓱꓛꓲꓤꓑ ꓱꓡꓯ�

THE CAT'S OUT
Tony's cat left home at 2 P.M. and returned at 8 A.M. the next day. How many hours was he gone?   18

DRAW THE PATH
Draw the path to get the End number.

START
6 — ×2 — −1
+3 — +7 — END 10

ELECTION TIME

VOTE
☒ Barb
☐ Madge
☐ Connie

A total of 42 people voted. Barb received twice as many votes as Madge, and Madge received twice as many votes as Connie. How many people voted for Barb?   24

NAIL IT DOWN!

480 grams

How much does one box of nails weigh?   60 g

© D. C. Heath and Company   S204   Problem solving

CHALKBOARD CHALLENGE

Use exercises 16–30 on page 120. Which exercise has a product that has

1. a *3* in the thousands place?
   Exercise 20
2. a *2* in the hundreds place?
   Exercise 22
3. a *7* in the hundredths place?
   Exercise 25
4. a *9* in the tenths place?
   Exercise 30

Left side — Chapter 5 Test worksheet

NAME _____ **CHAPTER 5 TEST**
(Form A)

Use the frequency table to answer each question. *(page 104)*

How many students

1. saw 5 movies? **1**
2. saw 1 movie? **12**
3. did not go to the movies? **4**
4. saw 3 or more movies? **8**
5. saw at least 1 movie? **29**
6. were in the survey? **33**

Number of Movies Attended Last Month

Number of Movies	Tally	Frequency
5	I	1
4	II	2
3	TNI	5
2	TNI IIII	9
1	TNI TNI II	12
0	IIII	4

ANSWERS
1. **1**
2. **12**
3. **4**
4. **8**
5. **29**
6. **33**
7. **Beth**
8. **16**
9. **Bob**
10. **3**
11. **12**
12. **$100**
13. **$280**
14. **6**
15. **7**
16. **$20**
17. **$40**

Use the bar graph to answer each question. *(page 106)*

7. Who spent the most time watching television? **Beth**
8. How many hours did Lori spend watching television? **16**
9. Who spent 11 hours watching television? **Bob**
10. How many watched more than 10 hours? **3**
11. How many more hours did Lori spend watching television than Alex? **12**

Television Viewed During Week

Use the line graph to answer each question. *(page 108)*

12. How much did Jill earn during the first 3 weeks? **$100**
13. How much did Jill earn during the 7 weeks? **$280**

During which week did Jill earn

14. $60? **6**
15. the most? **7**
16. How much did Jill earn during week 2? **$20**
17. How much more did Jill earn during week 6 than week 5? **$40**

Jill's Total Earnings

© D. C. Heath and Company   S17   Page 1

NAME _____ **CHAPTER 5 TEST**
(Form A)

Use the picture graph to answer each question. *(page 110)*

Who has

18. the most cassette tapes? **Terry**
19. 17 tapes? **Roger**

How many cassette tapes

20. does Mike have? **11**
21. do Carla and David have together? **34**

How many more cassette tapes does

22. Carla have than Mike? **9**
23. Roger have than Mike? **6**

Number of Cassette Tapes in Collection

Carla	☐☐☐☐☐
David	☐☐☐
Mike	☐☐◻
Roger	☐☐☐☐◻
Terry	☐☐☐☐☐☐

Each ☐ stands for 4 cassettes.

Use the list of scores to answer each question. *(pages 114, 116)*

What score did

24. Bob get in Game 1? **92**
25. Phillip get in Game 2? **109**

What is the mean of

26. Bob's three scores? **105**
27. scores for Game 1? **118**

What is the median of

28. scores for Game 1? **127**   29. scores for Game 3? **115**

What is the mode of

30. scores for Game 1? **127**   31. scores for Game 2? **109**

What is the range of

32. Craig's scores? **31**   33. Nancy's scores? **18**

Bowling Scores

Team Member	Game 1	Game 2	Game 3
Bob	92	118	105
Craig	127	101	96
Kim	131	128	122
Nancy	127	109	115
Phillip	113	109	122

ANSWERS
18. **Terry**
19. **Roger**
20. **11**
21. **34**
22. **9**
23. **6**
24. **92**
25. **109**
26. **105**
27. **118**
28. **127**
29. **115**
30. **127**
31. **109**
32. **31**
33. **18**

© D. C. Heath and Company   S18   Page 2

Right side — Chapter Review

Chapter REVIEW

Here are scrambled answers for the review exercises:

| 1 | 200 | 500 | circle | mean | mode | range |
| 4 | 300 | bar | line | median | picture | |

1. This type of graph is a ⟨?⟩ graph. The game at which the most popcorn was sold was Game ⟨?⟩. At Game 3, ⟨?⟩ boxes of popcorn were sold. *(page 106)*

FOOTBALL GAMES POPCORN SALES

2. This type of graph is called a ⟨?⟩ graph. About ⟨?⟩ boxes of popcorn were sold during the first quarter. *(page 108)*

GAME 1 — TOTAL POPCORN SALES

3. This type of graph is called a ⟨?⟩ graph. Each picture on this graph represents ⟨?⟩ people. *(page 110)*

HOME-GAME ATTENDANCE   ● = 200 people

4. This graph is called a ⟨?⟩ graph. The attendance at Games 2 and ⟨?⟩ made up one half of the total attendance. *(page 110)*

HOME-GAME ATTENDANCE (Game 1, Game 2, Game 3, Game 4)

5. Add the numbers on the temperature chart, then divide by 7 to find the ⟨?⟩ temperature.

Subtract 10 from 20 to find the ⟨?⟩ of the temperatures.

18° is the temperature that appears most often in the chart. It is called the ⟨?⟩.

Rank the temperatures. The temperature in the middle is called the ⟨?⟩. *(pages 114, 116)*

LOW TEMPERATURES (°F)
Jan. 1—Jan. 7

Jan. 1	10°
Jan. 2	18°
Jan. 3	17°
Jan. 4	11°
Jan. 5	18°
Jan. 6	12°
Jan. 7	20°

1. bar; 1; 500   **2.** line; 300   **3.** picture; 200   **4.** circle; 4   **5.** mean; range; mode; median

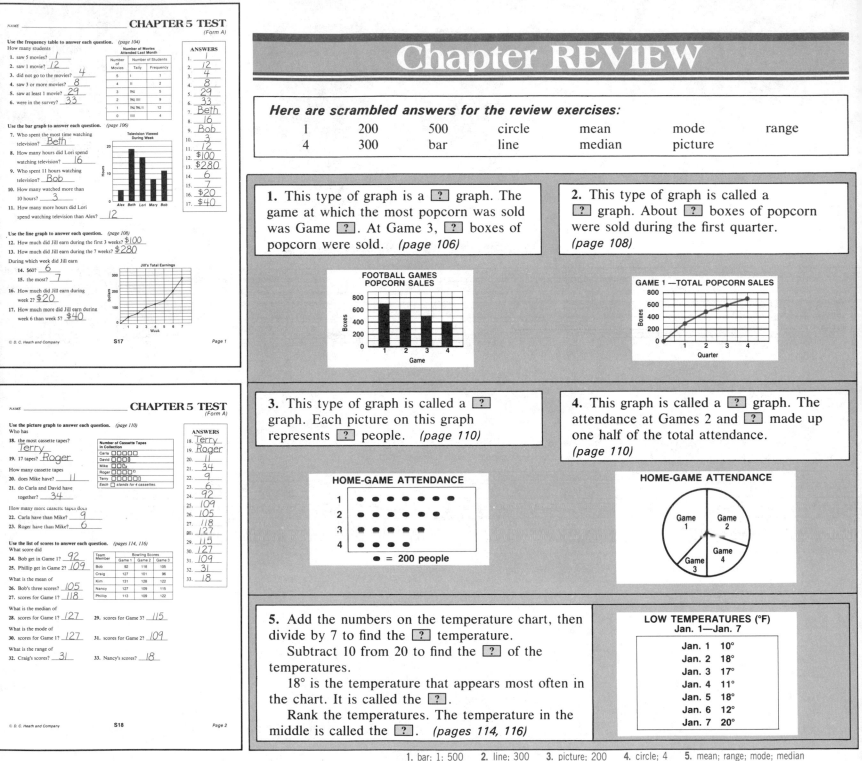

Chapter TEST

Use the frequency table to answer each question.
(page 104)

1. How many students saw 3 movies last month? 6
2. How many didn't go to a movie? 3
3. How many saw 2 or fewer movies? 17
4. How many students were in the survey? 26

Use the bar graph to answer each question.
(page 106)

5. Who spent the most time doing homework? Kim
6. How many hours did David spend doing homework? 12
7. How many hours did Jan spend doing homework? 18
8. How many more hours did Kim spend doing homework than Gayle? 4

Use the line graph to answer each question.
(page 108)

9. By the end of the second week, Anne had saved $8. How much had she saved by the end of the third week? $14
10. During which week did Anne save the most? 4
11. How much did Anne save during the six weeks? $30

Use the picture graph to answer each question.
(page 110)

12. Who has the most records? the fewest? Bob, Randy
13. How many records does Bob have? 28
14. How many records does Loni have? 21
15. How many records do Carl and Randy have together? 33

Use the list of scores to answer each question.
(pages 114, 116)

16. What is the mean of Kathleen's math test scores? 80
17. What is the median? 79
18. What is the mode? 77
19. What is the range of her math test scores? 7

NUMBER OF MOVIES ATTENDED LAST MONTH

Number of Movies	Number of Students	
	TALLY	FREQUENCY
4	III	3
3	₩⊦ I	6
2	₩⊦ ₩⊦ II	12
1	II	2
0	III	3

HOMEWORK DURING THE WEEK

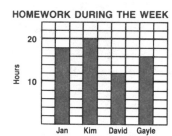

ANNE'S TOTAL SAVINGS

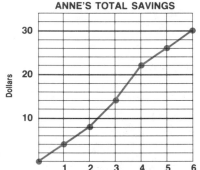

NUMBER OF RECORDS IN COLLECTION

Bob
Carl
Loni
Randy

Each ● stands for 4 records.

KATHLEEN'S MATH TEST SCORES

83 77 79 77 84

CHAPTER 5 TEST
(Form B)

NAME _____

Use the frequency table to answer each question. *(page 104)*
How many students

1. saw 5 movies? 2
2. saw 1 movie? 9
3. did not go to the movies? 4
4. saw 3 or more movies? 11
5. saw at least 1 movie? 31
6. were in the survey? 35

Number of Movies	Number of Students		
		Tally	Frequency
5		II	2
4		TH⊦ I	6
3		TH⊦ TH⊦ I	11
2		TH⊦ III	9
1		TH⊦ IIII	9
0		IIII	4

ANSWERS
1. 2
2. 9
3. 4
4. 11
5. 31
6. 35
7. Beth
8. 14
9. Mary
10. 3
11. 8
12. $100
13. $260
14. 2
15. 7
16. $40
17. $20

Use the bar graph to answer each question. *(page 106)*

7. Who spent the most time watching television? Beth
8. How many hours did Lori spend watching television? 14
9. Who spent 10 hours watching television? Mary
10. How many watched more than 10 hours? 3
11. How many more hours did Lori spend watching television than Alex? 8

Television Viewed During Week

Use the line graph to answer each question. *(page 108)*

12. How much did Jill earn during the first 3 weeks? $100
13. How much did Jill earn during the 7 weeks? $260
During which week did Jill earn
14. $50? 2
15. the most? 7
16. How much will Jill earn during week 3? $40
17. How much more did Jill earn during week 7 than week 6? $20

Jill's Total Earnings

© D. C. Heath and Company   S19   Page 1

CHAPTER 5 TEST
(Form B)

NAME _____

Use the picture graph to answer each question. *(page 110)*
Who has

18. the fewest cassette tapes? David
19. 18 tapes? Terry
How many cassette tapes
20. does Mike have? 15
21. do Carla and David have together? 38
How many more cassette tapes does
22. Carla have than Mike? 9
23. Roger have than Mike? 2

Number of Cassette Tapes in Collection

Carla	□□□□□□
David	□□□□□
Mike	□□□⫐
Roger	□□□□□
Terry	□□□□□

Each □ stands for 4 cassettes

ANSWERS
18. David
19. Terry
20. 15
21. 38
22. 9
23. 2
24. 96
25. 113
26. 108
27. 118
28. 115
29. 127
30. 122
31. 109
32. 26
33. 9

Use the list of scores to answer each question. *(pages 114, 116)*
What score did

24. Bob get in Game 1? 96
25. Phillip get in Game 2? 113
What is the mean of
26. Bob's three scores? 108
27. scores for Game 2? 118
What is the median of
28. scores for Game 1? 115
29. scores for Game 2? 127
What is the mode of
30. scores for Game 1? 122
31. scores for Game 3? 109
What is the range of
32. Craig's scores? 26
33. Nancy's scores? 9

Team Member	Bowling Scores		
	Game 1	Game 2	Game 3
Bob	96	127	101
Craig	105	92	118
Kim	115	127	109
Nancy	122	131	128
Phillip	122	113	109

© D. C. Heath and Company   S20   Page 2

Use Copymaster S336 to provide the students with an answer sheet in standardized test format.

Answers for Cumulative Test, Chapters 1–5

1. Ⓐ Ⓑ Ⓒ ●	2. Ⓐ Ⓑ ● Ⓓ	3. Ⓐ ● Ⓒ Ⓓ
4. Ⓐ Ⓑ ● Ⓓ	5. ● Ⓑ Ⓒ Ⓓ	6. Ⓐ ● Ⓒ Ⓓ
7. Ⓐ Ⓑ ● Ⓓ	8. Ⓐ ● Ⓒ Ⓓ	9. Ⓐ Ⓑ Ⓒ ●
10. ● Ⓑ Ⓒ Ⓓ	11. Ⓐ Ⓑ ● Ⓓ	12. ● Ⓑ Ⓒ Ⓓ

The table below correlates test items with student text pages.

Test Item	Page(s) Taught	Skill Practice
1	4	p. 112, exercises 1–14
2	12	p. 112, exercises 15–26
3	16	p. 112, exercises 27–35
4	20	p. 112, exercises 36–47
5	24	p. 112, exercises 48–56
6	46	p. 112, exercises 57–65
7	64	p. 120, exercises 1–15
8	68	p. 120, exercises 16–30
9	92	p. 120, exercises 31–45
10	94, 96	p. 120, exercises 46–60
11	114	p. 120, exercises 61–69
12	64	

Cumulative TEST Standardized Format

Choose the correct letter.

1. The standard numeral for 3 billion, 32 thousand is

A. 3,032,000
B. 3,320,000
C. 3,032,000,000
Ⓓ. none of these

2. 253,599 rounded to the nearest ten thousand is

A. 300,000
B. 254,000
Ⓒ. 250,000
D. none of these

3. The standard numeral for 16 and 64 thousandths is

A. 16.64
Ⓑ. 16.064
C. 16.0064
D. none of these

4. 7.695 rounded to the nearest hundredth is

A. 7.60
B. 7.69
Ⓒ. 7.70
D. none of these

5. Give the sum.

$6.4 + 0.65 + 12.9$

Ⓐ. 19.95
B. 25.8
C. 18.95
D. none of these

6. Give the difference.

$19.7 - 1.93$

A. 0.04
Ⓑ. 17.77
C. 17.83
D. none of these

7. Give the product.

23.6×1.09

A. 4.484
B. 25.474
Ⓒ. 25.724
D. none of these

8. Give the product.

5.772×1000

A. 577.2
Ⓑ. 5772
C. 57,720
D. none of these

9. Give the quotient.

$2.41 \div 100$

A. 241
B. 24.1
C. 0.241
Ⓓ. none of these

10. Give the quotient rounded to the nearest tenth.

$3.609 \div 3.4$

Ⓐ. 1.1
B. 1.6
C. 1.06
D. none of these

11. The mean of 80, 83, 87, 88, and 92 is

A. 9
B. 87
Ⓒ. 86
D. none of these

12. You bought 4 adult tickets for $2.75 each and 3 children's tickets for $1.25 each. How much did you spend?

Ⓐ. $14.75
B. $13.25
C. $14.25
D. none of these

CHAPTER 6
Fractions, Mixed Numbers, and Decimals

LESSON OBJECTIVES
To find equivalent fractions for a given fraction (*pages 126–127*)
To write fractions in lowest terms (*pages 128–129*)
To identify the least common denominator of a pair of fractions (*pages 130–131*)
To compare two fractions (*pages 132–133*)
To write whole numbers and mixed numbers as fractions (*pages 136–137*)
To write fractions as whole numbers or as mixed numbers (*pages 138–139*)
To write fractions and mixed numbers in simplest form (*pages 140–141*)
To write quotients as mixed numbers (*pages 142–143*)
To write fractions and mixed numbers as decimals (*pages 146–147*)
To write decimals as fractions or mixed numbers (*pages 148–149*)

PROBLEM-SOLVING SKILLS
Finding information in a display (*pages 126–127, 133, 142*)
Using logical reasoning (*pages 127, 129, 131, 137, 141, 143*)
Drawing a diagram (*page 131*)
Using data from a circle graph (*pages 132–133*)
Finding information in an ad (*pages 135, 138*)
Solving a multi-step problem (*pages 135, 145*)
Following instructions (*page 139*)
Choosing the correct operation (*pages 143, 145, 147, 151*)
Reading a map (*page 145*)
Finding information in a recipe (*pages 146–147*)
Looking for patterns (*page 147*)
Using a guess-and-check strategy (*page 149*)
Reading a cash-register receipt (*page 151*)

RESOURCES
- **VISUAL AIDS**
  Multiple strips from page 130 (*Visual Aid 20, Copymaster S125*)
  Picture of Mount Rushmore from page 132 (*Visual Aid 21, Copymaster S125*)
  Newspaper ad from page 135 (*Visual Aid 22, Copymaster S126*)
  Pizza pieces from page 136 (*Visual Aid 23, Copymaster S127*)
  Coupon pieces from page 138 (*Visual Aid 24, Copymaster S127*)
  Highlighted route from page 145 (*Visual Aid 25, Copymaster S128*)
  Dot grid (*Visual Aid 26, Copymaster S129*)
- **WORKSHEETS 53–65** (*Copymasters S205–S217 or Duplicating Masters S205–S217*)

LESSON OBJECTIVE
To find equivalent fractions for a given fraction

PROBLEM-SOLVING SKILLS
Finding information in a display
Using logical reasoning

STARTING THE LESSON
Before discussing exercises 1–6, sketch these shapes on the chalkboard:

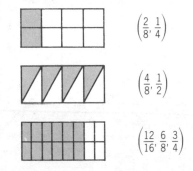

$\left(\frac{2}{8}, \frac{1}{4}\right)$

$\left(\frac{4}{8}, \frac{1}{2}\right)$

$\left(\frac{12}{16}, \frac{6}{8}, \frac{3}{4}\right)$

Ask the students to write as many fractions as they can to tell how much of each drawing is shaded. Then use exercises 1–6 on page 126 and the *Here's how* to acquaint the students with how to change a fraction to an equivalent fraction.

Equivalent fractions

Jan traded school pictures with her close friends. Here is her picture collection.

1. How many of Jan's friends are wearing glasses? 3

2. How many friends are pictured? 8

3. What fraction of her close friends are wearing glasses? $\frac{3}{8}$

4. $\frac{2}{8}$, or $\frac{1}{4}$, of Jan's close friends are boys. Do you agree or disagree with this statement? Agree

Here's how *to change a fraction to an equivalent fraction.*

To change a fraction to an equivalent fraction, multiply or divide both numerator and denominator by the same whole number (not 0).

$$\boxed{\times 2} \qquad \boxed{\div 2}$$

numerator → $\frac{1}{4} = \frac{2}{8}$ $\qquad$ $\frac{2}{8} = \frac{1}{4}$ ← denominator

$$\boxed{\times 2} \qquad \boxed{\div 2}$$

5. The *Here's how* shows that $\frac{1}{4}$ and $\boxed{?}$ are equivalent fractions. $\frac{2}{8}$

6. Complete these equivalent fractions.

   a. $\boxed{\times 3}$ $\frac{6}{5} = \frac{?}{15}$ 18 | You multiply 5 by 3 to get 15. So multiply 6 by 3 to find the missing numerator.
   $\boxed{\times 3}$

   b. $\boxed{\div 5}$ $\frac{15}{10} = \frac{?}{2}$ 3 | You have to divide 10 by 5 to get 2. So divide 15 by 5 to find the missing numerator.
   $\boxed{\div 5}$

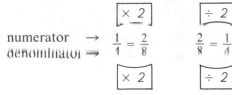

EXERCISES

Complete to get an equivalent fraction.

7. $\boxed{\times 3}$ $\frac{2}{5} = \frac{?}{15}$ 6
$\boxed{\times 3}$
$\boxed{\times 5}$

8. $\boxed{\times 2}$ $\frac{4}{3} = \frac{?}{6}$ 8
$\boxed{\times 2}$
$\boxed{\times 2}$

9. $\boxed{\div 2}$ $\frac{10}{12} = \frac{?}{6}$ 5
$\boxed{\div 2}$
$\boxed{\div 4}$

10. $\boxed{\div 3}$ $\frac{9}{15} = \frac{?}{5}$ 3
$\boxed{\div 3}$
$\boxed{\div 3}$

11. $\boxed{\div 6}$ $\frac{6}{24} = \frac{?}{1}$ 4
$\boxed{\div 6}$
$\boxed{\times 3}$

12. $\frac{1}{2} = \frac{?}{10}$ 5

13. $\frac{3}{8} = \frac{?}{16}$ 6

14. $\frac{12}{16} = \frac{?}{4}$ 3

15. $\frac{6}{9} = \frac{?}{3}$ 2

16. $\frac{7}{8} \frac{?}{21} \frac{?}{24}$

17. $\frac{1}{8} = \frac{?}{16}$ 2

18. $\frac{5}{2} = \frac{?}{10}$ 25

19. $\frac{4}{9} = \frac{?}{27}$ 12

20. $\frac{6}{8} = \frac{?}{4}$ 3

21. $\frac{5}{6} = \frac{?}{18}$ 15

22. $\frac{16}{10} = \frac{?}{5}$ 8

23. $\frac{9}{12} = \frac{?}{4}$ 3

24. $\frac{8}{12} = \frac{?}{3}$ 2

25. $\frac{4}{7} = \frac{?}{21}$ 12

26. $\frac{3}{18} = \frac{?}{6}$ 1

27. $\frac{10}{9} = \frac{?}{90}$ 100

28. $\frac{24}{30} = \frac{?}{15}$ 12

29. $\frac{25}{75} = \frac{?}{15}$ 5

30. $\frac{2}{9} = \frac{?}{45}$ 10

31. $\frac{30}{50} = \frac{?}{5}$ 3

Give the "next" three equivalent fractions.

32. $\frac{1}{2}, \frac{2}{4}, \frac{3}{6}, ?, ?, ?$ $\frac{4}{8} \frac{5}{10} \frac{6}{12}$

33. $\frac{2}{3}, \frac{4}{6}, \frac{6}{9}, ?, ?, ?$ $\frac{8}{12} \frac{10}{15} \frac{12}{18}$

34. $\frac{1}{4}, \frac{2}{8}, \frac{3}{12}, ?, ?, ?$ $\frac{4}{16} \frac{5}{20} \frac{6}{24}$

35. $\frac{1}{5}, \frac{2}{10}, ?, ?, ?$ $\frac{3}{15} \frac{4}{20} \frac{5}{25}$

36. $\frac{3}{4}, \frac{6}{8}, ?, ?, ?$ $\frac{9}{12} \frac{12}{16} \frac{15}{20}$

37. $\frac{4}{5}, \frac{8}{10}, ?, ?, ?$ $\frac{12}{15} \frac{16}{20} \frac{20}{25}$

38. $\frac{1}{6}, ?, ?, ?$ $\frac{2}{12} \frac{3}{18} \frac{4}{24}$

39. $\frac{3}{8}, ?, ?, ?$ $\frac{6}{16} \frac{9}{24} \frac{12}{32}$

40. $\frac{6}{5}, ?, ?, ?$ $\frac{12}{10} \frac{18}{15} \frac{24}{20}$

Solve. Use the collection of pictures on page 126.

41. What fraction of the pictures have been autographed? $\frac{5}{8}$

42. What fraction of the pictures have not been autographed? $\frac{3}{8}$

43. What fraction of those pictured are girls? Give two equivalent fractions. $\frac{6}{8}, \frac{3}{4}$

44. What fraction of the girls pictured wear glasses? Give two equivalent fractions. $\frac{2}{6}, \frac{1}{3}$

Smile!

45. Study the clues to find in what year this photograph was taken. 1902

Clues:

• The year rounded to the nearest ten is 1900.

• The sum of the digits is 12.

Fractions, Mixed Numbers, and Decimals **127**

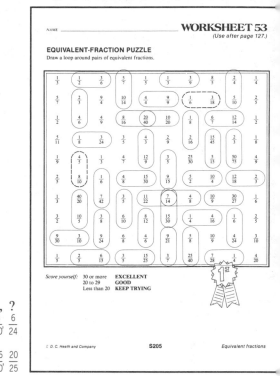

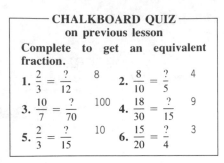
LESSON OBJECTIVE
To write fractions in lowest terms

PROBLEM-SOLVING SKILL
Using logical reasoning

STARTING THE LESSON
Sketch these divisor cards on the chalkboard:

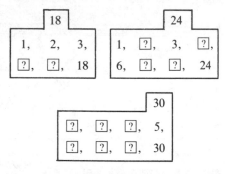

18	
1,	2,	3,
?,	?,	18

24	
1,	?,	3,	?,
6,	?,	?,	24

30	
?,	?,	?,	5,
?,	?,	?,	30

Before the students open their books, challenge them to find the missing numbers on each card. Then have the students check their answers with the divisor cards at the top of page 128.

Writing fractions in lowest terms

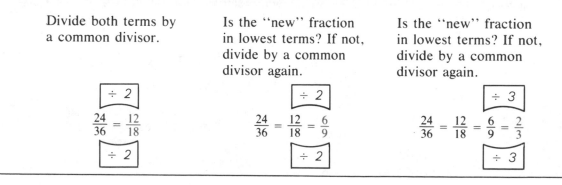

DIVISOR CARDS

1. Look at the divisor card for 12. Are 1, 2, 3, 4, 6, and 12 divisors of 12?
   Yes

2. What are the divisors of 18?   1, 2, 3, 6, 9, 18

3. What are the common divisors of 12 and 18 (divisors that divide both 12 and 18)?
                                    1, 2, 3, 6

4. What are the common divisors of 15 and 24?   1, 3

5. What are the common divisors of 30 and 36?   1, 2, 3, 6

Here's how *to write a fraction in* **lower terms.**

To write a fraction in **lower terms**, divide both terms (the numerator and the denominator) by a common divisor greater than 1.

$\overset{\div 2}{\frac{12}{18}} = \frac{6}{9} \leftarrow$ lower terms $\qquad \overset{\div 3}{\frac{30}{36}} = \frac{10}{12} \qquad \overset{\div 3}{\frac{24}{15}} = \frac{8}{5}$
$\underset{\div 2}{} \qquad\qquad\qquad\qquad \underset{\div 3}{} \qquad\qquad\qquad \underset{\div 3}{}$

A fraction is in **lowest terms** if 1 is the only common divisor of its terms.

6. Which fraction written above is in lowest terms? $\frac{8}{5}$

Here's how *to write a fraction in* **lowest terms.**

Divide both terms by a common divisor.	Is the "new" fraction in lowest terms? If not, divide by a common divisor again.	Is the "new" fraction in lowest terms? If not, divide by a common divisor again.
$\overset{\div 2}{\frac{24}{36}} = \frac{12}{18}$ $\underset{\div 2}{}$	$\overset{\div 2}{\frac{24}{36}} = \frac{12}{18} = \frac{6}{9}$ $\underset{\div 2}{}$	$\overset{\div 3}{\frac{24}{36}} = \frac{12}{18} = \frac{6}{9} = \frac{2}{3}$ $\underset{\div 3}{}$

7. Look at the *Here's how*. $\frac{24}{36}$ written in lowest terms is ▢ . $\frac{2}{3}$

EXERCISES

Is the "new" fraction in lowest terms? If not, write it in lowest terms.

8. $\frac{2}{8} = \frac{1}{4}$ Yes
9. $\frac{16}{4} = \frac{8}{2}$ No, $\frac{4}{1}$
10. $\frac{8}{12} = \frac{2}{3}$ Yes
11. $\frac{24}{16} = \frac{3}{2}$ Yes
12. $\frac{6}{18} = \frac{2}{6}$ No, $\frac{1}{3}$

13. $\frac{6}{4} = \frac{3}{2}$ Yes
14. $\frac{18}{27} = \frac{2}{3}$ Yes
15. $\frac{12}{20} = \frac{6}{10}$ No, $\frac{3}{5}$
16. $\frac{27}{45} = \frac{9}{15}$ No, $\frac{3}{5}$
17. $\frac{6}{9} = \frac{2}{3}$ Yes

18. $\frac{7}{21} = \frac{1}{3}$ Yes
19. $\frac{20}{12} = \frac{10}{6}$ No, $\frac{5}{3}$
20. $\frac{15}{12} = \frac{5}{4}$ Yes
21. $\frac{24}{48} = \frac{2}{4}$ No, $\frac{1}{2}$
22. $\frac{36}{18} = \frac{18}{9}$ No, $\frac{2}{1}$

Write each fraction in lowest terms.

Here are scrambled answers for the next row of exercises: $\frac{3}{5}$ $\frac{4}{5}$ $\frac{1}{2}$ $\frac{3}{4}$ $\frac{3}{1}$ $\frac{5}{8}$ $\frac{4}{9}$

23. $\frac{9}{12}$ $\frac{3}{4}$
24. $\frac{36}{12}$ $\frac{3}{1}$
25. $\frac{18}{30}$ $\frac{3}{5}$
26. $\frac{24}{30}$ $\frac{4}{5}$
27. $\frac{15}{24}$ $\frac{5}{8}$
28. $\frac{15}{30}$ $\frac{1}{2}$
29. $\frac{20}{45}$ $\frac{4}{9}$

30. $\frac{6}{8}$ $\frac{3}{4}$
31. $\frac{3}{9}$ $\frac{1}{3}$
32. $\frac{2}{6}$ $\frac{1}{3}$
33. $\frac{3}{12}$ $\frac{1}{4}$
34. $\frac{10}{30}$ $\frac{1}{3}$
35. $\frac{30}{36}$ $\frac{5}{6}$
36. $\frac{14}{42}$ $\frac{1}{3}$

37. $\frac{5}{15}$ $\frac{1}{3}$
38. $\frac{4}{6}$ $\frac{2}{3}$
39. $\frac{18}{15}$ $\frac{6}{5}$
40. $\frac{9}{6}$ $\frac{3}{2}$
41. $\frac{4}{12}$ $\frac{1}{3}$
42. $\frac{10}{15}$ $\frac{2}{3}$
43. $\frac{25}{10}$ $\frac{5}{2}$

44. $\frac{24}{8}$ $\frac{3}{1}$
45. $\frac{15}{10}$ $\frac{3}{2}$
46. $\frac{20}{50}$ $\frac{2}{5}$
47. $\frac{40}{50}$ $\frac{4}{5}$
48. $\frac{14}{24}$ $\frac{7}{12}$
49. $\frac{15}{25}$ $\frac{3}{5}$
50. $\frac{9}{24}$ $\frac{3}{8}$

51. $\frac{18}{14}$ $\frac{9}{7}$
52. $\frac{18}{6}$ $\frac{3}{1}$
53. $\frac{15}{45}$ $\frac{1}{3}$
54. $\frac{40}{30}$ $\frac{4}{3}$
55. $\frac{11}{22}$ $\frac{1}{2}$
56. $\frac{20}{24}$ $\frac{5}{6}$
57. $\frac{22}{33}$ $\frac{2}{3}$

58. $\frac{24}{32}$ $\frac{3}{4}$
59. $\frac{14}{16}$ $\frac{7}{8}$
60. $\frac{25}{15}$ $\frac{5}{3}$
61. $\frac{14}{6}$ $\frac{7}{3}$
62. $\frac{10}{40}$ $\frac{1}{4}$
63. $\frac{15}{20}$ $\frac{3}{4}$
64. $\frac{20}{40}$ $\frac{1}{2}$

65. $\frac{10}{24}$ $\frac{5}{12}$
66. $\frac{12}{18}$ $\frac{2}{3}$
67. $\frac{20}{32}$ $\frac{5}{8}$
68. $\frac{25}{20}$ $\frac{5}{4}$
69. $\frac{12}{24}$ $\frac{1}{2}$
70. $\frac{30}{20}$ $\frac{3}{2}$
71. $\frac{18}{21}$ $\frac{6}{7}$

72. $\frac{24}{18}$ $\frac{4}{3}$
73. $\frac{18}{36}$ $\frac{1}{2}$
74. $\frac{8}{24}$ $\frac{1}{3}$
75. $\frac{30}{18}$ $\frac{5}{3}$
76. $\frac{24}{36}$ $\frac{2}{3}$
77. $\frac{30}{24}$ $\frac{5}{4}$
78. $\frac{75}{100}$ $\frac{3}{4}$

No bones about it

Did you know there is only one bone in your skull that can move? It is the one in your lower jaw, which permits you to talk, laugh, and chew food!

79. How many bones are in your skull? 22
Clues:
- There are more than 12 but less than 30 bones.
- 11 is a divisor of the number of bones.

PRACTICE WORKSHEET

Copymaster S206 or Duplicating Master S206

LIFE-SKILL PROJECT

Reading a yardstick
Have the students find these measures on a yardstick. Tell them to compare their measures to the total length of the stick. Ask them what fractional part of a yard (in lowest terms) each measure is.

1. 12 inches $\frac{1}{3}$
2. 8 inches $\frac{2}{9}$
3. 9 inches $\frac{1}{4}$
4. 16 inches $\frac{4}{9}$
5. 18 inches $\frac{1}{2}$
6. 2 feet $\frac{2}{3}$
7. 27 inches $\frac{3}{4}$
8. 4 inches $\frac{1}{9}$

LESSON OBJECTIVE
To identify the least common denominator of a pair of fractions

PROBLEM-SOLVING SKILLS
Drawing a diagram
Using logical reasoning

STARTING THE LESSON
The multiple strips at the top of page 130 are also on **Visual Aid 20.** Before discussing exercises 1–4, challenge the students to look for the pattern and identify what the next four numbers on each strip would be. You may wish to cut the visual aid and use only the appropriate strips for discussing the first four exercises.

HERE'S HOW NOTE
Point out that the least common multiple of the denominators is the _least common denominator._ You may wish to go over several exercises from 5–59 orally before assigning the independent work.

Least common denominator

1. Look at the multiple strips for 3 and 4.
   a. Are 3, 6, 9, 12, 15, 18, 21, and 24 multiples of 3? Yes
   b. Are 4, 8, 12, 16, 20, 24, 28, and 32 multiples of 4? Yes
   c. Are 12 and 24 common multiples of 3 and 4? Yes
   d. Is 12 the least common multiple of 3 and 4? Yes

2. What is the least common multiple of 4 and 6? 12

3. What is the least common multiple of 5 and 6? 30

Multiple Strips

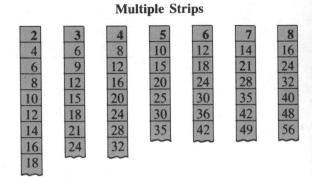

Here's how _to find the_ **least common denominator** _of_ $\frac{2}{3}$ _and_ $\frac{1}{4}$.

To find the **least common denominator** of two fractions, find the least common multiple of the denominators.

Find the least common multiple of 3 and 4.

$\frac{2}{3}$ and $\frac{1}{4}$

The least common denominator of $\frac{2}{3}$ _and_ $\frac{1}{4}$ _is 12._

Here is another method for finding the least common denominator.

Think about the multiples of one of the denominators (4).

From those, pick the first multiple that is a multiple of the other denominator (8).

$\frac{3}{4}$ and $\frac{5}{8}$

$\frac{3}{4}$ and $\frac{5}{8}$

The least common denominator is 8.

4. Look at the _Here's how._ What is the least common denominator of $\frac{3}{4}$ and $\frac{5}{8}$?

EXERCISES

Find the least common denominator.
Here are scrambled answers for the next row of exercises: 9 18 20 4 24

5. $\frac{1}{2}$ $\frac{3}{4}$ 4   6. $\frac{2}{9}$ $\frac{1}{3}$ 9   7. $\frac{1}{4}$ $\frac{3}{10}$ 20   8. $\frac{1}{2}$ $\frac{5}{9}$ 18   9. $\frac{1}{8}$ $\frac{1}{6}$ 24

10. $\frac{1}{5}$ $\frac{1}{6}$ 30   11. $\frac{2}{5}$ $\frac{1}{10}$ 10   12. $\frac{2}{3}$ $\frac{4}{9}$ 9   13. $\frac{4}{3}$ $\frac{1}{8}$ 24   14. $\frac{5}{6}$ $\frac{4}{3}$ 6

15. $\frac{5}{6}$ $\frac{3}{4}$ 12   16. $\frac{3}{4}$ $\frac{5}{12}$ 12   17. $\frac{3}{7}$ $\frac{1}{2}$ 14   18. $\frac{2}{3}$ $\frac{1}{12}$ 12   19. $\frac{4}{5}$ $\frac{1}{10}$ 10

20. $\frac{4}{7}$ $\frac{1}{4}$ 28   21. $\frac{2}{9}$ $\frac{1}{5}$ 45   22. $\frac{3}{5}$ $\frac{1}{4}$ 20   23. $\frac{1}{8}$ $\frac{2}{5}$ 40   24. $\frac{1}{6}$ $\frac{3}{7}$ 42

25. $\frac{1}{3}$ $\frac{1}{6}$ 6   26. $\frac{2}{5}$ $\frac{3}{2}$ 10   27. $\frac{1}{3}$ $\frac{5}{12}$ 12   28. $\frac{4}{3}$ $\frac{3}{8}$ 24   29. $\frac{1}{8}$ $\frac{1}{12}$ 24

30. $\frac{1}{2}$ $\frac{3}{20}$ 20   31. $\frac{1}{12}$ $\frac{7}{8}$ 24   32. $\frac{3}{4}$ $\frac{7}{6}$ 12   33. $\frac{5}{9}$ $\frac{7}{6}$ 18   34. $\frac{1}{10}$ $\frac{2}{15}$ 30

35. $\frac{4}{5}$ $\frac{1}{6}$ 30   36. $\frac{3}{8}$ $\frac{1}{6}$ 24   37. $\frac{3}{4}$ $\frac{9}{10}$ 20   38. $\frac{1}{8}$ $\frac{7}{10}$ 40   39. $\frac{1}{7}$ $\frac{1}{3}$ 21

40. $\frac{1}{7}$ $\frac{3}{8}$ 56   41. $\frac{2}{5}$ $\frac{3}{4}$ 20   42. $\frac{3}{7}$ $\frac{1}{5}$ 35   43. $\frac{1}{9}$ $\frac{3}{8}$ 72   44. $\frac{2}{15}$ $\frac{1}{30}$ 30

45. $\frac{1}{20}$ $\frac{3}{40}$ 40   46. $\frac{2}{11}$ $\frac{1}{33}$ 33   47. $\frac{1}{15}$ $\frac{5}{6}$ 30   48. $\frac{7}{3}$ $\frac{2}{11}$ 33   49. $\frac{4}{9}$ $\frac{1}{8}$ 72

50. $\frac{4}{5}$ $\frac{1}{3}$ 15   51. $\frac{5}{4}$ $\frac{2}{9}$ 36   52. $\frac{3}{4}$ $\frac{1}{12}$ 12   53. $\frac{1}{3}$ $\frac{7}{24}$ 24   54. $\frac{6}{7}$ $\frac{1}{4}$ 28

55. $\frac{2}{3}$ $\frac{1}{36}$ 36   56. $\frac{1}{10}$ $\frac{1}{100}$ 100   57. $\frac{3}{10}$ $\frac{1}{25}$ 50   58. $\frac{1}{8}$ $\frac{1}{80}$ 80   59. $\frac{2}{25}$ $\frac{7}{30}$ 150

Credit cutting

Credit-card companies suggest that expired cards be destroyed. With 3 straight cuts, this credit card was cut into 7 pieces.

60. What is the greatest number of pieces you can get with 5 straight cuts? *Hints: Draw a diagram. Use the clues to check your answer.* 16

   Clues:
   - There are more than 10 but less than 20 pieces.
   - The number of pieces is a multiple of 8.

PRACTICE WORKSHEET
Copymaster S207 or Duplicating Master S207

NAME _____   **WORKSHEET 55**
(Use after page 131.)

Complete each multiple strip.

5 | 5 | 10 | 15 | 20 | 25 | 30 | 35 | 40
6 | 6 | 12 | 18 | 24 | 30 | 36 | 42 | 48
8 | 8 | 16 | 24 | 32 | 40 | 48 | 56 | 64 | 72
9 | 9 | 18 | 27 | 36 | 45 | 54 | 63 | 72 | 81
10 | 10 | 20 | 30 | 40 | 50 | 60 | 70 | 80 | 90 | 100 | 110 | 120
12 | 12 | 24 | 36 | 48 | 60 | 72 | 84 | 96 | 108 | 120 | 132 | 144
15 | 15 | 30 | 45 | 60 | 75 | 90 | 105 | 120 | 135 | 150 | 165 | 180

Use your multiple strips to find the least common denominator of each set of fractions.

1. $\frac{3}{5}$ $\frac{1}{8}$ 40   2. $\frac{1}{3}$ $\frac{1}{6}$ $\frac{1}{10}$ 30   3. $\frac{5}{12}$ $\frac{3}{8}$ 24   4. $\frac{5}{6}$ $\frac{1}{9}$ 18
5. $\frac{1}{15}$ $\frac{7}{10}$ 30   6. $\frac{1}{12}$ $\frac{7}{15}$ 60   7. $\frac{7}{12}$ $\frac{1}{5}$ 60   8. $\frac{3}{10}$ $\frac{1}{12}$ 60
9. $\frac{4}{9}$ $\frac{2}{15}$ 45   10. $\frac{1}{6}$ $\frac{11}{15}$ 30   11. $\frac{2}{9}$ $\frac{11}{12}$ 36   12. $\frac{3}{8}$ $\frac{1}{10}$ 40
13. $\frac{2}{9}$ $\frac{4}{5}$ 45   14. $\frac{1}{3}$ $\frac{2}{5}$ 15   15. $\frac{5}{8}$ $\frac{3}{4}$ 24   16. $\frac{7}{9}$ $\frac{2}{15}$ 45
17. $\frac{1}{5}$ $\frac{5}{6}$ $\frac{3}{10}$ 30   18. $\frac{1}{6}$ $\frac{3}{8}$ $\frac{1}{12}$ 24   19. $\frac{5}{6}$ $\frac{1}{9}$ $\frac{7}{12}$ 36   20. $\frac{3}{10}$ $\frac{1}{12}$ $\frac{4}{15}$ 60

© D. C. Heath and Company   **S207**   *Least common denominator*

CHALKBOARD CHALLENGE

Jim's age this year is a multiple of 7. Next year his age will be a multiple of 5. His older sister is now 20. How old is Jim now? 14

LESSON OBJECTIVE
To compare two fractions

PROBLEM-SOLVING SKILLS
Using data from a circle graph
Using information from a display

STARTING THE LESSON
The picture of Mount Rushmore at the top of page 132 is also on **Visual Aid 21.** Use the picture of Mount Rushmore and take a student poll. Ask the students to name *one* of the presidents whose face is carved into Mount Rushmore. Use a frequency table to record the results of the poll.

Presidents	Tally
George Washington	
Thomas Jefferson	
Abraham Lincoln	
Theodore Roosevelt	

Have the students determine what fraction of the class named each president. Then have the students compare their polling results with the results in the graph on page 132.

Comparing fractions

MOUNT RUSHMORE RECALL

A group of high school students were asked to name one of the presidents whose face is carved into Mount Rushmore. The circle graph shows the results of the poll.

1. What fraction of the students named Abraham Lincoln? $\frac{3}{8}$

2. Thomas Jefferson was named by what fraction of the students? $\frac{1}{8}$

3. What two fractions would you compare to decide whether more students named Lincoln than named Jefferson? $\frac{3}{8}, \frac{1}{8}$

GEORGE WASHINGTON $\frac{1}{2}$

$\frac{3}{8}$ ABRAHAM LINCOLN

$\frac{1}{8}$ THOMAS JEFFERSON

Here's how *to compare two fractions with a common denominator.* $\frac{3}{8} \bullet \frac{1}{8}$

To compare fractions with a common denominator, compare the numerators.

$\frac{3}{8} > \frac{1}{8}$

3 is greater than 1. So $\frac{3}{8}$ is greater than $\frac{1}{8}$.

4. Which president, Abraham Lincoln or Thomas Jefferson, did more students name?

Abraham Lincoln

Here's how *to compare two fractions with different denominators.* $\frac{3}{8} \bullet \frac{1}{2}$

To compare fractions with different denominators, compare equivalent fractions with the same denominator.

Find the least common denominator.

$\frac{3}{8} \bullet \frac{1}{2}$

8

Write equivalent fractions.

$\frac{3}{8} \bullet \frac{1}{2}$

$\frac{3}{8}$ $\frac{4}{8}$

Compare.

$\frac{3}{8} \bullet \frac{1}{2}$

$\frac{3}{8} < \frac{4}{8}$

So $\frac{3}{8}$ is less than $\frac{1}{2}$.

5. Which president, Abraham Lincoln or George Washington, did more students name?

George Washington

EXERCISES

< or >?

6. $\frac{2}{5} \bullet \frac{3}{5}$ <

7. $\frac{5}{4} \bullet \frac{7}{4}$ <

8. $\frac{5}{7} \bullet \frac{3}{7}$ >

9. $\frac{5}{9} \bullet \frac{4}{9}$ >

10. $\frac{3}{8} \bullet \frac{0}{8}$ >

11. $\frac{4}{4} \bullet \frac{5}{4}$ <

12. $\frac{6}{5} \bullet \frac{7}{5}$ <

13. $\frac{7}{8} \bullet \frac{5}{8}$ >

14. $\frac{0}{6} \bullet \frac{1}{6}$ <

15. $\frac{7}{4} \bullet \frac{8}{4}$ <

16. $\frac{5}{3} \bullet \frac{3}{3}$ >

17. $\frac{3}{8} \bullet \frac{2}{8}$ >

18. $\frac{7}{9} \bullet \frac{4}{9}$ >

19. $\frac{11}{10} \bullet \frac{13}{10}$ <

20. $\frac{0}{5} \bullet \frac{1}{5}$ <

<, >, or =? *Hint: First write equivalent fractions with the same denominator.*

21. $\frac{1}{4} \bullet \frac{3}{8}$ <

$\boxed{\frac{2}{8}}$ $\boxed{\frac{3}{8}}$

22. $\frac{5}{6} \bullet \frac{2}{3}$ >

$\boxed{\frac{5}{6}}$ $\boxed{\frac{4}{6}}$

23. $\frac{1}{3} \bullet \frac{2}{7}$ >

$\boxed{\frac{7}{21}}$ $\boxed{\frac{6}{21}}$

24. $\frac{1}{3} \bullet \frac{1}{4}$ >

$\boxed{\frac{?}{12}}$ $\boxed{\frac{?}{12}}$

25. $\frac{3}{2} \bullet \frac{5}{4}$ >

$\boxed{\frac{?}{4}}$ $\boxed{\frac{?}{4}}$

26. $\frac{1}{3} \bullet \frac{3}{10}$ >

27. $\frac{3}{8} \bullet \frac{3}{4}$ <

28. $\frac{1}{6} \bullet \frac{1}{8}$ >

29. $\frac{2}{9} \bullet \frac{4}{18}$ =

30. $\frac{2}{5} \bullet \frac{1}{4}$ >

31. $\frac{3}{4} \bullet \frac{2}{3}$ >

32. $\frac{5}{6} \bullet \frac{3}{4}$ >

33. $\frac{3}{4} \bullet \frac{3}{5}$ >

34. $\frac{2}{3} \bullet \frac{7}{9}$ <

35. $\frac{0}{3} \bullet \frac{0}{7}$ =

36. $\frac{3}{7} \bullet \frac{9}{21}$ =

37. $\frac{9}{16} \bullet \frac{5}{8}$ <

38. $\frac{4}{7} \bullet \frac{5}{8}$ <

39. $\frac{7}{8} \bullet \frac{8}{9}$ <

40. $\frac{15}{12} \bullet \frac{5}{4}$ =

41. $\frac{7}{10} \bullet \frac{69}{100}$ >

42. $\frac{6}{100} \bullet \frac{55}{1000}$ >

43. $\frac{9}{1000} \bullet \frac{1}{10}$ <

44. $\frac{49}{1000} \bullet \frac{4}{100}$ >

45. $\frac{7}{10} \bullet \frac{73}{100}$ <

Solve.

46. On the day that Marcia visited Mount Rushmore, $\frac{1}{12}$ of the visitors were from Texas and $\frac{1}{8}$ were from California. From which state were there more visitors?
California

47. On another day, $\frac{1}{4}$ of the visitors were from North Dakota and $\frac{7}{20}$ of the visitors were from Nebraska. Were there more visitors from North Dakota or Nebraska? *Nebraska*

You're the statistical clerk!

Statistical clerks gather information from surveys and records. Business people depend on statistical clerks to help them make decisions.

48. Which statement is correct?
   a. A greater fraction of girls knew the location of Mount Rushmore.
   b. A greater fraction of boys knew the location of Mount Rushmore.

SURVEY FINDINGS
8 out of 15 boys knew that Mount Rushmore was located in South Dakota.
7 out of 12 girls knew its location.

PRACTICE WORKSHEET

Copymaster S208 or Duplicating Master S208

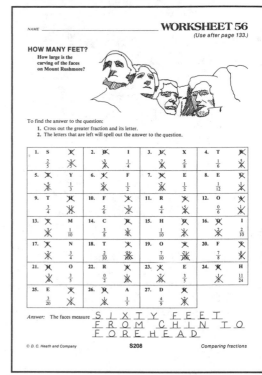

CHALKBOARD CHALLENGE

Match each fraction to a tag on the number line.

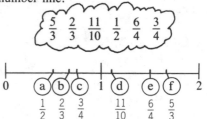

$$\frac{5}{3} \quad \frac{2}{3} \quad \frac{11}{10} \quad \frac{1}{2} \quad \frac{6}{4} \quad \frac{3}{4}$$

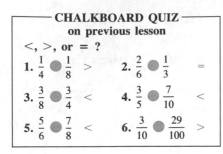

CHALKBOARD QUIZ
on previous lesson

$<$, $>$, or $=$?

1. $\frac{1}{4}$ ● $\frac{1}{8}$ $>$ 2. $\frac{2}{6}$ ● $\frac{1}{3}$ $=$

3. $\frac{3}{8}$ ● $\frac{3}{4}$ $<$ 4. $\frac{3}{5}$ ● $\frac{7}{10}$ $<$

5. $\frac{5}{6}$ ● $\frac{7}{8}$ $<$ 6. $\frac{3}{10}$ ● $\frac{29}{100}$ $>$

SKILLS REVIEWED

Writing the short word-name for a decimal
Adding decimals
Comparing decimals
Subtracting decimals

PROBLEM-SOLVING SKILLS

Finding information in a newspaper ad
Solving a multi-step problem

STARTING THE LESSON

Cumulative Skill Practice
Write these four answers on the chalkboard:

308 thousandths
10.93
84.39
361.8

Challenge the students to an answer hunt by saying, "Look for the four even-numbered exercises on page 134 that have these answers. You have four minutes to find as many of the exercises as you can." (Exercises 14, 24, 40, and 74)

STARTING THE LESSON

Problem Solving
The newspaper ad at the top of page 135 is also on **Visual Aid 22**. Use the ad and ask questions like these:

• What is the cost per month for the one-bedroom apartment? ($200)
• Is $200 per month enough money to rent an efficiency apartment in the new building? (No)
• Would it cost more or less than $2500 to rent the furnished three-bedroom apartment for one year? (More)

Write the short word-name. *(page 16)*

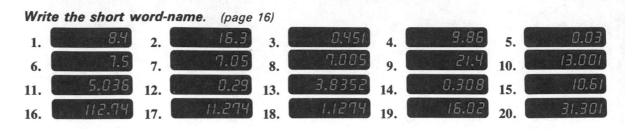

1. 8.4 2. 16.3 3. 0.451 4. 9.86 5. 0.03
6. 7.5 7. 7.05 8. 7.005 9. 21.4 10. 13.001
11. 5.036 12. 0.29 13. 3.8352 14. 0.308 15. 10.61
16. 112.74 17. 11.274 18. 1.1274 19. 16.02 20. 31.301

Give the sum. *(page 24)*

21. $8.24 + 6.59$ 14.83
22. $59.2 + 36.4$ 95.6
23. $6.095 + 4.968$ 11.063

24. $4.03 + 6.9$ 10.93
25. $5.74 + 3.692$ 9.432
26. $9 + 3.97$ 12.97

27. $4.7 + 3.52$ 8.22
28. $18.3 + 31$ 49.3
29. $0.368 + 0.44$ 0.808

30. $6.09 + 4.196$ 10.286
31. $15 + 12.9$ 27.9
32. $8.6 + 3.36$ 11.96

33. $2.3 + 4 + 5.8$ 12.1
34. $18 + 5.6 + 10$ 33.6
35. $8.4 + 6 + 5.9$ 20.3

36. $4.7 + 3.52 + 7.4$ 15.62
37. $18.3 + 31.9 + 7.53$ 57.73
38. $2.74 + 5.9 + 18$ 26.64

39. $16.34 + 21.7 + 32.5$ 70.54
40. $45.6 + 38 + 0.79$ 84.39
41. $56.7 + 42.3 + 87$ 186

$<$, $>$, or $=$? *(page 42)*

42. 0.6 ● 0.4 $>$
43. 0.05 ● 0.06 $<$
44. 0.008 ● 0.007 $>$

45. 24.3 ● 24.2 $>$
46. 9.63 ● 9.635 $<$
47. 0.32 ● 0.3 $>$

48. 52.58 ● 52.6 $<$
49. 3.060 ● 3.06 $=$
50. 0.914 ● 0.9 $>$

51. 17.1 ● 17.08 $>$
52. 0.034 ● 0.34 $<$
53. 6.804 ● 6.84 $<$

54. 28.24 ● 2.842 $>$
55. 2.0 ● 1.99 $>$
56. 3.008 ● 3.8 $<$

Give the difference. *(page 46)*

57. $9.8 - 3.4$ 6.4
58. $6.54 - 2.39$ 4.15
59. $12.346 - 7.591$ 4.755

60. $26.0 - 8.4$ 17.6
61. $16.02 - 5.88$ 10.14
62. $28.103 - 9.617$ 18.486

63. $8 - 3.4$ 4.6
64. $6.7 - 2.93$ 3.77
65. $5.467 - 2.18$ 3.287

66. $17 - 9.04$ 7.96
67. $18.3 - 2.67$ 15.63
68. $33.4 - 1.839$ 31.561

69. $5.43 - 2.976$ 2.454
70. $42.3 - 9.9$ 32.4
71. $100 - 2.46$ 97.54

72. $6.9 - 5.708$ 1.192
73. $227.9 - 34.88$ 193.02
74. $500.7 - 138.9$ 361.8

75. $36.8 - 8.37$ 28.43
76. $59 - 8.75$ 50.25
77. $1 - 0.399$ 0.601

Answers for page 134.
1. 8 and 4 tenths
2. 16 and 3 tenths
3. 451 thousandths
4. 9 and 86 hundredths
5. 3 hundredths
6. 7 and 5 tenths
7. 7 and 5 hundredths
8. 7 and 5 thousandths
9. 21 and 4 tenths
10. 13 and 1 thousandth
11. 5 and 36 thousandths
12. 29 hundredths
13. 3 and 8352 ten-thou
14. 308 thousandths
15. 10 and 61 hundredt

Problem solving

Use the ad to answer these questions.

1. How much would I spend per year for the first apartment listed? $2340

2. My "take-home" pay is $830 each month. How much would I have left after paying the rent on the second apartment listed? $480

3. Look at the third apartment listed. If the average cost of electricity is $74.50 per month, how much would you spend a year for rent and electricity? $4194

4. Suppose that you and 2 of your friends decided to rent the next-to-the-last apartment listed. What would your share of the rent be each month? Round your answer to the nearest cent. $83.33

5. Suppose that your "take-home" pay is $724 per month and that you rented the third apartment listed. If the electric bill was $89.76 the first month, how much would you have left after paying the rent and electric bill? $359.24

6. You decided that you could pay a maximum of $340 a month for rent and utilities. The monthly utilities for the efficiency apartment in the new building are estimated to be $76 for heat and $68 for electricity. Should you rent the apartment? No

7. According to a tenant of the last apartment listed, the total amount paid for the apartment and utilities for last year was $3762. How much did the utilities cost if the rent was the same last year as this year? $1362

8. Suppose that you and 4 of your friends rented a 3-bedroom apartment in the new building. How much would each of you pay in a year for rent? $948

9. The estimated total rent and utilities for a 3-bedroom apartment in the new building is $6480 per year. What is the estimated average monthly utility bill? $145

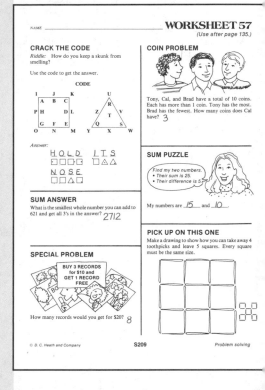

LESSON OBJECTIVE
To write whole numbers and mixed numbers as fractions

PROBLEM-SOLVING SKILL
Using logical reasoning

STARTING THE LESSON
Write the following list on the chalkboard:

$\frac{1}{2}$ $\frac{4}{3}$

2          $5\frac{1}{2}$

$4\frac{1}{2}$ 6

$\frac{8}{1}$ $6\frac{2}{5}$

Have the students identify which are fractions, which are whole numbers, and which are mixed numbers.

HERE'S HOW NOTE
The pizza pieces at the top of page 136 are also on **Visual Aid 23**. Cut out the pieces and use them when discussing the *Here's how* and exercises 1–5. Additional pieces are provided. Use these to illustrate other examples.

EXERCISE NOTE
Encourage the students to use a drawing like this to help them solve the problem in exercise 84.

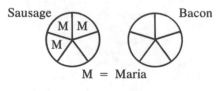

Sausage   Bacon

M = Maria

Writing whole numbers and mixed numbers as fractions

1. Look at a whole pizza. Does $1 = \frac{4}{4}$?   Yes

2. Look at 2 whole pizzas. Does $2 = \frac{8}{4}$?   Yes

Here's how *to change a whole number to a fraction.* $2 = \frac{?}{4}$

Write the whole number over the denominator 1.

$\frac{2}{1}$

Multiply the numerator and denominator by the same whole number (not 0).

$\underset{\times 4}{\overset{\times 4}{\frac{2}{1} = \frac{8}{4}}}$

There are 8 fourths in 2.

3. What would you have to multiply the numerator and denominator by to change $\frac{2}{1}$ to eighths?   8

4. Look at the pizzas. There are 2 whole pizzas plus [?] fourths.   3
   The mixed number $2\frac{3}{4}$ is read as "2 and $\frac{3}{4}$."

Here's how *to change a mixed number to a fraction.* $2\frac{3}{4} = ?$

Multiply the denominator by the whole number. (This gives the number of fourths in 2.)

$2\frac{3}{4}$

Add the numerator. (This gives the number of fourths in $2\frac{3}{4}$.)

$2\frac{3}{4} = \frac{11}{4}$

There are 11 fourths in $2\frac{3}{4}$.

5. Look at the pizzas. Does $2\frac{3}{4} = \frac{11}{4}$?   Yes

6. Check these examples. Are they correct?   Yes

   a. $3 = \frac{6}{2}$ **b.** $4 = \frac{12}{3}$ **c.** $1\frac{1}{2} = \frac{3}{2}$ **d.** $2\frac{2}{3} = \frac{8}{3}$

EXERCISES

Change to thirds.
Here are scrambled answers for the next row of exercises: $\frac{21}{3}$ $\frac{27}{3}$ $\frac{30}{3}$ $\frac{3}{3}$ $\frac{9}{3}$ $\frac{6}{3}$ $\frac{42}{3}$

7. $2\frac{6}{3}$ **8.** $9\frac{27}{3}$ **9.** $3\frac{9}{3}$ **10.** $1\frac{3}{3}$ **11.** $7\frac{21}{3}$ **12.** $10\frac{30}{3}$ $\frac{42}{3}$ **13.** 14

14. $6\frac{18}{3}$ **15.** $12\frac{36}{3}$ **16.** $4\frac{12}{3}$ **17.** $11\frac{33}{3}$ **18.** $5\frac{15}{3}$ **19.** $8\frac{24}{3}$ **20.** $15\ \frac{45}{3}$

Change to fifths.
21. $5\frac{25}{5}$ **22.** $1\frac{5}{5}$ **23.** $6\frac{30}{5}$ **24.** $2\frac{10}{5}$ **25.** $10\frac{50}{5}$ **26.** $7\frac{35}{5}$ $\frac{65}{5}$ **27.** 13

28. $4\frac{20}{5}$ **29.** $12\frac{60}{5}$ **30.** $9\frac{45}{5}$ **31.** $8\frac{40}{5}$ **32.** $3\frac{15}{5}$ **33.** $11\frac{55}{5}$ **34.** $15\ \frac{75}{5}$

Change each mixed number to a fraction.

35. $1\frac{1}{3}$ $\frac{4}{3}$ **36.** $1\frac{1}{2}$ $\frac{3}{2}$ **37.** $2\frac{1}{2}$ $\frac{5}{2}$ **38.** $2\frac{1}{3}$ $\frac{7}{3}$ **39.** $1\frac{1}{4}$ $\frac{5}{4}$ **40.** $3\frac{1}{4}$ $\frac{13}{4}$ **41.** $7\frac{3}{4}$ $\frac{31}{4}$

48. $9\frac{1}{6}$ $\frac{55}{6}$

42. $1\frac{2}{3}$ $\frac{5}{3}$ **43.** $2\frac{3}{4}$ $\frac{11}{4}$ **44.** $4\frac{1}{3}$ $\frac{13}{3}$ **45.** $3\frac{2}{3}$ $\frac{11}{3}$ **46.** $2\frac{2}{5}$ $\frac{12}{5}$ **47.** $3\frac{4}{5}$ $\frac{19}{5}$

49. $4\frac{3}{4}$ $\frac{19}{4}$ **50.** $4\frac{1}{6}$ $\frac{25}{6}$ **51.** $5\frac{3}{4}$ $\frac{23}{4}$ **52.** $4\frac{3}{5}$ $\frac{23}{5}$ **53.** $5\frac{5}{6}$ $\frac{35}{6}$ **54.** $2\frac{3}{8}$ $\frac{19}{8}$ **55.** $11\frac{1}{8}$ $\frac{89}{8}$

56. $6\frac{3}{8}$ $\frac{51}{8}$ **57.** $3\frac{5}{8}$ $\frac{29}{8}$ **58.** $6\frac{3}{10}$ $\frac{63}{10}$ **59.** $8\frac{7}{8}$ $\frac{71}{8}$ **60.** $4\frac{9}{10}$ $\frac{49}{10}$ **61.** $5\frac{5}{8}$ $\frac{45}{8}$ **62.** $7\frac{4}{5}$ $\frac{39}{5}$

63. $6\frac{1}{2}$ $\frac{13}{2}$ **64.** $3\frac{5}{6}$ $\frac{23}{6}$ **65.** $4\frac{7}{8}$ $\frac{39}{8}$ **66.** $4\frac{2}{3}$ $\frac{14}{3}$ **67.** $5\frac{4}{5}$ $\frac{29}{5}$ **68.** $2\frac{3}{5}$ $\frac{13}{5}$ **69.** $9\frac{2}{3}$ $\frac{29}{3}$

70. $2\frac{7}{8}$ $\frac{23}{8}$ **71.** $2\frac{1}{6}$ $\frac{13}{6}$ **72.** $6\frac{2}{3}$ $\frac{20}{3}$ **73.** $7\frac{5}{6}$ $\frac{47}{6}$ **74.** $3\frac{3}{4}$ $\frac{15}{4}$ **75.** $9\frac{3}{8}$ $\frac{75}{8}$ **76.** $13\frac{1}{4}$ $\frac{53}{4}$

77. $10\frac{3}{5}$ $\frac{53}{5}$ **78.** $12\frac{1}{2}$ $\frac{25}{2}$ **79.** $11\frac{2}{3}$ $\frac{35}{3}$ **80.** $15\frac{1}{2}$ $\frac{31}{2}$ **81.** $12\frac{3}{4}$ $\frac{51}{4}$ **82.** $10\frac{3}{8}$ $\frac{83}{8}$ **83.** $11\frac{1}{4}$ $\frac{45}{4}$

Pizza puzzle

84. Beth, Maria, and John ate one sausage and one bacon pizza. Study the clues to find what each person ate.

Clues:
- Each pizza was cut into fifths.
- Maria didn't eat bacon pizza.
- Maria ate 3 pieces.
- Beth didn't eat sausage pizza.
- Beth ate 1 more piece than John.

Hint: Draw a picture.

Beth—4 pieces of bacon pizza
Maria—3 pieces of sausage pizza
John—2 pieces of sausage and 1 piece of bacon

EXTRA PRACTICE
Page 428   Skill 34

PRACTICE WORKSHEET
Copymaster S210 or Duplicating Master S210

LIFE-SKILL PROJECT
Using a yardstick
Have each student measure his/her height, round it to the nearest inch, and use a mixed number to express the height in feet. For example, if a student is 63 inches tall, the student would rename that as $5\frac{1}{4}$ feet.

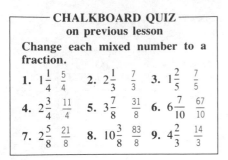
LESSON OBJECTIVE
To write fractions as whole numbers or as mixed numbers

PROBLEM-SOLVING SKILLS
Finding information in an ad
Following instructions

STARTING THE LESSON
Play 'What are the facts?' Have the students study the newspaper ad at the top of page 138 for 30 seconds. Then tell them to close their books and decide whether these statements are true or false:

• For each album you buy at the Stereo Connection, you get one fourth of a coupon. (True)
• If you have one half of a coupon, you can buy an album for half price. (False)
• When you buy four albums, you can use your coupon to get another album free. (True)

***HERE'S HOW* NOTE**
The coupons at the top of page 138 are also on **Visual Aid 24**. You may wish to cut out and rearrange the coupon fourths when discussing the *Here's how* and exercises 1–5. Additional coupon fourths are provided. Use these to illustrate other examples.

Writing fractions as whole numbers or as mixed numbers

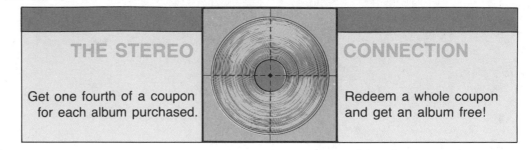

THE STEREO CONNECTION

Get one fourth of a coupon for each album purchased.

Redeem a whole coupon and get an album free!

1. How many fourths do you need to make a whole coupon? 4

2. If you have 8 fourths, how many whole coupons do you have? 2

Here's how *to change $\frac{8}{4}$ to a whole number.*

To change a fraction to a whole number, divide the numerator by the denominator.

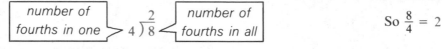

number of fourths in one $\quad 4\overline{)8}^{\,2}\quad$ number of fourths in all

So $\frac{8}{4} = 2$

3. $\frac{20}{4}$ is equal to what whole number? 5

Here's how *to change $\frac{11}{4}$ to a mixed number.*

To change a fraction to a mixed number, divide the numerator by the denominator.

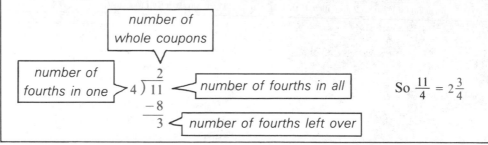

number of whole coupons

number of fourths in one $\quad 4\overline{)11}^{\,2}\quad$ number of fourths in all

$\underline{-8}$

$3 \quad$ number of fourths left over

So $\frac{11}{4} = 2\frac{3}{4}$

4. $\frac{21}{4}$ is equal to what mixed number? $5\frac{1}{4}$

5. A fraction can be changed to a whole number or mixed number if the denominator is $\underline{\quad\quad ? \quad\quad}$ the numerator. less than
less than/greater than

138

EXERCISES

Change each fraction to a whole number.
Here are scrambled answers for the next row of exercises: 5 4 2 1 8 6 3

6. $\frac{9}{3}$ 3   7. $\frac{10}{5}$ 2   8. $\frac{16}{2}$ 8   9. $\frac{6}{6}$ 1   10. $\frac{16}{4}$ 4   11. $\frac{18}{3}$ 6   12. $\frac{25}{5}$ 5

13. $\frac{15}{5}$ 3   14. $\frac{10}{2}$ 5   15. $\frac{3}{3}$ 1   16. $\frac{12}{4}$ 3   17. $\frac{16}{8}$ 2   18. $\frac{12}{6}$ 2   19. $\frac{24}{3}$ 8

20. $\frac{20}{10}$ 2   21. $\frac{24}{6}$ 4   22. $\frac{18}{2}$ 9   23. $\frac{24}{8}$ 3   24. $\frac{5}{5}$ 1   25. $\frac{12}{3}$ 4   26. $\frac{50}{25}$ 2

Change each fraction to a whole number or a mixed number.
Here are scrambled answers for the next row of exercises: 3 $1\frac{5}{6}$ $1\frac{1}{2}$ 2 $1\frac{1}{4}$ $2\frac{3}{5}$ 9

27. $\frac{3}{2}$ $1\frac{1}{2}$ 28. $\frac{5}{4}$ $1\frac{1}{4}$ 29. $\frac{9}{3}$ 3   30. $\frac{13}{5}$ $2\frac{3}{5}$ 31. $\frac{11}{6}$ $1\frac{5}{6}$ 32. $\frac{16}{8}$ 2   33. $\frac{81}{9}$ 9

34. $\frac{13}{10}$ $1\frac{3}{10}$ 35. $\frac{16}{4}$ 4   36. $\frac{5}{2}$ $2\frac{1}{2}$ 37. $\frac{7}{4}$ $1\frac{3}{4}$ 38. $\frac{17}{8}$ $2\frac{1}{8}$ 39. $\frac{10}{3}$ $3\frac{1}{3}$ 40. $\frac{11}{9}$ $1\frac{2}{9}$

41. $\frac{19}{5}$ $3\frac{4}{5}$ 42. $\frac{14}{3}$ $4\frac{2}{3}$ 43. $\frac{15}{4}$ $3\frac{3}{4}$ 44. $\frac{27}{10}$ $2\frac{7}{10}$ 45. $\frac{11}{2}$ $5\frac{1}{2}$ 46. $\frac{18}{3}$ 6   47. $\frac{27}{7}$ $3\frac{6}{7}$

48. $\frac{35}{5}$ 7   49. $\frac{25}{3}$ $8\frac{1}{3}$ 50. $\frac{30}{6}$ 5   51. $\frac{35}{2}$ $17\frac{1}{2}$ 52. $\frac{29}{6}$ $4\frac{5}{6}$ 53. $\frac{36}{4}$ 9   54. $\frac{36}{6}$ 6

55. $\frac{20}{5}$ 4   56. $\frac{13}{6}$ $2\frac{1}{6}$ 57. $\frac{37}{10}$ $3\frac{7}{10}$ 58. $\frac{20}{3}$ $6\frac{2}{3}$ 59. $\frac{19}{6}$ $3\frac{1}{6}$ 60. $\frac{42}{5}$ $8\frac{2}{5}$ 61. $\frac{21}{7}$ 3

62. $\frac{28}{3}$ $9\frac{1}{3}$ 63. $\frac{14}{14}$ 1   64. $\frac{8}{5}$ $1\frac{3}{5}$ 65. $\frac{50}{5}$ 10   66. $\frac{29}{3}$ $9\frac{2}{3}$ 67. $\frac{15}{3}$ 5   68. $\frac{19}{8}$ $2\frac{3}{8}$

A stack of singles!

69. The Beatles are considered the most successful recording group. If you stacked the single records that they sold between 1963 and 1973 in one stack, it would be [?] feet high.   3,493,590

To find [?], write a
- 0 in the ones place.
- 5 in the hundreds place.
- 4 in the hundred thousands place.
- 9 in both the tens place and the ten thousands place.
- 3 in both the millions place and the thousands place.

70. About how many miles high would the stack be? *Hint: There are 5280 feet in a mile.* About 662 miles

EXTRA PRACTICE
Page 429   Skill 35

PRACTICE WORKSHEET
Copymaster S211 or Duplicating Master S211

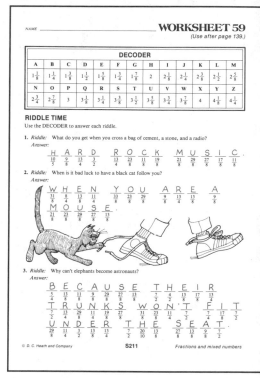

LIFE-SKILL PROJECT
Researching information
Have the students find out how mixed numbers are used in stock quotations. Ask them to find out how to read the stock quotations and share their findings with other class members.

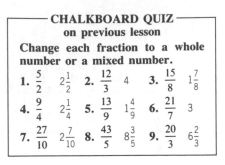
LESSON OBJECTIVE
To write fractions and mixed numbers in simplest form

PROBLEM-SOLVING SKILL
Using logical reasoning

STARTING THE LESSON
Write these fractions and mixed numbers on the chalkboard:

$\frac{7}{10}$ $4\frac{1}{2}$ $1\frac{1}{3}$

$\frac{1}{2}$ $6\frac{2}{5}$ $4\frac{5}{6}$

$\frac{5}{8}$ $2\frac{4}{8}$ $7\frac{1}{3}$

$\frac{3}{12}$ $8\frac{3}{4}$ $\frac{10}{7}$

Ask the students which fraction or mixed number does not belong in each group of numbers. ($\frac{3}{12}$, $2\frac{4}{8}$, and $\frac{10}{7}$ do not belong, since they are not written in simplest form.) Then discuss exercises 1–6 to acquaint the students with the rules for writing fractions and mixed numbers in simplest form.

Writing fractions and mixed numbers in simplest form

1. Look at the yellow cards. Which two fractions have numerators less than their denominators? $\frac{6}{8}$, $\frac{8}{12}$
   Are these fractions less than or greater than 1? Less than

Here's how *to write $\frac{6}{8}$ in simplest form.*

Write fractions less than 1 in lowest terms.

$$\frac{6}{8} = \frac{3}{4} \triangleleft \boxed{simplest\ form}$$

2. How would you write $\frac{8}{12}$ in simplest form? $\frac{2}{3}$

3. What two mixed numbers are written on the cards? $2\frac{2}{4}$, $3\frac{4}{6}$

Here's how *to write $2\frac{2}{4}$ in simplest form.*

Write mixed numbers with the fraction part less than 1 *and* in lowest terms.

$$2\frac{2}{4} = 2\frac{1}{2} \triangleleft \boxed{simplest\ form}$$

4. How would you write $3\frac{4}{6}$ in simplest form? $3\frac{2}{3}$

5. Look at the yellow cards. Which fractions are greater than or equal to 1? $\frac{6}{6}$, $\frac{18}{6}$, $\frac{14}{3}$, $\frac{20}{5}$, $\frac{18}{4}$

Here's how *to write $\frac{20}{5}$ and $\frac{14}{3}$ in simplest form.*

Write fractions that are greater than or equal to 1 as a whole number or as a mixed number in simplest form.

$$\frac{20}{5} = 4 \triangleleft \boxed{simplest\ form} \qquad \frac{14}{3} = 4\frac{2}{3} \triangleleft \boxed{simplest\ form}$$

6. Write each fraction in simplest form.

   a. $\frac{18}{6}$ 3   b. $\frac{18}{4}$ $4\frac{1}{2}$ c. $\frac{6}{6}$ 1

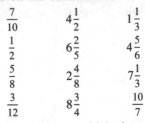

140

EXERCISES

Write in simplest form.

Here are scrambled answers for the next row of exercises: $\frac{3}{5}$ $\frac{1}{2}$ $\frac{3}{4}$ $\frac{5}{6}$ $\frac{1}{6}$ $\frac{2}{3}$ $\frac{4}{5}$

7. $\frac{6}{10}$ $\frac{3}{5}$ **8.** $\frac{2}{12}$ $\frac{1}{6}$ **9.** $\frac{5}{10}$ $\frac{1}{2}$ **10.** $\frac{6}{8}$ $\frac{3}{4}$ **11.** $\frac{4}{6}$ $\frac{2}{3}$ **12.** $\frac{15}{18}$ $\frac{5}{6}$ **13.** $\frac{20}{25}$ $\frac{4}{5}$

14. $\frac{6}{18}$ $\frac{1}{3}$ **15.** $\frac{8}{14}$ $\frac{4}{7}$ **16.** $\frac{10}{12}$ $\frac{5}{6}$ **17.** $\frac{5}{20}$ $\frac{1}{4}$ **18.** $\frac{16}{24}$ $\frac{2}{3}$ **19.** $\frac{14}{16}$ $\frac{7}{8}$ **20.** $\frac{6}{9}$ $\frac{2}{3}$

Write in simplest form.

21. $2\frac{2}{4}$ $2\frac{1}{2}$ **22.** $4\frac{2}{8}$ $4\frac{1}{4}$ **23.** $3\frac{4}{6}$ $3\frac{2}{3}$ **24.** $5\frac{2}{6}$ $5\frac{1}{3}$ **25.** $4\frac{6}{8}$ $4\frac{3}{4}$ **26.** $6\frac{10}{12}$ $6\frac{5}{6}$ **27.** $7\frac{4}{16}$ $7\frac{1}{4}$

28. $4\frac{3}{12}$ $4\frac{1}{4}$ **29.** $8\frac{5}{10}$ $8\frac{1}{2}$ **30.** $3\frac{3}{9}$ $3\frac{1}{3}$ **31.** $12\frac{10}{15}$ $12\frac{2}{3}$ **32.** $5\frac{9}{12}$ $5\frac{3}{4}$ **33.** $10\frac{8}{10}$ $10\frac{4}{5}$ **34.** $1\frac{9}{15}$ $1\frac{3}{5}$

35. $6\frac{4}{8}$ $6\frac{1}{2}$ **36.** $3\frac{8}{24}$ $3\frac{1}{3}$ **37.** $2\frac{15}{30}$ $2\frac{1}{2}$ **38.** $5\frac{10}{18}$ $5\frac{5}{9}$ **39.** $4\frac{5}{15}$ $4\frac{1}{3}$ **40.** $1\frac{7}{14}$ $1\frac{1}{2}$ **41.** $10\frac{8}{64}$ $10\frac{1}{8}$

Write in simplest form.

42. $\frac{6}{3}$ 2 **43.** $\frac{10}{2}$ 5 **44.** $\frac{12}{4}$ 3 **45.** $\frac{20}{4}$ 5 **46.** $\frac{36}{3}$ 12 **47.** $\frac{24}{8}$ 3 **48.** $\frac{14}{7}$ 2

49. $\frac{9}{2}$ $4\frac{1}{2}$ **50.** $\frac{8}{3}$ $2\frac{2}{3}$ **51.** $\frac{7}{4}$ $1\frac{3}{4}$ **52.** $\frac{9}{5}$ $1\frac{4}{5}$ **53.** $\frac{10}{3}$ $3\frac{1}{3}$ **54.** $\frac{11}{4}$ $2\frac{3}{4}$ **55.** $\frac{6}{1}$ 6

56. $\frac{17}{3}$ $5\frac{2}{3}$ **57.** $\frac{15}{4}$ $3\frac{3}{4}$ **58.** $\frac{12}{8}$ $1\frac{1}{2}$ **59.** $\frac{15}{10}$ $1\frac{1}{2}$ **60.** $\frac{16}{12}$ $1\frac{1}{3}$ **61.** $\frac{18}{12}$ $1\frac{1}{2}$ **62.** $\frac{34}{11}$ $3\frac{1}{11}$

63. $\frac{8}{10}$ $\frac{4}{5}$ **64.** $\frac{10}{8}$ $1\frac{1}{4}$ **65.** $\frac{16}{3}$ $5\frac{1}{3}$ **66.** $\frac{3}{6}$ $\frac{1}{2}$ **67.** $\frac{9}{8}$ $1\frac{1}{8}$ **68.** $\frac{16}{14}$ $1\frac{1}{7}$ **69.** $\frac{35}{30}$ $1\frac{1}{6}$

70. $\frac{33}{6}$ $5\frac{1}{2}$ **71.** $\frac{36}{5}$ $7\frac{1}{5}$ **72.** $\frac{24}{36}$ $\frac{2}{3}$ **73.** $\frac{18}{5}$ $3\frac{3}{5}$ **74.** $\frac{22}{16}$ $1\frac{3}{8}$ **75.** $\frac{28}{6}$ $4\frac{2}{3}$ **76.** $\frac{31}{7}$ $4\frac{3}{7}$

77. $\frac{8}{12}$ $\frac{2}{3}$ **78.** $\frac{6}{24}$ $\frac{1}{4}$ **79.** $\frac{8}{1}$ 8 **80.** $\frac{10}{25}$ $\frac{2}{5}$ **81.** $\frac{25}{10}$ $2\frac{1}{2}$ **82.** $\frac{18}{36}$ $\frac{1}{2}$ **83.** $\frac{35}{15}$ $2\frac{1}{3}$

84. $\frac{42}{6}$ 7 **85.** $\frac{6}{42}$ $\frac{1}{7}$ **86.** $\frac{25}{8}$ $3\frac{1}{8}$ **87.** $\frac{16}{18}$ $\frac{8}{9}$ **88.** $\frac{24}{32}$ $\frac{3}{4}$ **89.** $\frac{32}{24}$ $1\frac{1}{3}$ **90.** $\frac{13}{11}$ $1\frac{2}{11}$

Face fact

91. Study the clues to find how many muscles you use to smile and how many muscles you use to frown.

43 muscles to frown

17 muscles to smile

Clues:
- It takes more muscles to frown.
- If you add the numbers, you get 60.
- If you subtract the numbers, you get 26.

PRACTICE WORKSHEET

Copymaster S212 or Duplicating Master S212

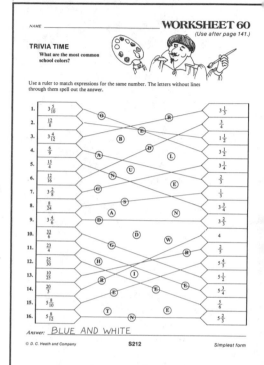

LIFE-SKILL PROJECT

Using a calculator

Have the students use a calculator to reduce each of these fractions to lowest terms:

1. $\frac{1920}{2560}$ $\frac{3}{4}$

2. $\frac{9702}{14,553}$ $\frac{2}{3}$

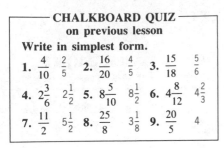

LESSON OBJECTIVE
To write quotients as mixed numbers

PROBLEM-SOLVING SKILLS
Finding information in a display
Choosing the correct operation
Using logical reasoning

STARTING THE LESSON
Write these division exercises on the chalkboard:

$3\overline{)42}$ $7\overline{)84}$ $4\overline{)51}$ $5\overline{)75}$

Ask the students which quotient does not belong in the group of division exercises. ($4\overline{)51}$ does not belong, since its quotient has a remainder.) Then use exercises 1–5 and the *Here's how* to show the students how to write quotients as mixed numbers.

Writing quotients as mixed numbers

1. How many photos can be mounted on one page of the album? 6

2. To find how many pages would be needed to mount 100 photos, you would divide 100 by what number? 6

Here's how *to write a quotient as a mixed number.*   *100 ÷ 6 = ?*

Step 1.
Divide.

$$\begin{array}{r} 16 \\ 6\overline{)100} \\ -6 \\ \hline 40 \\ -36 \\ \hline 4 \end{array}$$

number of full pages

number of photos remaining

Step 2.
Write the quotient as a mixed number.

$$\begin{array}{r} 16\frac{4}{6} \\ 6\overline{)100} \\ -6 \\ \hline 40 \\ -36 \\ \hline 4 \end{array}$$

Write the remainder over the divisor.

Step 3.
Write the mixed number in simplest form.

$$16\frac{4}{6} = 16\frac{2}{3}$$
$$\begin{array}{r} 6\overline{)100} \\ -6 \\ \hline 40 \\ -36 \\ \hline 4 \end{array}$$

3. Look at the first step in the *Here's how*. After 16 pages of the album were filled, how many photos would be left to be mounted?   4

4. Look at the last step of the *Here's how*. It would take 16 and ▢ $\frac{2}{3}$ pages to mount all the photos.

5. Check these examples. Are they correct? Yes

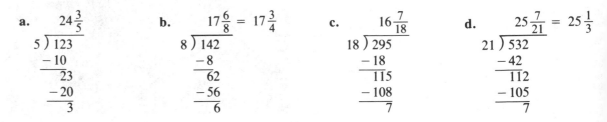

a.
$$\begin{array}{r} 24\frac{3}{5} \\ 5\overline{)123} \\ -10 \\ \hline 23 \\ -20 \\ \hline 3 \end{array}$$

b.
$$17\frac{6}{8} = 17\frac{3}{4}$$
$$\begin{array}{r} 8\overline{)142} \\ -8 \\ \hline 62 \\ -56 \\ \hline 6 \end{array}$$

c.
$$16\frac{7}{18}$$
$$\begin{array}{r} 18\overline{)295} \\ -18 \\ \hline 115 \\ -108 \\ \hline 7 \end{array}$$

d.
$$25\frac{7}{21} = 25\frac{1}{3}$$
$$\begin{array}{r} 21\overline{)532} \\ -42 \\ \hline 112 \\ -105 \\ \hline 7 \end{array}$$

EXERCISES

Divide. Write each quotient as a mixed number in simplest form.

Here are scrambled answers for the next row of exercises: $14\frac{2}{3}$ $5\frac{1}{3}$ $8\frac{1}{3}$ $4\frac{1}{2}$ $8\frac{2}{5}$

6. $4\overline{)18}$ $4\frac{1}{2}$ 7. $3\overline{)44}$ $14\frac{2}{3}$ 8. $6\overline{)50}$ $8\frac{1}{3}$ 9. $5\overline{)42}$ $8\frac{2}{5}$ 10. $9\overline{)48}$ $5\frac{1}{3}$

11. $7\overline{)45}$ $6\frac{3}{7}$ 12. $8\overline{)75}$ $9\frac{3}{8}$ 13. $6\overline{)74}$ $12\frac{1}{3}$ 14. $4\overline{)90}$ $22\frac{1}{2}$ 15. $9\overline{)78}$ $8\frac{2}{3}$

16. $5\overline{)162}$ $32\frac{2}{5}$ 17. $7\overline{)253}$ $36\frac{1}{7}$ 18. $8\overline{)153}$ $19\frac{1}{8}$ 19. $9\overline{)124}$ $13\frac{7}{9}$ 20. $3\overline{)124}$ $41\frac{1}{3}$

21. $12\overline{)283}$ $23\frac{7}{12}$ 22. $15\overline{)406}$ $27\frac{1}{15}$ 23. $21\overline{)592}$ $28\frac{4}{21}$ 24. $25\overline{)685}$ $27\frac{2}{5}$ 25. $18\overline{)665}$ $36\frac{17}{18}$

26. $24\overline{)862}$ $35\frac{11}{12}$ 27. $28\overline{)906}$ $32\frac{5}{14}$ 28. $32\overline{)900}$ $28\frac{1}{8}$ 29. $30\overline{)820}$ $27\frac{1}{3}$ 30. $36\overline{)912}$ $25\frac{1}{3}$

31. $44\overline{)2688}$ $61\frac{1}{11}$ 32. $42\overline{)2324}$ $55\frac{1}{3}$ 33. $48\overline{)3996}$ $83\frac{1}{4}$ 34. $60\overline{)2565}$ $42\frac{3}{4}$ 35. $40\overline{)2420}$ $60\frac{1}{2}$

36. $1450 \div 30$ $48\frac{1}{3}$ 37. $1480 \div 16$ $92\frac{1}{2}$ 38. $1850 \div 26$ $71\frac{2}{13}$ 39. $2187 \div 36$ $60\frac{3}{4}$

40. $3136 \div 42$ $74\frac{2}{3}$ 41. $2440 \div 60$ $40\frac{2}{3}$ 42. $2691 \div 72$ $37\frac{3}{8}$ 43. $3570 \div 64$ $55\frac{25}{32}$

44. $3475 \div 50$ $69\frac{1}{2}$ 45. $3396 \div 48$ $70\frac{3}{4}$ 46. $2282 \div 84$ $27\frac{1}{6}$ 47. $3660 \div 80$ $45\frac{3}{4}$

48. $4526 \div 30$ $150\frac{13}{15}$ 49. $4586 \div 15$ $305\frac{11}{15}$ 50. $8452 \div 12$ $704\frac{1}{3}$ 51. $6881 \div 17$ $404\frac{13}{17}$

52. $3146 \div 27$ $116\frac{14}{27}$ 53. $9107 \div 23$ $395\frac{22}{23}$ 54. $3106 \div 94$ $33\frac{2}{47}$ 55. $3524 \div 15$ $234\frac{14}{15}$

Solve.

56. You bought 2 rolls of film for $2.48 a roll. How much did you spend for the film? $4.96

57. You had 2 rolls of 24 developed for $6.79 a roll and 1 roll of 36 developed for $8.11. What was the total cost? $21.69

58. You can take 36 pictures on a large roll of film. If a large roll costs $3.69, how much does the film cost for each picture? Round the answer to the nearest cent. $.10

59. You have 68 photos to put in an album. If you put 6 photos on each page, how many pages will you need? Give the answer as a mixed number in simplest form. $11\frac{1}{3}$

Photo count!

60. Study these clues to find how many pictures are in the pile. 42

Clues:
- There are fewer than 50.
- If you put 8 on a page, you will have 2 left over.
- If you put 9 on a page, you will have 6 left over.

PRACTICE WORKSHEET
Copymaster S213 or Duplicating Master S213

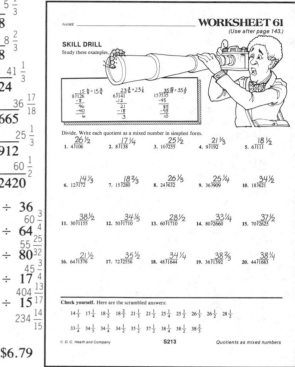

WORKSHEET 61
(Use after page 143.)

NAME _____

SKILL DRILL
Study these examples.

$8\overline{)126}$ $15\frac{6}{8}=15\frac{3}{4}$ $6\overline{)141}$ $23\frac{3}{6}=23\frac{1}{2}$ $15\overline{)535}$ $35\frac{10}{15}=35\frac{2}{3}$

Divide. Write each quotient as a mixed number in simplest form.

1. $4\overline{)106}$ $26\frac{1}{2}$ 2. $8\overline{)138}$ $17\frac{1}{4}$ 3. $10\overline{)255}$ $25\frac{1}{2}$ 4. $9\overline{)192}$ $21\frac{1}{3}$ 5. $6\overline{)111}$ $18\frac{1}{2}$

6. $12\overline{)172}$ $14\frac{1}{3}$ 7. $15\overline{)280}$ $18\frac{2}{3}$ 8. $24\overline{)632}$ $26\frac{1}{3}$ 9. $36\overline{)909}$ $25\frac{1}{4}$ 10. $18\overline{)621}$ $34\frac{1}{2}$

11. $30\overline{)1155}$ $38\frac{1}{2}$ 12. $50\overline{)1710}$ $34\frac{1}{5}$ 13. $60\overline{)1710}$ $28\frac{1}{2}$ 14. $80\overline{)2660}$ $33\frac{1}{4}$ 15. $70\overline{)2625}$ $37\frac{1}{2}$

16. $64\overline{)1376}$ $21\frac{1}{2}$ 17. $72\overline{)2556}$ $35\frac{1}{2}$ 18. $48\overline{)1644}$ $34\frac{1}{4}$ 19. $36\overline{)1392}$ $38\frac{2}{3}$ 20. $44\overline{)1683}$ $38\frac{1}{4}$

Check yourself. Here are the scrambled answers:

$14\frac{1}{3}$ $17\frac{1}{4}$ $18\frac{1}{2}$ $18\frac{2}{3}$ $21\frac{1}{3}$ $21\frac{1}{2}$ $25\frac{1}{4}$ $25\frac{1}{2}$ $26\frac{1}{3}$ $26\frac{1}{2}$ $28\frac{1}{2}$

$33\frac{1}{4}$ $34\frac{1}{5}$ $34\frac{1}{4}$ $34\frac{1}{2}$ $35\frac{1}{2}$ $37\frac{1}{2}$ $38\frac{1}{4}$ $38\frac{1}{2}$ $38\frac{2}{3}$

© D. C. Heath and Company   S213   *Quotients as mixed numbers*

CHALKBOARD CHALLENGE
Find the missing digits.

1.
```
        ⬚1⬚7 ⬚6
   6 )3 ⬚8 2 ⬚3
     - 3 6
       2 2
     - 1 8
         4 3
       - ⬚4 ⬚2
           ⬚1
```

2.
```
          ⬚5⬚ 14
   14 )9 1 ⬚7 5
      - ⬚8 ⬚4
          ⬚7 7
        - 7 0
            7 5
          - 7 0
              ⬚5
```

Fractions, Mixed Numbers, and Decimals **143**

Divide. Write each quotient as a
mixed number in simplest form.

1. $44 \div 5$ $8\frac{4}{5}$ **2.** $50 \div 8$ $6\frac{1}{4}$

3. $65 \div 7$ $9\frac{2}{7}$ **4.** $90 \div 4$ $22\frac{1}{2}$

5. $283 \div 10$ $28\frac{3}{10}$ **6.** $144 \div 50$ $2\frac{22}{25}$

SKILLS REVIEWED
Multiplying decimals
Multiplying by 10, 100, or 1000
Dividing decimals
Finding the median of a set of numbers

PROBLEM-SOLVING SKILLS
Reading a map
Choosing the correct operation
Solving a multi-step problem

STARTING THE LESSON
Cumulative Skill Practice
Challenge the students to an estimation
hunt by saying, "Pick the largest product
in the first row of exercises." (Exercise
3) Then have the students pick the largest product in the next six rows of
exercises. (Exercises 6, 9, 10, 13, 16,
and 20)

STARTING THE LESSON
Problem Solving
The route marked on the map on page
145 is on **Visual Aid 25**. Use the map
and ask questions like these:
• How many miles is it from Los An-
geles to San Bernardino? (65)
• What is the driving time from Santa
Barbara to Los Angeles? (1 hr
56 min)
• Is 3 hours enough driving time to travel
from Barstow to Death Valley? (No)

EXERCISE NOTE
Problem Solving
If some students have difficulty dealing
with the extra information on the map,
duplicate copies of **Visual Aid 25** for
them to use.

Cumulative Skill Practice

Give the product. *(page 64)*

1. 2.5×3 7.5   **2.** 4.2×2 8.4   **3.** 3.3×5 16.5

4. 2.74×7 19.18   **5.** 3.82×6 22.92   **6.** 7.23×9 65.07

7. 7.4×0.5 3.7   **8.** 9.24×0.2 1.848   **9.** 8.03×0.7 5.621

10. 6.84×0.6 4.104   **11.** 31.5×0.004 0.126   **12.** 0.98×0.09 0.0882

13. 24.96×12 299.52   **14.** 35.8×2.4 85.92   **15.** 2.694×5.1 13.7394

16. 5.07×38 192.66   **17.** 3.81×5.31 20.2311   **18.** 0.064×4.5 0.288

19. 283.4×1.38 391.092   **20.** 215×9.7 2085.5   **21.** 4.003×21.8 87.2654

Give the product. *(page 69)*

22. 42×10 420   **23.** 42×100 4200   **24.** 42×1000 42,000

25. 125×100 12,500   **26.** 74×10 740   **27.** 52×1000 52,000

28. 0.563×100 56.3   **29.** 0.563×10 5.63   **30.** 0.563×1000 563

31. 0.64×100 64   **32.** 0.64×10 6.4   **33.** 0.64×1000 640

34. 7.4×1000 7400   **35.** 7.4×10 74   **36.** 7.4×100 740

37. 56.39×10 563.9   **38.** 56.39×100 5639   **39.** 56.39×1000 56,390

40. 12.87×100 1287   **41.** 12.87×10 128.7   **42.** 12.87×1000 12,870

Give the quotient rounded to the nearest tenth. *(page 96)*

43. $3.8 \div 0.3$ 12.7   **44.** $7.4 \div 0.6$ 12.3   **45.** $9.1 \div 0.9$ 10.1

46. $9.4 \div 0.6$ 15.7   **47.** $8.3 \div 0.3$ 27.7   **48.** $2.73 \div 0.7$ 3.9

49. $5.64 \div 0.5$ 11.3   **50.** $8.422 \div 0.04$ 210.6   **51.** $5.75 \div 0.07$ 82.1

52. $34.32 \div 0.003$ 11,440   **53.** $56.5 \div 6$ 9.4   **54.** $19.4 \div 0.09$ 215.6

55. $42 \div 1.1$ 38.2   **56.** $6.38 \div 2.4$ 2.7   **57.** $74.26 \div 0.36$ 206.3

58. $96.32 \div 9.3$ 10.4   **59.** $6.389 \div 0.56$ 11.4   **60.** $9.62 \div 0.45$ 21.4

61. $0.084 \div 0.42$ 0.2   **62.** $0.9465 \div 8.3$ 0.1   **63.** $70.04 \div 5.2$ 13.5

Find the median. *(page 116)*

64. 93, 97, 58, 83, 86 86   **65.** 59, 63, 57, 55, 61 59   **66.** 39, 40, 40, 37, 35

67. 28, 27, 26, 30 27.5   **68.** 92, 96, 90, 89 91   **69.** 215, 217, 218, 216

70. 74, 70, 68, 75, 76 74   **71.** 23, 27, 24, 18 23.5   **72.** 53, 51, 47, 59 52

73. 308, 306, 312, 304 307   **74.** 66, 65, 68, 72 67   **75.** 71, 71, 75, 78, 73

Problem solving

The red numbers show the miles. The blue numbers show the driving time in hours and minutes. You decide to take the trip shown in yellow.

Solve.

1. How many miles is it from Los Angeles to Barstow? 138

2. What is the driving time from Barstow to Death Valley? 3 hours 38 minutes

3. You leave Death Valley at 8:00 A.M. If you plan two 15-minute rest stops and an hour for lunch, at what time should you arrive in Yosemite? 4:18 P.M.

4. Your fuel tank will hold 14.7 gallons. In San Francisco it takes 10.8 gallons to fill the tank. How many gallons were in the tank when you reached San Francisco? 3.9

5. If the fuel costs $1.32 per gallon, how much should you have paid for 10.8 gallons? $14.26

6. If you want to arrive at Monterey by noon, by what time should you leave San Francisco? 9:19 A.M.

7. On your way to Sequoia National Park, you fill the fuel tank. If the tank holds 14.7 gallons and your car gets 28.5 miles per gallon, how far can you drive before running out of fuel? 418.95 miles

8. You leave Sequoia and average 52.5 miles per hour for the first 2.5 hours. How far do you travel during this time? 131.25 miles

9. You plan to leave Sequoia and drive no more than 6 hours today. Can you reach Los Angeles today? No

10. Suppose that it takes 16.5¢ per mile to operate your car. What would be the total car expense for your trip? $268.29

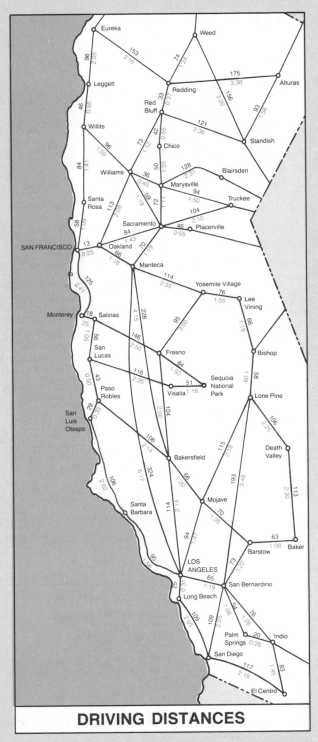

DRIVING DISTANCES

EXTRA PROBLEM SOLVING
Page 449   Even exercises

PROBLEM-SOLVING WORKSHEET
Copymaster S214 or Duplicating Master S214

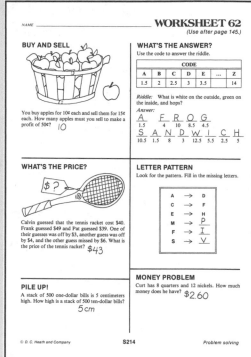

LIFE-SKILL PROJECT
Reading a map
Tell the students they can average 50 miles per hour on interstate highways, 45 miles per hour on numbered highways, and 40 miles per hour on other roads. Have them use a state road map, choose two cities, and use the distance information on the map to compute the shortest driving time between the pair of cities.

CHALKBOARD QUIZ
on previous lesson
Solve. Use the map on page 145.
1. How many miles is it from San Francisco to Monterey? 125
2. If you want to arrive at San Luis Obispo at 10 P.M., by what time should you leave Santa Barbara? 7:58 P.M.

LESSON OBJECTIVE
To write fractions and mixed numbers as decimals

PROBLEM-SOLVING SKILLS
Finding information in a recipe
Choosing the correct operation
Looking for patterns

STARTING THE LESSON
Before the students open their books, challenge them to name the meal. Read the recipe on page 146 and have them write what type of meal they think the recipe makes. Then have them open their books to page 146 and check their answers.

Writing fractions and mixed numbers as decimals

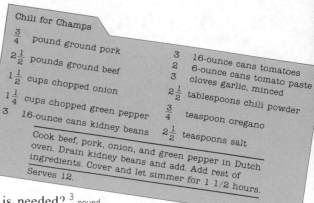

Chili for Champs
$\frac{3}{4}$ pound ground pork
$2\frac{1}{2}$ pounds ground beef
$1\frac{1}{2}$ cups chopped onion
$1\frac{1}{4}$ cups chopped green pepper
3 16-ounce cans kidney beans

3 16-ounce cans tomatoes
2 6-ounce cans tomato paste
3 cloves garlic, minced
$2\frac{1}{2}$ tablespoons chili powder
$\frac{3}{4}$ teaspoon oregano
$2\frac{1}{2}$ teaspoons salt

Cook beef, pork, onion, and green pepper in Dutch oven. Drain kidney beans and add. Add rest of ingredients. Cover and let simmer for 1 1/2 hours. Serves 12.

1. Look at the recipe. How much ground pork is needed? $\frac{3}{4}$ pound

2. How much ground pork is in the package? To decide whether the package contains the proper amount of ground pork for the recipe, you can change $\frac{3}{4}$ to a decimal. 0.75 pound

Here's how *to change $\frac{3}{4}$ to a decimal.*

To change a fraction to a decimal, divide the numerator by the denominator.

$$\begin{array}{r} 0.75 \\ 4\overline{)3.00} \\ -28 \\ \hline 20 \\ -20 \\ \hline 0 \end{array} \quad \text{So } \frac{3}{4} = 0.75$$

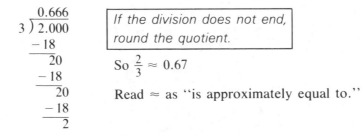

3. Look at the *Here's how.* Is $\frac{3}{4}$ pound the same as 0.75 pound? Yes

4. Does the package contain the proper amount of ground pork? Yes

5. Look at the recipe. How much ground beef is needed? $2\frac{1}{2}$ pounds

Study this example.

$$\begin{array}{r} 0.666 \\ 3\overline{)2.000} \\ -18 \\ \hline 20 \\ -18 \\ \hline 20 \\ -18 \\ \hline 2 \end{array}$$

If the division does not end, round the quotient.

So $\frac{2}{3} \approx 0.67$

Read $\approx$ as "is approximately equal to."

6. To what place was the decimal rounded? Hundredths

146

EXERCISES

Change each fraction to a decimal. *Here are scrambled answers for the next row of exercises:* 0.2 0.25 0.4 0.75 0.3 0.625 0.375

7. $\frac{1}{5}$ 0.2   **8.** $\frac{3}{10}$ 0.3   **9.** $\frac{1}{4}$ 0.25   **10.** $\frac{3}{4}$ 0.75   **11.** $\frac{2}{5}$ 0.4   **12.** $\frac{5}{8}$ 0.625   **13.** $\frac{3}{8}$ 0.375

14. $\frac{1}{16}$ 0.0625   **15.** $\frac{3}{16}$ 0.1875   **16.** $\frac{9}{20}$ 0.45   **17.** $\frac{7}{16}$ 0.4375   **18.** $\frac{5}{16}$ 0.3125   **19.** $\frac{12}{25}$ 0.48   **20.** $\frac{15}{5}$ 3

21. $\frac{9}{8}$ 1.125   **22.** $\frac{12}{5}$ 2.4   **23.** $\frac{15}{4}$ 3.75   **24.** $\frac{25}{8}$ 3.125   **25.** $\frac{9}{16}$ 0.5625   **26.** $\frac{13}{10}$ 1.3   **27.** $\frac{3}{20}$ 0.15

Change each mixed number to a decimal.

28. $2\frac{1}{2}$ $2\frac{1}{2} = 2 + \frac{1}{2}$
$\frac{1}{2} = 0.5$
$2\frac{1}{2} = 2.5$

29. $2\frac{3}{8}$ 2.375   **30.** $3\frac{1}{2}$ 3.5   **31.** $1\frac{1}{8}$ 1.125   **32.** $4\frac{3}{5}$ 4.6   **33.** $9\frac{1}{4}$ 9.25

34. $2\frac{1}{4}$ 2.25   **35.** $3\frac{4}{5}$ 3.8   **36.** $4\frac{2}{5}$ 4.4   **37.** $2\frac{5}{8}$ 2.625   **38.** $3\frac{3}{16}$ 3.1875

39. $7\frac{7}{8}$ 7.875   **40.** $5\frac{3}{8}$ 5.375   **41.** $4\frac{3}{4}$ 4.75   **42.** $3\frac{3}{8}$ 3.375   **43.** $6\frac{1}{5}$ 6.2   **44.** $4\frac{3}{10}$ 4.3   **45.** $5\frac{5}{8}$ 5.625

Change to a decimal rounded to the nearest hundredth.

46. $\frac{1}{3}$ 0.33   **47.** $\frac{1}{6}$ 0.17   **48.** $\frac{2}{3}$ 0.67   **49.** $\frac{1}{9}$ 0.11   **50.** $\frac{5}{6}$ 0.83   **51.** $\frac{5}{9}$ 0.56   **52.** $\frac{3}{14}$ 0.21

53. $\frac{5}{7}$ 0.71   **54.** $\frac{13}{3}$ 4.33   **55.** $\frac{1}{12}$ 0.08   **56.** $\frac{11}{6}$ 1.83   **57.** $\frac{17}{12}$ 1.42   **58.** $\frac{15}{6}$ 2.50   **59.** $\frac{7}{22}$ 0.32

60. $\frac{4}{9}$ 0.44   **61.** $\frac{5}{3}$ 1.67   **62.** $\frac{13}{6}$ 2.17   **63.** $\frac{5}{12}$ 0.42   **64.** $\frac{20}{3}$ 6.67   **65.** $\frac{17}{6}$ 2.83   **66.** $\frac{4}{7}$ 0.57

Solve. Use the recipe on page 146.

67. Ground beef costs $1.50 a pound. How much will the ground beef cost for the recipe? $3.75

68. A 6-ounce can of tomato paste costs $.48 and a 16-ounce can of tomatoes costs $.59. What will be the total cost of these ingredients for the recipe? $2.73

Can you spot it?

Divide. Find the fraction that does not belong in each group.

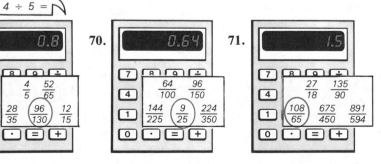

$4 \div 5 =$

69. 0.8 $\frac{4}{5}$ $\frac{52}{65}$ $\frac{28}{35}$ $\frac{96}{130}$ $\frac{12}{15}$

70. 0.64 $\frac{64}{100}$ $\frac{96}{150}$ $\frac{144}{225}$ $\frac{9}{25}$ $\frac{224}{350}$

71. 1.5 $\frac{27}{18}$ $\frac{135}{90}$ $\frac{108}{65}$ $\frac{675}{450}$ $\frac{891}{594}$

EXTRA PRACTICE
Page 430   Skill 37

PRACTICE WORKSHEET
Copymaster S215 or Duplicating Master S215

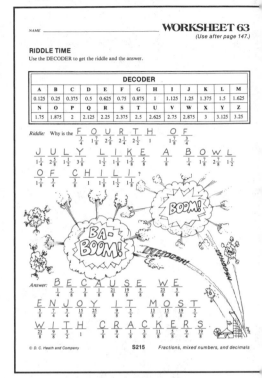

CHALKBOARD CHALLENGE

Find the decimal name for these fractions.

$\frac{1}{9} = ?$ 0.111... $\frac{2}{9} = ?$ 0.222...

$\frac{3}{9} = ?$ 0.333... $\frac{4}{9} = ?$ 0.444...

Look for the pattern. What is the decimal name for each of these fractions?

$\frac{5}{9} = ?$ 0.555... $\frac{6}{9} = ?$ 0.666...

$\frac{7}{9} = ?$ 0.777... $\frac{8}{9} = ?$ 0.888...

LESSON OBJECTIVE
To write decimals as fractions or mixed numbers

PROBLEM-SOLVING SKILL
Using a guess-and-check strategy

STARTING THE LESSON
Prepare **Visual Aid 26** (dot grid) or draw 10 x 10 grids on the chalkboard. Have the students use a decimal and a fraction in simplest form to tell what part of each square is shaded.

Record the answers on the chalkboard.

0.6 $\frac{6}{10} = \frac{3}{5}$

0.45 $\frac{45}{100} = \frac{9}{20}$

Then go over the exercises and the *Here's how* examples on page 148.

Writing decimals as fractions or mixed numbers

1. What decimal is shown on this calculator? 0.75

2. Is the decimal less than or greater than 1? Less than

Here's how *to change a decimal (less than 1) to a fraction in simplest form.*   *0.75 = ?*

Read the decimal.	Write as a fraction.	Write in simplest form.
0.75	$0.75 = \frac{75}{100}$	$0.75 = \frac{75}{100}$
$\boxed{75\ hundredths}$		$= \frac{3}{4}$

3. What decimal is shown on this calculator? 2.6

4. When 2.6 is changed to a mixed number, what should the whole-number part be? 2

Here's how *to change a decimal (greater than 1) to a mixed number in simplest form.*   *2.6 = ?*

Read the decimal.	Write as a mixed number.	Write in simplest form.
2.6	$2.6 = 2\frac{6}{10}$	$2.6 = 2\frac{6}{10}$
$\boxed{2\ and\ 6\ tenths}$		$= 2\frac{3}{5}$

EXERCISES

Change to a fraction in simplest form. Here are scrambled answers for the next row of exercises: $\frac{3}{4}$ $\frac{1}{4}$ $\frac{1}{8}$ $\frac{3}{5}$ $\frac{1}{2}$

5. 0.6 $\frac{3}{5}$ **6.** 0.25 $\frac{1}{4}$ **7.** 0.5 $\frac{1}{2}$ **8.** 0.75 $\frac{3}{4}$ **9.** 0.125 $\frac{1}{8}$

10. 0.8 $\frac{4}{5}$ **11.** 0.24 $\frac{6}{25}$ **12.** 0.48 $\frac{12}{25}$ **13.** 0.9 $\frac{9}{10}$ **14.** 0.150 $\frac{3}{20}$

15. 0.35 $\frac{7}{20}$ **16.** 0.375 $\frac{3}{8}$ **17.** 0.72 $\frac{18}{25}$ **18.** 0.4 $\frac{2}{5}$ **19.** 0.16 $\frac{4}{25}$

20. 0.36 $\frac{9}{25}$ **21.** 0.65 $\frac{13}{20}$ **22.** 0.875 $\frac{7}{8}$ **23.** 0.45 $\frac{9}{20}$ **24.** 0.05 $\frac{1}{20}$

Change to a mixed number in simplest form.

25. 2.25 $2\frac{1}{4}$ **26.** 1.4 $1\frac{2}{5}$ **27.** 2.400 $2\frac{2}{5}$ **28.** 5.5 $5\frac{1}{2}$ **29.** 9.35 $9\frac{7}{20}$

30. 7.8 $7\frac{4}{5}$ **31.** 3.75 $3\frac{3}{4}$ **32.** 6.08 $6\frac{2}{25}$ **33.** 12.375 $12\frac{3}{8}$ **34.** 4.04 $4\frac{1}{25}$

35. 6.28 $6\frac{7}{25}$ **36.** 8.44 $8\frac{11}{25}$ **37.** 6.85 $6\frac{17}{20}$ **38.** 4.50 $4\frac{1}{2}$ **39.** 3.6 $3\frac{3}{5}$

40. 8.52 $8\frac{13}{25}$ **41.** 3.875 $3\frac{7}{8}$ **42.** 10.350 $10\frac{7}{20}$ **43.** 6.15 $6\frac{3}{20}$ **44.** 5.625 $5\frac{5}{8}$

<, =, or >?

45. $\frac{1}{4}$ ● 0.2 >   **46.** 0.3 ● $\frac{1}{4}$ >   **47.** 0.1 ● $\frac{1}{10}$ =   **48.** $\frac{2}{3}$ ● 0.3 >

49. $\frac{1}{5}$ ● 0.25 <   **50.** $\frac{2}{5}$ ● 0.4 =   **51.** $\frac{1}{2}$ ● 0.6 <   **52.** $1\frac{3}{8}$ ● 1.38 <

53. 0.375 ● $\frac{2}{5}$ <   **54.** $\frac{3}{5}$ ● 0.625 <   **55.** $\frac{3}{4}$ ● 0.80 <   **56.** 0.62 ● $\frac{31}{50}$ =

57. 1.5 ● $1\frac{1}{2}$ =   **58.** $2\frac{3}{4}$ ● 2.7 >   **59.** $1\frac{7}{8}$ ● 1.85 >   **60.** $\frac{3}{4}$ ● 0.075 >

61. 3.4 ● $3\frac{3}{8}$ >   **62.** 2.08 ● $2\frac{1}{10}$ <   **63.** 3.625 ● $3\frac{5}{8}$ =   **64.** 1.05 ● $1\frac{1}{20}$ =

65. 2.5 ● $2\frac{1}{2}$ =   **66.** 3.15 ● $3\frac{3}{20}$ =   **67.** 2.66 ● $2\frac{2}{5}$ >   **68.** 4.77 ● $4\frac{3}{4}$ >

Four fun

69. Use the digit 4 four times to build each of the numbers from 1 through 10. You may add, subtract, multiply, and/or divide. Here are two examples:

$$44 \div 44 = 1$$
$$4 \times (4 - 4) + 4 = 4$$

PRACTICE WORKSHEET
Copymaster S216 or Duplicating Master S216

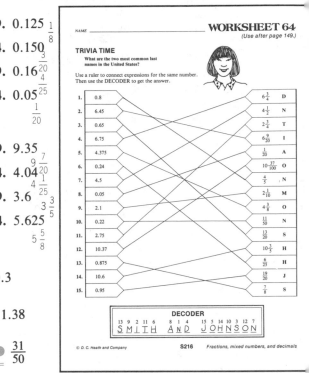

CHALKBOARD CHALLENGE

Unscramble the letters of each of these math words:

1. IARFCTNO — Fraction
2. ATENURMOR — Numerator
3. ALCDIEM — Decimal
4. EMXID UNBMRE — Mixed number

Answer for page 149.

69. Answers will vary. Sample answers are given.

$$4 \div 4 + 4 \div 4 = 2$$
$$(4 + 4 + 4) \div 4 = 3$$
$$(4 + 4 \times 4) \div 4 = 5$$
$$(4 + 4) \div 4 + 4 = 6$$
$$44 \div 4 - 4 = 7$$
$$4 + 4 \times 4 \div 4 = 8$$
$$4 + 4 + 4 \div 4 = 9$$
$$(44 - 4) \div 4 = 10$$

SKILLS REVIEWED
Comparing fractions
Writing fractions and mixed numbers in simplest form
Changing fractions and mixed numbers to decimals

PROBLEM-SOLVING SKILLS
Reading a cash-register receipt
Choosing the correct operation

STARTING THE LESSON
Write these four answers on the chalkboard:

$1\frac{4}{7}$ $\frac{4}{5}$ 1.3   2.8

Challenge the students to an answer hunt by saying, "Look for the four even-numbered exercises on page 150 that have these answers. You have four minutes to find as many of the exercises as you can." (Exercises 34, 40, 60, and 76)

STARTING THE LESSON
Problem Solving
Have the students use the information on the cash-register receipt to answer questions like these:
• Which food item costs $.59? (Celery)
• Which food item costs $1.19? (Cereal)
• Which item costs 5 cents more than the mushroom soup? (Carrots)

Cumulative Skill Practice

<, =, or >? *(page 132)*

1. $\frac{2}{5}$ ● $\frac{3}{5}$ < 2. $\frac{5}{8}$ ● $\frac{3}{8}$ > 3. $\frac{7}{10}$ ● $\frac{9}{10}$ < 4. $\frac{5}{9}$ ● $\frac{4}{9}$ > 5. $\frac{1}{6}$ ● $\frac{5}{6}$ <

6. $\frac{1}{2}$ ● $\frac{3}{4}$ < 7. $\frac{2}{3}$ ● $\frac{5}{6}$ < 8. $\frac{2}{4}$ ● $\frac{1}{2}$ = 9. $\frac{1}{4}$ ● $\frac{1}{3}$ < 10. $\frac{3}{8}$ ● $\frac{6}{16}$ =

11. $\frac{10}{15}$ ● $\frac{2}{3}$ = 12. $\frac{3}{10}$ ● $\frac{1}{3}$ < 13. $\frac{5}{12}$ ● $\frac{1}{4}$ > 14. $\frac{3}{4}$ ● $\frac{3}{8}$ > 15. $\frac{2}{3}$ ● $\frac{6}{9}$ =

16. $\frac{3}{2}$ ● $\frac{5}{2}$ < 17. $\frac{2}{5}$ ● $\frac{1}{4}$ > 18. $\frac{3}{4}$ ● $\frac{5}{6}$ < 19. $\frac{9}{4}$ ● $\frac{3}{2}$ > 20. $\frac{3}{4}$ ● $\frac{3}{5}$ >

Write in simplest form. *(page 140)*

21. $\frac{6}{8}$ $\frac{3}{4}$ 22. $\frac{9}{3}$ 3 23. $5\frac{4}{6}$ $5\frac{2}{3}$ 24. $\frac{10}{3}$ $3\frac{1}{3}$ 25. $\frac{6}{36}$ $\frac{1}{6}$ 26. $3\frac{2}{4}$ $3\frac{1}{2}$ 27. $\frac{17}{34}$ $\frac{1}{2}$

28. $\frac{12}{5}$ $2\frac{2}{5}$ 29. $\frac{5}{20}$ $\frac{1}{4}$ 30. $4\frac{5}{10}$ $4\frac{1}{2}$ 31. $\frac{18}{24}$ $\frac{3}{4}$ 32. $3\frac{6}{10}$ $3\frac{3}{5}$ 33. $1\frac{10}{12}$ $1\frac{5}{6}$ 34. $1\frac{8}{14}$ $1\frac{4}{7}$

35. $\frac{33}{5}$ $6\frac{3}{5}$ 36. $\frac{12}{16}$ $\frac{3}{4}$ 37. $\frac{18}{7}$ $2\frac{4}{7}$ 38. $\frac{10}{2}$ 5 39. $2\frac{3}{9}$ $2\frac{1}{3}$ 40. $\frac{8}{10}$ $\frac{4}{5}$ 41. $3\frac{7}{14}$ $3\frac{1}{2}$

42. $5\frac{3}{12}$ $5\frac{1}{4}$ 43. $\frac{25}{10}$ $2\frac{1}{2}$ 44. $\frac{4}{16}$ $\frac{1}{4}$ 45. $\frac{15}{12}$ $1\frac{1}{4}$ 46. $7\frac{6}{8}$ $7\frac{3}{4}$ 47. $\frac{10}{12}$ $\frac{5}{6}$ 48. $\frac{29}{12}$ $2\frac{5}{12}$

Change to a decimal. *(page 146)*

49. $\frac{1}{2}$ 0.5 50. $1\frac{1}{5}$ 1.2 51. $\frac{9}{10}$ 0.9 52. $\frac{1}{4}$ 0.25 53. $\frac{1}{16}$ 0.0625 54. $1\frac{1}{8}$ 1.125 55. $1\frac{3}{10}$ 1.3

56. $2\frac{2}{5}$ 2.4 57. $\frac{3}{8}$ 0.375 58. $\frac{3}{4}$ 0.75 59. $\frac{5}{2}$ 2.5 60. $\frac{13}{10}$ 1.3 61. $3\frac{3}{5}$ 3.6 62. $\frac{25}{16}$ 1.562

63. $1\frac{3}{16}$ 1.1875 64. $\frac{9}{2}$ 4.5 65. $\frac{7}{10}$ 0.7 66. $4\frac{7}{8}$ 4.875 67. $\frac{9}{4}$ 2.25 68. $\frac{5}{16}$ 0.3125 69. $\frac{9}{8}$ 1.125

70. $\frac{12}{5}$ 2.4 71. $6\frac{5}{8}$ 6.625 72. $\frac{4}{5}$ 0.8 73. $\frac{7}{4}$ 1.75 74. $\frac{9}{5}$ 1.8 75. $\frac{11}{2}$ 5.5 76. $2\frac{4}{5}$ 2.8

Change to a decimal rounded to the nearest hundredth. *(page 146)*

77. $\frac{1}{3}$ 0.33 78. $\frac{1}{6}$ 0.17 79. $\frac{1}{12}$ 0.08 80. $\frac{2}{3}$ 0.67 81. $\frac{1}{9}$ 0.11 82. $\frac{5}{3}$ 1.67 83. $\frac{4}{7}$ 0.57

84. $\frac{7}{12}$ 0.58 85. $\frac{11}{6}$ 1.83 86. $\frac{4}{9}$ 0.44 87. $\frac{5}{12}$ 0.42 88. $\frac{10}{9}$ 1.11 89. $\frac{7}{6}$ 1.17 90. $\frac{15}{9}$ 1.67

91. $\frac{5}{6}$ 0.83 92. $\frac{4}{3}$ 1.33 93. $\frac{2}{9}$ 0.22 94. $\frac{13}{6}$ 2.17 95. $\frac{7}{3}$ 2.33 96. $\frac{11}{12}$ 0.92 97. $\frac{3}{11}$ 0.27

150

Problem solving
COMPUTERS IN STORES

Most items sold in stores are marked with light and dark bands called the Universal Product Code (UPC).

An optical scanner reads and sends the code to a computer. The computer uses the code to search its memory for the price of the item. The price is then printed on a cash-register receipt.

Solve. Use the information on the receipt.

```
      **TRIPLE S**
       STORE #315

GRND BEEF          7.17
MM FROZEN OJ       1.01
MILK                .97
POTATOES           1.07
CARROTS             .44
DIET P COLA         .99
CELERY              .59
SUGAR              1.29
PNUT BUTTER        2.38
SLTN CRACKERS      1.35
MUSH SOUP           .39
CEREAL             1.19

     TOTAL        18.84

     CASH         20.00

     CHANGE        1.16

    THANK YOU
# 20416 C013 R 06 T12:40
```

7. A—MM FROZEN OJ
   and
  B—SUGAR
   or
  A—SLTN CRACKERS
   and
  B—CEREAL

    C—PNUT BUTTER
    D—CEREAL

1. What was the total cost of the vegetables? $2.10

2. Did the meat item cost more than 3 times as much as the vegetables? Yes

3. This purchase was made by 3 friends who share an apartment. What was each person's share of the cost? $6.28

4. The amount of this purchase is about $\frac{1}{5}$ of their weekly food allowance. About how much do they spend each week for food? $94.20

5. The ground beef will be used to prepare a meat loaf to serve 5 people. What is the average cost per serving? (Round to the nearest cent.) $1.43

6. What is the least number of coins that could be given in change? 3

7. Each of these UPCs is from an item printed on the receipt. Decide which item each code is on.

 costs 28¢ more than

74820 08030   71896 48853

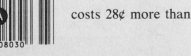 costs twice as much as

73361 64607   73361 64769

Fractions, Mixed Numbers, and Decimals **151**

REVIEW PRACTICE
Subtracting decimals
Page 418   Skill 13

PROBLEM-SOLVING WORKSHEET
Copymaster S217 or Duplicating Master S217

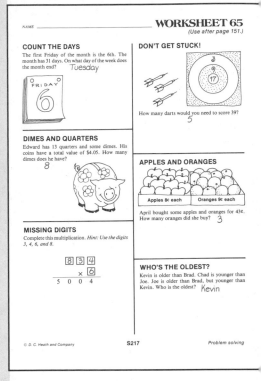

NAME _____ **WORKSHEET 65**
(Use after page 151.)

COUNT THE DAYS
The first Friday of the month is the 6th. The month has 31 days. On what day of the week does the month end? Tuesday

DON'T GET STUCK!
How many darts would you need to score 39? 5

DIMES AND QUARTERS
Edward has 13 quarters and some dimes. His coins have a total value of $4.05. How many dimes does he have? 8

APPLES AND ORANGES
Apples 8¢ each   Oranges 9¢ each
April bought some apples and oranges for 43¢. How many oranges did she buy? 3

MISSING DIGITS
Complete this multiplication. Hint: Use the digits 3, 4, 6, and 8.

$$\begin{array}{r} 8\;3\;4 \\ \times \quad 6 \\ \hline 5\;0\;0\;4 \end{array}$$

WHO'S THE OLDEST?
Kevin is older than Brad. Chad is younger than Joe. Joe is older than Brad, but younger than Kevin. Who is the oldest? Kevin

© D. C. Heath and Company   S217   Problem solving

CHALKBOARD CHALLENGE
Use the code to answer the riddle.

CODE

E	A	H
R	T I P	W
O	S N	C

Riddle: What did Baby Corn say to Mother Corn?

Answer: ⌐ ⌐ ⌐ ⌐ ⌐ ▽ △ ◁ ⌐ ⌐ ⌐ ?   Where is Pop Corn?

151

NAME _____ **CHAPTER 6 TEST**
(Form A)

Complete to get an equivalent fraction. *(page 126)*

1. $\frac{1}{2} = \frac{4}{8}$ 2. $\frac{1}{3} = \frac{4}{12}$ 3. $\frac{1}{4} = \frac{12}{16}$

4. $\frac{2}{3} = \frac{10}{15}$ 5. $\frac{3}{8} = \frac{9}{24}$

	ANSWERS
1.	4
2.	4
3.	12
4.	10
5.	9
6.	1/4
7.	1/4
8.	2/3
9.	5/7
10.	3/2
11.	4
12.	8
13.	12
14.	18
15.	12
16.	=
17.	>
18.	<
19.	>
20.	>
21.	4/3
22.	5/2
23.	11/8
24.	11/4
25.	23/6

Write each fraction in lowest terms. *(page 128)*

6. $\frac{2}{8} = 1/4$ 7. $\frac{4}{16} = 1/4$ 8. $\frac{6}{9} = 2/3$

9. $\frac{15}{21} = 5/7$ 10. $\frac{18}{12} = 3/2$

Find the least common denominator. *(page 130)*

11. $\frac{1}{2}, \frac{1}{4}$ 4   12. $\frac{3}{8}, \frac{3}{4}$ 8   13. $\frac{3}{4}, \frac{5}{6}$ 12

14. $\frac{1}{6}, \frac{5}{9}$ 18   15. $\frac{1}{2}, \frac{2}{3}, \frac{3}{4}$ 12

<, =, or >? *(page 132)*

16. $\frac{2}{4} = \frac{1}{2}$ 17. $\frac{5}{6} > \frac{3}{8}$ 18. $\frac{3}{8} < \frac{1}{2}$

19. $\frac{5}{6} > \frac{3}{4}$ 20. $\frac{2}{3} > \frac{5}{8}$

Change each mixed number to a fraction. *(page 136)*

21. $1\frac{1}{3} = 4/3$ 22. $2\frac{1}{2} = 5/2$ 23. $1\frac{3}{8} = 11/8$

24. $2\frac{3}{4} = 11/4$ 25. $3\frac{5}{6} = 23/6$

D. C. Heath and Company   S21   Page 1

NAME _____ **CHAPTER 6 TEST**
(Form A)

Change each fraction to a whole number or mixed number. *(page 138)*

26. $\frac{3}{2} = 1\frac{1}{2}$ 27. $\frac{9}{3} = 3$ 28. $\frac{11}{4} = 2\frac{3}{4}$

29. $\frac{15}{5} = 3$ 30. $\frac{23}{6} = 3\frac{5}{6}$

	ANSWERS
26.	1½
27.	3
28.	2 ¾
29.	3
30.	3⅚
31.	⅔
32.	5
33.	4¾
34.	3½
35.	3¾
36.	16 R1
37.	38⅔
38.	60¾
39.	47⅚
40.	59½
41.	0.5
42.	0.8
43.	0.875
44.	1.25
45.	2.375
46.	2/5
47.	1/4
48.	3/8
49.	1⅗
50.	2⅝

Write in simplest form. *(page 140)*

31. $\frac{4}{6} = 2/3$ 32. $\frac{10}{2} = 5$ 33. $\frac{19}{4} = 4\frac{3}{4}$

34. $\frac{21}{6} = 3\frac{1}{2}$ 35. $\frac{30}{8} = 3\frac{3}{4}$

Divide. Write each quotient as a mixed number in simplest form. *(page 142)*

36. $3\overline{)137}$ 37. $9\overline{)348}$ 38. $8\overline{)486}$

39. $12\overline{)574}$ 47⅚   40. $42\overline{)2499}$ 59½

Change to a decimal. *(pages 146, 147)*

41. $\frac{1}{2} = 0.5$ 42. $\frac{4}{5} = 0.8$ 43. $\frac{7}{8} = 0.875$

44. $1\frac{1}{4} = 1.25$ 45. $2\frac{3}{8} = 2.375$

Change to a fraction or mixed number in simplest form. *(page 148)*

46. 0.4 = 2/5   47. 0.25 = 1/4   48. 0.375 = 3/8

49. 1.6 = 1⅗   50. 2.625 = 2⅝

D. C. Heath and Company   S22   Page 2

Chapter REVIEW

Here are scrambled answers for the review exercises:

1	3	5	100	divisor	lowest	remainder
2	4	8	common	greater	mixed	tenth

1. To find the fraction equivalent to $\frac{5}{8}$, multiply 5 by ☐. *(page 126)*

$$\frac{5}{8} = \frac{?}{24}$$

2. This fraction is in lowest terms because ☐ is the only common divisor of its terms. *(page 128)*

$$\frac{2}{3}$$

3. The least common denominator of these fractions is ☐. *(page 130)*

$$\frac{3}{4} \text{ and } \frac{3}{8}$$

4. To compare these fractions, compare equivalent fractions with a ☐ denominator. *(page 132)*

$$\frac{2}{3} \quad \bullet \quad \frac{3}{4}$$

5. To change this mixed number to a fraction, multiply 5 by 4 and add ☐ to find the numerator and use ☐ for the denominator. *(page 136)*

$$4\frac{2}{5} = ?$$

6. To change this fraction to a mixed number, divide 13 by ☐. *(page 138)*

$$\frac{13}{4} = ?$$

7. To write this fraction in simplest form, write it in ☐ terms. *(page 140)*

$$\frac{10}{15} = ?$$

8. This mixed number is **not** in simplest form, since the fraction part is ☐ than 1. *(page 140)*

$$3\frac{6}{5}$$

9. To write this fraction in simplest form, you would change it to a ☐ number in simplest form. *(page 140)*

$$\frac{17}{3}$$

10. The last step in writing this quotient as a mixed number is to write the ☐ over the ☐. *(page 142)*

$$7\overline{)255} \quad \begin{array}{r} 36 \\ -21 \\ \hline 45 \\ -42 \\ \hline 3 \end{array}$$

11. The fraction $\frac{5}{6}$ written as a decimal rounded to the nearest ☐ is 0.8. *(page 146)*

$$\frac{5}{6} = ? \qquad 6\overline{)5.00} \quad \begin{array}{r} 0.83 \\ -48 \\ \hline 20 \\ -18 \\ \hline 2 \end{array}$$

12. To change this decimal to a fraction in simplest form, write 25 as the numerator and ☐ as the denominator. Then write the fraction in simplest form. *(page 148)*

$$0.25 = ?$$

1. 3   2. 1   3. 8   4. common   5. 2, 5
6. 4   7. lowest   8. greater   9. mixed
10. remainder, divisor   11. tenth   12. 100

Chapter TEST

Complete to get an equivalent fraction. (page 126)

1. $\frac{1}{4} = \frac{?}{8}$ 2
2. $\frac{1}{3} = \frac{?}{12}$ 4
3. $\frac{2}{3} = \frac{?}{9}$ 6
4. $\frac{5}{8} = \frac{?}{24}$ 15
5. $\frac{8}{14} = \frac{?}{7}$ 4
6. $\frac{12}{16} = \frac{?}{4}$ 3
7. $\frac{5}{10} = \frac{?}{2}$ 1
8. $\frac{16}{24} = \frac{?}{3}$ 2
9. $\frac{12}{28} = \frac{?}{7}$ 3
10. $\frac{3}{9} = \frac{?}{3}$ 1

Write each fraction in lowest terms. (page 128)

11. $\frac{6}{12}$ $\frac{1}{2}$
12. $\frac{6}{9}$ $\frac{2}{3}$
13. $\frac{9}{6}$ $\frac{3}{2}$
14. $\frac{6}{18}$ $\frac{1}{3}$
15. $\frac{20}{15}$ $\frac{4}{3}$
16. $\frac{21}{24}$ $\frac{7}{8}$
17. $\frac{50}{25}$ 2

Find the least common denominator. (page 130)

18. $\frac{3}{4}$ $\frac{1}{2}$ 4
19. $\frac{3}{10}$ $\frac{2}{5}$ 10
20. $\frac{1}{2}$ $\frac{1}{3}$ 6
21. $\frac{1}{3}$ $\frac{3}{8}$ 24
22. $\frac{5}{6}$ $\frac{2}{9}$ 18

<, =, or >? (page 132)

23. $\frac{3}{8} \bullet \frac{1}{4}$ >
24. $\frac{2}{3} \bullet \frac{5}{6}$ <
25. $\frac{1}{3} \bullet \frac{1}{4}$ >
26. $\frac{1}{3} \bullet \frac{5}{12}$ <
27. $\frac{4}{5} \bullet \frac{5}{6}$ <

Change each mixed number to a fraction. (page 136)

28. $1\frac{1}{2}$ $\frac{3}{2}$
29. $3\frac{1}{4}$ $\frac{13}{4}$
30. $2\frac{2}{3}$ $\frac{8}{3}$
31. $4\frac{3}{4}$ $\frac{19}{4}$
32. $2\frac{7}{8}$ $\frac{23}{8}$
33. $3\frac{5}{6}$ $\frac{23}{6}$
34. $7\frac{4}{5}$ $\frac{39}{5}$

Change each fraction to a whole number or a mixed number. (page 138)

35. $\frac{5}{2}$ $2\frac{1}{2}$
36. $\frac{8}{2}$ 4
37. $\frac{11}{4}$ $2\frac{3}{4}$
38. $\frac{12}{5}$ $2\frac{2}{5}$
39. $\frac{15}{3}$ 5
40. $\frac{23}{6}$ $3\frac{5}{6}$
41. $\frac{25}{8}$ $3\frac{1}{8}$

Write in simplest form. (page 140)

42. $\frac{6}{8}$ $\frac{3}{4}$
43. $\frac{8}{2}$ 4
44. $\frac{3}{2}$ $1\frac{1}{2}$
45. $\frac{5}{10}$ $\frac{1}{2}$
46. $2\frac{4}{8}$ $2\frac{1}{2}$
47. $\frac{16}{4}$ 4
48. $11\frac{11}{22}$ $11\frac{1}{2}$
49. $4\frac{2}{6}$ $4\frac{1}{3}$
50. $\frac{8}{12}$ $\frac{2}{3}$
51. $\frac{20}{6}$ $3\frac{1}{3}$
52. $\frac{9}{3}$ 3
53. $\frac{10}{15}$ $\frac{2}{3}$
54. $3\frac{6}{9}$ $3\frac{2}{3}$
55. $\frac{13}{4}$ $3\frac{1}{4}$

Divide. Write each quotient as a mixed number in simplest form. (page 142)

56. $3\overline{)127}$ $42\frac{1}{3}$
57. $4\overline{)925}$ $231\frac{1}{4}$
58. $9\overline{)384}$ $42\frac{2}{3}$
59. $12\overline{)7023}$ $585\frac{1}{4}$
60. $15\overline{)4316}$ $287\frac{11}{15}$
61. $28\overline{)2970}$ $106\frac{1}{14}$

Change to a decimal. (page 146)

62. $\frac{1}{4}$ 0.25
63. $6\frac{7}{10}$ 6.7
64. $6\frac{7}{8}$ 6.875
65. $\frac{1}{16}$ 0.0625
66. $\frac{9}{10}$ 0.9
67. $\frac{7}{8}$ 0.875
68. $3\frac{1}{10}$ 3.1
69. $3\frac{1}{20}$ 3.05
70. $2\frac{1}{4}$ 2.25
71. $2\frac{2}{5}$ 2.4
72. $5\frac{3}{8}$ 5.375
73. $2\frac{3}{4}$ 2.75
74. $4\frac{3}{100}$ 4.03
75. $\frac{4}{5}$ 0.8

Change to a fraction or mixed number in simplest form. (page 148)

76. 0.6 $\frac{3}{5}$
77. 0.25 $\frac{1}{4}$
78. 0.2 $\frac{1}{5}$
79. 0.75 $\frac{3}{4}$
80. 0.375 $\frac{3}{8}$
81. 0.450 $\frac{9}{20}$
82. 1.42 $1\frac{21}{50}$
83. 1.4 $1\frac{2}{5}$
84. 2.8 $2\frac{4}{5}$
85. 1.50 $1\frac{1}{2}$
86. 3.08 $3\frac{2}{25}$
87. 4.300 $4\frac{3}{10}$
88. 3.625 $3\frac{5}{8}$
89. 6.02 $6\frac{1}{50}$

Use Copymaster S336 to provide the students with an answer sheet in standardized test format.

Answers for Cumulative Test, Chapters 1–6

1. Ⓐ Ⓑ © ⑩   2. Ⓐ Ⓑ © ⑩   3. Ⓐ Ⓑ © ⑩
4. Ⓐ Ⓑ © ⑩   5. Ⓐ Ⓑ © ⑩   6. Ⓐ Ⓑ © ⑩
7. Ⓐ Ⓑ © ⑩   8. Ⓐ Ⓑ © ⑩   9. Ⓐ Ⓑ © ⑩
10. Ⓐ Ⓑ © ⑩   11. Ⓐ Ⓑ © ⑩   12. Ⓐ Ⓑ © ⑩

The table below correlates test items with student text pages.

Test Item	Page Taught	Skill Practice
1	16	p. 134, exercises 1–20
2	24	p. 134, exercises 21–41
3	42	p. 134, exercises 42–56
4	46	p. 134, exercises 57–77
5	64	p. 144, exercises 1–21
6	68	p. 144, exercises 22–42
7	96	p. 144, exercises 43–63
8	116	p. 144, exercises 64–75
9	132	p. 150, exercises 1–20
10	140	p. 150, exercises 21–48
11	146	p. 150, exercises 77–97
12	106	

154

Cumulative TEST — Standardized Format

Choose the correct letter.

1. The short word-name for 50.012 is
A. 50 and 12 hundredths
B. 50 and 12 thousandths
C. 50 and 12 tenths
D. none of these

2. Give the sum.
$36.09 + 14.8 + 321.7$
A. 372.59
B. 69.74
C. 83.06
D. none of these

3. Which number is less than 0.04?
A. 0.3
B. 0.05
C. 0.041
D. none of these

4. Give the difference.
$52.46 - 3.521$
A. 17.25
B. 48.941
C. 48.938
D. none of these

5. Give the product.
4.03×4.6
A. 185.38
B. 18.538
C. 18.428
D. none of these

6. Give the product.
10.463×100
A. 0.10463
B. 104.63
C. 1046.3
D. none of these

7. Give the quotient rounded to the nearest tenth.
$3.742 \div 1.9$
A. 2.0
B. 1.9
C. 0.2
D. none of these

8. The median of 38, 42, 36, 36, and 43 is
A. 38
B. 36
C. 39
D. none of these

9. $\frac{1}{3} < ?$
A. $\frac{1}{4}$
B. $\frac{3}{10}$
C. $\frac{3}{8}$
D. none of these

10. $\frac{24}{16}$ in simplest form is
A. $\frac{3}{2}$
B. $1\frac{8}{16}$
C. $1\frac{1}{2}$
D. none of these

11. Change to a decimal rounded to the nearest hundredth.
$\frac{5}{6} = ?$
A. 0.83
B. 0.84
C. 1.20
D. none of these

12.

SAL'S EARNINGS

Sal's total earnings were
A. $80
B. $70
C. $130
D. none of these

CHAPTER 7
Adding and Subtracting Fractions and Mixed Numbers

LESSON OBJECTIVES
To add fractions with common denominators (*pages 156–157*)
To add fractions with different denominators (*pages 158–159*)
To add mixed numbers (*pages 160–161*)
To subtract fractions with common denominators
   (*pages 164–165*)
To subtract fractions with different denominators
   (*pages 166–167*)
To subtract mixed numbers without regrouping (*pages 168–169*)
To subtract mixed numbers with regrouping (*pages 170–171*)

PROBLEM-SOLVING SKILLS
Choosing information from a display (*pages 156–157, 164–165,
   168–169, 173*)
Making a list (*page 157*)
Reading a map (*pages 158–159*)
Selecting information from a chart (*pages 160–161, 170–171*)
Following instructions and checking answers (*page 161*)
Drawing a picture (*page 163*)
Choosing the correct operation (*pages 163, 173*)
Using a drawing (*page 165*)
Reading a circle graph (*pages 166–167*)
Checking answers (*page 167*)
Using logical reasoning (*page 169*)
Reading a map and a map scale (*pages 170, 171*)

RESOURCES
• **VISUAL AIDS**
   Map from page 158 (*Visual Aid 27, Copymaster S130*)
   Dashboard gauges from page 164 (*Visual Aid 28, Copymaster
   S131*)
   Map from page 171 (*Visual Aid 29, Copymaster S132*)
• **WORKSHEETS 66–74** (*Copymasters S218–S226 or Duplicating
   Masters S218–S226*)

LESSON OBJECTIVE
To add fractions with common denominators

PROBLEM-SOLVING SKILLS
Choosing information from a display
Making a list

STARTING THE LESSON
Write these coins and weights on the
chalkboard:

penny $\frac{2}{28}$ ounce

nickel $\frac{3}{28}$ ounce

dime $\frac{5}{28}$ ounce

quarter $\frac{6}{28}$ ounce

Ask the students to use their estimation
skills to match each coin with its weight.
Then have the students open their books
to page 156 to check their answers.

EXERCISE NOTE
Encourage the students to make a list
to solve the problem in exercises 42
and 43.

COINS		
dimes	**nickels**	**pennies**
✓✓	✓	
✓✓		✓✓✓✓✓
✓	✓✓✓	

Adding fractions with common denominators

1. What is the weight of a nickel? $\frac{5}{28}$ ounce

2. Which coin weighs $\frac{2}{28}$ ounce?   Dime

3. You have 3 coins that are worth 35¢. What three fractions would you add to find how many ounces they weigh?
$\frac{5}{28}$, $\frac{5}{28}$, and $\frac{6}{28}$

$\frac{3}{28}$ ounce

$\frac{6}{28}$ ounce

$\frac{5}{28}$ ounce

$\frac{2}{28}$ ounce

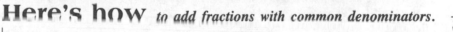
Here's how *to add fractions with common denominators.* $\frac{5}{28} + \frac{5}{28} + \frac{6}{28} = ?$

Add the numerators and use the common denominator.

nickel   quarter
      nickel
$\frac{5}{28} + \frac{5}{28} + \frac{6}{28} = \frac{16}{28}$

$= \frac{4}{7}$

4. Look at the *Here's how*. What is the total weight of the 3 coins? $\frac{4}{7}$

5. Check these examples. Give each sum in simplest form.

a. $\frac{3}{28} + \frac{5}{28} = \frac{8}{28}$
$= ?$ $\frac{2}{7}$

b. $\frac{2}{3} + \frac{1}{3} = \frac{3}{3}$
$= ?$ 1

c. $\frac{4}{5} + \frac{2}{5} + \frac{3}{5} = \frac{9}{5}$
$= ?$ $1\frac{4}{5}$

156

EXERCISES

Add. Write the sum in simplest form.
Here are scrambled answers for the next row of exercises: $1\frac{1}{4}$ $\frac{5}{7}$ $\frac{2}{5}$ $\frac{1}{2}$ 1

6. $\frac{3}{8} + \frac{1}{8}$ $\frac{1}{2}$

7. $\frac{3}{10} + \frac{1}{10}$ $\frac{2}{5}$

8. $\frac{2}{7} + \frac{3}{7}$ $\frac{5}{7}$

9. $\frac{3}{8} + \frac{7}{8}$ $1\frac{1}{4}$

10. $\frac{1}{3} + \frac{2}{3}$ 1

11. $\frac{5}{9} + \frac{1}{9}$ $\frac{2}{3}$

12. $\frac{1}{5} + \frac{2}{5}$ $\frac{3}{5}$

13. $\frac{5}{12} + \frac{3}{12}$ $\frac{2}{3}$

14. $\frac{2}{5} + \frac{3}{5}$ 1

15. $\frac{1}{6} + \frac{5}{6}$ 1

16. $\frac{3}{10} + \frac{2}{10}$ $\frac{1}{2}$

17. $\frac{7}{12} + \frac{7}{12}$ $1\frac{1}{6}$

18. $\frac{5}{8} + \frac{7}{8}$ $1\frac{1}{2}$

19. $\frac{1}{4} + \frac{3}{4}$ 1

20. $\frac{3}{5} + \frac{4}{5}$ $1\frac{2}{5}$

21. $\frac{4}{15} + \frac{1}{15}$ $\frac{1}{3}$

22. $\frac{31}{50} + \frac{9}{50}$ $\frac{4}{5}$

23. $\frac{17}{100} + \frac{33}{100}$ $\frac{1}{2}$

24. $\frac{5}{16} + \frac{7}{16}$ $\frac{3}{4}$

25. $\frac{7}{10} + \frac{9}{10}$ $1\frac{3}{5}$

26. $\frac{3}{10} + \frac{1}{10} + \frac{2}{10}$ $\frac{3}{5}$

27. $\frac{1}{6} + \frac{1}{6} + \frac{5}{6}$ $1\frac{1}{6}$

28. $\frac{1}{12} + \frac{5}{12} + \frac{3}{12}$ $\frac{3}{4}$

29. $\frac{1}{8} + \frac{3}{8} + \frac{5}{8}$ $1\frac{1}{8}$

30. $\frac{1}{5} + \frac{2}{5} + \frac{4}{5}$ $1\frac{2}{5}$

31. $\frac{2}{5} + \frac{1}{5} + \frac{1}{5}$ $\frac{4}{5}$

32. $\frac{6}{7} + \frac{3}{7} + \frac{2}{7}$ $1\frac{4}{7}$

33. $\frac{5}{9} + \frac{2}{9} + \frac{5}{9}$ $1\frac{1}{3}$

Solve. Use the coin facts on page 156.

34. What coins are worth 40¢ and weigh $\frac{13}{28}$ ounce? 1 quarter, 1 dime 1 nickel

35. What coins are worth 15¢ and weigh $\frac{15}{28}$ ounce? 3 nickels

36. What coins are worth 15¢ and weigh $\frac{17}{28}$ ounce? 1 dime, 5 pennies

37. What coins are worth 50¢ and weigh $\frac{15}{28}$ ounce? 1 quarter, 2 dimes, 1 nickel

38. What coins are worth 60¢ and weigh $\frac{1}{2}$ ounce? 2 quarters, 1 dime

39. What coins are worth 30¢ and weigh $\frac{3}{4}$ ounce? 1 quarter, 5 pennies

Change, please

40. How many ways can you make change for a nickel? 1

41. How many ways can you make change for a dime? *Hint: The answer is not 2.* 3

42. How many ways can you make change for a quarter? *Hint: Make a list.* 12

43. How many ways can you make change for a half-dollar? 49

PRACTICE WORKSHEET
Copymaster S218 or Duplicating Master S218

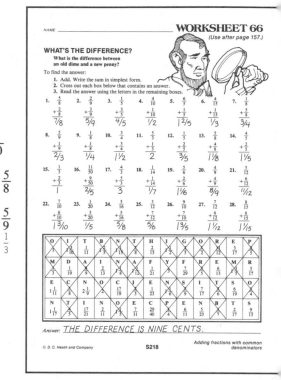

CHALKBOARD CHALLENGE
Use this code and find the three-letter word on page 157 that has a sum of $1\frac{7}{26}$. the

a	b	c	. . . . .	z
$\frac{1}{26}$	$\frac{2}{26}$	$\frac{3}{26}$	. . . . .	$\frac{26}{26}$

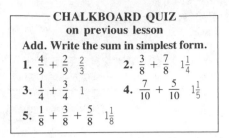
LESSON OBJECTIVE
To add fractions with different denominators.

PROBLEM-SOLVING SKILL
Reading a map

STARTING THE LESSON
The map at the top of page 158 is also on **Visual Aid 27**. Use the map and ask these questions:
- Which scenic point is between Dry Gulch and Deer Pond? (Rainbow Falls)
- Which scenic point is seven eighths of a mile from Roaring Rapids? (Lost Mine)
- Is it more or less than one-half mile from Ranger's Tower to Fox Ridge? (More)

Then use the map to discuss exercises 1–3.

EXERCISE NOTE
Point out that sometimes, as in the first example in exercise 4, only one of the fractions will have to be renamed, since the other one has a denominator that can be the common denominator.

Adding fractions with different denominators

This map shows the distance between scenic points on a hiking trail.

1. What is the shortest hiking distance from the Trail Entrance to Dry Gulch? $\frac{1}{4}$ mile

2. What two fractions would you add to compute the distance in miles from Rainbow Falls through Deer Pond to Lost Mine? $\frac{1}{2}$ and $\frac{2}{3}$

Here's how *to add fractions with different denominators.* $\frac{1}{2} + \frac{2}{3} = ?$

Find the least common denominator.

Change to equivalent fractions.

Add. Write the sum in simplest form.

$$\begin{array}{c} \frac{1}{2} \\ +\frac{2}{3} \end{array} \rangle 6$$

$$\begin{array}{c} \frac{1}{2} = \frac{3}{6} \\ +\frac{2}{3} = +\frac{4}{6} \end{array}$$

$$\begin{array}{c} \frac{1}{2} = \frac{3}{6} \\ +\frac{2}{3} = +\frac{4}{6} \\ \hline \frac{2}{3} \quad \frac{7}{6} = 1\frac{1}{6} \end{array}$$

3. Look at the *Here's how*. How far is it from Rainbow Falls to Lost Mine? $1\frac{1}{6}$

4. Check these examples. Give each sum in simplest form.

a. $\frac{1}{2} + \frac{3}{4} = \frac{2}{4} + \frac{3}{4}$
   $= \frac{5}{4}$
   $= ?$ $1\frac{1}{4}$

b. $\frac{1}{4} + \frac{1}{3} + \frac{1}{2} = \frac{3}{12} + \frac{4}{12} + \frac{6}{12}$
   $= \frac{13}{12}$
   $= ?$ $1\frac{1}{12}$

EXERCISES

Add. Give the sum in simplest form.
Here are scrambled answers for the next row of exercises: $\frac{5}{8}$ $1\frac{1}{8}$ $\frac{7}{24}$ $1\frac{5}{24}$ $\frac{3}{5}$ $\frac{3}{4}$ 1

5. $\frac{1}{2} + \frac{1}{4} = \frac{3}{4}$
6. $\frac{1}{6} + \frac{1}{8} = \frac{7}{24}$
7. $\frac{3}{8} + \frac{1}{4} = \frac{5}{8}$
8. $\frac{3}{10} + \frac{7}{10} = 1$
9. $\frac{2}{5} + \frac{1}{5} = \frac{3}{5}$
10. $\frac{5}{8} + \frac{1}{2} = 1\frac{1}{8}$
11. $\frac{5}{6} + \frac{3}{8} = 1\frac{5}{24}$

12. $\frac{7}{16} + \frac{1}{4} = \frac{11}{16}$
13. $\frac{1}{3} + \frac{5}{9} = \frac{8}{9}$
14. $\frac{5}{12} + \frac{2}{3} = 1\frac{1}{12}$
15. $\frac{5}{6} + \frac{1}{4} = 1\frac{1}{12}$
16. $\frac{3}{10} + \frac{1}{2} = \frac{4}{5}$
17. $\frac{2}{3} + \frac{3}{4} = 1\frac{5}{12}$
18. $\frac{5}{9} + \frac{5}{6} = 1\frac{7}{18}$

19. $\frac{1}{3} + \frac{1}{6} = \frac{1}{2}$
20. $\frac{3}{4} + \frac{1}{8} = \frac{7}{8}$
21. $\frac{3}{5} + \frac{7}{10} = 1\frac{3}{10}$
22. $\frac{5}{8} + \frac{1}{2} = 1\frac{1}{8}$
23. $\frac{1}{3} + \frac{1}{4} = \frac{7}{12}$
24. $\frac{1}{5} + \frac{3}{10} = \frac{1}{2}$
25. $\frac{2}{3} + \frac{2}{3} = 1\frac{1}{3}$

26. $\frac{2}{3} + \frac{1}{5} = \frac{13}{15}$
27. $\frac{1}{2} + \frac{11}{16} = 1\frac{3}{16}$
28. $\frac{2}{5} + \frac{1}{4} = \frac{13}{20}$
29. $\frac{5}{8} + \frac{1}{6} = \frac{19}{24}$
30. $\frac{9}{16} + \frac{1}{2} = 1\frac{1}{16}$
31. $\frac{2}{5} + \frac{3}{10} = \frac{7}{10}$
32. $\frac{5}{9} + \frac{1}{6} = \frac{13}{18}$

33. $\frac{1}{2} + \frac{1}{4} + \frac{1}{8}$ $\frac{7}{8}$
34. $\frac{3}{4} + \frac{3}{8} + \frac{1}{2}$ $1\frac{5}{8}$
35. $\frac{1}{16} + \frac{3}{8} + \frac{1}{4}$ $\frac{11}{16}$
36. $\frac{1}{8} + \frac{5}{16} + \frac{3}{4}$ $1\frac{3}{16}$

Solve. Use the map on page 158.

37. What is the shortest hiking distance from the Trail Entrance to Roaring Rapids? $\frac{3}{4}$ mi

38. What is the shortest hiking distance from Lost Mine to the Ranger's Tower? $1\frac{5}{8}$ mi

39. If you hiked at 1 mile per hour, could you hike from the Trail Entrance to Lost Mine in less than $1\frac{1}{2}$ hours? No

40. Which is the shorter route from the Trail Entrance to Ranger's Tower, over Fox Ridge or through Dry Gulch and past Roaring Rapids? Over Fox Ridge

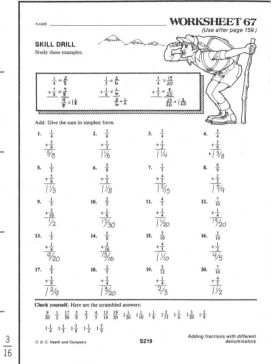

WORKSHEET 67 (Use after page 159.)

NAME _____

SKILL DRILL
Study these examples.

$\frac{1}{4}=\frac{2}{8}$ $\frac{1}{3}=\frac{2}{6}$ $\frac{3}{4}=\frac{15}{20}$
$+\frac{7}{8}=\frac{7}{8}$ $+\frac{1}{6}=\frac{1}{6}$ $+\frac{2}{5}=\frac{8}{20}$
$\frac{9}{8}=1\frac{1}{8}$ $\frac{3}{6}=\frac{1}{2}$ $\frac{23}{20}=1\frac{3}{20}$

Add. Give the sum in simplest form.

1. $\frac{1}{4} + \frac{3}{8} = \frac{5}{8}$
2. $\frac{5}{6} + \frac{1}{3} = 1\frac{1}{6}$
3. $\frac{3}{4} + \frac{1}{2} = 1\frac{1}{4}$
4. $\frac{3}{4} + \frac{5}{8} = 1\frac{3}{8}$
5. $\frac{1}{2} + \frac{5}{6} = 1\frac{1}{3}$
6. $\frac{5}{8} + \frac{1}{2} = 1\frac{1}{8}$
7. $\frac{1}{3} + \frac{5}{6} = 1\frac{2}{5}$
8. $\frac{8}{9} + \frac{3}{5} = 1\frac{5}{9}$
9. $\frac{1}{5} + \frac{3}{10} = \frac{1}{2}$
10. $\frac{2}{5} + \frac{1}{6} = \frac{17}{30}$
11. $\frac{4}{5} + \frac{1}{4} = 1\frac{1}{20}$
12. $\frac{7}{10} + \frac{1}{4} = 1\frac{9}{20}$
13. $\frac{1}{5} + \frac{1}{4} = \frac{9}{20}$
14. $\frac{3}{8} + \frac{1}{2} = 1\frac{3}{16}$
15. $\frac{5}{8} + \frac{4}{5} = 1\frac{1}{10}$
16. $\frac{3}{10} + \frac{1}{2} = \frac{4}{5}$
17. $\frac{2}{3} + \frac{5}{9} = 1\frac{2}{9}$
18. $\frac{2}{5} + \frac{3}{4} = 1\frac{3}{20}$
19. $\frac{5}{12} + \frac{1}{4} = \frac{2}{3}$
20. $\frac{7}{10} + \frac{4}{5} = 1\frac{1}{2}$

Check yourself. Here are the scrambled answers:
$\frac{9}{20}$ $\frac{2}{3}$ $\frac{17}{30}$ $\frac{3}{8}$ $\frac{3}{4}$ $\frac{13}{16}$ $\frac{4}{5}$ $1\frac{5}{20}$ $1\frac{1}{10}$ $1\frac{3}{13}$ $1\frac{1}{6}$ $1\frac{3}{20}$ $1\frac{2}{9}$ $1\frac{1}{4}$ $1\frac{1}{3}$ $1\frac{3}{8}$ $1\frac{1}{2}$ $1\frac{5}{9}$

© D. C. Heath and Company   S219   *Adding fractions with different denominators*

CHALKBOARD CHALLENGE
Find the missing digit.

1. $\frac{1}{3} + \frac{1}{\boxed{2}} = \frac{5}{6}$ 2. $\frac{1}{\boxed{5}} + \frac{3}{4} = \frac{19}{20}$
3. $\frac{\boxed{3}}{8} + \frac{1}{3} = \frac{17}{24}$ 4. $\frac{1}{4} + \frac{\boxed{1}}{6} = \frac{5}{12}$

Where are you? Reading a map

Use the map. At which scenic points would you find these trail signs?

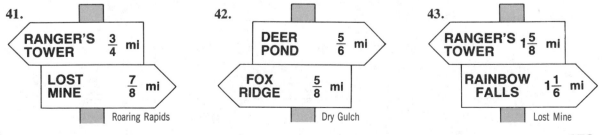

41. RANGER'S TOWER $\frac{3}{4}$ mi / LOST MINE $\frac{7}{8}$ mi — Roaring Rapids

42. DEER POND $\frac{5}{6}$ mi / FOX RIDGE $\frac{5}{8}$ mi — Dry Gulch

43. RANGER'S TOWER $1\frac{5}{8}$ mi / RAINBOW FALLS $1\frac{1}{6}$ mi — Lost Mine

LESSON OBJECTIVE
To add mixed numbers

PROBLEM-SOLVING SKILLS
Selecting information from a chart
Following instructions and checking answers

STARTING THE LESSON
Before the students open their books, have them guess how many cups of dog food a 12-week-old Chihuahua should be fed each day. Have the students write their guesses. Record the high and low guesses on the chalkboard. Then say, "Open your book to page 160. Read the chart. What answer does the book give?" ($2\frac{1}{3}$ cups)

Adding mixed numbers

RECOMMENDED DAILY AMOUNTS OF FOOD		
DOG SIZE	AGE 5-9 WEEKS	AGE 10-15 WEEKS
SMALL Scottish Terrier Chihuahua	$1\frac{1}{4}$ cups	$2\frac{1}{3}$ cups
MEDIUM Poodle Welsh Terrier	$2\frac{1}{2}$ cups	$4\frac{1}{2}$ cups
LARGE Greyhound Schnauzer	$3\frac{2}{3}$ cups	$6\frac{3}{4}$ cups

1. How many cups of food should you feed an 8-week-old poodle each day? $2\frac{1}{2}$

2. How much daily food is recommended for a 13-week-old schnauzer? $6\frac{3}{4}$

3. You have a 6-week-old greyhound and a 12-week-old poodle. What two mixed numbers would you add to find the total number of cups of food you should feed them each day? $3\frac{2}{3}$ and $4\frac{1}{2}$

Here's how *to add mixed numbers.* $3\frac{2}{3} + 4\frac{1}{2} = ?$

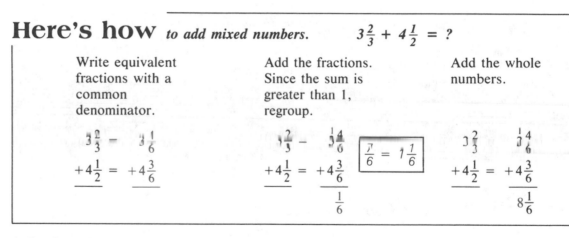

Write equivalent fractions with a common denominator.

$3\frac{2}{3} \rightarrow 3\frac{4}{6}$
$+4\frac{1}{2} = +4\frac{3}{6}$

Add the fractions. Since the sum is greater than 1, regroup.

$3\frac{2}{3} \rightarrow 3\frac{4}{6}$
$+4\frac{1}{2} = +4\frac{3}{6}$
$\frac{7}{6}$

$\boxed{\frac{7}{6} = 1\frac{1}{6}}$

Add the whole numbers.

$3\frac{2}{3} \rightarrow 3\frac{4}{6}$
$+4\frac{1}{2} = +4\frac{3}{6}$
$8\frac{1}{6}$

4. Look at the *Here's how*. How many cups of food should you feed your 6-week-old greyhound and 12-week-old poodle each day? $8\frac{1}{6}$

5. Copy and complete these examples.

a. $3\frac{2}{3}$
$+2\frac{1}{3}$ $\boxed{\frac{3}{3} = 1}$
$\frac{}{6}$

b. $2\frac{1}{2} = 2\frac{2}{4}$
$+6\frac{3}{4} = +6\frac{3}{4}$ $\boxed{\frac{5}{4} = 1\frac{1}{4}}$
$9\frac{1}{4}$

c. $4\frac{5}{6} = 4\frac{20}{24}$
$+4\frac{3}{8} = +4\frac{9}{24}$ $\boxed{\frac{29}{24}}$
$9\frac{5}{24}$

160

EXERCISES

Add. Write the sum in simplest form.

Here are scrambled answers for the next row of exercises: $8\frac{7}{8}$ $10\frac{1}{8}$ $8\frac{1}{4}$ $7\frac{3}{4}$ $9\frac{1}{8}$ $6\frac{1}{6}$

6. $3\frac{1}{2}$
$+4\frac{1}{4}$
$\overline{\quad 7\frac{3}{4}\quad}$

7. $5\frac{3}{4}$
$+2\frac{1}{2}$
$\overline{\quad 8\frac{1}{4}\quad}$

8. $3\frac{1}{8}$
$+5\frac{3}{4}$
$\overline{\quad 8\frac{7}{8}\quad}$

9. $6\frac{3}{4}$
$+2\frac{3}{8}$
$\overline{\quad 9\frac{1}{8}\quad}$

10. $3\frac{1}{2}$
$+6\frac{5}{8}$
$\overline{\quad 10\frac{1}{8}\quad}$

11. $4\frac{2}{3}$
$+1\frac{1}{2}$
$\overline{\quad 6\frac{1}{6}\quad}$

12. $7\frac{3}{4}$
$+3\frac{1}{4}$
$\overline{\quad 11\quad}$

13. $8\frac{1}{6}$
$+4\frac{1}{9}$
$\overline{\quad 12\frac{5}{18}\quad}$

14. $9\frac{5}{6}$
$+5\frac{1}{4}$
$\overline{\quad 15\frac{1}{12}\quad}$

15. 8
$+8\frac{3}{4}$
$\overline{\quad 16\frac{3}{4}\quad}$

16. $5\frac{1}{2}$
$+6\frac{7}{8}$
$\overline{\quad 12\frac{3}{8}\quad}$

17. $4\frac{2}{5}$
$+1\frac{1}{2}$
$\overline{\quad 5\frac{9}{10}\quad}$

18. $4\frac{2}{3}$
$+9\frac{5}{6}$
$\overline{\quad 14\frac{1}{2}\quad}$

19. $8\frac{5}{12}$
$+6\frac{7}{8}$
$\overline{\quad 15\frac{7}{24}\quad}$

20. 5
$+5\frac{3}{8}$
$\overline{\quad 10\frac{3}{8}\quad}$

21. $7\frac{3}{8}$
$+9\frac{7}{12}$
$\overline{\quad 16\frac{23}{24}\quad}$

22. $9\frac{3}{5}$
$+8\frac{2}{5}$
$\overline{\quad 18\quad}$

23. $6\frac{1}{3}$
$+4\frac{2}{3}$
$\overline{\quad 11\quad}$

24. $9\frac{4}{5} + 5\frac{3}{10}$ $15\frac{1}{10}$ **25.** $7\frac{5}{12} + 4\frac{1}{3}$ $11\frac{3}{4}$ **26.** $6\frac{1}{2} + 5\frac{3}{10}$ $11\frac{4}{5}$ **27.** $9\frac{1}{10} + 3\frac{1}{2}$ $12\frac{3}{5}$ **28.** $1\frac{1}{5} + 3\frac{3}{10}$ $4\frac{1}{2}$

29. $3\frac{5}{12} + 2\frac{1}{2}$ $5\frac{11}{12}$ **30.** $6\frac{1}{2} + 2\frac{1}{3}$ $8\frac{5}{6}$ **31.** $1\frac{1}{4} + 3\frac{2}{5}$ $4\frac{13}{20}$ **32.** $2\frac{7}{8} + 1\frac{1}{2}$ $4\frac{3}{8}$ **33.** $4\frac{1}{6} + 2\frac{2}{3}$ $6\frac{5}{6}$

Solve. Use the chart on page 160.

34. Is $4\frac{5}{6}$ cups of food enough food for a 6-week-old Welsh terrier and a 14-week-old Chihuahua?   Yes

35. Is $9\frac{5}{12}$ cups of food enough food for a 7-week-old greyhound and a 14-week-old schnauzer?   No

Check the sums

36. Find and correct the two wrong answers.

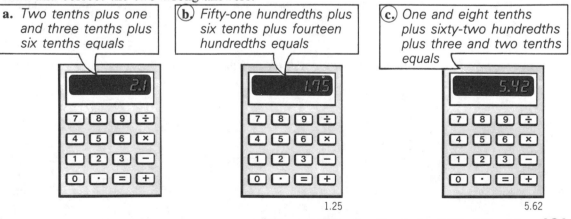

a. *Two tenths plus one and three tenths plus six tenths equals* [display: 2.1]

b. *Fifty-one hundredths plus six tenths plus fourteen hundredths equals* [display: 1.75]   1.25

c. *One and eight tenths plus sixty-two hundredths plus three and two tenths equals* [display: 5.42]   5.62

EXTRA PRACTICE
Page 432   Skill 41

PRACTICE WORKSHEET
Copymaster S220 or Duplicating Master S220

NAME _____   **WORKSHEET 68**
(Use after page 161.)

HOW MANY POUNDS?

The heaviest dog on record was a Wisconsin Saint Bernard. How many pounds did it weigh?

To find the answer:
1. Add. Give the answer in simplest form.
2. Write the letter under its matching number in the DECODER.

1. $7\frac{1}{2}$ $+ 3\frac{1}{4}$ $\overline{10\frac{3}{4}}$ G	2. $3\frac{3}{4}$ $+ 6\frac{1}{2}$ $\overline{11\frac{1}{4}}$ V	3. $5\frac{5}{6}$ $+ 4\frac{1}{3}$ $\overline{10\frac{1}{6}}$ D	4. $5\frac{4}{5}$ $+ 5\frac{1}{2}$ $\overline{11\frac{3}{10}}$ Y
5. $9\frac{3}{4}$ $+ 2\frac{5}{8}$ $\overline{12\frac{3}{8}}$ R	6. $5\frac{1}{2}$ $+ 2\frac{7}{10}$ $\overline{8\frac{1}{5}}$ I	7. $6\frac{2}{3}$ $+ 6\frac{1}{4}$ $\overline{12\frac{11}{12}}$ A	8. $5\frac{1}{4}$ $+ 9\frac{1}{2}$ $\overline{14\frac{3}{4}}$ O
9. $8\frac{2}{3}$ $+ 1\frac{7}{12}$ $\overline{10\frac{1}{4}}$ U	10. $4\frac{1}{3}$ $+ 2\frac{4}{5}$ $\overline{7\frac{2}{5}}$ W	11. $1\frac{2}{3}$ $+ 5\frac{1}{5}$ $\overline{6\frac{13}{15}}$ P	12. $8\frac{2}{3}$ $+ 4\frac{1}{2}$ $\overline{13\frac{1}{6}}$ N
13. $5\frac{3}{5}$ $+ 8\frac{1}{2}$ $\overline{14\frac{1}{10}}$ H	14. $4\frac{1}{2}$ $+ 5\frac{3}{8}$ $\overline{8\frac{1}{8}}$ F	15. $1\frac{3}{5}$ $+ 6\frac{2}{3}$ $\overline{8\frac{1}{24}}$ T	16. $13\frac{1}{3}$ $+ 1\frac{1}{6}$ $\overline{14\frac{1}{2}}$ E

DECODER

$8\frac{7}{15}$ $7\frac{2}{5}$ $14\frac{3}{4}$	$14\frac{1}{10}$ $10\frac{1}{4}$ $13\frac{1}{6}$ $10\frac{1}{6}$ $12\frac{3}{8}$ $14\frac{1}{2}$ $10\frac{1}{6}$
T W O	H U N D R E D
$13\frac{1}{6}$ $8\frac{1}{5}$ $13\frac{1}{6}$ $14\frac{1}{2}$ $8\frac{1}{24}$ $11\frac{3}{10}$	$8\frac{1}{8}$ $8\frac{1}{5}$ $11\frac{1}{4}$ $14\frac{1}{2}$
N I N E T Y - F I V E	
$6\frac{13}{15}$ $10\frac{1}{4}$ $14\frac{3}{4}$	$10\frac{1}{6}$ $12\frac{11}{12}$ $14\frac{1}{2}$ $8\frac{1}{24}$ $11\frac{3}{10}$ $8\frac{1}{8}$ $8\frac{1}{5}$ $11\frac{1}{4}$ $14\frac{1}{2}$
P O U N D s	A T A G E F I V E

LIFE-SKILL PROJECT

Researching information

Have the students look in grocery stores for the cost of different-sized packages of dry dog food. Have them use their findings and the chart on page 160 to compute the cost of feeding a 5-week-old Schnauzer for 4 weeks.

162 Chapter 7

SKILLS REVIEWED
Adding and subtracting decimals
Multiplying decimals
Dividing by 10, 100, or 1000
Dividing a decimal by a decimal

PROBLEM-SOLVING SKILLS
Drawing a picture
Choosing the correct operation

STARTING THE LESSON
Cumulative Skill Practice
Write these four answers on the chalkboard:

43.1   1.782
6.9   8.772

Challenge students to an answer hunt by saying, "Look for the four even-numbered exercises on page 162 that have these answers. You have four minutes to find as many of the exercises as you can." (Exercises 6, 14, 26, and 34)

STARTING THE LESSON
Problem Solving
Draw this picture on the chalkboard:

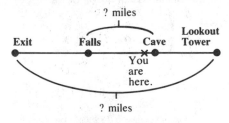

Have the students use the information on the signpost at the top of page 163 to find the missing number of miles in the drawing. (Falls to Cave, $3\frac{1}{4}$ miles; Exit to Lookout Tower, $9\frac{3}{4}$ miles)

Cumulative Skill Practice

Give the sum.   *(page 24)*

1. 3.4 + 4.56 7.96
2. 6.87 + 3.9 10.77
3. 7.24 + 45.6 52.84
4. 3.24 + 6.2 + 8.4 17.84
5. 25.6 + 52.5 + 2.85 80.95
6. 36 + 5.3 + 1.8 43.1
7. 0.25 + 0.6 + 3 3.85
8. 6.7 + 5 + 0.92 12.62
9. 13 + 2.5 + 0.35 15.85
10. 0.39 + 7 + 4.215 11.605
11. 3.7 + 24 + 0.146 27.846
12. 7.5 + 0.01 + 0.461 7.971

Give the difference.   *(page 46)*

13. 63.5 − 49.7 13.8
14. 20.7 − 13.8 6.9
15. 8.00 − 4.47 3.53
16. 8.7 − 5.99 2.71
17. 30 − 7.24 22.76
18. 43.2 − 3.64 39.56
19. 8.6 − 2.73 5.87
20. 13 − 4.53 8.47
21. 10.18 − 8.45 1.73
22. 4.5 − 3.06 1.44
23. 17 − 3.205 13.795
24. 6 − 3.91 2.09

Give the product.   *(page 64)*

25. 3.7 × 0.8 2.96
26. 2.97 × 0.6 1.782
27. 47.5 × 0.5 23.75
28. 5.2 × 0.68 3.536
29. 0.28 × 1.3 0.364
30. 24 × 0.41 9.84
31. 3.62 × 3.06 11.0772
32. 2.05 × 61 125.05
33. 7.03 × 4.41 31.0023
34. 4.3 × 2.04 8.772
35. 5.1 × 32 163.2
36. 2.1 × 3.05 6.405

Give the quotient.   *(page 92)*

37. 63 ÷ 10 6.3
38. 534.2 ÷ 100 5.342
39. 629.8 ÷ 1000 0.6298
40. 242 ÷ 100 2.42
41. 71.5 ÷ 1000 0.0715
42. 6 ÷ 100 0.06
43. 3.03 ÷ 10 0.303
44. 4.29 ÷ 100 0.0429
45. 7012 ÷ 1000 7.012
46. 7.34 ÷ 100 0.0734
47. 2.09 ÷ 10 0.209
48. 346 ÷ 1000 0.346
49. 5.14 ÷ 10 0.514
50. 3.6 ÷ 100 0.036
51. 4.9 ÷ 100 0.049

Give the quotient rounded to the nearest hundredth.   *(page 96)*

52. $0.3\overline{)1.4}$ 4.67
53. $0.7\overline{)0.52}$ 0.74
54. $1.2\overline{)6.4}$ 5.33
55. $2.6\overline{)3.24}$ 1.25
56. $0.06\overline{)0.5}$ 8.33
57. $2.2\overline{)4.96}$ 2.25
58. $0.006\overline{)0.04}$ 6.67
59. $0.12\overline{)0.5}$ 4.17
60. $3.2\overline{)7.5}$ 2.34
61. $0.04\overline{)2.93}$ 73.25
62. $0.7\overline{)3.4}$ 4.86
63. $2.1\overline{)3.43}$ 1.63
64. $4.5\overline{)2.8}$ 0.62
65. $6.2\overline{)3.52}$ 0.57
66. $1.7\overline{)3.96}$ 2.33
67. $2.3\overline{)3.85}$ 1.67

Problem solving

YOU'RE THE TRAIL GUIDE!

CAVE	$\frac{1}{2}$ mi
FALLS	$2\frac{3}{4}$ mi
LOOKOUT TOWER	$3\frac{1}{2}$ mi
EXIT	$6\frac{1}{4}$ mi

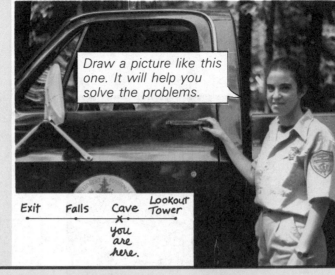

Draw a picture like this one. It will help you solve the problems.

Exit   Falls   Cave   Lookout Tower

you are here.

Use the picture to answer these hikers' questions.

1. *How many miles is it from the cave to the falls?* $3\frac{1}{4}$

2. *When I get to the lookout tower, how far will I be from the exit?* $9\frac{3}{4}$ miles

3. "How many miles is it from the falls to the lookout tower?" $6\frac{1}{4}$

4. "How far is it from the cave to the exit?" $6\frac{3}{4}$ miles

5. "When I'm at the cave, how far is it to the lookout tower?" 3 miles

6. "Which is closer to the cave, the falls or the lookout tower?" The lookout tower

Draw another picture to solve these problems.

SCENIC VIEW	6 mi
LEDGE	3 mi
POND	8 mi
ENTRANCE	4 mi

7. How many miles is the round trip from the entrance to the scenic view and back again? 20

8. Suppose you started at the entrance and hiked 7 miles toward the pond. How far are you from the scenic view? 3 miles

9. When you are halfway between the scenic view and the pond, how far are you from the entrance? 11 miles

10. Is the ledge closer to the pond or to the scenic view? How much closer? Scenic view, 2 miles

---

EXTRA PROBLEM SOLVING
Page 450   Odd exercises

PROBLEM-SOLVING WORKSHEET
Copymaster S221 or Duplicating Master S221

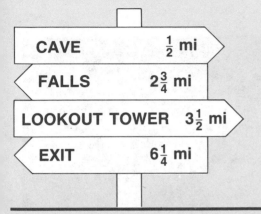

NAME _____

WORKSHEET 69
(Use after page 163.)

PEANUT PROBLEM

SPECIAL PEANUTS	$2.40/lb			
Pounds	$\frac{1}{4}$	$\frac{1}{2}$	$\frac{3}{4}$	1
Cost	$.60	$1.20	$1.80	$2.40

Amy bought $1\frac{1}{2}$ pounds of peanuts. She spent $3.60

Brian gave the clerk $5 and got $.20 in change. He bought 2 pounds of peanuts.

MISSING DIGITS
Fill in the missing digits.

```
      2 ⬜ 8
    ×  ⬜ 2 ⬜
      7 7 4
    5 1 ⬜
  1 5 4 8
  1 ⬜ 0 ⬜ 3 4
```

COUNT YOUR CHANGE!

You bought this record. You gave the clerk $2. What 5 coins did you get back in change?

quarter   quarter
nickel   penny
penny

© D. C. Heath and Company   S221   Problem solving

TRIANGLE TANGLE
How many triangles are there? *Hint: There are more than 10.* 13

COUNTING PENNIES
Sidney has some pennies. When he counts them by fives, there are three left over. When he counts them by tens, there are eight left over. Sidney has almost 50¢ in pennies. How many pennies does he have? 48

TIME IT

TIME CARD

Name *Jan Baker*
Week Ending *May 15*

DAY	A.M. HOURS	P.M. HOURS	TOTAL HOURS
M	$3\frac{1}{2}$	4	$7\frac{1}{2}$
T	$2\frac{1}{2}$	3	$5\frac{1}{2}$
W	4	$2\frac{1}{2}$	$6\frac{1}{2}$
Th	3	4	7
F	$4\frac{1}{2}$	$1\frac{1}{2}$	6
		Total:	$32\frac{1}{2}$

Fill in the time card. On which day did Jan earn $24 if she was paid $4 an hour?
Friday

LIFE-SKILL PROJECT

Reading a map
Have the students use the map on page 11 to find the missing mileage on these road signs:

1.
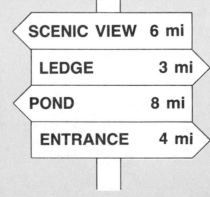

Radd	10 mi
Ridgeway	? mi	11
Fairmont	? mi	74

2.
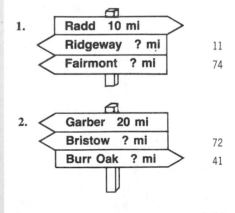

Garber	20 mi
Bristow	? mi	72
Burr Oak	? mi	41

163

Subtracting fractions with common denominators

You won first prize at a sports-car rally.

BEFORE RALLY

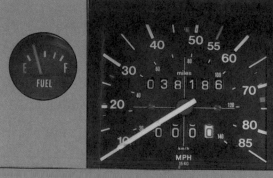

AFTER RALLY

1. Fuel check! What fraction of a tank did you have before the rally? $\frac{3}{4}$

2. Fuel check! What fraction of a tank did you have after the rally? $\frac{1}{4}$

3. Would you add or subtract to compute what fraction of a tank you used?
   Subtract

Here's how *to subtract fractions with a common denominator.*

$$\frac{3}{4} - \frac{1}{4} = ?$$

Subtract the numerators and use $\frac{3}{4} - \frac{1}{4} = \frac{2}{4}$
the common denominator. $= \frac{1}{2}$

4. Look at the *Here's how.* What fraction of a tank did you use on the rally? $\frac{1}{2}$

5. Check these examples. Give each difference in simplest form.

   a. $\frac{7}{8} - \frac{3}{8} = \frac{4}{8}$ **b.** $\frac{5}{12} - \frac{1}{12} = \frac{4}{12}$ **c.** $\frac{5}{2} - \frac{2}{2} = \frac{3}{2}$

   $= ?$ $\frac{1}{2}$ $= ?$ $\frac{1}{3}$ $= ?$ $1\frac{1}{2}$

164

EXERCISES

Subtract. Write the difference in simplest form.
Here are scrambled answers for the next row of exercises: $\frac{5}{6}$ $\frac{1}{4}$ $\frac{1}{6}$ $\frac{1}{2}$ 0 $\frac{2}{5}$

6. $\frac{3}{5} - \frac{1}{5}$ $\frac{2}{5}$ 7. $\frac{2}{4} - \frac{1}{4}$ $\frac{1}{4}$ 8. $\frac{6}{6} - \frac{1}{6}$ $\frac{5}{6}$ 9. $\frac{4}{6} - \frac{3}{6}$ $\frac{1}{6}$ 10. $\frac{5}{8} - \frac{1}{8}$ $\frac{1}{2}$ 11. $\frac{3}{8} - \frac{3}{8}$ 0

12. $\frac{5}{8} - \frac{3}{8}$ $\frac{1}{4}$ 13. $\frac{5}{9} - \frac{0}{9}$ $\frac{5}{9}$ 14. $\frac{5}{4} - \frac{1}{4}$ 1   15. $\frac{7}{6} - \frac{3}{6}$ $\frac{2}{3}$ 16. $\frac{5}{6} - \frac{1}{6}$ $\frac{2}{3}$ 17. $\frac{6}{4} - \frac{2}{4}$ 1

18. $\frac{3}{5} - \frac{0}{5}$ $\frac{3}{5}$ 19. $\frac{11}{8} - \frac{5}{8}$ $\frac{3}{4}$ 20. $\frac{5}{9} - \frac{2}{9}$ $\frac{1}{3}$ 21. $\frac{12}{8} - \frac{6}{8}$ $\frac{3}{4}$ 22. $\frac{11}{4} - \frac{3}{4}$ 2   23. $\frac{7}{4} - \frac{4}{4}$ $\frac{3}{4}$

24. $\frac{9}{4} - \frac{3}{4}$ $1\frac{1}{2}$ 25. $\frac{5}{8} - \frac{4}{8}$ $\frac{1}{8}$ 26. $\frac{8}{6} - \frac{2}{6}$ 1   27. $\frac{5}{3} - \frac{2}{3}$ 1   28. $\frac{7}{6} - \frac{2}{6}$ $\frac{5}{6}$ 29. $\frac{10}{9} - \frac{4}{9}$ $\frac{2}{3}$

30. $\frac{12}{4} - \frac{3}{4}$ $2\frac{1}{4}$ 31. $\frac{7}{8} - \frac{3}{8}$ $\frac{1}{2}$ 32. $\frac{13}{4} - \frac{3}{4}$ $2\frac{1}{2}$ 33. $\frac{10}{8} - \frac{2}{8}$ 1   34. $\frac{9}{6} - \frac{6}{6}$ $\frac{1}{2}$ 35. $\frac{10}{4} - \frac{2}{4}$ 2

36. $\frac{2}{3} - \frac{2}{3}$ 0   37. $\frac{7}{4} - \frac{3}{4}$ 1   38. $\frac{8}{9} - \frac{3}{9}$ $\frac{5}{9}$ 39. $\frac{4}{5} - \frac{2}{5}$ $\frac{2}{5}$ 40. $\frac{9}{8} - \frac{3}{8}$ $\frac{3}{4}$ 41. $\frac{13}{7} - \frac{8}{7}$ $\frac{5}{7}$

42. $\frac{12}{10} - \frac{7}{10}$ $\frac{1}{2}$ 43. $\frac{7}{8} - \frac{4}{8}$ $\frac{3}{8}$ 44. $\frac{6}{4} - \frac{2}{4}$ 1   45. $\frac{5}{6} - \frac{5}{6}$ 0   46. $\frac{6}{5} - \frac{3}{5}$ $\frac{3}{5}$ 47. $\frac{5}{6} - \frac{3}{6}$ $\frac{1}{3}$

Solve. Look at the top of page 164.

48. How many miles had your car been driven before the rally? 38,016

49. How many miles had your car been driven after the rally? 38,186

50. How many miles was the rally? *Hint: Use your answers to problems 48 and 49.* 170

51. If you used 7.8 gallons of gasoline on the rally, how many miles did you average per gallon? Round the answer to the nearest tenth. 21.8

Where are they?   Making a sketch

52. Study the clues to find out how far Carol and Joe are from the checkpoint at Clara's Corner. *Hint: Make a sketch.*

Clues: 9.9 miles
- They left Bruskville and drove 18.6 miles east to Clara's Corner.
- They turned right on Highway 26 and drove 13.9 miles to the second checkpoint at Harold's Hollow.
- They drove 6.4 miles beyond Harold's Hollow.
- They turned around and started back for Clara's Corner. They drove 10.4 miles toward Clara's Corner.

Adding and Subtracting Fractions and Mixed Numbers **165**

EXTRA PRACTICE
Page 432   Skill 42

PRACTICE WORKSHEET
Copymaster S222 or Duplicating Master S222

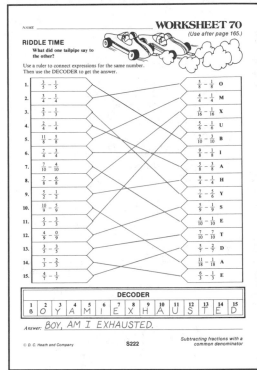

LIFE-SKILL PROJECT
Using library resources
Have each of the students use an almanac to find the mileage (miles per gallon) that his/her favorite sports car gets. Have them use their findings to compute the number of gallons it would take for them to drive in the sports-car rally described on page 164. (The mileage information can be found in *The World Almanac and Book of Facts*.)

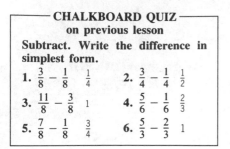

LESSON OBJECTIVE
To subtract fractions with different denominators

PROBLEM-SOLVING SKILLS
Reading a circle graph
Checking answers

STARTING THE LESSON
Sketch this circle graph on the chalkboard:

FAVORITE AFTER-SCHOOL SPORTS OF TEENAGERS

Swimming
Jogging
Cycling
Other Sports

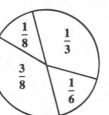

Before the students open their books, have them guess which fraction of the circle graph represents each sport. Then say, "Open your books to page 166 and check your guesses with the graph at the top of the page."

Subtracting fractions with different denominators

The circle graph shows the results of a teenage survey. Each teenager was asked to name his/her favorite after-school sport.

1. What fraction of those surveyed preferred swimming? $\frac{1}{6}$

2. What fraction preferred cycling? $\frac{3}{8}$

3. What fraction preferred jogging? $\frac{1}{3}$

4. Would you add or subtract to find how much greater the fraction for cycling is than the fraction for jogging? Subtract

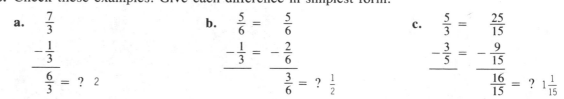

FAVORITE AFTER-SCHOOL SPORTS OF TEENAGERS

Here's how *to subtract fractions with different denominators.* $\frac{3}{8} - \frac{1}{3} = ?$

Find the least common denominator.	Change to equivalent fractions.	Subtract.
$\begin{array}{r}\frac{3}{8}\\[4pt]\frac{1}{3}\end{array}$ $\boxed{24}$	$\begin{array}{r}\frac{3}{8} = \frac{9}{24}\\[4pt]-\frac{1}{3} = -\frac{8}{24}\end{array}$	$\begin{array}{r}\frac{3}{8} = \frac{9}{24}\\[4pt]-\frac{1}{3} = -\frac{8}{24}\\\hline \frac{1}{24}\end{array}$

5. Look at the *Here's how*. How much greater was the fraction of teenagers who preferred cycling than the fraction who preferred jogging? $\frac{1}{24}$

6. Check these examples. Give each difference in simplest form.

a. $\begin{array}{r}\frac{7}{3}\\[4pt]-\frac{1}{3}\\\hline \frac{6}{3} = ?\ 2\end{array}$

b. $\begin{array}{r}\frac{5}{6} = \frac{5}{6}\\[4pt]-\frac{1}{3} = -\frac{2}{6}\\\hline \frac{3}{6} = ?\ \frac{1}{2}\end{array}$

c. $\begin{array}{r}\frac{5}{3} = \frac{25}{15}\\[4pt]-\frac{3}{5} = -\frac{9}{15}\\\hline \frac{16}{15} = ?\ 1\frac{1}{15}\end{array}$

EXERCISES

Subtract. Give the difference in simplest form.

Here are scrambled answers for the next row of exercises: $\frac{3}{4}$ $\frac{3}{10}$ $\frac{1}{9}$ $\frac{1}{3}$ $\frac{5}{12}$ $\frac{13}{24}$ $\frac{1}{4}$

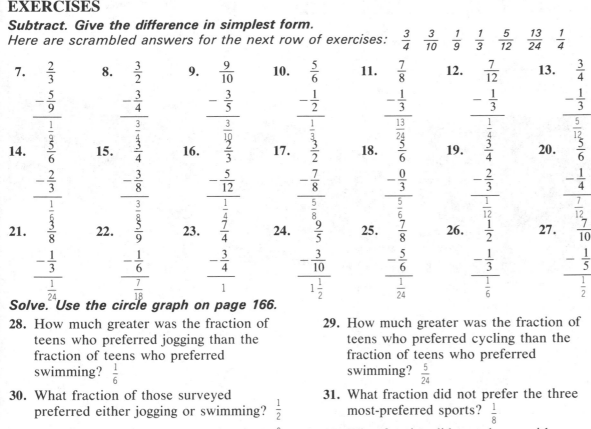

7. $\frac{2}{3} - \frac{5}{9} = \frac{1}{9}$

8. $\frac{3}{2} - \frac{3}{4} = \frac{3}{4}$

9. $\frac{9}{10} - \frac{3}{5} = \frac{3}{10}$

10. $\frac{5}{6} - \frac{1}{2} = \frac{1}{3}$

11. $\frac{7}{8} - \frac{1}{3} = \frac{13}{24}$

12. $\frac{7}{12} - \frac{1}{3} = \frac{1}{4}$

13. $\frac{3}{4} - \frac{1}{3} = \frac{5}{12}$

14. $\frac{5}{6} - \frac{2}{3} = \frac{1}{6}$

15. $\frac{3}{4} - \frac{3}{8} = \frac{3}{8}$

16. $\frac{2}{3} - \frac{5}{12} = \frac{1}{4}$

17. $\frac{3}{2} - \frac{7}{8} = \frac{5}{8}$

18. $\frac{5}{6} - \frac{0}{3} = \frac{5}{6}$

19. $\frac{3}{4} - \frac{2}{3} = \frac{1}{12}$

20. $\frac{5}{6} - \frac{1}{4} = \frac{7}{12}$

21. $\frac{3}{8} - \frac{1}{3} = \frac{1}{24}$

22. $\frac{5}{9} - \frac{1}{6} = \frac{7}{18}$

23. $\frac{7}{4} - \frac{3}{4} = 1$

24. $\frac{9}{5} - \frac{3}{10} = 1\frac{1}{2}$

25. $\frac{7}{8} - \frac{5}{6} = \frac{1}{24}$

26. $\frac{1}{2} - \frac{1}{3} = \frac{1}{6}$

27. $\frac{7}{10} - \frac{1}{5} = \frac{1}{2}$

Solve. Use the circle graph on page 166.

28. How much greater was the fraction of teens who preferred jogging than the fraction of teens who preferred swimming? $\frac{1}{6}$

29. How much greater was the fraction of teens who preferred cycling than the fraction of teens who preferred swimming? $\frac{5}{24}$

30. What fraction of those surveyed preferred either jogging or swimming? $\frac{1}{2}$

31. What fraction did not prefer the three most-preferred sports? $\frac{1}{8}$

32. What fraction did not choose jogging? $\frac{2}{3}$

33. What fraction did not choose either cycling or swimming? $\frac{11}{24}$

Check the differences

34. Find and correct the two wrong answers.

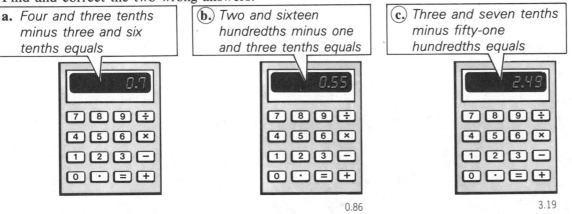

a. Four and three tenths minus three and six tenths equals
(0.7)

b. Two and sixteen hundredths minus one and three tenths equals
(0.55) — 0.86

c. Three and seven tenths minus fifty-one hundredths equals
(2.49) — 3.19

PRACTICE WORKSHEET

Copymaster S223 or Duplicating Master S223

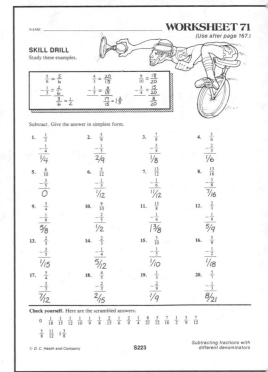

NAME _____

WORKSHEET 71
(Use after page 167.)

SKILL DRILL
Study these examples.

$\frac{5}{6} = \frac{5}{6}$ $\frac{4}{3} = \frac{20}{15}$ $\frac{9}{10} = \frac{18}{20}$
$-\frac{1}{3} = \frac{2}{6}$ $-\frac{1}{5} = \frac{3}{15}$ $-\frac{3}{4} = \frac{15}{20}$
$\frac{3}{6} = \frac{1}{2}$ $\frac{17}{15} = 1\frac{2}{15}$ $\frac{3}{20}$

Subtract. Give the answer in simplest form.

1. $\frac{1}{2} - \frac{1}{4} = \frac{1}{4}$
2. $\frac{5}{9} - \frac{1}{3} = \frac{2}{9}$
3. $\frac{7}{8} - \frac{3}{4} = \frac{1}{8}$
4. $\frac{5}{6} - \frac{2}{3} = \frac{1}{6}$

5. $\frac{6}{10} - \frac{3}{5} = 0$
6. $\frac{5}{12} - \frac{1}{3} = \frac{1}{12}$
7. $\frac{13}{12} - \frac{1}{6} = 1\frac{1}{12}$
8. $\frac{13}{16} - \frac{3}{8} = \frac{7}{16}$

9. $\frac{3}{4} - \frac{1}{8} = \frac{5}{8}$
10. $\frac{9}{10} - \frac{2}{5} = \frac{1}{2}$
11. $\frac{13}{8} - \frac{1}{4} = 1\frac{3}{8}$
12. $\frac{2}{3} - \frac{1}{9} = \frac{5}{9}$

13. $\frac{2}{3} - \frac{3}{5} = \frac{1}{15}$
14. $\frac{2}{3} - \frac{1}{4} = \frac{5}{12}$
15. $\frac{3}{5} - \frac{1}{2} = \frac{1}{10}$
16. $\frac{2}{3} - \frac{5}{9} = \frac{1}{18}$

17. $\frac{5}{4} - \frac{2}{3} = \frac{7}{12}$
18. $\frac{4}{5} - \frac{2}{3} = \frac{2}{15}$
19. $\frac{1}{3} - \frac{2}{9} = \frac{1}{9}$
20. $\frac{5}{7} - \frac{1}{3} = \frac{8}{21}$

Check yourself. Here are the scrambled answers:

0 $\frac{1}{18}$ $\frac{1}{15}$ $\frac{1}{13}$ $\frac{1}{10}$ $\frac{1}{9}$ $\frac{1}{8}$ $\frac{1}{6}$ $\frac{2}{9}$ $\frac{4}{8}$ $\frac{8}{21}$ $\frac{7}{12}$ $\frac{1}{16}$ $\frac{2}{5}$ $\frac{7}{9}$ $\frac{9}{12}$

$\frac{5}{8}$ $\frac{11}{12}$ $1\frac{3}{8}$

CHALKBOARD CHALLENGE

Find the missing digits.

1. $\frac{5}{\boxed{8}} - \frac{1}{4} = \frac{3}{8}$

2. $\frac{3}{4} - \frac{1}{\boxed{3}} = \frac{5}{12}$

3. $\frac{\boxed{5}}{9} - \frac{1}{3} = \frac{2}{9}$

4. $\frac{5}{6} - \frac{\boxed{2}}{3} = \frac{1}{6}$

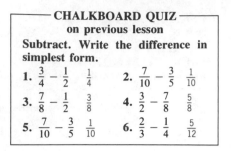
LESSON OBJECTIVE
To subtract mixed numbers without regrouping

PROBLEM-SOLVING SKILLS
Selecting information from a display
Using logical reasoning

STARTING THE LESSON
Play 'What are the facts?' Allow students 30 seconds to study the comments at the top of page 168. Then have them close their books and try to decide from memory whether these statements are true or false:

• Steve said he was $68\frac{3}{4}$ inches tall. (True)
• Arlo said he was shorter than Steve. (True)
• The girl said she was shorter than Steve. (True)
• The girl's name is Polly. (False)

Subtracting mixed numbers without regrouping

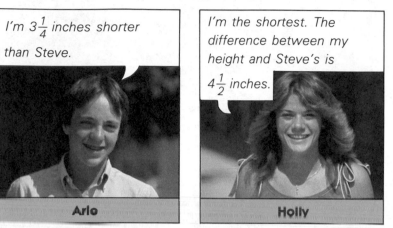

I'm $3\frac{1}{4}$ inches shorter than Steve.

Arlo

I'm the shortest. The difference between my height and Steve's is $4\frac{1}{2}$ inches.

Holly

I'm $68\frac{3}{4}$ inches tall.

Steve

1. Who is the shortest? Holly

2. Who is the tallest? Steve

3. To find how many inches tall Holly is, you subtract $4\frac{1}{2}$ from what number? $68\frac{3}{4}$

Here's how *to subtract mixed numbers.* $68\frac{3}{4} - 4\frac{1}{2} = ?$

Write equivalent fractions with a common denominator.

$$68\frac{3}{4} = 68\frac{3}{4}$$
$$-\ 4\frac{1}{2} = -4\frac{2}{4}$$

Subtract the fractions.
Subtract the whole numbers.

$$68\frac{3}{4} = 68\frac{3}{4}$$
$$-\ 4\frac{1}{2} = -4\frac{2}{4}$$
$$64\frac{1}{4}$$

---

4. Look at the *Here's how*. How tall is Holly? $64\frac{1}{4}$ inches

5. Check these examples. Is Arlo $65\frac{1}{2}$ inches or 72 inches tall? $65\frac{1}{2}$

a.
$$68\frac{3}{4}$$
$$+\ 3\frac{1}{4}$$
$$71\frac{4}{4} = 72$$

b.
$$68\frac{3}{4}$$
$$-\ 3\frac{1}{4}$$
$$65\frac{2}{4} = 65\frac{1}{2}$$

EXERCISES

Subtract. Give each difference in simplest form.
Here are scrambled answers for the next row of exercises: $3\frac{3}{8}$ $4\frac{1}{8}$ $2\frac{1}{4}$ $1\frac{1}{4}$ $5\frac{1}{4}$ $2\frac{3}{8}$

6. $\begin{aligned}4\frac{3}{8}\\-2\frac{1}{8}\\\hline 2\frac{1}{4}\end{aligned}$ 7. $\begin{aligned}8\frac{1}{2}\\-5\frac{1}{8}\\\hline 3\frac{3}{8}\end{aligned}$ 8. $\begin{aligned}10\frac{3}{4}\\-5\frac{1}{2}\\\hline 5\frac{1}{4}\end{aligned}$ 9. $\begin{aligned}6\frac{7}{8}\\-2\frac{3}{4}\\\hline 4\frac{1}{8}\end{aligned}$ 10. $\begin{aligned}3\frac{1}{2}\\-2\frac{1}{4}\\\hline 1\frac{1}{4}\end{aligned}$ 11. $\begin{aligned}4\frac{5}{8}\\-2\frac{1}{4}\\\hline 2\frac{3}{8}\end{aligned}$

12. $\begin{aligned}19\frac{4}{5}\\-8\frac{3}{10}\\\hline 11\frac{1}{2}\end{aligned}$ 13. $\begin{aligned}17\frac{5}{12}\\-14\frac{1}{3}\\\hline 3\frac{1}{12}\end{aligned}$ 14. $\begin{aligned}36\frac{1}{2}\\-25\frac{3}{10}\\\hline 11\frac{1}{5}\end{aligned}$ 15. $\begin{aligned}17\frac{3}{8}\\-12\frac{1}{8}\\\hline 5\frac{1}{4}\end{aligned}$ 16. $\begin{aligned}3\frac{4}{5}\\-\frac{3}{5}\\\hline 3\frac{1}{5}\end{aligned}$ 17. $\begin{aligned}2\frac{5}{9}\\-1\frac{1}{3}\\\hline 1\frac{2}{9}\end{aligned}$

18. $\begin{aligned}5\frac{1}{3}\\-2\frac{1}{4}\\\hline 3\frac{1}{12}\end{aligned}$ 19. $\begin{aligned}3\frac{2}{3}\\-1\frac{1}{2}\\\hline 2\frac{1}{6}\end{aligned}$ 20. $\begin{aligned}12\frac{3}{4}\\-1\frac{1}{6}\\\hline 11\frac{7}{12}\end{aligned}$ 21. $\begin{aligned}8\frac{3}{4}\\-2\frac{2}{5}\\\hline 6\frac{7}{20}\end{aligned}$ 22. $\begin{aligned}9\frac{1}{4}\\-3\frac{1}{6}\\\hline 6\frac{1}{12}\end{aligned}$ 23. $\begin{aligned}10\frac{2}{9}\\-3\frac{1}{10}\\\hline 7\frac{11}{90}\end{aligned}$

24. $12\frac{3}{5} - 3\frac{1}{10}$ $9\frac{1}{2}$
25. $16\frac{1}{2} - 8\frac{1}{4}$ $8\frac{1}{4}$
26. $38\frac{1}{2} - 21\frac{3}{10}$ $17\frac{1}{5}$
27. $15\frac{3}{4} - 9\frac{1}{8}$ $6\frac{5}{8}$

28. $9\frac{7}{8} - 3\frac{1}{2}$ $6\frac{3}{8}$
29. $15\frac{1}{4} - 3\frac{1}{6}$ $12\frac{1}{12}$
30. $2\frac{7}{10} - 1\frac{3}{5}$ $1\frac{1}{10}$
31. $8\frac{4}{5} - 6\frac{11}{20}$ $2\frac{1}{4}$

32. $16\frac{1}{2} - 4\frac{1}{5}$ $12\frac{3}{10}$
33. $3\frac{5}{12} - 1\frac{1}{4}$ $2\frac{1}{6}$
34. $6\frac{4}{9} - 2\frac{1}{3}$ $4\frac{1}{9}$
35. $7\frac{5}{8} - 6\frac{11}{24}$ $1\frac{1}{6}$

How many pounds? Logical reasoning

Solve. Use the clues.

36. How much does Holly weigh? $110\frac{1}{2}$ pounds
   Clues: • Steve guessed 115 pounds and missed by $4\frac{1}{2}$ pounds.
   • Arlo guessed 100 pounds and missed by $10\frac{1}{2}$ pounds.

37. How much does Arlo weigh? $145\frac{3}{4}$ pounds
   Clues: • Holly guessed 140 pounds and missed by $5\frac{3}{4}$ pounds.
   • Steve guessed 148 pounds and missed by $2\frac{1}{4}$ pounds.

38. How much does Steve weigh? $143\frac{1}{2}$ pounds
   Clues: • Arlo guessed 160 pounds and missed by $16\frac{1}{2}$ pounds.
   • Holly guessed 150 pounds and missed by $6\frac{1}{2}$ pounds.

39. Who do you think is the best guesser, Arlo, Holly, or Steve? Why?
   Answers will vary.

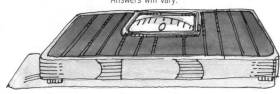

EXTRA PRACTICE
Page 433   Skill 44

PRACTICE WORKSHEET
Copymaster S224 or Duplicating Master S224

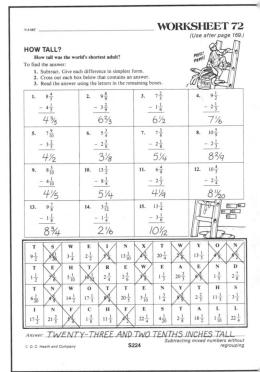

NAME _____ **WORKSHEET 72**
(Use after page 169.)

HOW TALL?
How tall was the world's shortest adult?
To find the answer:
1. Subtract. Give each difference in simplest form.
2. Cross out each box below that contains an answer.
3. Read the answer using the letters in the remaining boxes.

1. $8\frac{4}{5}$ $-4\frac{1}{5}$ $=4\frac{3}{5}$	2. $9\frac{8}{9}$ $-3\frac{2}{9}$ $=6\frac{2}{3}$	3. $7\frac{2}{3}$ $-1\frac{1}{6}$ $=6\frac{1}{2}$	4. $9\frac{1}{2}$ $-2\frac{1}{3}$ $=7\frac{1}{6}$
5. $7\frac{9}{10}$ $-3\frac{2}{5}$ $=4\frac{1}{2}$	6. $5\frac{3}{4}$ $-2\frac{5}{8}$ $=3\frac{1}{8}$	7. $7\frac{3}{8}$ $-2\frac{1}{8}$ $=5\frac{1}{4}$	8. $10\frac{5}{9}$ $-2\frac{1}{3}$ $=8\frac{2}{9}$
9. $8\frac{3}{10}$ $-4\frac{1}{10}$ $=4\frac{1}{5}$	10. $13\frac{1}{2}$ $-8\frac{1}{4}$ $=5\frac{1}{4}$	11. $6\frac{4}{9}$ $-2\frac{1}{3}$ $=4\frac{1}{9}$	12. $10\frac{4}{5}$ $-2\frac{1}{4}$ $=8\frac{11}{20}$
13. $9\frac{7}{8}$ $-1\frac{1}{8}$ $=8\frac{3}{4}$	14. $3\frac{5}{12}$ $-1\frac{1}{4}$ $=2\frac{1}{6}$	15. $13\frac{1}{4}$ $-3\frac{1}{6}$ $=10\frac{1}{12}$	

Answer: TWENTY-THREE AND TWO TENTHS INCHES TALL
© D. C. Heath and Company   **S224**
Subtracting mixed numbers without regrouping

CHALKBOARD CHALLENGE
Put each digit in a box to get the answer.

1.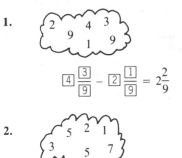
   2 4 3
   9 1 9

   $\boxed{4}\frac{\boxed{3}}{\boxed{9}} - \boxed{2}\frac{\boxed{1}}{\boxed{9}} = 2\frac{2}{9}$

2.
   5 2 1
   3 5 7

   $\boxed{7}\frac{\boxed{3}}{\boxed{5}} - \boxed{1}\frac{\boxed{2}}{\boxed{5}} = 6\frac{1}{5}$

LESSON OBJECTIVE

To subtract mixed numbers with regrouping

PROBLEM-SOLVING SKILLS

Selecting information from a chart
Reading a map and a map scale

STARTING THE LESSON

Before discussing exercises 1–3, have the students use the chart at the top of page 170 to answer these questions:

- On a clear day, how far can you see from a hot-air balloon at a height of 50 feet? ($8\frac{1}{2}$ miles)
- Can you see more or less than 60 miles at a height of 3000 feet? (More)
- Are you above or below 100 feet if you can see a distance of 10 miles? (Below)

EXERCISE NOTE

The map at the bottom of page 171 is also on **Visual Aid 29**. Use the map when discussing exercises 38–40. You may want to make duplicate copies of **Visual Aid 29** for students to use. They can cut out the scale of miles and use it to measure distances between cities.

Subtracting mixed numbers with regrouping

At 300 feet I can see 22 miles!

HEIGHT OF BALLOON (IN FEET)	DISTANCE SEEN FROM BALLOON (IN MILES)
10	$3\frac{7}{8}$
50	$8\frac{1}{2}$
100	$12\frac{3}{8}$
200	$17\frac{3}{8}$
300	22
1000	$38\frac{3}{4}$
3000	$67\frac{1}{8}$

1. Your hot-air balloon is 3000 feet above the ground. Your friend's balloon is at 100 feet. Look at the chart. What two numbers would you use to compute how many more miles you can see than your friend? $67\frac{1}{8}$ and $12\frac{3}{8}$

Here's how *to subtract mixed numbers.* $67\frac{1}{8} - 12\frac{3}{8} = ?$

Not enough eighths!	Regroup 1 for $\frac{8}{8}$.	Subtract.
$67\frac{1}{8}$ $-12\frac{3}{8}$	$\overset{66\ 9}{\cancel{67}\frac{\cancel{1}}{8}}$ $12\frac{3}{8}$	$\overset{66\ 9}{\cancel{67}\frac{\cancel{1}}{8}}$ $-12\frac{3}{8}$ $\overline{54\frac{6}{8} = 54\frac{3}{4}}$

2. Look at the *Here's how*. How many miles farther can you see? $54\frac{3}{4}$

3. Study these examples. Is each difference in simplest form? Yes

a. $22 = 21\frac{2}{2}$ *Regrouped 1 for $\frac{2}{2}$.*
    $-8\frac{1}{2} = -8\frac{1}{2}$
    $\overline{\qquad\quad 13\frac{1}{2}}$

b. $8\frac{1}{2} = \overset{7\ 12}{\cancel{8}\frac{\cancel{4}}{8}}$ *Changed to a common denominator.*
    $-3\frac{7}{8} = -3\frac{7}{8}$ *Regrouped 1 for $\frac{8}{8}$.*
    $\overline{\qquad\quad 4\frac{5}{8}}$

EXERCISES

Subtract. Write the difference in simplest form.
Here are scrambled answers for the next row of exercises: $3\frac{1}{4}$ $4\frac{3}{5}$ $7\frac{2}{9}$ $3\frac{3}{4}$ $2\frac{6}{7}$ $3\frac{4}{5}$

4. $6\frac{1}{8}$
$-2\frac{3}{8}$
$\overline{3\frac{3}{4}}$

5. $8\frac{7}{9}$
$-1\frac{5}{9}$
$\overline{7\frac{2}{9}}$

6. $9\frac{1}{8}$
$-5\frac{7}{8}$
$\overline{3\frac{1}{4}}$

7. $6\frac{5}{7}$
$-3\frac{6}{7}$
$\overline{2\frac{6}{7}}$

8. $8\frac{2}{5}$
$-3\frac{4}{5}$
$\overline{4\frac{3}{5}}$

9. 6
$-2\frac{1}{5}$
$\overline{3\frac{4}{5}}$

10. $4\frac{3}{7}$
$-1\frac{5}{7}$
$\overline{2\frac{5}{7}}$

11. $6\frac{5}{9}$
$-3\frac{8}{9}$
$\overline{2\frac{2}{3}}$

12. 7
$-3\frac{1}{2}$
$\overline{3\frac{1}{2}}$

13. $12\frac{1}{2}$
$-6\frac{1}{4}$
$\overline{6\frac{1}{4}}$

14. 20
$-8\frac{5}{8}$
$\overline{11\frac{3}{8}}$

15. $2\frac{2}{9}$
$-1\frac{1}{3}$
$\overline{\frac{8}{9}}$

16. $4\frac{1}{8}$
$-2\frac{1}{2}$
$\overline{1\frac{5}{8}}$

17. $5\frac{3}{4}$
$-3\frac{1}{2}$
$\overline{2\frac{1}{4}}$

18. $9\frac{1}{10}$
$-3\frac{1}{5}$
$\overline{5\frac{9}{10}}$

19. $5\frac{3}{8}$
$-2\frac{1}{4}$
$\overline{3\frac{1}{8}}$

20. $14\frac{1}{8}$
$-6\frac{3}{4}$
$\overline{7\frac{3}{8}}$

21. $13\frac{1}{4}$
$-2\frac{1}{2}$
$\overline{10\frac{3}{4}}$

22. $8\frac{1}{3}$
$-2\frac{1}{2}$
$\overline{5\frac{5}{6}}$

23. $10\frac{1}{4}$
$-2\frac{2}{3}$
$\overline{7\frac{7}{12}}$

24. $6\frac{3}{8}$
$-4\frac{5}{6}$
$\overline{1\frac{13}{24}}$

25. $7\frac{7}{8}$
$-1\frac{3}{4}$
$\overline{6\frac{1}{8}}$

26. $15\frac{7}{8}$
$-12\frac{1}{4}$
$\overline{3\frac{5}{8}}$

27. $14\frac{1}{6}$
$-3\frac{2}{3}$
$\overline{10\frac{1}{2}}$

28. $6\frac{3}{4} - 1\frac{3}{5}$ $5\frac{3}{20}$
29. $8\frac{1}{2} - 4\frac{2}{3}$ $3\frac{5}{6}$
30. $7\frac{1}{5} - 2\frac{1}{10}$ $5\frac{1}{10}$
31. $10\frac{3}{4} - 3\frac{7}{8}$ $6\frac{7}{8}$
32. $10 - 6\frac{1}{2}$ $3\frac{1}{2}$

33. $29\frac{2}{3} - 8\frac{1}{2}$ $21\frac{1}{6}$
34. $24\frac{1}{2} - 1\frac{3}{4}$ $22\frac{3}{4}$
35. $14\frac{2}{3} - 3\frac{1}{2}$ $11\frac{1}{6}$
36. $10\frac{5}{8} - 4\frac{3}{4}$ $5\frac{7}{8}$
37. $30 - 8\frac{3}{4}$ $21\frac{1}{4}$

Oh, say can you see? Reading a map

Use the map scale and the chart on page 170 to solve these problems.

38. You are in a hot-air balloon 100 feet above Boone, Nebraska. What 4 cities can you see? Boone, St. Edward, Albion, Newman Grove

39. Now you are 300 feet above Petersburg. What 9 cities can you see? Petersburg, Neligh, Tilden, Elgin, Newman Grove, Albion, Spalding, Boone, St. Edward

40. When you are 3000 feet above O'Neill, can you see as far as Greeley? Yes

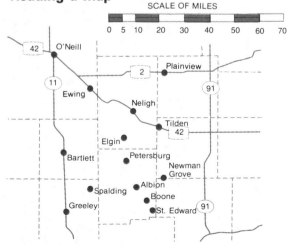

SCALE OF MILES
0 5 10 20 30 40 50 60 70

42 O'Neill
Plainview
2
11
91
Ewing
Neligh
Tilden
42
Elgin
Bartlett
Petersburg
Newman Grove
Spalding
Albion
Boone
Greeley
St. Edward
91

PRACTICE WORKSHEET

Copymaster S225 or Duplicating Master S225

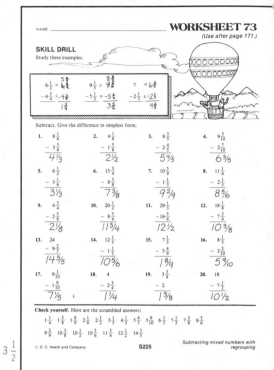

NAME _____   **WORKSHEET 73**
(Use after page 171.)

SKILL DRILL
Study these examples.

$6\frac{1}{2} = 6\frac{4}{8}$ $9\frac{1}{3} = 9\frac{4}{12}$ $7 = 6\frac{8}{8}$
$-4\frac{3}{4} = -4\frac{6}{8}$ $-5\frac{1}{2} = -5\frac{6}{12}$ $-2\frac{1}{3} = -2\frac{3}{8}$
$\overline{1\frac{7}{8}}$ $\overline{3\frac{10}{12}}$ $\overline{4\frac{5}{8}}$

Subtract. Give the difference in simplest form.

1. $8\frac{1}{6}$
$-3\frac{5}{6}$
$\overline{4\frac{1}{3}}$

2. $4\frac{1}{8}$
$-1\frac{5}{8}$
$\overline{2\frac{1}{2}}$

3. $8\frac{1}{5}$
$-2\frac{4}{5}$
$\overline{5\frac{1}{5}}$

4. $9\frac{1}{10}$
$-2\frac{1}{10}$
$\overline{6\frac{3}{5}}$

5. $6\frac{1}{6}$
$-3\frac{1}{6}$
$\overline{3\frac{1}{3}}$

6. $15\frac{1}{8}$
$-8\frac{3}{8}$
$\overline{7\frac{3}{8}}$

7. $10\frac{5}{9}$
$-1\frac{1}{9}$
$\overline{9\frac{2}{9}}$

8. $11\frac{1}{6}$
$-2\frac{1}{3}$
$\overline{8\frac{5}{6}}$

9. $4\frac{3}{8}$
$-2\frac{5}{8}$
$\overline{2\frac{1}{8}}$

10. $20\frac{1}{2}$
$-8\frac{3}{4}$
$\overline{11\frac{3}{4}}$

11. $29\frac{1}{8}$
$-16\frac{5}{6}$
$\overline{12\frac{1}{2}}$

12. $18\frac{1}{8}$
$-7\frac{3}{4}$
$\overline{10\frac{3}{8}}$

13. 24
$-9\frac{2}{5}$
$\overline{14\frac{3}{5}}$

14. $12\frac{1}{5}$
$-1\frac{1}{2}$
$\overline{10\frac{5}{8}}$

15. $7\frac{1}{3}$
$-5\frac{4}{9}$
$\overline{1\frac{8}{9}}$

16. $8\frac{1}{5}$
$-2\frac{3}{10}$
$\overline{5\frac{9}{10}}$

17. $9\frac{1}{10}$
$-1\frac{9}{10}$
$\overline{7\frac{1}{5}}$

18. $3\frac{3}{8}$
$-2\frac{1}{8}$
$\overline{1\frac{1}{4}}$

19. $3\frac{3}{8}$
-2
$\overline{1\frac{3}{8}}$

20. 18
$-7\frac{1}{2}$
$\overline{10\frac{1}{2}}$

Check yourself. Here are the scrambled answers:

$1\frac{1}{4}$ $1\frac{3}{8}$ $1\frac{8}{9}$ $2\frac{1}{8}$ $2\frac{1}{2}$ $3\frac{1}{3}$ $4\frac{1}{3}$ $5\frac{1}{5}$ $5\frac{9}{10}$ $6\frac{3}{5}$ $7\frac{1}{5}$ $7\frac{3}{8}$ $8\frac{5}{6}$

$9\frac{2}{9}$ $10\frac{3}{8}$ $10\frac{1}{2}$ $10\frac{5}{8}$ $11\frac{3}{4}$ $12\frac{1}{2}$ $14\frac{3}{5}$

© D. C. Heath and Company   S225   *Subtracting mixed numbers with regrouping*

CHALKBOARD CHALLENGE

Copy and complete this Magic Square so that the sums along every row, column, and diagonal are $16\frac{7}{8}$.

9	$1\frac{1}{8}$	$6\frac{3}{4}$
$3\frac{3}{8}$	$5\frac{5}{8}$	$7\frac{7}{8}$
$4\frac{1}{2}$	$10\frac{1}{8}$	$2\frac{1}{4}$

┌─ CHALKBOARD QUIZ ─┐
on previous lesson
Subtract. Write the difference in simplest form.

1. $6\frac{1}{4} - 1\frac{3}{4}$ $4\frac{1}{2}$ **2.** $4\frac{1}{8} - 2\frac{3}{8}$ $1\frac{3}{4}$

3. $10 - 6\frac{1}{3}$ $3\frac{2}{3}$ **4.** $4\frac{1}{3} - 1\frac{1}{2}$ $2\frac{5}{6}$

5. $3\frac{2}{3} - 1\frac{1}{4}$ $2\frac{5}{12}$ **6.** $10\frac{3}{8} - 4\frac{3}{4}$ $5\frac{5}{8}$

SKILLS REVIEWED
Computing the mean
Writing fractions as decimals
Changing a decimal to a fraction or mixed number in simplest form
Adding and subtracting mixed numbers

PROBLEM-SOLVING SKILLS
Using information on a display
Choosing the correct operation

STARTING THE LESSON
Cumulative Skill Practice
Write these four answers on the chalkboard:

$0.8 \qquad \frac{9}{20} \qquad 3\frac{11}{15} \qquad 2\frac{1}{6}$

Challenge the students to an answer hunt by saying: "Look for the four even-numbered exercises on page 172 that have these answers. You have four minutes to find as many of the exercises as you can." (Exercises 18, 36, 60, and 64)

STARTING THE LESSON
Problem Solving
Have the students read the paragraph above each of the Fuel Data Panel displays. Then ask the students which buttons were pushed to display

- the miles per gallon the car is getting at this instant. (Button on the left)
- the number of miles you can travel on the fuel remaining in the tank. (Button on the right)
- the gallons of fuel used since the last fill-up. (Push the button on the right twice.)

Cumulative Skill Practice

Find the mean. Round the answer to the nearest tenth. (page 114)

1. 19, 35, 28 27.3

2. 13, 42, 27 27.3

3. 28, 36, 1 21.7

4. 2.8, 4.7, 1.8 3.1

5. 1.8, 2.8, 1.9, 10.8 4.3

6. 28, 56, 32, 45 40.3

7. 13, 20, 17, 19, 15 16.8

8. 28, 14, 25, 13, 20 20

9. 3.7, 4.3, 4.4, 5.6 4.

Write as a decimal. (page 146)

10. $\frac{1}{2}$ 0.5 **11.** $\frac{7}{8}$ 0.875 **12.** $\frac{3}{4}$ 0.75 **13.** $\frac{2}{5}$ 0.4 **14.** $\frac{5}{8}$ 0.625 **15.** $3\frac{1}{2}$ 3.5 **16.** $4\frac{3}{8}$ 4.37

17. $\frac{3}{10}$ 0.3 **18.** $\frac{4}{5}$ 0.8 **19.** $1\frac{3}{5}$ 1.6 **20.** $4\frac{1}{2}$ 4.5 **21.** $6\frac{1}{8}$ 6.125 **22.** $6\frac{2}{5}$ 6.4 **23.** $3\frac{1}{10}$ 3.1

24. $11\frac{1}{4}$ 11.25 **25.** $16\frac{7}{10}$ 16.7 **26.** $18\frac{1}{5}$ 18.2 **27.** $21\frac{3}{20}$ 21.15 **28.** $12\frac{7}{8}$ 12.8/5 **29.** $42\frac{3}{4}$ 42.75 **30.** $13\frac{1}{2}$ 13.

Change to a fraction or mixed number in simplest form. (page 148)

31. 0.6 $\frac{3}{5}$ **32.** 0.08 $\frac{2}{25}$ **33.** 0.25 $\frac{1}{4}$ **34.** 0.8 $\frac{4}{5}$ **35.** 0.5 $\frac{1}{2}$ **36.** 0.45 $\frac{9}{20}$ **37.** 0.75 $\frac{3}{4}$

38. 0.625 $\frac{5}{8}$ **39.** 1.75 $1\frac{3}{4}$ **40.** 2.5 $2\frac{1}{2}$ **41.** 6.125 $6\frac{1}{8}$ **42.** 5.6 $5\frac{3}{5}$ **43.** 9.45 $9\frac{9}{20}$ **44.** 6.375 6

Add. Give the sum in simplest form. (page 160)

45. $8\frac{1}{3}$
$+4\frac{1}{6}$
$12\frac{1}{2}$

46. $5\frac{1}{8}$
$+6\frac{3}{4}$
$11\frac{7}{8}$

47. $6\frac{5}{8}$
$+3\frac{1}{4}$
$9\frac{7}{8}$

48. $3\frac{1}{6}$
$+5\frac{5}{12}$
$8\frac{7}{12}$

49. $2\frac{1}{6}$
$+7\frac{2}{3}$
$9\frac{5}{6}$

50. $7\frac{2}{3}$
$+6\frac{1}{4}$
$13\frac{11}{12}$

51. $8\frac{1}{5}$
$+3\frac{1}{2}$
$11\frac{7}{10}$

52. $7\frac{2}{3}$
$+9\frac{1}{6}$
$16\frac{5}{6}$

53. $12\frac{1}{8}$
$+ 4\frac{1}{2}$
$16\frac{5}{8}$

54. $14\frac{3}{4}$
$+ 8\frac{1}{8}$
$22\frac{7}{8}$

Subtract. Give the difference in simplest form. (pages 168, 170)

55. $6\frac{7}{8}$
$-3\frac{1}{8}$
$3\frac{3}{4}$

56. $12\frac{5}{6}$
$- 9\frac{1}{6}$
$3\frac{2}{3}$

57. $23\frac{7}{8}$
$-17\frac{1}{4}$
$6\frac{5}{8}$

58. $29\frac{2}{3}$
$-18\frac{1}{6}$
$11\frac{1}{2}$

59. $24\frac{1}{3}$
$- 7\frac{5}{6}$
$16\frac{1}{2}$

60. $6\frac{1}{3}$
$-2\frac{3}{5}$
$3\frac{11}{15}$

61. $11\frac{3}{8}$
$- 8\frac{5}{6}$
$2\frac{13}{24}$

62. $8\frac{1}{2}$
$-6\frac{7}{8}$
$1\frac{5}{8}$

63. $14\frac{3}{5}$
$- 9\frac{7}{10}$
$4\frac{9}{10}$

64. $9\frac{5}{6}$
$-7\frac{2}{3}$
$2\frac{1}{6}$

172

Problem solving

COMPUTERS IN AUTOMOBILES

You recently purchased a new car that has an advanced electronics system and a built-in computer. You are in your car driving up a steep hill and decide to use the Fuel Data Panel.

There are three buttons on the panel. You press the one on the left. The digital display shows the miles per gallon your car is producing at this instant.

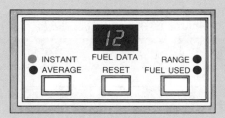

1. a. At this rate, how far will your car travel on 22 gallons of fuel? 264 miles

   b. If the rate improves to 18 miles per gallon, how much further will your car travel at this new rate? 132 miles

You want to know how many miles you can travel on the fuel remaining in the tank. You press the button on the right.

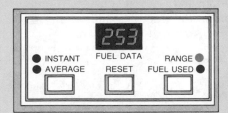

3. You plan to drive 185 miles to Lancaster and then drive on to Colebrook, another 91 miles. If the computer's estimate is accurate, can you make the trip to Colebrook without stopping for fuel? No

You want to know your car's average miles per gallon since the system was last reset. (To reset the system, you press the middle button.) You press the button on the left a second time.

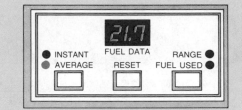

2. a. At this rate, how many gallons have been used if the car was driven 247 miles? (Round the answer to the nearest tenth of a gallon.) 11.4

   b. At this rate, how many miles would the car have been driven if 17.5 gallons of fuel had been used? 379.75

You want to know how many gallons of fuel you have used since your last fill-up. You press the button on the right a second time.

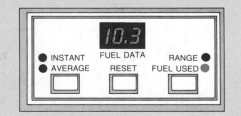

4. a. Your fuel tank holds 22 gallons of fuel. How many gallons are left in the tank? 11.7

   b. Gasoline costs $1.39 per gallon. Can you fill your tank for $15.00? Yes

EXTRA PROBLEM SOLVING
Page 450   Even exercises

PROBLEM-SOLVING WORKSHEET
Copymaster S226 or Duplicating Master S226

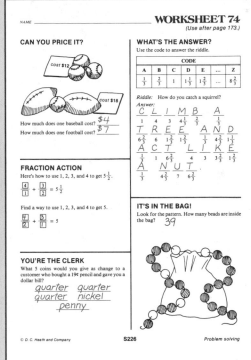

LIFE-SKILL PROJECT

Estimating sums

Have the students estimate which two decimals in exercises 31–44 on page 172 have a sum of:

1. 2.75   2.5 + 0.25
2. 0.95   0.5 + 0.45
3. 6.2   0.6 + 5.6
4. 6.925   0.8 + 6.125

If calculators are available have the students use them to see whether they make the correct choices.

Add. Write the sum in simplest form. *(pages 156, 158)*

1. $\frac{1}{7} + \frac{2}{7} = \frac{5}{7}$ 2. $\frac{2}{5} + \frac{3}{5} = 1$ 3. $\frac{3}{4} + \frac{3}{4} = 1\frac{1}{2}$

4. $\frac{2}{3} + \frac{1}{6} = \frac{5}{6}$ 5. $\frac{1}{4} + \frac{1}{2} = \frac{3}{4}$ 6. $\frac{1}{4} + \frac{3}{8} = \frac{5}{8}$

7. $\frac{1}{2} + \frac{1}{3} = \frac{5}{6}$ 8. $\frac{3}{4} + \frac{5}{6} = 1\frac{7}{12}$ 9. $\frac{1}{6} + \frac{5}{9} = \frac{13}{18}$

10. $\frac{3}{4} + \frac{2}{3} = 1\frac{5}{12}$ 11. $\frac{5}{6} + \frac{7}{8} = 1\frac{17}{24}$ 12. $\frac{2}{3} + \frac{5}{8} = 1\frac{7}{24}$

13. $\frac{9}{10} + \frac{0}{4} = \frac{9}{10}$

	ANSWERS
1.	$\frac{5}{7}$
2.	1
3.	$1\frac{1}{2}$
4.	$\frac{5}{6}$
5.	$\frac{3}{4}$
6.	$\frac{5}{8}$
7.	$\frac{5}{6}$
8.	$1\frac{7}{12}$
9.	$\frac{13}{18}$
10.	$1\frac{5}{12}$
11.	$1\frac{17}{24}$
12.	$1\frac{7}{24}$
13.	$\frac{9}{10}$
14.	$7\frac{1}{2}$
15.	$5\frac{3}{5}$
16.	6
17.	7
18.	$8\frac{1}{4}$
19.	$10\frac{1}{2}$
20.	$10\frac{1}{8}$
21.	$12\frac{5}{8}$
22.	$13\frac{1}{3}$
23.	$16\frac{5}{24}$
24.	$12\frac{5}{12}$
25.	$16\frac{1}{8}$

Add. Write the sum in simplest form. *(page 160)*

14. $4\frac{1}{2}$ $+3$ = $7\frac{1}{2}$ 15. $3\frac{3}{5}$ $+2\frac{1}{5}$ = $5\frac{3}{5}$ 16. $2\frac{1}{2}$ $+3\frac{1}{2}$ = 6 17. $4\frac{1}{3}$ $+2\frac{2}{3}$ = 7

18. $+3$ = $8\frac{1}{4}$ 19. $+5\frac{5}{6}$ = $10\frac{1}{2}$ 20. $6\frac{3}{4}$ $+3\frac{3}{8}$ = $10\frac{1}{8}$ 21. $4\frac{1}{4}$ $+8\frac{1}{3}$ = $12\frac{5}{8}$

22. $6\frac{2}{3}$ $+6\frac{3}{3}$ = $13\frac{1}{3}$ 23. $7\frac{5}{6}$ $+8\frac{1}{8}$ = $16\frac{5}{24}$ 24. $5\frac{2}{3}$ $+6\frac{3}{4}$ = $12\frac{5}{12}$ 25. $7\frac{4}{8}$ $+8\frac{1}{8}$ = $16\frac{1}{8}$

Subtract. Write the difference in simplest form. *(pages 164, 166)*

26. $\frac{3}{5} - \frac{1}{5} = \frac{2}{5}$ 27. $\frac{3}{4} - \frac{1}{4} = \frac{1}{2}$ 28. $\frac{7}{8} - \frac{1}{8} = \frac{3}{4}$

29. $\frac{2}{3} - \frac{1}{6} = \frac{1}{2}$ 30. $\frac{5}{6} - \frac{1}{3} = \frac{1}{2}$ 31. $\frac{5}{8} - \frac{1}{4} = \frac{3}{8}$

32. $\frac{3}{4} - \frac{1}{4} = \frac{1}{2}$ 33. $\frac{7}{8} - \frac{1}{3} = \frac{13}{24}$ 34. $\frac{4}{5} - \frac{5}{9} = \frac{5}{10}$

	ANSWERS
26.	$\frac{2}{5}$
27.	$\frac{1}{2}$
28.	$\frac{3}{4}$
29.	$\frac{1}{2}$
30.	$\frac{1}{2}$
31.	$\frac{3}{8}$
32.	$\frac{1}{2}$
33.	$\frac{13}{24}$
34.	$\frac{5}{18}$
35.	$2\frac{2}{3}$
36.	$4\frac{1}{2}$
37.	$3\frac{1}{3}$
38.	$6\frac{3}{4}$
39.	$4\frac{1}{4}$
40.	$2\frac{3}{8}$
41.	$4\frac{1}{6}$
42.	$5\frac{1}{2}$
43.	$5\frac{5}{8}$
44.	$5\frac{3}{4}$
45.	$4\frac{17}{24}$
46.	$2\frac{11}{12}$
47.	$\frac{3}{4}$ cup
48.	$1\frac{1}{4}$
49.	$\frac{3}{4}$ cup
50.	$\frac{1}{2}$ cup

Subtract. Write the difference in simplest form. *(pages 168, 170)*

35. $4\frac{2}{3}$ -2 = $2\frac{2}{3}$ 36. $5\frac{3}{4}$ $-1\frac{1}{4}$ = $4\frac{1}{2}$ 37. $6\frac{5}{9}$ $-3\frac{1}{3}$ = $3\frac{1}{3}$ 38. $8\frac{5}{8}$ $-2\frac{3}{4}$ = $6\frac{3}{4}$

39. $9\frac{3}{4}$ $-5\frac{1}{2}$ = $4\frac{1}{4}$ 40. $7\frac{5}{8}$ $-5\frac{1}{4}$ = $2\frac{3}{8}$ 41. $8\frac{5}{6}$ $-4\frac{3}{4}$ = $4\frac{1}{6}$ 42. $6\frac{3}{4}$ $-1\frac{1}{3}$ = $5\frac{1}{2}$

43. 8 $-2\frac{3}{8}$ = $5\frac{5}{8}$ 44. $9\frac{1}{2}$ $-3\frac{3}{4}$ = $5\frac{3}{4}$ 45. $6\frac{1}{3}$ $-1\frac{5}{8}$ = $4\frac{17}{24}$ 46. $7\frac{3}{4}$ $-4\frac{5}{6}$ = $2\frac{11}{12}$

Solve.

Date-Nut Muffins
1¼ cups milk
1 egg
1¼ cups bleached flour
½ cup brown sugar
¼ cup white sugar
1 cup whole-wheat flour
¼ cup walnuts
½ cup pecans
1 teaspoon salt
¾ cup dates
3 teaspoons baking powder
¼ cup butter

47. How much sugar is needed? $\frac{3}{4}$ cup

48. How many cups of nuts are needed? $1\frac{1}{4}$

49. How much more bleached flour is needed than whole-wheat flour? $\frac{3}{4}$ cup

50. You have $\frac{3}{4}$ cup of milk. How much more do you need? $\frac{1}{2}$ cup

Chapter REVIEW

Here are scrambled answers for the review exercises:

8	add	equivalent	numerators	subtract
12	common	fractions	regroup	whole
20	denominator	numbers	simplest	

1. add

1. To complete this sum, you would [?] the numerators and use the common denominator. *(page 156)*

$$\frac{3}{5} + \frac{1}{5} = \frac{?}{?}$$

2. common, 12

2. To complete this sum, you would first change to equivalent fractions with a [?] denominator. The least common denominator is [?]. *(page 158)*

$$\frac{3}{4} + \frac{2}{3} = \frac{?}{?} + \frac{?}{?}$$

3. fractions, whole, simplest

3. To complete this addition exercise, you would add the [?] and then add the [?] numbers. The last step would be to write the sum in [?] form. *(page 160)*

$$2\frac{2}{3} = 2\frac{4}{6}$$
$$+ 1\frac{1}{2} = +1\frac{3}{6}$$

4. subtract, denominator

4. To complete this difference, you would [?] the numerators and use the common [?]. *(page 164)*

$$\frac{5}{9} - \frac{4}{9} = \frac{?}{?}$$

5. equivalent, numerators

5. To complete this difference, you would first change to [?] fractions with a common denominator. Then you would subtract the [?] and use the common denominator. *(page 166)*

$$\frac{5}{6} - \frac{2}{3} = \frac{?}{?} - \frac{?}{?}$$

6. 20, numbers

6. To complete this subtraction exercise, you would first change to equivalent fractions using the least common denominator, [?]. Then you would subtract the fractions and whole [?]. *(page 168)*

$$4\frac{4}{5} = 4\frac{?}{?}$$
$$- 2\frac{1}{4} = -2\frac{?}{?}$$

7. regroup, 8

7. The next step in this subtraction exercise would be to [?] one for [?] eighths. *(page 170)*

$$5\frac{1}{8} = 5\frac{1}{8}$$
$$- 3\frac{1}{2} = -3\frac{4}{8}$$

Add. Write the sum in simplest form. *(pages 156, 158)*

1. $\frac{5}{9} + \frac{2}{9}$ $\frac{7}{9}$
2. $\frac{1}{8} + \frac{3}{8}$ $\frac{1}{2}$
3. $\frac{5}{6} + \frac{3}{6}$ $1\frac{1}{3}$
4. $\frac{2}{3} + \frac{1}{3}$ 1
5. $\frac{7}{9} + \frac{4}{9}$ $1\frac{2}{9}$
6. $\frac{1}{6} + \frac{2}{3}$ $\frac{5}{6}$
7. $\frac{1}{2} + \frac{1}{3}$ $\frac{5}{6}$
8. $\frac{5}{8} + \frac{3}{4}$ $1\frac{3}{8}$
9. $\frac{3}{4} + \frac{2}{3}$ $1\frac{5}{12}$
10. $\frac{3}{4} + \frac{1}{2}$ $1\frac{1}{4}$

Add. Write the sum in simplest form. *(page 160)*

11. $3\frac{1}{3}$
  $+2\frac{1}{3}$
  $5\frac{2}{3}$
12. $2\frac{1}{2}$
  $+1\frac{1}{2}$
  4
13. $5\frac{3}{5}$
  $+3\frac{1}{5}$
  $8\frac{4}{5}$
14. $4\frac{3}{8}$
  $+4\frac{1}{8}$
  $8\frac{1}{2}$
15. $2\frac{4}{9}$
  $+4\frac{5}{9}$
  7
16. $4\frac{3}{7}$
  $+8\frac{5}{7}$
  $13\frac{1}{7}$

17. $5\frac{2}{5}$
  $+2\frac{1}{2}$
  $7\frac{9}{10}$
18. $3\frac{1}{2}$
  $+6\frac{1}{3}$
  $9\frac{5}{6}$
19. $4\frac{2}{3}$
  $+5\frac{5}{6}$
  $10\frac{1}{2}$
20. $6\frac{3}{4}$
  $+2\frac{5}{6}$
  $9\frac{7}{12}$
21. $5\frac{7}{8}$
  $+5\frac{1}{2}$
  $11\frac{3}{8}$
22. $4\frac{1}{5}$
  $+3\frac{1}{10}$
  $7\frac{3}{10}$

Subtract. Write the difference in simplest form. *(pages 164, 166)*

23. $\frac{4}{5} - \frac{1}{5}$ $\frac{3}{5}$
24. $\frac{5}{6} - \frac{1}{6}$ $\frac{2}{3}$
25. $\frac{5}{8} - \frac{1}{8}$ $\frac{1}{2}$
26. $\frac{8}{9} - \frac{2}{9}$ $\frac{2}{3}$
27. $\frac{5}{7} - \frac{1}{7}$ $\frac{4}{7}$
28. $\frac{1}{2} - \frac{1}{4}$ $\frac{1}{4}$
29. $\frac{3}{4} - \frac{1}{3}$ $\frac{5}{12}$
30. $\frac{5}{9} - \frac{1}{6}$ $\frac{7}{18}$
31. $\frac{7}{8} - \frac{1}{3}$ $\frac{13}{24}$
32. $\frac{1}{2} - \frac{3}{8}$ $\frac{1}{8}$

Subtract. Write the difference in simplest form. *(pages 168, 170)*

33. $5\frac{3}{5}$
  $-2\frac{1}{5}$
  $3\frac{2}{5}$
34. $6\frac{3}{4}$
  $-4\frac{1}{4}$
  $2\frac{1}{2}$
35. $7\frac{2}{3}$
  $-1\frac{1}{6}$
  $6\frac{1}{2}$
36. $8\frac{4}{5}$
  $-3\frac{1}{4}$
  $5\frac{11}{20}$
37. $6\frac{7}{8}$
  $-2\frac{2}{3}$
  $4\frac{5}{24}$
38. $9\frac{4}{5}$
  $-3\frac{1}{2}$
  $6\frac{3}{10}$

39. $9\frac{1}{4}$
  $-6\frac{1}{2}$
  $2\frac{3}{4}$
40. $7\frac{1}{2}$
  $-4\frac{3}{5}$
  $2\frac{9}{10}$
41. 8
  $-5\frac{5}{6}$
  $2\frac{1}{6}$
42. 5
  $-2\frac{7}{8}$
  $2\frac{1}{8}$
43. $6\frac{2}{3}$
  $-3\frac{3}{4}$
  $2\frac{11}{12}$
44. $8\frac{1}{3}$
  $-2\frac{4}{9}$
  $5\frac{8}{9}$

Solve. Write the answer in simplest form.

45. How many cups of flour are needed? $6\frac{1}{4}$

46. You have $\frac{3}{4}$ cup of milk. How much more do you need? $\frac{3}{4}$

SEEDLESS RYE BREAD

$2\frac{3}{4}$ cups rye flour
$3\frac{1}{2}$ cups white flour
1 tablespoon sugar
2 teaspoons salt
1 package yeast

2 tablespoons honey
1 tablespoon butter
$1\frac{1}{2}$ cups milk
$\frac{1}{4}$ cup water

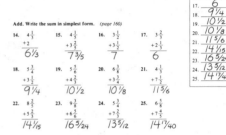
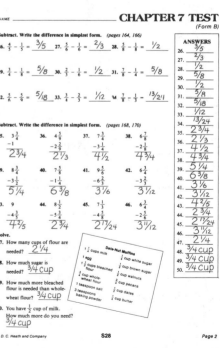

Use Copymaster S336 to provide the students with an answer sheet in standardized test format.

Cumulative TEST
Standardized Format

Choose the correct letter.

Answers for Cumulative Test, Chapters 1–7

1. Ⓐ Ⓑ C D   2. Ⓐ Ⓑ ● D   3. Ⓐ B ● D
4. Ⓐ B ● D   5. Ⓐ B ● D   6. ● B C D
7. Ⓐ ● C D   8. Ⓐ B ● D   9. ● B C D
10. Ⓐ B C ●   11. Ⓐ B C ●   12. Ⓐ B ● D

The table below correlates test items with student text pages.

Test Item	Page(s) Taught	Skill Practice
1	24	p. 162, exercises 1–12
2	46	p. 162, exercises 13–24
3	64	p. 162, exercises 25–36
4	92	p. 162, exercises 37–51
5	96	p. 162, exercises 52–67
6	114	p. 172, exercises 1–9
7	146	p. 172, exercises 10–30
8	148	p. 172, exercises 31–44
9	160	p. 172, exercises 45–54
10	168, 170	p. 172, exercises 55–64
11	108	
12	170	

1. Give the sum.

$81.6 + 42.53 + 231.5$

A. 355.63
B. 73.84
C. 354.63
D. none of these

2. Give the difference.

$64.03 - 2.946$

A. 34.57
B. 3.457
C. 61.084
D. none of these

3. Give the product.

20.6×1.28

A. 26.268
B. 26.368
C. 263.68
D. none of these

4. Give the quotient.

$516.3 \div 100$

A. 51,630
B. 0.5163
C. 5.163
D. none of these

5. Give the quotient rounded to the nearest hundredth.

$21.57 \div 3.7$

A. 5.82
B. 0.58
C. 5.83
D. none of these

6. The mean of 48, 52, 46, 46, and 53 is

A. 49
B. 46
C. 48
D. none of these

7. $2\frac{7}{8} = ?$

A. 0.875
B. 2.875
C. 2.125
D. none of these

8. $1.75 = ?$

A. $\frac{3}{4}$
B. $1\frac{1}{4}$
C. $1\frac{3}{4}$
D. none of these

9. Add. $3\frac{3}{4}$
$+2\frac{2}{3}$

A. $6\frac{5}{12}$ C. $5\frac{5}{7}$
B. $5\frac{5}{12}$ D. none of these

10. Subtract. $5\frac{1}{3}$
$-3\frac{1}{2}$

A. $2\frac{1}{6}$
B. $2\frac{5}{6}$
C. $1\frac{1}{6}$
D. none of these

11. QUIZ SCORES

The score on the third quiz was

A. 60   B. 55
C. 50   D. 45

12. You volunteer to work 12 hours on a class project. You work $2\frac{1}{2}$ hours on Friday and $6\frac{3}{4}$ hours on Saturday. How many hours do you have left to work?

A. $7\frac{3}{4}$ B. $3\frac{3}{4}$
C. $2\frac{3}{4}$ D. none of these

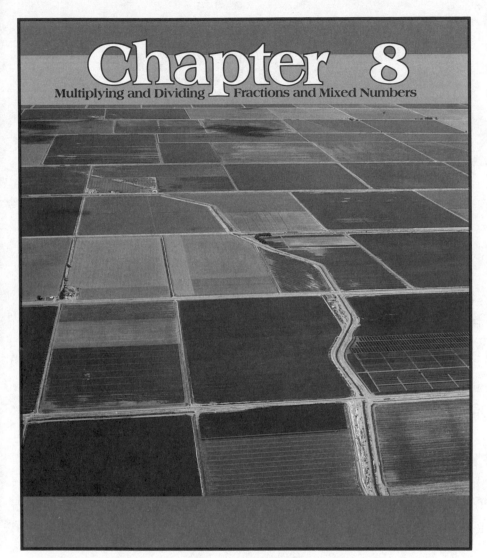

Chapter 8
Multiplying and Dividing Fractions and Mixed Numbers

CHAPTER 8
Multiplying and Dividing Fractions and Mixed Numbers

LESSON OBJECTIVES
To multiply a fraction by a fraction (*pages 178–179*)
To find a fraction of a whole number (*pages 180–181*)
To multiply mixed numbers (*pages 182–183*)
To relate fractions to customary units of measure
  (*pages 184–185*)
To identify reciprocals (*pages 188–189*)
To divide by a fraction (*pages 188–189*)
To divide a fraction by a whole number (*pages 188–189*)
To divide mixed numbers (*pages 190–191*)

PROBLEM-SOLVING SKILLS
Finding information in a display (*pages 178, 190–191*)
Solving a multi-step problem (*pages 179, 187*)
Selecting information from a newspaper ad (*pages 180–181*)
Choosing the correct operation (*pages 181, 183, 191*)
Using logical reasoning (*page 181*)
Finding information in a recipe (*pages 182–183*)
Following directions and checking answers (*pages 183, 191*)
Analyzing a sequence of events (*page 185*)
Using a table (*page 187*)
Using a picture to solve a problem (*page 188*)
Reading a chart (*page 189*)
Using a drawing (*page 193*)
Following instructions (*page 193*)

RESOURCES
- **VISUAL AIDS**
  Chart from page 187 (*Visual Aid 30, Copymaster S132*)
  Electrode display from page 193 (*Visual Aid 31, Copymaster S133*)
- **WORKSHEETS 75–82** (*Copymasters S227–S234 or Duplicating Masters S227–S234*)

LESSON OBJECTIVE
To multiply a fraction by a fraction

PROBLEM-SOLVING SKILLS
Finding information in a display
Solving a multi-step problem

STARTING THE LESSON
Before discussing exercises 1–6, draw a square on the chalkboard. Ask a student to draw a line that divides your square into halves. Ask another student to draw a line that divides each half into halves. Shade in one section.

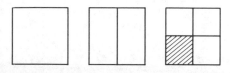

Write $\frac{1}{2}$ of $\frac{1}{2}$ = ? on the chalkboard. Point out to the students that their diagram shows that $\frac{1}{2}$ of $\frac{1}{2}$ is $\frac{1}{4}$. Repeat with thirds. Write $\frac{1}{3}$ of $\frac{1}{3}$ = $\frac{1}{9}$ on the chalkboard.

Multiplying fractions

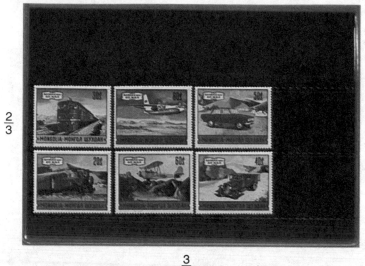

1. How many stamps are on the page? 6

2. How many stamps can be mounted on a full page? 12

3. What fraction of the page is covered with stamps? $\frac{6}{12}$ or $\frac{1}{2}$

4. To find what fraction of the page is covered with stamps, you could multiply $\frac{2}{3}$ by what fraction? $\frac{3}{4}$

Here's how *to multiply fractions.* $\frac{2}{3} \times \frac{3}{4} = ?$

Multiply the numerators to get the numerator of the product and multiply the denominators to get the denominator of the product.

Multiply numerators.
Multiply denominators.

Write the product
in simplest form.

$$\frac{2}{3} \times \frac{3}{4} = \frac{6}{12}$$

$$\frac{2}{3} \times \frac{3}{4} = \frac{6}{12}$$
$$= \frac{1}{2}$$

---

5. Look at the *Here's how*. What fraction of the page is covered with stamps? $\frac{1}{2}$

6. Check these examples. Give each product in simplest form.

a. $\frac{2}{3} \times \frac{3}{8} = \frac{6}{24}$
     $= ?$ $\frac{1}{4}$

b. $2 \times \frac{3}{4} = \frac{2}{1} \times \frac{3}{4}$
     $\boxed{\frac{2}{1}}$ $= ?$ $1\frac{1}{2}$

178

EXERCISES

Multiply. Write the product in simplest form.

Here are scrambled answers for the next row of exercises: $\frac{5}{8}$ 1 $\frac{1}{5}$ $2\frac{1}{4}$ $\frac{1}{16}$ $\frac{2}{7}$

7. $\frac{1}{2} \times \frac{2}{5}$ $\frac{1}{5}$
8. $3 \times \frac{3}{4}$ $2\frac{1}{4}$
9. $\frac{5}{6} \times \frac{3}{4}$ $\frac{5}{8}$
10. $\frac{2}{3} \times \frac{3}{2}$ 1
11. $\frac{1}{4} \times \frac{1}{4}$ $\frac{1}{16}$
12. $\frac{2}{3} \times \frac{3}{7}$ $\frac{2}{7}$

13. $\frac{2}{3} \times 2$ $1\frac{1}{3}$
14. $\frac{1}{2} \times \frac{2}{3}$ $\frac{1}{3}$
15. $\frac{1}{2} \times \frac{1}{3}$ $\frac{1}{6}$
16. $\frac{1}{4} \times \frac{5}{8}$ $\frac{5}{32}$
17. $3 \times \frac{1}{3}$ 1
18. $\frac{1}{5} \times \frac{1}{5}$ $\frac{1}{25}$

19. $\frac{4}{3} \times \frac{2}{5}$ $\frac{8}{15}$
20. $\frac{3}{2} \times \frac{3}{4}$ $1\frac{1}{8}$
21. $4 \times \frac{3}{4}$ 3
22. $\frac{3}{8} \times \frac{2}{3}$ $\frac{1}{4}$
23. $\frac{0}{3} \times \frac{4}{5}$ 0
24. $\frac{2}{7} \times \frac{7}{3}$ $\frac{2}{3}$

25. $\frac{2}{5} \times \frac{3}{2}$ $\frac{3}{5}$
26. $\frac{3}{4} \times \frac{2}{3}$ $\frac{1}{2}$
27. $4 \times \frac{2}{3}$ $2\frac{2}{3}$
28. $\frac{5}{6} \times \frac{1}{3}$ $\frac{5}{18}$
29. $\frac{3}{4} \times \frac{3}{4}$ $\frac{9}{16}$
30. $10 \times \frac{4}{5}$ 8

31. $\frac{3}{4} \times 3$ $2\frac{1}{4}$
32. $\frac{3}{2} \times \frac{1}{4}$ $\frac{3}{8}$
33. $\frac{5}{2} \times \frac{2}{5}$ 1
34. $\frac{2}{9} \times \frac{3}{4}$ $\frac{1}{6}$
35. $\frac{3}{2} \times \frac{0}{2}$ 0
36. $\frac{3}{5} \times \frac{5}{8}$ $\frac{3}{8}$

37. $\frac{1}{3} \times \frac{3}{4}$ $\frac{1}{4}$
38. $\frac{5}{8} \times \frac{4}{5}$ $\frac{1}{2}$
39. $3 \times \frac{5}{6}$ $2\frac{1}{2}$
40. $\frac{9}{2} \times \frac{4}{3}$ 6
41. $\frac{3}{8} \times \frac{3}{8}$ $\frac{9}{64}$
42. $\frac{1}{2} \times \frac{1}{2}$ $\frac{1}{4}$

43. $\frac{5}{8} \times \frac{2}{5}$ $\frac{1}{4}$
44. $\frac{6}{5} \times \frac{15}{2}$ 9
45. $\frac{7}{10} \times \frac{5}{4}$ $\frac{7}{8}$
46. $6 \times \frac{3}{10}$ $1\frac{4}{5}$
47. $\frac{5}{6} \times \frac{6}{5}$ 1
48. $\frac{3}{5} \times \frac{5}{3}$ 1

49. $2 \times \frac{1}{2}$ 1
50. $\frac{5}{12} \times \frac{3}{2}$ $\frac{5}{8}$
51. $\frac{4}{3} \times \frac{3}{4}$ 1
52. $\frac{4}{3} \times \frac{7}{12}$ $\frac{7}{9}$
53. $\frac{15}{16} \times \frac{4}{5}$ $\frac{3}{4}$
54. $4 \times \frac{3}{4}$ 3

55. $5 \times \frac{2}{5}$ 2
56. $\frac{3}{5} \times \frac{1}{3}$ $\frac{1}{5}$
57. $\frac{1}{5} \times \frac{1}{4}$ $\frac{1}{20}$
58. $8 \times \frac{9}{8}$ 9
59. $\frac{2}{7} \times \frac{1}{2}$ $\frac{1}{7}$
60. $\frac{12}{13} \times \frac{1}{2}$ $\frac{6}{13}$

61. $\frac{1}{6} \times \frac{2}{3}$ $\frac{1}{9}$
62. $\frac{1}{2} \times \frac{4}{5}$ $\frac{2}{5}$
63. $6 \times \frac{1}{2}$ 3
64. $\frac{1}{3} \times \frac{2}{5}$ $\frac{2}{15}$
65. $6 \times \frac{1}{6}$ 1
66. $9 \times \frac{4}{3}$ 12

Solve.

67. Two thirds of the stamps in a collection are U.S. stamps. One fourth of the U.S. stamps are airmail stamps. What fraction of the stamps are U.S. airmail stamps? $\frac{1}{6}$

68. One eighth of the stamps in an album were from Germany and one third of the stamps were from France. What fraction of the stamps were not from Germany or France? $\frac{13}{24}$

Airmail error

69. The most valuable United States stamp was printed in 1918. Its value resulted from a printer's error (the airplane was upside down). In 1979, 4 of these 24¢ stamps sold for a total of $500,000. The sale price was how many times the face value? Round the answer to the nearest tenth. 520,833.3

PRACTICE WORKSHEET
Copymaster S227 or Duplicating Master S227

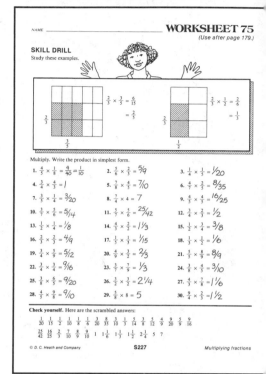

NAME _____ **WORKSHEET 75**
(Use after page 179.)

SKILL DRILL
Study these examples.

$\frac{2}{3} \times \frac{3}{5} = \frac{6}{15} = \frac{2}{5}$

$\frac{2}{3} \times \frac{1}{2} = \frac{2}{6} = \frac{1}{3}$

Multiply. Write the product in simplest form.

1. $\frac{4}{5} \times \frac{1}{8} = \frac{4}{40} = \frac{1}{10}$
2. $\frac{5}{6} \times \frac{2}{3} = \frac{5}{9}$
3. $\frac{1}{4} \times \frac{1}{5} = \frac{1}{20}$
4. $\frac{3}{4} \times \frac{4}{3} = 1$
5. $\frac{7}{8} \times \frac{4}{5} = \frac{7}{10}$
6. $\frac{4}{7} \times \frac{2}{5} = \frac{8}{35}$
7. $\frac{3}{5} \times \frac{1}{4} = \frac{3}{20}$
8. $\frac{7}{4} \times 4 = 7$
9. $\frac{4}{5} \times \frac{4}{5} = \frac{16}{25}$
10. $\frac{3}{7} \times \frac{5}{6} = \frac{5}{14}$
11. $\frac{5}{7} \times \frac{5}{6} = \frac{25}{42}$
12. $\frac{3}{4} \times \frac{2}{3} = \frac{1}{2}$
13. $\frac{1}{2} \times \frac{1}{4} = \frac{1}{8}$
14. $\frac{4}{3} \times \frac{2}{4} = 1\frac{1}{3}$
15. $\frac{1}{2} \times \frac{3}{4} = \frac{3}{8}$
16. $\frac{2}{3} \times \frac{2}{3} = \frac{4}{9}$
17. $\frac{1}{5} \times \frac{1}{3} = \frac{1}{15}$
18. $\frac{1}{3} \times \frac{1}{2} = \frac{1}{6}$
19. $\frac{3}{4} \times \frac{4}{9} = \frac{5}{12}$
20. $\frac{4}{9} \times \frac{3}{2} = \frac{2}{3}$
21. $\frac{5}{3} \times \frac{8}{5} = \frac{8}{9}$
22. $\frac{3}{4} \times \frac{3}{4} = \frac{9}{16}$
23. $\frac{3}{7} \times \frac{7}{9} = \frac{1}{3}$
24. $\frac{3}{8} \times \frac{4}{5} = \frac{3}{10}$
25. $\frac{3}{8} \times \frac{6}{5} = \frac{9}{20}$
26. $\frac{3}{2} \times \frac{3}{2} = 2\frac{1}{4}$
27. $\frac{4}{3} \times \frac{7}{8} = 1\frac{1}{6}$
28. $\frac{4}{5} \times \frac{9}{8} = \frac{9}{10}$
29. $\frac{5}{8} \times 8 = 5$
30. $\frac{9}{4} \times \frac{2}{3} = 1\frac{1}{2}$

Check yourself. Here are the scrambled answers:

$\frac{1}{20}$ $\frac{1}{15}$ $\frac{2}{3}$ $\frac{1}{10}$ $\frac{1}{8}$ $\frac{1}{6}$ $\frac{3}{20}$ $\frac{8}{35}$ $\frac{3}{10}$ $\frac{3}{1}$ $\frac{3}{14}$ $\frac{8}{12}$ $\frac{4}{9}$ $\frac{9}{20}$ $\frac{9}{9}$ $\frac{5}{16}$

$\frac{25}{42}$ $\frac{16}{25}$ $\frac{2}{3}$ $\frac{7}{10}$ $\frac{8}{9}$ $\frac{9}{10}$ 1 $1\frac{1}{6}$ $1\frac{1}{3}$ $1\frac{1}{2}$ $2\frac{1}{4}$ 5 7

© D. C. Heath and Company   S227   Multiplying fractions

CHALKBOARD CHALLENGE
Find a way to fold a piece of notebook paper to show that $\frac{3}{4} \times \frac{1}{2} = \frac{3}{8}$.

LESSON OBJECTIVE
To find a fraction of a whole number

PROBLEM-SOLVING SKILLS
Selecting information from a newspaper ad
Choosing the correct operation
Using logical reasoning

STARTING THE LESSON
Play 'What are the facts?' Have the students study the ad at the top of page 180 for 30 seconds. Then tell them to close their books and try to decide whether these statements are true or false:

• There are two types of men's shoes on sale. (True)
• The sale price of the women's jogging shoes is less than $36. (True)
• The men's tennis shoes are on sale for one-half the regular price. (True)
• The regular price of the men's jogging shoes is $54. (False)

A fraction of a whole number

SHOE SALE!

Regular price **$36**
$\frac{2}{3}$ of Regular Price
Women's Jogging Shoes

Regular price **$40**
$\frac{1}{2}$ of Regular Price
Men's Tennis Shoes

Regular price **$44**
$\frac{3}{4}$ of Regular Price
Men's Jogging Shoes

1. What is the regular price of the women's jogging shoes? $36

2. The sale price of the women's jogging shoes is what fraction of the regular price? $\frac{2}{3}$

3. To find the sale price, you would find $\frac{2}{3}$ of what price? $36

Here's how *to find a fraction of a number.* $\frac{2}{3}$ *of $36 = ?*

SHORTCUT METHOD!
When the denominator is a divisor of the whole number, you can divide the whole number by the denominator and then multiply the result by the numerator.

$$\boxed{36 \div 3 \times 2 = 24}$$

$\frac{2}{3}$ of $36 = $24

Note:

Dividing a number by 3 gives $\frac{1}{3}$ of the number.

Multiplying that result by 2 gives $\frac{2}{3}$ of the number.

REGULAR METHOD
Change the whole number to a fraction and multiply.

$$\frac{2}{3} \text{ of } \$36 = \frac{2}{3} \times \frac{\$36}{1}$$
$$= \frac{\$72}{3}$$
$$= \$24$$

---

4. Look at the *Here's how*. What is the sale price of the women's jogging shoes? $24

5. In which method was the computing easier?   Shortcut method

6. You can use the shortcut when the $\dfrac{?}{\text{numerator/denominator}}$ of the fraction is a divisor of the whole number.

denominator

EXERCISES

Use the shortcut to complete each exercise.
Here are scrambled answers for the next row of exercises: 4   12   3   27

7. $\frac{1}{4}$ of 12 = ?   3   **8.** $\frac{2}{3}$ of 18 = ?   12   **9.** $\frac{3}{4}$ of 36 = ?   27   **10.** $\frac{2}{5}$ of 10 = ?   4

11. $\frac{3}{5}$ of 20 = ?   12   **12.** $\frac{3}{8}$ of 48 = ?   18   **13.** $\frac{1}{5}$ of 15 = ?   3   **14.** $\frac{5}{6}$ of 30 = ?   25

15. $\frac{3}{10}$ of 60 = ?   18   **16.** $\frac{1}{3}$ of 33 = ?   11   **17.** $\frac{5}{8}$ of 48 = ?   30   **18.** $\frac{3}{4}$ of 48 = ?   36

19. $\frac{2}{3}$ of \$30 = ?   \$20   **20.** $\frac{3}{5}$ of \$30 = ?   \$18   **21.** $\frac{1}{2}$ of \$32 = ?   \$16   **22.** $\frac{9}{10}$ of \$100 = ?   \$90

23. $\frac{1}{8}$ of \$48 = ?   \$6   **24.** $\frac{7}{10}$ of \$60 = ?   \$42   **25.** $\frac{4}{5}$ of \$45 = ?   \$36   **26.** $\frac{7}{8}$ of \$56 = ?   \$49

You decide which method to use. Give the answer in simplest form.
Here are scrambled answers for the next row of exercises: $10\frac{1}{2}$ 21   15 $15\frac{1}{3}$

27. $\frac{1}{2}$ of 21 = ? $10\frac{1}{2}$ **28.** $\frac{3}{4}$ of 28 = ?   21   **29.** $\frac{2}{3}$ of 23 = ? $15\frac{1}{3}$ **30.** $\frac{5}{6}$ of 18 = ?   15

31. $\frac{4}{5}$ of 25 = ?   20   **32.** $\frac{2}{3}$ of 16 = ? $10\frac{2}{3}$ **33.** $\frac{1}{6}$ of 24 = ?   4   **34.** $\frac{3}{8}$ of 31 = ? $11\frac{5}{8}$

35. $\frac{3}{4}$ of 15 = ? $11\frac{1}{4}$ **36.** $\frac{1}{3}$ of 28 = ? $9\frac{1}{3}$ **37.** $\frac{7}{10}$ of 20 = ?   14   **38.** $\frac{7}{8}$ of 27 = ? $23\frac{5}{8}$

39. $\frac{11}{12}$ of 12 = ?   11   **40.** $\frac{2}{5}$ of 12 = ? $4\frac{4}{5}$ **41.** $\frac{1}{5}$ of 12 = ? $2\frac{2}{5}$ **42.** $\frac{3}{4}$ of 12 = ?   9

43. $\frac{3}{8}$ of \$40 = ?   \$15   **44.** $\frac{4}{5}$ of \$35 = ?   \$28   **45.** $\frac{5}{6}$ of \$48 = ?   \$40   **46.** $\frac{2}{3}$ of \$60 = ?   \$40

Solve. Use the ad on page 180.

47. What is the sale price of the men's tennis shoes?   \$20

48. What is the sale price of the men's jogging shoes?   \$33

49. What is the difference in the sale price of the two men's styles?   \$13

50. How much would one save by buying the men's jogging shoes on sale?   \$11

Pick-a-pair   Using logical reasoning

51. You have 4 pairs of brown socks and 5 pairs of blue socks. It is dark and the lights go out in your room! How many socks must you pick to be sure that you have a pair that matches?   3

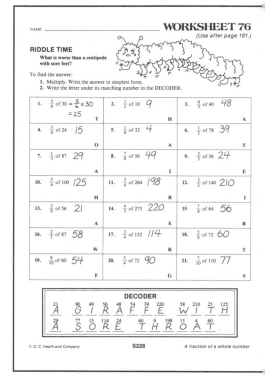

EXTRA PRACTICE
Page 435   Skill 47

PRACTICE WORKSHEET
Copymaster S228 or Duplicating Master S228

LIFE-SKILL PROJECT
Using a glossary
Have the students look for these words in the Glossary of their math book:

1. Find a 4-letter math word. One half of the letters must be a.   area

2. Find a 10-letter math word. One fifth of the letters must be f.   difference

3. Find a 9-letter math word. Four ninths of the letters must be a vowel.   numerator

Answers will vary.
  numerator
  perimeter
  trapezoid
  remainder
  decimeter
  dekameter
  kilometer
  opposites

---CHALKBOARD QUIZ---
on previous lesson
Give the answer in simplest form.

1. $\frac{1}{3}$ of 21   7   2. $\frac{2}{3}$ of 15   10

3. $\frac{3}{10}$ of 40   12   4. $\frac{4}{5}$ of 30   24

5. $\frac{1}{2}$ of 15 $7\frac{1}{2}$ 6. $\frac{3}{4}$ of 5 $3\frac{3}{4}$

7. $\frac{3}{8}$ of 8   3   8. $\frac{5}{6}$ of 48   40

LESSON OBJECTIVE
To multiply mixed numbers

PROBLEM-SOLVING SKILLS
Finding information in a recipe
Choosing the correct operation
Following directions and checking answers

STARTING THE LESSON
Have the students look at the recipe card on page 182. "How many bars does the recipe make?" (48) Ask the students to find the amount of each ingredient that would be needed to double the recipe, that is, to make 8 dozen, or 96, bars.

Multiplying mixed numbers

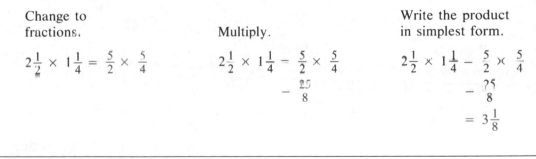

SPICE BARS

Makes 4 dozen bars

$1\frac{1}{2}$ cups all-purpose flour $\frac{3}{4}$ teaspoon salt

$1\frac{1}{4}$ cups sugar   1 teaspoon baking soda

$\frac{1}{2}$ cup milk $1\frac{1}{4}$ teaspoons cinnamon

$\frac{1}{2}$ cup vegetable oil   1 teaspoon cloves

2 eggs $\frac{1}{2}$ cup chopped nuts

$\frac{1}{2}$ cup raisins

Preheat oven to 350°F. Grease 9" x 10" jelly-roll pan. Combine all ingredients in large bowl and mix well. Turn batter into prepared pan, spreading evenly. Bake until golden, about 20 minutes. Cool in pan on rack 10 minutes. Cut into bars.

1. How many bars does this recipe make?   48

2. How much sugar is needed to make the recipe? $1\frac{1}{4}$ cups

3. You want to make $2\frac{1}{2}$ times the recipe. What two mixed numbers should you multiply to find how many cups of sugar you will need? $2\frac{1}{2}$ and $1\frac{1}{4}$

Here's how *to multiply mixed numbers.* $2\frac{1}{2} \times 1\frac{1}{4} = ?$

Change each mixed number to a fraction and multiply.

Change to fractions.

$$2\frac{1}{2} \times 1\frac{1}{4} = \frac{5}{2} \times \frac{5}{4}$$

Multiply.

$$2\frac{1}{2} \times 1\frac{1}{4} = \frac{5}{2} \times \frac{5}{4}$$
$$= \frac{25}{8}$$

Write the product in simplest form.

$$2\frac{1}{2} \times 1\frac{1}{4} = \frac{5}{2} \times \frac{5}{4}$$
$$= \frac{25}{8}$$
$$= 3\frac{1}{8}$$

4. Look at the *Here's how*. How many cups of sugar will you need? Does the answer seem reasonable? $3\frac{1}{8}$, Yes

5. Check these examples. Give each product in simplest form.

a. $3 \times 2\frac{2}{3} = \frac{3}{1} \times \frac{8}{3}$
$= \frac{24}{3}$
$= ?$ 8

b. $2\frac{3}{4} \times 4\frac{2}{5} = \frac{11}{4} \times \frac{22}{5}$
$= \frac{242}{20}$
$= ?$ $12\frac{1}{10}$

182

EXERCISES

Multiply. Write the product in simplest form.
Here are scrambled answers for the next row of exercises: $5\frac{1}{2}$ $4\frac{1}{6}$ 7 2 $6\frac{3}{5}$

6. $2 \times 3\frac{1}{2}$ 7 **7.** $1\frac{1}{2} \times 1\frac{1}{3}$ 2 **8.** $2\frac{3}{4} \times 2$ $5\frac{1}{2}$ **9.** $1\frac{2}{3} \times 2\frac{1}{2}$ $4\frac{1}{6}$ **10.** $2\frac{1}{5} \times 3$ $6\frac{3}{5}$

11. $2\frac{1}{4} \times 3\frac{1}{2}$ $7\frac{7}{8}$ **12.** $2\frac{4}{5} \times 3$ $8\frac{2}{5}$ **13.** $3\frac{1}{2} \times 1\frac{3}{4}$ $6\frac{1}{8}$ **14.** $2\frac{1}{2} \times 3\frac{1}{2}$ $8\frac{3}{4}$ **15.** $2\frac{1}{2} \times 2\frac{1}{2}$ $6\frac{1}{4}$

16. $2\frac{1}{3} \times 4\frac{1}{2}$ $10\frac{1}{2}$ **17.** $3\frac{1}{6} \times 2\frac{3}{4}$ $8\frac{17}{24}$ **18.** $3\frac{3}{4} \times 6$ $22\frac{1}{2}$ **19.** $5\frac{1}{2} \times 4\frac{3}{4}$ $26\frac{1}{8}$ **20.** $4\frac{1}{3} \times 3\frac{1}{2}$ $15\frac{1}{6}$

21. $2\frac{3}{8} \times 4$ $9\frac{1}{2}$ **22.** $3\frac{2}{3} \times 4\frac{1}{3}$ $15\frac{8}{9}$ **23.** $5\frac{3}{4} \times 2\frac{1}{2}$ $14\frac{3}{8}$ **24.** $2\frac{2}{3} \times 3\frac{1}{6}$ $8\frac{4}{9}$ **25.** $2\frac{1}{5} \times 1\frac{1}{2}$ $3\frac{3}{10}$

26. $4\frac{1}{5} \times 5\frac{3}{8}$ $22\frac{23}{40}$ **27.** $3 \times 5\frac{2}{3}$ 17 **28.** $1\frac{5}{8} \times 4\frac{1}{2}$ $7\frac{5}{16}$ **29.** $3\frac{3}{8} \times 6\frac{3}{4}$ $22\frac{25}{32}$ **30.** $1\frac{1}{3} \times 6$ 8

31. $4\frac{1}{2} \times 3$ $13\frac{1}{2}$ **32.** $1\frac{1}{2} \times 2\frac{1}{3}$ $3\frac{1}{2}$ **33.** $4 \times 2\frac{1}{2}$ 10 **34.** $3\frac{1}{3} \times 4\frac{1}{3}$ $14\frac{4}{9}$ **35.** $1\frac{2}{3} \times 6$ 10

Solve. Use the recipe on page 182.

36. You make $1\frac{1}{2}$ times the recipe. How many bars do you make? 72

37. How much more baking soda than salt is used in the recipe? $\frac{1}{4}$ tsp

38. How much flour is needed to double the recipe? 3 cups

39. How many teaspoons of spices (cinnamon and cloves) are used in the recipe? $2\frac{1}{4}$

40. You want to make $3\frac{1}{2}$ times the recipe. How much sugar will you need? $4\frac{3}{8}$ cups

41. You have $1\frac{3}{4}$ cups of raisins. Do you have enough to make $3\frac{1}{2}$ times the recipe? Yes

Check the products

42. Find and correct the two wrong answers.

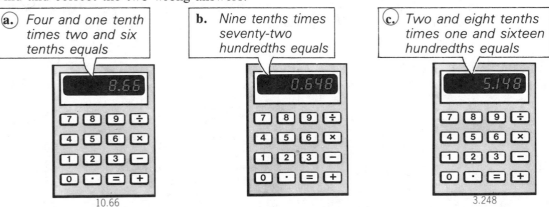

a. *Four and one tenth times two and six tenths equals* 8.66 10.66

b. *Nine tenths times seventy-two hundredths equals* 0.648

c. *Two and eight tenths times one and sixteen hundredths equals* 5.148 3.248

PRACTICE WORKSHEET
Copymaster S229 or Duplicating Master S229

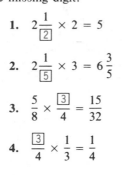

NAME _____   **WORKSHEET 77**
(Use after page 183.)

SKILL DRILL
Study these examples.

$$3\frac{1}{4} \times 1\frac{2}{3} = \frac{13}{4} \times \frac{5}{3} \qquad 2\frac{3}{4} \times 1\frac{1}{3} = \frac{11}{4} \times \frac{4}{3}$$
$$= \frac{65}{12} \qquad\qquad = \frac{44}{12}$$
$$= 5\frac{5}{12} \qquad\qquad = 3\frac{8}{12} \text{ or } 3\frac{2}{3}$$

Multiply. Write the product in simplest form.

1. $3\frac{1}{4} \times 2\frac{1}{4}$ $7\frac{7}{8}$ 2. $1\frac{1}{3} \times 1\frac{1}{2}$ 2 3. $2\frac{2}{3} \times 2\frac{1}{2}$ $6\frac{2}{3}$

4. $2\frac{1}{3} \times 1\frac{1}{4}$ $2\frac{11}{12}$ 5. $1\frac{1}{4} \times 2\frac{1}{2}$ $3\frac{1}{8}$ 6. $3\frac{2}{3} \times 5\frac{1}{2}$ $20\frac{1}{6}$

7. $3\frac{2}{3} \times 2\frac{1}{4}$ $10\frac{1}{2}$ 8. $2\frac{1}{3} \times 1\frac{2}{3}$ $3\frac{8}{9}$ 9. $1\frac{1}{2} \times 1\frac{1}{2}$ $2\frac{1}{4}$

10. $1\frac{2}{3} \times 2\frac{4}{5}$ $4\frac{2}{3}$ 11. $2\frac{1}{4} \times 2\frac{1}{4}$ $5\frac{1}{16}$ 12. $3\frac{1}{2} \times 4\frac{1}{2}$ $15\frac{15}{16}$

13. $1\frac{1}{3} \times 1\frac{1}{3}$ $1\frac{4}{5}$ 14. $5\frac{1}{6} \times 1\frac{1}{4}$ $9\frac{1}{24}$ 15. $2\frac{1}{4} \times 2\frac{1}{4}$ $5\frac{5}{8}$

16. $2\frac{1}{2} \times 3\frac{2}{5}$ $8\frac{1}{2}$ 17. $1\frac{1}{3} \times 1\frac{1}{3}$ $1\frac{11}{25}$ 18. $2\frac{1}{5} \times 3\frac{1}{4}$ $7\frac{3}{20}$

19. $2\frac{4}{5} \times 3\frac{1}{3}$ $9\frac{5}{8}$ 20. $1\frac{1}{4} \times 1\frac{1}{4}$ $2\frac{3}{16}$ 21. $2\frac{1}{4} \times 1\frac{1}{8}$ $2\frac{7}{32}$

22. $1\frac{1}{6} \times 3\frac{1}{2}$ $4\frac{1}{2}$ 23. $1\frac{1}{3} \times 2\frac{2}{3}$ $3\frac{9}{10}$ 24. $1\frac{1}{3} \times 1\frac{3}{5}$ $2\frac{1}{3}$

Check yourself. Here are the scrambled answers:

$1\frac{11}{25}$ $1\frac{4}{5}$ 2 $2\frac{3}{16}$ $2\frac{1}{4}$ $2\frac{1}{3}$ $2\frac{17}{32}$ $2\frac{11}{12}$ $3\frac{1}{8}$ $3\frac{8}{9}$ $4\frac{1}{12}$ $3\frac{7}{10}$ $4\frac{2}{3}$

$5\frac{1}{16}$ $5\frac{5}{8}$ $15\frac{15}{16}$ $6\frac{2}{3}$ $7\frac{3}{20}$ $7\frac{7}{8}$ $8\frac{1}{2}$ $9\frac{1}{24}$ $9\frac{5}{8}$ $10\frac{1}{2}$ $20\frac{1}{6}$

© D. C. Heath and Company   **S229**   *Multiplying mixed numbers*

CHALKBOARD CHALLENGE
Find the missing digit.

1. $2\frac{1}{\boxed{2}} \times 2 = 5$

2. $2\frac{1}{\boxed{5}} \times 3 = 6\frac{3}{5}$

3. $\frac{5}{8} \times \frac{\boxed{3}}{4} = \frac{15}{32}$

4. $\frac{\boxed{3}}{4} \times \frac{1}{3} = \frac{1}{4}$

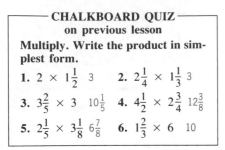

CHALKBOARD QUIZ
on previous lesson

Multiply. Write the product in simplest form.

1. $2 \times 1\frac{1}{2}$ 3   2. $2\frac{1}{4} \times 1\frac{1}{3}$ 3

3. $3\frac{2}{5} \times 3$ $10\frac{1}{5}$ 4. $4\frac{1}{2} \times 2\frac{3}{4}$ $12\frac{3}{8}$

5. $2\frac{1}{5} \times 3\frac{1}{8}$ $6\frac{7}{8}$ 6. $1\frac{2}{3} \times 6$ 10

LESSON OBJECTIVE
To relate fractions to customary units of measure

PROBLEM-SOLVING SKILL
Analyzing a sequence of events

STARTING THE LESSON
Write these measurement facts and numbers on the chalkboard:

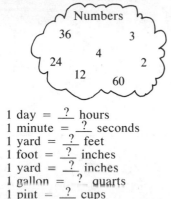

Numbers

36   3
24   4   2
12   60

1 day = __?__ hours
1 minute = __?__ seconds
1 yard = __?__ feet
1 foot = __?__ inches
1 yard = __?__ inches
1 gallon = __?__ quarts
1 pint = __?__ cups

Before the students open their books, have them choose the numbers to complete the measurement facts. Then tell them to open their books to pages 184 and 185 and check their answers.

More on a fraction of a whole number

1. How many hours are there in 2 days? 48

2. How many hours are there in $\frac{1}{2}$ of a day? 12

3. If you know the number of hours in 2 days and the number of hours in $\frac{1}{2}$ of a day, how could you find the number of hours in $2\frac{1}{2}$ days? add

1 day = 24 hours (h)
1 h = 60 minutes (min)
1 min = 60 seconds (s)

Here's how *to find the number of hours in $2\frac{1}{2}$ days.*

SHORTCUT METHOD!
First find the hours in 2 days and in $\frac{1}{2}$ of a day. Then add.

$2\frac{1}{2}$ days = 48 hours + 12 hours

= 60 hours

24 hours

REGULAR METHOD
Change the mixed number to a fraction and multiply.

$2\frac{1}{2}$ days = $2\frac{1}{2} \times 24$ hours

= $\frac{5}{2} \times \frac{24}{1}$ hours

24 hours

= $\frac{120}{2}$ hours

= 60 hours

4. Look at the *Here's how.*

a. How many hours are there in $2\frac{1}{2}$ days? 60

b. Does the answer make sense? Is it between the number of hours in 2 days (48) and the number of hours in 3 days (72)? Yes, Yes

EXERCISES

Complete. Here are scrambled answers for the next row of exercises: 100 66 90

5. $2\frac{3}{4}$ days = __?__ h 66

6. $1\frac{1}{2}$ h = __?__ min 90

7. $1\frac{2}{3}$ h = __?__ min 100

8. $1\frac{1}{3}$ min = __?__ s 80

9. $1\frac{3}{4}$ h = __?__ min 105

10. $1\frac{2}{3}$ days = __?__ h 40

11. $1\frac{5}{6}$ min = __?__ s 110

12. $2\frac{3}{8}$ days = __?__ h 57

13. $3\frac{2}{3}$ h = __?__ min 220

1 yard (yd) = 3 feet (ft)
1 ft = 12 inches (in.)
1 yd = 36 in.

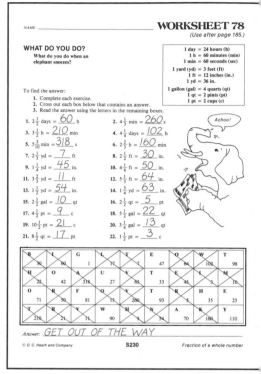

WORKSHEET 78
(Use after page 185.)

NAME _____

WHAT DO YOU DO?
What do you do when an
elephant sneezes?

| 1 day = 24 hours (h) |
| 1 h = 60 minutes (min) |
| 1 min = 60 seconds (sec) |
| 1 yard (yd) = 3 feet (ft) |
| 1 ft = 12 inches (in.) |
| 1 yd = 36 in. |
| 1 gallon (gal) = 4 quarts (qt) |
| 1 qt = 2 pints (pt) |
| 1 pt = 2 cups (c) |

To find the answer:
1. Complete each exercise.
2. Cross out each box below that contains an answer.
3. Read the answer using the letters in the remaining boxes.

Achoo!

1. $2\frac{1}{2}$ days = __60__ h
2. $4\frac{1}{3}$ min = __260__ s
3. $3\frac{1}{2}$ h = __210__ min
4. $4\frac{1}{4}$ days = __102__ h
5. $5\frac{3}{10}$ min = __318__ s
6. $2\frac{2}{3}$ h = __160__ min
7. $2\frac{1}{3}$ ft = __7__ ft
8. $2\frac{1}{2}$ ft = __30__ in.
9. $1\frac{1}{4}$ yd = __45__ in.
10. $4\frac{1}{6}$ ft = __50__ in.
11. $3\frac{2}{3}$ yd = __11__ ft
12. $5\frac{1}{3}$ ft = __64__ in.
13. $1\frac{1}{2}$ yd = __54__ in.
14. $1\frac{3}{4}$ yd = __63__ in.
15. $2\frac{1}{2}$ gal = __10__ qt
16. $2\frac{1}{2}$ qt = __5__ pt
17. $4\frac{1}{2}$ pt = __9__ c
18. $5\frac{1}{2}$ gal = __22__ qt
19. $10\frac{1}{2}$ pt = __21__ c
20. $3\frac{1}{4}$ gal = __13__ qt
21. $8\frac{1}{2}$ qt = __17__ pt
22. $1\frac{1}{2}$ pt = __3__ c

B		I		G		L		E		Q		W		T
30		60		1		7		47		64		102		98
H		O		A		U		T		T		E		M
22		42		318		27		63		33		44		10
O		R		F		Q		V		T		R		E
71		50		81		15		260		93		35		25
T		R		U		W		H		N		A		Y
210		21		11		90		50		54		70		160		110

Answer: GET OUT OF THE WAY

© D. C. Heath and Company   S230   Fraction of a whole number

---

14. $1\frac{1}{3}$ yd = __?__ ft 4

15. $1\frac{1}{2}$ ft = __?__ in. 18

16. $1\frac{1}{3}$ yd = __?__ in. 48

17. $1\frac{3}{4}$ ft = __?__ in. 21

18. $2\frac{1}{3}$ yd = __?__ ft 7

19. $1\frac{3}{4}$ yd = __?__ in. 63

20. $2\frac{2}{3}$ yd = __?__ ft. 8

21. $2\frac{1}{2}$ yd = __?__ in. 90

22. $2\frac{3}{4}$ ft = __?__ in. 33

23. $3\frac{2}{3}$ yd = __?__ ft 11

24. $3\frac{2}{3}$ ft = __?__ in. 44

25. $3\frac{3}{4}$ yd = __?__ in. 135

1 gallon (gal) = 4 quarts (qt)
1 qt = 2 pints (pt)
1 pt = 2 cups (c)

26. $1\frac{1}{2}$ gal = __?__ qt 6

27. $1\frac{1}{2}$ qt = __?__ pt 3

28. $2\frac{1}{2}$ pt = __?__ c 5

29. $4\frac{1}{2}$ qt = __?__ pt 9

30. $2\frac{3}{4}$ gal = __?__ qt 11

31. $4\frac{1}{2}$ pt = __?__ c 9

32. $3\frac{1}{2}$ gal = __?__ qt 14

33. $3\frac{1}{2}$ pt = __?__ c 7

34. $2\frac{1}{2}$ qt = __?__ pt 5

35. $2\frac{1}{4}$ gal = __?__ qt 9

36. $3\frac{1}{2}$ qt = __?__ pt 7

37. $5\frac{1}{2}$ pt = __?__ c 11

LIFE-SKILL PROJECT
Using a calculator
Let the students use a calculator to compute how many years old they will be when they have lived 10 million minutes.

19 years old

What's the time?

38. A thunderstorm caused a power failure at 10:05 P.M. The next morning at 7:55 the electric clock showed 6:05. 1 h 50 min

a. How long was the electricity off?

b. At what time did the electricity come on again? 11:55 P.M.

Complete.

1. $1\frac{1}{2}$ days = __?__ hours   36

2. $1\frac{3}{4}$ hours = __?__ minutes   105

3. $5\frac{1}{4}$ minutes = __?__ seconds   315

4. $1\frac{1}{3}$ yards = __?__ feet   4

5. $6\frac{1}{2}$ feet = __?__ inches   78

6. $2\frac{3}{4}$ gallons = __?__ quarts   11

SKILLS REVIEWED
Adding and subtracting decimals
Multiplying and dividing decimals
Comparing fractions

PROBLEM-SOLVING SKILLS
Using a table
Solving a multi-step problem

STARTING THE LESSON
Cumulative Skill Practice
Write these four answers on the chalkboard:

13.74	2.1
3.27	27.72

Challenge the students to an answer hunt by saying: "Look for the four even-numbered exercises on page 186 that have these answers. You have four minutes to find as many of the exercises as you can." (Exercises 4, 18, 30, and 44)

STARTING THE LESSON
Problem Solving
The chart at the top of page 187 is also on **Visual Aid 30**. Use the chart and ask questions like these:

• Which cost more per pound, Delicious apples or McIntosh apples? (McIntosh apples)

• Is one dollar enough money to buy two pounds of Delicious apples? (No)

• What is the cost of $1\frac{3}{4}$ pounds of Granny Smith apples? ($1.75)

186

Cumulative Skill Practice

Give the sum.   *(page 24)*

1. $3.4 + 2.36$ 5.76   2. $1.78 + 4.7$ 6.48   3. $6.14 + 15.9$ 22.04

4. $6.3 + 2.14 + 5.3$ 13.74   5. $20 + 0.5 + 2.9$ 23.4   6. $5.5 + 13 + 0.3$ 18.8

7. $40 + 3.7 + 0.25$ 43.95   8. $0.2 + 0.24 + 0.3$ 0.74   9. $12 + 2.5 + 0.75$ 15

10. $5.7 + 36 + 2.1$ 43.8   11. $6.34 + 18 + 96$ 120.34   12. $35 + 2.4 + 3.1$ 40.5

13. $9.03 + 4 + 1.2$ 14.23   14. $1.4 + 0.03 + 2$ 3.43   15. $14 + 6.2 + 4.05$ 24

Give the difference.   *(page 46)*

16. $32.4 - 18.6$ 13.8   17. $20.6 - 15.8$ 4.8   18. $6.00 - 2.73$ 3.27   19. $4.02 - 3.8$ 22

20. $3.4 - 1.26$ 2.14   21. $16 - 12.5$ 3.5   22. $9.6 - 5.45$ 4.15   23. $6.4 - 3.91$ 2.49

24. $32.1 - 2.84$ 29.26   25. $9.7 - 2.74$ 6.96   26. $14 - 3.62$ 10.38   27. $15 - 2.8$ 12.2

28. $6.5 - 2.01$ 4.49   29. $16.8 - 3.24$ 13.56   30. $3.2 - 1.1$ 2.1   31. $2.8 - 2$ 0.8

32. $3.8 - 1.57$ 2.23   33. $2.91 - 1.7$ 1.21   34. $6 - 3.9$ 2.1   35. $6.9 - 3.15$ 3.75

Give the product.   *(page 64)*

36. 2.3×0.4 0.92   37. 2.6×0.21 0.546   38. 0.44×0.6 0.264   39. 0.2×0.35 0.07

40. 14×1.2 16.8   41. 0.56×2.8 1.568   42. 3.21×1.1 3.531   43. 2.11×3.8 8.0

44. 9.24×3 27.72   45. 14.5×2.6 37.70   46. 125×1.4 175.0   47. 286×3.1 886.6

48. 6.1×4.2 25.62   49. 4.8×11 52.8   50. 37×0.2 7.4   51. 351×4.2 1474

52. 7.35×0.01 0.0735   53. 3.4×2.9 9.86   54. 6.01×3.7 22.237   55. 368×1.11 408

Give the quotient rounded to the nearest tenth.   *(page 96)*

56. $4.64 \div 0.5$ 9.3   57. $8.43 \div 0.02$ 421.5   58. $56.3 \div 3$ 18.8   59. $8.65 \div 2$ 4.3

60. $42 \div 0.7$ 60   61. $3.8 \div 0.2$ 19   62. $6.38 \div 1.2$ 5.3   63. $3.78 \div 2.4$ 1.6

64. $0.8465 \div 7.1$ 0.1   65. $60.04 \div 5.2$ 11.5   66. $0.072 \div 0.36$ 0.2   67. $0.54 \div 0.21$ 2.6

68. $56 \div 0.24$ 233.3   69. $0.08 \div 2.5$ 0.0   70. $10.2 \div 2.8$ 3.6   71. $6.3 \div 0.5$ 12.6

Less than (<), equal to (=), or greater than (>)?   *(page 132)*

72. $\frac{4}{5}$ ● $\frac{3}{5}$ >   73. $\frac{7}{5}$ ● $\frac{3}{5}$ >   74. $\frac{5}{9}$ ● $\frac{4}{9}$ >   75. $\frac{1}{7}$ ● $\frac{3}{7}$ <   76. $\frac{4}{3}$ ● $\frac{7}{3}$ <

77. $\frac{1}{8}$ ● $\frac{1}{6}$ <   78. $\frac{5}{8}$ ● $\frac{1}{2}$ >   79. $\frac{1}{4}$ ● $\frac{1}{5}$ >   80. $\frac{3}{4}$ ● $\frac{2}{3}$ >   81. $\frac{0}{5}$ ● $\frac{0}{4}$ =

82. $\frac{2}{5}$ ● $\frac{1}{2}$ <   83. $\frac{7}{3}$ ● $\frac{5}{2}$ <   84. $\frac{2}{3}$ ● $\frac{7}{10}$ <   85. $\frac{1}{9}$ ● $\frac{1}{8}$ <   86. $\frac{4}{5}$ ● $\frac{2}{3}$ >

Problem solving

You're the clerk

Use the information in the table to answer each customer's question.

APPLES	POUNDS				
	$\frac{1}{4}$	$\frac{1}{2}$	$\frac{3}{4}$	1	2
Granny Smith	$.25	$.50	$.75	$1.00	$2.00
Delicious	$.15	$.30	$.45	$.60	$1.20
McIntosh	$.18	$.36	$.54	$.72	$1.44

1. What is the cost of 2 pounds of McIntosh apples? $1.44

2. What is the cost of $1\frac{1}{2}$ pounds of Granny Smith apples? $1.50

3. How many pounds of Delicious apples can I buy for $1.80? 3

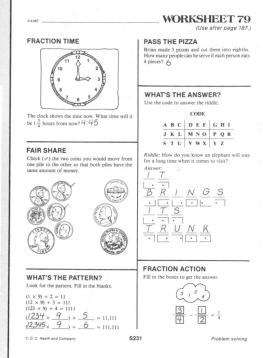

4. "What is the cost of $2\frac{1}{2}$ pounds of McIntosh apples?" $1.80

5. "How many pounds of Delicious apples can I buy for $1.50?" $2\frac{1}{2}$

6. "What is the cost of $2\frac{3}{4}$ pounds of Granny Smith apples?" $2.75

7. "How many pounds of McIntosh apples can I buy for $.90?" $1\frac{1}{4}$

Solve. Use the apple prices.

8. Mike gave the clerk $5 for $2\frac{3}{4}$ pounds of Delicious apples. How much change did he get? $3.35

9. Karen spent $3.60 for a 5-pound bag of apples. What kind of apples did she buy? McIntosh

10. There are 4 pounds of apples in a bag. The total cost is $2.40. What kind of apples are in the bag? Delicious

11. How much more do 10 pounds of McIntosh apples cost than 10 pounds of Delicious apples? $1.20

12. A customer bought $1\frac{1}{2}$ pounds of Granny Smith apples and some Delicious apples. She spent a total of $3.30. How many pounds of Delicious apples did the customer buy? 3

13. How much does a 6-pound bag of apples cost if it is $\frac{1}{3}$ Granny Smith apples and $\frac{2}{3}$ Delicious apples? $4.40

Multiplying and Dividing Fractions and Mixed Numbers **187**

EXTRA PROBLEM SOLVING
Page 451   Odd exercises

PROBLEM-SOLVING WORKSHEET
Copymaster S231 or Duplicating Master S231

NAME _____

WORKSHEET 79
(Use after page 187.)

FRACTION TIME

The clock shows the time now. What time will it be $1\frac{3}{4}$ hours from now? 4:45

FAIR SHARE

Check (✓) the two coins you would move from one pile to the other so that both piles have the same amount of money.

WHAT'S THE PATTERN?

Look for the pattern. Fill in the blanks.

$(1 \times 9) + 2 = 11$
$(12 \times 9) + 3 = 111$
$(123 \times 9) + 4 = 1111$
$(\underline{1234} \times \underline{9}) + \underline{5} = 11,111$
$(\underline{12,345} \times \underline{9}) + \underline{6} = 111,111$

PASS THE PIZZA

Brian made 3 pizzas and cut them into eighths. How many people can he serve if each person eats 4 pieces? 6

WHAT'S THE ANSWER?

Use the code to answer the riddle.

CODE

A B C	D E F	G H I
J K L	M N O	P Q R
S T U	V W X	Y Z

Riddle: How do you know an elephant will stay for a long time when it comes to visit?

Answer:

I T

B R I N G S

I T S

T R U N K

FRACTION ACTION

Fill in the boxes to get the answer.

$\frac{3}{4} - \frac{1}{2} = \frac{1}{4}$

© D. C. Heath and Company   S231   Problem solving

CHALKBOARD CHALLENGE
Unscramble the letters of these math words.

1. MUS   Sum
2. CROPDUT   Product
3. RAGHP   Graph
4. EDMO   Mode
5. NUOIQTET   Quotient

LESSON OBJECTIVES
To identify reciprocals
To divide by a fraction
To divide a fraction by a whole number

PROBLEM-SOLVING SKILLS
Using a picture to solve a problem
Reading a chart

STARTING THE LESSON
Use exercises 1 and 2 to show the students that dividing by $\frac{1}{4}$ is the same as multiplying by 4.

Dividing fractions

1. **a.** How far is it around the track? $\frac{1}{4}$ mile
   b. How many times would you have to run around the track to run $\frac{1}{2}$ mile? 2

2. **a.** How many times would you have to run around the track to run 2 miles? 8
   b. Answer part **a** by dividing.

$$
\begin{array}{ccc}
\text{total} & \text{miles in} & \\
\text{miles} & \text{each lap} & \text{laps} \\
2 & \div \quad \frac{1}{4} & = \boxed{?} \quad 8
\end{array}
$$

It's $\frac{1}{4}$ mile around this track.

   c. Answer part **a** by multiplying.

$$
\begin{array}{ccc}
\text{total} & \text{laps for} & \\
\text{miles} & \text{each mile} & \text{laps} \\
2 & \times \quad 4 & = \boxed{?} \quad 8
\end{array}
$$

   d. Look at parts b and c. Dividing by $\frac{1}{4}$ is the same as multiplying by what number? 4

TIME OUT! $\frac{3}{8} \times \frac{8}{3} = 1$

$\frac{8}{3}$ is the reciprocal of $\frac{3}{8}$.

$\frac{3}{8}$ is the reciprocal of $\frac{8}{3}$.

Two numbers are **reciprocals** if their product is 1.

For a fraction not equal to 0, you can find the reciprocal by inverting the fraction.

Here's how *to divide by a fraction.*

To divide by a fraction, multiply by its reciprocal.

$$
\begin{aligned}
\frac{1}{2} \div \frac{1}{4} &= \frac{1}{2} \times \frac{4}{1} \\
&= \frac{4}{2} \\
&= 2
\end{aligned}
\qquad
\begin{aligned}
2 \div \frac{1}{4} &= \frac{2}{1} \times \frac{4}{1} \\
&= \frac{8}{1} \\
&= 8
\end{aligned}
$$

3. Check each division exercise. Then complete the statement.

   a. $\frac{5}{2} \div \frac{2}{3} = \frac{5}{2} \times \frac{3}{2}$ To divide by $\frac{2}{3}$,

   $= \frac{15}{4}$ multiply by $\boxed{?}$
   $\frac{3}{2}$

   $= 3\frac{3}{4}$

   b. $\frac{4}{5} \div 4 = \frac{4}{5} \times \frac{1}{4}$ To divide by 4, multiply by $\boxed{?}$
   $\frac{1}{4}$

   $= \frac{4}{20}$

   $= \frac{1}{5}$

EXERCISES

Give the reciprocal of each number.

4. 5 — $\frac{1}{5}$ 5. $\frac{1}{3}$ — 3 6. $\frac{1}{8}$ — 8 7. $\frac{3}{8}$ — $\frac{8}{3}$ 8. $\frac{5}{7}$ — $\frac{7}{5}$ 9. $\frac{2}{5}$ — $\frac{5}{2}$ 10. 3 — $\frac{1}{3}$

11. 6 — $\frac{1}{6}$ 12. $\frac{3}{5}$ — $\frac{5}{3}$ 13. $\frac{6}{5}$ — $\frac{5}{6}$ 14. $\frac{3}{2}$ — $\frac{2}{3}$ 15. $\frac{9}{10}$ — $\frac{10}{9}$ 16. 8 — $\frac{1}{8}$ 17. $\frac{14}{3}$ — $\frac{3}{14}$

Divide. Write the quotient in simplest form.

Here are scrambled answers for the next row of exercises: $6\quad 1\quad \frac{1}{6}\quad 1\frac{1}{8}\quad \frac{9}{16}\quad \frac{2}{3}$

$\boxed{\frac{2}{3} \times \frac{1}{4}}$ $\boxed{\frac{3}{2} \times \frac{4}{1}}$ $\boxed{\frac{3}{4} \times \frac{3}{2}}$ $\boxed{\frac{7}{5} \times \frac{5}{7}}$ $\boxed{\frac{3}{8} \times \frac{3}{2}}$ $\boxed{\frac{2}{9} \times \frac{3}{1}}$

18. $\frac{2}{3} \div 4$ $\frac{1}{6}$ 19. $\frac{3}{2} \div \frac{1}{4}$ 6 20. $\frac{3}{4} \div \frac{2}{3}$ $1\frac{1}{8}$ 21. $\frac{7}{5} \div \frac{7}{5}$ 1 22. $\frac{3}{8} \div \frac{2}{3}$ $\frac{9}{16}$ 23. $\frac{2}{9} \div \frac{1}{3}$ $\frac{2}{3}$

24. $\frac{5}{9} \div \frac{1}{3}$ $1\frac{2}{3}$ 25. $\frac{5}{8} \div 2$ $\frac{5}{16}$ 26. $\frac{4}{5} \div \frac{3}{3}$ $\frac{4}{5}$ 27. $\frac{2}{3} \div \frac{5}{9}$ $1\frac{1}{5}$ 28. $5 \div \frac{2}{5}$ $12\frac{1}{2}$ 29. $\frac{2}{7} \div \frac{5}{14}$ $\frac{4}{5}$

30. $\frac{3}{5} \div \frac{2}{5}$ $1\frac{1}{2}$ 31. $\frac{3}{2} \div \frac{2}{3}$ $2\frac{1}{4}$ 32. $\frac{7}{9} \div \frac{4}{3}$ $\frac{7}{12}$ 33. $\frac{2}{5} \div 5$ $\frac{2}{25}$ 34. $\frac{7}{8} \div \frac{3}{4}$ $1\frac{1}{6}$ 35. $\frac{3}{7} \div \frac{27}{49}$ $\frac{7}{9}$

36. $\frac{4}{3} \div \frac{4}{3}$ 1 37. $\frac{3}{8} \div \frac{3}{2}$ $\frac{1}{4}$ 38. $\frac{3}{2} \div \frac{3}{8}$ 4 39. $\frac{2}{5} \div \frac{1}{4}$ $1\frac{3}{5}$ 40. $\frac{9}{10} \div \frac{4}{5}$ $1\frac{1}{8}$ 41. $\frac{1}{5} \div \frac{1}{25}$ 5

42. $4 \div \frac{5}{8}$ $6\frac{2}{5}$ 43. $\frac{9}{4} \div \frac{7}{8}$ $2\frac{4}{7}$ 44. $6 \div \frac{3}{2}$ 4 45. $\frac{7}{2} \div \frac{9}{4}$ $1\frac{5}{9}$ 46. $\frac{7}{8} \div \frac{5}{16}$ $2\frac{4}{5}$ 47. $8 \div \frac{1}{2}$ 16

48. $\frac{0}{5} \div \frac{5}{6}$ 0 49. $8 \div \frac{2}{5}$ 20 50. $\frac{5}{9} \div \frac{4}{3}$ $\frac{5}{12}$ 51. $\frac{5}{4} \div 3$ $\frac{5}{12}$ 52. $\frac{5}{12} \div \frac{5}{12}$ 1 53. $\frac{2}{3} \div 1$ $\frac{2}{3}$

Solve.

54. How many $\frac{1}{4}$-mile laps must you run to run 4 miles? *Hint:* $4 \div \frac{1}{4} = ?$ 16

55. You are on a $\frac{1}{2}$-mile relay team. Each runner runs $\frac{1}{8}$ mile. How many runners are on your team? *Hint:* $\frac{1}{2} \div \frac{1}{8} = ?$ 4

You're the coach Reading a chart

Use the 100-yard-dash times.

56. Which two runners would make the fastest 2-person 200-yard relay team? Kim, Sandy

57. Which two runners would make the slowest 200-yard relay team? Jenny, Tom

58. Which of these teams should win a 200-yard relay, Jenny and Dan or Tom and Sandy? Tom and Sandy

100-yard Dash	
NAME	TIME
Jenny	15.7 seconds
Kim	13.9 seconds
Tom	16.1 seconds
Dan	14.3 seconds
Sandy	13.2 seconds

PRACTICE WORKSHEET
Copymaster S232 or Duplicating Master S232

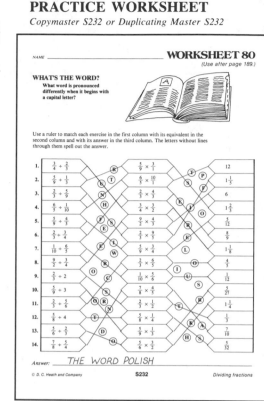

CHALKBOARD CHALLENGE
Find the missing number.

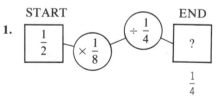

1. START $\frac{1}{2}$ $\times \frac{1}{8}$ $\div \frac{1}{4}$ END ? $\frac{1}{4}$

2. START ? $\times \frac{1}{4}$ $\div \frac{1}{4}$ END 8   8

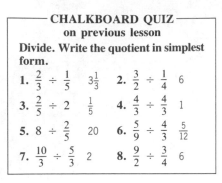
LESSON OBJECTIVE
To divide mixed numbers

PROBLEM-SOLVING SKILLS
Selecting information from a display
Choosing the correct operation
Following directions and checking
  answers

STARTING THE LESSON
Play 'What are the facts?' Have the students study the auto-repair chart at the top of page 190 for 30 seconds. Then tell them to close their books and answer these questions from memory:
• Which job takes longer, a minor tune-up or a major tune-up?
  (Major tune-up)
• Which job takes $1\frac{1}{4}$ hours?
  (Minor tune-up)
• Does it take more or less than half an hour to do an oil change? (Less)
• How many cars can have wheel alignments in one hour? (2)

Dividing mixed numbers

1. How much time is needed for an oil change? $\frac{1}{3}$ hour

2. How many hours does a minor tune-up take? $1\frac{1}{4}$

3. To find how many minor tune-ups can be completed in $3\frac{3}{4}$ hours, the service manager would divide $3\frac{3}{4}$ by what number? $1\frac{1}{4}$

H & W AUTO REPAIR	
JOB	TIME
Oil Change	$\frac{1}{3}$ hour
Wheel Alignment	$\frac{1}{2}$ hour
Minor Tune-up	$1\frac{1}{4}$ hours
Major Tune-up	$2\frac{1}{3}$ hours

Here's how *to divide mixed numbers.*

Change to fractions.

$$3\frac{3}{4} \div 1\frac{1}{4} = \frac{15}{4} \div \frac{5}{4}$$

Divide. Write the quotient in simplest form.

$$3\frac{3}{4} \div 1\frac{1}{4} = \frac{15}{4} \div \frac{5}{4}$$
$$= \frac{15}{4} \times \frac{4}{5}$$
$$= \frac{60}{20}$$
$$= 3$$

4. Look at the *Here's how*. How many minor tune-ups can be completed in $3\frac{3}{4}$ hours? 3

5. Check these examples. Then answer the questions.

$$2\frac{1}{2} \div \frac{1}{2} = \frac{5}{2} \div \frac{1}{2}$$
$$= \frac{5}{2} \times \frac{2}{1}$$
$$= \frac{10}{2}$$
$$= 5$$

$$7 \div 2\frac{1}{3} = \frac{7}{1} \div \frac{7}{3}$$
$$= \frac{7}{1} \times \frac{3}{7}$$
$$= \frac{21}{7}$$
$$= 3$$

a. How many cars can have wheel alignments in $2\frac{1}{2}$ hours? 5

b. How many major tune-ups can be done in 7 hours? 3

190

EXERCISES

Divide. Write each quotient in simplest form.

Here are scrambled answers for the next row of exercises: $1\frac{1}{4}$ $4\frac{1}{8}$ $1\frac{4}{5}$ $2\frac{1}{7}$ $2\frac{1}{4}$

6. $2\frac{1}{4} \div 1\frac{1}{4}$ $1\frac{4}{5}$ 7. $5\frac{1}{2} \div 1\frac{1}{3}$ $4\frac{1}{8}$ 8. $5 \div 2\frac{1}{3}$ $2\frac{1}{7}$ 9. $4\frac{1}{2} \div 2$ $2\frac{1}{4}$ 10. $2\frac{1}{2} \div 2$ $1\frac{1}{4}$

11. $6\frac{1}{2} \div 2\frac{2}{3}$ $2\frac{7}{16}$ 12. $6\frac{1}{2} \div 2\frac{1}{4}$ $2\frac{8}{9}$ 13. $8 \div 2\frac{1}{4}$ $3\frac{5}{9}$ 14. $6\frac{1}{4} \div 1\frac{1}{4}$ 5 15. $1\frac{1}{6} \div 1\frac{1}{2}$ $\frac{7}{9}$

16. $5\frac{7}{8} \div 1\frac{3}{4}$ $3\frac{5}{14}$ 17. $7 \div 2\frac{1}{3}$ 3 18. $4\frac{1}{3} \div 2\frac{1}{2}$ $1\frac{11}{15}$ 19. $2 \div 1\frac{1}{2}$ $1\frac{1}{3}$ 20. $4\frac{1}{2} \div 4$ $1\frac{1}{8}$

21. $2\frac{3}{8} \div 1\frac{1}{3}$ $1\frac{25}{32}$ 22. $6\frac{3}{4} \div 3$ $2\frac{1}{4}$ 23. $1\frac{1}{5} \div 5$ $\frac{6}{25}$ 24. $8\frac{1}{2} \div 1\frac{3}{4}$ $4\frac{6}{7}$ 25. $6 \div 1\frac{1}{2}$ 4

26. $3\frac{3}{5} \div 1\frac{1}{5}$ 3 27. $6\frac{2}{3} \div 2$ $3\frac{1}{3}$ 28. $9\frac{1}{4} \div 2\frac{1}{4}$ $4\frac{1}{9}$ 29. $8 \div 2\frac{1}{2}$ $3\frac{1}{5}$ 30. $2 \div \frac{2}{3}$ 3

31. $6 \div 4\frac{1}{2}$ $1\frac{1}{3}$ 32. $9 \div 2\frac{1}{4}$ 4 33. $2\frac{1}{3} \div 2\frac{1}{3}$ 1 34. $2\frac{1}{2} \div 1\frac{1}{4}$ 2 35. $3\frac{1}{2} \div 3\frac{1}{2}$ 1

36. $1\frac{1}{2} \div 2$ $\frac{3}{4}$ 37. $7\frac{1}{2} \div 1\frac{1}{2}$ 5 38. $3\frac{2}{3} \div 1\frac{1}{3}$ $2\frac{3}{4}$ 39. $6 \div 1\frac{1}{3}$ $4\frac{1}{2}$ 40. $1\frac{1}{2} \div \frac{1}{2}$ 3

41. $4\frac{4}{5} \div 4$ $1\frac{1}{5}$ 42. $3\frac{1}{3} \div 6$ $\frac{5}{9}$ 43. $7\frac{1}{2} \div \frac{1}{2}$ 15 44. $5\frac{1}{2} \div 10$ $\frac{11}{20}$ 45. $10 \div \frac{1}{2}$ 20

Solve. Use the auto-repair information on page 190.

46. How many oil changes can be done in $2\frac{2}{3}$ hours? 8

47. How many hours should it take for a major tune-up and an oil change? $2\frac{2}{3}$

48. How many hours should it take to do wheel alignments on 7 cars? $3\frac{1}{2}$

49. A mechanic starts a minor tune-up at 10:20. At what time should the job be done? 11:35

Check the quotients

50. Find and correct the two wrong answers.

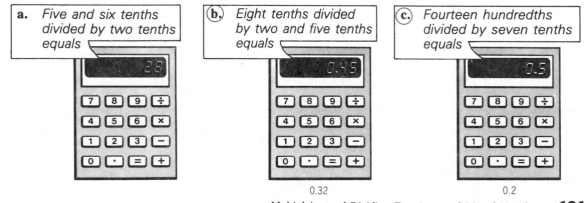

a. Five and six tenths divided by two tenths equals ▸ 28

b. Eight tenths divided by two and five tenths equals ▸ 0.45   0.32

c. Fourteen hundredths divided by seven tenths equals ▸ 0.5   0.2

Multiplying and Dividing Fractions and Mixed Numbers **191**

EXTRA PRACTICE
Page 437   Skill 51

PRACTICE WORKSHEET
Copymaster S233 or Duplicating Master S233

NAME _____ **WORKSHEET 81**
(Use after page 191.)

SKILL DRILL
Study these examples.

$1\frac{3}{4} \div 2\frac{1}{2} = \frac{7}{4} \div \frac{5}{2}$ *To divide, multiply by the reciprocal.*
$= \frac{7}{4} \times \frac{2}{5}$
$= \frac{14}{20}$
$= \frac{7}{10}$

$7 \div 1\frac{3}{4} = \frac{7}{1} \div \frac{7}{4}$
$= \frac{7}{1} \times \frac{4}{7}$
$= \frac{28}{7}$
$= 4$

Divide. Write each quotient in simplest form.

1. $5\frac{1}{2} \div 1\frac{1}{3}$ $4\frac{1}{8}$ 2. $5 \div 2\frac{1}{3}$ $2\frac{1}{7}$ 3. $1\frac{1}{4} \div 4\frac{1}{2}$ $\frac{7}{18}$

4. $3\frac{1}{2} \div 1\frac{1}{8}$ $3\frac{1}{9}$ 5. $4 \div 1\frac{1}{9}$ $3\frac{3}{5}$ 6. $4\frac{1}{3} \div 2\frac{1}{2}$ $1\frac{11}{15}$

7. $5\frac{5}{8} \div 1\frac{1}{2}$ $3\frac{3}{4}$ 8. $6\frac{1}{4} \div 1\frac{1}{4}$ 5 9. $5\frac{1}{4} \div 2\frac{1}{2}$ $2\frac{1}{10}$

10. $7 \div 2\frac{1}{3}$ 3 11. $8\frac{1}{3} \div 1\frac{1}{4}$ $6\frac{2}{3}$ 12. $9 \div 2\frac{1}{4}$ 4

13. $2\frac{1}{3} \div \frac{1}{2}$ $4\frac{1}{6}$ 14. $1\frac{1}{4} \div 1\frac{1}{2}$ $1\frac{1}{6}$ 15. $10\frac{1}{2} \div 1\frac{1}{2}$ 7

16. $3\frac{1}{2} \div 2\frac{3}{4}$ $1\frac{3}{11}$ 17. $1\frac{1}{2} \div \frac{3}{4}$ 2 18. $7\frac{2}{3} \div 1\frac{1}{6}$ $6\frac{4}{7}$

Check yourself. Here are the scrambled answers:
$\frac{7}{18}$ $1\frac{1}{6}$ $1\frac{3}{11}$ $1\frac{11}{15}$ 2 $2\frac{1}{10}$ $2\frac{1}{7}$ $3\frac{3}{4}$ 3 $3\frac{1}{9}$ $3\frac{3}{5}$ 4 $4\frac{1}{6}$ $4\frac{1}{8}$ 5 $6\frac{4}{7}$ $6\frac{2}{3}$ 7

© D. C. Heath and Company   **S233**   Dividing mixed numbers

LIFE-SKILL PROJECT
Collecting data
Have the students count the number of sheets in a $\frac{1}{2}$-inch stack of paper. Then have them divide to compute the thickness of a single sheet of paper.

SKILLS REVIEWED
Changing fractions to decimals
Adding and subtracting fractions
Multiplying and dividing mixed numbers

PROBLEM-SOLVING SKILLS
Using a drawing
Following instructions

STARTING THE LESSON
Cumulative Skill Practice
Challenge the students to an estimation hunt by saying, "Find the five sums in exercises 22–39 that are greater than 1." (Exercises 25, 30, 34, 38, and 39) Then have the students find the three products in exercises 58–72 that are greater than 10. (Exercises 61, 69, and 71)

STARTING THE LESSON
Problem Solving
The diagram showing the 24 electrodes is also on **Visual Aid 31**. Shade in the propriate electrodes so that *6:23* is displayed. Have the students tell which electrodes were charged to display:
• the *6*. (Electrodes D, C, B, Q, P, and O)
• the colon. (Electrode R)
• the *2*. (Electrodes H, I, F, S, and T)
• the *3*. (Electrodes L, M, J, X, and W)
Use the visual aid to display other times and ask similar questions.

EXERCISE NOTE
Problem Solving
You may wish to make copies of **Visual Aid 31** for the students to use in solving exercises 3 and 4 on page 193.

192

Cumulative Skill Practice

Change to a decimal rounded to the nearest hundredth. *(page 146)*

1. $\frac{1}{6}$ 0.17   2. $\frac{1}{3}$ 0.33   3. $\frac{13}{3}$ 4.33   4. $\frac{1}{9}$ 0.11   5. $\frac{5}{3}$ 1.67   6. $\frac{7}{3}$ 2.33   7. $\frac{10}{9}$ 1.1

8. $\frac{1}{12}$ 0.08   9. $\frac{4}{9}$ 0.44   10. $\frac{2}{3}$ 0.67   11. $\frac{6}{11}$ 0.55   12. $\frac{5}{6}$ 0.83   13. $\frac{5}{7}$ 0.71   14. $\frac{3}{7}$ 0.43

15. $\frac{11}{6}$ 1.83   16. $\frac{5}{9}$ 0.56   17. $\frac{16}{3}$ 5.33   18. $\frac{7}{9}$ 0.78   19. $\frac{5}{12}$ 0.42   20. $\frac{1}{7}$ 0.14   21. $\frac{11}{9}$ 1.2

Give the sum in simplest form. *(page 158)*

22. $\frac{3}{5} + \frac{1}{5}$ $\frac{4}{5}$ 23. $\frac{1}{3} + \frac{1}{2}$ $\frac{5}{6}$ 24. $\frac{1}{6} + \frac{1}{3}$ $\frac{1}{2}$ 25. $\frac{3}{5} + \frac{7}{10}$ $1\frac{3}{10}$ 26. $\frac{1}{8} + \frac{3}{4}$ $\frac{7}{8}$ 27. $\frac{2}{5} + \frac{1}{10}$ $\frac{1}{2}$

28. $\frac{1}{4} + \frac{1}{3}$ $\frac{7}{12}$ 29. $\frac{3}{10} + \frac{1}{5}$ $\frac{1}{2}$ 30. $\frac{4}{9} + \frac{2}{3}$ $1\frac{1}{9}$ 31. $\frac{1}{8} + \frac{9}{16}$ $\frac{11}{16}$ 32. $\frac{1}{2} + \frac{1}{4}$ $\frac{3}{4}$ 33. $\frac{1}{9} + \frac{2}{3}$ $\frac{7}{9}$

34. $\frac{1}{2} + \frac{3}{4}$ $1\frac{1}{4}$ 35. $\frac{1}{4} + \frac{5}{8}$ $\frac{7}{8}$ 36. $\frac{9}{16} + \frac{3}{8}$ $\frac{15}{16}$ 37. $\frac{1}{8} + \frac{1}{2}$ $\frac{5}{8}$ 38. $\frac{5}{12} + \frac{2}{3}$ $1\frac{1}{12}$ 39. $\frac{3}{4} + \frac{1}{2}$ $1\frac{1}{4}$

Give the difference in simplest form. *(pages 164, 166)*

40. $\frac{3}{4} - \frac{1}{4}$ $\frac{1}{2}$ 41. $\frac{7}{10} - \frac{1}{10}$ $\frac{3}{5}$ 42. $\frac{3}{2} - \frac{3}{4}$ $\frac{3}{4}$ 43. $\frac{2}{3} - \frac{4}{9}$ $\frac{2}{9}$ 44. $\frac{9}{10} - \frac{2}{5}$ $\frac{1}{2}$ 45. $\frac{4}{5} - \frac{1}{2}$ $\frac{3}{10}$

46. $\frac{7}{8} - \frac{1}{3}$ $\frac{13}{24}$ 47. $\frac{5}{12} - \frac{1}{3}$ $\frac{1}{12}$ 48. $\frac{3}{4} - \frac{2}{3}$ $\frac{1}{12}$ 49. $\frac{3}{2} - \frac{5}{8}$ $\frac{7}{8}$ 50. $\frac{5}{6} - \frac{0}{4}$ $\frac{5}{6}$ 51. $\frac{2}{3} - \frac{1}{9}$ $\frac{5}{9}$

52. $\frac{5}{6} - \frac{1}{4}$ $\frac{7}{12}$ 53. $\frac{3}{3} - \frac{1}{4}$ $\frac{3}{4}$ 54. $\frac{9}{5} - \frac{3}{10}$ $1\frac{1}{2}$ 55. $\frac{7}{5} - \frac{2}{3}$ $\frac{11}{15}$ 56. $\frac{7}{8} - \frac{5}{6}$ $\frac{1}{24}$ 57. $\frac{5}{8} - \frac{1}{2}$ $\frac{1}{8}$

Give the product in simplest form. *(page 182)*

58. $2 \times 1\frac{1}{2}$ 3   59. $3 \times 2\frac{1}{3}$ 7   60. $4 \times 1\frac{2}{3}$ $6\frac{2}{3}$ 61. $3\frac{1}{4} \times 5$ $16\frac{1}{4}$ 62. $4 \times 2\frac{1}{2}$ 10

63. $1\frac{1}{3} \times 1\frac{1}{2}$ 2   64. $1\frac{1}{2} \times 1\frac{2}{3}$ $2\frac{1}{2}$ 65. $2\frac{1}{4} \times 3\frac{1}{2}$ $7\frac{7}{8}$ 66. $3 \times 2\frac{2}{5}$ $7\frac{1}{5}$ 67. $3\frac{1}{2} \times 1\frac{1}{4}$ $4\frac{3}{8}$

68. $3\frac{1}{2} \times 1\frac{3}{4}$ $6\frac{1}{8}$ 69. $2\frac{2}{3} \times 4\frac{1}{3}$ $11\frac{5}{9}$ 70. $1\frac{3}{4} \times 1\frac{2}{3}$ $2\frac{11}{12}$ 71. $2\frac{2}{3} \times 3\frac{4}{5}$ $10\frac{2}{15}$ 72. $1\frac{1}{2} \times 2\frac{1}{3}$ $3\frac{1}{2}$

Give the quotient in simplest form. *(page 190)*

73. $1\frac{1}{2} \div 2$ $\frac{3}{4}$ 74. $3\frac{3}{4} \div 3$ $1\frac{1}{4}$ 75. $2 \div 1\frac{1}{3}$ $1\frac{1}{2}$ 76. $4 \div 2\frac{3}{4}$ $1\frac{5}{11}$ 77. $12\frac{1}{2} \div 6$ $2\frac{1}{12}$

78. $5\frac{1}{2} \div 1\frac{1}{3}$ $4\frac{1}{8}$ 79. $8 \div 2\frac{1}{2}$ $3\frac{1}{5}$ 80. $6\frac{1}{4} \div 1\frac{1}{4}$ 5   81. $5\frac{7}{8} \div 1\frac{3}{4}$ $3\frac{5}{14}$ 82. $6\frac{1}{2} \div 2$ $3\frac{1}{4}$

Problem solving

COMPUTERS IN WATCHES

A tiny, battery-powered computer controls the electronic circuits used to display the time on a digital watch.

The diagram shows 24 electrodes. Each electrode controls a part of the display. When the electrode is charged, the part controlled by the computer turns black.

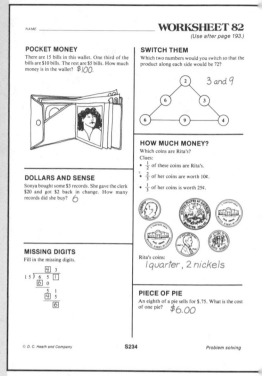

A B C D E   F G H I J K L M

N O P Q R S T U V W X

ELECTRODES SHOWN IN RED ARE CHARGED.

Solve. Use the diagram.

1. In the diagram, electrodes B, C, D, F, H, I, J, L, M, O, P, Q, R, S, T, W, and X are charged.
   a. What time is displayed? 6:23
   b. If electrode E was also charged, what time would be displayed? 8:23

2. After one minute passes, the computer will change the *3* to a *4*. To make this change, the computer
   a. removes the charge from electrodes L and ☐. W
   b. charges electrode ☐. K

3. For each set of charged electrodes, give the time that would be displayed.
   a. E, F, G, I, J, K, L, M, Q, R, U, W, and X 1:49
   b. A, E, I, M, N, Q, R, U, and X 11:11
   c. A, B, D, E, F, H, I, K, L, M, N, O, P, R, T, U, V, W, and X 12:30

4. When *10:00* is displayed, all but 3 of the electrodes are charged. 8:08, 10:06, 10:09, 10:28, 10:38, 10:58, 12:08
   a. Can you find seven more times that use all but 3 of the electrodes?
   b. Can you find a time that uses all but 2 of the electrodes? 10:08

5. A computer can also make it possible for a watch to include a calendar, an alarm, and a calculator. What is the sale price of this watch? $12

Reg. $15
1/5 off

EXTRA PROBLEM SOLVING
Page 451   Even exercises

PROBLEM-SOLVING WORKSHEET
Copymaster S234 or Duplicating Master S234

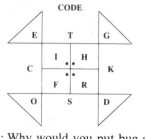

NAME _____ **WORKSHEET 82**
(Use after page 193.)

POCKET MONEY
There are 15 bills in this wallet. One third of the bills are $10 bills. The rest are $5 bills. How much money is in the wallet? $100

SWITCH THEM
Which two numbers would you switch so that the product along each side would be 72? 3 and 9
(2, 6, 3, 6, 9, 4)

DOLLARS AND SENSE
Sonya bought some $3 records. She gave the clerk $20 and got $2 back in change. How many records did she buy? 6

HOW MUCH MONEY?
Which coins are Rita's?
Clues:
• ½ of these coins are Rita's.
• ⅔ of her coins are worth 10¢.
• ⅓ of her coins is worth 25¢.

Rita's coins: 1 quarter, 2 nickels

MISSING DIGITS
Fill in the missing digits.
15) 6 5 1
(with digits filled)

PIECE OF PIE
An eighth of a pie sells for $.75. What is the cost of one pie? $6.00

© D. C. Heath and Company   S234   *Problem solving*

CHALKBOARD CHALLENGE
Use the code to answer the riddle.

CODE

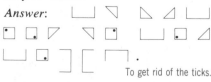

E T G
C I H K
F R
O S D

Riddle: Why would you put bug spray on your watch?

Answer: ⬜ ◺ ◿ ◺ ⬜
◰ ⬜ ◳ ◹ ⬜ ⬜ ⬜ ◺
⬜ ⬜ ⬜ ⬜ ⬜ ⬜

To get rid of the ticks.

NAME ____________ **CHAPTER 8 TEST**
(Form A)

Multiply. Write the product in simplest form. *(page 178)*

1. $3 \times \frac{1}{3} =$ 1 2. $4 \times \frac{1}{2} =$ 2 3. $\frac{2}{3} \times \frac{1}{5} =$ 2/15
4. $\frac{3}{5} \times \frac{1}{6} =$ 1/10 5. $\frac{9}{4} \times \frac{2}{5} =$ 9/10 6. $\frac{2}{3} \times \frac{3}{4} =$ 1/2
7. $\frac{0}{2} \times \frac{5}{3} =$ 0 8. $\frac{3}{2} \times \frac{4}{3} =$ 2 9. $\frac{3}{8} \times \frac{8}{3} =$ 1

Complete. *(page 180)*

10. $\frac{1}{2}$ of 16 = 8 11. $\frac{2}{3}$ of 21 = 14
12. $\frac{3}{4}$ of 32 = 24 13. $\frac{1}{4}$ of \$20 = \$5
14. $\frac{3}{5}$ of \$40 = \$24 15. $\frac{5}{6}$ of \$36 = \$30
16. $\frac{3}{8}$ of \$24 = \$9

Multiply. Write the product in simplest form. *(page 182)*

17. $2 \times 1\frac{1}{2} =$ 3 18. $3 \times 1\frac{1}{4} =$ 3 3/4
19. $2\frac{1}{2} \times 4 =$ 10 20. $1\frac{1}{2} \times 1\frac{1}{3} =$ 2
21. $1\frac{1}{4} \times 2\frac{1}{2} =$ 3 1/8 22. $1\frac{1}{3} \times 1\frac{2}{3} =$ 2 2/9
23. $2\frac{2}{3} \times 2\frac{1}{2} =$ 6 2/3 24. $3\frac{5}{8} \times 2\frac{1}{4} =$ 8 5/32
25. $3\frac{3}{4} \times 1\frac{7}{8} =$ 7 1/32

ANSWERS

1. 1
2. 2
3. 2/15
4. 1/10
5. 9/10
6. 1/2
7. 0
8. 2
9. 1
10. 8
11. 14
12. 24
13. \$5
14. \$24
15. \$30
16. \$9
17. 3
18. 3 3/4
19. 10
20. 2
21. 3 1/8
22. 2 2/9
23. 6 2/3
24. 8 5/32
25. 7 1/32

© D. C. Heath and Company S29 Page 1

NAME ____________ **CHAPTER 8 TEST**
(Form A)

Complete. *(pages 184, 185)*

26. $1\frac{1}{2}$ days = 36 h 27. $1\frac{3}{4}$ h = 105 min
28. $1\frac{1}{3}$ yd = 4 ft 29. $2\frac{2}{3}$ ft = 32 in.
30. $2\frac{1}{2}$ gal = 10 qt 31. $1\frac{1}{2}$ qt = 3 pt

Divide. Write each quotient in simplest form. *(page 188)*

32. $\frac{2}{3} \div 2 =$ 1/3 33. $\frac{3}{4} \div 3 =$ 1/4 34. $\frac{3}{5} \div \frac{1}{5} =$ 3
35. $\frac{5}{8} \div \frac{1}{4} =$ 2 1/2 36. $\frac{2}{3} \div \frac{5}{6} =$ 4/5 37. $\frac{3}{5} \div \frac{5}{2} =$ 6/25
38. $\frac{0}{4} \div \frac{1}{2} =$ 0 39. [illegible] $\div 3 =$ 1/6

Divide. Write each quotient in simplest form. *(page 190)*

40. $3 \div 1\frac{1}{2} =$ 2 41. $2\frac{1}{4} \div 2 =$ 1 1/8
42. $3\frac{1}{2} \div 1\frac{3}{4} =$ 2 43. $2\frac{1}{2} \div 1\frac{1}{8} =$ 2 2/9
44. $1\frac{2}{3} \div 2\frac{1}{5} =$ 25/33 45. $3\frac{1}{3} \div 1\frac{1}{4} =$ 2 2/3
46. $4\frac{2}{3} \div 3\frac{1}{6} =$ 1 9/19 47. $1\frac{1}{2} \div 4 =$ 3/8

Solve.

48. How many miles is it from Eagle Ledge to Blue Lake if you hike by Crystal Falls? 6
49. You are at Crystal Falls. You plan to hike at the rate of $2\frac{1}{2}$ miles per hour for the next $1\frac{3}{4}$ hours. How far will you be from Crystal Falls then? 4 3/8 miles
50. You hiked from Hermit Cave to Eagle Ledge in $1\frac{1}{4}$ hours. How many miles per hour did you average? 2 3/5

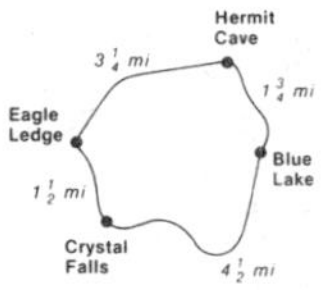

Hermit Cave
3 1/4 mi
1 3/4 mi
Eagle Ledge
Blue Lake
1 1/2 mi
Crystal Falls
4 1/2 mi

ANSWERS

26. 36
27. 105
28. 4
29. 32
30. 10
31. 3
32. 1/3
33. 1/4
34. 3
35. 2 1/2
36. 4/5
37. 6/25
38. 0
39. 1/6
40. 2
41. 1 1/8
42. 2
43. 2 2/9
44. 25/33
45. 2 2/3
46. 1 9/19
47. 3/8
48. 6
49. 4 3/8 miles
50. 2 3/5

© D. C. Heath and Company S30 Page 2

Chapter REVIEW

Here are scrambled answers for the review exercises:

1	3	add	fraction	reciprocal
2	4	denominators	inverting	simplest
		divide	numerators	whole

1. numerators, denominators

1. To multiply these two fractions, you would multiply the [?] to get the numerator of the product and multiply the [?] to get the denominator of the product. *(page 178)*

$\frac{3}{4} \times \frac{1}{2} = ?$

2. 4, 3

2. To compute this fraction of a number, you could first divide 36 by [?] and then multiply the result by [?]. *(page 180)*

$\frac{3}{4}$ of $36 = ?$

3. whole

3. To compute this fraction of a number, you would change the [?] number to a fraction and multiply. *(page 180)*

$\frac{2}{5}$ of $17 = ?$

4. fraction

4. To multiply these mixed numbers, change each mixed number to a [?] and multiply. *(page 182)*

$2\frac{1}{2} \times 1\frac{1}{4} = ?$

5. 2, add

5. To change $2\frac{1}{2}$ feet to inches, you could first find how many inches in [?] feet and in $\frac{1}{2}$ of a foot and then [?]. *(page 184)*

$2\frac{1}{2}$ feet = ? inches

6. 1, inverting

6. Two numbers are reciprocals if their product is [?]. For a fraction not equal to 0, you can find the reciprocal by [?] the fraction. *(page 188)*

7. reciprocal, divide

7. To divide by a fraction, you would multiply by its [?]. To divide mixed numbers, change each mixed number to a fraction and [?]. *(pages 188, 190)*

8. simplest

8. The last step in this division exercise is to write the quotient in [?] form. *(page 190)*

$$2\frac{1}{2} \div 1\frac{3}{4} = \frac{5}{2} \div \frac{7}{4}$$
$$= \frac{5}{2} \times \frac{4}{7}$$
$$= \frac{20}{14}$$
$$= ?$$

Chapter TEST

Multiply. Write the product in simplest form.   *(page 178)*

1. $2 \times \frac{1}{2}$ 1   **2.** $\frac{1}{3} \times \frac{1}{3}$ $\frac{1}{9}$ **3.** $\frac{2}{5} \times \frac{1}{3}$ $\frac{2}{15}$ **4.** $\frac{3}{4} \times \frac{1}{2}$ $\frac{3}{8}$ **5.** $\frac{2}{3} \times \frac{3}{5}$ $\frac{2}{5}$ **6.** $\frac{2}{5} \times \frac{1}{2}$ $\frac{1}{5}$

7. $4 \times \frac{1}{2}$ 2   **8.** $4 \times \frac{1}{8}$ $\frac{1}{2}$ **9.** $\frac{5}{2} \times \frac{4}{3}$ $3\frac{1}{3}$ **10.** $\frac{4}{5} \times \frac{5}{4}$ 1   **11.** $\frac{8}{3} \times \frac{5}{2}$ $6\frac{2}{3}$ **12.** $4 \times \frac{5}{4}$ 5

Complete.   *(page 180)*

13. $\frac{1}{2}$ of 12 = ? 6   **14.** $\frac{1}{3}$ of 24 = ? 8   **15.** $\frac{2}{3}$ of 18 = ? 12   **16.** $\frac{3}{4}$ of $20 = ? $15   **17.** $\frac{3}{4}$ of $8 = ? $6

Multiply. Write the product in simplest form.   *(page 182)*

18. $2 \times 1\frac{1}{2}$ 3   **19.** $2\frac{1}{3} \times 3$ 7   **20.** $3 \times 1\frac{1}{4}$ $3\frac{3}{4}$ **21.** $2\frac{2}{3} \times 4$ $10\frac{2}{3}$ **22.** $5 \times 1\frac{1}{2}$ $7\frac{1}{2}$

23. $1\frac{2}{3} \times 2\frac{1}{2}$ $4\frac{1}{6}$ **24.** $2\frac{3}{4} \times 2\frac{3}{4}$ $7\frac{9}{16}$ **25.** $2\frac{5}{6} \times 1\frac{1}{4}$ $3\frac{13}{24}$ **26.** $1\frac{3}{8} \times 3\frac{3}{5}$ $4\frac{19}{20}$ **27.** $1\frac{1}{3} \times 1\frac{2}{3}$ $2\frac{2}{9}$

Complete.   *(page 184)*

28. $2\frac{1}{2}$ days = ? h 60   **29.** $1\frac{3}{4}$ h = ? min 105   **30.** $2\frac{1}{2}$ min = ? sec 150   **31.** $1\frac{1}{3}$ yd = ? ft 4

Divide. Write each quotient in simplest form.   *(page 188)*

32. $\frac{3}{4} \div 2$ $\frac{3}{8}$ **33.** $3 \div \frac{3}{8}$ 8   **34.** $\frac{2}{3} \div \frac{1}{3}$ 2   **35.** $\frac{1}{2} \div \frac{1}{3}$ $1\frac{1}{2}$ **36.** $\frac{1}{3} \div \frac{1}{2}$ $\frac{2}{3}$ **37.** $4 \div \frac{1}{2}$ 8

38. $\frac{5}{6} \div \frac{3}{4}$ $1\frac{1}{9}$ **39.** $6 \div \frac{3}{5}$ 10   **40.** $\frac{3}{5} \div 6$ $\frac{1}{10}$ **41.** $\frac{5}{8} \div \frac{3}{4}$ $\frac{5}{6}$ **42.** $\frac{3}{10} \div \frac{2}{5}$ $\frac{3}{4}$ **43.** $\frac{1}{2} \div \frac{3}{4}$ $\frac{2}{3}$

Divide. Write each quotient in simplest form.   *(page 190)*

44. $2\frac{1}{2} \div 1\frac{1}{4}$ 2   **45.** $3 \div 1\frac{1}{2}$ 2   **46.** $2\frac{1}{2} \div 2$ $1\frac{1}{4}$ **47.** $8 \div 2\frac{1}{3}$ $3\frac{3}{7}$ **48.** $5 \div \frac{1}{2}$ 10

49. $3\frac{1}{4} \div 6$ $\frac{13}{24}$ **50.** $4\frac{3}{4} \div 1\frac{1}{2}$ $3\frac{1}{3}$ **51.** $9 \div 3\frac{3}{8}$ $2\frac{2}{3}$ **52.** $5\frac{5}{6} \div 3\frac{1}{2}$ $1\frac{2}{3}$ **53.** $2\frac{1}{3} \div 3$ $\frac{7}{9}$

Solve.

54. How many miles is it from Round Lake to Clear Falls if you hike by Lookout Point? $5\frac{3}{4}$

55. Which is the shorter route from Round Lake to Clear Falls? By Lookout Point

56. How many miles long is the hiking trail? 12

57. You hiked the trail in $5\frac{1}{4}$ hours. How many miles per hour did you average? $2\frac{2}{7}$

LOOKOUT POINT

$1\frac{1}{4}$ mi

$4\frac{1}{2}$ mi

CLEAR FALLS

ROUND LAKE

$1\frac{1}{2}$ mi

BLACK CAVE

$4\frac{3}{4}$ mi

NAME _____   **CHAPTER 8 TEST**
(Form B)

Multiply. Write the product in simplest form.   *(page 178)*

1. $2 \times \frac{1}{2}$ 1   2. $6 \times \frac{1}{3}$ 2   3. $\frac{3}{4} \times \frac{1}{4}$ $\frac{3}{16}$

4. $\frac{2}{3} \times \frac{1}{6}$ $\frac{1}{15}$ 5. $\frac{7}{4} \times \frac{2}{5}$ $\frac{7}{10}$ 6. $\frac{3}{4} \times \frac{2}{3}$ $\frac{1}{2}$

7. $\frac{0}{2} \times \frac{5}{2}$ 0   8. $\frac{5}{2} \times \frac{4}{5}$ 2   9. $\frac{5}{8} \times \frac{8}{5}$ 1

Complete.   *(page 180)*

10. $\frac{1}{2}$ of 14 = 7   11. $\frac{2}{3}$ of 18 = 12

12. $\frac{3}{4}$ of 36 = 27   13. $\frac{1}{3}$ of $36 = $12

14. $\frac{2}{5}$ of $40 = $16   15. $\frac{5}{6}$ of $24 = $20

16. $\frac{5}{8}$ of $16 = $10

Multiply. Write the product in simplest form.   *(page 182)*

17. $3 \times 1\frac{1}{3}$ 4   18. $2 \times 2\frac{1}{2}$ 5

19. $3 \times 1\frac{1}{4}$ $3\frac{3}{4}$ 20. $1\frac{1}{3} \times 1\frac{1}{2}$ 2

21. $2\frac{1}{4} \times 1\frac{1}{2}$ $3\frac{3}{8}$ 22. $1\frac{1}{4} \times 1\frac{3}{4}$ $2\frac{3}{16}$

23. $2\frac{1}{2} \times 2\frac{2}{3}$ $6\frac{2}{3}$ 24. $3\frac{1}{4} \times 2\frac{3}{8}$ $7\frac{23}{32}$

25. $1\frac{5}{8} \times 2\frac{3}{4}$ $4\frac{15}{32}$

ANSWERS
1. 1
2. 2
3. $\frac{3}{16}$
4. $\frac{1}{15}$
5. $\frac{7}{10}$
6. $\frac{1}{2}$
7. 0
8. 2
9. 1
10. 7
11. 12
12. 27
13. $12
14. $16
15. $20
16. $10
17. 4
18. 5
19. $3\frac{3}{4}$
20. 2
21. $3\frac{3}{8}$
22. $2\frac{3}{16}$
23. $6\frac{2}{3}$
24. $7\frac{23}{32}$
25. $4\frac{15}{32}$

D. C. Heath and Company   S31   Page 1

NAME _____   **CHAPTER 8 TEST**
(Form B)

Complete.   *(pages 184, 185)*

26. $1\frac{1}{4}$ days = 30 h   27. $1\frac{2}{3}$ h = 100 min

28. $2\frac{1}{3}$ yd = 7 ft   29. $1\frac{3}{4}$ ft = 21 in.

30. $2\frac{1}{4}$ gal = 9 qt   31. $2\frac{1}{2}$ qt = 5 pt

Divide. Write each quotient in simplest form.   *(page 188)*

32. $\frac{3}{4} \div 3$ $\frac{1}{4}$ 33. $\frac{4}{5} \div ?$ $\frac{1}{3}$ 34. $\frac{4}{5} \div \frac{1}{5}$ 4

35. $\frac{7}{8} \div \frac{1}{4}$ $3\frac{1}{2}$ 36. $\frac{4}{5} \div \frac{2}{3}$ $1\frac{1}{5}$ 37. $\frac{5}{9} \div \frac{5}{4}$ $\frac{4}{9}$

38. $\frac{0}{6} \div \frac{2}{3}$ 0   39. $\frac{2}{3} \div 2$ $\frac{1}{5}$

Divide. Write each quotient in simplest form.   *(page 190)*

40. $5 \div 2\frac{1}{2}$ 2   41. $2\frac{1}{3} \div 2$ $1\frac{1}{6}$

42. $3\frac{1}{4} \div 1\frac{5}{8}$ 2   43. $2\frac{3}{4} \div 1\frac{1}{2}$ $1\frac{7}{9}$

44. $4\frac{3}{4} \div 2\frac{1}{3}$ $2\frac{1}{28}$ 45. $3\frac{1}{3} \div 2\frac{3}{4}$ $1\frac{1}{5}$

46. $1\frac{5}{9} \div 2\frac{3}{5}$ $\frac{55}{78}$ 47. $2\frac{1}{2} \div 4$ $\frac{5}{8}$

Solve.

48. How many miles is it from Eagle Ledge to Blue Lake if you hike by Hermit Cave? 5

49. You are at Eagle Ledge. You plan to hike at the rate of $2\frac{1}{4}$ miles per hour for the next $1\frac{1}{2}$ hours. How far will you be from Eagle Ledge then? $3\frac{3}{8}$ miles

50. You hiked from Blue Lake to Crystal Falls in $1\frac{3}{4}$ hours. How many miles per hour did you average? $2\frac{4}{7}$

Hermit Cave
$3\frac{1}{4}$ mi
Eagle Ledge
$1\frac{1}{4}$ mi
Blue Lake
$1\frac{1}{3}$ mi
Crystal Falls
$4\frac{1}{4}$ mi

ANSWERS
26. 30
27. 100
28. 7
29. 21
30. 9
31. 5
32. $\frac{1}{4}$
33. $\frac{1}{3}$
34. 4
35. $3\frac{1}{2}$
36. $1\frac{1}{5}$
37. $\frac{4}{9}$
38. 0
39. $\frac{1}{5}$
40. 2
41. $1\frac{1}{6}$
42. 2
43. $1\frac{7}{9}$
44. $2\frac{1}{28}$
45. $1\frac{1}{5}$
46. $\frac{55}{78}$
47. $\frac{5}{8}$
48. 5
49. $3\frac{3}{8}$
50. $2\frac{4}{7}$

D. C. Heath and Company   S32   Page 2

CUMULATIVE TEST
(*Chapters 1–8*)

Use Copymaster S336 to provide the students with an answer sheet in standardized test format.

Cumulative TEST Standardized Format

Choose the correct letter.

Answers for Cumulative Test, Chapters 1–8

1. Ⓐ Ⓑ ⓒ Ⓓ	2. Ⓐ ⓑ ⓒ Ⓓ	3. ⓐ Ⓑ Ⓒ Ⓓ
4. Ⓐ Ⓑ ⓒ Ⓓ	5. Ⓐ Ⓑ Ⓒ ⓓ	6. ⓐ Ⓑ Ⓒ Ⓓ
7. Ⓐ Ⓑ ⓒ Ⓓ	8. Ⓐ ⓑ Ⓒ Ⓓ	9. Ⓐ Ⓑ Ⓒ ⓓ
10. ⓐ Ⓑ Ⓒ Ⓓ	11. Ⓐ ⓑ Ⓒ Ⓓ	12. Ⓐ Ⓑ Ⓒ ⓓ

The table below correlates test items with student text pages.

Test Item	Page(s) Taught	Skill Practice
1	24	p. 186, exercises 1–15
2	46	p. 186, exercises 16–35
3	64	p. 186, exercises 36–55
4	96	p. 186, exercises 56–71
5	132	p. 186, exercises 72–86
6	146	p. 192, exercises 1–21
7	158	p. 192, exercises 22–39
8	164, 166	p. 192, exercises 40–57
9	182	p. 192, exercises 58–72
10	190	p. 192, exercises 73–82
11	110	
12	160	

1. Give the sum.

$23.5 + 4.28 + 60.7$

A. 12.70   **B.** 127.0
C. 88.48   **D.** none of these

2. Give the difference.

$286.5 - 13.74$

A. 273.24   **B.** 272.76
C. 149.1   **D.** none of these

3. Give the product.

3.57×2.70

A. 9.6390   **B.** 8.199
C. 963.90   **D.** none of these

4. Give the quotient rounded to the nearest tenth.

$423.8 \div 1.62$

A. 2.6   **B.** 0.3
C. 261.6   **D.** none of these

5. $\frac{7}{8} < ?$

A. $\frac{1}{2}$ **B.** $\frac{4}{5}$
C. $\frac{5}{6}$ **D.** none of these

6. Change to a decimal rounded to the nearest hundredth.

$\frac{5}{6} = ?$

A. 0.83   **B.** 0.84
C. 11.2   **D.** none of these

7. Give the sum in simplest form.

$\frac{2}{3} + \frac{3}{4}$

A. $\frac{5}{7}$ **B.** $\frac{1}{2}$
C. $1\frac{5}{12}$ **D.** none of these

8. Give the difference in simplest form.

$\frac{5}{6} - \frac{3}{8}$

A. 1   **B.** $\frac{11}{24}$
C. $\frac{1}{12}$ **D.** none of these

9. Give the product in simplest form.

$2\frac{1}{2} \times 1\frac{1}{4}$

A. 2   **B.** $6\frac{1}{4}$
C. $12\frac{1}{2}$ **D.** none of these

10. Give the quotient in simplest form.

$6 \div 3\frac{3}{4}$

A. $1\frac{3}{5}$
B. $\frac{3}{8}$
C. $22\frac{1}{2}$
D. none of these

11. STUDENT TRYOUTS

Football	↑↑↑↑↑↑↑↑↑
Basketball	↑↑↑↑↑
Baseball	↑↑↑↑↑
Each ↑ stands for 6 students.	

How many more students tried out for football than baseball?

A. 2   **B.** 12
C. 18   **D.** none of these

12. Sara jogged 3 miles one day and $4\frac{1}{2}$ miles on each of the next two days. How many miles did she average per day?

A. $3\frac{3}{7}$ **B.** $3\frac{3}{4}$
C. $4\frac{1}{14}$ **D.** none of these

NAME _____ **SECOND-QUARTER TEST**
(Chapters 5 through 8)

Choose the correct letter.
Sample:

Student	Tickets Sold
Beth	
Greg	

How many tickets did Greg sell?
A. 14
B. 12
C. 22
D. none of these

Ⓐ Ⓑ Ⓒ Ⓓ

First decide which answer is correct. Then find the problem number on your answer sheet and darken in the space for the correct answer. In the sample, D is the correct answer.

1.
Student	Free Throws Made
Jan	
Sean	

How many free throws did Sean make?
A. 14
Ⓑ 11
C. 13
D. none of these

2. **Homework During Week**
How many hours did Carol spend doing homework?
A. 3 Ⓑ 5
C. 10 D. none of these

3. Look at the graph in exercise 2. Who spent 8 hours doing homework?
A. Carol Ⓑ Mark
C. Rodney
D. none of these

4. **Sue's Weekly Savings**
How much did Sue save during week 4?
A. $9 Ⓑ $4
C. $10 Ⓓ none of these

5. Look at the graph in exercise 4. During which week did Sue save $13?
A. 2 Ⓑ 4
Ⓒ 5 D. none of these

6. **Number of Books Read**
Ruth ■ ■ ■ ■
Samuel ■ ■ ■ ■ ■
Tom ■ ■ ■
Each ■ stands for 4 books.
How many books did Samuel read?
A. 5 B. 10
C. 16 Ⓓ none of these

7. Look at the graph in exercise 6. Sam read how many more books than Tom?
A. 2 Ⓑ 6
C. 8 D. none of these

8. The mean of 23, 35, 37, 37, 34, and 32 is
A. 14 Ⓑ 33
C. 37 D. none of these

9. The median of 58, 46, 53, 49, and 54 is
Ⓐ 53 B. 52
C. 12 D. none of these

10. The mode of 133, 118, 127, 118, 122, and 120 is
Ⓐ 118 B. 121
C. 123 D. none of these

© D. C. Heath and Company   S73   Page 1

NAME _____ **SECOND-QUARTER TEST**
(Chapters 5 through 8)

Choose the correct letter.

11. The range of 132, 109, 127, 125, and 127 is
Ⓐ 23
B. 124
C. 127
D. none of these

12. $\frac{3}{4} = \underline{?}$
A. $\frac{4}{3}$
Ⓑ $\frac{9}{12}$
C. $\frac{8}{9}$
D. none of these

13. $\frac{12}{18}$ written in lowest terms is
A. $\frac{6}{9}$
B. $\frac{4}{6}$
Ⓒ $\frac{2}{3}$
D. none of these

14. The least common denominator of $\frac{5}{6}$ and $\frac{4}{9}$ is
A. 9
Ⓑ 18
C. 54
D. none of these

15. $\frac{2}{3} < \underline{?}$
A. $\frac{1}{3}$
B. $\frac{5}{8}$
C. $\frac{5}{9}$
Ⓓ $\frac{7}{10}$

16. $\frac{3}{4} > \underline{?}$
Ⓐ $\frac{7}{8}$
B. $\frac{3}{4}$
C. $\frac{5}{4}$
D. $\frac{5}{6}$

17. $3\frac{2}{3} = \underline{?}$
A. $\frac{9}{3}$
B. $\frac{8}{3}$
Ⓒ $\frac{11}{3}$
D. none of these

18. $\frac{24}{6} = \underline{?}$
Ⓐ 4
B. 6
C. 8
D. none of these

19. $\frac{20}{3} = \underline{?}$
A. $6\frac{1}{3}$
B. $6\frac{2}{3}$
C. $7\frac{1}{3}$
D. none of these

20. $\frac{12}{30}$ written in simplest form is
A. $\frac{12}{30}$
B. $\frac{4}{10}$
Ⓒ $\frac{2}{5}$
D. none of these

21. $\frac{9}{6}$ written in simplest form is
A. $\frac{2}{3}$
B. $\frac{3}{2}$
Ⓒ $1\frac{1}{2}$
D. none of these

22. Divide. $6\overline{)382}$
A. $66\frac{1}{3}$
B. $36\frac{2}{3}$
C. $66\frac{2}{3}$
Ⓓ none of these

23. $\frac{3}{5} = \underline{?}$
Ⓐ 0.6
B. 0.66
C. 0.35
D. none of these

24. $2\frac{3}{8} = \underline{?}$
A. 2.25
B. 2.625
C. 0.375
Ⓓ none of these

25. $0.4 = \underline{?}$
A. $\frac{4}{5}$
B. $\frac{1}{25}$
Ⓒ $\frac{2}{5}$
D. none of these

© D. C. Heath and Company   S74   Page 2

NAME _____ **SECOND-QUARTER TEST**
(Chapters 5 through 8)

Choose the correct letter.

26. $1.625 = \underline{?}$
Ⓐ $1\frac{5}{8}$
B. $1\frac{3}{8}$
C. $1\frac{5}{6}$
D. none of these

27. $\frac{5}{8} + \frac{3}{8} = \underline{?}$
A. $\frac{8}{16}$
B. $\frac{1}{8}$
Ⓒ 1
D. none of these

28. $\frac{3}{4} + \frac{2}{3} = \underline{?}$
A. $\frac{5}{4}$
B. $\frac{5}{12}$
Ⓒ $1\frac{5}{12}$
D. none of these

29. $2\frac{1}{4} + 1\frac{2}{5} = \underline{?}$
Ⓐ $\frac{13}{20}$
B. $3\frac{3}{20}$
C. $3\frac{1}{3}$
D. none of these

30. $3\frac{5}{8} + 1\frac{2}{3} = \underline{?}$
A. $4\frac{7}{11}$
B. $4\frac{7}{24}$
C. $4\frac{7}{8}$
Ⓓ none of these

31. $\frac{5}{6} - \frac{1}{6} = \underline{?}$
A. $\frac{1}{3}$
B. 1
Ⓒ $\frac{2}{3}$
D. none of these

32. $\frac{7}{12} - \frac{1}{4} = \underline{?}$
Ⓐ $\frac{1}{3}$
B. $\frac{1}{2}$
C. $\frac{3}{4}$
D. none of these

33. $3\frac{5}{9} - 1\frac{2}{3} = \underline{?}$
A. $1\frac{1}{3}$
Ⓑ $2\frac{1}{3}$
C. $2\frac{2}{9}$
D. none of these

34. $5\frac{5}{8} - 3\frac{1}{2} = \underline{?}$
A. $2\frac{1}{3}$
B. $2\frac{1}{2}$
Ⓒ $2\frac{1}{8}$
D. none of these

35. Subtract.
$6 - 4\frac{3}{4}$
A. $2\frac{3}{4}$
B. $2\frac{1}{4}$
Ⓒ $1\frac{1}{4}$
D. none of these

36. One cookie recipe calls for $1\frac{3}{4}$ cups of flour, and another calls for $2\frac{1}{2}$ cups of flour. How many cups of flour are needed for both recipes?
A. $\frac{3}{4}$
B. $3\frac{1}{4}$
Ⓒ $4\frac{1}{4}$
D. none of these

37. A cake recipe calls for 3 cups of sugar. You have $1\frac{1}{4}$ cups of sugar. How many more cups of sugar will you need?
A. $4\frac{3}{4}$
B. $2\frac{1}{4}$
C. $2\frac{3}{4}$
Ⓓ none of these

38. $\frac{2}{3} \times \frac{5}{6} = \underline{?}$
Ⓐ $\frac{5}{9}$
B. $\frac{4}{5}$
C. $1\frac{2}{3}$
D. none of these

39. $\frac{1}{4}$ of 32 = $\underline{?}$
Ⓐ 8
B. 16
C. 24
D. none of these

40. $\frac{4}{5}$ of 40 = $\underline{?}$
A. 50
Ⓑ 32
C. 24
D. none of these

© D. C. Heath and Company   S75   Page 3

NAME _____ **SECOND-QUARTER TEST**
(Chapters 5 through 8)

Choose the correct letter.

41. $4 \times 2\frac{1}{2} = \underline{?}$
A. $8\frac{1}{2}$
B. 6
Ⓒ 10
D. none of these

42. $1\frac{1}{2} \times 2\frac{2}{3} = \underline{?}$
Ⓐ 4
B. $\frac{9}{16}$
C. $1\frac{5}{6}$
D. none of these

43. $2\frac{1}{2}$ days = $\underline{?}$ h
A. 24
B. 40
C. 48
Ⓓ none of these

44. $1\frac{3}{4}$ ft = $\underline{?}$ in.
A. 28
B. 21
Ⓒ 21
D. none of these

45. $1\frac{3}{4}$ gal = $\underline{?}$ qt
Ⓐ 7
B. 4
C. 10
D. none of these

46. $\frac{4}{5} + \frac{2}{3} = \underline{?}$
A. $\frac{5}{6}$
B. $\frac{8}{15}$
Ⓒ $1\frac{1}{5}$
D. none of these

47. $1\frac{1}{2} \div 2 = \underline{?}$
A. 3
B. $1\frac{1}{4}$
C. $\frac{1}{3}$
Ⓓ none of these

48. $2\frac{5}{8} + 1\frac{1}{6} = \underline{?}$
Ⓐ $2\frac{1}{4}$
B. $\frac{2}{3}$
C. $3\frac{1}{16}$
D. none of these

49. You hiked at the rate of $2\frac{1}{2}$ miles per hour for $1\frac{3}{4}$ hours. How many miles did you hike?
A. $1\frac{3}{7}$
B. $\frac{7}{10}$
Ⓒ $4\frac{3}{8}$
D. none of these

50. You hiked $6\frac{3}{4}$ miles in $2\frac{1}{4}$ hours. How many miles did you average per hour?
A. 18
B. $\frac{1}{18}$
C. $2\frac{17}{32}$
Ⓓ none of these

© D. C. Heath and Company   S76   Page 4

SECOND-QUARTER TEST

The second-quarter test shown on these two pages is in standardized format so that the students can become accustomed to taking standardized tests.

196A

Use Copymaster S92 or Duplicating Master S92 to provide the students with an answer sheet in standardized test format.

Copymaster S106 has a quick-score answer key for the second-quarter test.

The table below correlates test items with student text pages.

Test Item	Text Page	Test Item	Text Page	Test Item	Text Page	Test Item	Text Page
1	p. 104	14	p. 130	27	p. 156	40	p. 180
2	p. 106	15	p. 132	28	p. 158	41	p. 182
3	p. 106	16	p. 132	29	p. 160	42	p. 182
4	p. 108	17	p. 136	30	p. 160	43	p. 184
5	p. 108	18	p. 138	31	p. 164	44	p. 184
6	p. 110	19	p. 138	32	p. 166	45	p. 184
7	p. 110	20	p. 140	33	p. 168	46	p. 188
8	p. 114	21	p. 140	34	p. 168	47	p. 190
9	p. 116	22	p. 142	35	p. 170	48	p. 190
10	p. 116	23	p. 146	36	p. 160	49	p. 182
11	p. 116	24	p. 147	37	p. 170	50	p. 190
12	p. 126	25	p. 148	38	p. 178		
13	p. 128	26	p. 148	39	p. 180		

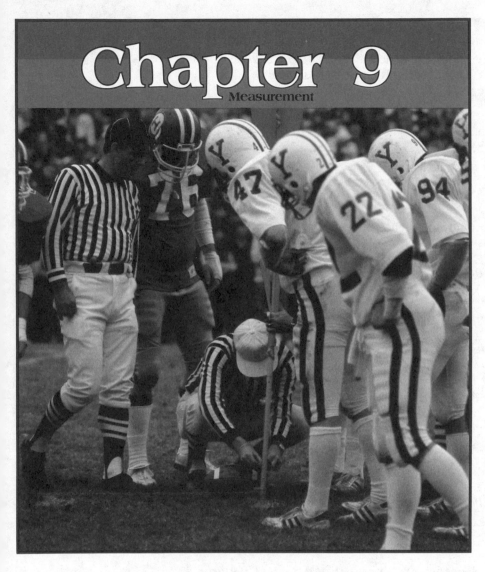

CHAPTER 9
Measurement

LESSON OBJECTIVES
To measure lengths with centimeters and millimeters
 (*pages 198–199*)
To become familiar with metric units of length   (*pages 200–201*)
To make conversions between metric units of length
 (*pages 202–203*)
To become familiar with metric units of liquid volume
 (*pages 204–205*)
To make conversions between metric units of liquid volume
 (*pages 204–205*)
To become familiar with metric units of weight (mass)
 (*pages 206–207*)
To make conversions between metric units of weight (mass)
 (*pages 206–207*)
To measure lengths in inches   (*pages 210–211*)
To make conversions between customary units of length
 (*pages 212–213*)
To make conversions between customary liquid-volume
 units   (*pages 214–215*)
To make conversions between customary units of weight
 (*pages 216–217*)
To compute with customary units   (*pages 218–219*)

PROBLEM-SOLVING SKILLS
Finding information in a display   (*page 198–199, 214–216, 221*)
Reading a ruler   (*pages 198–199, 210–211*)
Choosing the correct operation   (*pages 199, 209, 215, 217,
 219, 221*)
Reading a map   (*page 201*)
Using a guess-and-check strategy   (*page 201*)
Utilizing metric relationships   (*pages 203, 207*)
Using logical reasoning   (*pages 203, 213, 215, 217*)
Selecting information in an ad   (*page 205*)
Solving a multi-step problem   (*pages 209, 217*)
Following directions   (*page 211*)
Utilizing relationships between customary units of length
 (*page 213*)
Reading a table   (*page 219*)

RESOURCES
- **VISUAL AIDS**
 Centimeter and millimeter ruler from page 198   (*Visual Aid 32,
 Copymaster S133*)
 List of metric units of length from page 200   (*Visual Aid 33,
 Copymaster S134*)
 Map from page 201   (*Visual Aid 34, Copymaster S135*)
 Inch ruler   (*Visual Aid 35, Copymaster S135*)
- **WORKSHEETS 83–94**   (*Copymasters S235–S246 or Duplicating
 Masters S235–S246*)

197

LESSON OBJECTIVE
To measure lengths with centimeters and millimeters

PROBLEM-SOLVING SKILLS
Finding information in a display
Reading a metric ruler
Choosing the correct operation

STARTING THE LESSON
Choose a student to read the first paragraph orally. Discuss exercises 1–4. You may wish to use **Visual Aid 32** (centimeter and millimeter rulers) for demonstration purposes during the *Here's how* discussion.

Using a metric ruler

The **centimeter** (cm) is a unit of length in the metric system. The length of the 18K (18-carat) gold chain measured to the nearest centimeter is 6 centimeters.

1. What is the length of the 14K gold chain measured to the nearest centimeter? 10 cm

Here's how *to measure to the nearest millimeter.*

Notice that one tenth of a centimeter is 1 millimeter (mm).

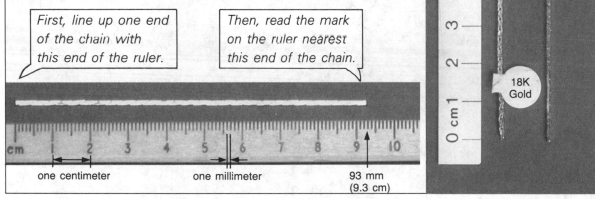

First, line up one end of the chain with this end of the ruler.

Then, read the mark on the ruler nearest this end of the chain.

one centimeter   one millimeter   93 mm (9.3 cm)

2. Look at the *Here's how*. What is the length of the chain measured to the nearest millimeter? 93 mm

3. What is the length of the chain to the nearest tenth of a centimeter? to the nearest centimeter? 9.3 cm, 9 cm

4. Look at the ruler. How many millimeters are in 1 centimeter? 10

EXERCISES

Use a metric ruler. Measure each chain to the nearest centimeter.

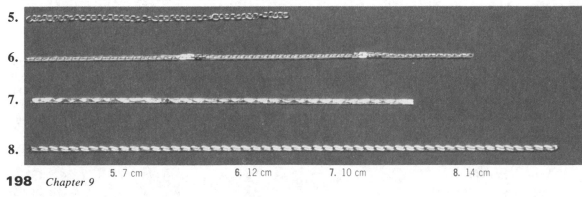

5. 7 cm   6. 12 cm   7. 10 cm   8. 14 cm

Measure each chain to the nearest millimeter. Answers will vary slightly. (± 2 mm)

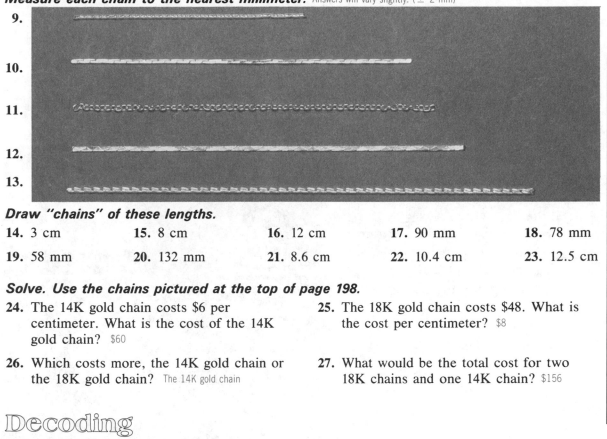

9.

10.

11.

12.

13.

Draw "chains" of these lengths.

14. 3 cm	**15.** 8 cm	**16.** 12 cm	**17.** 90 mm	**18.** 78 mm
19. 58 mm	**20.** 132 mm	**21.** 8.6 cm	**22.** 10.4 cm	**23.** 12.5 cm

Solve. Use the chains pictured at the top of page 198.

24. The 14K gold chain costs $6 per centimeter. What is the cost of the 14K gold chain? $60

25. The 18K gold chain costs $48. What is the cost per centimeter? $8

26. Which costs more, the 14K gold chain or the 18K gold chain? The 14K gold chain

27. What would be the total cost for two 18K chains and one 14K chain? $156

Decoding

28. Use the code to get the answer to the riddle.

CODE: H   O   E   T C   W   I   D   A   J   S   L   F   N   R

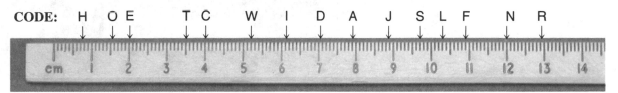

RIDDLE: What's the difference between a jeweler and a jailer?

ANSWER: 1.5 cm * 12 cm * 2 cm

9.7 cm * 20 mm * 10.3 cm * 103 mm * 97 mm

5.2 cm * 79 mm * 35 mm * 4 cm * 7 mm * 20 mm * 9.7 cm

52 mm * 0.7 cm * 6.1 cm * 103 mm * 2 cm

3.5 cm * 7 mm * 20 mm

15 mm * 3.5 cm * 7 mm * 2 cm * 129 mm

52 mm * 7.9 cm * 3.5 cm * 40 mm * 0.7 cm * 2 cm * 97 mm

4 cm * 20 mm * 10.3 cm * 103 mm * 9.7 cm.

One sells watches while the other watches cells.

REVIEW PRACTICE
Multiplying by 10, 100, 1000
Page 421   Skill 20

PRACTICE WORKSHEET
Copymaster S235 or Duplicating Master S235

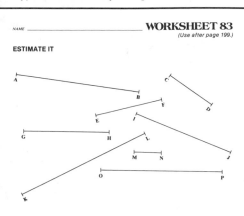

NAME _____   WORKSHEET 83
(Use after page 199.)

ESTIMATE IT

Complete the table by first estimating and then measuring the length of each segment. *Answers may vary slightly.*

	Segment	Estimated length to nearest centimeter	Measured length to nearest 0.1-centimeter	Difference between estimated length and measured length
1.	$\overline{AB}$		9.5 cm	
2.	$\overline{CD}$		3.9 cm	
3.	$\overline{EF}$	Answers	5.2 cm	Answers
4.	$\overline{GH}$	will	6.5 cm	will
5.	$\overline{IJ}$	vary.	7.8 cm	vary.
6.	$\overline{KL}$		10.5 cm	
7.	$\overline{MN}$		2.1 cm	
8.	$\overline{OP}$		9.3 cm	

© D. C. Heath and Company   S235   Using a metric ruler

LIFE-SKILL PROJECT
Collecting data
Have each student measure to the nearest centimeter his/her height, shoe size, and arm span. Then have the students use their measurements to find the class averages. (If centimeter tapes are not available, the students can use a string and then measure the string using a meterstick or centimeter ruler.)

CHALKBOARD QUIZ
on previous lesson

Draw line segments having these lengths.
1. 4 cm   2. 70 mm
3. 9 cm   4. 125 mm
5. 10.5 cm 6. 55 mm

LESSON OBJECTIVE
To become familiar with metric units of length

PROBLEM-SOLVING SKILLS
Reading a map
Using a guess-and-check strategy

STARTING THE LESSON
Play 'What are the facts?' Have the students study the first two paragraphs and the *Here's how* on page 200 for one minute. Then tell them to close their books and choose *millimeter, centimeter, meter,* or *kilometer* to complete each of these statements:

• The width of a fingernail is about one __?__. (cm)
• The length of a baseball bat is about one __?__. (m)
• The thickness of an eyeglass lens is about one __?__. (mm)
• One thousand long steps measure about one __?__. (km)

The list of metric equivalences at the top of the page is also on **Visual Aid 33.** Use the list to help the students see that the metric system is based on powers of 10.

EXERCISE NOTE
The map on page 201 is also on **Visual Aid 34.** Use the map when discussing exercises 17–20.

Metric units of length

Could you hit a baseball 100 meters? *Hint: The longest home run ever hit went 188.4 meters. It was hit by Roy "Dizzy" Carlyle.*

The basic unit for measuring length in the metric system is the **meter** (m). A baseball bat is about 1 meter long.

These units are used to measure length in the metric system:

1 **kilometer (km)** = **1000 meters**
1 hectometer (hm) = 100 meters
1 **dekameter (dam)** = **10 meters**
1 meter (m) = 1 meter
1 decimeter (dm) = 0.1 meter
1 **centimeter (cm)** = **0.01 meter**
1 **millimeter (mm)** = **0.001 meter**

Note: The units listed in red are used most often.

Here's how
to estimate metric units of length.

width of a fingernail— about 1 cm

thickness of an eyeglass lens—about 1 mm

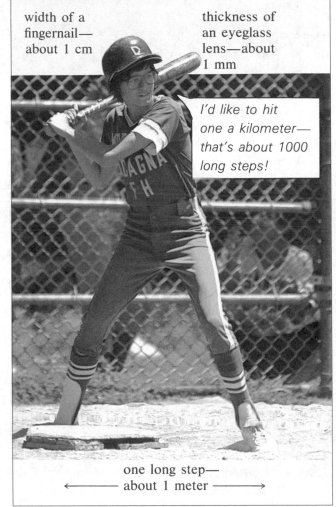

I'd like to hit one a kilometer— that's about 1000 long steps!

one long step— ←————— about 1 meter —————→

EXERCISES
Choose mm, cm, m, or km.

1. The distance from home plate to first base is 24.4 __?__. m

2. The height of a first baseman is 182 __?__. cm

3. The thickness of a dime is 1 __?__. mm

4. The length of a river is 450 __?__. km

5. The length of a tennis court is 20 __?__. m

6. The length of a paper clip is 3 __?__. cm

7. The width of a door is 0.6 __?__. m

8. The length of a new pencil is 190 __?__. mm

Which measurement is reasonable?

9. Length of a dollar bill:
a. 16 mm **(b.)** 16 cm **c.** 16 m

10. Length of an automobile:
a. 4.75 cm **b.** 4.75 mm **(c.)** 4.75 m

11. Length of a baseball bat:
a. 92 mm **(b.)** 92 cm **c.** 92 m

12. Height of a nine-story building:
a. 30 cm **(b.)** 30 m **c.** 30 km

13. Height of a soup can:
a. 10 mm **(b.)** 10 cm **c.** 10 m

14. Width of a thumb:
(a.) 20 mm **b.** 20 cm **c.** 20 m

15. Thickness of a nickel:
(a.) 2 mm **b.** 2 cm **c.** 2 m

16. Thickness of a dollar bill:
(a.) 0.1 mm **b.** 0.1 cm **c.** 0.1 m

AIR DISTANCES

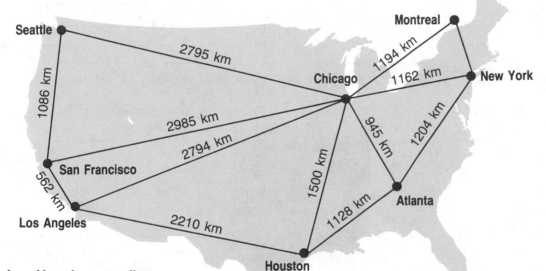

Seattle — 2795 km — **Chicago**
Seattle 1086 km
Montreal 1194 km **Chicago**
Chicago 1162 km **New York**
Chicago 2985 km
Chicago 2794 km
San Francisco 562 km **Los Angeles**
Chicago 945 km
Chicago 1500 km
New York 1204 km
Los Angeles 2210 km **Houston**
Houston 1128 km **Atlanta**

Solve. Use the map distances.

17. How far is it from
 a. San Francisco to New York through Chicago? 4147 miles
 b. New York to Houston through Atlanta? 2332 miles

18. How much farther is it from
 a. Chicago to Los Angeles than from Chicago to Houston? 1294 miles
 b. San Francisco to Chicago than from Los Angeles to Chicago? 191 miles

Play ball!

Use the information on the map to answer the questions.

19. From New York the Mets baseball team flew to [?] to play a game. Then they flew to [?] to play another game. They traveled 2149 kilometers altogether. In which two cities did they play games?

Atlanta, Chicago

20. The Dodgers flew from Los Angeles to [?] and then to [?] to play ball games. They traveled about 4300 kilometers altogether. In which two cities did they play games? Chicago, Houston

Measurement **201**

REVIEW PRACTICE
Multiplying whole numbers
Page 419   Skill 15

PRACTICE WORKSHEET
Copymaster S236 or Duplicating Master S236

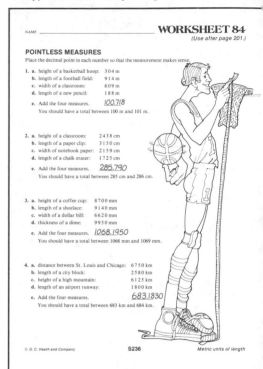

NAME _____   **WORKSHEET 84**
(Use after page 201.)

POINTLESS MEASURES
Place the decimal point in each number so that the measurement makes sense.

1. a. height of a basketball hoop: 3 0 4 m
   b. length of a football field: 9 1 4 m
   c. width of a classroom: 6 0 9 m
   d. length of a new pencil: 1 8 8 m
   e. Add the four measures. 100.718
   You should have a total between 100 m and 101 m.

2. a. height of a classroom: 2 4 3 8 cm
   b. length of a paper clip: 3 1 5 0 cm
   c. width of notebook paper: 2 1 5 9 cm
   d. length of a chalk eraser: 1 7 2 5 cm
   e. Add the four measures. 285.790
   You should have a total between 285 cm and 286 cm.

3. a. height of a coffee cup: 8 7 0 0 mm
   b. length of a shoelace: 9 1 4 0 mm
   c. width of a dollar bill: 6 6 2 0 mm
   d. thickness of a dime: 9 9 5 0 mm
   e. Add the four measures. 1068.1950
   You should have a total between 1068 mm and 1069 mm.

4. a. distance between St. Louis and Chicago: 6 7 5 0 km
   b. length of a city block: 2 5 8 0 km
   c. height of a high mountain: 6 1 2 5 km
   d. length of an airport runway: 1 8 0 0 km
   e. Add the four measures. 683.1830
   You should have a total between 683 km and 684 km.

© D. C. Heath and Company   **S236**   Metric units of length

LIFE-SKILL PROJECT
Estimating length
Have the students work in pairs. One student holds a metric ruler and the other estimates 8.5 centimeters by pointing to the back of the ruler. The other member of the pair tells his/her partner how close he/she was to the given measurement. Let the students take turns, one naming the length and the other estimating.

LESSON OBJECTIVE
To make conversions between metric units of length

PROBLEM-SOLVING SKILLS
Utilizing metric relationships
Using logical reasoning

STARTING THE LESSON
Have the students read the information on the entry blanks at the top of the page. Have them record who they think caught the bigger fish. Tell them they will be able to check their answers after completing exercises 1–4.

EXERCISE NOTE
In exercises 5–37, encourage the students to first decide whether they are converting to a smaller or larger unit. If the conversion is to a smaller unit, multiplication is used. If the conversion is to a larger unit, division is used. Remind the students that the list of metric equivalences on page 200 is helpful when converting from one metric unit to another.

Changing units in the metric system

WHO CAUGHT THE BIGGER FISH?

To change units in the metric system, multiply or divide by 10, 100, or 1000.

FISHING CONTEST
Prizes:
1st: $100.00 CASH
2nd: PICKWICK ULTRA LIGHT FISHING POLE
3rd: STAY-DRY HIP WADERS

Name *Mel Criser*
Address *2347 South Vine*
Wichita, Kansas
Length *0.38 m*

Name *Nancy Perkins*
Address *42 Falls Road*
Salt Lake City, Utah
Length *475 mm*

Here's how *to change from one unit of length to another.*

Mel's fish
0.38 m = _?_ cm

Since I'm changing to a smaller unit, I should get a larger number. So I should multiply.

Remember: 1 m = 100 cm

0.38 m = 38 cm
  └ × 100 ┘

Nancy's fish
475 mm = _?_ cm

Now I'm changing to a larger unit, so I should get a smaller number. Therefore I should divide.

Remember: 10 mm = 1 cm

475 mm = 47.5 cm
  └ ÷ 10 ┘

1. Look at the *Here's how*. To change from meters to centimeters, multiply by ▢ . 100

2. To change from millimeters to centimeters, divide by ▢ . 10

3. Who caught the larger fish, Mel or Nancy? Nancy

4. Check these examples. Have the units been changed correctly? Yes

   a. 1395 m = _?_ km

   Think: Changing smaller to larger units, so divide.

   Remember: 1000 m = 1 km
   1395 m = 1.395 km
     └ ÷ 1000 ┘

   b. 8.53 km = _?_ m

   Think: Changing larger to smaller units, so multiply.

   Remember: 1 km = 1000 m
   8.53 km = 8530 m
     └ × 1000 ┘

EXERCISES

Copy and complete.

5. 7 cm = _?_ mm 70

6. 3 m = _?_ cm 300

7. 8 km = _?_ m 8000

8. 45 cm = _?_ m 0.45

9. 63 mm = _?_ cm 6.3

10. 18 km = _?_ m 18,000

11. 4265 m = _?_ km 4.265

12. 7.3 km = _?_ m 7300

13. 4.2 cm = _?_ mm 42

14. 95 m = _?_ cm 9500

15. 4.8 m = _?_ cm 480

16. 420 cm = _?_ m 4.20

17. 68 mm = _?_ cm 6.8

18. 3.25 km = _?_ m 3250

19. 1575 m = _?_ km 1.575

20. 15 m = _?_ cm 1500

21. 14 mm = _?_ cm 1.4

22. 7.8 cm = _?_ mm 78

23. 250 km = _?_ m 250,000

24. 300 mm = _?_ m 0.300

25. 0.4 m = _?_ mm 400

26. 5 cm + 4 mm = _?_ mm 54

27. 20 cm + 4 mm = _?_ mm 204

28. 30 cm + 5 mm = _?_ cm 30.5

29. 10 cm + 12 mm = _?_ cm 11.2

30. 8 m + 75 cm = _?_ cm 875

31. 5 m + 125 cm = _?_ cm 625

32. 4 m + 50 cm = _?_ m 4.5

33. 7 m + 200 cm = _?_ m 9

Solve.

34. The largest salt water fish caught was a 1852-centimeter whale shark. How many meters was that? 18.52

35. The smallest fresh water fish caught was a dwarf pygmy goby. It was only 0.7 centimeter long. How many millimeters was that? 7

36. The greatest depth at which a fish was caught was 8299 meters in the Puerto Rico Trough. How many kilometers was that? 8.299

37. The fastest fish is the cosmopolitan sailfish. It can swim 110 kilometers per hour. How many meters per hour is that? 110,000

You be the judge Logical reasoning

38. Who caught the biggest fish? Rita
How big was it? 61 cm

Clues:
- Susan's fish was 4 cm longer than Wilda's fish.
- Wilda's fish was 5 cm shorter than Rita's fish.
- Rita's fish was 1 cm longer than Monica's fish.
- Monica caught a 60-cm fish.

REVIEW PRACTICE
Multiplying whole numbers
Page 419   Skill 16

PRACTICE WORKSHEET
Copymaster S237 or Duplicating Master S237

NAME _____

WORKSHEET 85
(Use after page 203.)

RIDDLE TIME
Why are fishermen such good correspondents?

To find the answer:
1. Complete.
2. Write the letter under its matching number in the DECODER.

1. 75 mm = _7.5_ cm
   E
2. 75 cm = _0.75_ m
   Y
3. 3.25 km = _3250_ m
   R
4. 3.25 m = _325_ cm
   H
5. 200 cm = _2_ m
   P
6. 2 m = _2000_ mm
   U
7. 6.8 cm = _68_ mm
   K
8. 68 m = _6800_ cm
   N
9. 55 m = _5500_ cm
   C
10. 550 cm = _5.5_ m
    B
11. 1.4 m = _1400_ m
    O
12. 1400 m = _1.4_ km
    S
13. 8 m = _8000_ mm
    T
14. 80 mm = _8_ cm
    A
15. 75 m = _7500_ cm
    W
16. 7.5 km = _7500_ m
    D
17. 300 cm = _3_ m
    I
18. 300 mm = _0.3_ m
    L

DECODER

| 5.5 | 7.5 | 5500 | 8 | 2000 | 1.4 | 7.5 | 8000 | 325 | 7.5 | 0.75 |
| B | E | C | A | U | S | E | | T | H | E | Y |

| 8 | 0.3 | 7500 | 8 | 2000 | 1.4 | 0.3 | 68 | 8.5 | 8000 | 1400 |
| A | L | W | A | Y | S | | L | I | K | E | T | O |

| 7500 | 3250 | 1400 | 2 | | 8 | | 0.3 | 3 | 6800 | 7.5 |
| D | R | O | P | | A | | L | I | N | E | . |

© D. C. Heath and Company   S237   *Changing metric units*

LIFE-SKILL PROJECT
Estimating length
Have each of the students use their normal step as a unit of measure. Then have them estimate, by counting steps, how many kilometers they walk during a school day.

LESSON OBJECTIVES
To become familiar with metric units
  of liquid volume
To make conversions between metric
  units of liquid volume

PROBLEM-SOLVING SKILL
Selecting information in an ad

STARTING THE LESSON
Before discussing exercises 1–4, play
'What are the facts?' Have the students
study the information at the top of page
204 for one minute. Then have them
close their books and answer these
questions:
• An eyedropper holds about how many
  milliliters? (1)
• Four glasses of perfume is about how
  many liters? (1)
• One liter equals how many milliliters?
  (1000)
• About how much would one liter of
  the world's most expensive perfume
  cost? ($15,000)

Liquid volume—metric system

WOULD YOU BELIEVE IT!

One drop of the world's most expensive
perfume costs $1.50. One liter of the same
perfume would cost about $15,000!

A unit for measuring liquid volume in the
metric system is the **liter** (L). The **milliliter** (mL)
is used to measure small liquid volumes.

1 L = 1000 mL

About 4
glasses

About 10
drops

1 milliliter of perfume

**10 milliliters
of perfume**

**1 liter of
perfume**

1. Which is more, 999 milliliters or 1 liter?   1 liter

2. Choose mL or L.
   a. A 250-[?] bottle of shampoo costs $1.99.   **b.** A 0.5-[?] bottle of liquid soap costs $1.89.
          mL   L

Here's how *to change from one unit of liquid volume to another.*

250 mL = <u> ? </u> L	0.5 L = <u> ? </u> mL
Think: Changing from smaller units to larger units, so divide.	*Think:* Changing from larger units to smaller units, so multiply.
Remember: 1000 mL = 1 L	*Remember:* 1 L = 1000 mL
250 mL = 0.250 L └─ ÷ 1000 ─┘	0.5 L = 500 mL └─ × 1000 ─┘

3. Look at the *Here's how*. To change from milliliters to liters, divide by [?].   1000

4. To change from liters to milliliters, multiply by [?].   1000

EXERCISES

Which liquid volume seems reasonable?

5. A coffee cup:
  (**a.**) 300 mL   **b.** 30 mL   **c.** 3 mL

7. A bathtub:
  a. 3 L   **b.** 30 L   (**c.**) 300 L

9. A thermos bottle:
  a. 80 mL   (**b.**) 800 mL   **c.** 8000 mL

11. An eyedropper:
  (**a.**) 1 mL   **b.** 10 mL   **c.** 100 mL

6. A soft drink can:
  a. 4 mL   **b.** 40 mL   (**c.**) 400 mL

8. A tablespoon:
  a. 0.5 mL   (**b.**) 5 mL   **c.** 50 mL

10. A fruit-juice pitcher:
  a. 0.1 L   (**b.**) 1 L   **c.** 10 L

12. An automobile gas tank:
  a. 6 L   (**b.**) 60 L   **c.** 600 L

Copy and complete.

13. 6 L = _?_ mL   6000

14. 15 L = _?_ mL   15,000

15. 2.7 L = _?_ mL   2700

16. 4000 mL = _?_ L   4

17. 1725 mL = _?_ L   1.725

18. 500 mL = _?_ L   0.500

19. 5.75 L = _?_ mL   5750

20. 0.756 L = _?_ mL   756

21. 0.35 L = _?_ mL   350

22. 12,000 mL = _?_ L   12

23. 870 mL = _?_ L   0.870

24. 25 mL = _?_ L   0.025

25. 6.05 L = _?_ mL   6050

26. 175 mL = _?_ L   0.175

27. 100 mL = _?_ L   0.100

28. 986 mL = _?_ L   0.986

29. 790 L = _?_ mL   790,000

30. 2800 L = _?_ mL   2,800,000

31. 210 mL = _?_ L   0.210

32. 60 mL = _?_ L   0.060

33. 5640 L = _?_ mL   5,640,000

34. 2 L + 500 mL = _?_ mL   2500

35. 5 L + 125 mL = _?_ mL   5125

36. 4 L + 100 mL = _?_ L   4.1

37. 3 L + 625 mL = _?_ L   3.625

38. 46 L + 18 mL = _?_ mL   46,018

39. 16 L + 200 mL _?_ L   16.2

40. 75 L + 500 mL = _?_ mL   75,500

41. 35 L + 600 mL = _?_ L   35.6

Special smells

Use the information in the advertisement. Complete the sentences.

42. A 50-milliliter bottle of [?] costs $5.00.   Sweet Rose

43. A [?]-milliliter bottle of Sweet Rose costs $8.00.   80

44. A 40-milliliter bottle of Twilight costs [?] dollars. $2.00

45. A 20-milliliter bottle of Twilight and a [?]-milliliter bottle of New Spice cost a total of $10.00.   30

PERFUME $PECIAL$

Twilight . . . . $.05 per mL
Sweet Rose . . . . $.10 per mL
Always Yours . . . . $.20 per mL
New Spice . . . . $.30 per mL

REVIEW PRACTICE
Multiplying whole numbers
Page 420   Skill 17

PRACTICE WORKSHEET
Copymaster S238 or Duplicating Master S238

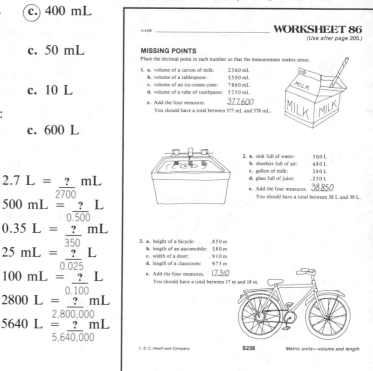

NAME _____   **WORKSHEET 86**
(Use after page 205.)

MISSING POINTS
Place the decimal point in each number so that the measurement makes sense.

1. a. volume of a carton of milk: 2360 mL
  b. volume of a tablespoon: 5500 mL
  c. volume of an ice-cream cone: 7860 mL
  d. volume of a tube of toothpaste: 5750 mL
  e. Add the four measures.   377.600
  You should have a total between 377 mL and 378 mL.

2. a. sink full of water: 300 L
  b. shoebox full of air: 480 L
  c. gallon of milk: 380 L
  d. glass full of juice: 250 L
  e. Add the four measures.   38.850
  You should have a total between 38 L and 39 L.

3. a. height of a bicycle: .850 m
  b. length of an automobile: 5.80 m
  c. width of a door: .910 m
  d. length of a classroom: 9.75 m
  e. Add the four measures.   17.310
  You should have a total between 17 m and 18 m.

© D. C. Heath and Company   **S238**   *Metric units—volume and length*

LIFE-SKILL PROJECT
Collecting data
Ask the students to estimate and then measure the amount of water that would be lost from a dripping faucet in 1 day.

Copy and complete.
1. 4 L = $\underline{?}$ mL   4000
2. 25 L = $\underline{?}$ mL   25,000
3. 6.5 L = $\underline{?}$ mL   6500
4. 5000 mL = $\underline{?}$ L   5
5. 875 mL = $\underline{?}$ L   0.875
6. 25 mL = $\underline{?}$ L   0.025

LESSON OBJECTIVES
To become familiar with metric units of weight (mass)
To make conversions between metric units of weight (mass)

PROBLEM-SOLVING SKILL
Utilizing metric relationships

STARTING THE LESSON
Before discussing exercises 1–3, play 'What are the facts?' Have the students study the information at the top of page 206 for one minute. Then have them close their books and answer these questions from memory:
• One kilogram equals how many grams? (1000)
• How many milligrams does it take to equal 1 gram? (1000)
• Does a paper clip weigh 1 gram or 1 kilogram? (1 g)
• Does a wing of a honeybee weigh 1 milligram or 1 gram? (1 mg)
• Can a honeybee carry more or less than 300 times its own weight? (More)

Weight—metric system

AMAZING FACT!

Did you know that a honeybee can lift more than 300 times its own weight!

A unit for measuring weight (mass) in the metric system is the **gram** (g). The weight of a large paper clip is about 1 gram.

Here are some other units for measuring weight.

$$1 \text{ kilogram (kg)} = 1000 \text{ g}$$
$$1 \text{ milligram (mg)} = 0.001 \text{ g}$$

The weight of this textbook is about 1 kilogram.

1. Which is heavier, 999 grams or 1 kilogram?
       1 kilogram
2. Which is heavier, 999 milligrams or 1 gram?
       1 gram

Would you believe . . . A honeybee can lift an object as heavy as an egg!

Wing— about 1 mg

Honeybee— about 200 mg

Here's how *to change from one metric unit of weight to another.*

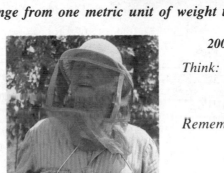

0.06 kg = $\underline{?}$ g

Changing from larger to smaller units, so multiply.

Remember: 1 kg = 1000 g

0.06 kg = 60 g
    ⌐× 1000 ⌐

200 mg = $\underline{?}$ g

Think: Changing from smaller to larger units, so divide.

Remember: 1000 mg = 1 g

200 mg = 0.2 g
    ⌐÷ 1000 ⌐

3. Check these examples. Have the unit changes been done correctly? Yes

   a. 4.6 g = $\underline{?}$ mg

     Think: Changing from larger to smaller units, so multiply.

     Remember: 1 g = 1000 mg

       4.6 g = 4600 mg
         ⌐× 1000 ⌐

   b. 358 g = $\underline{?}$ kg

     Think: Changing from smaller to larger units, so divide.

     Remember: 1000 g = 1 kg

       358 g = 0.358 kg
         ⌐÷ 1000 ⌐

EXERCISES

Which weight seems reasonable?

4. A bicycle:
  a. 12 mg   **b.** 12 g   **c.** 12 kg ⓒ

5. A dime:
  a. 3 mg   **b.** 3 g ⓑ   **c.** 3 kg

6. A straight pin:
  a. 130 mg ⓐ   **b.** 130 g   **c.** 130 kg

7. An automobile:
  a. 2000 mg   **b.** 2000 g   **c.** 2000 kg ⓒ

8. A can of tomatoes:
  a. 464 mg   **b.** 464 g ⓑ   **c.** 464 kg

9. An apple:
  a. 330 mg   **b.** 330 g ⓑ   **c.** 330 kg

Copy and complete.

10. 6000 mg = _?_ g 6

11. 4125 mg = _?_ g 4.125

12. 765 mg = _?_ g 0.765

13. 5000 g = _?_ kg 5

14. 7617 g = _?_ kg 7.617

15. 326 g = _?_ kg 0.326

16. 7 kg = _?_ g 7000

17. 4.2 kg = _?_ g 4200

18. 1.27 kg = _?_ g 1270

19. 4 g = _?_ mg 4000

20. 6.5 g = _?_ mg 6500

21. 0.425 g = _?_ mg 425

22. 3.5 kg = _?_ g 3500

23. 315 g = _?_ kg 0.315

24. 775 mg = _?_ g 0.775

25. 86.3 kg = _?_ g 86,300

26. 489 g = _?_ kg 0.489

27. 9163 g = _?_ kg 9.163

28. 1653 mg = _?_ g 1.653

29. 25.8 kg = _?_ g 25,800

30. 41.3 g = _?_ mg 41,300

31. 6 g + 325 mg = _?_ mg 6325

32. 6 kg + 3500 g = _?_ g 9500

33. 35 g + 1800 mg = _?_ mg 36,800

34. 85 kg + 6000 g = _?_ kg 91

35. 8 g + 435 mg = _?_ mg 8435

36. 25 g + 1500 mg = _?_ mg 26,500

37. 4 g + 666 mg = _?_ g 4.666

38. 12 g + 2545 mg = _?_ g 14.545

39. 6 kg + 825 g = _?_ g 6825

40. 5 kg + 2000 g = _?_ g 7000

41. 9 kg + 125 g = _?_ kg 9.125

42. 3 kg + 3000 g = _?_ kg 6

Are you as strong as an ant?

43. a. An ant weighing 200 mg can lift (with its teeth) a weight of 10 g. How many times its weight can an ant lift? 50

b. Suppose that you could lift the same number of times your weight. How much weight would that be? Answers will vary.

c. Are you as strong as an ant? No

REVIEW PRACTICE
Multiplying decimals
Page 420   Skill 18

PRACTICE WORKSHEET
Copymaster S239 or Duplicating Master S239

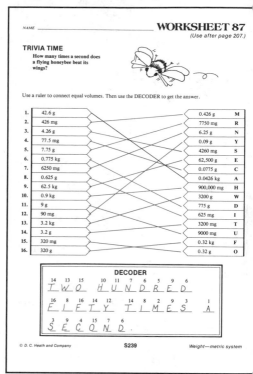

LIFE-SKILL PROJECT
Estimating and measuring weight
Provide the students with common classroom objects (pencil, eraser, chalk, book, etc.). Have them complete the chart by first estimating each object's weight and then finding its actual weight by using a metric scale.

Object	Estimate	Actual weight

CHALKBOARD QUIZ
on previous lesson
Copy and complete.
1. 7000 mg = __?__ g   7
2. 8000 g = __?__ kg   8
3. 9 kg = __?__ g   9000
4. 4.5 g = __?__ mg   4500
5. 625 mg = __?__ g   0.625
6. 3.5 kg = __?__ g   3500

SKILLS REVIEWED
Multiplying and dividing decimals
Changing fractions to decimals
Changing decimals to mixed numbers
Adding mixed numbers

PROBLEM-SOLVING SKILLS
Choosing the correct operation
Solving a multi-step problem

STARTING THE LESSON
Cumulative Skill Practice
Challenge the students to an estimation
hunt by saying, "Find the five products
in exercises 1–18 that are greater than
30." (Exercises 1, 8, 9, 10, and 16)
Then have the students find the two
quotients in exercises 19–33 that are
greater than 100. (Exercises 23 and 32)

STARTING THE LESSON
Problem Solving
Challenge the students to an operation
hunt. Have them look at problems 1–5
on page 209 to answer these questions:
• Which problem could you solve by dividing? (Problem 3)
• Which problem could you solve by subtracting? (Problem 1)
• Which problem could you solve by multiplying and subtracting? (Problem 2)

Cumulative Skill Practice

Multiply. *(page 64)*

1. $\begin{array}{r}1.2\\ \times 38\\ \hline 45.6\end{array}$	2. $\begin{array}{r}5.9\\ \times 3.2\\ \hline 18.88\end{array}$	3. $\begin{array}{r}0.63\\ \times 7.4\\ \hline 4.662\end{array}$	4. $\begin{array}{r}0.82\\ \times 23\\ \hline 18.86\end{array}$	5. $\begin{array}{r}0.48\\ \times 9.6\\ \hline 4.608\end{array}$	6. $\begin{array}{r}6.09\\ \times 3.4\\ \hline 20.706\end{array}$
7. $\begin{array}{r}0.61\\ \times 0.55\\ \hline 0.3355\end{array}$	8. $\begin{array}{r}0.46\\ \times 72\\ \hline 33.12\end{array}$	9. $\begin{array}{r}9.2\\ \times 9.2\\ \hline 84.64\end{array}$	10. $\begin{array}{r}5.12\\ \times 35\\ \hline 179.20\end{array}$	11. $\begin{array}{r}3.75\\ \times 0.38\\ \hline 1.4250\end{array}$	12. $\begin{array}{r}2.15\\ \times 0.2\\ \hline 0.430\end{array}$
13. $\begin{array}{r}4.25\\ \times 5.4\\ \hline 22.950\end{array}$	14. $\begin{array}{r}8.91\\ \times 0.58\\ \hline 5.1678\end{array}$	15. $\begin{array}{r}30.4\\ \times 0.71\\ \hline 21.584\end{array}$	16. $\begin{array}{r}55.5\\ \times 1.93\\ \hline 107.115\end{array}$	17. $\begin{array}{r}7.62\\ \times 2.06\\ \hline 15.6972\end{array}$	18. $\begin{array}{r}3.88\\ \times 1.01\\ \hline 3.9188\end{array}$

Divide. Round the quotient to the nearest hundredth. *(page 96)*

19. $0.3 \overline{)1.7}$ → 5.67 20. $0.6 \overline{)1.77}$ → 7.95 21. $0.09 \overline{)2.4}$ → 26.67 22. $0.06 \overline{)5.8}$ → 96.67 23. $0.03 \overline{)25}$ → 833.33

24. $0.6 \overline{)0.5}$ → 0.83 25. $0.09 \overline{)7.9}$ → 87.78 26. $0.13 \overline{)0.7}$ → 5.38 27. $0.27 \overline{)4.26}$ → 15.78 28. $0.35 \overline{)29.5}$ → 84.29

29. $2.3 \overline{)0.8}$ → 0.35 30. $5.4 \overline{)3.4}$ → 0.63 31. $2.8 \overline{)46.6}$ → 16.64 32. $0.77 \overline{)80.5}$ → 104.55 33. $0.81 \overline{)3.05}$ → 3.77

Change to a decimal. *(page 146)*

34. $\frac{1}{4}$ 0.25 35. $\frac{4}{5}$ 0.8 36. $\frac{7}{8}$ 0.875 37. $\frac{3}{5}$ 0.6 38. $\frac{1}{2}$ 0.5 39. $\frac{1}{5}$ 0.2 40. $\frac{3}{4}$ 0.75

41. $\frac{1}{8}$ 0.125 42. $\frac{3}{10}$ 0.3 43. $\frac{3}{8}$ 0.375 44. $\frac{5}{8}$ 0.625 45. $\frac{9}{10}$ 0.9 46. $\frac{2}{5}$ 0.4 47. $\frac{7}{10}$ 0.7

48. $1\frac{3}{8}$ 1.375 49. $3\frac{4}{5}$ 3.8 50. $2\frac{7}{8}$ 2.875 51. $5\frac{7}{10}$ 5.7 52. $4\frac{5}{16}$ 4.3125 53. $1\frac{1}{2}$ 1.5 54. $2\frac{3}{5}$ 2.6

Change to a mixed number in simplest form. *(page 148)*

55. 2.4 $2\frac{2}{5}$ 56. 3.5 $3\frac{1}{2}$ 57. 4.8 $4\frac{4}{5}$ 58. 9.6 $9\frac{3}{5}$ 59. 5.2 $5\frac{1}{5}$ 60. 6.9 $6\frac{9}{10}$

61. 4.50 $4\frac{1}{2}$ 62. 6.60 $6\frac{3}{5}$ 63. 2.25 $2\frac{1}{4}$ 64. 7.75 $7\frac{3}{4}$ 65. 8.35 $8\frac{7}{20}$ 66. 3.14 $3\frac{7}{50}$

67. 3.125 $3\frac{1}{8}$ 68. 6.625 $6\frac{5}{8}$ 69. 9.875 $9\frac{7}{8}$ 70. 8.200 $8\frac{1}{5}$ 71. 8.300 $8\frac{3}{10}$ 72. 2.190 $2\frac{19}{100}$

Add. Give each sum in simplest form. *(page 160)*

| 73. $\begin{array}{r}8\frac{1}{2}\\ +2\frac{1}{4}\\ \hline 10\frac{3}{4}\end{array}$ | 74. $\begin{array}{r}3\frac{1}{2}\\ +4\frac{1}{3}\\ \hline 7\frac{5}{6}\end{array}$ | 75. $\begin{array}{r}7\frac{3}{8}\\ +1\frac{1}{4}\\ \hline 8\frac{5}{8}\end{array}$ | 76. $\begin{array}{r}9\frac{2}{5}\\ +1\frac{1}{5}\\ \hline 10\frac{3}{5}\end{array}$ | 77. $\begin{array}{r}8\\ +2\frac{2}{3}\\ \hline 10\frac{2}{3}\end{array}$ | 78. $\begin{array}{r}6\frac{1}{2}\\ +3\frac{1}{3}\\ \hline 9\frac{5}{6}\end{array}$ |
| 79. $\begin{array}{r}4\frac{2}{5}\\ +1\frac{3}{5}\\ \hline 6\end{array}$ | 80. $\begin{array}{r}6\frac{2}{3}\\ +2\frac{1}{3}\\ \hline 9\end{array}$ | 81. $\begin{array}{r}2\frac{3}{4}\\ +2\frac{3}{4}\\ \hline 5\frac{1}{2}\end{array}$ | 82. $\begin{array}{r}6\\ +4\frac{1}{2}\\ \hline 10\frac{1}{2}\end{array}$ | 83. $\begin{array}{r}8\frac{7}{8}\\ +3\frac{3}{4}\\ \hline 12\frac{5}{8}\end{array}$ | 84. $\begin{array}{r}4\frac{5}{9}\\ +6\frac{1}{3}\\ \hline 10\frac{8}{9}\end{array}$ |

Problem solving

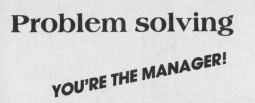

YOU'RE THE MANAGER!

1. You sell a certain brand of plain jeans for $19.98 and the designer jeans for $27.65. How much more do you charge for the designer jeans? $7.67

2. You buy 72 pairs of jeans for $12.45 each and sell them for $18.69 each. How much profit do you make on 72 pairs? $449.28

3. One day 42 customers spent $964.50 in your store. What was the average amount spent per customer? Round the answer to the nearest cent. $22.96

4. One day you sold 60 pairs of jeans. Twenty-four pairs were designer jeans. What fraction of the jeans were not designer jeans? Give the answer in simplest form. $\frac{3}{5}$

5. A denim shirt regularly sells for $18.60. You put it on sale for $\frac{2}{3}$ of the regular price. What is the sale price? $12.40

6. Your store has an area of 996 square feet. Your yearly rent is $14 per square foot. How much is your yearly rent? your monthly rent? $13,944; $1162

7. You pay each employee $5.75 an hour. Your store hours are from 9:00 A.M. to 6:00 P.M. If an employee takes 1 hour off for lunch, how much does it cost per day for each full-time employee? $46

8. One employee works from 9:00 A.M. to 12:45 P.M. How many hours does she work each day? Give the answer as a mixed number in simplest form. $3\frac{3}{4}$

9. a. One employee works from 1:30 P.M. to 6:00 P.M. How many hours is that? Give your answer as a decimal. 4.5

   b. At $5.75 per hour, how much will you pay him each day? Round the answer to the nearest cent. $25.88

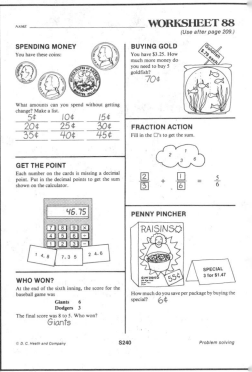

EXTRA PROBLEM SOLVING
Page 452   Odd exercises

PROBLEM-SOLVING WORKSHEET
Copymaster S240 or Duplicating Master S240

NAME _____   **WORKSHEET 88**
(Use after page 209.)

SPENDING MONEY
You have these coins:

What amounts can you spend without getting change? Make a list.

5¢	10¢	15¢
20¢	25¢	30¢
35¢	40¢	45¢

BUYING GOLD
You have $3.25. How much more money do you need to buy 5 goldfish?
70¢

FRACTION ACTION
Fill in the □'s to get the sum.

$\frac{2}{3} + \frac{1}{6} = \frac{5}{6}$

GET THE POINT
Each number on the cards is missing a decimal point. Put in the decimal points to get the sum shown on the calculator.

46.75

1 4.8   7.3 5   2 4.6

PENNY PINCHER

SPECIAL
3 for $1.47

55¢

How much do you save per package by buying the special? 6¢

WHO WON?
At the end of the sixth inning, the score for the baseball game was

Giants   6
Dodgers   3

The final score was 8 to 5. Who won?
Giants

© D. C. Heath and Company   S240   Problem solving

LIFE-SKILL PROJECT
Reading a newspaper ad
Have the students use newspaper ads to make up problems similar to problems 1–5 on page 209.

210

LESSON OBJECTIVE
To measure lengths in inches

PROBLEM-SOLVING SKILLS
Reading an inch ruler
Following directions

STARTING THE LESSON
Have the students do exercise 1 and record their guesses on the chalkboard. Then do exercises 2–4. You may wish to use **Visual Aid 35** (inch ruler) for demonstration purposes during the *Here's how* discussion.

EXERCISE NOTE
The map on page 211 is also on **Visual Aid 36**. Use the map and **Visual Aid 35** (inch ruler) when discussing exercise 25. Some students may wish to draw line segments as they follow the steps to find the treasure. Duplicate copies of **Visual Aid 35** for them to use.

Length—customary units

GUESS AND CHECK

1. Guess which pencil is longer. (Later, you will check your guess by measuring each pencil with an inch ruler.)
   Answers will vary.

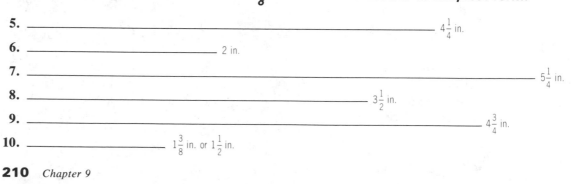

Here's how *to measure with an inch ruler.*

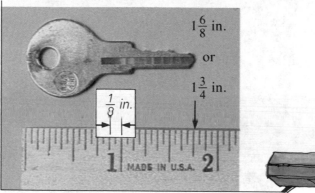

$1\frac{6}{8}$ in.

or

$1\frac{3}{4}$ in.

$\frac{1}{8}$ in.

2. Look at the *Here's how*. What is the length of the key measured to the nearest $\frac{1}{8}$ inch? (Give the answer in simplest form.) $1\frac{3}{4}$ in.

3. **a.** Measure the orange pencil to the nearest $\frac{1}{8}$ inch. $3\frac{5}{8}$ in.

   b. Measure the green pencil to the nearest $\frac{1}{8}$ inch. $3\frac{1}{2}$ in.

   c. Which pencil is longer? Orange

4. Was your guess for question 1 correct? Answers will vary.

EXERCISES

Measure each segment to the nearest $\frac{1}{8}$ inch. Give the answer in simplest form.

5. _____ $4\frac{1}{4}$ in.

6. _____ 2 in.

7. _____ $5\frac{1}{4}$ in.

8. _____ $3\frac{1}{2}$ in.

9. _____ $4\frac{3}{4}$ in.

10. _____ $1\frac{3}{8}$ in. or $1\frac{1}{2}$ in.

Draw segments having these lengths.

11. $1\frac{1}{2}$ inches   12. $2\frac{1}{8}$ inches   13. $3\frac{3}{4}$ inches   14. $\frac{7}{8}$ inch

15. $4\frac{5}{8}$ inches   16. $6\frac{1}{4}$ inches   17. $\frac{1}{2}$ inch   18. $5\frac{3}{8}$ inches

19. $2\frac{1}{2}$ inches   20. $1\frac{1}{8}$ inches   21. $5\frac{5}{8}$ inches   22. $3\frac{7}{8}$ inches

23. Draw a segment that is 3 inches long.

    a. How many $\frac{1}{2}$ inches long is it?   6

    b. How many $\frac{1}{4}$ inches long is it?   12

24. Draw a segment that is $4\frac{3}{4}$ inches long.

    a. How many $\frac{1}{4}$ inches long is it?   19

    b. How many $\frac{1}{8}$ inches long is it?   38

Find the treasure   Following directions

This treasure map was found in a bottle on a deserted island. Use the map to locate the buried treasure.

25. At the base of which tree would you dig to find the treasure?   B

To find the treasure on the map:

Start at "X" on the boulder.

Go west $1\frac{3}{4}$ inches to a tree.

Then go 4 inches to another tree.

Go north $3\frac{1}{8}$ inches to a tree.

Then go $3\frac{7}{8}$ inches to another tree.

Go $1\frac{1}{2}$ inches east to a tree.

Then go $1\frac{3}{4}$ inches northwest to another tree.

Next, go $2\frac{3}{4}$ inches to another tree.

Dig at the base of the last tree.

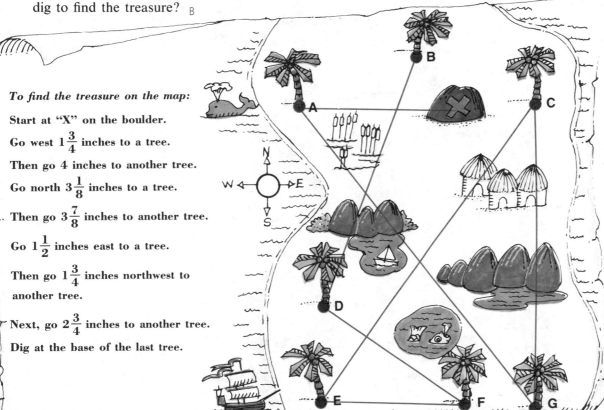

REVIEW PRACTICE
Simplifying expressions
Page 421   Skill 19

PRACTICE WORKSHEET
Copymaster S241 or Duplicating Master S241

NAME _____   **WORKSHEET 89**
(Use after page 211.)

WHY IS IT?
Why is a bad joke like an unsharpened pencil?

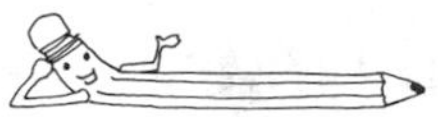

To find out:
Measure each segment to the nearest one-eighth inch. Then write the letter below the measurement in the DECODER.

S •————————————————• 5⅝ in.
N •————————————• 4¼ in.
T •———• 1⅛ in.
C •—————• 2⅛ in.
E •————————• 3⅞ in.
U •————• 2½ in.
H •——————————————• 5¾ in.
B •————————• 3⅝ in.
A •———————————• 5 in.
I •—————————• 4¾ in.
P •—————• 2⅜ in.
O •——————————————————• 6⅛ in.

DECODER

3⅝ in.	3⅞ in.	2⅛ in.	5 in.	2½ in.	5⅝ in.	3⅞ in.	4¾ in.	1⅛ in.
B	E	C	A	U	S	E	I	T

5¾ in.	5 in.	5⅝ in.	4¼ in.	6⅛ in.	2⅜ in.	6⅛ in.	4¾ in.	4¼ in.	1⅛ in.
H	A	S	N	O	P	O	I	N	T

© D. C. Heath and Company   S241   *Length—customary units*

LIFE-SKILL PROJECT
Estimating length
Have the students work in pairs. One student holds a ruler and the other estimates $5\frac{1}{2}$ inches by pointing to the back of the ruler. The other member of the pair tells his/her partner how close he/she was to the given measurement. Let students take turns, one naming the length and the other estimating.

LESSON OBJECTIVE
To make conversions between customary units of length

PROBLEM-SOLVING SKILLS
Utilizing relationships among customary units of length
Using logical reasoning

STARTING THE LESSON
Before discussing exercises 1 and 2, have the students read the information at the top of the page. Ask them to decide, without computing, whether a 185-inch apple peel is a new record.

EXERCISE NOTE
In exercises 3–32, encourage the students to first decide whether they are converting to a smaller or a larger unit. If the conversion is to a larger unit, they should divide. If the conversion is to a smaller unit, they should multiply.

Changing units of length—customary

RECORD BREAKER?

Is 185 inches of apple peel a new world record? The longest unbroken apple peel is 57 yards 1 foot by Kathy Wafler of Wolcott, New York.

Here are the facts you will need to know to change from one unit of length to another:

12 inches (in.) = 1 foot (ft)
3 ft = 1 yard (yd)
36 in. = 1 yd
5280 ft = 1 mile (mi)

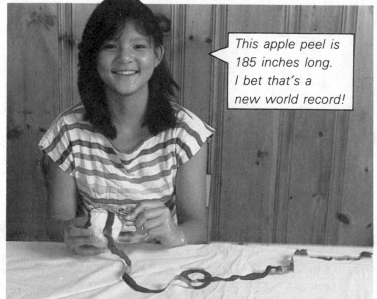

This apple peel is 185 inches long. I bet that's a new world record!

Here's how *to change from one unit of length to another.*

185 in. = _?_ ft _?_ in.

Think: Changing to a larger unit, so divide.

Remember: 12 in. = 1 ft

```
      15
  12 ) 185
      -12
      ___
       65      185 in. = 15 ft 5 in.
      -60
      ___
        5
```

57 yd 1 ft = _?_ ft

Think: Change to a smaller unit, so multiply.

Remember: 1 yd = 3 ft

```
     57
   ×  3
   ____
    171
   +  1      57 yd 1 ft = 172 ft
   ____
    172
```

1. Look at the *Here's how.* Is 185 inches of apple peel a new world record? No

2. Check these examples. Have the unit changes been done correctly? Yes

   a. 2 mi = _?_ ft

   Think: Changing to a smaller unit, so multiply.

   Remember: 1 mi = 5280 ft
   2 mi = 10,560 ft
   └── × 5280 ──┘

   b. 66 ft = _?_ yd

   Think: Changing to a larger unit, so divide.

   Remember: 3 ft = 1 yd
   66 ft = 22 yd
   └── ÷ 3 ──┘

EXERCISES

Copy and complete.

3. 6 ft = _?_ in. 72

4. 5 yd = _?_ ft 15

5. 1 mi = _?_ ft 5280

6. 48 in. = _?_ ft 4

7. 12 ft = _?_ yd 4

8. 3 mi = _?_ ft 15,840

9. 36 in. = _?_ yd 1

10. 3 yd = _?_ in. 108

11. 5 ft = _?_ in. 60

12. 120 ft = _?_ yd 40

13. 13 yd = _?_ ft 39

14. 72 in. = _?_ yd 2

15. 26 in. = 2 ft _?_ in. 2

16. 7 ft = 2 yd _?_ ft 1

17. 40 in. = 1 yd _?_ in. 4

18. 50 in. = 4 ft _?_ in. 2

19. 11 ft = 3 yd _?_ ft 2

20. 49 in. = 1 yd _?_ in. 13

21. 80 in. = 6 ft _?_ in. 8

22. 17 ft = 5 yd _?_ ft 2

23. 68 in. = 1 yd _?_ in. 32

24. 2 ft 3 in. = _?_ in. 27

25. 3 yd 1 ft = _?_ ft 10

26. 2 yd 4 in. = _?_ in. 76

27. 3 ft 7 in. = _?_ in. 43

28. 7 yd 2 ft = _?_ ft 23

29. 3 yd 10 in. = _?_ in. 118

30. 4 ft 3 in. = _?_ in. 51

31. 8 yd 3 ft = _?_ ft 27

32. 7 yd 6 in. = _?_ in. 258

Solve.

33. The record for spitting watermelon seeds is 65 feet 4 inches. How many inches is that? 784

34. The record for an egg to be thrown and then caught without breaking is 116 yards 2 feet. How many feet is that? 350

35. The record for catching a thrown grape in the mouth is 319 feet 8 inches. Suppose you caught a grape that was thrown 89 yards 10 inches. Would you break the record? No

36. The record for throwing a 2-pound rolling pin is 175 feet 5 inches. Suppose you threw a 2-pound rolling pin 58 yards 1 foot. Would you break the record? No

How many apples? Logical reasoning

37. Study the clues to find how many apples are in the bag.

Clues:
- There are fewer than 30.
- If you divided them among 4 people, you would have 3 left over.
- If you divided them among 5 people, you would have 4 left over. 19

REVIEW PRACTICE
Multiplying decimals by 10, 100, 1000
Page 421   Skill 20

PRACTICE WORKSHEET
Copymaster S242 or Duplicating Master S242

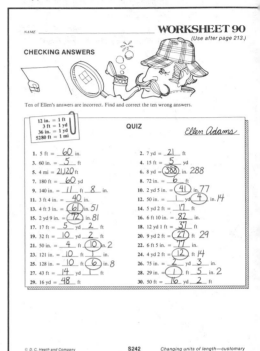

LIFE-SKILL PROJECT
Using a calculator

Have the students compute the height in miles of the 40 billion hamburgers sold by a famous fast-food chain. Tell the students to suppose the hamburgers are stacked one on top of the other and each hamburger is 1.5 inches thick. You may wish to give the students the following hints:

- There are 5280 feet in a mile.
- First compute the height of 40 million hamburgers and then multiply by 1000.

946,969.7 miles high

LESSON OBJECTIVE
To make conversions in customary liquid-volume units

PROBLEM-SOLVING SKILLS
Selecting information from a recipe
Choosing the correct operation
Using logical reasoning

STARTING THE LESSON
Have the students read the ingredients on the recipe card at the top of the page. Ask them to write what dessert they think the recipe makes. (Ice cream)

Liquid volume— customary units

CAN YOU NAME THIS DESSERT?

20 cups sugar
5 teaspoons salt
12 quarts milk

48 eggs
2 cups vanilla
10 quarts whipping cream

2 cups (c) = 1 pint (pt)
2 pints = 1 quart (qt)
4 quarts = 1 gallon (gal)

1 cup　　1 pint　　1 quart　　1 gallon

1. Read the recipe. How many quarts of milk are needed to make the dessert? 12

2. How many quarts are in 1 gallon? 4

3. To compute the number of gallons of milk, you would divide 12 by what number? 4

Here's how *to change from one unit of liquid volume to another.*

12 qt = _?_ gal

Think: Changing to a larger unit, so divide.

Remember: 4 qt = 1 gal
12 qt = 3 gal
└ ÷ 4 ┘

10 qt = _?_ pt

Think: Changing to a smaller unit, so multiply.

Remember: 1 qt = 2 pt
10 qt = 20 pt
└ × 2 ┘

4. Check these examples. Have the units been changed correctly? Yes

a. 13 qt = _?_ gal _?_ qt

Remember: 4 qt = 1 gal

$$4\overline{)13} \quad \begin{array}{r} 3 \\ \underline{-12} \\ 1 \end{array}$$

13 qt = 3 gal 1 qt

b. 11 pt 1 c = _?_ c

Remember: 1 pt = 2 c

$$\begin{array}{r} 11 \\ \times 2 \\ \hline 22 \\ +1 \\ \hline 23 \end{array}$$

11 pt 1 c = 23 c

214

EXERCISES

Copy and complete.

5. 18 pt = __?__ qt 9

6. 12 c = __?__ pt 6

7. 8 qt = $\frac{?}{2}$ gal

8. 6 qt = __?__ pt 12

9. 3 gal = __?__ qt 12

10. 6 pt = $\frac{?}{12}$ c

11. 1 qt = __?__ pt 2

12. 1 qt = __?__ c 4

13. 1 gal = $\frac{?}{16}$ c

14. 4 c = __?__ qt 1

15. 8 pt = __?__ gal 1

16. 16 c = $\frac{?}{1}$ gal

17. 3 pt 1 c = __?__ c 7

18. 5 qt 1 pt = __?__ pt 11

19. 3 gal 2 qt = $\frac{?}{14}$ qt

20. 3 gal 2 pt = __?__ qt 13

21. 8 qt 2 c = __?__ pt 17

22. 1 qt 1 pt = $\frac{?}{6}$ c

23. 15 pt = __?__ qt 1 pt 7

24. 19 qt = __?__ gal 3 qt 4

25. 34 pt = $\frac{?}{4}$ gal 1 qt

26. 17 pt = 8 qt __?__ pt 1

27. 15 qt = 3 gal __?__ qt 3

28. 25 pt = 3 gal $\frac{?}{1}$ pt

Solve. Use the recipe on page 214.

29. a. How many dozen eggs are needed? 4
    b. If eggs cost $.89 a dozen, what will be the total cost of the eggs? $3.56

30. a. How many cups of whipping cream are needed? 40
    b. If whipping cream costs $.98 a cup, what will be the total cost of the whipping cream? $39.20

31. a. How many $\frac{1}{4}$-cup bottles of vanilla are needed? 8
    b. If a $\frac{1}{4}$-cup bottle of vanilla costs $1.98, what will be the total cost for the vanilla? $15.84

32. a. The recipe makes 40 quarts of vanilla ice cream. How many gallons is that? 10
    b. If you bought the same amount of ice cream for $4.89 per gallon, what would be the total cost? $48.90

What's number one?

33. What is the most popular flavor of ice cream? Vanilla

Clues:
- More people like vanilla than cherry.
- More people like chocolate than strawberry.
- Fewer people like chocolate than vanilla.

REVIEW PRACTICE
Dividing whole numbers
Page 422   Skill 21

PRACTICE WORKSHEET
Copymaster S243 or Duplicating Master S243

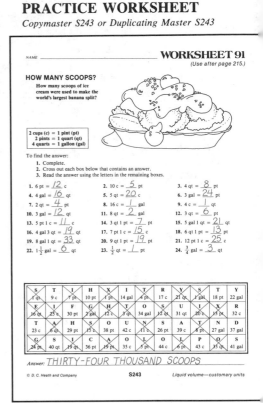

WORKSHEET 91
(Use after page 215.)

HOW MANY SCOOPS?
How many scoops of ice cream were used to make the world's largest banana split?

2 cups (c) = 1 pint (pt)
2 pints = 1 quart (qt)
4 quarts = 1 gallon (gal)

To find the answer:
1. Complete.
2. Cross out each box below that contains an answer.
3. Read the answer using the letters in the remaining boxes.

1. 6 pt = 12 c   2. 10 c = 5 pt   3. 4 qt = 8 pt
4. 4 gal = 16 qt   5. 5 qt = 20 c   6. 3 gal = 24 pt
7. 2 qt = 4 pt   8. 16 c = 1 gal   9. 4 c = 1 pt
10. 3 gal = 12 qt   11. 8 qt = 2 gal   12. 3 qt = 6 pt
13. 5 pt 1 c = 11 c   14. 3 qt 1 pt = 7 pt   15. 5 gal 1 qt = 21 qt
16. 4 gal 3 qt = 19 qt   17. 7 pt 1 c = 15 c   18. 6 qt 1 pt = 13 pt
19. 8 gal 1 qt = 33 qt   20. 9 qt 1 pt = 19 pt   21. 12 pt 1 c = 25 c
22. 1½ gal = 6 qt   23. ½ qt = 1 pt   24. ¾ gal = 3 qt

S 1 qt	T 9 c	H 7 pt	X 10 pt	I 1 pt	T 14 gal	R 4 pt	Y 17 c	S 21 qt	T 1 gal	T 18 pt	Y 22 gal
E 16 qt	I 25 c	F 30 pt	G 2 gal	H 12 c	T 3 qt	O 34 gal	U 12 qt	S 31 qt	I 20 c	X 13 pt	R 32 c
T 23 c	A 6 qt	H 29 pt	S 15 c	O 38 pt	U 42 c	N 26 pt	S 39 c	A 8 pt	T 27 gal	N 37 gal	D
G 24 pt	S 40 qt	I 19 qt	C 36 pt	A 19 pt	O 35 c	L 5 pt	O 44 c	L 6 pt	X 43 c	P 33 qt	S 41 gal

Answer: THIRTY-FOUR THOUSAND SCOOPS

© D. C. Heath and Company   S243   Liquid volume—customary units

LIFE-SKILL PROJECT
Collecting data
Have the students determine how much water they use to brush their teeth if they let the water run the whole time. Have them use their data to compute how many gallons of water they would use yearly in brushing their teeth.

LESSON OBJECTIVE
To make conversions between customary units of weight

PROBLEM-SOLVING SKILLS
Selecting information from a display
Choosing the correct operation
Solving a multi-step problem
Using logical reasoning

STARTING THE LESSON
Before discussing exercises 1–6, have the students study the clues at the top of the page. Ask them to write what fruit they think is in the bag. (Apples)

Weight—customary units

SALE
Apples .... $.80/lb
Oranges $1.00/lb
Pears $1.20/lb

16 ounces (oz) = 1 pound (lb)
2000 lb = 1 ton (T)

1. What is the weight of the bag of fruit? 32 oz

2. How many ounces equal 1 pound? 16

3. To compute the number of pounds of fruit in the bag, you would divide 32 by what number? 16

$1 60

32 oz

WHAT'S IN THE BAG?
APPLES,
ORANGES,
OR PEARS?

Here's how *to change from one unit of weight to another.*

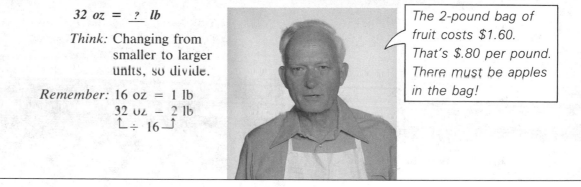

$32 \ oz = \underline{\ ?\ } \ lb$

Think: Changing from smaller to larger units, so divide.

Remember: 16 oz = 1 lb
$$32 \ oz = 2 \ lb$$
$$\llcorner \div 16 \lrcorner$$

The 2-pound bag of fruit costs $1.60. That's $.80 per pound. There must be apples in the bag!

4. Use the sale prices. How much would 32 ounces of pears cost? $2.40

5. How much would a ton of oranges cost? $2000

6. Check these examples. Have the units been changed correctly? Yes
   a. 6000 lb = _?_ T

      Think: Changing to a larger unit, so divide.
      $$6000 \ lb = 3 \ T$$
      $$\llcorner \div 2000 \lrcorner$$

   b. 2 lb 5 oz = _?_ oz

      Think: Changing to a smaller unit, so multiply.
      $$2 \ lb \ 5 \ oz = 37 \ oz$$
      $$\llcorner \times 16 + 5 \lrcorner$$

EXERCISES

Copy and complete.

7. 3 lb = _?_ oz 48

8. 48 oz = _?_ lb 3

9. 4 T = _?_ lb 8000

10. 8000 lb = _?_ T 4

11. 10 lb = _?_ oz 160

12. 160 oz = _?_ lb 10

13. 80 oz = _?_ lb 5

14. 10,000 lb = _?_ T 5

15. 14 lb = _?_ oz 224

16. 1 lb 8 oz = _?_ oz 24

17. 2 lb 3 oz = _?_ oz 35

18. 4 lb 10 oz = _?_ oz 74

19. 20 oz = _?_ lb 4 oz 1

20. 52 oz = _?_ lb 4 oz 3

21. 30 oz = _?_ lb 14 oz 1

22. 7500 lb = _?_ T 1500 lb 3

23. 9050 lb = 4 T _?_ lb 1050

24. 2060 lb = _?_ T 60 lb 1

25. 18 oz = 1 lb _?_ oz 2

26. 5000 lb = _?_ T 1000 lb 2

27. 100 oz = _?_ lb 4 oz 6

28. 22 lb = _?_ oz 352

29. 64 oz = _?_ lb 4

30. 56,000 lb = _?_ T 28

31. 6016 lb = 3T _?_ lb 16

32. 40 oz = 2 lb _?_ oz 8

33. 2500 lb = 1T _?_ lb 500

Solve.

34. An empty truck weighs 12,500 pounds. When full of apples, it weighs 8 tons. What is the weight of the apples in pounds? 3500

35. A truck contained 3 tons of oranges. After some oranges were unloaded, 1 ton 450 pounds of oranges remained. How many pounds of oranges were unloaded? 3550

36. A 2-pound bag of bananas costs 78¢. A 16-ounce bag of bananas costs 45¢. Which costs less per pound? 2 lb bag

37. A 2-pound 8-ounce bag of peaches costs $4.00. A 1-pound 4-ounce bag of peaches costs $2.25. Which costs less per ounce? 2 lb 8 oz bag

Fruit salad! Logical reasoning

38. Study the clues to find how many apples, oranges, and pears are in the fruit salad.

Clues:
- There are 12 oranges.
- If you add the number of pears and apples, you get 2 more than the number of oranges.
- There are 4 more pears than apples.

12 oranges,
9 pears,
5 apples

REVIEW PRACTICE
Dividing whole numbers
Page 422   Skill 22

PRACTICE WORKSHEET
Copymaster S244 or Duplicating Master S244

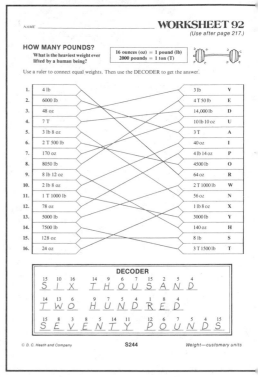

LIFE-SKILL PROJECT
Estimating weight
Have the students estimate the number of apples in a ton. Then have them weigh one apple and calculate an answer. Have them compare their estimate with the calculated answer.

LESSON OBJECTIVE
To compute with customary units

PROBLEM-SOLVING SKILLS
Choosing the correct operation
Reading a table

STARTING THE LESSON
Write these measurement facts and numbers on the chalkboard:

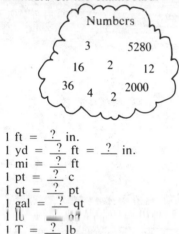

Numbers

3   5280
16   2   12
36   4   2000

1 ft = _?_ in.
1 yd = _?_ ft = _?_ in.
1 mi = _?_ ft
1 pt = _?_ c
1 qt = _?_ pt
1 gal = _?_ qt
1 lb = _?_ oz
1 T = _?_ lb

Before the students open their books, have them choose the numbers to complete the measurement facts. Then tell them to use the chart at the top of page 218 and check their answers.

HERE'S HOW NOTE
Go over the examples carefully. In each case, stress the regrouping that was done. Point out that in computing with customary units, the regrouping is not always 10 for 1 or 1 for 10, but rather it varies according to the units used.

Computing with customary units

DO YOU REMEMBER THESE MEASUREMENT FACTS?

LENGTH	LIQUID VOLUME	WEIGHT
1 ft = 12 in.	1 pt = 2 c	1 lb = 16 oz
1 yd = 3 ft = 36 in.	1 qt = 2 pt	1 T = 2000 lb
1 mi = 5280 ft	1 gal = 4 qt	

Here's how
to compute with customary units of measurement.

EXAMPLE 1.   *15 ft 4 in. + 12 ft 10 in. = ?*

Step 1.
Add inches and regroup.

```
      1 ft
   15 ft  4 in.
 + 12 ft 10 in.
 ─────────────
          2 in.
```

Step 2.
Add feet.

```
      1 ft
   15 ft  4 in.
 + 12 ft 10 in.
 ─────────────
   28 ft  2 in.
```

| 14 in. = 1 ft 2 in. |

EXAMPLE 2.   *14 lb 9 oz − 8 lb 12 oz = ?*

Step 1.
Regroup.

| 16 oz + 9 oz |

```
   13 lb 25 oz
   14 lb  9 oz
 −  8 lb 12 oz
```

Step 2.
Subtract.

```
   13 lb 25 oz
   14 lb  9 oz
 −  8 lb 12 oz
 ─────────────
    5 lb 13 oz
```

EXERCISES

Add. Here are scrambled answers
for the next row of exercises: *6 ft 7 in.   6 yd   6 ft 3 in.   7 yd 1 ft*

1.   3 ft 8 in.
      +2 ft 7 in.
      ─────────
        6 ft 3 in.

2.   2 yd 2 ft
      +4 yd 2 ft
      ─────────
        7 yd 1 ft

3.   4 ft 10 in.
      +1 ft 9 in.
      ─────────
        6 ft 7 in.

4.   1 yd 1 ft
      +4 yd 2 ft
      ─────────
        6 yd

5.
```
   3 gal 3 qt
 + 1 gal 2 qt
```
5 gal 1 qt

6.
```
   4 qt 1 pt
 + 3 qt 1 pt
```
8 qt

7.
```
   2 gal 2 qt
 + 5 gal 1 qt
```
7 gal 3 qt

8.
```
   2 pt 1 c
 + 4 pt 1 c
```
7 pt

9.
```
   6 lb 12 oz
 + 3 lb  8 oz
```
10 lb 4 oz

10.
```
   2 T 1500 lb
 + 3 T 1400 lb
```
6 T 900 lb

11.
```
   8 lb 14 oz
 + 9 lb 10 oz
```
18 lb 8 oz

12.
```
   6 T 1000 lb
 + 3 T 1800 lb
```
10 T 800 lb

*Here are scrambled answers
for the next row of exercises:* 3 yd 1 ft   2 ft 6 in.   2 ft 11 in.   2 yd 2 ft

13.
```
   5 ft  9 in.
 - 2 ft 10 in.
```
2 ft 11 in.

14.
```
   4 yd 1 ft
 - 1 yd 2 ft
```
2 yd 2 ft

15.
```
   7 ft 2 in.
 - 4 ft 8 in.
```
2 ft 6 in.

16.
```
   6 yd
 - 2 yd 2 ft
```
3 yd 1 ft

17.
```
   5 lb  2 oz
 - 2 lb 12 oz
```
2 lb 6 oz

18.
```
   6 T  500 lb
 - 3 T 1000 lb
```
2 T 1500 lb

19.
```
   4 lb 10 oz
 - 1 lb 11 oz
```
2 lb 15 oz

20.
```
   30 T 1800 lb
 -  9 T 1900 lb
```
20 T 1900 lb

21.
```
   4 gal 1 qt
 - 1 gal 2 qt
```
2 gal 3 qt

22.
```
   4 qt
 - 2 qt 1 pt
```
1 qt 1 pt

23.
```
   5 gal 2 qt
 - 2 gal 3 qt
```
2 gal 3 qt

24.
```
   4 gal
 - 1 gal 1 qt
```
2 gal 3 qt

Solve.

25. You and a friend cut a watermelon into two pieces. Your piece weighed 14 pounds 9 ounces, and her piece weighed 12 pounds 10 ounces. How much more did your piece weigh? *1 lb 15 oz*

26. You bought 3 pounds 7 ounces of green grapes and 2 pounds 9 ounces of red grapes. How many pounds of grapes did you buy altogether? *6*

Antique math   Reading a table

Use the table to complete each exercise.

27. 27 barleycorns = __?__ in. *9*

28. 15 in. = __?__ palms *5*

29. 2 spans + 1 hand = __?__ in. *22*

30. 1 pace + 1 cubit = __?__ in. *54*

31. 1 pace = __?__ cubits *2*

32. 6 palms = __?__ spans *2*

33. 2 cubits = __?__ spans *4*

34. 3 hands = __?__ palms *4*

35. 1 pace − 1 cubit = __?__ spans *2*

36. 1 cubit − 1 span = __?__ palms *3*

37. 1 hand + 1 palm = __?__ barleycorns *21*

38. 1 hand − 1 palm = __?__ barleycorns *3*

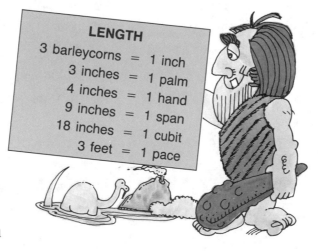

LENGTH
3 barleycorns = 1 inch
3 inches = 1 palm
4 inches = 1 hand
9 inches = 1 span
18 inches = 1 cubit
3 feet = 1 pace

REVIEW PRACTICE
Dividing whole numbers
Page 423   Skill 23

PRACTICE WORKSHEET
Copymaster S245 or Duplicating Master S245

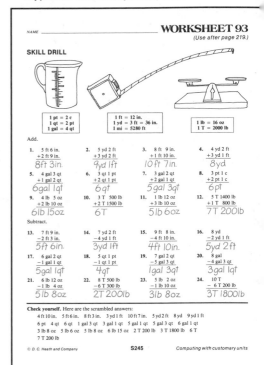

CHALKBOARD CHALLENGE
Unscramble the letters in these math words:

1. OLAGLN   Gallon
2. DOPUN   Pound
3. RUQAT   Quart
4. EIML   Mile
5. EUONC   Ounce
6. ELIKOMTRE   Kilometer
7. RAGM   Gram
8. RTLIE   Liter

220

SKILLS REVIEWED
Subtracting mixed numbers
Multiplying and dividing fractions
Making conversions between metric units
Subtracting customary units

PROBLEM-SOLVING SKILLS
Finding information in a computer display
Choosing the correct operation

STARTING THE LESSON
Cumulative Skill Practice
Write these five answers on the chalkboard:

$5\frac{3}{4}$ 1   4

5.8   2 ft 5 in.

Challenge the students to an answer hunt by saying, "Look for the five even-numbered exercises on page 220 that have these answers. You have five minutes to find as many of the exercises as you can." (Exercises 6, 28, 36, 44, and 52)

STARTING THE LESSON
Problem Solving
Have the students read the paragraph at the top of page 221. Ask the students, "What did Richard Dorr do to get the information displayed on Screen B?" (He selected "4".) "What did he do to get the information displayed on Screen C?" (He selected "10".) "How did he get Screen D?" (He pressed the ENTER key.)

220

Cumulative Skill Practice

Subtract. Give the difference in simplest form. *(page 168, 170)*

1. $3\frac{3}{4}$ $-1\frac{1}{4}$ $2\frac{1}{2}$
2. $5\frac{5}{6}$ $-2\frac{1}{6}$ $3\frac{2}{3}$
3. 4 $-2\frac{1}{3}$ $1\frac{2}{3}$
4. 6 $-4\frac{1}{2}$ $1\frac{1}{2}$
5. 9 $-3\frac{3}{5}$ $5\frac{2}{5}$
6. $8\frac{1}{2}$ $-2\frac{3}{4}$ $5\frac{3}{4}$

7. $7\frac{1}{3}$ $-1\frac{1}{2}$ $5\frac{5}{6}$
8. $3\frac{5}{8}$ $-2\frac{3}{4}$ $\frac{7}{8}$
9. $6\frac{1}{3}$ $-4\frac{3}{8}$ $1\frac{23}{24}$
10. $16\frac{3}{4}$ $-10\frac{7}{8}$ $5\frac{7}{8}$
11. $20\frac{3}{10}$ $-12\frac{5}{6}$ $7\frac{7}{15}$
12. $14\frac{5}{8}$ $-\frac{15}{16}$ $13\frac{11}{16}$

Give the product in simplest form. *(page 178)*

13. $\frac{1}{3} \times \frac{1}{3}$ $\frac{1}{9}$
14. $\frac{3}{4} \times \frac{2}{3}$ $\frac{1}{2}$
15. $\frac{3}{2} \times \frac{3}{2}$ $2\frac{1}{4}$
16. $\frac{5}{9} \times \frac{3}{2}$ $\frac{5}{6}$
17. $\frac{4}{5} \times \frac{7}{2}$ $2\frac{4}{5}$

18. $\frac{7}{8} \times \frac{4}{3}$ $1\frac{1}{6}$
19. $\frac{0}{2} \times \frac{3}{8}$ 0
20. $\frac{3}{4} \times \frac{4}{3}$ 1
21. $\frac{5}{6} \times \frac{10}{3}$ $2\frac{7}{9}$
22. $\frac{5}{9} \times \frac{3}{3}$ $\frac{5}{9}$

Give the quotient in simplest form. *(page 188)*

23. $\frac{4}{9} \div \frac{1}{3}$ $1\frac{1}{3}$
24. $6 \div \frac{2}{3}$ 9
25. $\frac{5}{6} \div \frac{1}{2}$ $1\frac{2}{3}$
26. $4 \div \frac{2}{3}$ 6
27. $\frac{5}{8} \div \frac{1}{4}$ $2\frac{1}{2}$

28. $\frac{9}{4} \div \frac{9}{4}$ 1
29. $\frac{3}{2} \div \frac{3}{4}$ 2
30. $\frac{2}{5} \div 4$ $\frac{1}{10}$
31. $\frac{3}{5} \div \frac{3}{8}$ $1\frac{3}{5}$
32. $\frac{3}{10} \div \frac{2}{5}$ $\frac{3}{4}$

33. $\frac{5}{6} \div 3$ $\frac{5}{18}$
34. $\frac{9}{5} \div \frac{3}{8}$ $4\frac{4}{5}$
35. $\frac{1}{8} \div \frac{1}{4}$ $\frac{1}{2}$
36. $\frac{2}{3} \div \frac{1}{6}$ 4
37. $\frac{0}{4} \div \frac{1}{2}$ 0

Complete. *(page 202)*

38. 9 cm = ? mm 90
39. 4 m = ? cm 400
40. 3 km = ? m 3000

41. 3715 m = ? km 3.715
42. 5.9 km = ? m 5900
43. 6.3 cm = ? mm 63

44. 58 mm = ? cm 5.8
45. 35 cm = ? m 0.35
46. 26 km = ? m 26,000

47. 1368 m = ? km 1.368
48. 5.75 km = ? m 5750
49. 1.6 m = ? mm 1600

Subtract. *(page 218)*

50.   6 ft 4 in.
    − 2 ft 8 in. 3 ft 8 in.
51.   6 yd 1 ft
    − 3 yd 2 ft 2 yd 2 ft
52.   8 ft
    − 5 ft 7 in. 2 ft 5 in.
53.   9 yd
    − 2 yd 1 ft 6 yd 2

54.   8 lb 3 oz
    − 2 lb 10 oz 5 lb 9 oz
55.   4 T 200 lb
    − 2 T 500 lb 1 T 1700 lb
56.   10 lb 6 oz
    − 3 lb 12 oz 6 lb 10 oz
57.   6 T
    − 2 T 1000 lb 3 T

58.   3 gal 1 qt
    − 1 gal 2 qt 1 gal 3 qt
59.   8 qt
    − 2 qt 1 pt 5 qt 1 pt
60.   4 gal 2 qt
    − 2 gal 3 qt 1 gal 3 qt
61.   5 gal
    − 3 gal 1 qt 1 gal 3

Problem solving

GARDENING WITH A COMPUTER

Richard Dorr used his home computer to help his family plan their garden. THE HOME GARDENER program helped them decide how much to plant, how much seed to buy, and how much fertilizer to buy. The steps used to plan one part of the garden are shown below.

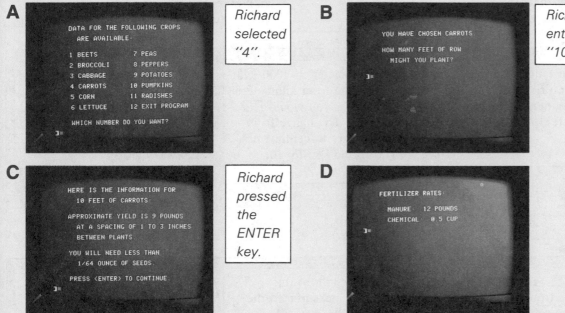

A

```
DATA FOR THE FOLLOWING CROPS
ARE AVAILABLE:

1 BEETS       7 PEAS
2 BROCCOLI    8 PEPPERS
3 CABBAGE     9 POTATOES
4 CARROTS    10 PUMPKINS
5 CORN       11 RADISHES
6 LETTUCE    12 EXIT PROGRAM

WHICH NUMBER DO YOU WANT?
```

Richard selected "4".

B

```
YOU HAVE CHOSEN CARROTS.

HOW MANY FEET OF ROW
MIGHT YOU PLANT?
```

Richard entered "10".

C

```
HERE IS THE INFORMATION FOR
10 FEET OF CARROTS:

APPROXIMATE YIELD IS 9 POUNDS
AT A SPACING OF 1 TO 3 INCHES
BETWEEN PLANTS.

YOU WILL NEED LESS THAN
1/64 OUNCE OF SEEDS.

PRESS <ENTER> TO CONTINUE.
```

Richard pressed the ENTER key.

D

```
FERTILIZER RATES:

MANURE:   12 POUNDS
CHEMICAL:  0.5 CUP
```

Use the data from the screens to solve these problems.

1. How many different crops does the program provide data for? 11

2. The progam assumes that the crops are planted in rows. How long a row of carrots was planned? 10 feet

3. a. What is the suggested spacing for the seeds? 1 to 3 inches

   b. If they used the widest spacing suggested, would they have more than 3 dozen plants in the row? Yes

4. a. How many pounds of carrots should they expect to grow? 9 pounds

   b. A similar row of tomato plants would yield 3 times the weight yielded by the carrot plants. How many pounds of tomatoes could they grow in the row? 27 pounds

5. Richard's father found about 6 ounces of chemical fertilizer left in a bottle. Was this enough fertilizer for the row of carrots? (*Hint: There are 8 ounces in a cup.*) Yes

6. Assume the weight of the seeds used to plant the row of carrots was $\frac{1}{64}$ ounce. How many pounds of carrots could they grow if they planted 1 ounce of seeds? 576 pounds

Measurement **221**

EXTRA PROBLEM SOLVING
Page 452   Even exercises

PROBLEM-SOLVING WORKSHEET
Copymaster S246 or Duplicating Master S246

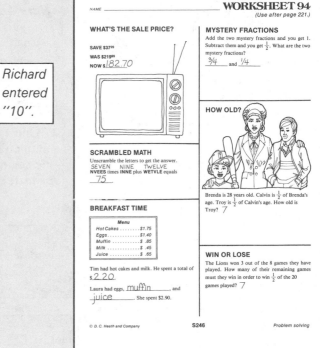

NAME _____   **WORKSHEET 94**
(Use after page 221.)

WHAT'S THE SALE PRICE?

SAVE $37⁹⁹
WAS $219⁹⁹
NOW $ 182.70

MYSTERY FRACTIONS
Add the two mystery fractions and you get 1. Subtract them and you get $\frac{1}{2}$. What are the two mystery fractions?
3/4 and 1/4

SCRAMBLED MATH
Unscramble the letters to get the answer.
SEVEN NINE TWELVE
NVEES times INNE plus WETVLE equals
75

HOW OLD?
Brenda is 28 years old. Calvin is $\frac{1}{2}$ of Brenda's age. Troy is $\frac{1}{2}$ of Calvin's age. How old is Troy? 7

BREAKFAST TIME

Menu	
Hot Cakes	$1.75
Eggs	$1.40
Muffin	$ .85
Milk	$ .45
Juice	$ .65

Tim had hot cakes and milk. He spent a total of $ 2.20.
Laura had eggs, muffin, and juice. She spent $2.90.

WIN OR LOSE
The Lions won 3 out of the 8 games they have played. How many of their remaining games must they win in order to win $\frac{1}{2}$ of the 20 games played? 7

© D. C. Heath and Company   S246   Problem solving

CHALKBOARD CHALLENGE
Use the code to answer the riddle.

CODE

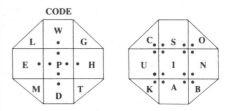

Riddle: When is a gardener like a mystery writer?

Answer:

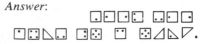

When she digs up a plot.

221

NAME

CHAPTER 9 TEST
(Form A)

Give each length to the nearest centimeter. *(page 198)*

1. ___4___ cm 2. ___5___ cm

3. ___11___ cm

ANSWERS	
1.	4
2.	5
3.	11
4.	b
5.	a
6.	c
7.	c
8.	50
9.	3000
10.	0.24
11.	8.2
12.	460
13.	4250
14.	6000
15.	1400
16.	1.32
17.	375
18.	0.85
19.	0.065
20.	3
21.	2
22.	2500
23.	6400
24.	0.265
25.	0.465

Which measurement is reasonable? *(page 200)*

4. Length of a toothbrush:
   a. 15 mm   **b.** 15 cm   c. 15 m
5. Length of a paper clip:
   a. 25 mm   b. 25 cm   c. 25 m
6. Height of your desk:
   a. 0.7 mm   b. 0.7 cm   **c.** 0.7 m
7. Length of a bridge:
   a. 0.4 cm   b. 0.4 m   **c.** 0.4 km

Complete. *(pages 202, 204, 206)*

8. 5 cm = ___50___ mm 9. 3 km = ___3000___ m
10. 24 cm = ___0.24___ m 11. 82 mm = ___8.2___ cm
12. 4.6 m = ___460___ cm 13. 4.25 km = ___4250___ m
14. 6 L = ___6000___ mL 15. ___1400___ L
16. 1320 mL = ___1.32___ L 17. 0.375 L = ___375___ mL
18. 850 mL = ___0.85___ L 19. 65 mL = ___0.065___ L
20. 3000 mg = ___3___ g 21. 2000 g = ___2___ kg
22. 2.5 kg = ___2500___ g 23. 6.4 g = ___6400___ mg
24. 265 mg = ___0.265___ g 25. 465 g = ___0.465___ kg

D. C. Heath and Company   **S33**   *Page 1*

NAME

CHAPTER 9 TEST
(Form A)

Give each length to the nearest $\frac{1}{8}$ inch. Give the answer in the simplest form.

26. ___$2\frac{1}{2}$___ in. 27. ___$1\frac{3}{4}$___ in.

28. ___$4\frac{3}{8}$___ in.

ANSWERS	
26.	$2\frac{1}{2}$
27.	$1\frac{3}{4}$
28.	$4\frac{3}{8}$
29.	96
30.	21
31.	5280
32.	6
33.	2
34.	11
35.	10
36.	18
37.	5
38.	7
39.	6
40.	1
41.	32
42.	5
43.	4000
44.	4
45.	7200
46.	2
47.	6 ft 1 in.
48.	11 lb 5 oz
49.	6 yd 2 ft
50.	1 gal 1 qt

Complete. *(pages 212, 214, 216)*

29. 8 ft = ___96___ in. 30. 7 yd = ___21___ ft
31. 1 mi = ___5280___ ft 32. 30 in. = ___2___ ft
33. 17 ft = 5 yd ___2___ ft 34. 3 yd 2 ft = ___11___ ft
35. 5 qt = ___10___ pt 36. 9 pt = ___18___ c
37. 20 qt = ___5___ gal 38. 1 gal 3 qt = ___7___ qt
39. 13 pt = ___6___ qt 1 pt 40. 15 c = ___7___ pt ___1___ c
41. 2 lb = ___32___ oz 42. 80 oz = ___5___ lb
43. 2 T = ___4000___ lb 44. 20 oz = 1 lb ___4___ oz
45. 3200 lb = 1 T ___1200___ lb 46. 35 oz = ___2___ lb 3 oz

Add or subtract. *(page 218)*

47. 3 ft 4 in.
    + 2 ft 9 in.
    ___6 ft 1 in.___

48. 6 lb 13 oz
    + 4 lb 8 oz
    ___11 lb 5 oz___

49. 9 yd 1 ft
    − 2 yd 2 ft
    ___6 yd 2 ft___

50. 3 gal
    − 1 gal 3 qt
    ___1 gal 1 qt___

D. C. Heath and Company   **S34**   *Page 2*

Chapter REVIEW

Here are scrambled answers for the review exercises:

1000	feet	kilogram	multiply
5280	gallon	meters	pound
centimeter	grams	milliliters	ton
divide	inch	millimeters	yard

1. centimeter, millimeters **2.** meters, multiply, divide **3.** milliliters, 1000

1. One tenth of a [?] is 1 millimeter. The length of this segment is 23 [?]. *(page 198)*

2. 1 kilometer = 1000 [?]. To change from kilometers to meters, you would [?] by 1000. To change from millimeters to centimeters, you would [?] by 10. *(pages 200, 202)*

$$6000\ km = \underline{?}\ m$$
$$700\ mm = \underline{?}\ cm$$

3. 1 liter = 1000 [?]. To change from milliliters to liters, you would divide by [?]. *(page 204)*

$$8000\ mL = \underline{?}\ L$$

4. kilograms, grams **5.** inch **6.** feet, 5280

4. 1 [?] = 1000 grams. To change from kilograms to [?], you would multiply by 1000. *(page 206)*

$$6\ kg = \underline{?}\ g$$

5. The length of this segment measured to the nearest $\frac{1}{8}$ [?] is $1\frac{3}{8}$ inches. *(page 210)*

6. 5280 [?] = 1 mile. To change from miles to feet, you would multiply by [?]. *(page 212)*

$$3\ mi = \underline{?}\ ft$$

7. gallon, ton **8.** pound **9.** yard

7. 4 quarts = 1 [?]. 2000 pounds = 1 [?]. *(pages 214, 216)*

8. To do this addition exercise, you would first add the ounces and then regroup 16 ounces for 1 [?]. *(page 218)*

$$5\ lb\ 9\ oz + 3\ lb\ 11\ oz$$

9. To do this subtraction exercise, you would first need to regroup 1 [?] for 3 feet. *(page 218)*

$$9\ yd\ 1\ ft - 5\ yd\ 2\ ft$$

Chapter TEST

Measure each length to the nearest centimeter. *(page 198)*

1. _____ 6 cm

2. _____ 5 cm

3. _____ 5 cm

4. _____ 7 cm

5. _____ 14 cm

Which measurement is reasonable? *(page 200)*

6. Length of a key:
   (a.) 52 mm   **b.** 52 cm   **c.** 52 m

7. Length of a baseball bat:
   a. 91 mm   (b.) 91 cm   **c.** 91 m

8. Height of a door:
   a. 2.1 cm   (b.) 2.1 m   **c.** 2.1 km

9. Length of a train:
   a. 0.6 cm   **b.** 0.6 m   (c.) 0.6 km

Copy and complete. *(pages 202, 204, 206)*

10. 6 cm = _?_ mm   60
11. 4 m = _?_ cm   400
12. 9 km = _?_ m   9000

13. 82 mm = _?_ cm   8.2
14. 3.8 m = _?_ cm   380
15. 7.4 cm = _?_ mm   74

16. 8 L = _?_ mL   8000
17. 1.5 L = _?_ mL   1500
18. 1250 mL = _?_ L   1.25

19. 0.475 L = _?_ mL   475
20. 750 mL = _?_ L   0.750
21. 65 mL = _?_ L   0.065

22. 5000 mg = _?_ g   5
23. 3000 g = _?_ kg   3
24. 2.1 kg = _?_ g   2100

25. 8.4 g = _?_ mg   8400
26. 438 mg = _?_ g   0.438
27. 395 g = _?_ kg   0.395

Measure each segment to the nearest $\frac{1}{8}$ inch. Give the answer in simplest form. *(page 210)*

28. _____ $2\frac{3}{8}$ in.

29. _____ $2\frac{1}{8}$ in.

30. _____ $5\frac{3}{4}$ in.

Copy and complete. *(pages 212, 214, 216)*

31. 7 ft = _?_ in.   84
32. 1 mi = _?_ ft   5280
33. 33 ft = _?_ yd   11

34. 72 in. = _?_ yd   2
35. 2 ft 4 in. = _?_ in.   28
36. 4 yd 1 ft = _?_ ft   13

37. 16 pt = _?_ qt   8
38. 14 c = _?_ pt   7
39. 16 qt = _?_ gal   4

40. 8 c = _?_ qt   2
41. 13 pt = 6 qt _?_ pt   1
42. 9 qt = 2 gal _?_ qt   1

43. 4 lb = _?_ oz   64
44. 64 oz = _?_ lb   4
45. 3 T = _?_ lb   6000

46. 24 oz = 1 lb _?_ oz   8
47. 3500 lb = 1 T _?_ lb   1500
48. 36 oz = _?_ lb 4 oz   2

Add or subtract. *(page 218)*

49.　5 ft 9 in.
　　+3 ft 8 in.
　　‾‾‾‾‾‾‾‾‾
　　9 ft 5 in.

50.　8 lb 14 oz
　　+5 lb 7 oz
　　‾‾‾‾‾‾‾‾‾
　　14 lb 5 oz

51.　7 yd 1 ft
　　−2 yd 2 ft
　　‾‾‾‾‾‾‾‾‾
　　4 yd 2 ft

52.　4 gal
　　−1 gal 3 qt
　　‾‾‾‾‾‾‾‾‾
　　2 gal 1 qt

Use Copymaster S336 to provide the students with an answer sheet in standardized test format.

Answers for Cumulative Test, Chapters 1–9

1. Ⓐ Ⓑ Ⓒ Ⓓ   2. Ⓐ Ⓑ Ⓒ Ⓓ   3. Ⓐ Ⓑ Ⓒ Ⓓ
4. Ⓐ Ⓑ Ⓒ Ⓓ   5. Ⓐ Ⓑ Ⓒ Ⓓ   6. Ⓐ Ⓑ Ⓒ Ⓓ
7. Ⓐ Ⓑ Ⓒ Ⓓ   8. Ⓐ Ⓑ Ⓒ Ⓓ   9. Ⓐ Ⓑ Ⓒ Ⓓ
10. Ⓐ Ⓑ Ⓒ Ⓓ   11. Ⓐ Ⓑ Ⓒ Ⓓ   12. Ⓐ Ⓑ Ⓒ Ⓓ

The table below correlates test items with student text pages.

Test Item	Page Taught	Skill Practice
1	64	p. 208, exercises 1–18
2	96	p. 208, exercises 19–33
3	146	p. 208, exercises 34–54
4	148	p. 208, exercises 55–72
5	106	
6	160	p. 208, exercises 73–84
7	168	p. 220, exercises 1–12
8	178	p. 220, exercises 13–22
9	188	p. 220, exercises 23–37
10	202	p. 220, exercises 38–49
11	218	p. 220, exercises 50–61
12	64	

Cumulative TEST
Standardized Format

Choose the correct letter.

1. Multiply. 5.637
$\times 2.04$

A. 114.9948
B. 13.5288
C. 11.49948
D. none of these

2. Divide. Round the quotient to the nearest hundredth.

$0.65 \overline{)6.69}$

A. 1.03
B. 1.29
C. 10.29
D. none of these

3. Change to a decimal.

$2\frac{7}{8} = ?$

A. 2.78
B. 3.375
C. 2.875
D. none of these

4. Change to a mixed number in simplest form.

3.200

A. $3\frac{1}{4}$
B. $3\frac{200}{1000}$
C. $3\frac{1}{5}$
D. none of these

5.

MATH TEST GRADES

How many students made a grade of C or better?

A. 8   B. 11
C. 13   D. none of these

6. Add. $3\frac{2}{3}$
$+2\frac{3}{4}$

A. $5\frac{5}{12}$
B. $6\frac{5}{12}$
C. $5\frac{5}{7}$
D. none of these

7. Subtract. $4\frac{1}{5}$
$-2\frac{1}{2}$

A. $2\frac{3}{10}$ B. $2\frac{7}{10}$
C. $1\frac{7}{10}$ D. none of these

8. Give the product.
$\frac{3}{8} \times \frac{4}{5} = ?$

A. $\frac{3}{10}$ B. $\frac{7}{40}$
C. $\frac{12}{13}$ D. none of these

9. Give the quotient.
$\frac{6}{5} \div \frac{3}{4} = ?$

A. $1\frac{1}{9}$ B. $\frac{9}{10}$
C. $1\frac{3}{5}$ D. none of these

10. Complete.
$236 \text{ cm} = \underline{\ ?\ } \text{ m}$

A. 23.6
B. 236
C. 23,600
D. none of these

11. Subtract.   8 ft 2 in.
$-$ 3 ft 9 in.

A. 5 ft 7 in.
B. 4 ft 5 in.
C. 4 ft 3 in.
D. none of these

12. You had $27. Then you worked 2.5 hours for $3.80 per hour. How much money did you have then?

A. $36.50   B. $30.80
C. $71.30   D. none of these

CHAPTER 10
Ratio and Proportion

LESSON OBJECTIVES
To give the ratio of two quantities (*pages 226–227*)
To change ratios to higher or lower terms (*pages 226–227*)
To compare the cross products to tell whether the ratios are equal or not equal (*pages 228–229*)
To solve proportions (*pages 230–231*)
To solve rate problems using proportions (*pages 232–233*)
To solve problems that involve scale drawings by using proportions (*pages 236–237*)
To use proportions to find missing measurements of sides of similar figures (*pages 238–239*)
To use similar triangles to solve indirect measurement problems (*pages 240–241*)

PROBLEM-SOLVING SKILLS
Using information in a display (*pages 226–227, 230–231, 235*)
Finding information in a table (*pages 228–229*)
Using logical reasoning (*page 229*)
Checking answers (*page 231*)
Using a proportion to solve a problem (*pages 232–233, 235–236, 239*)
Choosing the correct operation (*pages 235, 237*)
Reading a map (*pages 236–237*)
Solving a multi-step problem (*page 237*)
Selecting information from a drawing (*pages 238–241*)
Using a drawing and proportion to solve a problem (*pages 238–241, 243*)
Reading a computer display (*page 243*)

RESOURCES
- **VISUAL AIDS**
  Map from page 236 (*Visual Aid 37, Copymaster S136*)
  Centimeter and millimeter ruler from page 198 (*Visual Aid 32, Copymaster S133*)
  Pictures from page 238 (*Visual Aid 38, Copymaster S137*)
  Picture from page 240 (*Visual Aid 39, Copymaster S137*)
  Pictures from page 241 (*Visual Aid 40, Copymaster S138*)
- **WORKSHEETS 95–103** (*Copymasters S247–S255 or Duplicating Masters S247–S255*)

Ratios

You can use a **ratio** to compare two numbers. The paint for the birdhouse was a custom mixture of yellow and blue. The ratio of yellow paint to blue paint was 2 to 3. Here are three ways to write the ratio:

$$2 \text{ to } 3 \qquad \frac{2}{3} \qquad 2 : 3$$

Read each ratio as "2 to 3."

1. Look at the jars of paint shown above. What is the ratio of jars of yellow paint to jars of blue paint? 2 to 3

2. What is the ratio of jars of blue paint to jars of yellow paint? 3 to 2

3. Suppose that you wanted to mix the same color and use 4 jars of yellow paint. How many jars of blue paint should you use? 6

Here's how *to find equal ratios.*

You can find equal ratios by thinking about equivalent fractions.

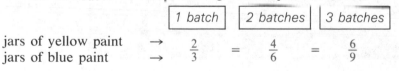

	1 batch	2 batches	3 batches
jars of yellow paint →	$\frac{2}{3}$ =	$\frac{4}{6}$ =	$\frac{6}{9}$
jars of blue paint →			

4. Look at the *Here's how*.
   a. How many jars of yellow paint would you mix with 6 jars of blue paint? 4

   b. How many jars of blue paint would you mix with 6 jars of yellow paint? 9

   c. You would have to multiply both the numerator and the denominator of $\frac{2}{3}$ by ? to get $\frac{4}{6}$. 2

   d. You would have to divide both numerator and denominator of $\frac{6}{9}$ by ? to get $\frac{2}{3}$ 3

5. Suppose you decide to use 12 jars of yellow paint. How many jars of blue paint would you need to mix the custom green? 18

EXERCISES

Give each ratio as a fraction in lowest terms.
Here are scrambled answers for the next row of exercises: $\frac{4}{3}$ $\frac{1}{4}$ $\frac{5}{2}$ $\frac{1}{2}$ $\frac{4}{9}$

6. 4 to 8 $\frac{1}{2}$ **7.** 3 to 12 $\frac{1}{4}$ **8.** 15 to 6 $\frac{5}{2}$ **9.** 8 to 6 $\frac{4}{3}$ **10.** 16 to 36 $\frac{4}{9}$

11. $\frac{14}{21}$ $\frac{2}{3}$ **12.** $\frac{10}{4}$ $\frac{5}{2}$ **13.** $\frac{16}{6}$ $\frac{8}{3}$ **14.** $\frac{9}{45}$ $\frac{1}{5}$ **15.** $\frac{18}{27}$ $\frac{2}{3}$

16. 12 : 20 $\frac{3}{5}$ **17.** 14 : 8 $\frac{7}{4}$ **18.** 18 : 32 $\frac{9}{16}$ **19.** 12 : 18 $\frac{2}{3}$ **20.** 24 : 18 $\frac{4}{3}$

21. 32 : 18 $\frac{16}{9}$ **22.** 17 : 51 $\frac{1}{3}$ **23.** 70 : 50 $\frac{7}{5}$ **24.** 26 : 39 $\frac{2}{3}$ **25.** 22 : 33 $\frac{2}{3}$

Copy and complete. Hint: Think about equivalent fractions.

26. $\frac{3}{4} = \frac{?}{8}$ 6   **27.** $\frac{1}{4} = \frac{?}{12}$ 3   **28.** $\frac{8}{5} = \frac{40}{?}$ 25   **29.** $\frac{4}{3} = \frac{12}{?}$ 9

30. $\frac{8}{3} = \frac{?}{21}$ 56   **31.** $\frac{?}{16} = \frac{5}{4}$ 20   **32.** $\frac{?}{3} = \frac{10}{30}$ 1   **33.** $\frac{1}{3} = \frac{?}{12}$ 4

34. $\frac{12}{?} = \frac{24}{22}$ 11   **35.** $\frac{?}{15} = \frac{2}{3}$ 10   **36.** $\frac{15}{30} = \frac{3}{?}$ 6   **37.** $\frac{7}{9} = \frac{?}{54}$ 42

38. $\frac{6}{5} = \frac{36}{?}$ 30   **39.** $\frac{5}{7} = \frac{?}{28}$ 20   **40.** $\frac{4}{?} = \frac{16}{28}$ 7   **41.** $\frac{?}{3} = \frac{50}{30}$ 5

42. $\frac{1}{3} = \frac{?}{75}$ 25   **43.** $\frac{3}{20} = \frac{9}{?}$ 60   **44.** $\frac{10}{3} = \frac{100}{?}$ 30   **45.** $\frac{16}{18} = \frac{?}{9}$ 8

46. $\frac{2}{3} = \frac{?}{24}$ 16   **47.** $\frac{3}{4} = \frac{27}{?}$ 36   **48.** $\frac{5}{8} = \frac{?}{32}$ 20   **49.** $\frac{3}{2} = \frac{30}{?}$ 20

50. $\frac{7}{8} = \frac{21}{?}$ 24   **51.** $\frac{?}{100} = \frac{9}{5}$ 180   **52.** $\frac{4}{3} = \frac{40}{?}$ 30   **53.** $\frac{?}{100} = \frac{4}{5}$ 80

54. $\frac{?}{24} = \frac{3}{8}$ 9   **55.** $\frac{6}{5} = \frac{?}{50}$ 60   **56.** $\frac{?}{18} = \frac{5}{3}$ 30   **57.** $\frac{5}{2} = \frac{100}{?}$ 40

You mix it!

To get Sunset Orange, mix 1 part white, 3 parts yellow, and 2 parts red.

1 : 3 : 2

58. How many jars of white paint would you need if you used 4 jars of red? 2

59. How many jars of red would you need to mix with 9 jars of yellow? 6

60. Suppose you needed 12 jars of Sunset Orange. How many jars of each of the three colors would you need?
2 white, 6 yellow, 4 red

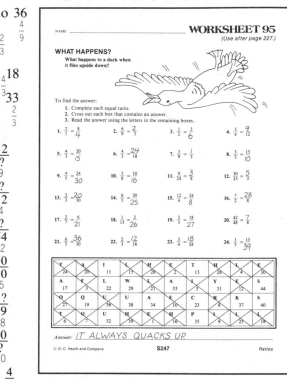
Ratio and Proportion **227**

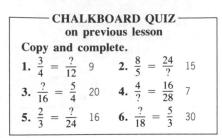

CHALKBOARD QUIZ
on previous lesson

Copy and complete.

1. $\frac{3}{4} = \frac{?}{12}$ 9   2. $\frac{8}{5} = \frac{24}{?}$ 15

3. $\frac{?}{16} = \frac{5}{4}$ 20   4. $\frac{4}{?} = \frac{16}{28}$ 7

5. $\frac{2}{3} = \frac{?}{24}$ 16   6. $\frac{?}{18} = \frac{5}{3}$ 30

LESSON OBJECTIVE

To compare the cross products to tell whether the ratios are equal or not equal

PROBLEM-SOLVING SKILLS

Finding information in a table
Using logical reasoning

STARTING THE LESSON

Before going over exercises 1–6, have the students study the table at the top of the page. Ask them to write who they think is the better free-throw shooter, Nancy or Ingrid. After completing exercise 6, ask the students again who they think is the better free-throw shooter, Nancy or Ingrid. (Ingrid)

EXERCISE NOTE

You may wish to use several of exercises 7–16 as oral exercises before making a written assignment. Have the students verbalize the method they are using in comparing the cross products.

Proportions

PLAYER	FREE THROWS MADE	FREE THROWS ATTEMPTED
Nancy B.	|||	||||
Linda D.	||||	|||| |||
Ingrid G.	||||	||||	
Susan L.	|||	||||	
Amanda M.	||||	|||| ||||	
Paige R.	||||		|||| ||||
Kathy R.	||||		|||| ||||
Maria T.	||||	|||| |||| ||

FREE THROWS DURING GAMES

1. Look at the table. How many free throws did Nancy make? 3

2. How many free throws did Nancy attempt? 5

3. What is Nancy's ratio of free throws made to free throws attempted? $\frac{3}{5}$

4. What is Kathy's ratio of free throws made to free throws attempted? $\frac{6}{10}$

TIME OUT!   An equation stating that two ratios are equal is called a **proportion.** Every proportion has a related multiplication equation.

Proportion		**Multiplication Equation**
Nancy's ratio	$\frac{3}{5} \leftarrow = \rightarrow \frac{6}{10}$ Kathy's ratio	$3 \times 10 = 5 \times 6$

The two products 3×10 and 5×6 are called **cross products.**

Here's how   *to use the cross products to tell whether or not two ratios are equal.*

If the cross products are equal, then the ratios are equal.	If the cross products are not equal, then the ratios are not equal.
Nancy's ratio $\frac{3}{5}$ ● $\frac{6}{10}$ Kathy's ratio	Nancy's ratio $\frac{3}{5}$ ● $\frac{4}{6}$ Ingrid's ratio
Since $3 \times 10 = 5 \times 6$ we know that $\frac{3}{5} = \frac{6}{10}$.	Since $3 \times 6 \neq 5 \times 4$ we know that $\frac{3}{5} \neq \frac{4}{6}$.

5. Look at the *Here's how*. Is Nancy's ratio equal to Kathy's ratio?   Yes

6. Is Nancy's ratio equal to Ingrid's ratio?   No

228

EXERCISES

Tell whether the ratios are equal (=) or not equal (≠). *Hint: Compare the cross products.*

7. $\frac{1}{2} \bullet \frac{3}{4}$ ≠

8. $\frac{4}{12} \bullet \frac{1}{3}$ =

9. $\frac{5}{9} \bullet \frac{2}{5}$ ≠

10. $\frac{3}{2} \bullet \frac{9}{6}$ =

11. $\frac{4}{7} \bullet \frac{3}{5}$ ≠

12. $\frac{5}{8} \bullet \frac{3}{5}$ ≠

13. $\frac{3}{9} \bullet \frac{4}{12}$ =

14. $\frac{5}{10} \bullet \frac{2}{4}$ =

15. $\frac{5}{4} \bullet \frac{3}{2}$ ≠

16. $\frac{7}{2} \bullet \frac{12}{4}$ ≠

17. $\frac{14}{8} \bullet \frac{21}{12}$ =

18. $\frac{13}{16} \bullet \frac{9}{12}$ ≠

19. $\frac{12}{15} \bullet \frac{8}{10}$ =

20. $\frac{6}{9} \bullet \frac{4}{6}$ =

21. $\frac{15}{9} \bullet \frac{14}{8}$ ≠

22. $\frac{2}{12} \bullet \frac{3}{18}$ =

23. $\frac{8}{10} \bullet \frac{16}{20}$ =

24. $\frac{9}{8} \bullet \frac{6}{5}$ ≠

25. $\frac{13}{15} \bullet \frac{11}{13}$ ≠

26. $\frac{14}{16} \bullet \frac{35}{40}$ =

27. $\frac{3}{4} \bullet \frac{0.5}{1}$ ≠

28. $\frac{2}{0.5} \bullet \frac{8}{2}$ =

29. $\frac{5}{0.75} \bullet \frac{4}{1}$ ≠

30. $\frac{5}{1} \bullet \frac{2}{0.4}$ =

31. $\frac{0.6}{2} \bullet \frac{3}{5}$ ≠

32. $\frac{6}{9} \bullet \frac{0.4}{0.6}$ =

33. $\frac{0.6}{0.5} \bullet \frac{4}{3}$ ≠

34. $\frac{0.3}{0.6} \bullet \frac{0.4}{0.8}$ =

35. $\frac{4.5}{6.0} \bullet \frac{7.5}{10.0}$ =

36. $\frac{1.5}{0.5} \bullet \frac{6.0}{2.0}$ =

37. $\frac{3}{4} \bullet \frac{1\frac{1}{2}}{2}$ =

38. $\frac{3}{2} \bullet \frac{2}{1\frac{1}{4}}$ ≠

39. $\frac{1\frac{1}{3}}{4} \bullet \frac{2}{6}$ =

40. $\frac{2}{1\frac{3}{8}} \bullet \frac{5}{3}$ ≠

41. $\frac{2\frac{1}{2}}{5} \bullet \frac{4}{9}$ ≠

42. $\frac{9}{3} \bullet \frac{7\frac{1}{2}}{2\frac{1}{2}}$ =

43. $\frac{1\frac{1}{4}}{7\frac{1}{2}} \bullet \frac{2}{12}$ =

44. $\frac{1\frac{1}{4}}{2} \bullet \frac{2\frac{1}{8}}{3}$ ≠

45. $\frac{2\frac{2}{3}}{1\frac{1}{2}} \bullet \frac{3}{2\frac{3}{4}}$ ≠

46. $\frac{3\frac{3}{5}}{2\frac{1}{4}} \bullet \frac{1\frac{1}{5}}{1}$ ≠

Solve. Use the table on page 228.

47. What is Linda's ratio of free throws made to free throws attempted? $\frac{4}{8}$

48. What is Susan's ratio of free throws made to free throws attempted? $\frac{3}{6}$

49. Compare the ratios from exercises 47 and 48. Is Linda's ratio equal to Susan's ratio? Yes

50. Which player's ratio (free throws made to free throws attempted) is equal to Ingrid's ratio? Paige's

51. What is Paige's ratio of free throws missed to free throws attempted? $\frac{3}{9}$

52. What is Amanda's ratio of free throws made to free throws missed? $\frac{5}{6}$

Who won?

53. With only two minutes left to play, the Jefferson Tigers were ahead of the Washington Badgers 48 to 47. During the last two minutes, the two teams made a total of 3 field goals (2-point goals) and no free throws. Both teams scored 50 or more points. Which team won, and what was the final score? Badgers, 51 to 50

Ratio and Proportion **229**

REVIEW PRACTICE
Simplifying expressions
Page 424   Skill 25

PRACTICE WORKSHEET
Copymaster S248 or Duplicating Master S248

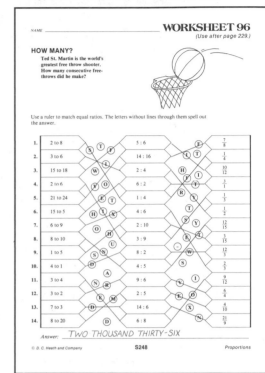

CHALKBOARD CHALLENGE

Use a clockface to help you answer these questions.

1. What time is it when the ratio of hours past noon to hours until midnight is 7 to 5? 7 P.M.

2. What time is it when the ratio of hours past noon to hours until midnight is 1 to 2? 4 P.M.

CHALKBOARD QUIZ
on previous lesson
Tell whether the ratios are equal (=) or not equal (≠).

1. $\frac{3}{4}$ ● $\frac{7}{9}$ ≠   2. $\frac{3}{2}$ ● $\frac{9}{6}$ =

3. $\frac{3}{9}$ ● $\frac{4}{12}$ =   4. $\frac{5}{4}$ ● $\frac{3}{2}$ ≠

5. $\frac{3}{4}$ ● $\frac{0.5}{1}$ ≠   6. $\frac{5}{1}$ ● $\frac{2}{0.4}$ =

LESSON OBJECTIVE
To solve proportions

PROBLEM-SOLVING SKILLS
Using information in a display
Checking answers

STARTING THE LESSON
Play 'What are the facts?' Have the students study the information and pictures at the top of page 230 for one minute. Then tell them to close their books, and challenge them to decide whether these statements are true or false:

- Amelia Earhart was the first woman pilot to fly solo and nonstop across the Atlantic ocean. (True)
- A team of Air Force pilots were the first to fly around the world. (False)
- Amelia Earhart made her flight in a *Lockheed Vega*. (True)
- The wingspan of a *Lockheed Vega* is greater than a *Douglas Chicago*. (False)

HERE'S HOW NOTE
Emphasize how the proportion is set up so that both numerators refer to the models and both denominators refer to the real airplanes.

Solving proportions

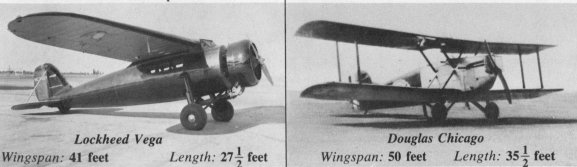

In 1932 Amelia Earhart became the first woman to fly across the Atlantic solo and nonstop.

In 1924 a team of U.S. Army pilots were the first to fly around the world.

Lockheed Vega
Wingspan: **41 feet**   *Length:* **27$\frac{1}{2}$ feet**

Douglas Chicago
Wingspan: **50 feet**   *Length:* **35$\frac{1}{2}$ feet**

1. What is the wingspan of the 1924 *Douglas Chicago*? 50 feet

A model of the *Douglas Chicago* is to be $\frac{1}{20}$ the size of the real airplane.

To find how many feet the wingspan of the model should be, you can set up and solve a proportion.

Here's how *to set up and solve a proportion.*

When setting up a proportion, make sure that the ratios are in the same order.

wingspan of model airplane → $\frac{n}{50} = \frac{1}{20}$ ← model airplane
wingspan of real airplane →

Write the multiplication equation. $20n = 50 \times 1$ 20n *is a short way to write* $20 \times n$.

Solve the multiplication equation. $20n = 50$

$n = \frac{50}{20}$ Since 20 times *n* equals 50, divide 50 by 20 to find *n*.

$n = 2\frac{1}{2}$

Check: $\frac{2\frac{1}{2}}{50} = \frac{1}{20}$ $2\frac{1}{2} \times 20 = 50 \times 1$

2. Look at the *Here's how*. If the model is $\frac{1}{20}$ the size of the real airplane, how long should the wingspan of the model be? $2\frac{1}{2}$ feet

EXERCISES

Copy and complete. Give answers in simplest form.
Here are scrambled answers for the next row of exercises: 20 $3\frac{1}{2}$ $4\frac{4}{5}$ 3

3. $\frac{5}{2} = \frac{n}{8}$ $\boxed{\begin{array}{l}2n = 40\\ n = ?\end{array}}$ 20

4. $\frac{8}{6} = \frac{4}{n}$ $\boxed{\begin{array}{l}8n = 24\\ n = ?\end{array}}$ 3

5. $\frac{n}{8} = \frac{3}{5}$ $\boxed{\begin{array}{l}5n = 24\\ n = ?\end{array}}$ $4\frac{4}{5}$

6. $\frac{1}{2} = \frac{n}{7}$ $\boxed{\begin{array}{l}2n = 7\\ n = ?\end{array}}$ $3\frac{1}{2}$

7. $\frac{2}{n} = \frac{4}{1\frac{1}{2}}$ $\boxed{\begin{array}{l}4n = 2 \times 1\frac{1}{2}\\ 4n = 3\\ n = ?\end{array}}$ $\frac{3}{4}$

8. $\frac{2\frac{1}{2}}{4} = \frac{n}{8}$ $\boxed{\begin{array}{l}4n = 2\frac{1}{2} \times 8\\ 4n = 20\\ n = ?\end{array}}$ 5

9. $\frac{3}{5} = \frac{n}{2\frac{1}{2}}$ $\boxed{\begin{array}{l}5n = 3 \times 2\frac{1}{2}\\ 5n = 7\frac{1}{2}\\ n = ?\end{array}}$ $1\frac{1}{2}$

10. $\frac{n}{1\frac{3}{4}} = \frac{4}{5}$ $\boxed{\begin{array}{l}5n = 1\frac{3}{4} \times 4\\ 5n = 7\\ n = ?\end{array}}$ $1\frac{2}{5}$

Solve each proportion. Give the answer in simplest form.

11. $\frac{1}{2} = \frac{6}{n}$ 12

12. $\frac{1}{4} = \frac{12}{n}$ 3

13. $\frac{n}{5} = \frac{2}{10}$ 1

14. $\frac{5}{n} = \frac{10}{20}$ 10

15. $\frac{1}{6} = \frac{7}{n}$ 42

16. $\frac{3}{10} = \frac{n}{5}$ $1\frac{1}{2}$

17. $\frac{7}{12} = \frac{4}{n}$ $6\frac{6}{7}$

18. $\frac{8}{n} = \frac{10}{3}$ $2\frac{2}{5}$

19. $\frac{n}{6} = \frac{5}{9}$ $3\frac{1}{3}$

20. $\frac{11}{4} = \frac{n}{12}$ 33

21. $\frac{1\frac{1}{2}}{3} = \frac{n}{2}$ 1

22. $\frac{10}{7} = \frac{1\frac{1}{4}}{n}$ $\frac{7}{8}$

23. $\frac{4}{n} = \frac{8}{2\frac{3}{4}}$ $1\frac{3}{8}$

24. $\frac{n}{2\frac{1}{2}} = \frac{4}{6}$ $1\frac{2}{3}$

25. $\frac{5}{4} = \frac{1\frac{1}{4}}{n}$ 1

Solve. Refer to the airplanes pictured on page 230.

26. Suppose that you want to make a model of the *Lockheed Vega* that is $\frac{1}{30}$ the size of the real airplane.

a. What should the wingspan of the model be? $1\frac{11}{30}$ feet

b. How long should the model be? $\frac{11}{12}$ foot

Check it out!

27. Find and correct the two wrong answers.

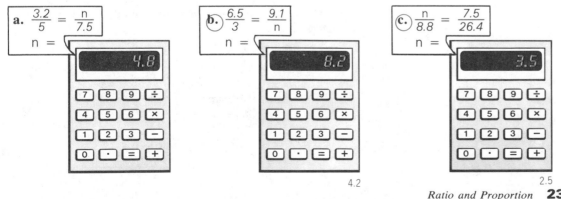

a. $\frac{3.2}{5} = \frac{n}{7.5}$ n = `4.8`

b. $\frac{6.5}{3} = \frac{9.1}{n}$ n = `8.2` 4.2

c. $\frac{n}{8.8} = \frac{7.5}{26.4}$ n = `3.5` 2.5

EXTRA PRACTICE
Page 437   Skill 52

PRACTICE WORKSHEET
Copymaster S249 or Duplicating Master S249

NAME _____   **WORKSHEET 97**
(Use after page 231.)

SKILL DRILL
Study these examples.

$\frac{n}{8} = \frac{3}{5}$
$5n = 3 \times 8$
$5n = 24$
$n = 4\frac{4}{5}$

$4\frac{4}{5}$ $\frac{24}{5}$ -20

$\frac{3}{7} = \frac{n}{5}$
$7n = 3 \times 5$
$7n = 15$
$n = 2\frac{1}{7}$

$\frac{3}{4} = \frac{10}{n}$
$3n = 4 \times 10$
$3n = 40$
$n = 13\frac{1}{3}$

Solve each proportion. Give the answer in simplest form.

1. $\frac{n}{4} = \frac{7}{5}$ $5\frac{3}{5}$
2. $\frac{4}{5} = \frac{n}{3}$ $2\frac{2}{5}$
3. $\frac{4}{9} = \frac{32}{n}$ 72
4. $\frac{7}{8} = \frac{5}{n}$ $5\frac{5}{7}$

5. $\frac{n}{6} = \frac{8}{9}$ $5\frac{1}{3}$
6. $\frac{2}{n} = \frac{7}{8}$ $2\frac{2}{7}$
7. $\frac{7}{5} = \frac{2}{n}$ $1\frac{5}{9}$
8. $\frac{6}{n} = \frac{8}{3}$ $2\frac{1}{4}$

9. $\frac{n}{5} = \frac{3}{2}$ $7\frac{1}{2}$
10. $\frac{3}{n} = \frac{6}{5}$ $2\frac{1}{2}$
11. $\frac{4}{9} = \frac{n}{9}$ 12
12. $\frac{n}{10} = \frac{8}{4}$ 20

13. $\frac{6}{12} = \frac{9}{n}$ 18
14. $\frac{15}{3} = \frac{n}{8}$ 40
15. $\frac{3}{5} = \frac{2}{n}$ $3\frac{1}{3}$
16. $\frac{2}{9} = \frac{3}{n}$ $13\frac{1}{2}$

17. $\frac{1}{4} = \frac{n}{5}$ $1\frac{1}{4}$
18. $\frac{3}{4} = \frac{5}{n}$ $6\frac{2}{3}$
19. $\frac{n}{3} = \frac{4}{5}$ $1\frac{3}{5}$
20. $\frac{8}{3} = \frac{n}{2}$ $3\frac{1}{5}$

21. $\frac{5}{3} = \frac{n}{8}$ $13\frac{1}{3}$
22. $\frac{4}{9} = \frac{3}{n}$ $6\frac{3}{4}$
23. $\frac{5}{2} = \frac{n}{5}$ $12\frac{1}{2}$
24. $\frac{2}{n} = \frac{5}{20}$ 8

Check yourself. Here are the scrambled answers:

$1\frac{1}{4}$ $1\frac{4}{5}$ $1\frac{3}{5}$ $2\frac{1}{4}$ $2\frac{2}{7}$ $2\frac{2}{5}$ $2\frac{1}{2}$ $3\frac{1}{3}$ $3\frac{1}{5}$ $5\frac{1}{3}$ $5\frac{3}{5}$ $5\frac{5}{7}$ $6\frac{2}{3}$
$6\frac{3}{4}$ $7\frac{1}{2}$ 8 12 $12\frac{1}{2}$ $13\frac{1}{3}$ $13\frac{1}{2}$ 18 20 40 72

S249   Solving proportions

LIFE-SKILL PROJECT
Reading a recipe
Have the students choose a favorite recipe. Tell them to use proportions to alter the recipe so that there is just enough to serve the entire class.

LESSON OBJECTIVE

To solve rate problems using proportions

PROBLEM-SOLVING SKILLS

Using a proportion to solve a problem
Finding information from a display

STARTING THE LESSON

Write this problem on the chalkboard:

You spent $12.50 for 9 gallons of gasoline. At that rate, how much would you spend for 14 gallons?

Before the students open their books, have them estimate the cost of 14 gallons of gasoline. Record the high and low estimates on the chalkboard. Then have the students study problem 1 on page 232 to see if their estimate was close to the exact cost, $19.44.

Rates

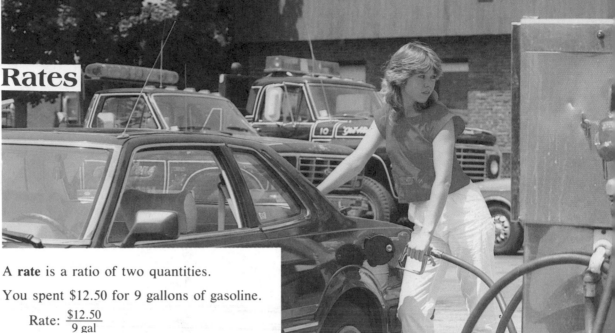

A **rate** is a ratio of two quantities.

You spent $12.50 for 9 gallons of gasoline.

Rate: $\dfrac{\$12.50}{9 \text{ gal}}$

Read as "$12.50 per 9 gallons."

Here's how *to use proportions to solve rate problems.*

PROBLEM 1. If you spent $12.50 for 9 gallons of gasoline, how much would you spend for 14 gallons?

dollars → $\dfrac{12.50}{9} = \dfrac{n}{14}$ ← dollars
gallons →   ← gallons

$9n = 12.50 \times 14$
$9n = 175$
$n \approx 19.44$

$$9\overline{)175.000} = 19.444$$

Remember: When setting up a proportion, you must be sure that the ratios are in the same order!

Read $\approx$ as "is approximately equal to."

So, at that rate, you would spend $19.44 for 14 gallons of gasoline.

PROBLEM 2. You drive 196 miles in 4 hours. At that rate, how many hours will it take you to drive 320 miles?

miles → $\dfrac{196}{4} = \dfrac{320}{n}$ ← miles
hours →   ← hours

$196n = 4 \times 320$
$196n = 1280$
$n \approx 6.53$

$$196\overline{)1280.0000} = 6.5306$$

So, at that rate, it would take you about 6.53 hours to drive 320 miles.

EXERCISES

Solve by using proportions. If an answer does not come out evenly, round it to the nearest hundredth.

1. You spend $18 for 12 gallons of gasoline. At that price,

   a. how many gallons could you buy for $15? 10

$$\text{Hint: } \frac{18}{12} = \frac{15}{n}$$

   b. how many gallons could you buy for $6.50? 4.33

   c. how much would 9 gallons cost? $13.50

   d. how much would 10.4 gallons cost? $15.60

2. You drive 128 miles in 3 hours. At that speed,

   a. how many miles could you drive in 5 hours? 213.33

$$\text{Hint: } \frac{128}{3} = \frac{n}{5}$$

   b. how many miles could you drive in 7 hours? 298.67

   c. how many hours would it take you to drive 200 miles? 4.69

   d. how many hours would it take you to drive 286 miles? 6.70

3. You drive 124 miles and use 4.8 gallons of gasoline. At that rate,

   a. how many miles could you drive on 8 gallons? 206.67

   b. how many miles could you drive on 15 gallons? 387.5

   c. how many gallons would you need for 200 miles? 7.74

   d. how many gallons would you need for 260 miles? 10.06

4. You spend $3.60 to drive 110 miles on a toll road. At that rate,

   a. how many miles could you drive for $1.60? 48.89

   b. how many miles could you drive for $2.00? 61.11

   c. how much would it cost to drive 150 miles? $4.91

   d. how much would it cost to drive 85 miles? $2.78

5. During the first 2 days of your trip you spend $43 for meals. At that rate,

   a. how much will your meals cost for 5 days? $107.50

   b. how many days of meals could you buy for $215? 10

6. You drive 4 hours and use 8.2 gallons of gasoline. At that rate,

   a. how many hours could you drive on 6 gallons? 2.93

   b. how many gallons would you need to drive 7 hours? 14.35

Check your instruments

7. You are 157 miles from Chicago. You want to be in Chicago by 11 o'clock. You look at your speedometer and clock.

Will you be on time if you keep driving at the same rate? No

REVIEW PRACTICE
Dividing decimals
Page 424   Skill 26

PRACTICE WORKSHEET
Copymaster S250 or Duplicating Master S250

NAME _____ **WORKSHEET 98**
(Use after page 233.)

SKILL DRILL
Solve each proportion.

1. $\frac{5}{4} = \frac{12}{n}$ $9\frac{3}{5}$ **2.** $\frac{9}{2} = \frac{n}{8}$ 36   **3.** $\frac{3}{2} = \frac{14}{n}$ 21   **4.** $\frac{n}{9} = \frac{4}{6}$ 6

5. $\frac{3}{8} = \frac{n}{4}$ $1\frac{1}{2}$ **6.** $\frac{15}{n} = \frac{10}{4}$ 6   **7.** $\frac{5}{6} = \frac{n}{18}$ 15   **8.** $\frac{6}{9} = \frac{n}{12}$ 8

Solve by using a proportion.

9. Brian earned $7 in 2 hours. At that rate, how long would it take him to earn $56?
Hint: $\frac{7}{2} = \frac{56}{n} \leftarrow \frac{dollars}{hours}$ 16 hours

10. Mr. Larson can drive 90 miles in 2 hours. At that rate, how far can he drive in 5 hours?
Hint: $\frac{90}{2} = \frac{n}{5} \leftarrow \frac{miles}{hours}$ 225 miles

11. Martha's pulse beats 24 times in 20 seconds. At that rate, how many times does it beat in 60 seconds?   72

12. Melons were on sale at 3 for $2. How many melons could be bought for $10?   15

13. Jill can type 90 words in 2 minutes. At that rate, how many minutes would it take her to type 1350 words?   30

14. Bananas are sold at 3 pounds for $1.00. What is the cost to the nearest cent of 2 pounds of bananas?   67¢

15. Tony had 4 hits out of 15 times at bat. At that rate, how many hits would he have in 60 times at bat?   16

16. Doughnuts cost $2 per dozen. How much will 30 doughnuts cost? $5.00

© D. C. Heath and Company   S250   Rates

LIFE-SKILL PROJECT
Collecting data and using proportions
Have the students take their pulse for 15 seconds. Then have the students use their individual pulse rate to compute how many times their heart will beat in 1 minute and in 1 hour. Have the students compute how many hours it takes for their heart to beat 1,000,000 times.

SKILLS REVIEWED
Multiplying and dividing decimals
Comparing fractions
Changing a fraction to a decimal
Adding fractions

PROBLEM-SOLVING SKILLS
Finding information in a display
Choosing the correct operation
Using a proportion to solve a problem

STARTING THE LESSON
Cumulative Skill Practice
Challenge the students to an estimation hunt by saying, "Pick the largest product in the first row of exercises." (Exercise 1) Then have the students pick the largest answers in the next five rows of exercises. (Exercises 10, 16, 23, 25, and 32)

STARTING THE LESSON
Problem Solving
Have the students use the information at the top of page 235 to answer questions such as, "Who is older than McGrath but younger than Delano?" (Cleaver) "Who is taller than Howe but shorter than Cleaver?" (Delano) "Who is heavier than Howe but lighter than Cleaver?" (Delano)

234

Cumulative Skill Practice

Multiply. *(page 64)*

1. 1.4×52 = 72.8	2. 4.9×5.2 = 25.48	3. 0.58×6.8 = 3.944	4. 0.94×37 = 34.78	5. 0.39×9.7 = 3.783	6. 2.04×3.1 = 6.324
7. 0.78×0.44 = 0.3432	8. 0.53×66 = 34.98	9. 8.4×8.4 = 70.56	10. 4.18×41 = 171.38	11. 2.67×0.71 = 1.8957	12. 6.11×0.23 = 1.4053
13. 4.56×3.6 = 16.416	14. 8.03×0.62 = 4.9786	15. 50.8×0.73 = 37.084	16. 66.6×1.84 = 122.544	17. 8.49×2.05 = 17.4045	18. 9.14×3.23 = 29.5222

Divide. Round the quotient to the nearest tenth. *(page 90)*

19. $0.6 \overline{)4.3}$ = 7.2
20. $0.3 \overline{)3.91}$ = 13.0
21. $0.09 \overline{)5.2}$ = 57.8
22. $0.03 \overline{)8.7}$ = 290
23. $0.06 \overline{)50}$ = 833.3

24. $1.3 \overline{)5.3}$ = 4.1
25. $0.11 \overline{)37}$ = 336.4
26. $2.7 \overline{)3.7}$ = 1.4
27. $3.7 \overline{)5.04}$ = 1.4
28. $0.65 \overline{)9.1}$ = 14

29. $0.41 \overline{)7.5}$ = 18.3
30. $9.7 \overline{)5.09}$ = 0.5
31. $3.3 \overline{)0.66}$ = 0.2
32. $0.55 \overline{)79}$ = 143.6
33. $9.3 \overline{)4.05}$ = 0.4

<, =, or >? *(page 132)*

34. $\frac{1}{2} \bullet \frac{4}{8}$ =
35. $\frac{3}{8} \bullet \frac{5}{8}$ <
36. $\frac{1}{2} \bullet \frac{1}{4}$ >
37. $\frac{3}{9} \bullet \frac{1}{3}$ =
38. $\frac{1}{3} \bullet \frac{1}{2}$ <

39. $\frac{5}{8} \bullet \frac{3}{4}$ <
40. $\frac{2}{3} \bullet \frac{10}{15}$ =
41. $\frac{3}{4} \bullet \frac{2}{3}$ >
42. $\frac{5}{6} \bullet \frac{7}{8}$ <
43. $\frac{5}{6} \bullet \frac{3}{4}$ >

44. $\frac{12}{16} \bullet \frac{3}{4}$ =
45. $\frac{9}{16} \bullet \frac{5}{8}$ <
46. $\frac{9}{10} \bullet \frac{7}{8}$ >
47. $\frac{4}{5} \bullet \frac{5}{4}$ <
48. $\frac{1}{2} \bullet \frac{50}{100}$ =

Change to a decimal rounded to the nearest hundredth. *(page 146)*

49. $\frac{1}{3}$ 0.33
50. $\frac{1}{9}$ 0.11
51. $\frac{1}{6}$ 0.17
52. $\frac{1}{8}$ 0.13
53. $\frac{1}{16}$ 0.06
54. $\frac{3}{4}$ 0.75
55. $\frac{5}{8}$ 0.63

56. $\frac{2}{3}$ 0.67
57. $\frac{5}{6}$ 0.83
58. $\frac{3}{8}$ 0.38
59. $\frac{9}{16}$ 0.56
60. $\frac{7}{12}$ 0.58
61. $\frac{7}{8}$ 0.88
62. $\frac{5}{16}$ 0.31

63. $\frac{11}{9}$ 1.22
64. $\frac{15}{6}$ 2.50
65. $\frac{19}{8}$ 2.38
66. $\frac{21}{12}$ 1.75
67. $\frac{25}{16}$ 1.56
68. $\frac{13}{4}$ 3.25
69. $\frac{16}{3}$ 5.33

Give the sum in simplest form. *(page 158)*

70. $\frac{3}{4} + \frac{1}{4}$ 1
71. $\frac{1}{2} + \frac{1}{4}$ $\frac{3}{4}$
72. $\frac{5}{9} + \frac{1}{3}$ $\frac{8}{9}$
73. $4 + \frac{2}{5}$ $4\frac{2}{5}$
74. $\frac{2}{3} + 3$ $3\frac{2}{3}$

75. $\frac{7}{8} + \frac{3}{4}$ $1\frac{5}{8}$
76. $\frac{1}{2} + \frac{3}{8}$ $\frac{7}{8}$
77. $\frac{3}{10} + \frac{1}{5}$ $\frac{1}{2}$
78. $\frac{5}{6} + \frac{2}{3}$ $1\frac{1}{2}$
79. $\frac{2}{3} + \frac{3}{4}$ $1\frac{11}{12}$

Problem solving

Use the facts and fingerprints above.
Find the missing information.

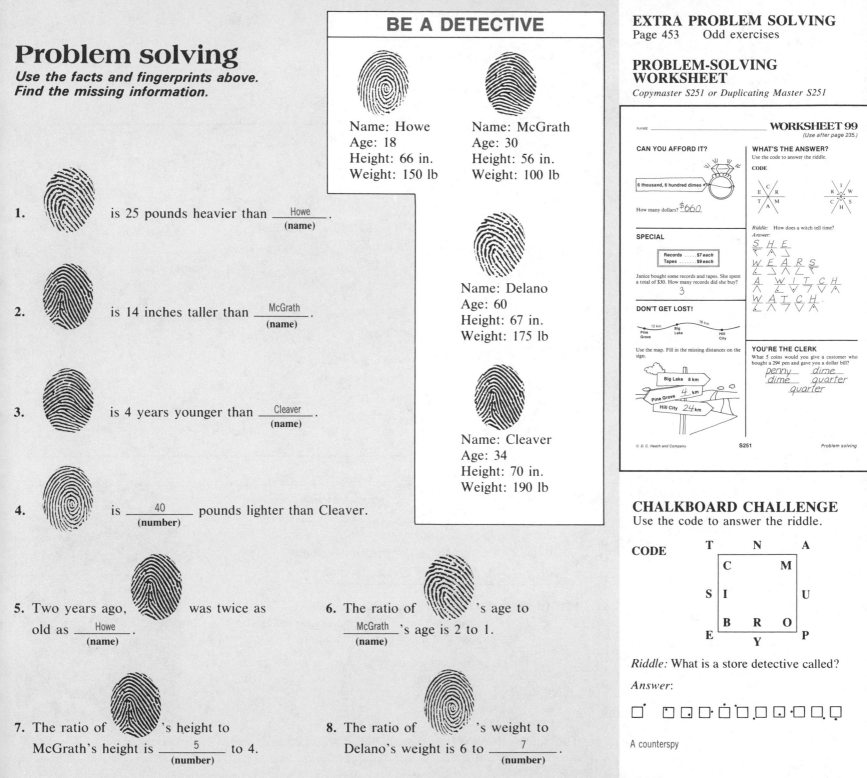

BE A DETECTIVE

Name: Howe
Age: 18
Height: 66 in.
Weight: 150 lb

Name: McGrath
Age: 30
Height: 56 in.
Weight: 100 lb

Name: Delano
Age: 60
Height: 67 in.
Weight: 175 lb

Name: Cleaver
Age: 34
Height: 70 in.
Weight: 190 lb

1. ⬤ is 25 pounds heavier than ___Howe___.
   (name)

2. ⬤ is 14 inches taller than ___McGrath___.
   (name)

3. ⬤ is 4 years younger than ___Cleaver___.
   (name)

4. ⬤ is ___40___ pounds lighter than Cleaver.
   (number)

5. Two years ago, ⬤ was twice as
   old as ___Howe___.
   (name)

6. The ratio of ⬤'s age to
   ___McGrath___'s age is 2 to 1.
   (name)

7. The ratio of ⬤'s height to
   McGrath's height is ___5___ to 4.
   (number)

8. The ratio of ⬤'s weight to
   Delano's weight is 6 to ___7___.
   (number)

EXTRA PROBLEM SOLVING
Page 453   Odd exercises

PROBLEM-SOLVING WORKSHEET
Copymaster S251 or Duplicating Master S251

NAME _____   **WORKSHEET 99**
(Use after page 235.)

CAN YOU AFFORD IT?

6 thousand, 6 hundred dimes

How many dollars? $660

WHAT'S THE ANSWER?
Use the code to answer the riddle.

CODE

Riddle: How does a witch tell time?
Answer:
S H E
W E A R S
A W I T C H
W A T C H.

SPECIAL

| Records | ..... $7 each |
| Tapes | .... $9 each |

Janice bought some records and tapes. She spent
a total of $30. How many records did she buy?
3

DON'T GET LOST!

12 km   Big Lake   16 km
Pine Grove   Hill City

Use the map. Fill in the missing distances on the
sign.

Big Lake 8 km
Pine Grove 4 km
Hill City 24 km

YOU'RE THE CLERK
What 5 coins would you give a customer who
bought a 29¢ pen and gave you a dollar bill?
penny   dime
dime   quarter
quarter

© D. C. Heath and Company   S251   *Problem solving*

CHALKBOARD CHALLENGE
Use the code to answer the riddle.

CODE

```
      T      N      A
   ┌─────────────────┐
 C │                 │ M
   │                 │
 S │ I             U │
   │                 │
 B │ R           O   │
   └─────────────────┘
 E      Y             P
```

Riddle: What is a store detective called?

Answer:

□ □□□□ □ □□ □□□ □□ □□

A counterspy

235

CHALKBOARD QUIZ
on previous lesson

Complete. Use the information at the top of page 235.

1. $\underset{\text{(Name)}}{\underline{\text{Delano}}}$ is 25 pounds heavier than Howe.

2. The ratio of Delano's age to $\underset{\text{(Name)}}{\underline{\text{McGrath's}}}$ age is 2 to 1.

3. The ratio of Cleaver's age to $\underset{\text{(Name)}}{\underline{\text{Howe's}}}$ age is 17 to 9.

LESSON OBJECTIVE
To solve problems that involve scale drawings by using proportions

PROBLEM-SOLVING SKILLS
Reading a map
Using a ruler and a map scale
Choosing the correct operation
Solving a multi-step problem

STARTING THE LESSON
The map at the top of page 236 is also on **Visual Aid 37**. Before going over the *Here's how*, use the map and ask questions like these:
- Which city is closer to Chicago, Pittsburgh or Cincinnati? (Cincinnati)
- According to the scale on the map, 1 centimeter stands for how many kilometers? (150)
- What real distance would 2 centimeters on the map represent? (300 km)

EXERCISE NOTE
You may wish to use **Visual Aid 37** (map) and **Visual Aid 32** (millimeter ruler) when discussing exercises 11–21.

Scale drawings

A map is an example of a scale drawing.
On this map, 1 centimeter stands for 150 kilometers.

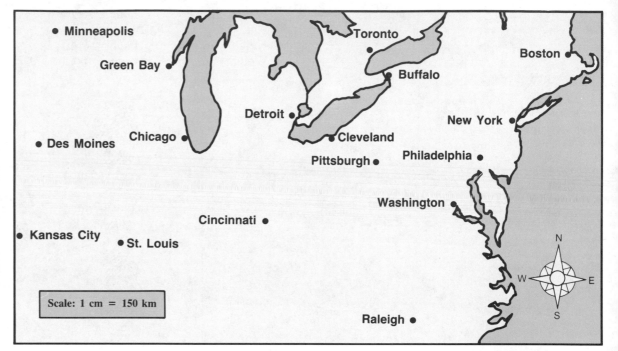

Scale: 1 cm = 150 km

Here's how *to solve a scale-drawing problem.*

> Since we know the scale, we can measure a distance on the map and solve a proportion to find the actual distance.

PROBLEM. The distance from Minneapolis to Cincinnati on the map is 7.5 centimeters. What is the actual distance from Minneapolis to Cincinnati?

$$\begin{array}{l}\text{cm on map} \rightarrow \\ \text{actual km} \rightarrow \end{array} \frac{1}{150} = \frac{7.5}{n} \begin{array}{l} \leftarrow \text{cm on map} \\ \leftarrow \text{actual km}\end{array}$$

$$n = 7.5 \times 150$$
$$n = 1125$$

The actual distance from Minneapolis to Cincinnati is about 1125 kilometers.

EXERCISES

Find the actual distance between the cities. The map distances from page 236 are given.

1. Chicago to Raleigh, 7.8 cm _1170 km_
2. Detroit to New York, 5.9 cm _885 km_
3. Minneapolis to Toronto, 8.3 cm _1245 km_
4. Boston to Washington, 4.8 cm _735 km_
5. Green Bay to Buffalo, 5.8 cm _870 km_
6. Chicago to New York, 8.6 cm _1290 km_
7. St. Louis to Detroit, 5.6 cm _840 km_
8. Detroit to Cleveland, 1.2 cm _180 km_
9. Minneapolis to Raleigh, 12.3 cm _1845 km_
10. Kansas City to Toronto, 10.4 cm _1560 km_

Solve. Use a ruler and the map on page 236. _Answers for 11–16 may vary slightly._

11. How far is it from Minneapolis to Detroit? _1005 km_
12. How far is it from Cleveland to Boston? _990 km_
13. How far is it from Minneapolis to Detroit to Washington? _1740 km_
14. How far is it from Toronto to Washington to Raleigh? _1170 km_
15. How much farther is it from Chicago to Pittsburgh than from Cincinnati to Pittsburgh? _270 km_
16. How much farther is it from Kansas City to Pittsburgh than from St. Louis to Pittsburgh? _390 km_
17. Which city is about 1350 kilometers east of Des Moines? _Pittsburgh_
18. Which city is about 700 kilometers northwest of Raleigh? _Cincinnati or Pittsburgh_

You be the pilot!

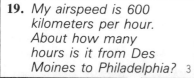

19. My airspeed is 600 kilometers per hour. About how many hours is it from Des Moines to Philadelphia? _3_

20. I'm flying from Philadelphia to St. Louis. My airspeed is 750 kilometers per hour. About how many hours should the flight take? _2_

21. At 600 kilometers per hour, how many hours will it take to fly from St. Louis to Toronto? _2_

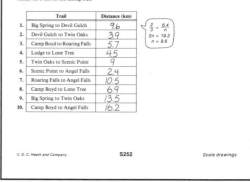

REVIEW PRACTICE
Dividing decimals by 10, 100, 1000
Page 425   Skill 27

PRACTICE WORKSHEET
Copymaster S252 or Duplicating Master S252

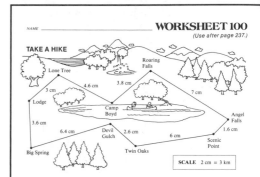

NAME _____   **WORKSHEET 100**
(Use after page 237.)

TAKE A HIKE

SCALE 2 cm = 3 km

Use a proportion to find the actual length of each trail. Notice that 2 cm on the map stands for 3 km on the hiking trail.

	Trail	Distance (km)
1.	Big Spring to Devil Gulch	9.6
2.	Devil Gulch to Twin Oaks	3.9
3.	Camp Boyd to Roaring Falls	5.7
4.	Lodge to Lone Tree	4.5
5.	Twin Oaks to Scenic Point	9
6.	Scenic Point to Angel Falls	2.4
7.	Roaring Falls to Angel Falls	10.5
8.	Camp Boyd to Lone Tree	6.9
9.	Big Spring to Twin Oaks	13.5
10.	Camp Boyd to Angel Falls	16.2

$$\frac{2}{3} = \frac{6.4}{n}$$
$$2n = 19.2$$
$$n = 9.6$$

© D. C. Heath and Company   S252   *Scale drawings*

LIFE-SKILL PROJECT
Making a scale drawing
Have the students find the outside dimensions of the school building. Tell them to make a scale drawing of the building using the scale 1 centimeter = 1 meter.

CHALKBOARD QUIZ
on previous lesson

Solve.
Use the scale 1 cm = 125 km.
1. The distance on the map is 7 cm. How many kilometers is the real distance? 875
2. How far is the real distance if the distance on the map is 9.4 cm? 1175 km

LESSON OBJECTIVE
To use proportions to find missing measurements of sides of similar figures

PROBLEM-SOLVING SKILLS
Finding information in a drawing
Using a proportion to solve a problem

STARTING THE LESSON
The boats pictured at the top of page 238 are also on **Visual Aid 38**. Use the picture and ask questions like these:
• Are the large sail on the box and the large sail on the model the same shape? (Yes)
• Are the small sail on the box and the small sail on the model the same shape? (Yes)
• Two figures are similar if they have the same shape but not necessarily the same size. Are the flag on the box and the flag on the model similar figures? (Yes)

Similar figures

The sails on the box and on the model are the same shape. They are **similar figures.**

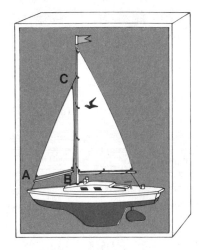

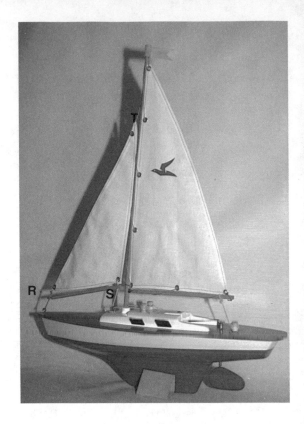

Look at the small sail on the box and on the model.

Side *AB* corresponds to side *RS*.
Side *AC* corresponds to side *RT*.
Side *BC* corresponds to side *ST*.

In similar figures, the ratios of the lengths of corresponding sides are equal.

Here's how *to use a proportion to solve a similar-figures problem.*

PROBLEM. These two flags are similar. What is the length of side *n*?

Step 1. Write a proportion.

small flag → $\frac{1.5}{2.5} = \frac{3}{n}$ ← small flag
large flag →   ← large flag

Step 2. Solve the proportion.

$1.5n = 3 \times 2.5$
$1.5n = 7.5$
$n = 5$

$$1.5\overline{)7.5} \quad \begin{array}{r} 5. \\ \underline{-75} \\ 0 \end{array}$$

The length of side *n* is 5 centimeters.

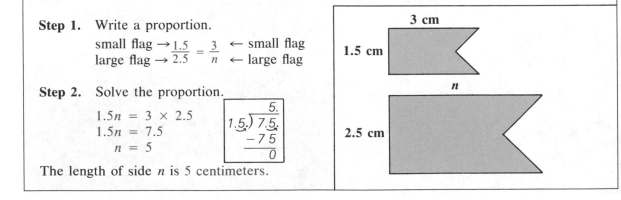

3 cm
1.5 cm
n
2.5 cm

EXERCISES

The two figures are similar. Solve a proportion to find the length of side n.

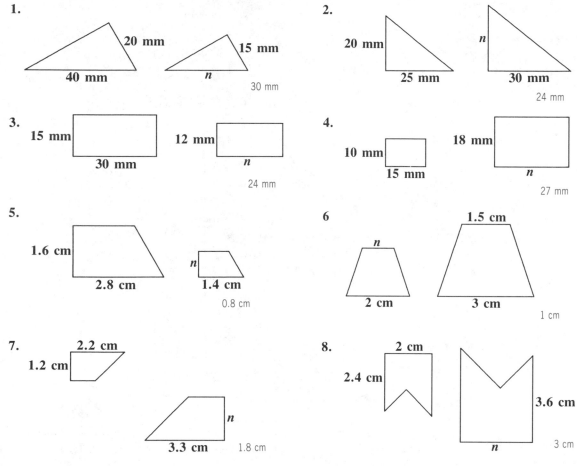

1.

20 mm
40 mm
15 mm
n
30 mm

2.

20 mm
25 mm
n
30 mm
24 mm

3.

15 mm
30 mm
12 mm
n
24 mm

4.

10 mm
15 mm
18 mm
n
27 mm

5.

1.6 cm
2.8 cm
n
1.4 cm
0.8 cm

6

n
2 cm
1.5 cm
3 cm
1 cm

7.

2.2 cm
1.2 cm
n
3.3 cm
1.8 cm

8.

2 cm
2.4 cm
3.6 cm
n
3 cm

Size it up!

Solve a proportion to answer the question.

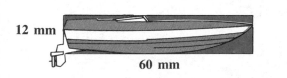

12 mm
60 mm

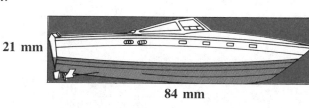

21 mm
84 mm

9. The *Starfire* is actually 1.64 meters high. What is its actual length? 8.2 m

10. The *Sport Special* is actually 2.9 meters high. What is its actual length? 11.6 m

Ratio and Proportion **239**

REVIEW PRACTICE
Dividing decimals
Page 425   Skill 28

PRACTICE WORKSHEET
Copymaster S253 or Duplicating Master S253

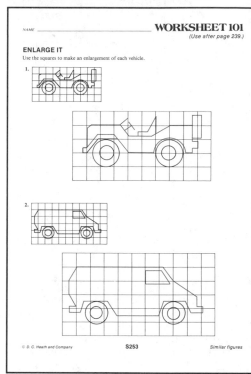

NAME _____   **WORKSHEET 101**
(Use after page 239.)

ENLARGE IT
Use the squares to make an enlargement of each vehicle.

1.

2.

© D. C. Heath and Company   **S253**   *Similar figures*

CHALKBOARD CHALLENGE
Show how to arrange four figures like Figure A to get a larger figure that is similar to Figure A.

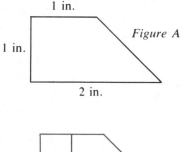

1 in.
Figure A
1 in.
2 in.

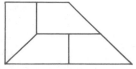

239

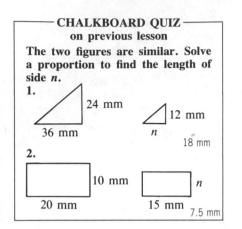
LESSON OBJECTIVE
To use similar triangles to solve indirect measurement problems

PROBLEM-SOLVING SKILLS
Selecting information from a drawing
Using a drawing and proportion to solve a problem

STARTING THE LESSON
The picture at the top of page 240 is on **Visual Aid 39**. Before discussing the *Here's how* example, use the picture and have the students guess the height of the loop-the-loop ride. Record the high and low guesses. Then go over the *Here's how* example and have the students check their guesses.

EXERCISE NOTE
The pictures at the top of page 241 are also on **Visual Aid 40**. Use the pictures when discussing exercises 1–4.

Indirect measurement

MAKE A GUESS!

WHAT IS THE HEIGHT OF THE LOOP-THE-LOOP RIDE?

2 m

0.5 m

5 m

Here's how *similar triangles can be used to find lengths that are difficult to measure directly.*

The triangle made by the man and his shadow is similar to the triangle made by the loop-the-loop ride and its shadow. We can use this proportion to find the height of the ride.

height of loop-the-loop → $\dfrac{n}{2} = \dfrac{5}{0.5}$ ← shadow of loop-the-loop

height of man → ← shadow of man

$$0.5n = 2 \times 5$$

$$0.5n = 10$$

$$n = 20$$

The height of the loop-the-loop ride is 20 meters.

EXERCISES

Solve. Round the answer to the nearest hundredth of a meter.

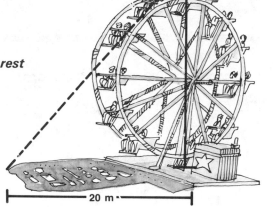

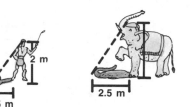

2 m

1.5 m

2.5 m

20 m

1. The elephant casts a 2.5-meter shadow. A man 2 meters tall casts a 1.5-meter shadow. How tall is the elephant? 3.33 m

2. The Ferris wheel casts a 20-meter shadow. How tall is the Ferris wheel? Round the answer to the nearest hundredth of a meter. *Hint: Use the facts about the man and his shadow.* 26.67 m

Make your own drawings. Then solve the problem.

3. A high-diving pole casts a 21-meter shadow. A man 2 meters tall casts a 1-meter shadow. How tall is the high-diving pole? 42 m

4. A woman 1.5 meters tall casts a 0.75-meter shadow. A diving tank casts a 1.2-meter shadow. How deep is the diving tank? 2.4 m

5. An animal trainer is 2 meters tall and casts a 2.2-meter shadow. A black bear casts a 3.3-meter shadow. How tall is the black bear? 3 m

6. A 2-meter sign casts a 3-meter shadow. A flagpole casts a 45-meter shadow. How tall is the flagpole? 30 m

7. A TV tower is 30 meters high and casts a 10-meter shadow. How tall is a nearby tree that casts a 6-meter shadow? 18 m

8. The fence around a water tower is 2.5 meters high and casts a 4-meter shadow. The water tower casts a 48-meter shadow. How tall is the water tower? 30 m

Animal tracks

9. Unscramble the letters to name each animal.

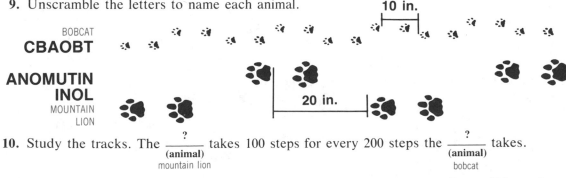

10 in.

20 in.

BOBCAT
CBAOBT

ANOMUTIN INOL
MOUNTAIN LION

10. Study the tracks. The  takes 100 steps for every 200 steps the ―?― takes.
(animal) — mountain lion   (animal) — bobcat

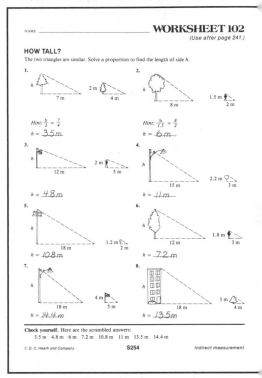

WORKSHEET 102
(Use after page 241.)

HOW TALL?
The two triangles are similar. Solve a proportion to find the length of side *h*.

1. 2 m, 7 m, 4 m
   Hint: $\frac{h}{2} = \frac{7}{4}$
   h = 3.5 m

2. 8 m, 1.5 m, 2 m
   Hint: $\frac{h}{1.5} = \frac{8}{2}$
   h = 6 m

3. 12 m, 2 m, 5 m
   h = 4.8 m

4. 15 m, 2.2 m, 3 m
   h = 11 m

5. 18 m, 1.2 m, 2 m
   h = 10.8 m

6. 12 m, 1.8 m, 3 m
   h = 7.2 m

7. 18 m, 4 m, 5 m
   h = 14.4 m

8. 18 m, 3 m, 4 m
   h = 13.5 m

Check yourself. Here are the scrambled answers:
3.5 m   4.8 m   6 m   7.2 m   10.8 m   11 m   13.5 m   14.4 m

© D. C. Heath and Company   S254   *Indirect measurement*

LIFE-SKILL PROJECT
Making indirect measurements
Wait for a sunny day. Then have the students take a meterstick and measuring tape outside. Have them find the height of a flagpole or tree by using the shadow and its relationship to a meterstick and its shadow.

$$\frac{\text{meterstick}}{\text{stick's shadow}} = \frac{\text{flagpole}}{\text{pole's shadow}}$$

Solve. Draw a sketch.

1. A building casts a 150-meter shadow. At the same time, a man 2 meters tall casts a 3-meter shadow. How tall is the building? **100 m**

2. A tree casts a 30-meter shadow. At the same time, a 15-meter stick casts a 2-meter shadow. How tall is the tree? **225 m**

SKILLS REVIEWED
Subtracting fractions
Finding a fraction of a whole number
Dividing mixed numbers
Making conversions between metric units
Computing with customary units
Solving proportions

PROBLEM-SOLVING SKILLS
Reading a computer display
Using a proportion to solve a problem

STARTING THE LESSON
Cumulative Skill Practice
Challenge the students to an estimation hunt by saying, "Find the difference in exercises 1–15 that is greater than one half." (Exercise 12) Then have them find the four quotients in exercises 24–35 that are greater than two. (Exercises 28, 29, 30, and 32)

STARTING THE LESSON
Problem Solving
Discuss the displays on screens 1 and 2. Ask the students which numbers and letters would be used to locate the sections that contain the corners of the triangle. (Sections 3B, 3E, and 6D) Then go over exercises 1–3.

Cumulative Skill Practice

Give the difference in simplest form. *(page 166)*

1. $\frac{3}{5} - \frac{1}{5}$ $\frac{2}{5}$
2. $\frac{3}{4} - \frac{1}{4}$ $\frac{1}{2}$
3. $\frac{1}{2} - \frac{1}{4}$ $\frac{1}{4}$
4. $\frac{1}{3} - \frac{1}{6}$ $\frac{1}{6}$
5. $\frac{3}{8} - \frac{1}{4}$ $\frac{1}{8}$

6. $\frac{7}{8} - \frac{3}{4}$ $\frac{1}{8}$
7. $\frac{1}{2} - \frac{3}{8}$ $\frac{1}{8}$
8. $\frac{3}{10} - \frac{1}{5}$ $\frac{1}{10}$
9. $\frac{5}{6} - \frac{2}{3}$ $\frac{1}{6}$
10. $\frac{2}{3} - \frac{5}{12}$ $\frac{1}{4}$

11. $1 - \frac{7}{10}$ $\frac{3}{10}$
12. $1 - \frac{2}{5}$ $\frac{3}{5}$
13. $\frac{5}{6} - \frac{3}{4}$ $\frac{1}{12}$
14. $\frac{9}{16} - \frac{3}{8}$ $\frac{3}{16}$
15. $\frac{7}{12} - \frac{11}{24}$ $\frac{1}{8}$

Complete. *(page 180)*

16. $\frac{1}{2}$ of 12 = ? 6
17. $\frac{1}{3}$ of 15 = ? 5
18. $\frac{2}{3}$ of 18 = ? 12
19. $\frac{3}{4}$ of 24 = ? 18

20. $\frac{7}{8}$ of 16 = ? 14
21. $\frac{3}{5}$ of 25 = ? 15
22. $\frac{5}{8}$ of 32 = ? 20
23. $\frac{3}{4}$ of 48 = ? 36

Give the quotient in simplest form. *(page 190)*

24. $1\frac{1}{2} \div 3$ $\frac{1}{2}$
25. $2\frac{1}{2} \div 2$ $1\frac{1}{4}$
26. $2 \div 1\frac{1}{2}$ $1\frac{1}{3}$
27. $4 \div 2\frac{1}{4}$ $1\frac{7}{9}$

28. $2\frac{2}{3} \div 1\frac{1}{4}$ $2\frac{2}{15}$
29. $5\frac{1}{2} \div 1\frac{3}{8}$ 4
30. $6\frac{1}{4} \div 1\frac{1}{4}$ 5
31. $3\frac{3}{4} \div 2\frac{1}{3}$ $1\frac{17}{28}$

32. $6 \div 2\frac{2}{3}$ $2\frac{1}{4}$
33. $3\frac{5}{8} \div 2\frac{1}{4}$ $1\frac{11}{18}$
34. $4\frac{5}{6} \div 2\frac{5}{12}$ 2
35. $5\frac{7}{8} \div 4$ $1\frac{15}{32}$

Complete. *(page 204)*

36. 5 L = ? mL 5000
37. 12 L = ? mL 12,000
38. 3.4 L = ? mL 3400

39. 3000 mL = ? L 3
40. 1635 mL = ? L 1.635
41. 400 mL = ? L 0.4

42. 4.75 L = ? mL 4750
43. 0.530 L = ? mL 530
44. 0.75 mL = ? L 0.00075

Add. *(page 218)*

45.
```
  4 ft  7 in.
+ 2 ft 10 in.
```
7 ft 5 in.

46.
```
  3 yd 2 ft
+ 1 yd 2 ft
```
5 yd 1 ft

47.
```
  5 ft 9 in.
+ 3 ft 8 in.
```
9 ft 5 in.

48.
```
  4 gal 3 qt
+ 1 gal 2 qt
```
6 gal 1 qt

49.
```
  5 qt 1 pt
+ 2 qt 1 pt
```
8 qt

50.
```
  2 gal 3 qt
+ 3 gal 3 qt
```
6 gal 2 qt

51.
```
  4 pt 1 c
+ 4 pt 1 c
```
9 pt

52.
```
  8 lb 9 oz
+ 5 lb 9 oz
```
14 lb 2 oz

Solve. Give the answer in simplest form. *(page 230)*

53. $\frac{1}{4} = \frac{n}{12}$ 3
54. $\frac{5}{6} = \frac{7}{n}$ $8\frac{2}{5}$
55. $\frac{5}{n} = \frac{3}{15}$ 25
56. $\frac{n}{12} = \frac{5}{8}$ $7\frac{1}{2}$
57. $\frac{9}{n} = \frac{2}{3}$ $13\frac{1}{2}$

58. $\frac{2}{7} = \frac{5}{n}$ $17\frac{1}{2}$
59. $\frac{4}{8} = \frac{n}{9}$ $4\frac{1}{2}$
60. $\frac{9}{6} = \frac{n}{4}$ 6
61. $\frac{5}{2} = \frac{n}{3}$ $7\frac{1}{2}$
62. $\frac{3}{5} = \frac{10}{n}$ $16\frac{2}{3}$

Problem solving

USING COMPUTER SOFTWARE

Maria Cataldo uses a **software** package to draw geometric figures on her computer screen. The software also allows her to enlarge any part of the drawing.

Maria uses a number and a letter to locate each section in her drawing.

> This is section "5C".

When Maria commands the computer to enlarge section 5C, the computer screen looks like this:

> The ratio of enlargement is 1 to 7. This line segment is 7 times as long as the same segment on Screen 1.

Screen 1

Screen 2

Which section from Screen 1 has been enlarged?

1. 3B

2. 5D

3. 3E

Complete.

4. If the ratio of enlargement is 1 to 7, a 2-inch line segment in an original picture would be ☐ inches in an enlargement. 14

5. If the ratio of enlargement is 1 to 8, a 1.5-inch line segment in an original picture would be ☐ inches in an enlargement. 12

6. An original picture has a line segment that is 2 inches long. The same line segment is 12 inches long in an enlargement. The ratio of enlargement is 1 to ☐. 6

7. A line segment is enlarged from 1.75 inches in the original drawing to 15.75 inches in an enlargement. The ratio of enlargement is 1 to ☐. 9

Ratio and Proportion **243**

EXTRA PROBLEM SOLVING
Page 453   Even exercises

PROBLEM-SOLVING WORKSHEET
Copymaster S255 or Duplicating Master S255

NAME _____   **WORKSHEET 103**
(Use after page 243.)

TRUTH OR BALONEY?

> There are more minutes in a day than there are pounds in a ton!

> I don't believe it! You're wrong.

Pam   Tom

Who is right, Pam or Tom?

Tom

EARNING MONEY

Babysitter needed
1:30 to 5:00 P.M. $2/hr.
Call 999-4173.

How much could you earn per day as a babysitter? $7

SQUARE COUNT

How many squares can you count? *Hint: There are more than 10.*

14

LETTER PATTERN
Look for the pattern. Fill in the missing letters.

AE → C
FH → G
AG → D
CE → D
JN → L
AM → G

WHAT'S THE NUMBER?
What number is equal to the number of letters in its name?

Four

CAN YOU GAUGE IT?
Our gas tank holds 16 gallons. According to the gauge, how many gallons are left in the tank?

E   F
6

© D. C. Heath and Company   S255   Problem solving

CHALKBOARD CHALLENGE

Unscramble the letters in these math words:

1. OIART   Ratio
2. SRCOS CTRPOUD   Cross product
3. ROPOPTRINO   Proportion
4. ECSAL NADWRIG   Scale drawing
5. RLISMIA IGFRUES   Similar figures

243

CHAPTER 10 TEST
(Form A)

Write each ratio as a fraction in lowest terms. *(page 226)*

1. 2 to 4 $\frac{1}{2}$ 2. 3 to 12 $\frac{1}{4}$ 3. 6 to 9 $\frac{2}{3}$

4. $\frac{15}{20}$ $\frac{3}{4}$ 5. $\frac{18}{12}$ $\frac{3}{2}$ 6. $\frac{24}{18}$ $\frac{4}{3}$

7. 6 : 18 $\frac{1}{3}$ 8. 10 : 12 $\frac{5}{6}$ 9. 15 : 36 $\frac{5}{12}$

10. 15 : 10 $\frac{3}{2}$ 11. 21 : 15 $\frac{7}{5}$ 12. 36 : 24 $\frac{3}{2}$

Tell whether the ratios are equal (=) or not equal (≠). *(page 228)*

13. $\frac{1}{2} \bigcirc \frac{3}{6}$ 14. $\frac{2}{5} \bigcirc \frac{3}{7}$ 15. $\frac{10}{15} \bigcirc \frac{2}{3}$

16. $\frac{2}{3} \bigcirc \frac{3}{4}$ 17. $\frac{8}{6} \bigcirc \frac{4}{3}$ 18. $\frac{8}{7} \bigcirc \frac{9}{8}$

19. $\frac{4}{9} \bigcirc \frac{3}{7}$ 20. $\frac{4}{6} \bigcirc \frac{6}{9}$ 21. $\frac{9}{5} \bigcirc \frac{5}{3}$

22. $\frac{16}{3} \bigcirc \frac{18}{4}$ 23. $\frac{25}{20} \bigcirc \frac{20}{16}$ 24. $\frac{14}{16} \bigcirc \frac{13}{12}$

25. $\frac{12}{10} \bigcirc \frac{18}{15}$

ANSWERS
1. $\frac{1}{2}$
2. $\frac{1}{4}$
3. $\frac{2}{3}$
4. $\frac{3}{4}$
5. $\frac{3}{2}$
6. $\frac{4}{3}$
7. $\frac{1}{3}$
8. $\frac{5}{6}$
9. $\frac{5}{12}$
10. $\frac{3}{2}$
11. $\frac{7}{5}$
12. $\frac{3}{2}$
13. =
14. ≠
15. =
16. ≠
17. =
18. ≠
19. ≠
20. =
21. ≠
22. ≠
23. =
24. ≠
25. =

S37   Page 1

CHAPTER 10 TEST
(Form A)

Solve each proportion. Give the answer in simplest form. *(page 230)*

26. $\frac{6}{8} = \frac{n}{12}$ 9   27. $\frac{2}{7} = \frac{8}{n}$ 28   28. $\frac{n}{6} = \frac{11}{3}$ 22

29. $\frac{4}{n} = \frac{6}{9}$ 6   30. $\frac{n}{8} = \frac{9}{4}$ 18   31. $\frac{3}{9} = \frac{n}{15}$ 5

32. $\frac{8}{10} = \frac{12}{n}$ 15   33. $\frac{25}{n} = \frac{10}{6}$ 15   34. $\frac{n}{15} = \frac{16}{12}$ 20

35. $\frac{3}{7} = \frac{2}{n}$ 4⅔   36. $\frac{n}{3} = \frac{4}{5}$ 3¾   37. $\frac{4}{6} = \frac{n}{8}$ 5⅓

38. $\frac{n}{4} = \frac{6}{7}$ 3³⁄₇   39. $\frac{10}{3} = \frac{n}{5}$ 16⅔   40. $\frac{n}{6} = \frac{6}{8}$ 4½

41. $\frac{9}{5} = \frac{7}{n}$ 3⁸⁄₉   42. $\frac{5}{8} = \frac{n}{9}$ 14²⁄₅

Solve by using a proportion. If the answer does not come out evenly, round it to the nearest hundredth. *(page 232)*

43. You jog 3.6 miles in 30 minutes. At that rate, how long will it take you to jog 4.8 miles?   40 min

44. You buy 3 cassette tapes for $18.48. At that rate, how much will 4 tapes cost? $24.64

45. You earn $33 in 8 hours. At that rate, how much would you earn in 5 hours? $20.63

46. You read 500 words in 3 minutes. At that rate, how many words would you read in 20 minutes?   3333.33

The two figures are similar. Solve a proportion to find the length of side n. *(page 238)*

47.   18m

48.   3.2 m

Solve. *(page 240)*

49. A boy 1.6 m tall casts a 2.4-m shadow. How tall is a nearby streetlight that casts a 7.2-m shadow?   4.8m

50. A flagpole is 12.5 m tall. It casts a 17.5-m shadow. How tall is a nearby radio tower that casts a 61.25-m shadow?   43.75m

ANSWERS
26. 9
27. 28
28. 22
29. 6
30. 18
31. 5
32. 15
33. 15
34. 20
35. 4⅔
36. 3¾
37. 5⅓
38. 3³⁄₇
39. 16⅔
40. 4½
41. 3⁸⁄₉
42. 14²⁄₅
43. 40min
44. $24.64
45. $20.63
46. 3333.33
47. 18m
48. 3.2m
49. 4.8m
50. 43.75m

S38   Page 2

244   Copymasters S37 and S38
or Duplicating Masters S37 and S38

Chapter REVIEW

Here are scrambled answers for the review exercises:

approximately   divide   height   proportion   scale
corresponds   equal   multiplication   rate   similar
cross   fractions   order   ratio

1. ratio, fractions   **2.** proportion, multiplication

1. You can use a ? to compare two numbers. You can find equal ratios by thinking about equivalent ? . *(page 226)*

2. A ? is an equation that says two ratios are equal. Every proportion has a related ? equation. *(page 228)*

3. cross   **4.** divide   **5.** order, approximately

3. You can use the ? products to find whether these two ratios are equal. Since 3 × 15 = 5 × 9, you know that the ratios are equal. *(page 228)*

$$\frac{3}{5} \bullet \frac{9}{15}$$

4. The last step in solving this proportion is to ? 24 by 5. *(page 230)*

$$\frac{5}{6} = \frac{4}{n}$$
$$5n = 6 \times 4$$
$$5n = 24$$

5. When setting up a proportion, you must be sure that the ratios are in the same ? . In this proportion, n is ? equal to 3.11. *(pages 230, 232)*

$$\frac{9}{4} = \frac{7}{n}$$
$$9n = 28$$
$$n \approx 3.11$$

6. rate, scale   **7.** similar, corresponds, equal   **8.** height

6. A ? is a ratio of two quantities. A map is an example of a ? drawing. *(pages 232, 236)*

7. Figures that are the same shape are called ? figures. In these similar figures, side AB ? to side RS. In similar figures, the ratios of the lengths of corresponding sides are ? . *(page 238)*

8. You can solve this proportion to find the ? of the flagpole. *(page 240)*

$$\frac{n}{1.9} = \frac{7.2}{2.4}$$

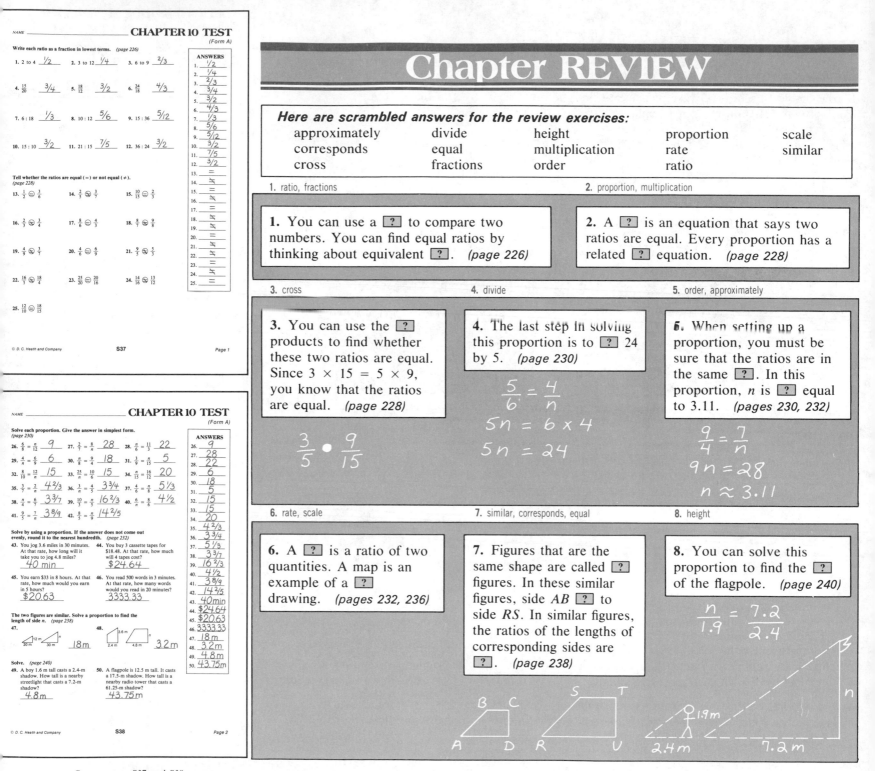

244   *Chapter 10*

Chapter TEST

Give each ratio as a fraction in lowest terms. *(page 226)*

1. 3 to 9 $\frac{1}{3}$
2. 8 to 12 $\frac{2}{3}$
3. 16 to 10 $\frac{8}{5}$
4. 18 to 24 $\frac{3}{4}$
5. 7 to 14 $\frac{1}{2}$
6. 12 : 16 $\frac{3}{4}$
7. 15 : 10 $\frac{3}{2}$
8. 21 : 14 $\frac{3}{2}$
9. 32 : 8 $\frac{4}{1}$
10. 56 : 16 $\frac{7}{2}$

Tell whether the ratios are equal (=) or not equal (≠). *(page 228)*

11. $\frac{3}{4} \bullet \frac{9}{12}$ =
12. $\frac{5}{6} \bullet \frac{7}{8}$ ≠
13. $\frac{5}{2} \bullet \frac{7}{4}$ ≠
14. $\frac{4}{6} \bullet \frac{6}{9}$ =
15. $\frac{4}{8} \bullet \frac{2}{4}$ =
16. $\frac{4}{3} \bullet \frac{5}{4}$ ≠
17. $\frac{8}{5} \bullet \frac{9}{6}$ ≠
18. $\frac{6}{16} \bullet \frac{9}{24}$ =
19. $\frac{4}{7} \bullet \frac{7}{12}$ ≠
20. $\frac{5}{6} \bullet \frac{2}{3}$ ≠

Solve each proportion. Give the answer in simplest form. *(page 230)*

21. $\frac{2}{3} = \frac{n}{9}$ 6
22. $\frac{1}{4} = \frac{10}{n}$ $2\frac{1}{2}$
23. $\frac{5}{8} = \frac{n}{4}$ $2\frac{1}{2}$
24. $\frac{2}{3} = \frac{9}{n}$ $13\frac{1}{2}$
25. $\frac{4}{5} = \frac{8}{n}$ 10
26. $\frac{n}{20} = \frac{3}{4}$ 15
27. $\frac{11}{n} = \frac{5}{4}$ $8\frac{4}{5}$
28. $\frac{3}{n} = \frac{2}{3}$ $4\frac{1}{2}$
29. $\frac{2}{n} = \frac{5}{8}$ $3\frac{1}{5}$
30. $\frac{1}{5} = \frac{2}{n}$ 10
31. $\frac{6}{10} = \frac{n}{8}$ $4\frac{4}{5}$
32. $\frac{4}{7} = \frac{12}{n}$ 21
33. $\frac{7}{n} = \frac{2}{3}$ $10\frac{1}{2}$
34. $\frac{7}{10} = \frac{n}{8}$ $5\frac{3}{5}$
35. $\frac{2}{7} = \frac{n}{5}$ $1\frac{3}{7}$

Solve by using a proportion. *(page 232)*

36. You jog 4.5 miles in 36 minutes. At that rate, how long will it take to jog 6 miles? 48 minutes

37. You buy 3 record albums for $16.50. At that rate, how much will 5 records cost? $27.50

38. You earn $48 in 12 hours. At that rate, how much would you earn in 7 hours? $28

39. You type 129 words in 3 minutes. At that rate, how many words could you type in 10 minutes? 430

The two figures are similar. Solve a proportion to find the length of side n. *(page 238)*

40.
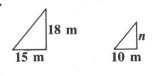
12 m

41.
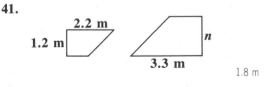
2.2 m
1.2 m
3.3 m
n
1.8 m

Make a drawing and solve the problem. *(page 240)*

42. A woman 1.8 m tall casts a 1.2-meter shadow. How tall is a nearby building that casts a 14.4-meter shadow? 21.6 m

43. A tower is 60 m high. It casts a 45-meter shadow. How tall is a nearby telephone pole that casts a 6-meter shadow? 8 m

Use Copymaster S336 to provide the students with an answer sheet in standardized test format.

Answers for Cumulative Test, Chapters 1–10

1. Ⓐ Ⓑ Ⓒ Ⓓ	2. Ⓐ Ⓑ Ⓒ Ⓓ	3. Ⓐ Ⓑ Ⓒ Ⓓ
4. Ⓐ Ⓑ Ⓒ Ⓓ	5. Ⓐ Ⓑ Ⓒ Ⓓ	6. Ⓐ Ⓑ Ⓒ Ⓓ
7. Ⓐ Ⓑ Ⓒ Ⓓ	8. Ⓐ Ⓑ Ⓒ Ⓓ	9. Ⓐ Ⓑ Ⓒ Ⓓ
10. Ⓐ Ⓑ Ⓒ Ⓓ	11. Ⓐ Ⓑ Ⓒ Ⓓ	12. Ⓐ Ⓑ Ⓒ Ⓓ

The table below correlates test items with student text pages.

Test Item	Page Taught	Skill Practice
1	64	p. 234, exercises 1–18
2	96	p. 234, exercises 19–33
3	132	p. 234, exercises 34–48
4	146	p. 234, exercises 49–69
5	158	p. 234, exercises 70–79
6	166	p. 242, exercises 1–15
7	180	p. 242, exercises 16–23
8	190	p. 242, exercises 24–35
9	204	p. 242, exercises 36–44
10	218	p. 242, exercises 45–52
11	230	p. 242, exercises 53–62
12	232	

Cumulative TEST — Standardized Format

Choose the correct letter.

1. Multiply.
$$3.954 \times 36.5$$
A. 117.4790
Ⓑ. 144.3210
C. 1174.790
D. none of these

2. Divide. Round the quotient to the nearest tenth.
$$2.03 \overline{)3.959}$$
A. 1.95
B. 1.9
Ⓒ. 2.0
D. none of these

3. $\frac{5}{8} < ?$
A. $\frac{1}{2}$
B. $\frac{4}{9}$
C. $\frac{3}{5}$
Ⓓ. none of these

4. Change to a decimal rounded to the nearest hundredth.
$$\frac{2}{3} = ?$$
Ⓐ. 0.67
B. 0.66
C. 0.667
D. none of these

5. Give the sum.
$$\frac{5}{6} + \frac{3}{4}$$
A. $\frac{4}{5}$
B. $\frac{1}{3}$
Ⓒ. $1\frac{7}{12}$
D. none of these

6. Give the difference.
$$\frac{7}{8} - \frac{1}{3}$$
A. $\frac{7}{12}$
B. $1\frac{1}{5}$
C. $\frac{1}{4}$
Ⓓ. none of these

7. Complete.
$$\frac{3}{4} \text{ of } 24 = ?$$
A. 32
Ⓑ. 18
C. 16
D. none of these

8. Give the quotient.
$$2\frac{1}{3} \div 1\frac{1}{2}$$
Ⓐ. $1\frac{5}{9}$
B. $\frac{2}{7}$
C. $3\frac{1}{2}$
D. none of these

9. Complete.
$$1.235 \text{ L} = \underline{\ ?\ } \text{ mL}$$
A. 123.5
B. 0.001235
Ⓒ. 1235
D. none of these

10. Add.
$$\begin{array}{r} 5 \text{ lb } 9 \text{ oz} \\ + 2 \text{ lb } 11 \text{ oz} \end{array}$$
A. 9 lb
B. 8 lb 8 oz
C. 7 lb 4 oz
Ⓓ. none of these

11. Solve. $\frac{9}{n} = \frac{2}{3}$
A. 9
Ⓑ. $13\frac{1}{2}$
C. $1\frac{1}{2}$
D. none of these

12. You work 9 hours and earn $35. At that rate, how much would you earn in 13 hours? Round the answer to the nearest cent.
Ⓐ. $50.56
B. $3.34
C. $24.23
D. none of these

CHAPTER 11
Percent

LESSON OBJECTIVES
To change a percent to a fraction (*pages 248–249*)
To change a fraction to a percent (*pages 250–251*)
To change a percent to a decimal (*pages 252–253*)
To change a decimal to a percent (*page 253*)
To find a percent of a number by multiplying by a fraction or decimal equivalent to the percent (*pages 256–257*)
To find a percent of a number by solving a proportion (*pages 258–259*)
To use a proportion to find a number when a percent of the number is known (*pages 260–261*)
To solve percent problems by using proportions (*pages 262–263*)

PROBLEM-SOLVING SKILLS
Finding information in a circle graph (*pages 248–249*)
Choosing the correct operation (*pages 249, 255, 261, 265*)
Interpreting directions correctly (*pages 249, 261*)
Reading a chart (*pages 250–251, 258–259*)
Reading a map (*pages 252–253*)
Selecting information from a sign (*page 255*)
Solving a multi-step problem (*page 255*)
Selecting information in a sale ad (*pages 256–257, 262*)
Using a guess-and-check strategy (*page 257*)
Making a list (*page 259*)
Setting up a proportion to solve any kind of percent problem (*pages 262, 263*)
Finding information in a computer display (*page 265*)

RESOURCES
- **VISUAL AIDS**
  Circle graph from page 248 (*Visual Aid 41, Copymaster S138*)
  Map from page 252 (*Visual Aid 42, Copymaster S139*)
- **WORKSHEETS 104–112** (*Copymasters S256–S264 or Duplicating Masters S256–S264*)

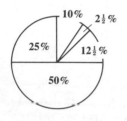
Changing a percent to a fraction

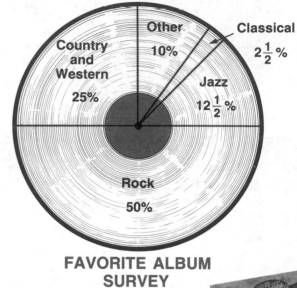

In a survey of high school students, each person was asked to name his or her favorite album. Each album was placed in one of five categories. The graph shows the results of the survey.

Notice that 50% (50 percent) of those surveyed chose a rock album. This means that 50 out of 100, or $\frac{50}{100}$, chose a rock album.

FAVORITE ALBUM SURVEY

1. What two categories of albums were most popular?
   Rock, Country and Western
2. Were classical music albums more popular than country and western albums?
   No
3. What percent of those surveyed chose a country and western album?
   25%
4. What percent of those surveyed chose a jazz album?
   $12\frac{1}{2}$%

Here's how *to change a percent to a fraction.*

To change a percent to a fraction, first write the percent as a fraction with a denominator of 100. Then write the fraction in simplest form.

Country and Western

$25\% = \frac{25}{100}$

$\quad = \frac{1}{4}$

Jazz

$12\frac{1}{2}\% = \frac{12\frac{1}{2}}{100}$

$\quad = 12\frac{1}{2} \div 100$

$\quad = \frac{25}{2} \div 100$

$\quad = \frac{25}{2} \times \frac{1}{100}$

$\quad = \frac{25}{200}$

$\quad = \frac{1}{8}$

> Divide the numerator by the denominator.

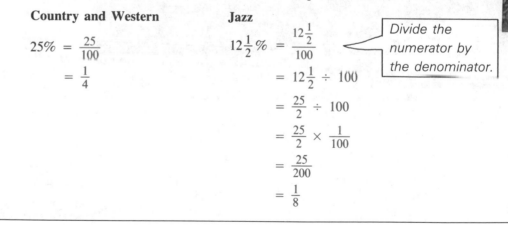

5. Look at the *Here's how*. What fraction of those surveyed chose a country and western album? $\frac{1}{4}$

6. What fraction of those surveyed chose a jazz album? $\frac{1}{8}$

EXERCISES

Change to a fraction, whole number, or mixed number.
Give the answer in simplest form.
Here are scrambled answers for the next row of exercises: $\frac{1}{4}$ $\frac{7}{10}$ $\frac{1}{2}$ $\frac{18}{25}$ 1 $1\frac{1}{4}$

7. 50% $\frac{1}{2}$ **8.** 125% $1\frac{1}{4}$ **9.** 25% $\frac{1}{4}$ **10.** 72% $\frac{18}{25}$ **11.** 100% 1 **12.** 70% $\frac{7}{10}$

13. 120% $1\frac{1}{5}$ **14.** 85% $\frac{17}{20}$ **15.** 96% $\frac{24}{25}$ **16.** 10% $\frac{1}{10}$ **17.** 44% $\frac{11}{25}$ **18.** 45% $\frac{9}{20}$

19. 32% $\frac{8}{25}$ **20.** 15% $\frac{3}{20}$ **21.** 75% $\frac{3}{4}$ **22.** 220% $2\frac{1}{5}$ **23.** 300% 3 **24.** 175% $1\frac{3}{4}$

25. 66% $\frac{33}{50}$ **26.** 48% $\frac{12}{25}$ **27.** 210% $2\frac{1}{10}$ **28.** 20% $\frac{1}{5}$ **29.** 60% $\frac{3}{5}$ **30.** 200% 2

31. 225% $2\frac{1}{4}$ **32.** 30% $\frac{3}{10}$ **33.** 150% $1\frac{1}{2}$ **34.** 400% 4 **35.** 74% $\frac{37}{50}$ **36.** 250% $2\frac{1}{2}$

37. 375% $3\frac{3}{4}$ **38.** 16% $\frac{4}{25}$ **39.** 110% $1\frac{1}{10}$ **40.** 35% $\frac{7}{20}$ **41.** 275% $2\frac{3}{4}$ **42.** 160% $1\frac{3}{5}$

43. 40% $\frac{2}{5}$ **44.** 325% $3\frac{1}{4}$ **45.** 90% $\frac{9}{10}$ **46.** 350% $3\frac{1}{2}$ **47.** 80% $\frac{4}{5}$ **48.** 5% $\frac{1}{20}$

49. $33\frac{1}{3}$% $\frac{1}{3}$ **50.** $106\frac{1}{4}$% $1\frac{1}{16}$ **51.** $137\frac{1}{2}$% $1\frac{3}{8}$ **52.** $18\frac{3}{4}$% $\frac{3}{16}$ **53.** $62\frac{1}{2}$% $\frac{5}{8}$ **54.** $8\frac{1}{3}$% $\frac{1}{12}$

55. $66\frac{2}{3}$% $\frac{2}{3}$ **56.** $16\frac{2}{3}$% $\frac{1}{6}$ **57.** $81\frac{1}{4}$% $\frac{13}{16}$ **58.** $133\frac{1}{3}$% $1\frac{1}{3}$ **59.** $87\frac{1}{2}$% $\frac{7}{8}$ **60.** $162\frac{1}{2}$% $1\frac{5}{8}$

61. $166\frac{2}{3}$% $1\frac{2}{3}$ **62.** $212\frac{1}{2}$% $2\frac{1}{8}$ **63.** $233\frac{1}{3}$% $2\frac{1}{3}$ **64.** $206\frac{1}{4}$% $2\frac{1}{16}$ **65.** $187\frac{1}{2}$% $1\frac{7}{8}$ **66.** $116\frac{2}{3}$% $1\frac{1}{6}$

Solve. Use the graph on page 248.

67. What fraction of those surveyed chose a classical album? $\frac{1}{40}$

68. What fraction chose either a rock or a country and western album? $\frac{3}{4}$

69. What fraction of those surveyed chose either a jazz or a rock album? $\frac{5}{8}$

70. What fraction of those surveyed did not choose a jazz album? $\frac{7}{8}$

Name that year

71. The first phonograph was made by Thomas Alva Edison. You can find the year by pressing the calculator keys as shown below.

$\boxed{1}\,\boxed{4}\,\boxed{4}\,\boxed{\div}\,\boxed{4}\,\boxed{=}\,\boxed{\times}\,\boxed{4}\,\boxed{8}\,\boxed{=}\,\boxed{+}\,\boxed{1}\,\boxed{6}\,\boxed{6}\,\boxed{=}\,\boxed{-}\,\boxed{1}\,\boxed{7}\,\boxed{=}$ 1877

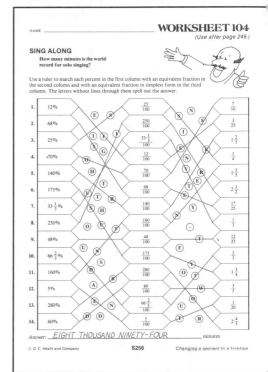

PRACTICE WORKSHEET
Copymaster S256 or Duplicating Master S256

LIFE-SKILL PROJECT
Taking a survey
Have a group of students survey 100 students to determine which of these kinds of music they like best.

Classical
Country and Western
Jazz
Rock
Other

After they have tallied the results, have them find what percent of the students chose the different kinds of music.

LESSON OBJECTIVE
To change a fraction to a percent

PROBLEM-SOLVING SKILL
Reading a chart

STARTING THE LESSON
Before going over exercises 1–6, have the students look at the helmets at the top of page 250. Challenge the students to see how many of the teams they can name.

Pittsburg Steelers	Buffalo Bills	Atlanta Falcons	Denver Broncos
Green Bay Packers	Kansas City Chiefs	Los Angeles Rams	New England Patriots
New York Giants	New York Jets	Dallas Cowboys	Washington Redskins
Cincinnati Bengals	St. Louis Cardinals	Cleveland Browns	Miami Dolphins
Indianapolis Colts	Chicago Bears	Seattle Seahawks	Minnesota Vikings
San Diego Chargers	Detroit Lions	Houston Oilers	New Orleans Saints

EXERCISE NOTE
Some students may benefit from making a chart and exploring simpler problems to solve problem 53.

FIRST TICKET SOLD	LAST TICKET SOLD	NUMBER OF TICKETS SOLD
#10394	#10395	2
#10394	#10396	3
#10394	#10397	4

Changing a fraction to a percent

Look at the football helmets. Can you name the team for each helmet?

This question was part of a football survey conducted at Lancaster High School. The results are shown in the table.

NAME	NUMBER OF TEAMS NAMED CORRECTLY
Marty	12
Jill	16
David	18
Robert	14
Ann	20
Terry	17

1. How many teams did Marty name correctly? 12

2. How many teams are there in all? 24

3. What fraction of the teams did Marty name correctly? $\frac{1}{2}$

4. What fraction of the teams did Jill name correctly? $\frac{2}{3}$

ATTENTION, FOOTBALL FANS!

Here's how *to change a fraction to a percent.*

Changing Marty's fraction to a percent

Method 1. Change to an equivalent fraction with a denominator of 100. Then write as a percent.

$$\frac{1}{2} = \frac{50}{100}$$
$$= 50\%$$

Changing Jill's fraction to a percent

Method 2. Since there is no whole number that you can multiply by 3 to get the denominator of 100, solve a proportion.

$$\frac{2}{3} = \frac{n}{100}$$
$$3n = 200$$
$$n = 66\frac{2}{3}$$

So $\frac{2}{3} = \frac{66\frac{2}{3}}{100}$

$$= 66\frac{2}{3}\%$$

5. Which method would you use to change $\frac{3}{4}$ to a percent? Method 1

6. Which method would you use to change $\frac{1}{6}$ to a percent? Method 2

250

EXERCISES

Change to a percent. Hint: First change to an equivalent fraction with a denominator of 100. Here are scrambled answers for the next row of exercises: 225%   40%   60%   90%   50%   125%

7. $\frac{2}{5}$ 40%   **8.** $\frac{9}{4}$ 225%   **9.** $\frac{9}{10}$ 90%   **10.** $\frac{3}{5}$ 60%   **11.** $\frac{5}{4}$ 125%   **12.** $\frac{1}{2}$ 50%

13. $\frac{1}{5}$ 20%   **14.** $\frac{1}{4}$ 25%   **15.** $\frac{4}{5}$ 80%   **16.** 1 100%   **17.** $\frac{1}{10}$ 10%   **18.** $\frac{3}{10}$ 30%

19. $\frac{3}{2}$ 150%   **20.** 2 200%   **21.** $\frac{7}{5}$ 140%   **22.** $\frac{3}{4}$ 75%   **23.** $\frac{5}{2}$ 250%   **24.** $\frac{7}{4}$ 175%

Change to a percent. Hint: You may need to solve a proportion. Here are scrambled answers for the next row of exercises: 175% $16\frac{2}{3}$% $33\frac{1}{3}$%   120% $133\frac{1}{3}$% $83\frac{1}{3}$%

25. $\frac{1}{3}$ $33\frac{1}{3}$%   **26.** $\frac{1}{6}$ $16\frac{2}{3}$%   **27.** $\frac{7}{4}$ 175%   **28.** $\frac{6}{5}$ 120%   **29.** $\frac{5}{6}$ $83\frac{1}{3}$%   **30.** $\frac{4}{3}$ $133\frac{1}{3}$%

31. $\frac{9}{16}$ $56\frac{1}{4}$%   **32.** $\frac{9}{25}$ 36%   **33.** $\frac{5}{9}$ $55\frac{5}{9}$%   **34.** $\frac{7}{2}$ 350%   **35.** $\frac{2}{3}$ $66\frac{2}{3}$%   **36.** $\frac{3}{8}$ $37\frac{1}{2}$%

37. $\frac{4}{9}$ $44\frac{4}{9}$%   **38.** $\frac{9}{20}$ 45%   **39.** $\frac{31}{50}$ 62%   **40.** $\frac{5}{3}$ $166\frac{2}{3}$%   **41.** $\frac{5}{12}$ $41\frac{2}{3}$%   **42.** $\frac{1}{12}$ $8\frac{1}{3}$%

43. $\frac{7}{25}$ 28%   **44.** $\frac{17}{10}$ 170%   **45.** $\frac{7}{8}$ $87\frac{1}{2}$%   **46.** 3 300%   **47.** $\frac{5}{8}$ $62\frac{1}{2}$%   **48.** $\frac{11}{25}$ 44%

Solve. Use the survey results on page 250.

49. What percent of the teams did David name correctly? 75%

50. What percent of the teams did Robert name correctly? $58\frac{1}{3}$%

51. What percent of the students surveyed knew more than 15 of the teams? $66\frac{2}{3}$%

52. What percent of the students surveyed knew 15 or fewer of the teams? (*Hint: Use your answer from exercise 51.*) $33\frac{1}{3}$%

How many fans?

The number on the first ticket sold for a ball game was 10394. The number on the last ticket was 19017.

53. How many tickets were sold? Be careful! 8624

54. Three hundred of the tickets sold were not used. How many people were at the ball game? 8324

EXTRA PRACTICE
Page 438   Skill 54

PRACTICE WORKSHEET
Copymaster S257 or Duplicating Master S257

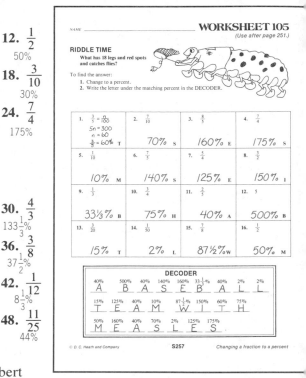

NAME _____ **WORKSHEET 105**
(Use after page 251.)

RIDDLE TIME
What has 18 legs and red spots and catches flies?

To find the answer:
1. Change to a percent.
2. Write the letter under the matching percent in the DECODER.

1. $\frac{3}{5} = \frac{n}{100}$ $5n = 300$ $n = 60$ $\frac{3}{5} = 60\%$ T	2. $\frac{7}{10}$ 70% S	3. $\frac{8}{5}$ 160% E	4. $\frac{7}{4}$ 175% S
5. $\frac{1}{10}$ 10% M	6. $\frac{7}{5}$ 140% S	7. $\frac{5}{4}$ 125% E	8. $\frac{3}{2}$ 150% I
9. $\frac{1}{3}$ $33\frac{1}{3}$% B	10. $\frac{3}{4}$ 75% H	11. $\frac{2}{5}$ 40% A	12. 5 500% B
13. $\frac{3}{20}$ 15% T	14. $\frac{1}{50}$ 2% L	15. $\frac{7}{8}$ $87\frac{1}{2}$% W	16. $\frac{1}{2}$ 50% M

DECODER

| 40% | 500% | 40% | 140% | 160% | $33\frac{1}{3}$% | 40% | 2% | 2% |
| A | B | A | S | E | B | A | L | L |

| 15% | 125% | 40% | 10% | $87\frac{1}{2}$% | 150% | 60% | 75% |
| T | E | A | M | W | I | T | H |

| 50% | 160% | 40% | 70% | 10% | 175% |
| M | E | A | S | L | E | S |

© D. C. Heath and Company   S257   Changing a fraction to a percent

LIFE-SKILL PROJECT

Taking a survey
Use the football helmets on page 250. Have the students survey other students to see if they can name the team for each helmet. Tell the students to find what percent of the teams each student named correctly.

LESSON OBJECTIVES
To change a percent to a decimal
To change a decimal to a percent

PROBLEM-SOLVING SKILL
Reading a map

STARTING THE LESSON
Before the students open their books, have them list which states share part of their border with Texas. Then have them use the map on page 252 to check their answers.

EXERCISE NOTE
The map at the top of page 252 is also on **Visual Aid 42**. You may wish to use the visual aid when discussing exercises 1, 2, and 51–56.

Percents and decimals

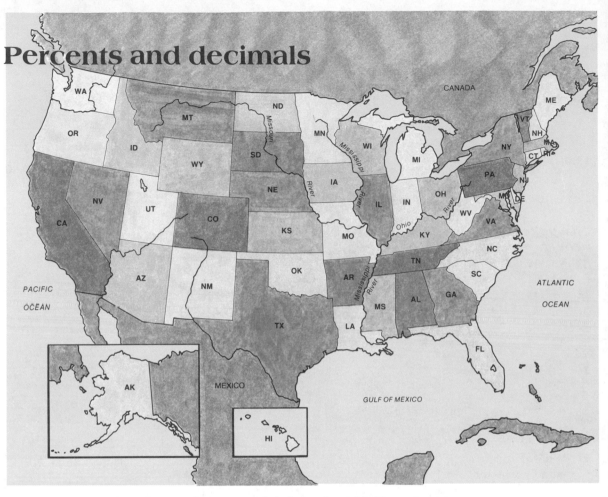

1. What percent of the states share part of their border with Texas? 8%

2. What percent of the states have names beginning with the letter M? 16%

Here's how *to change a percent to a decimal.*

$8\% = \frac{8}{100}$ $16\% = \frac{16}{100}$ $33\frac{1}{3}\% = \frac{33\frac{1}{3}}{100}$

$= 0.08$ $= 0.16$ $= 0.33\frac{1}{3}$

Here is a **SHORTCUT.**

To change a percent to a decimal, move the decimal point two places to the left and remove the percent sign.

$8\% = 0.08$ $29.5\% = 0.295$

$16\% = 0.16$ $115\% = 1.15$

$33\frac{1}{3}\% = 0.33\frac{1}{3}$

Here's how *to change a decimal to a percent.*

$$0.36 = \frac{36}{100} \qquad 0.8 = \frac{8}{10} = \frac{80}{100} \qquad 0.66\frac{2}{3} = \frac{66\frac{2}{3}}{100}$$
$$= 36\% \qquad\qquad\qquad = 80\% \qquad\qquad\qquad = 66\frac{2}{3}\%$$

Here is a **SHORTCUT**.

To change a decimal to a percent, move the decimal point two places to the right and write the percent sign.

$$0.36 = 36\% \qquad 0.02 = 2\%$$
$$0.8 = 80\% \qquad 1.375 = 137.5\%$$
$$0.66\frac{2}{3} = 66\frac{2}{3}\%$$

EXERCISES

Change each percent to a decimal. Hint: Use the SHORTCUT.

3. 5% 0.05 **4.** 9% 0.09 **5.** 6% 0.06 **6.** 25% 0.25 **7.** 72% 0.72 **8.** 44% 0.44

9. 125% 1.25 **10.** 150% 1.5 **11.** 238% 2.38 **12.** 282% 2.82 **13.** 360% 3.6 **14.** 400% 4

15. 6.25% 0.0625 **16.** 37.5% 0.375 **17.** 9.6% 0.096 **18.** 8.75% 0.0875 **19.** 62.5% 0.625 **20.** 4.8% 0.048

21. $33\frac{1}{3}\%$ $0.33\frac{1}{3}$ **22.** $16\frac{2}{3}\%$ $0.16\frac{2}{3}$ **23.** $37\frac{1}{2}\%$ $0.37\frac{1}{2}$ **24.** $166\frac{2}{3}\%$ $1.66\frac{2}{3}$ **25.** $162\frac{1}{2}\%$ $1.62\frac{1}{2}$ **26.** $187\frac{1}{2}\%$ $1.87\frac{1}{2}$

Change each decimal to a percent. Hint: Use the SHORTCUT.

27. 0.06 6% **28.** 0.08 8% **29.** 0.02 2% **30.** 0.38 38% **31.** 0.65 65% **32.** 0.93 93%

33. 0.5 50% **34.** 0.8 80% **35.** 0.7 70% **36.** 0.6 60% **37.** 0.2 20% **38.** 0.4 40%

39. 1.50 150% **40.** 2.5 250% **41.** 1.375 137.5% **42.** 2.875 287.5% **43.** 0.002 0.2% **44.** 0.085 8.5%

45. $0.12\frac{1}{2}$ $12\frac{1}{2}\%$ **46.** $0.33\frac{1}{3}$ $33\frac{1}{3}\%$ **47.** $0.66\frac{2}{3}$ $66\frac{2}{3}\%$ **48.** $1.37\frac{1}{2}$ $137\frac{1}{2}\%$ **49.** $2.16\frac{2}{3}$ $216\frac{2}{3}\%$ **50.** $2.83\frac{1}{3}$ $283\frac{1}{3}\%$

Solve. Use the map on page 252.

51. What percent of the states are east of the Mississippi River? 52%

52. What percent of the states have names beginning with the letter N? 16%

53. What fraction of the states share part of their border with Mexico? $\frac{2}{25}$

54. What fraction of the states are completely surrounded by water? $\frac{1}{50}$

Map madness!

55. Which 4 states share a common corner?
Utah, Colorado, Arizona, and New Mexico

56. Which state borders on the greatest number of other states? Tennessee

EXTRA PRACTICE
Page 439   Skills 55 and 56

PRACTICE WORKSHEET
Copymaster S258 or Duplicating Master S258

NAME _____ **WORKSHEET 106**
(Use after page 253.)

PERCENT RIDDLE
What do you call a dance attended only by fortune tellers?

To find the answer:
1. Find what percent of the square was used to make each letter.
2. Write the letter below its matching percent in the DECODER.

1. T 28%	2. A 14%	3. S 25%	4. Y 8%
5. R 34%	6. L 26%	7. A 41%	8. L 36%
9. L 10%	10. B 35%	11. C 24%	12. A 20%

DECODER

14%	24%	34%	8%	25%	28%	41%	10%	35%	20%	26%	36%
A		C R Y S T A L						B A L L			

© D. C. Heath and Company   S258   Decimals and percents

LIFE-SKILL PROJECT

Taking a survey
Use the map on page 252. Have the students survey the people in their families to find out what percent of the states they have visited.

Percent **253**

SKILLS REVIEWED
Multiplying and dividing decimals
Finding the mean
Adding and subtracting fractions

PROBLEM-SOLVING SKILLS
Selecting information from a sign
Choosing the correct operation
Solving a multi-step problem

STARTING THE LESSON
Cumulative Skill Practice
Challenge the students to an estimation hunt by saying, "Find the five products in exercises 1–18 that are greater than 50." (Exercises 1, 6, 9, 10, and 18) Then have the students find the five quotients in exercises 19–33 that are greater than 100. (Exercises 21, 22, 23, 25, and 32)

STARTING THE LESSON
Problem Solving
Use the Trail Rules and Information sign and ask questions like these:
- Which trail is less than five miles long? (Clear Falls)
- Which trails take less than three hours to hike? (Deer and Pine Ridge)
- If it is 3:30 P.M., is there time to hike Pine Ridge Trail? (Yes)
- Which trail is the hardest trail to hike? (Clear Falls)

254

Cumulative Skill Practice

Multiply.   *(page 64)*

1. $64 \times 1.3 = 83.2$
2. $5.7 \times 4.7 = 26.79$
3. $0.65 \times 9.4 = 6.110$
4. $0.86 \times 48 = 41.28$
5. $0.36 \times 7.2 = 2.592$
6. $8.3 \times 21 = 174.3$

7. $0.85 \times 0.55 = 0.4675$
8. $0.31 \times 76 = 23.56$
9. $9.3 \times 9.3 = 86.49$
10. $5.06 \times 42 = 212.52$
11. $3.74 \times 0.52 = 1.9448$
12. $2.23 \times 0.14 = 0.3122$

13. $3.42 \times 2.7 = 9.234$
14. $7.05 \times 0.46 = 3.2430$
15. $20.5 \times 0.83 = 17.015$
16. $22.8 \times 1.14 = 25.992$
17. $9.46 \times 3.06 = 28.9476$
18. $4.13 \times 31.2 = 128.856$

Divide. Round the quotient to the nearest tenth.   *(page 96)*

19. $0.4 \overline{)7.2}$ = 18
20. $0.3 \overline{)2.81}$ = 9.4
21. $0.06 \overline{)6.2}$ = 103.3
22. $0.03 \overline{)6.5}$ = 216.7
23. $0.09 \overline{)20}$ = 222.2

24. $2.3 \overline{)5.7}$ = 2.5
25. $0.12 \overline{)32}$ = 266.7
26. $3.6 \overline{)5.2}$ = 1.4
27. $3.9 \overline{)6.01}$ = 1.5
28. $0.56 \overline{)8.9}$ = 15.9

29. $0.51 \overline{)9.4}$ = 18.4
30. $7.3 \overline{)5.07}$ = 0.7
31. $5.5 \overline{)0.71}$ = 0.1
32. $0.33 \overline{)97}$ = 293.9
33. $6.8 \overline{)8.05}$ = 1.2

Give the mean. Round the answer to the nearest tenth.   *(page 114)*

34. 46, 49, 51   48.7
35. 681, 694, 700   691.7
36. 89.6, 90.4, 100.7   93.6

37. 78, 65, 93, 88   81
38. 345, 361, 402, 390   374.5
39. 9.82, 7.55, 6.09, 10.32   8.4

40. 19, 36, 22, 27, 30   26.8
41. 309, 211, 213, 215, 217   233
42. 8.3, 9.4, 6.5, 8.0, 7.2   7.9

Give the sum in simplest form.   *(page 158)*

43. $\frac{1}{2} + \frac{1}{4}$ $\frac{3}{4}$
44. $\frac{2}{3} + \frac{5}{6}$ $1\frac{1}{2}$
45. $\frac{1}{4} + \frac{5}{8}$ $\frac{7}{8}$
46. $3 + \frac{2}{3}$ $3\frac{2}{3}$
47. $\frac{4}{5} + \frac{3}{10}$ $1\frac{1}{10}$

48. $\frac{1}{4} + \frac{5}{12}$ $\frac{2}{3}$
49. $\frac{3}{5} + 2$ $2\frac{3}{5}$
50. $\frac{5}{9} + \frac{2}{3}$ $1\frac{2}{9}$
51. $\frac{1}{3} + \frac{1}{2}$ $\frac{5}{6}$
52. $\frac{2}{3} + \frac{4}{5}$ $1\frac{7}{15}$

53. $\frac{3}{4} + \frac{2}{3}$ $1\frac{5}{12}$
54. $\frac{2}{5} + \frac{3}{5}$ 1
55. $\frac{5}{8} + \frac{5}{16}$ $\frac{15}{16}$
56. $\frac{7}{12} + \frac{5}{8}$ $1\frac{5}{24}$
57. $\frac{5}{9} + \frac{3}{4}$ $1\frac{11}{36}$

Give the difference in simplest form.   *(page 166)*

58. $\frac{3}{4} - \frac{1}{4}$ $\frac{1}{2}$
59. $\frac{7}{8} - \frac{3}{4}$ $\frac{1}{8}$
60. $1 - \frac{2}{3}$ $\frac{1}{3}$
61. $\frac{1}{2} - \frac{3}{8}$ $\frac{1}{8}$
62. $\frac{3}{10} - \frac{1}{5}$ $\frac{1}{10}$

63. $\frac{2}{3} - \frac{1}{4}$ $\frac{5}{12}$
64. $\frac{3}{4} - \frac{3}{8}$ $\frac{3}{8}$
65. $\frac{1}{2} - \frac{1}{3}$ $\frac{1}{6}$
66. $\frac{5}{6} - \frac{2}{3}$ $\frac{1}{6}$
67. $\frac{3}{4} - \frac{2}{3}$ $\frac{1}{12}$

68. $2 - \frac{5}{8}$ $1\frac{3}{8}$
69. $\frac{9}{10} - \frac{3}{5}$ $\frac{3}{10}$
70. $\frac{5}{6} - \frac{1}{4}$ $\frac{7}{12}$
71. $\frac{9}{16} - \frac{1}{2}$ $\frac{1}{16}$
72. $\frac{9}{10} - \frac{2}{5}$ $\frac{1}{2}$

Problem solving

YOU'RE THE PARK RANGER

TRAIL RULES AND INFORMATION

All children under 12 years of age must be accompanied by an adult.
All litter is to be carried out by hikers.
All trails are closed at 6:00 P.M.

TRAIL NAME	DISTANCE *(miles)*	HIKING TIME *(hours)*
Deer	5.8	$2\frac{1}{2}$
Clear Falls	4.9	$3\frac{3}{4}$
Pine Ridge	5.6	$2\frac{1}{4}$

Use the trail information to answer each hiker's question.

$4\frac{3}{4}$ hours

1. What is the total distance of the 2 shorter trails? 10.5 miles

2. How long would it take us to hike both Deer Trail and Pine Ridge Trail?

3. "How much longer would it take me to hike Clear Falls Trail than Pine Ridge Trail?" $1\frac{1}{2}$ hours

4. "We've hiked 2.8 miles of Pine Ridge Trail. How far is it to the end of the trail?" 2.8 miles

5. "I've hiked $\frac{1}{2}$ of Deer Trail. How far is it to the end of the trail?" 2.9 miles

6. "It is now 8:00 A.M. Would we have time to hike both Deer Trail and Clear Falls Trail by 12:30 P.M.?" No

Solve.

7. During the first 15 days of July there were 403 hikers. At that rate, how many hikers would there be for the entire month of July? Round your answer to the nearest whole number. 833

8. Small postcards cost $.50 each, large postcards cost $.85 each, and a photo book of all 3 trails costs $5.97. A hiker buys 3 small postcards, 2 large postcards, and a photo book. How much change should he get from a $10 bill? $.83

Percent **255**

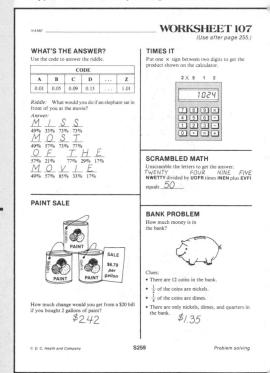
LIFE-SKILL PROJECT

Estimating products

Have the students look through exercises 1–18 on page 254 to find which exercise has a product of about

1. 6.1   Exercise 3
2. 2.6   Exercise 5
3. 0.5   Exercise 7
4. 1.9   Exercise 11
5. 9.2   Exercise 13

If calculators are available, have the students use them to see whether they made the correct choices.

LESSON OBJECTIVE
To find a percent of a number by multiplying by a fraction or decimal equivalent to the percent

PROBLEM-SOLVING SKILLS
Selecting information in a sale ad
Using a guess-and-check strategy

STARTING THE LESSON
Play 'What are the facts?' Have the students study the sale ad at the top of page 256 for 60 seconds and then tell them to close their books. Challenge them to answer these questions from memory:
• Which item had a regular price of $120? (Tent)
• Was the regular price of the boots more or less than $50? (More)
• Which item could you buy for 10% off the regular price? (Lantern)
• Was the sale price of the binoculars more or less than $63? (Less)
• Was there a camp stove on sale? (No)

EXERCISE NOTE
Some students may benefit from using a guess-and-check approach to solve problem 46.

Finding a percent of a number

Camping Equipment Sale!

20% off
Reg. $80
Sportsman's Boots

18% off
Reg. $22
Swiss Army Knife

25% off Reg. $120
Two Person Tent

16% off
Reg. $63
Binoculars

50% off
Reg. $29.98
Trail Pack

10% off
Reg. $16.50
Candle Lantern

To find the sale price of an item, you can first compute the discount. The discount is the amount that is subtracted from the regular price.

1. What is the regular price of the tent? $120

2. The discount on the tent is what percent of the regular price? 25%

3. What is the regular price of the binoculars? $63

4. The discount on the binoculars is what percent of the regular price? 16%

Here's how *to find a percent of a number.*

Change the percent to a fraction or decimal and multiply.

Discount on Tent
25% of $120 = n

Change the percent to a fraction and multiply.

25% of $120 = $\frac{1}{4} \times$ $120
= $30

Discount on Binoculars
16% of $63 = n

Change the percent to a decimal and multiply.

16% of $63 = 0.16 × $63
= $10.08

$$\begin{array}{r} 63 \\ \times\,0.16 \\ \hline 3\ 78 \\ 6\ 3 \\ \hline 10.08 \end{array}$$

5. Look at the *Here's how*. What is the discount on the price of the tent? $30

6. What is the sale price of the tent? $90

7. What is the sale price of the binoculars? $52.92

EXERCISES

Solve by changing the percent to a fraction and multiplying.
Here are scrambled answers for the next row of exercises: 15 18 10

8. 50% of 36 = n 18
9. 25% of 40 = n 10
10. 60% of 25 = n 15

11. 75% of 24 = n 18
12. 30% of 60 = n 18
13. 10% of 80 = n 8

14. 20% of 30 = n 6
15. 40% of 40 = n 16
16. 25% of 44 = n 11

17. 75% of 32 = n 24
18. 100% of 24 = n 24
19. 150% of 18 = n 27

Solve by changing the percent to a decimal and multiplying.
Here are scrambled answers for the next row of exercises: 4.20 4.68 17.94

20. 12% of 35 = n 4.20
21. 9% of 52 = n 4.68
22. 23% of 78 = n 17.94

23. 32% of 156 = n 49.92
24. 54% of 264 = n 142.56
25. 78% of 165 = n 128.7

26. 5.6% of 61 = n 3.416
27. 8.75% of 46 = n 4.025
28. 12.5% of 132 = n 16.5

29. 0.75% of 50 = n 0.375
30. 0.35% of 21.5 = n 0.07525
31. 14.8% of 36.7 = n 5.4316

Solve. Hint: First try to decide which method would be easier.

32. 50% of 18 = n 9
33. 14% of 32 = n 4.48
34. 25% of 48 = n 12

35. 25% of 73 = n 18.25
36. 7.5% of 56 = n 4.2
37. 80% of 20 = n 16

38. 10% of 125 = n 12.5
39. 16.5% of 80 = n 13.2
40. 20% of 50 = n 10

Solve. Look at the items on page 256.

41. a. What is the discount on the price of the boots? $16
   b. What is the sale price of the boots? $64

42. a. What is the discount on the price of the knife? $3.96
   b. What is the sale price of the knife? $18.04

43. What is the sale price of the lantern? $14.85

44. What is the sale price of the small pack? $14.99

Be a super shopper

45. On which camping item can you save the largest amount of money? Two Person Tent

46. Your rich uncle gave you a $100 bill. You bought two of the camping items on sale. You got $21.15 in change. What did you buy? Boots and the lantern

PRACTICE WORKSHEET
Copymaster S260 or Duplicating Master S260

NAME _____   **WORKSHEET 108**
(Use after page 257.)

CAMPING OUT
Graeme Hurry of England holds the world record for camping out. How many consecutive nights did he sleep out?

To find the answer:
1. Solve each problem.
2. Write the letter under its matching number in the DECODER.

1. 50% of 44	2. 75% of 64	3. 80% of 25	4. 25% of 40
22 S	48 R	20 I	10 E
5. 100% of 45	**6.** 150% of 24	**7.** 5% of 20	**8.** 10% of 80
45 D	36 O	1 N	8 T
9. 180% of 35	**10.** 175% of 20	**11.** 90% of 150	**12.** 200% of 7
63 A	35 U	135 N	14 R
13. 120% of 80	**14.** 60% of 90	**15.** 40% of 40	**16.** 250% of 10
96 Y	54 F	16 H	25 X

DECODER

O N E   T H O U S A N D
F O U R   H U N D R E D
S I X T Y

© D. C. Heath and Company   S260   Finding a percent of a number

CHALKBOARD CHALLENGE

Arrange the digits in the boxes to get the answer.

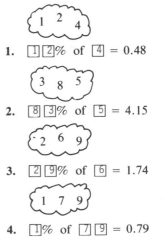

1, 2, 4

1. ☐☐% of ☐ = 0.48

3, 8, 5

2. ☐☐% of ☐ = 4.15

2, 6, 9

3. ☐☐% of ☐ = 1.74

1, 7, 9

4. ☐% of ☐☐ = 0.79

LESSON OBJECTIVE
To find a percent of a number by solving a proportion

PROBLEM-SOLVING SKILLS
Reading a chart
Making a list

STARTING THE LESSON
Write these foods on the chalkboard:

Chicken   Potatoes
Hamburgers   Steak
Pizza   Tacos

Before the students open their books, take an opinion poll. Ask them which of these foods they think was most often named as a favorite food when 600 teenagers were surveyed. Then have the students use the chart at the top of page 258 to get the answer. (Pizza)

More on finding a percent of a number

The "menu" shows the results of a survey of 600 teenagers. They were asked to list some favorite foods and some least-favorite foods.

TEENAGER MENU

FAVORITE FOODS

Pizza 47%
Steak .... $33\frac{1}{3}$%
Hamburgers ... 25%
Chicken .... $18\frac{1}{6}$%
Potatoes .... $12\frac{1}{2}$%
Tacos 10%

LEAST-FAVORITE FOODS

Spinach 20%
Liver .... $16\frac{2}{3}$%
Beans .... $8\frac{1}{3}$%
Broccoli 8%
Peas 6%
Fish 5%

1. What percent of those surveyed listed pizza as a favorite food? 47%

2. How many teenagers were surveyed? 600

3. What decimal would you multiply 600 by to compute the number of teenagers who listed pizza as a favorite food? 0.47

4. What fraction would you multiply 600 by to compute the number of teenagers who listed tacos as a favorite? $\frac{1}{10}$

5. What percent of those surveyed listed liver as a least-favorite food? $16\frac{2}{3}$%

Here's how *to find a percent of a number by solving a proportion.*

To find the number of those surveyed who listed liver as a least-favorite food, you would need to solve the equation $16\frac{2}{3}$% *of 600 = n.*

When you cannot easily change the percent to a fraction or decimal, find n by solving a proportion.

$16\frac{2}{3}$ out of 100 ... $\dfrac{16\frac{2}{3}}{100} = \dfrac{n}{600}$ ... is how many out of 600?

$$100n = 16\frac{2}{3} \times 600$$
$$= \frac{50}{3} \times 600$$
$$= 10,000$$
$$n = 100$$

6. Look at the *Here's how*. How many of those surveyed listed liver as a least-favorite food? 100

258

EXERCISES

Solve by solving a proportion. Round answers to the nearest hundredth.
Here are scrambled answers for the next row of exercises: 3.75 1.71 3.12

| $6\frac{1}{3}$ out of 100 is equal to how many out of 27? | $8\frac{2}{3}$ out of 100 is equal to how many out of 36? | $12\frac{1}{2}$ out of 100 is equal to how many out of 30? |

7. $6\frac{1}{3}\%$ of $27 = n$ 1.71

8. $8\frac{2}{3}\%$ of $36 = n$ 3.12

9. $12\frac{1}{2}\%$ of $30 = n$ 3.75

10. $33\frac{1}{3}\%$ of $48 = n$ 16

11. $66\frac{2}{3}\%$ of $69 = n$ 46

12. $16\frac{2}{3}\%$ of $39 = n$ 6.5

13. $6\frac{3}{4}\%$ of $45 = n$ 3.04

14. $8\frac{7}{8}\%$ of $56 = n$ 4.97

15. $5\frac{1}{3}\%$ of $18 = n$ 0.96

Solve by multiplying by a fraction, by multiplying by a decimal, or by solving a proportion. *Hint: Look for the easiest method.*

16. 10% of $50 = n$ 5

17. 23% of $125 = n$ 28.75

18. $8\frac{1}{3}\%$ of $21 = n$ 1.75

19. 22.5% of $86 = n$ 19.35

20. 75% of $92 = n$ 69

21. $66\frac{2}{3}\%$ of $33 = n$ 22

22. 80% of $12 = n$ 9.6

23. 8.5% of $120 = n$ 10.2

24. 150% of $29 = n$ 43.5

25. 20% of $144 = n$ 28.8

26. 6.5% of $66 = n$ 4.29

27. 1.9% of $164 = n$ 3.116

28. $4\frac{2}{3}\%$ of $30 = n$ 1.4

29. 50% of $124 = n$ 62

30. 11% of $63 = n$ 6.93

Solve. Use the survey on page 258.

31. How many of those surveyed listed hamburgers as a favorite food?   150

32. How many of those surveyed listed pizza as a favorite food?   282

33. How many listed spinach as a least favorite food?   120

34. How many more listed spinach than broccoli as a least-favorite food?   72

35. How many more listed hamburgers than chicken as a favorite food?   41

36. How many did not list tacos as a favorite food?   540

37. How many did not list the most popular favorite food?   318

38. Which food was chosen as a favorite food by 75 of the teenagers surveyed?   Potatoes

Your order, please

39. A vendor sells only hot dogs and hamburgers. You cannot order more than 3 sandwiches. How many different orders can you place? *Hint: Make a list.*   4

EXTRA PRACTICE
Page 440   Skill 58

PRACTICE WORKSHEET
Copymaster S261 or Duplicating Master S261

NAME _____ **WORKSHEET 109**
(Use after page 259.)

SKILL DRILL
Solve.

1. 35% of 80 = *n*   28

2. 70% of 16 = *n*   11.2

3. 150% of 39 = *n*   58.5

4. 99% of 200 = *n*   198

5. 120% of 60 = *n*   72

6. 75% of 84 = *n*   63

7. 5% of 40 = *n*   2

8. 7.5% of 60 = *n*   4.5

9. 30% of 200 = *n*   60

10. 22% of 50 = *n*   11

11. 25% of 56 = *n*   14

12. 60% of 150 = *n*   90

13. 1.5% of 200 = *n*   3

14. 18% of 50 = *n*   9

15. 9% of 80 = *n*   7.2

16. 56% of 80 = *n*   44.8

17. 150% of 8 = *n*   12

18. 300% of 9 = *n*   27

Check yourself. Here are the scrambled answers:
2 3 4.5 7.2 9 11 11.2 12 14 27 28 44.8 58.5 60 63 72
90 198

© D. C. Heath and Company   **S261**   Finding a percent of a number

LIFE-SKILL PROJECT

Using a calculator

Have the students develop a calculator code to use for finding 40% of 105. Possible codes are:

$0.40 \boxed{\times} 105 \boxed{=}$

$105 \boxed{\times} 40 \boxed{\%} \boxed{=}$

Let the students use their calculator codes to do exercises 31–38.

CHALKBOARD QUIZ
on previous lesson
Solve.
1. 20% of 60 = n   12
2. 6.5% of 34 = n   2.21
3. $33\frac{1}{3}$% of 66 = n   22
4. 50% of 142 = n   71
5. $8\frac{1}{3}$% of 24 = n   2

LESSON OBJECTIVE
To use a proportion to find a number when a percent of the number is known

PROBLEM-SOLVING SKILLS
Choosing the correct operation
Interpreting directions correctly

STARTING THE LESSON
Before discussing exercises 1–4, have the students study items 1–6 of the driver's test for 60 seconds. Tell them to close their books. Then read test items 1–6 and have the students answer 'True' or 'False' to each item.

Finding the number when a percent is known

RULES OF THE ROAD

Here are the first few items on a driver's test.

1. What percent of the total items did Ann get correct? 80%

2. How many of the total items did she get correct? 52

3. Were there more or fewer than 52 items on the whole test?

More

Name *Ann Bender*

Number correct *52*

Percent correct *80%*

Part A.   True or false?

t 1. The RED LIGHT requires a stop at the marked stop line. If there is no marked stop line, stop before entering the crosswalk on the near side of the intersection.

X *f* 2. The YELLOW LIGHT warns that the signal is changing from green to red. When the red light appears, you are prohibited from entering the intersection.

t 3. The GREEN LIGHT means you may proceed if it is safe to do so. You must first, however, yield the right-of-way to pedestrians and vehicles that are still within the intersection or an adjacent crosswalk.

t 4. A YELLOW ARROW may appear after a green arrow. It means that the green arrow movement is ending.

t 5. A GREEN ARROW, pointing right or left, means you may make a turn in the direction of the arrow, if you are in the proper lane for such a turn, after yielding the right-of-way to vehicles and pedestrians within the intersection.

f 6. A GREEN ARROW pointing upward means you may turn left or right.

t 7. A GREEN ARROW...

Here's how *to find the number when a percent is known.*

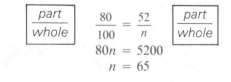

To find the number of items on the test taken by Ann, you would need to solve the equation

80% of n = 52

You can find *n* by solving a proportion.

$$\boxed{\frac{part}{whole}} \qquad \frac{80}{100} = \frac{52}{n} \qquad \boxed{\frac{part}{whole}}$$
$$80n = 5200$$
$$n = 65$$

4. Look at the *Here's how*. How many items were on the test Ann took? 65

EXERCISES

Solve by solving a proportion.
Here are scrambled answers for the next row of exercises: 64 48 75

5. 25% of n = 12   48

6. 20% of n = 15   75

7. 75% of n = 48   64

8. 60% of n = 42   70

9. 40% of n = 56   140

10. 5% of n = 8   160

11. 50% of n = 17   34

12. 6% of n = 12   200

13. 80% of n = 20   25

14. 9% of n = 45   500

15. 10% of n = 18   180

16. 30% of n = 15   50

Solve. Round each answer to the nearest tenth.

17. 12.5% of n = 10.2   81.6

18. 6.4% of n = 1.3   20.3

19. 9.3% of n = 4.7   50.5

20. 5.8% of n = 6.4   110.3

21. 0.5% of n = 0.9   180

22. 0.8% of n = 1.3   162.5

23. 1.2% of n = 4.2   3.5

24. 4.8% of n = 1.2   25

25. 5.6% of n = 3.6   64.3

26. 125% of n = 2.3   1.8

27. 175% of n = 12.4   7.1

28. 150% of n = 10.5   7

Solve.

29. You took a test that had 72 questions. You got 18 questions wrong.
  a. What fraction of the questions did you get right? $\frac{3}{4}$
  b. What percent of the questions did you get right? 75%

30. You took a test that had 60 questions. You got 30 questions right.
  a. What fraction of the questions did you get right? $\frac{1}{2}$
  b. What percent of the questions did you get right? 50%

31. You took a test that had 120 questions. You got 80% of the questions right. How many questions did you get right? *Hint: 80% of 120 = n*   96

32. You scored $66\frac{2}{3}$% on a 96-question test. How many questions did you get right?   64

33. You got 60 questions on a test right. You scored 75%. How many questions were on the test? *Hint: 75% of n = 60.*   80

34. You scored 90% on a test. You got 135 of the questions right. How many questions were on the test? 150

What a jam!

35. The longest traffic jam ever reported was that of February 16, 1980. It stretched northward from Lyon, France, [?] miles toward Paris.   109.3

To find [?], write a *9* in the ones place, a *3* in the tenths place, a *0* in the tens place, and a *1* in the hundreds place.

EXTRA PRACTICE
Page 441   Skill 59

PRACTICE WORKSHEET
Copymaster S262 or Duplicating Master S262

NAME _____

WORKSHEET 110
(Use after page 261.)

BACKING UP
Charles Creighton and James Hargis hold the world record for driving in reverse. They drove their Ford Model A 1929 roadster in reverse from New York City to [?] without stopping the engine once.

To find the city:
1. Solve each equation by using a proportion.
2. Cross out each box below that contains an answer.
3. Read the name of the city using the letters in the remaining boxes.

1. 30% of n = 15
  $\frac{30}{100} = \frac{15}{n}$
  30n = 1500
  n = 50

2. 6% of n = 9   150

3. 80% of n = 20   25

4. 25% of n = 44   176

5. 20% of n = 16   80

6. 10% of n = 13   130

7. 40% of n = 36   90

8. 50% of n = 55   110

9. 5% of n = 10   200

10. 75% of n = 225   300

11. 2% of n = 10   500

12. 150% of n = 15   10

| C | E | H | L | K | O | A | S | N |
|590|90|190|176|200|75|25|150|30|80|

| A | C | N | G | I | E | T | L | E | S |
|20|10|40|36|130|11|150|60|300|45|75|

Answer: LOS ANGELES

© D. C. Heath and Company   S262   Finding the number when the percent is known

CHALKBOARD CHALLENGE
Unscramble the letters of each of these math words.
1. CREPETN   Percent
2. UISDCOTN   Discount
3. ELAS CRPIE   Sale price
4. ITROPPORON   Proportion

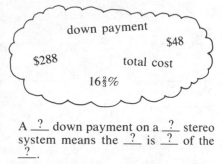

CHALKBOARD QUIZ
on previous lesson
Solve by using a proportion.
1. 25% of $n = 24$ 96
2. 40% of $n = 30$ 75
3. 50% of $n = 17$ 34
4. 125% of $n = 40$ 32
5. 200% of $n = 150$ 75

LESSON OBJECTIVE
To solve percent problems by using proportions

PROBLEM-SOLVING SKILLS
Reading a sale ad
Setting up a proportion to solve any kind of percent problem
Interpreting directions correctly

STARTING THE LESSON
Write this on the chalkboard:

down payment
$48
$288
total cost
$16\frac{2}{3}\%$

A __?__ down payment on a __?__ stereo system means the __?__ is __?__ of the __?__.

Before the students open their books, tell them to use the words, dollar amounts, and percent to fill in the blanks so the sentence makes sense. Then have them look at the first *Here's how* on page 262 to check on whether they filled in the blanks correctly.

More on percent

SYSTEM A	SYSTEM B	SYSTEM C
[?]% DOWN $48 DOWN	$[?] DOWN $33\frac{1}{3}$% DOWN	$37\frac{1}{2}$% DOWN $92 DOWN

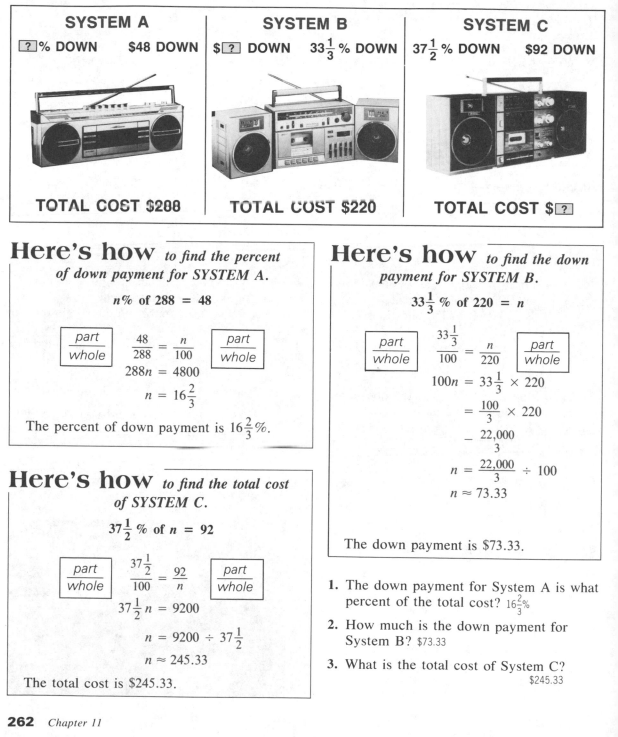

TOTAL COST $288   **TOTAL COST $220**   **TOTAL COST $[?]**

Here's how *to find the percent of down payment for SYSTEM A.*

$$n\% \text{ of } 288 = 48$$

$\frac{part}{whole}$ $\frac{48}{288} = \frac{n}{100}$ $\frac{part}{whole}$

$$288n = 4800$$
$$n = 16\frac{2}{3}$$

The percent of down payment is $16\frac{2}{3}\%$.

Here's how *to find the total cost of SYSTEM C.*

$$37\frac{1}{2}\% \text{ of } n = 92$$

$\frac{part}{whole}$ $\frac{37\frac{1}{2}}{100} = \frac{92}{n}$ $\frac{part}{whole}$

$$37\frac{1}{2}n = 9200$$
$$n = 9200 \div 37\frac{1}{2}$$
$$n \approx 245.33$$

The total cost is $245.33.

Here's how *to find the down payment for SYSTEM B.*

$$33\frac{1}{3}\% \text{ of } 220 = n$$

$\frac{part}{whole}$ $\frac{33\frac{1}{3}}{100} = \frac{n}{220}$ $\frac{part}{whole}$

$$100n = 33\frac{1}{3} \times 220$$
$$= \frac{100}{3} \times 220$$
$$= \frac{22,000}{3}$$
$$n = \frac{22,000}{3} \div 100$$
$$n \approx 73.33$$

The down payment is $73.33.

1. The down payment for System A is what percent of the total cost? $16\frac{2}{3}\%$

2. How much is the down payment for System B? $73.33

3. What is the total cost of System C? $245.33

EXERCISES

Solve. *Here are scrambled answers for the next row of exercises:* 75 125 5

4. $n\%$ of 4 = 3 75

5. $n\%$ of 4 = 5 125

6. $n\%$ of 20 = $\frac{1}{5}$

7. $n\%$ of 8 = 4 50

8. $n\%$ of 16 = 4 25

9. $n\%$ of 1 = $\frac{5}{500}$

Solve. *Here are scrambled answers for the next row of exercises:* 0.32 0.075 0.36

10. $2\frac{2}{3}\%$ of 12 = n 0.32

11. $1\frac{1}{4}\%$ of 6 = n 0.075

12. $4\frac{1}{2}\%$ of 8 = n 0.36

13. $16\frac{2}{3}\%$ of 72 = n 12

14. $33\frac{1}{3}\%$ of 42 = n 14

15. $8\frac{1}{3}\%$ of 96 = $\frac{n}{8}$

Solve. *Here are scrambled answers for the next row of exercises:* 34 45 48

16. 20% of n = 9 45

17. 25% of n = 12 48

18. 50% of n = $\frac{17}{34}$

19. 9% of n = 36 400

20. 1% of n = 2.56 256

21. 24% of n = $\frac{12.48}{52}$

22. $12\frac{1}{2}\%$ of n = 6 48

23. $16\frac{2}{3}\%$ of n = 24 144

24. $33\frac{1}{3}\%$ of n = $\frac{17}{51}$

Solve. *Here are scrambled answers for the next row of exercises:* 120 $31\frac{1}{4}$ 6

25. $12\frac{1}{2}\%$ of n = 15 120

26. $16\frac{2}{3}\%$ of 36 = n 6

27. $n\%$ of 16 = $\frac{5}{31\frac{1}{4}}$

28. $33\frac{1}{3}\%$ of 18 = n 6

29. $n\%$ of 8 = 7 $87\frac{1}{2}$

30. 22% of n = $\frac{11}{50}$

Solve.

31. A stereo system that costs $224 has a down payment of $56. What percent of the total cost is the down payment? 25%

32. A tape deck sells for $279. The down payment is $33\frac{1}{3}\%$ of the selling price. How much is the down payment? $93

33. A set of speakers can be purchased for a down payment of $24. The down payment is $16\frac{2}{3}\%$ of the price. What is the price of the speakers? $144

34. A car radio sells for $275. The down payment is 25% of the selling price. How much is the down payment? $68.75

Name that year

35. You can find the year the radio was invented by pressing these calculator keys. 1896

| 4 | 0 | × | 4 | 0 | = | + | 3 | 0 | 0 | = | − | 4 | = |

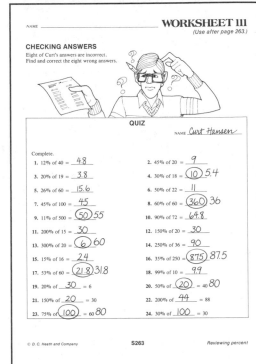

REVIEW PRACTICE
Equivalent fractions
Page 426   Skill 30

PRACTICE WORKSHEET
Copymaster S263 or Duplicating Master S263

NAME _____   **WORKSHEET 111**
(Use after page 263.)

CHECKING ANSWERS
Eight of Curt's answers are incorrect.
Find and correct the eight wrong answers.

QUIZ   NAME *Curt Hansen*

Complete.

1. 12% of 40 = 4.8
2. 45% of 20 = 9
3. 20% of 19 = 3.8
4. 30% of 18 = (10) 5.4
5. 26% of 60 = 15.6
6. 50% of 22 = 11
7. 45% of 100 = 45
8. 60% of 60 = (360) 36
9. 11% of 500 = (50) 55
10. 90% of 72 = 64.8
11. 200% of 15 = 30
12. 150% of 20 = 30
13. 300% of 20 = (6) 60
14. 250% of 36 = 90
15. 15% of 16 = 24
16. 35% of 250 = (875) 87.5
17. 53% of 60 = (21.8) 31.8
18. 99% of 10 = 99
19. 20% of 30 = 6
20. 50% of (20) = 40 80
21. 150% of 20 = 30
22. 200% of 44 = 88
23. 75% of (100) = 60 80
24. 30% of 100 = 30

© D. C. Heath and Company   S263   Reviewing percent

LIFE-SKILL PROJECT

Checking sale ads
Have the students look for uses of percents in ads. Have them check the computations involving the percents to see if they can find errors or misleading information.

SKILLS REVIEWED

Multiplying and dividing fractions
Making conversions between metric units of measure
Subtracting customary units
Solving proportions
Changing percents to fractions

PROBLEM-SOLVING SKILLS

Finding information in a computer display
Choosing the correct operation

STARTING THE LESSON

Cumulative Skill Practice
Write these five answers on the chalkboard:

$$\frac{3}{7} \qquad \frac{1}{36} \qquad 0.238$$

$$1 \text{ ft } 7 \text{ in.} \qquad \frac{3}{5}$$

Challenge the students to an answer hunt by saying, "Look for the five even-numbered exercises on page 264 that have these answers. You have five minutes to find as many of the exercises as you can." (Exercises 6, 30, 40, 48, and 70)

STARTING THE LESSON

Problem Solving
Have the students read the paragraphs at the top of page 265. Ask the students, "What did Eric Jeffrey do to get the information displayed on Screen B?" (Eric selected "2".) "Screen C?" (Eric entered $7.50.) "Screen D?" (Eric entered "4".) "Screen E?" (Eric pushed the ENTER key.) "Screen F?" (Eric entered 1.00.)

Cumulative Skill Practice

Give the product in simplest form.   *(page 178)*

1. $\frac{2}{3} \times \frac{4}{4}$ $\frac{2}{3}$
2. $\frac{1}{2} \times \frac{1}{4}$ $\frac{1}{8}$
3. $\frac{1}{6} \times \frac{1}{8}$ $\frac{1}{48}$
4. $\frac{3}{4} \times \frac{2}{3}$ $\frac{1}{2}$
5. $\frac{2}{5} \times \frac{5}{6}$ $\frac{1}{3}$
6. $\frac{3}{4} \times \frac{4}{7}$ $\frac{3}{7}$

7. $2 \times \frac{3}{5}$ $1\frac{1}{5}$
8. $\frac{3}{8} \times \frac{3}{8}$ $\frac{9}{64}$
9. $\frac{0}{2} \times \frac{1}{6}$ 0
10. $\frac{3}{4} \times \frac{2}{5}$ $\frac{3}{10}$
11. $4 \times \frac{2}{9}$ $\frac{8}{9}$
12. $5 \times \frac{1}{2}$ $2\frac{1}{2}$

13. $\frac{9}{10} \times \frac{2}{3}$ $\frac{3}{5}$
14. $4 \times \frac{5}{6}$ $3\frac{1}{3}$
15. $\frac{2}{3} \times \frac{3}{10}$ $\frac{1}{5}$
16. $\frac{7}{16} \times \frac{4}{5}$ $\frac{7}{20}$
17. $3 \times \frac{11}{12}$ $2\frac{3}{4}$
18. $\frac{1}{2} \times \frac{1}{3}$ $\frac{1}{6}$

Give the quotient in simplest form.   *(page 188)*

19. $2 \div \frac{1}{2}$ 4
20. $\frac{1}{2} \div \frac{2}{3}$ $\frac{3}{4}$
21. $3 \div \frac{2}{3}$ $4\frac{1}{2}$
22. $\frac{3}{4} \div \frac{3}{8}$ 2
23. $\frac{2}{3} \div \frac{1}{2}$ $1\frac{1}{3}$
24. $4 \div \frac{1}{5}$ 20

25. $\frac{3}{5} \div \frac{3}{8}$ $1\frac{3}{5}$
26. $\frac{3}{10} \div \frac{1}{5}$ $1\frac{1}{2}$
27. $\frac{5}{8} \div \frac{1}{4}$ $2\frac{1}{2}$
28. $\frac{5}{6} \div 2$ $\frac{5}{12}$
29. $\frac{3}{10} \div \frac{3}{4}$ $\frac{2}{5}$
30. $\frac{1}{6} \div 6$ $\frac{1}{36}$

31. $\frac{2}{3} \div \frac{3}{4}$ $\frac{8}{9}$
32. $\frac{5}{16} \div \frac{3}{8}$ $\frac{5}{6}$
33. $\frac{9}{10} \div \frac{3}{5}$ $1\frac{1}{2}$
34. $\frac{3}{4} \div \frac{2}{3}$ $1\frac{1}{8}$
35. $\frac{11}{12} \div \frac{5}{6}$ $1\frac{1}{10}$
36. $\frac{2}{3} \div \frac{2}{3}$ 1

Complete.   *(page 206)*

37. $4000 \text{ mg} = \underline{?} \text{ g}$ 4
38. $582 \text{ mg} = \underline{?} \text{ g}$ 0.582
39. $2000 \text{ g} = \underline{?} \text{ kg}$ 2

40. $238 \text{ g} = \underline{?} \text{ kg}$ 0.238
41. $5 \text{ kg} = \underline{?} \text{ g}$ 5000
42. $2.64 \text{ kg} = \underline{?} \text{ g}$ 2640

43. $2 \text{ g} = \underline{?} \text{ mg}$ 2000
44. $8.3 \text{ g} = \underline{?} \text{ mg}$ 8300
45. $0.375 \text{ g} = \underline{?} \text{ mg}$ 375

Subtract.   *(page 218)*

46. 5 ft 6 in. − 2 ft 9 in.   2 ft 9 in.
47. 5 yd 1 ft − 1 yd 2 ft   3 yd 2 ft
48. 8 ft 4 in. − 6 ft 9 in.   1 ft 7 in.
49. 3 gal 2 qt − 1 gal 3 qt   1 gal 3 qt

50. 3 qt − 1 qt 1 pt   1 qt 1 pt
51. 4 gal 1 qt − 2 gal 3 qt   1 gal 2 qt
52. 5 pt − 3 pt 1 c   1 pt 1 c
53. 9 lb 6 oz − 5 lb 10 oz   3 lb 12 oz

Solve.   *(page 230)*

54. $\frac{2}{4} = \frac{n}{2}$ 1
55. $\frac{n}{6} = \frac{10}{12}$ 5
56. $\frac{5}{6} = \frac{11}{n}$ $13\frac{1}{5}$
57. $\frac{8}{3} = \frac{13}{n}$ $4\frac{7}{8}$
58. $\frac{n}{8} = \frac{7}{10}$ $5\frac{3}{5}$

59. $\frac{3}{n} = \frac{4}{8}$ 6
60. $\frac{7}{4} = \frac{n}{8}$ 14
61. $\frac{n}{12} = \frac{15}{8}$ $22\frac{1}{2}$
62. $\frac{10}{9} = \frac{16}{n}$ $14\frac{2}{5}$
63. $\frac{8}{n} = \frac{5}{12}$ $19\frac{1}{5}$

64. $\frac{n}{18} = \frac{6}{4}$ 27
65. $\frac{20}{n} = \frac{16}{9}$ $11\frac{1}{4}$
66. $\frac{13}{20} = \frac{n}{18}$ $11\frac{7}{10}$
67. $\frac{6}{8} = \frac{9}{n}$ 12
68. $\frac{6}{n} = \frac{3}{7}$ 14

Change to a fraction in simplest form.   *(page 248)*

69. 20% $\frac{1}{5}$
70. 60% $\frac{3}{5}$
71. 25% $\frac{1}{4}$
72. 80% $\frac{4}{5}$
73. 50% $\frac{1}{2}$

74. 75% $\frac{3}{4}$
75. 40% $\frac{2}{5}$
76. 100% 1
77. 125% $1\frac{1}{4}$
78. 275% $2\frac{3}{4}$

79. $33\frac{1}{3}\%$ $\frac{1}{3}$
80. $37\frac{1}{2}\%$ $\frac{3}{8}$
81. $66\frac{2}{3}\%$ $\frac{2}{3}$
82. $6\frac{1}{4}\%$ $\frac{1}{16}$
83. $116\frac{2}{3}\%$ $1\frac{1}{6}$

264

Problem solving

COMPUTERS AT HOME

Eric Jeffrey's home computer uses the telephone to communicate with a large **main frame** computer. This communication link allows him to use a wide variety of programs stored in the large computer.

Eric has just received a raise, and he uses a HOME MANAGEMENT program to answer some questions about his raise.

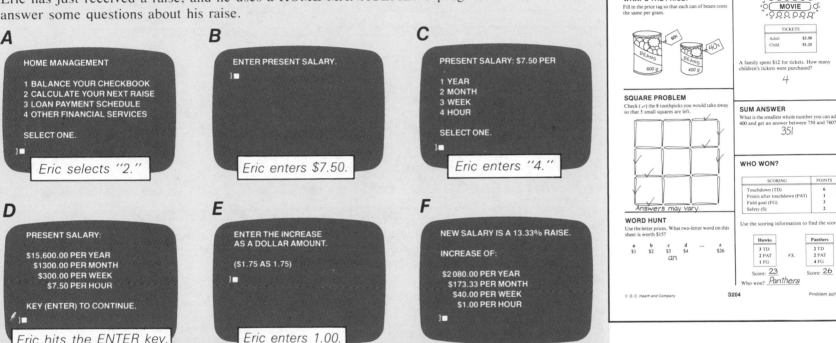

A

HOME MANAGEMENT

1 BALANCE YOUR CHECKBOOK
2 CALCULATE YOUR NEXT RAISE
3 LOAN PAYMENT SCHEDULE
4 OTHER FINANCIAL SERVICES

SELECT ONE.

]■

Eric selects "2."

B

ENTER PRESENT SALARY.

]■

Eric enters $7.50.

C

PRESENT SALARY: $7.50 PER

1 YEAR
2 MONTH
3 WEEK
4 HOUR

SELECT ONE.

]■

Eric enters "4."

D

PRESENT SALARY:

$15,600.00 PER YEAR
$1300.00 PER MONTH
$300.00 PER WEEK
$7.50 PER HOUR

KEY (ENTER) TO CONTINUE.

]■

Eric hits the ENTER key.

E

ENTER THE INCREASE
AS A DOLLAR AMOUNT.

($1.75 AS 1.75)

]■

Eric enters 1.00.

F

NEW SALARY IS A 13.33% RAISE.

INCREASE OF:

$2 080.00 PER YEAR
$173.33 PER MONTH
$40.00 PER WEEK
$1.00 PER HOUR

]■

Use Screen D to answer these questions.

1. Is the weekly salary equal to 40 × $7.50? Yes

2. How did the computer calculate Eric's salary per year?
   Multiplied $7.50 × 40 × 52.

3. How did the computer calculate Eric's salary per month?
   Divided $15,600 by 12.

Use Screen F to answer these questions.

4. What is the percent of increase of Eric's raise? 13.33%

5. How much more money will Eric earn per week? $40.

Use Screens D and F to answer these questions.

6. $1.00 is 13.33% of what amount? $7.50

7. What will Eric's new salary per year be? $17,680

Percent **265**

EXTRA PROBLEM SOLVING
Page 454   Even exercises

PROBLEM-SOLVING WORKSHEET
Copymaster S264 or Duplicating Master S264

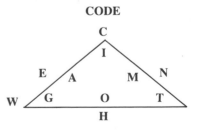

WORKSHEET 112
(Use after page 265.)

NAME _____

WHAT'S THE PRICE?
Fill in the price tag so that each can of beans costs the same per gram.

BEANS 600 g   60¢
BEANS 400 g   40¢

MOVIE

TICKETS	
Adult	$3.50
Child	$1.25

A family spent $12 for tickets. How many children's tickets were purchased?
4

SQUARE PROBLEM
Check (✓) the 8 toothpicks you would take away so that 5 small squares are left.

Answers may vary.

SUM ANSWER
What is the smallest whole number you can add to 400 and get an answer between 750 and 760?
351

WORD HUNT
Use the letter prices. What two-letter word on this sheet is worth $15?

a	b	c	d	...	z
$1	$2	$3	$4		$26

an

WHO WON?
Use the scoring information to find the score.

SCORING	POINTS
Touchdown (TD)	6
Points after touchdown (PAT)	1
Field goal (FG)	3
Safety (S)	2

Hawks		Panthers
3 TD		2 TD
2 PAT	*vs.*	2 PAT
1 FG		4 FG

Score: 23   Score: 26
Who won? Panthers

© D. C. Heath and Company   3264   Problem solving

CHALKBOARD CHALLENGE
Use the code to answer the riddle.

CODE

C
I
E   A   M   N
W   G   O   T
H

Riddle: Who earns a living without doing a day's work?

△ △ △ △ △
△ △ △ △ △ △ △

A night watchman

265

CHAPTER 11 TEST
(Form A)

NAME _____

Change to a fraction or mixed number in simplest form. *(page 248)*

1. 40% = $\frac{2}{5}$ 2. 25% = $\frac{1}{4}$ 3. 5% = $\frac{1}{20}$

4. 150% = $1\frac{1}{2}$ 5. $12\frac{1}{2}$% = $\frac{1}{8}$ 6. $66\frac{2}{3}$% = $\frac{2}{3}$

Change to a percent. *(page 250)*

7. $\frac{1}{2}$ = 50% 8. $\frac{3}{5}$ = 60% 9. 2 = 200%

10. $\frac{6}{5}$ = 120% 11. $\frac{1}{3}$ = $33\frac{1}{3}$% 12. $\frac{7}{6}$ = $116\frac{2}{3}$%

Change each percent to a decimal. *(page 252)*

13. 15% = 0.15 14. 8% = 0.08

15. 160% = 1.60 16. 12.5% = 0.125

17. 4.7% = 0.047 18. $33\frac{1}{3}$% = $0.33\frac{1}{3}$

19. $62\frac{1}{2}$% = $0.62\frac{1}{2}$

Change each decimal to a percent. *(page 253)*

20. 0.06 = 6% 21. 0.45 = 45%

22. 0.9 = 90% 23. 0.875 = 87.5%

24. $0.37\frac{1}{2}$ = $37\frac{1}{2}$% 25. $1.83\frac{1}{3}$ = $183\frac{1}{3}$%

ANSWERS
1. $\frac{2}{5}$
2. $\frac{1}{4}$
3. $\frac{1}{20}$
4. $1\frac{1}{2}$
5. $\frac{1}{8}$
6. $\frac{2}{3}$
7. 50%
8. 60%
9. 200%
10. 120%
11. $33\frac{1}{3}$%
12. $116\frac{2}{3}$%
13. 0.15
14. 0.08
15. 1.60
16. 0.125
17. 0.047
18. $0.33\frac{1}{3}$
19. $0.62\frac{1}{2}$
20. 6%
21. 45%
22. 90%
23. 87.5%
24. $37\frac{1}{2}$%
25. $183\frac{1}{3}$%

© D. C. Heath and Company   S41   Page 1

CHAPTER 11 TEST
(Form A)

NAME _____

Solve. *(pages 256, 258)*

26. 25% of 36 = n ___9___ 27. 75% of 64 = n ___48___ 28. 40% of 80 = n ___32___

29. 23% of 32 = n __7.36__ 30. 6.4% of 44 = n __2.816__ 31. 0.75% of 15.4 = n __0.1155__

32. 0.8% of 150 = n __1.2__ 33. $33\frac{1}{3}$% of 51 = n __17__ 34. $16\frac{2}{3}$% of 72 = n __12__

35. $37\frac{1}{2}$% of 96 = n __36__

Solve. *(pages 260, 262)*

36. 50% of n = 16 __32__ 37. 80% of n = 40 __50__ 38. 5% of n = 11 __220__

39. 20% of n = 13 __65__ 40. 75% of n = 48 __64__ 41. 150% of n = 93 __62__

42. 12.5% of n = 18 __144__ 43. 62.5% of n = 55 __88__ 44. $33\frac{1}{3}$% of n = 37 __111__

45. $66\frac{2}{3}$% of n = 62 __93__ 46. $16\frac{2}{3}$% of n = 2 __3__

Solve. *(page 262)*

47. For the movie camera, the down payment is what percent of the total cost? __25%__

48. How much is the down payment for the television? __$84.15__

49. What is the total cost of the cassette player? __$120__

50. How much would you owe after making the down payment for the cassette player? __$102__

TELEVISION — 20% DOWN $? DOWN — TOTAL COST $420.75

MOVIE CAMERA — ?% DOWN $90 DOWN — TOTAL COST $360

CASSETTE PLAYER — 15% DOWN $18 DOWN — TOTAL COST $?

ANSWERS
26. 9
27. 48
28. 32
29. 7.36
30. 2.816
31. 0.1155
32. 1.2
33. 17
34. 12
35. 36
36. 32
37. 50
38. 220
39. 65
40. 64
41. 62
42. 144
43. 88
44. 111
45. 93
46. 3
47. 25%
48. $84.15
49. $120
50. $102

© D. C. Heath and Company   S42   Page 2

Chapter REVIEW

Here are scrambled answers for the review exercises:

7   75   denominator   equivalent   multiply   proportion   simplest
12   100   divide   left   percent   right

1. 100, denominator, simplest   2. equivalent, percent   3. proportion

1. 25% means 25 out of [?]. To change a percent to a fraction, you can first write the percent as a fraction with a [?] of 100. Then you can write the fraction in [?] form. *(page 248)*

25%

2. To change this fraction to a percent, you could first write the [?] fraction with a denominator of 100. Then you would write that fraction as a [?]. *(page 250)*

$\frac{3}{4}$

3. To change $\frac{5}{6}$ to a percent, you could solve this [?]. *(page 250)*

$$\frac{5}{6} = \frac{n}{100}$$

4. left, right   5. multiply, 12, 17

4. To change a percent to a decimal, you can move the decimal point two places to the [?] and remove the percent sign.
To change a decimal to a percent, you can move the decimal point two places to the [?] and write a percent sign. *(pages 252, 253)*

5. To find a percent of a number, you can change the percent to a fraction or decimal and [?].
25% of 48 is [?].
14% of 50 is [?].
(page 256)

6. divide   7. 75

6. You can find $8\frac{1}{3}$% of 60 by solving this proportion. The next step in solving the proportion would be to [?] both sides of the equation by 100. *(page 258)*

$$8\frac{1}{3}\% \text{ of } 60 = n$$
$$\frac{8\frac{1}{3}}{100} = \frac{n}{60}$$
$$100n = 8\frac{1}{3} \times 60$$
$$= 500$$

7. You can solve a proportion to find the number when a percent of it is known. If you solve the proportion, you will find that n = [?]. *(page 260)*

$$24\% \text{ of } n = .18$$
$$\frac{24}{100} = \frac{18}{n}$$

Chapter TEST

Change to a fraction in simplest form.   *(page 248)*

1. 20% $\frac{1}{5}$ 2. 25% $\frac{1}{4}$ 3. 80% $\frac{4}{5}$ 4. 75% $\frac{3}{4}$ 5. 50% $\frac{1}{2}$ 6. 5% $\frac{1}{20}$

7. 150% $1\frac{1}{2}$ 8. 225% $2\frac{1}{4}$ 9. $12\frac{1}{2}$% $\frac{1}{8}$ 10. $62\frac{1}{2}$% $\frac{5}{8}$ 11. $33\frac{1}{3}$% $\frac{1}{3}$ 12. $66\frac{2}{3}$% $\frac{2}{3}$

Change to a percent.   *(page 250)*

13. $\frac{1}{2}$ 50%   14. $\frac{2}{5}$ 40%   15. $\frac{3}{4}$ 75%   16. $\frac{1}{4}$ 25%   17. 2 200%   18. 4 400%

19. $\frac{7}{5}$ 140%   20. $\frac{9}{4}$ 225%   21. $\frac{1}{3}$ $33\frac{1}{3}$%   22. $\frac{1}{6}$ $16\frac{2}{3}$%   23. $\frac{5}{8}$ $62\frac{1}{2}$%   24. $\frac{7}{8}$ $87\frac{1}{2}$%

Change each percent to a decimal.   *(page 252)*

25. 12% 0.12   26. 9% 0.09   27. 56% 0.56   28. 125% 1.25   29. 160% 1.6   30. 250% 2.5

31. 15.3% 0.153   32. 1.5% 0.015   33. 6.85% 0.0685   34. $16\frac{2}{3}$% $0.16\frac{2}{3}$ 35. $37\frac{1}{2}$% $0.37\frac{1}{2}$ or 0.375   36. $33\frac{1}{3}$% $0.33\frac{1}{3}$

Change each decimal to a percent.   *(page 253)*

37. 0.05 5%   38. 0.09 9%   39. 0.54 54%   40. 0.8 80%   41. 0.575 57.5%   42. 0.625 62.5%

43. 1.375 137.5%   44. 2.326 232.6%   45. 0.004 0.4%   46. $0.12\frac{1}{2}$ $12\frac{1}{2}$%   47. $0.66\frac{2}{3}$ $66\frac{2}{3}$%   48. $1.33\frac{1}{3}$ $133\frac{1}{3}$%

Solve.   *(pages 256, 258)*

49. 25% of 44 = n 11   50. 75% of 52 = n 39   51. 6.2% of 32 = n 1.984

52. 0.75% of 12.4 = n 0.093   53. $8\frac{1}{3}$% of 60 = n 5   54. $16\frac{2}{3}$% of 72 = n 12

Solve.   *(page 260)*

55. 50% of n = 19   38   56. 40% of n = 36   90   57. 5% of n = 15   300

58. 150% of n = 51   34   59. 12.5% of n = 3   24   60. $33\frac{1}{3}$% of n = 21   63

Solve.   *(page 262)*

61. How much is the down payment? $120

$[?] DOWN

25% DOWN

TOTAL COST $480

62. What is the total cost? $560

$112 DOWN

20% DOWN

TOTAL COST $[?]

Use Copymaster S336 to provide the students with an answer sheet in standardized test format.

Cumulative TEST Standardized Format

Answers for Cumulative Test, Chapters 1–11

1. Ⓐ Ⓑ ● Ⓓ   2. Ⓐ ● Ⓒ Ⓓ   3. ● Ⓑ Ⓒ Ⓓ
4. Ⓐ Ⓑ Ⓒ ●   5. Ⓐ ● Ⓒ Ⓓ   6. ● Ⓑ Ⓒ Ⓓ
7. Ⓐ Ⓑ ● Ⓓ   8. Ⓐ Ⓑ Ⓒ ●   9. Ⓐ ● Ⓒ Ⓓ
10. Ⓐ Ⓑ ● Ⓓ   11. ● Ⓑ Ⓒ Ⓓ   12. Ⓐ Ⓑ ● Ⓓ

The table below correlates test items with student text pages.

Test Item	Page Taught	Skill Practice
1	64	p. 254, exercises 1–18
2	96	p. 254, exercises 19–33
3	114	p. 254, exercises 34–42
4	158	p. 254, exercises 43–57
5	166	p. 254, exercises 58–72
6	178	p. 264, exercises 1–18
7	188	p. 264, exercises 19–36
8	206	p. 264, exercises 37–45
9	218	p. 264, exercises 46–53
10	230	p. 264, exercises 54–68
11	248	p. 264, exercises 69–83
12	256	

Choose the correct letter.

1. Multiply.

$$4.239 \times 8.07$$

A. 342.0873
B. 36.8793
Ⓒ. 34.20873
D. none of these

2. Divide. Round the quotient to the nearest tenth.

$$62.5 \overline{)191.27}$$

A. 3.06
Ⓑ. 3.1
C. 3.6
D. none of these

3. The mean of 81.5, 83.4, 86.9, 87.4, and 90.3 is

Ⓐ. 85.9
B. 86.9
C. 87.9
D. none of these

4. Give the sum.

$$\frac{5}{6} + \frac{5}{8}$$

A. $\frac{5}{7}$
B. $\frac{5}{24}$
C. $1\frac{1}{4}$
Ⓓ. none of these

5. Give the difference.

$$\frac{7}{8} - \frac{2}{3}$$

A. 1
Ⓑ. $\frac{5}{24}$
C. $\frac{5}{11}$
D. none of these

6. Give the product.

$$\frac{5}{6} \times \frac{3}{8}$$

Ⓐ. $\frac{5}{16}$
B. $2\frac{2}{9}$
C. $\frac{9}{20}$
D. none of these

7. Give the quotient.

$$\frac{7}{8} \div \frac{3}{4}$$

A. $\frac{21}{32}$
B. $\frac{6}{7}$
Ⓒ. $1\frac{1}{6}$
D. none of these

8. Complete.

275 mg = __?__ g

A. 2.75
B. 275
C. 27.5
Ⓓ. none of these

9. Subtract.

9 gal 2 qt
−3 gal 3 qt

A. 6 gal 1 qt
Ⓑ. 5 gal 3 qt
C. 5 gal 1 qt
D. none of these

10. Solve.

$$\frac{7}{n} = \frac{5}{9}$$

A. 3.89
B. 6.43
Ⓒ. 12.6
D. none of these

11. Change to a fraction.

$$16\frac{2}{3}\% = ?$$

Ⓐ. $\frac{1}{6}$ B. $\frac{1}{16}$
C. $\frac{1}{8}$ D. none of these

12. You took a 72-problem math test. You got 75% of the problems correct. How many was that?

A. 96
B. 36
Ⓒ. 54
D. none of these

CHAPTER 12
Consumer Mathematics

LESSON OBJECTIVES
To compute earnings   (*pages 270–271*)
To learn about some kinds of payroll deductions   (*page 271*)
To compute discounts and sale prices   (*pages 272–273*)
To compute unit prices   (*pages 274–275*)
To determine which of two sizes is more expensive in terms of unit price   (*pages 274–275*)
To solve problems by relating discounts and coupons to real situations   (*pages 276–277*)
To understand checking accounts and checks   (*pages 280–281*)
To balance a checking account   (*page 281*)
To understand savings accounts and passbooks   (*pages 282–283*)
To understand compound interest   (*page 283*)
To compute simple interest   (*pages 284–285*)
To understand monthly bills and payments   (*pages 286–287*)

PROBLEM-SOLVING SKILLS
Reading a Help Wanted ad   (*page 270*)
Reading a statement of withholdings and deductions   (*page 271*)
Reading a sale ad   (*pages 272–277*)
Choosing the correct operation   (*pages 277, 287, 289*)
Selecting information from a chart   (*page 279*)
Selecting information from checks and a check register
   (*pages 280–281*)
Selecting information from a savings-account passbook
   (*page 282*)
Reading a graph   (*page 283*)
Interpreting directions correctly   (*page 283*)
Selecting information from a display   (*page 284*)
Reading an auto-loan application   (*page 285*)
Finding information in a bill   (*pages 286–287*)
Reading a telephone-rate table   (*page 287*)
Reading a computer display   (*page 289*)
Using a guess-and-check strategy   (*page 289*)

RESOURCES
- **VISUAL AIDS**
  Statements from page 271   (*Visual Aid 43, Copymaster S140*)
  Checks from page 280   (*Visual Aid 44, Copymaster S141*)
  Check register from page 281   (*Visual Aid 45, Copymaster S142*)
  Passbook from page 282   (*Visual Aid 46, Copymaster S143*)
  Graph from page 283   (*Visual Aid 47, Copymaster S144*)
  Bills from page 286   (*Visual Aid 48, Copymaster S145*)
- **WORKSHEETS 113–122**   (*Copymasters S265–S274 or Duplicating Masters S265–S274*)

LESSON OBJECTIVES
To compute earnings
To learn about some kinds of payroll deductions

PROBLEM-SOLVING SKILLS
Reading a help-wanted ad
Reading a statement of withholdings and deductions

STARTING THE LESSON
Have the students use the information in the Help Wanted ads to find the occupation of each person in exercises 1–4.

EXERCISE NOTE
The check and statement of withholdings and deductions on page 271 are also on **Visual Aid 43.** You may wish to use the visual aid when discussing exercises 8–14.

Earning money

Read the want ads to find the jobs.

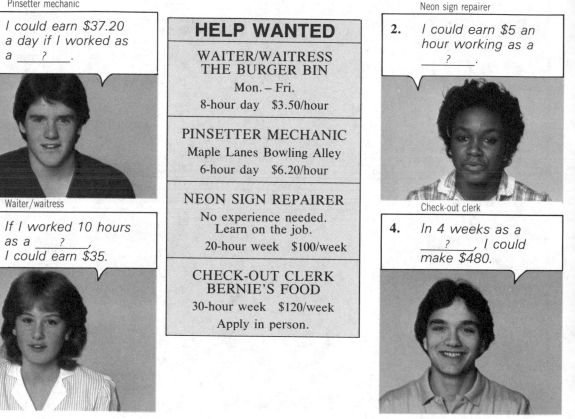

Pinsetter mechanic

1. *I could earn $37.20 a day if I worked as a ___?___.*

Waiter/waitress

3. *If I worked 10 hours as a ___?___, I could earn $35.*

HELP WANTED

WAITER/WAITRESS
THE BURGER BIN
Mon. – Fri.
8-hour day $3.50/hour

PINSETTER MECHANIC
Maple Lanes Bowling Alley
6-hour day $6.20/hour

NEON SIGN REPAIRER
No experience needed.
Learn on the job.
20-hour week $100/week

CHECK-OUT CLERK
BERNIE'S FOOD
30-hour week $120/week
Apply in person.

Neon sign repairer

2. *I could earn $5 an hour working as a ___?___.*

Check-out clerk

4. *In 4 weeks as a ___?___, I could make $480.*

EXERCISES

Solve.

5. The Ace Trucking Company pays its drivers 20¢ a mile.

   a. How much would an Ace driver be paid for an 840-mile trip? $168

   b. How many miles would a driver have to drive to make $150? 750

6. The Tip Top Café pays its cooks $5.40 an hour.

   a. How much would a Tip Top cook be paid for a 7.5-hour day? $40.50

   b. How much would a cook be paid for a 37.5-hour week? $202.50

7. The Happy Day Card Company pays its salespeople a commission of 20% on all sales.

   a. How much would you earn for selling $300 worth of Happy Day cards? *Hint: What is 20% of $300?* $60

   b. To earn $100 commission, would you have to sell more or less than $400 worth of Happy Day cards? More

270

Cindy Davis is a cashier at Showtime Cinemas. Each week she receives with her paycheck a **statement of withholdings and deductions.** This statement lists the amount that her employer is required by law to deduct from her weekly paycheck.

SHOWTIME CINEMAS
College Mall
Cedar City

No 1914

March 8 19 85   53-7122
2113

PAY TO THE ORDER OF _Cindy Davis_ $ 95.62

Ninety-five and ⁶²/₁₀₀ ——————— DOLLARS

Middle Savings Bank

Carol DeBold

EMPLOYEE	CHECK #	WEEK ENDING	HOURLY WAGE	HOURS	GROSS PAY	NET PAY
Davis, Cindy	1914	03/08/85	$3.80	32.5	$123.50	$95.62

TAX DEDUCTIONS			PERSONAL DEDUCTIONS		
FIT	FICA	STATE	LOCAL	MEDICAL	UNION DUES
$16.50	$8.54	$2.84	—	—	—

8. How much was Cindy paid per hour? $3.80

9. How many hours did she work? 32.5

10. To find Cindy's gross pay, $3.80 was multiplied by what number? 32.5

11. Social Security (FICA) withholding is for retirement income and disability income. How much was withheld for Social Security? $8.54

12. How much did her employer withhold for federal income tax (FIT)? State income tax? $16.50, $2.84

13. How much was deducted altogether from Cindy's gross pay? $27.88

14. How much was Cindy's net, or "take home", pay? $95.62

You're the boss

15. Complete this statement by computing Cindy's gross and net pay.

EMPLOYEE	CHECK #	WEEK ENDING	HOURLY WAGE	HOURS	GROSS PAY	NET PAY
Davis, Cindy	1972	03/15/85	$3.80	29.5	? $112.10	? $86.43

TAX DEDUCTIONS			PERSONAL DEDUCTIONS		
FIT	FICA	STATE	LOCAL	MEDICAL	UNION DUES
$15.68	$7.42	$2.57	—	—	—

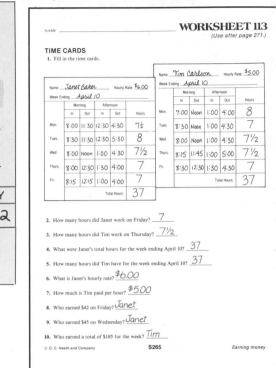

LIFE-SKILL PROJECT
Researching information
Have the students investigate job opportunities in types of work that interest them. Have them find out about education requirements, working conditions, and beginning salaries. (This information can be found in the *Occupational Outlook Handbook.*)

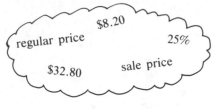
Buying on sale

BIG VALUES

FLANNEL SHIRTS Reg. **$24.75**   NOW 20% OFF

LEATHER BOOTS Reg. **$66.60**   NOW 15% OFF

JEANS Reg. **$32.80**   NOW 25% OFF

1. What is the regular price of the jeans? $32.80
2. Will the sale price of the jeans be more or less than $32.80? Less

Here's how *to find the sale price of a pair of jeans.*

METHOD 1.

$$\begin{array}{r} \$32.80 \leftarrow \text{Regular price} \\ \times\ 0.25 \\ \hline 16400 \\ 6560 \\ \hline \$8.2000 \leftarrow \text{Discount is } \$8.20. \end{array}$$

$$\begin{array}{r} \$32.80 \leftarrow \text{Regular price} \\ -\ 8.20 \leftarrow \text{Discount} \\ \hline \$24.60 \leftarrow \text{Sale price} \end{array}$$

METHOD 2.

$$\begin{array}{r} \$32.80 \leftarrow \text{Regular price} \\ \times\ 0.75 \\ \hline 16400 \\ 22960 \\ \hline \$24.6000 \leftarrow \text{Sale price is } \$24.60. \end{array}$$

If the discount is 25%, the sale price is 75% of the regular price.

3. Look at the *Here's how*. How much is the savings on a pair of jeans during the sale? $8.20
4. What is the sale price of a pair of jeans? $24.60
5. What is the sale price of a pair of leather boots? $56.61
6. What is the sale price of a flannel shirt? $19.80

EXERCISES

Find the sale price of each item.

7. $80.55

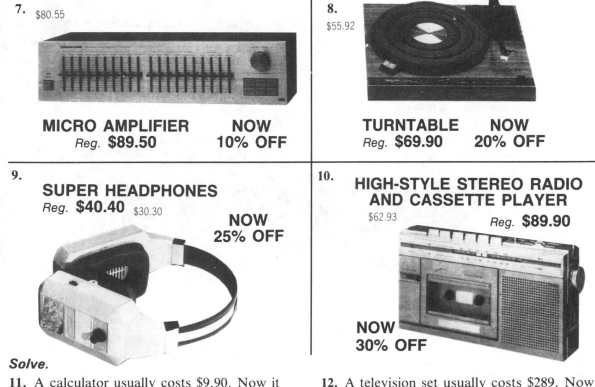

MICRO AMPLIFIER   **NOW**
Reg. **$89.50**   **10% OFF**

8. $55.92

TURNTABLE   **NOW**
Reg. **$69.90**   **20% OFF**

9.

SUPER HEADPHONES
Reg. **$40.40** $30.30

NOW
25% OFF

10.

**HIGH-STYLE STEREO RADIO
AND CASSETTE PLAYER**

$62.93

Reg. **$89.90**

NOW
30% OFF

Solve.

11. A calculator usually costs $9.90. Now it is marked 10% off. What is the sale price? $8.91

12. A television set usually costs $289. Now it is on sale at a 20% discount. What is the sale price? $231.20

13. A radio is on sale at a 25% discount. The regular price is $39.88. How much would you save when buying the radio on sale? $9.97

14. How much would you save by purchasing a stereo set at 30% off the regular price? The regular price is $186. $55.80

Check the ads

15. Two of these ads are incorrect. Find and correct the two wrong sale prices.

a. **SAVE $1.99**

Reg. **$7.29**
SALE $4.30
$5.30

b. $\frac{1}{3}$ **OFF**

Reg. **$8.49**

NOW
$5.66

c. **15% OFF**

Reg. **$6.80**
SALE $5.69
$5.78

Consumer Mathematics **273**

REVIEW PRACTICE
Finding least common denominators
Page 427   Skill 32

PRACTICE WORKSHEET
Copymaster S266 or Duplicating Master S266

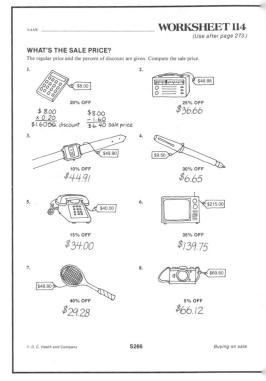

LIFE-SKILL PROJECT

Using a calculator
Have the students collect newspaper ads that give the percent of discount. When the regular price and the sale price are given, have the students use a calculator to check the amounts to see whether the correct percent is listed.

LESSON OBJECTIVES
To compute unit prices
To determine which of two sizes is more expensive in terms of unit price

PROBLEM-SOLVING SKILL
Selecting information from an ad

STARTING THE LESSON
Before discussing exercises 1–3, have the students read the people's comments at the top of the page. Ask them how they would decide which is the better buy, the 4.5-pound bag of apples or the 8-pound bag.

Comparison buying
WHO'S RIGHT?

Which is the better buy, the 4.5-pound bag of apples or the 8-pound bag?

If the apples in each bag are the same quality and you could use either amount, you should compute the **unit price** (price per pound) to decide which is the better buy.

This 4.5-pound bag of apples is a better buy.

No! This 8-pound bag of apples costs less per pound.

$1.79   Orchard Fresh Fruit

$2.99

Here's how *to find the unit price*.

To compute the unit price of the apples, divide the price by the number of pounds. That will tell you the price per pound.

Small bag | 4.5 pounds for $1.79 | **Large bag** | 8 pounds for $2.99 |

$$
\begin{array}{r}
\$\ 0.397 \\
4.5\overline{)\ \$1.7900} \\
-135 \\
\hline
440 \\
-405 \\
\hline
350 \\
-315 \\
\hline
35
\end{array}
$$

$$
\begin{array}{r}
\$0.373 \\
8\overline{)\ \$2.990} \\
-24 \\
\hline
59 \\
-56 \\
\hline
30 \\
-24 \\
\hline
6
\end{array}
$$

Round each unit price to the nearest cent.

Small bag
$.40 per pound

Large bag
$.37 per pound

1. Look at the *Here's how*. Which size bag of apples costs less per pound? Large bag

2. If both bags of apples are the same quality, which size bag is the better buy? Large bag

3. If you only need 4 pounds of apples, which size bag should you buy? Small bag

274

EXERCISES

Compute the unit price. Round each answer to the nearest cent.

4. Grapes $.95
2 pounds for $1.89

5. Pickles $.09
9 ounces for $.79

> Hint: The unit price is the cost per ounce.

6. Crackers
10 ounces for 98¢ $.10

7. Ketchup
8 ounces for 69¢ $.09

8. Tomatoes
3 pounds for $2.69 $.90

9. Apples
4 pounds for $1.75 $.44

10. Peanuts
1.1 pounds for $1.99 $1.81

11. Bread
14 ounces for $1.10 $.08

12. Sunflower seeds
6.5 ounces for 89¢ $.14

13. Spaghetti sauce
12 ounces for 99¢ $.08

Suppose that you could use either amount. Tell which is the better buy.

Hint: Compute and compare the unit prices.

14. Cheese
  (a.) 3 pounds for $3.19
  b. 2 pounds for $2.29

15. Bananas
  a. 3 pounds for $.89
  (b.) 5 pounds for $1.39

16. Carrots
  a. 0.5 pound for $.29
  (b.) 2 pounds for $.99

17. Beans
  (a.) 8-ounce can for $.49
  b. 12-ounce can for $.89

18. Cereal
  a. 18-ounce box for $1.09
  (b.) 12-ounce box for $.63

19. Olives
  (a.) 6-ounce jar for $.99
  b. 10-ounce jar for $1.79

20. Dinner napkins
  (a.) 100 for $.85
  b. 150 for $1.75

21. Milk
  a. 1 quart for $.99
  (b.) $\frac{1}{2}$ gallon for $1.79

What's in the bag?

Use the ad to find what fruit is in each bag.

22. Cherries

23. Grapes

PRODUCE SALE

PEARS	$ .88/lb
PEACHES	$ .75/lb
CHERRIES	$1.80/lb
GRAPES	$1.20/lb

PRACTICE WORKSHEET
Copymaster S267 or Duplicating Master S267

NAME _____   **WORKSHEET 115**
(Use after page 275.)

COMPARISON SHOPPING
Compute the unit price to answer the questions.

1. a. What does one ounce of the large jar of jelly cost? $.06
  b. What does one ounce of the small jar of jelly cost? $.069
  c. Do you save money by buying the larger size? Yes

JELLY 16 oz $.96
JELLY 10 oz $.69

2. a. Which size bag of walnuts costs $0.105 per ounce? Small
  b. Which size bag costs $0.095 per ounce? Large
  c. Which size bag of walnuts is the better buy? Large

WALNUTS 8 oz $.84
WALNUTS 12 oz $1.14

3. a. How much does one apple in the large bag cost? $.129
  b. How much does one apple in the small bag cost? $.115
  c. Which size bag of apples is the better buy? Small

APPLES Large Bag 10 for $1.29
APPLES Small Bag 6 for $.69

4. a. Which size box of cereal costs $0.075 per ounce? Giant
  b. Which size box of cereal costs $0.08 per ounce? Medium
  c. Which size box of cereal is the best buy? Giant

GIANT SIZE CEREAL $1.35 18 oz
MEDIUM CEREAL $.96 12 oz
SMALL CEREAL $.64 8 oz

© D. C. Heath and Company   S267   Comparison buying

LIFE-SKILL PROJECT
Computing unit prices
Have a contest to find the food item in the kitchen that cost the most per ounce. Encourage the students to use a calculator to compute the unit prices.

LESSON OBJECTIVE
To solve problems by relating discounts and coupons to real situations

PROBLEM-SOLVING SKILLS
Selecting information from sale ads and coupons
Choosing the correct operation

STARTING THE LESSON
Write this on the chalkboard:

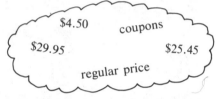

$4.50   coupons
$29.95 $25.45
regular price

Shoppers who use __?__ pay less than the __?__. For example, with a __?__ off coupon, a __?__ camera will cost __?__.

Before the students open their books, tell them to use the words and dollar amounts to fill in the blanks so the sentences make sense. Then have them use the item prices and coupon information on page 276 to check on whether they filled in the blanks correctly.

Bargain buying

Shoppers who use coupons pay less than the regular price. They get the price reduced by the value of the coupon. For example, with the coupon, the pocket camera will cost $25.45.

POCKET CAMERA
Reg. **$29.95**

$29.95	regular price
− 4.50	value of coupon
$25.45	

CAMERA BAG
Reg. **$48.29**

MOVIE PROJECTOR
$\frac{1}{4}$ OFF   *Reg.* **$240.00**

MOVIE CAMERA
10% OFF
Reg. **$199.00**

$4.50   STORE COUPON $4.50
$4.50 OFF POCKET CAMERA
LIMIT 1 PER CUSTOMER

STORE COUPON
30¢ OFF
ON 1 ROLL
OF 24-EXPOSURE
COLOR FILM
Reg. $2.49
$2.19

STORE COUPON
SAVE $1.99
ON
CAMERA BAG
LIMITED QUANTITY

STORE COUPON
COLOR PRINT PROCESSING

	Reg.	WITH COUPON
12-EXPOSURE	$2.25	$1.99
20-EXPOSURE	$4.35	$3.79
36-EXPOSURE	$6.45	$5.89

BRING THIS COUPON WITH ORDER   NO LIMIT

EXERCISES

Solve.

1. What is the regular price of a
   a. pocket camera? $29.95
   b. roll of 24-exposure color film? $2.49

2. With a coupon, how much can you save when you buy a
   a. pocket camera? $4.50
   b. camera bag? $1.99

3. How much more will it cost to process a roll of 36-exposure color film without a coupon? $.56

4. With a coupon, how much would you pay for a camera bag? $46.30

5. You bought a movie camera. What was the sale price? $179.10

6. You are interested in buying a movie projector. How much can you save by buying it during the sale? $60

7. Mrs. Kelly bought a roll of 24-exposure color film and a camera bag. How much did she save by using coupons? $2.29

8. A customer paid for 2 rolls of 24-exposure color film with a $10 bill and got $5.62 in change. Did the customer use coupons? Yes

9. Janet has a $15 gift certificate. How much more money does she need to buy a pocket camera using a coupon? $10.45

10. Mr. Harms was charged $13.05 to have 3 rolls of 20-exposure color film processed. Did he have a coupon? No

11. Using only one coupon, what would be the total cost for two pocket cameras?
    $55.40

12. Which is the better buy, getting 10% off the regular price of a roll of 24-exposure color film or using the coupon?
    Using the coupon

You decide!

Use the coupons and the prices on page 276 to answer these questions.

13. *I bought a roll of 24-exposure color film and a pocket camera. I spent $27.94. Which coupon did I clip out and use?* $4.50 off pocket camera

14. *I bought a camera bag, a pocket camera, and a roll of 24-exposure film. I spent a total of $78.44. Which coupons did I clip out and use?* Coupons for camera bag and film

REVIEW PRACTICE
Writing mixed numbers as fractions
Page 428   Skill 34

PRACTICE WORKSHEET
Copymaster S268 or Duplicating Master S268

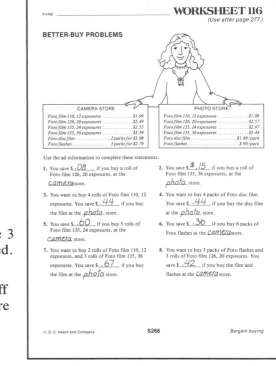

NAME _____   **WORKSHEET 116**
(Use after page 277.)

BETTER-BUY PROBLEMS

CAMERA STORE		PHOTO STORE	
Foto film 110, 12 exposures	$1.99	Foto film 110, 12 exposures	$1.88
Foto film 126, 20 exposures	$2.49	Foto film 126, 20 exposures	$2.57
Foto film 135, 24 exposures	$2.55	Foto film 135, 24 exposures	$2.67
Foto film 135, 36 exposures	$3.59	Foto film 135, 36 exposures	$3.44
Foto disc film	2 packs for $3.98	Foto disc film	$1.88/pack
Foto flashes	3 packs for $2.79	Foto flashes	$.99/pack

Use the ad information to complete these statements.

1. You save $ .08 if you buy a roll of Foto film 126, 20 exposures, at the *camera* store.

2. You save $ .15 if you buy a roll of Foto film 135, 36 exposures, at the *photo* store.

3. You want to buy 4 rolls of Foto film 110, 12 exposures. You save $ .44 if you buy the film at the *photo* store.

4. You want to buy 4 packs of Foto disc film. You save $ .44 if you buy the disc film at the *photo* store.

5. You save $ .60 if you buy 5 rolls of Foto film 135, 24 exposures, at the *camera* store.

6. You save $ .36 if you buy 6 packs of Foto flashes at the *camera* store.

7. You want to buy 2 rolls of Foto film 110, 12 exposures, and 3 rolls of Foto film 135, 36 exposures. You save $ .67 if you buy the film at the *photo* store.

8. You want to buy 3 packs of Foto flashes and 3 rolls of Foto film 126, 20 exposures. You save $ .42 if you buy the film and flashes at the *camera* store.

© D. C. Heath and Company   S268   Bargain buying

LIFE-SKILL PROJECT
Using coupons
Have the students look through magazines and newspapers for coupons their families could use. Have them determine how much money they could save if their families used the coupons.

SKILLS REVIEWED
Adding and subtracting mixed numbers
Multiplying and dividing mixed numbers
Making conversions between metric units of measure

PROBLEM-SOLVING SKILL
Selecting information from a chart

STARTING THE LESSON
Cumulative Skill Practice
Challenge the students to an estimation hunt by saying, "Find the five sums in exercises 1–12 that are less than 6. (Exercises 1, 2, 3, 4, and 6) Then have the students find the five differences in exercises 13–24 that are less than 4. (Exercises 14, 15, 16, 18, and 21)

STARTING THE LESSON
Problem Solving
Have the students use the budgets at the top of page 279 to answer questions like these:
• Which person budgets a total of $17 for movies and lunches? (Rhonda)
• Who budgets $\frac{1}{6}$ of total earnings for movies? (Walter)
• Who saves 20% of total earnings? (Kelly)

Cumulative Skill Practice

Add. Write the sum in simplest form. *(page 160)*

1. $3\frac{2}{3}$ $+1\frac{1}{2}$ $5\frac{1}{6}$
2. $2\frac{1}{3}$ $+2\frac{3}{4}$ $5\frac{1}{12}$
3. $1\frac{5}{6}$ $+2\frac{2}{3}$ $4\frac{1}{2}$
4. $1\frac{3}{4}$ $+1\frac{1}{2}$ $3\frac{1}{4}$
5. $4\frac{1}{2}$ $+2\frac{1}{4}$ $6\frac{3}{4}$
6. $3\frac{1}{3}$ $+2\frac{1}{2}$ $5\frac{5}{6}$

7. $12\frac{2}{3}$ $+6\frac{1}{2}$ $19\frac{1}{6}$
8. $10\frac{1}{3}$ $+8\frac{4}{5}$ $19\frac{2}{15}$
9. $16\frac{5}{9}$ $+7$ $23\frac{5}{9}$
10. $15\frac{7}{8}$ $+12\frac{3}{4}$ $28\frac{5}{8}$
11. $23\frac{2}{3}$ $+17\frac{3}{5}$ $41\frac{4}{15}$
12. $20\frac{1}{3}$ $+6\frac{1}{5}$ $26\frac{8}{15}$

Subtract. Write the difference in simplest form. *(page 170)*

13. $6\frac{3}{4}$ $-1\frac{1}{2}$ $5\frac{1}{4}$
14. $5\frac{2}{3}$ -3 $2\frac{2}{3}$
15. $4\frac{1}{2}$ $-1\frac{3}{4}$ $2\frac{3}{4}$
16. $5\frac{1}{8}$ $-2\frac{1}{2}$ $2\frac{5}{8}$
17. $6\frac{3}{5}$ $-2\frac{1}{2}$ $4\frac{1}{10}$
18. $7\frac{2}{7}$ $-3\frac{1}{2}$ $3\frac{11}{14}$

19. 8 $-2\frac{1}{3}$ $5\frac{2}{3}$
20. 14 $-2\frac{5}{6}$ $11\frac{1}{6}$
21. $11\frac{3}{8}$ $-9\frac{1}{2}$ $1\frac{7}{8}$
22. $15\frac{1}{9}$ $-10\frac{5}{6}$ $4\frac{5}{18}$
23. $24\frac{2}{3}$ $-16\frac{3}{4}$ $7\frac{11}{12}$
24. $25\frac{1}{2}$ $-13\frac{5}{8}$ $11\frac{7}{8}$

Give the product in simplest form. *(page 182)*

25. $3\frac{1}{2} \times 2\frac{1}{4}$ $7\frac{7}{8}$ 26. $1\frac{1}{3} \times 1\frac{1}{2}$ 2 27. $4\frac{1}{2} \times 2\frac{1}{3}$ $10\frac{1}{2}$ 28. $2\frac{1}{2} \times 1\frac{1}{4}$ $3\frac{1}{8}$ 29. $1\frac{1}{4} \times 2\frac{1}{3}$ $2\frac{11}{12}$

30. $1\frac{2}{3} \times 2\frac{1}{2}$ $4\frac{1}{6}$ 31. $1\frac{1}{3} \times 1\frac{1}{3}$ $1\frac{7}{9}$ 32. $2\frac{3}{4} \times 3\frac{2}{3}$ $10\frac{1}{12}$ 33. $2\frac{3}{8} \times 3$ $7\frac{1}{8}$ 34. $2\frac{2}{3} \times 1\frac{3}{4}$ $4\frac{2}{3}$

35. $2\frac{1}{4} \times 2\frac{1}{4}$ $5\frac{1}{16}$ 36. $4 \times 3\frac{2}{3}$ $14\frac{2}{3}$ 37. $1\frac{3}{4} \times 1\frac{3}{4}$ $3\frac{1}{16}$ 38. $4\frac{2}{5} \times 3\frac{3}{4}$ $16\frac{1}{2}$ 39. $1\frac{5}{8} \times 9$ $14\frac{5}{8}$

Give the quotient in simplest form. *(page 190)*

40. $3\frac{3}{4} \div 1\frac{1}{4}$ 3 41. $5 \div 2\frac{1}{2}$ 2 42. $5\frac{5}{6} \div 2\frac{1}{3}$ $2\frac{1}{2}$ 43. $5\frac{1}{2} \div 2\frac{1}{4}$ $2\frac{4}{9}$ 44. $6\frac{2}{3} \div 1\frac{1}{6}$ $5\frac{5}{7}$

45. $6\frac{1}{4} \div 1\frac{1}{4}$ 5 46. $5\frac{5}{8} \div 1\frac{1}{2}$ $3\frac{3}{4}$ 47. $5\frac{1}{4} \div 2\frac{1}{2}$ $2\frac{1}{10}$ 48. $10\frac{1}{2} \div 1\frac{3}{4}$ 6 49. $8 \div 1\frac{2}{3}$ $4\frac{4}{5}$

50. $6\frac{1}{2} \div 2\frac{1}{4}$ $2\frac{8}{9}$ 51. $7 \div 2\frac{1}{3}$ 3 52. $8\frac{1}{3} \div 1\frac{1}{4}$ $6\frac{2}{3}$ 53. $12\frac{3}{4} \div 2\frac{1}{2}$ $5\frac{1}{10}$ 54. $3\frac{2}{3} \div 4$ $\frac{11}{12}$

Complete. *(page 202)*

55. 9 cm = _?_ mm 90   56. 6 km = _?_ m 6000   57. 62 mm = _?_ cm 6.2

58. 3450 m = _?_ km 3.450   59. 8.4 km = _?_ m 8400   60. 5.6 cm = _?_ m 0.056

278

Problem solving

A **budget** is a plan for using one's money. Here's my weekly budget.

I use a budget to keep track of my spending so that I won't run out of money between paychecks.

I keep a budget to make sure I put some money into savings each week.

Kelly
EARNINGS: $30/week
BUDGET
Savings: $6.00
Clothing: 4.50
Movies: 3.50
Records: 3.00
Lunches: 9.00
Other: 4.00

Rhonda
EARNINGS: $40/week
BUDGET
Savings: $ 4.00
Clothing: 10.00
Movies: 7.00
Records: 3.00
Lunches: 10.00
Other: 6.00

Walter
EARNINGS: $24/week
BUDGET
Savings: $3.00
Clothing: 6.50
Movies: 4.00
Records: 2.00
Lunches: 6.50
Other: 2.00

Use the budgets to answer the questions.

1. Who budgets a total of $6 for movies and records? Walter

2. Who budgets $2.50 more for clothing than for movies? Walter

3. Which person budgets $\frac{1}{4}$ of total earnings for clothing? Rhonda

4. Who budgets $\frac{1}{8}$ of total earnings for savings? Walter

5. What fraction of Rhonda's total earnings does she save? Give the answer in lowest terms. $\frac{1}{10}$

6. What fraction of his earnings does Walter save? Give the answer in lowest terms. $\frac{1}{8}$

7. Who spends 10% of total earnings for records? Kelly

8. Who spends 50% of total earnings for clothing and lunches? Rhonda

Solve.

9. Holly Moore earns $50 a week. She plans her budget using percents. Find the amount she plans to spend for each category.

10. How much more money does Holly plan to spend for clothing than for recreation? $2.50

HOLLY'S BUDGET		
CATEGORY	PERCENT	AMOUNT
Clothing	30%	$15.00
Savings	10%	?
Recreation	25%	?
Personal	15%	?
Other	20%	?

9. Savings—$5.00; Recreation—$12.50;
Personal—$7.50; Other—$10.00

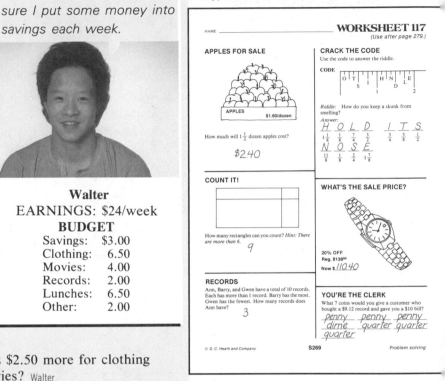

Solve. Use the budgets shown at the top of page 279.

1. How many dollars of her earnings did Rhonda budget for movies? $7

2. What fraction of his earnings did Walter budget for savings? $\frac{1}{8}$

3. What percent of her earnings did Kelly budget for records? 10%

LESSON OBJECTIVES
To understand checking accounts and checks
To balance a checking account

PROBLEM-SOLVING SKILL
Selecting information from checks and a check register

STARTING THE LESSON
The three checks at the top of page 280 are also on **Visual Aid 44**. Have the students use the checks and the clues in exercises 1 and 2 to find out whose checks paid for the stereo and the TV set.

EXERCISE NOTE
The check register at the top of page 281 is on **Visual Aid 45**. You may wish to use this in discussing exercises 7–14.

Checking accounts
CHECK IT OUT!

1. Whose check paid for the stereo? Tony Perez's
   Clues:
   - The check was written for more than $300.
   - The check was dated in early March.

2. Whose check paid for a TV set? Frank Horowitz's
   Clues:
   - The check number is less than 500.
   - The check was written for less than $400.

Check No. 175, March 28, 1985. PAY TO THE ORDER OF Ace Electronics $426.93. Four hundred twenty-six and 93/100 DOLLARS. FIRST NATIONAL BANK, Lexington, MA. Julie Adams. 0513 0421 127 415 0175

Check No. 326, March 15, 1985. PAY TO THE ORDER OF Ace Electronics $283.17. Two hundred eighty-three and 17/100 DOLLARS. UNITED BANK OF LEXINGTON, Lexington, MA. Frank Horowitz. 5711 2371 741 105 0326

Check No. 1215, March 6, 1985. PAY TO THE ORDER OF Ace Electronics $379.86. Three hundred seventy-nine and 86/100 DOLLARS. PEOPLE'S BANK, LEXINGTON, MA. Tony Perez. 910 710 170 416 913 1215

EXERCISES
Use the checks to answer the questions.

3. Find check No. 175. Who signed the check? What was the amount of the check?
   Julie Adams, $426.93

4. Who signed the check that tells the United Bank of Lexington to pay Ace Electronics $283.17 from his account? Frank Horowitz

5. What is the amount of check No. 1215? Why do you think the amount is written in both numerals and words? $379.86 So that the amount cannot be changed.

6. Julie Adams keeps her money in the First National Bank. Her checking-account number is 127 415. Whose checking-account number is 741 105? What is Tony Perez's checking-account number? Frank Horowitz's, 416 913

Julie's checkbook has a section called a **check register** in which she keeps a record of her checking account.

NUMBER	DATE	DESCRIPTION OF TRANSACTION	AMOUNT OF CHECK	✓	AMOUNT OF DEPOSIT	BALANCE $173 96
173	3/14/85	Top Supervalue	$ 72.14		$	101 82
	3/16/85				500.00	601 82
174	3/21/85	cash	50.00			551 82
175	3/28/85	Ace Electronics	426.93			124 89
176	4/2/85	Reed Bookstore	13.21			

7. On what date was a $500 deposit made? 3/16/85

8. For how much was the check that was written to Top Supervalue? $72.14

9. To whom was a check for $426.93 written? Ace Electronics

10. Check No. 174 was written for what amount? $50.00

11. What was the balance in Julie's account after check 174 was written? $551.82

12. What two numbers would you use to find the balance in her account on April 2? Would you add or subtract to find the balance? $124.89, $13.21, Subtract

13. What was the balance in her account after check No. 176 was written? $111.68

14. On April 4, Julie wrote check No. 177 for $17.65. What was her balance after that? $94.03

Can you figure it?

Find each new balance.

15.

	AMOUNT OF CHECK	✓	AMOUNT OF DEPOSIT	BALANCE 745 32
692.22 **a.**	53.10			?
674.94 **b.**	17.28			?
779.94 **c.**			105.00	?
496.77 **d.**	283.17			?
542.52 **e.**			45.75	?
484.14 **f.**	58.38			?

16.

	AMOUNT OF CHECK	✓	AMOUNT OF DEPOSIT	BALANCE 434 80
371.68 **a.**	63.12			?
353.29 **b.**	18.39			?
225.36 **c.**	127.93			?
475.36 **d.**			250.00	?
95.50 **e.**	379.86			?
84.43 **f.**	11.07			?

REVIEW PRACTICE
Writing fractions as mixed numbers
Page 429   Skill 35

PRACTICE WORKSHEET
Copymaster S270 or Duplicating Master S270

NAME _____   **WORKSHEET 118**
(Use after page 281.)

CHECKS AND BALANCES
Complete each check.
1. Write a check to Midtown Hardware for $53.20.

Tony Perez
1750 Oakland
Sometown, U.S.A.   No. 1216
March 7 19 85
Pay to the order of Midtown Hardware $ 53.20
Fifty-three and 20/100 _____ Dollars
First National Bank   Tony Perez
⑆0431⑆0213⑆ 1216

2. Write a check to EZ Cleaners for $17.89.

Tony Perez
1750 Oakland
Sometown, U.S.A.   No. 1217
March 7 19 85
Pay to the order of EZ Cleaners $ 17.89
Seventeen and 89/100 _____ Dollars
First National Bank   Tony Perez
⑆0431⑆0213⑆ 1217

Complete each balance.

	CHECK NO.	DATE	PAY TO	AMOUNT	DEPOSIT	BALANCE 623 78
3.	1211	March 1	Crosstown Motors	275.50		348 28
4.	1212	March 1	Bell Telephone	36.52		311 76
5.		March 2			385.16	696 92
6.	1213	March 2	Adams Insurance Co.	59.65		637 27
7.	1214	March 2	Cash	75.00		562 27
8.	1215	March 4	Power and Gas	69.65		492 62
9.	1216	March 7	Midtown Hardware	53.20		439 42
10.	1217	March 7	EZ Cleaners	17.89		421 53
	1218	March 8	Cash	10.00		411 53

© D. C. Heath and Company   S270   Checking accounts

LIFE-SKILL PROJECT
Researching information
Have the students find the answers to these questions:
1. What does "overdrawn" mean?
2. What is a "service charge"?
3. What does it mean to make a check out to "cash"?
4. What is a "cashier's check"?

CHALKBOARD QUIZ
on previous lesson

Solve. Use the check register shown at the top of page 281.

1. What is the number of the check written to Ace Electronics?   175

2. On what date was a $13.21 check written?   4/2/85

3. What was the balance in the account after check 173 was written? $101.82

LESSON OBJECTIVES

To understand savings accounts and passbooks
To understand compound interest

PROBLEM-SOLVING SKILLS

Selecting information from a savings-account passbook
Reading a graph
Interpreting directions correctly

STARTING THE LESSON

Have the students take the savings-account quiz shown at the top of page 282. Correct the quizzes before assigning the exercises.

EXERCISE NOTE

The passbook on page 282 and the compound-interest graph on page 283 are also on **Visual Aids 46 and 47.**

Savings accounts

CAN YOU PASS THIS SAVINGS ACCOUNT QUIZ?

Word list

| added | interest | subtracted |
| deposit | passbook | withdrawal |

Use the word list to complete each statement.

1. To open a savings account, you must make a ?. Each time you make a deposit, it is ? to the balance of your account.
   deposit, added

2. A ? is an amount of money you take out of your savings account. When you make a withdrawal, it is ? from your balance.   withdrawal, subtracted

3. You may receive a ? when you open a savings account. Bank tellers use it to record all deposits, withdrawals, ? earned, and the new balance.
   passbook, interest

EXERCISES

Use James Stickney's passbook to answer the questions.

1. How much money did James deposit on January 19? $250.00

2. How much money did he withdraw on March 12? $65.50

3. What was the balance in his account on March 12? $302.44

4. On what date did James get $2.22 interest?
   April 1

5. What was the balance on June 1? $489.94

6. How much interest did James receive for January 19 through June 1? $9.19

DEPOSITOR: JAMES STICKNEY ACCOUNT NO. 26-01432				
DATE	WITHDRAWAL	DEPOSIT	INTEREST	BALANCE
01-19		250.00		250.00
02-01			.65	250.65
02-18		115.50		366.15
03-01			1.79	367.94
03-12	65.50			302.44
04-01			2.22	304.66
05-01			2.01	306.67
05-17	180.75			487.42
06-01			2.52	?

The interest on savings accounts is often compounded daily. This means that the interest is added to the account each day. That way, you earn interest on your interest. Answers for 7–9 may vary slightly.

Use the graph to answer the questions.

7. At 6% interest, about how much would a $1000 deposit be worth at the end of 3 years? 5 years? 7 years? $1175, $1325, $1500

8. At 9% interest, about how much would a $1000 deposit be worth at the end of 3 years? 5 years? 7 years? $1300, $1525, $1825

9. At 12% interest, about how much would a $1000 deposit be worth at the end of 3 years? 5 years? 7 years? $1400, $1775, $2225

10. About how many years does it take to double a $1000 deposit at 9% interest? 8

11. About how many years does it take to double a $1000 deposit at 12% interest? 6

12. Suppose you deposited $1000 at 9% interest and a friend deposited $1000 at 6% interest.

   a. About how much more money would you have than your friend at the end of 4 years? $150

   b. About how much more money would you have than your friend at the end of 8 years? $400

Want to be a millionaire?

Here's how to make $1,000,000.

13. Put [?] dollars in a savings account that pays [?]% interest compounded yearly. Then wait [?] years and your account will be worth $1,000,981.

   To find [?], write a 5 in the ones place, a 6 in the hundreds place, and a 9 in the tens place. 695

   To find [?], write a 1 in the tens place and a 6 in the ones place. 16

   To find [?], write a 9 in the ones place and a 4 in the tens place. 49

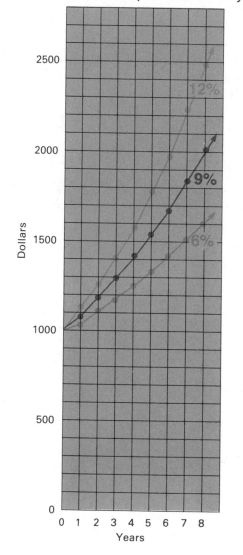

HOW $1000 GROWS
(Interest Compounded Daily)

Dollars / Years (12%, 9%, 6%)

REVIEW PRACTICE
Simplifying fractions
Page 429   Skill 36

PRACTICE WORKSHEET
Copymaster S271 or Duplicating Master S271

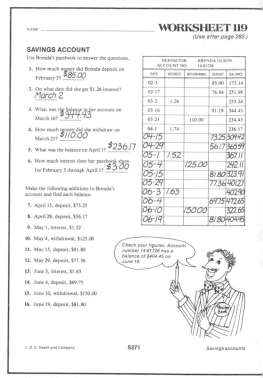

WORKSHEET 119
(Use after page 283.)

SAVINGS ACCOUNT
Use Brenda's passbook to answer the questions.

1. How much money did Brenda deposit on February 3? $85.00

2. On what date did she get $1.26 interest? March 2

3. What was the balance in her account on March 16? $344.43

4. How much money did she withdraw on March 21? $110.00

5. What was the balance on April 1? $236.17

6. How much interest does her passbook show for February 3 through April 1? $3.00

Make the following additions to Brenda's account and find each balance.

7. April 15, deposit, $73.25
8. April 29, deposit, $56.17
9. May 1, interest, $1.52
10. May 4, withdrawal, $125.00
11. May 15, deposit, $81.80
12. May 29, deposit, $77.36
13. June 3, interest, $1.63
14. June 4, deposit, $69.75
15. June 10, withdrawal, $150.00
16. June 19, deposit, $81.80

Check your figures. Account number 14-81726 has a balance of $404.45 on June 19.

LIFE-SKILL PROJECT
Using library resources
Have the students use an almanac to find the largest United States commercial bank. Challenge the students to write the amount of the bank's deposits in words. (This information can be found in *The World Almanac and Book of Facts*.)

Borrowing money

The amount of **interest** (rent for using the money) depends on the **principal** (the amount borrowed), the **rate** (percent of interest charged), and the **time** for which the money is borrowed.

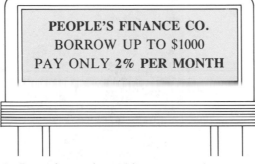

PEOPLE'S FINANCE CO.
BORROW UP TO $1000
PAY ONLY **2% PER MONTH**

I'll lend you the $500 at 18% for 1 year.

1. In order to buy this car, you have to borrow $500 for 6 months. Which loan would you choose, People's Finance Company's or Honest Abe's?
   Answers will vary.

Here's how *to use a formula to find the interest (I) for a $500 loan for 6 months.*

People's Finance Co.
Principal (*p*) = $500
Rate (*r*) = 2% per month
Time (*t*) = 6 months

Honest Abe
Principal = $500
Rate = 18% per year
Time = 6 months ($\frac{1}{2}$ year)

FORMULA $I = p \times r \times t$
$I = \$500 \times 0.02 \times 6$
$= \$60$

$I = p \times r \times t$
$I = \$500 \times 0.18 \times 0.5$
$= \$45$

The time units must be the same. Since the rate is a yearly rate, use 0.5 of a year for t.

2. Look at the *Here's how*. How much interest is People's Finance Company charging? How much interest is Honest Abe charging? $60, $45

3. Who is offering the better deal, People's Finance Company, or Honest Abe? Honest Abe

EXERCISES

Compute the interest.
Here are scrambled answers for the next row of exercises: $4.50 $240 $30

4. Principal = $1000
Rate = 12% per year
Time = 2 years $240

5. Principal = $600
Rate = 10% per year
Time = 6 months $30

6. Principal = $100
Rate = 1.5% per month
Time = 3 months
$4.50

7. Principal = $300
Rate = 16% per year
Time = 1 year $48

8. Principal = $450
Rate = 1% per month
Time = 8 months $36

9. Principal = $700
Rate = 14% per year
Time = 9 months
$73.50

10. Principal = $200
Rate = 15% per year
Time = 1.5 years $45

11. Principal = $4000
Rate = 12% per year
Time = 4 years $1920

12. Principal = $300
Rate = 18.5% per year
Time = 18 months
$83.25

Solve.

13. Brian borrowed $1500 for 1 year to buy a car. The yearly rate was 14%.
a. How much interest will he owe at the end of the year? $210
b. What is the total amount he will have to repay at the end of a year? $1710

14. You need $300 to buy a motorcycle.
a. A bank will lend you the money at 15% for 1 year. How much interest is that? $45
b. A finance company will loan you the money at 1.5% per month for 12 months. How much interest is that? $54
c. Which loan is the better deal, the bank's or the finance company's? The bank's

You're the loan officer

15. You work at a bank. Part of your job is to review loan applications. Complete the loan application. Then decide whether or not you would approve the loan.

FIRST NATIONAL BANK   APPLICATION FOR AUTO LOAN

NAME *Amy Higgins*   OCCUPATION *editor*

MONTHLY INCOME
(after deductions) $1400
MONTHLY EXPENSES
HOUSE PAYMENT   550
UTILITIES   180
LIVING   360
INSURANCE   80
OTHER LOAN PAYMENTS   50
OTHER   120
TOTAL EXPENSES   ?
$1340

COST OF AUTO $7200
DOWN PAYMENT   1000
BALANCE OWED
(cost minus down payment)   6200
?
FINANCE CHARGE   2770
TOTAL LOAN (balance owed plus finance charge) $8970
?
NUMBER OF MONTHLY PAYMENTS   30
MONTHLY PAYMENT   ?
$299

Do not write below this line

BANK USE ONLY
Check one   Loan ( ) approved (X) not approved

REVIEW PRACTICE
Writing fractions as decimals
Page 430   Skill 37

PRACTICE WORKSHEET
Copymaster S272 or Duplicating Master S272

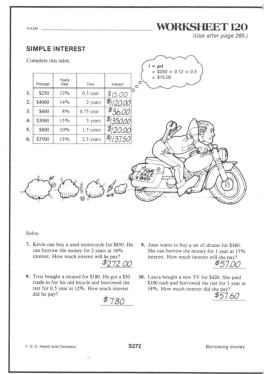

NAME _____   **WORKSHEET 120**
(Use after page 285.)

SIMPLE INTEREST
Complete this table.

$I = prt$
$= $250 \times 0.12 \times 0.5$
$= 15.00

	Principal	Yearly Rate	Time	Interest
1.	$250	12%	0.5 year	$15.00
2.	$4000	14%	2 years	$120.00
3.	$600	8%	0.75 year	$36.00
4.	$3000	15%	3 years	$350.00
5.	$800	10%	1.5 years	$120.00
6.	$3500	13%	2.5 years	$1137.50

Solve.

7. Kevin can buy a used motorcycle for $850. He can borrow the money for 2 years at 16% interest. How much interest will he pay? $272.00

8. Joan wants to buy a set of drums for $380. She can borrow the money for 1 year at 15% interest. How much interest will she pay? $57.00

9. Troy bought a moped for $180. He got a $50 trade-in for his old bicycle and borrowed the rest for 0.5 year at 12%. How much interest did he pay? $7.80

10. Laura bought a new TV for $420. She paid $100 cash and borrowed the rest for 1 year at 18%. How much interest did she pay? $57.60

© D. C. Heath and Company   S272   Borrowing money

LIFE-SKILL PROJECT
Buying a car
Give the students a copy of the classified section of a local newspaper containing automobiles for sale. Have the students pick out an automobile. Ask them to suppose that they have enough cash to pay 20% of the listed price and that they borrow the rest of the money for 2 years at a yearly rate of 15%. Have the students figure out how much interest they will have to pay and how much they will have to pay each month to pay off the loan.

LESSON OBJECTIVE

To understand monthly bills and payments

PROBLEM-SOLVING SKILLS

Finding information in a bill
Choosing the correct operation
Reading a telephone-rate table

STARTING THE LESSON

The bills on page 286 are also on **Visual Aid 48**. Before assigning the exercises, help the students understand how to read monthly bills by asking questions like these:

- Look at the Bank Card statement. How much was charged at Yen Foo Restaurant? ($16.25)
- How much is the finance charge for the month on the Bank Card statement? ($4.09)
- Look at the telephone bill. On what date was a 6-minute telephone call made to St. Louis? (3/24)
- How much is the monthly service charge for the telephone? ($10.98)

Paying bills

BILLS, BILLS, BILLS!

At the end of each month, bills are sent to customers. Here are some monthly bills that George Mumby received.

BANK CARD STATEMENT

ACCOUNT NUMBER	CREDIT LIMIT	AVAILABLE CREDIT	STATEMENT DATE	PAYMENT DUE DATE	MINIMUM PAYMENT DUE
431 025 1506	$1000	$400	03/24	04/19	$30.00

DATE OF TRANSACTION	REFERENCE NUMBER	CHARGES SINCE LAST STATEMENT	AMOUNT
02/20	753152	QUIK-SERV CLEANERS	$ 7.15
02/22	817615	RALPH'S APPLIANCES	215.74
02/25	044162	YEN FOO RESTAURANT	16.25
02/28	516234	CORNER GIFT SHOP	12.50
03/04	711276	A-1 RENTALS	22.16
03/10	144261	C & C MUFFLER SHOP	47.72

PREVIOUS BALANCE	PAYMENTS	UNPAID BALANCE	FINANCE CHARGE	PURCHASES ADDED	NEW BALANCE
$322.79	$50.00	$272.79	$4.09	$321.52	$598.40

CITY ELECTRIC
Account Number   7050682

PRESENT READING (KWH)	PREVIOUS READING (KWH)	KWH USED	AMOUNT
2012	1170	842	$44.55

ELECTRIC REFUND CREDIT $5.08

PREVIOUS BILL $48.26   TOTAL AMOUNT DUE ▶ $39.47
TOTAL PAYMENT $48.26   PAYMENT DUE DATE ▶ 04/15
PREVIOUS BALANCE $0.00

State Telephone Company   PAGE 1
                           ACCOUNT NO. 216-9045

FINAL CHARGES FOR MARCH 1 THRU MARCH 31
PAYMENT DUE BY APRIL 15

ITEMIZED CALLS $ 9.03
MONTHLY SERVICE CHARGE   10.98
FEDERAL TAX   .24

                    PAY THIS AMOUNT ➝ $20.25

State Telephone Company   PAGE 2

DETAILS OF ITEMIZED CALLS

DATE	TIME	PLACE CALLED	AREA	TEL NO	MIN	AMOUNT
03/09	8:21 AM	COLUMBUS, OH	614	666-8059	2	$2.16
03/15	3:15 PM	BOSTON, MA	617	999-4301	8	3.21
03/22	1:49 PM	MELBOURNE, FL	305	888-0122	11	2.25
03/24	5:05 PM	ST. LOUIS, MO	314	333-3001	6	1.41

TOTAL CHARGE FOR ITEMIZED CALLS $9.03

EXERCISES

Use the electric bill to answer these questions.

1. How many kilowatt hours (KWH) of electricity were used during the month? 842

2. What is the total amount George owes the electric company? On what date is the payment due? $39.47, April 15

3. What was the previous month's electricity bill? How much more was it than this month's bill? $48.26, $8.79

Use the Bank Card statement to answer these questions.

4. How much did George charge at the Corner Gift Shop? $12.50

5. What was the amount of the charge at the C & C Muffler Shop? $47.72

6. What was the total amount of new charges? $321.52

7. What two numbers would you use to check the amount of the unpaid balance? Would you add or subtract? $322.79, $50, Subtract

8. Bank Card charges 1.5% per month interest (finance charge) on the unpaid balance. How much was last month's finance charge? $4.09

9. What three numbers would you add to check the amount of the new balance? $272.79, $4.09, $321.52

10. George's new balance is $598.40. If he makes the minimum payment, how much will he still owe? $568.40

11. At 1.5% per month, how much will the finance charge be on an unpaid balance of $570? $8.55

Use the telephone bill to answer these questions.

12. When must the telephone bill be paid? How much does George owe? by April 15, $20.25

13. How much federal tax is included in the bill? $.24

14. What is the monthly charge for service? $10.98

15. On March 15, George made a long-distance call to Boston, Massachusetts. How many minutes long was the call? What was the charge for the call? 8, $3.21

16. How much did it cost per minute for George to call Columbus, Ohio? $1.08

17. If George makes a long-distance call between 11:00 P.M. and 8:00 A.M., he gets a 60% discount. How much would he have saved if he had made the call to Melbourne, Florida, between 11:00 P.M. and 8:00 A.M.? $1.35

Answer the phone

Use the phone rates to answer the questions.

18. Julie called a friend at 10 A.M. on Wednesday. They talked for 5 minutes. How much was she charged for the call? $1.44

19. Julie was charged $1.28 for a call she made on Friday at 9:30 P.M. How long was the call? 6 minutes

LONG DISTANCE IN-STATE PHONE RATES Monday through Friday		
	8 A.M.—5 P.M.	5 P.M.—8 A.M.
First minute	$.44	$.28
Each additional minute	$.25	$.20

PRACTICE WORKSHEET
Copymaster S273 or Duplicating Master S273

NAME _____   **WORKSHEET 121**
(Use after page 287.)

MONTHLY PAYMENTS

BANK CARD STATEMENT					
ACCOUNT NUMBER	CREDIT LIMIT	AVAILABLE CREDIT	STATEMENT DATE	PAYMENT DUE DATE	MINIMUM PAYMENT DUE
431 025 1506	$1000	⑥ $773.10	06/10/85	06/25/85	⑤ $22.69

DATE OF TRANSACTION	REFERENCE NUMBER	CHARGES SINCE LAST STATEMENT	AMOUNT
05/18	612435	UPTOWN MOTORS	$ 41.10
05/23	127067	TED'S CAMERA SHOP	16.95
05/28	427106	PRO SPORTSWEAR	39.65
05/30	372111	HARRY'S RESTAURANT	27.70

PREVIOUS BALANCE	PAYMENTS	UNPAID BALANCE	FINANCE CHARGE	PURCHASES ADDED	NEW BALANCE
175.15	75.15	① $100.00	② $1.50	③ $125.40	④ $226.90

Use the monthly bank card statement to answer the questions. Then use the answers to complete the bank card statement.

1. Subtract the payments from the previous balance to get the unpaid balance. What is the unpaid balance? $100.00

2. The finance charge is computed by multiplying 0.015 (1.5%) times the unpaid balance. What is the finance charge? $1.50

3. Add the charges since the last payment to get the purchases added. What is the total of the purchases added? $125.40

4. Add the unpaid balance, finance charge, and purchases added to get the new balance. What is the new balance? $226.90

5. The minimum payment is computed by multiplying 0.10 (10%) times the new balance. What is the minimum payment? $22.69

6. Subtract the new balance from the credit limit to get the available credit for the next month. What is the available credit? $773.10

© D. C. Heath and Company   S273   Paying bills

CHALKBOARD CHALLENGE
Unscramble the letters of each of these consumer math words.
1. INUT CPERI   Unit price
2. SVNAIGS UCACONT   Savings account
3. EDUBGT   Budget
4. ETINERST   Interest

SKILLS REVIEWED

Adding with customary units of measure
Changing a percent to a fraction
Changing a fraction to a percent
Solving percent problems

PROBLEM-SOLVING SKILLS

Reading a computer display
Choosing the correct operation
Using a guess-and-check strategy

STARTING THE LESSON

Cumulative Skill Practice
Write these five answers on the chalkboard:

6 yd $\frac{1}{8}$ 350%   40   49.5

Challenge the students to an answer hunt by saying, "Look for the five even-numbered exercises on page 288 that have these answers. You have five minutes to find as many of the exercises as you can." (Exercises 4, 32, 48, 66, and 76)

STARTING THE LESSON

Problem Solving
Have the students read the paragraphs at the top of page 289. Have the students use the information on Screens A and B and ask them to answer questions like these:

• Use Screen B. What are the order number and cost of the Friendship Bouquet? (204, $23.95)
• What is the cost of order 219? ($19.50)
• Use Screen A. What number would you select to get the order numbers and the costs of the Happy Birthday! selections? (5)

Cumulative Skill Practice

Add. *(page 218)*

1. 4 ft 9 in.
   + 1 ft 8 in.
   _____
   6 ft 5 in.

2. 3 yd 2 ft
   + 2 yd 2 ft
   _____
   6 yd 1 ft

3. 3 ft 9 in.
   + 1 ft 8 in.
   _____
   5 ft 5 in.

4. 2 yd 1 ft
   + 3 yd 2 ft
   _____
   6 yd

5. 2 gal 3 qt
   + 1 gal 1 qt
   _____
   4 gal

6. 2 qt 1 pt
   + 1 qt 1 pt
   _____
   4 qt

7. 3 gal 1 qt
   + 2 gal 3 qt
   _____
   6 gal

8. 3 pt 1 c
   + 1 pt 1 c
   _____
   5 pt

9. 7 lb 12 oz
   + 5 lb 8 oz
   _____
   13 lb 4 oz

10. 4 T 1200 lb
    + 1 T 1300 lb
    _____
    6 T 500 lb

11. 8 lb 11 oz
    + 2 lb 9 oz
    _____
    11 lb 4 oz

12. 6 T 1600 lb
    + 3 T 1500 lb
    _____
    10 T 1100 lb

Change to a fraction or mixed number in simplest form. *(page 248)*

13. 10% $\frac{1}{10}$ 14. 50% $\frac{1}{2}$ 15. 60% $\frac{3}{5}$ 16. 5% $\frac{1}{20}$ 17. 30% $\frac{3}{10}$ 18. 40% $\frac{2}{5}$

19. 25% $\frac{1}{4}$ 20. 75% $\frac{3}{4}$ 21. 90% $\frac{9}{10}$ 22. 36% $\frac{9}{25}$ 23. 72% $\frac{18}{25}$ 24. 15% $\frac{3}{20}$

25. 120% $1\frac{1}{5}$ 26. 150% $1\frac{1}{2}$ 27. 175% $1\frac{3}{4}$ 28. 200% 2 29. 250% $2\frac{1}{2}$ 30. 340% 3

31. $33\frac{1}{3}$% $\frac{1}{3}$ 32. $12\frac{1}{2}$% $\frac{1}{8}$ 33. $66\frac{2}{3}$% $\frac{2}{3}$ 34. $6\frac{1}{4}$% $\frac{1}{16}$ 35. $87\frac{1}{2}$% $\frac{7}{8}$ 36. $3\frac{1}{8}$% $\frac{1}{32}$

Change to a percent. *(page 250)*

37. $\frac{2}{5}$ 40%   38. $\frac{1}{10}$ 10%   39. $\frac{1}{2}$ 50%   40. $\frac{3}{4}$ 75%   41. $\frac{1}{5}$ 20%   42. $\frac{4}{5}$ 80%   43. $\frac{2}{9}$ 2

44. $\frac{9}{10}$ 90%   45. $\frac{3}{5}$ 60%   46. $\frac{1}{4}$ 25%   47. 4 400%   48. $\frac{7}{2}$ 350%   49. 3 300%   50. $\frac{9}{6}$

Solve. *(page 258)*

51. 10% of 60 = n 6

52. 25% of 44 = n 11

53. 60% of 45 = n 27

54. 12% of 34 = n 4.08

55. 9% of 41.5 = n 3.735

56. 150% of 27 = n 40.5

57. 8.5% of 136 = n 11.56

58. 11.4% of 52 = n 5.928

59. 16.2% of 48.5 = n 7.85

60. $12\frac{1}{2}$% of 56 = n 7

61. $33\frac{1}{3}$% of 63 = n 21

62. $83\frac{1}{3}$% of 72 = n

63. 10.8% of 265 = n 28.62

64. 75% of 156 = n 117

65. $62\frac{1}{2}$% of 250 = n 156.

Solve. *(page 260)*

66. 10% of n = 4 40

67. 20% of n = 11 55

68. 25% of n = 16 64

69. 50% of n = 13 26

70. 75% of n = 48 64

71. 150% of n = 39 26

Solve. Round each answer to the nearest tenth. *(page 260)*

72. 4.5% of n = 6 133.3

73. 9.5% of n = 12 126.3

74. 6.4% of n = 15 234.

75. 1.5% of n = 7.3 486.7

76. 21.4% of n = 10.6 49.5

77. 7.8% of n = 12.4 1

Problem solving

SHOPPING BY COMPUTER

Diane Milotte can use her home computer to order flowers to be sent almost anywhere in the world. Her computer can be linked by telephone to a large computer that will select a florist, place the order, and charge it to Diane's account number.

The screens below show some of the decisions Diane has to make when she places an order.

Screen A

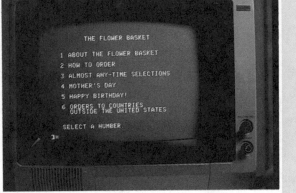

THE FLOWER BASKET

1 ABOUT THE FLOWER BASKET
2 HOW TO ORDER
3 ALMOST ANY-TIME SELECTIONS
4 MOTHER'S DAY
5 HAPPY BIRTHDAY!
6 ORDERS TO COUNTRIES OUTSIDE THE UNITED STATES

SELECT A NUMBER

Diane selected "3".
The computer then displayed Screen B.

Screen B

SELECTIONS
FOR ALMOST ANY OCCASION

ROSES $46.95
ORDER 107
WISH'N WELL BOUQUET $24.95
ORDER 292
FRIENDSHIP BOUQUET $23.95
ORDER 204
FORGET-ME-NOT BOUQUET $19.50
ORDER 219

TO ORDER ENTER A 3-DIGIT NUMBER

Diane entered "219".
Additional screens requested more information to complete her order.

Solve.

1. Use Screen A. What information would Diane be asking for if she selected number 2 on Screen A? How to order

2. Use Screen B. What are the order number and the cost of the Wish'n Well Bouquet? 292, $24.95

3. Use Screen A.

  a. What number should Diane select to order a special bouquet for her aunt's birthday? 5

  b. Diane wants to order flowers for her sister in Paris, France. What number should she select? 6

4. Use Screen B.

  a. What 3-digit number should Diane enter to order the least expensive bouquet? 219

  b. If Diane decided to spend $23.95, what 3-digit number should she enter? 204

5. Diane ordered bouquets 107, 292, and 219. How much money was charged to her account? $91.40

6. One month Diane ordered 2 different bouquets. She spent a total of $43.45. Which bouquets did she order? Friendship and Forget-Me-Not

Consumer Mathematics **289**

EXTRA PROBLEM SOLVING
Page 455   Even exercises

PROBLEM-SOLVING WORKSHEET
Copymaster S274 or Duplicating Master S274

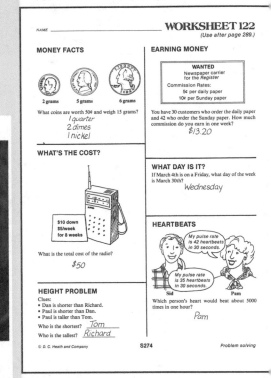

NAME _____

WORKSHEET 122
(Use after page 289.)

MONEY FACTS

2 grams   5 grams   6 grams

What coins are worth 50¢ and weigh 15 grams?
1 quarter
2 dimes
1 nickel

EARNING MONEY

WANTED
Newspaper carrier
for the *Register*
Commission Rates:
5¢ per daily paper
10¢ per Sunday paper

You have 30 customers who order the daily paper and 42 who order the Sunday paper. How much commission do you earn in one week?
$13.20

WHAT'S THE COST?

$10 down
$5/week
for 8 weeks

What is the total cost of the radio?
$50

WHAT DAY IS IT?
If March 4th is on a Friday, what day of the week is March 30th?
Wednesday

HEIGHT PROBLEM
Clues:
• Dan is shorter than Richard.
• Paul is shorter than Dan.
• Paul is taller than Tom.
Who is the shortest? Tom
Who is the tallest? Richard

HEARTBEATS
My pulse rate is 42 heartbeats in 30 seconds.
My pulse rate is 35 heartbeats in 30 seconds.
Sid   Pam
Which person's heart would beat about 5000 times in one hour?
Pam

© D. C. Heath and Company   S274   Problem solving

CHALKBOARD CHALLENGE
Use this code and find the two-letter word in the first paragraph on page 289 that has a sum of 35. to

CODE

a	b	c	d	e	. . .	z
1	2	3	4	5	. . .	26

CHAPTER 12 TEST
(Form A)

Solve. *(pages 270, 271)*

1. How many hours would you work each week? **40**
2. How much does the job pay each week? **$174**
3. Suppose that $27.40 is withheld for federal income tax and $12.35 is withheld for Social Security. What would your net pay be? **$134.25**
4. How much less would the net pay be than the gross pay? **$39.75**

SALES CLERK
Monday–Friday
8-hr day $4.35/hr
Apply in person.
Pedal Power Bike Shop

Solve. *(page 272)*

5. What is the regular price of the sander? **$54.60**
6. How much is the discount on the sander? **$8.19**
7. What is the sale price of the sander? **$46.41**

Reg. $54.60
SANDER
15% OFF

Complete. Round each unit price to the nearest cent. *(page 274)*

8. The unit price of the smaller bag of apples is **$.33** per pound.
9. The unit price of the larger bag of apples is **$.32** per pound.
10. The **larger** bag is the better buy.

APPLES
3 pounds $1.00   5 pounds $1.59

Solve. *(page 276)*

With a coupon, how much can you save when you buy a

11. small pizza? **$.95**
12. medium pizza? **$1.48**
13. large pizza? **$1.97**
14. How much more do you save on a large pizza than on a small one? **$1.02**
15. How much would you have to pay for 2 medium pizzas if you used a coupon? **$13.32**
16. You had $20. You bought a medium pizza with a coupon and paid the regular price for a small pizza. How much money did you have left? **$8.13**

PIZZA PALACE COUPON
Save on ONE Super Combo pizza.

	Reg.	With coupon
Small	$3.90	$3.00
Medium	$7.40	$5.92
Large	$8.95	$6.98

Limit 1 per customer.

ANSWERS
1. 40
2. $174
3. $134.25
4. $39.75
5. $54.60
6. $8.19
7. $46.41
8. $.33
9. $.32
10. larger
11. $.95
12. $1.48
13. $1.97
14. $1.02
15. $13.32
16. $8.13

© D. C. Heath and Company   S45   Page 1

CHAPTER 12 TEST
(Form A)

Solve. *(page 280)*

17. What is the check number? **106**
18. To whom was the check written? **Hal Lee**
19. Who signed the check? **Jo Davis**
20. Before Jo Davis wrote check no. 106, she had a balance of $406.38. What was the balance after she wrote check no. 106? **$371.75**

NO. 106
March 16, '85
Pay to the order of Hal Lee
Thirty-four and 63/100
People's Bank
Lexington, MA
Jo Davis

Solve. *(page 282)*

21. How much money was deposited on April 3? **$500**
22. On what date was $50 withdrawn? **April 23**
23. How much interest was paid on May 1? **$2.06**
24. What was the balance after the interest was paid on May 1? **$452.06**
25. What would the balance be if $39.65 was deposited on May 16? **$616.71**
26. What would the balance be if $39.65 was deposited on May 16 and $50.00 withdrawn on May 17? **$566.71**

DEPOSITOR: RUTH WEAVER   ACCOUNT NO. 41-0808

DATE	WITHDRAWAL	DEPOSIT	INTEREST	BALANCE
		800.00		800.00
04-03		800.00		800.00
04-23	50.00			550.00
05-01			2.06	452.06
05-16		188.00		577.06

Compute the interest. Round to the nearest cent. *(page 284)*

27. Principal = $100
Rate = 10% per year
Time = 1 year
Interest = **$10**

28. Principal = $240
Rate = 12% per year
Time = 2 years
Interest = **$57.60**

29. Principal = $850
Rate = 1.5% per year
Time = 1 year
Interest = **$12.75**

Solve. *(page 286)*

30. What is the total amount owed to the electric company? **$55.36**
31. On what date is the payment due? **May 15**
32. How much more was the previous bill? **$13.63**
33. How many kilowatt hours (KWH) of electricity were used? **1181**

CITY ELECTRIC

PRESENT READING (KWH)	PREVIOUS READING (KWH)	KWH USED	AMOUNT
4806	3625	1181	$62.49

ELECTRIC REFUND CREDIT $7.13
Previous Bill $68.99
Total Payment $68.99 Total Amount Due $55.36
Previous Balance $ 0.00 Payment Due Date 5/15

ANSWERS
17. 106
18. Hal Lee
19. Jo Davis
20. $371.75
21. $500
22. April 23
23. $2.06
24. $452.06
25. $616.71
26. $566.71
27. $10
28. $57.60
29. $12.75
30. $55.36
31. May 15
32. $13.63
33. 1181

© D. C. Heath and Company   S46   Page 2

Chapter REVIEW

Here are scrambled answers for the review exercises:

| 18 | 40 | 72 | 200 | interest | net | Robert Thayer | subtracted |
| 38 | 60 | 75 | added | less | pounds | Security | time |

1. Security, net   **2.** 75, 72   **3.** pounds, 38

1. An employer is required by law to deduct from a paycheck money for federal income tax and social **?**. "Take home" pay is called an employee's **?** pay. *(page 271)*

2. If an item is on sale for 25% off the regular price, you can compute the sale price by taking **?**% of the regular price. The sale price of this TV is $**?**. *(page 272)*

Reg. $96
Now 25% off

3. To find the price per pound of these oranges, you divide the price by the number of **?**. The unit price of the oranges rounded to the nearest cent is **?**¢. *(page 274)*

5 pounds $1.89

4. 200, 40, Robert Thayer, 60

4. The check number is **?**. The check was written for **?** dollars. **?** signed the check. *(page 280)*
The balance in the checking account before the check was written was $100. The balance after the check was written was **?** dollars. *(page 280)*

March 3 19 85   No. 200
PAY TO THE ORDER OF   Mike's Market $40.00
Forty and 00/100 _____ DOLLARS
Savings Bank
Robert Thayer
⑈211371227⑈ 1234025431⑈ 200

5. added, subtracted   **6.** time, interest   **7.** 18

5. Each time you make a deposit in a savings account, the amount is **?** to the balance of your account. Each time you make a withdrawal from a savings account, the amount is **?** from the balance of your account. *(page 282)*

6. The amount of interest charged for a loan depends on the principal, the interest rate, and the **?** for which the money is borrowed. You can use this formula to compute the **?** on a loan. *(page 284)*

$I = p \times r \times t$

7. The interest for this loan would be $**?**. *(page 284)*

Principal = $300
Rate = 12% per year
Time = 6 months

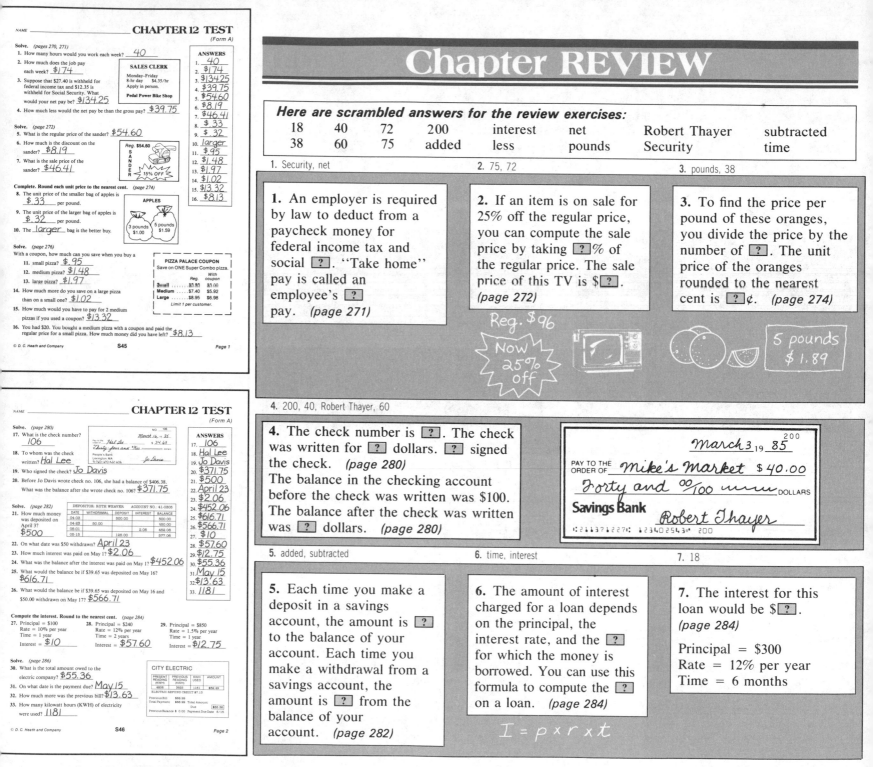

Chapter TEST

Solve. *(page 270, 271)*

1. a. How much does the job pay each week?

   b. Suppose that Camper's Supply $170 withheld $23.75 for federal income tax and $11.50 for Social Security. What would the net pay be? $134.75

   c. How much less would the net pay be than the gross pay? $35.25

SALES CLERK
No experience
necessary.
Mon—Fri
8-hr day $4.25/hr
Apply in person
CAMPER'S SUPPLY

Compute the sale price. *(page 272)*

2. **HIKING BOOTS** $51.60
   Reg. $64.50
   20% OFF!

3. **TENT** $84
   Reg. $112
   25% OFF!

4. **BACK PACK** $39.20
   Reg. $56
   30% OFF!

Solve. *(pages 274, 276)*

3. What is the unit price of the smaller bag of trail mix? $.16

4. Which is the better buy, the small bag or the large bag?
   Small bag

5. Camper's Supply Store gave out a 50¢ coupon that could be used on the purchase of a large bag of trail mix. If a customer used a coupon, how much would 3 small bags and 1 large bag of trail mix cost? $7.86

$2.69   16 ounces
$1.89   12 ounces

Solve. *(page 280)*

6. Who signed the check?   David Jones

7. What is the number of the check?   2003

8. What is the amount of the check? $48.93

9. To whom was the check written?   Camper's Supply

10. David James had a balance of $167.34 in his checking account before he wrote the check. What was his balance after he wrote the check? $118.41

March 4, 19 85   2003
PAY TO THE ORDER OF   Camper's Supply $48.93
Forty-eight and 93/100   DOLLARS
Savings Bank
David Jones

Solve. *(pages 282, 284)*

11. On March 24 you had a balance of $124 in your savings account. On March 25 you withdrew $35, and on March 31 the bank paid you $.82 interest. What was your balance then? $89.82

12. How much interest will you pay if you borrow $240 for 6 months if you are charged 1% per month? $14.40

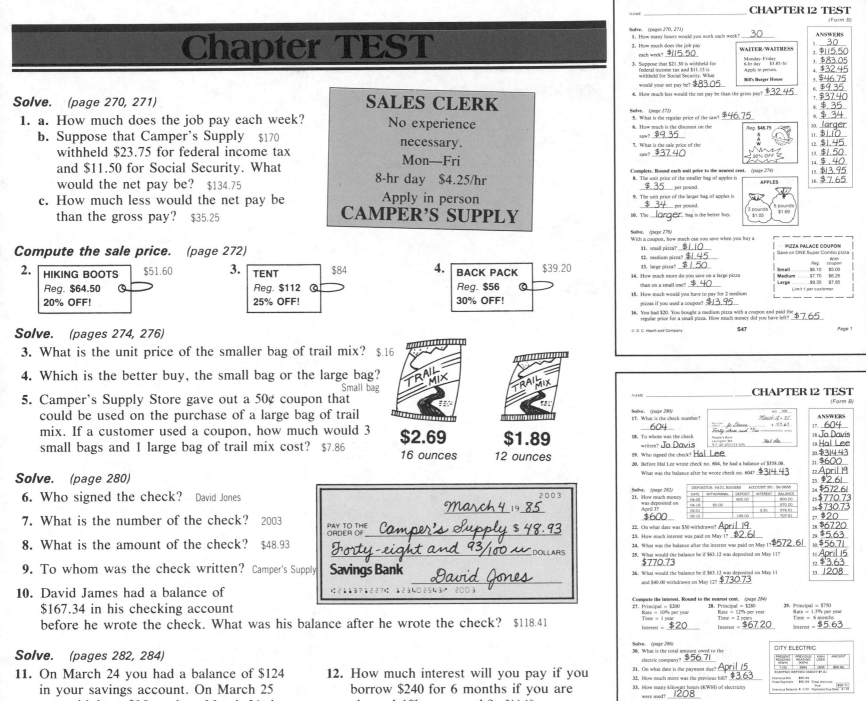

Solve. *(pages 270, 271)*

1. How many hours would you work each week?   30

2. How much does the job pay each week? $115.50

   WAITER/WAITRESS
   Monday–Friday
   6-hr day $3.85/hr
   Apply in person
   Bill's Burger House

3. Suppose that $21.30 is withheld for federal income tax and $11.15 is withheld for Social Security. What would your net pay be? $83.05

4. How much less would the net pay be than the gross pay? $32.45

Solve. *(page 272)*

5. What is the regular price of the saw? $46.75

6. How much is the discount on the saw? $9.35

   Reg. $46.75   S A W   20% OFF

7. What is the sale price of the saw? $37.40

Complete. Round each unit price to the nearest cent. *(page 274)*

8. The unit price of the smaller bag of apples is $.35   per pound.

9. The unit price of the larger bag of apples is $.34   per pound.

   APPLES   3 pounds $1.05   5 pounds $1.69

10. The larger bag is the better buy.

Solve. *(page 276)*

With a coupon, how much can you save when you buy a

11. small pizza? $1.10

12. medium pizza? $1.45

13. large pizza? $1.50

14. How much more do you save on a large pizza than on a small one? $.40

15. How much would you have to pay for 2 medium pizzas if you used a coupon? $13.95

16. You had $20. You bought a medium pizza with a coupon and paid the regular price for a small pizza. How much money did you have left? $7.65

PIZZA PALACE COUPON		
Save on ONE Super Combo pizza.		
	Reg.	With coupon
Small	$6.10	$5.00
Medium	$7.70	$6.25
Large	$9.35	$7.85
	Limit 1 per customer.	

	ANSWERS
1.	30
2.	$115.50
3.	$83.05
4.	$32.45
5.	$46.75
6.	$9.35
7.	$37.40
8.	$.35
9.	$.34
10.	larger
11.	$1.10
12.	$1.45
13.	$1.50
14.	$.40
15.	$13.95
16.	$7.65

© D. C. Heath and Company   S47   Page 1

Solve. *(page 280)*

17. What is the check number?   604

18. To whom was the check written?   Jo Davis

19. Who signed the check?   Hal Lee

20. Before Hal Lee wrote check no. 604, he had a balance of $358.06. What was the balance after he wrote check no. 604? $314.43

NO. 604   March 17, 19 85 $43.63
PAY TO   Jo Davis
Forty-three and 63/100
People's Bank
Lexington MA
4/7-10-170-123-604
Hal Lee

Solve. *(page 282)*

21. How much money was deposited on April 3? $600

DATE	WITHDRAWAL	DEPOSIT	INTEREST	BALANCE
04-03		600.00		600.00
04-19	30.00			570.00
05-01			2.61	572.61
05-10		198.00		707.61

22. On what date was $30 withdrawn?   April 19

23. How much interest was paid on May 1? $2.61

24. What was the balance after the interest was paid on May 1? $572.61

25. What would the balance be if $63.12 was deposited on May 11? $770.73

26. What would the balance be if $63.12 was deposited on May 11 and $40.00 withdrawn on May 12? $730.73

Compute the interest. Round to the nearest cent. *(page 284)*

27. Principal = $200
    Rate = 10% per year
    Time = 1 year
    Interest = $20

28. Principal = $280
    Rate = 12% per year
    Time = 2 years
    Interest = $67.20

29. Principal = $750
    Rate = 1.5% per year
    Time = 6 months
    Interest = $5.63

Solve. *(page 286)*

30. What is the total amount owed to the electric company? $56.71

31. On what date is the payment due?   April 15

32. How much more was the previous bill? $3.63

33. How many kilowatt hours (KWH) of electricity were used?   1208

CITY ELECTRIC

PRESENT READING (KWH)	PREVIOUS READING (KWH)	KWH USED	AMOUNT
7152	5944	1208	$60.92

ELECTRIC REFUND CREDIT $7.41
Previous Bill $60.34
Total Payment $60.34   Total Amount Due $56.71
Previous Balance $ 0.00   Payment Due Date 4-15

	ANSWERS
17.	604
18.	Jo Davis
19.	Hal Lee
20.	$314.43
21.	$600
22.	April 19
23.	$2.61
24.	$572.61
25.	$770.73
26.	$730.73
27.	$20
28.	$67.20
29.	$5.63
30.	$56.71
31.	April 15
32.	$3.63
33.	1208

© D. C. Heath and Company   S48   Page 2

Use Copymaster S336 to provide the students with an answer sheet in standardized test format.

Cumulative TEST Standardized Format

Choose the correct letter.

Answers for Cumulative Test, Chapters 1–12

1. Ⓐ Ⓑ ● Ⓓ   2. Ⓐ ● Ⓒ Ⓓ   3. ● Ⓑ Ⓒ Ⓓ
4. Ⓐ Ⓑ ● Ⓓ   5. Ⓐ Ⓑ Ⓒ ●   6. Ⓐ Ⓑ Ⓒ ●
7. ● Ⓑ Ⓒ Ⓓ   8. Ⓐ Ⓑ ● Ⓓ   9. Ⓐ ● Ⓒ Ⓓ
10. Ⓐ ● Ⓒ Ⓓ   11. Ⓐ ● Ⓒ Ⓓ   12. Ⓐ Ⓑ Ⓒ ●

The table below correlates test items with student text pages.

Test Item	Page Taught	Skill Practice
1	160	p. 278, exercises 1–12
2	170	p. 278, exercises 13–24
3	182	p. 278, exercises 25–39
4	190	p. 278, exercises 40–54
5	202	p. 278, exercises 55–60
6	218	p. 288, exercises 1–12
7	248	p. 288, exercises 13–36
8	250	p. 288, exercises 37–50
9	258	p. 288, exercises 51–65
10	260	p. 288, exercises 66–71
11	232	
12	284	

1. Add. $2\frac{5}{8}$
   $+1\frac{1}{2}$

   A. $3\frac{1}{8}$
   B. $3\frac{3}{5}$
   ⓒ $4\frac{1}{8}$
   D. none of these

2. Subtract. $3\frac{1}{4}$
   $-1\frac{1}{3}$

   A. $2\frac{11}{12}$
   Ⓑ $1\frac{11}{12}$
   C. $2\frac{1}{12}$
   D. none of these

3. Give the product.
   $2\frac{1}{2} \times 1\frac{1}{4}$

   Ⓐ $3\frac{1}{8}$
   B. 2
   C. $\frac{8}{25}$
   D. none of these

4. Give the quotient.
   $4\frac{2}{3} \div 1\frac{3}{4}$

   A. $8\frac{1}{6}$
   B. $\frac{3}{8}$
   ⓒ $2\frac{2}{3}$
   D. none of these

5. 425 mm = _?_ m
   A. 4.25
   B. 42.5
   C. 4250
   Ⓓ none of these

6. Add.   4 lb 9 oz
   $+$ 5 lb 8 oz

   A. 10 lb 7 oz
   B. 10 lb 5 oz
   C. 10 lb 3 oz
   Ⓓ none of these

7. Change to a fraction.
   $33\frac{1}{3}\% = ?$

   Ⓐ $\frac{1}{3}$
   B. $\frac{2}{3}$
   C. 3
   D. none of these

8. Change to a percent.
   $\frac{5}{6} = ?$

   A. $16\frac{2}{3}\%$
   B. $66\frac{2}{3}\%$
   ⓒ $83\frac{1}{3}\%$
   D. none of these

9. Solve.
   12% of 42 = n

   A. 350
   Ⓑ 5.04
   C. 50.4
   D. none of these

10. Solve.
    5% of n = 12

    A. 60
    Ⓑ 240
    C. 0.6
    D. none of these

11. You jog 3 miles in 24 minutes. At that rate, how far can you jog in 36 minutes?

    A. 6 miles
    Ⓑ 4.5 miles
    C. 1.5 miles
    D. none of these

12. Compute the interest.
    Principal = $650
    Rate = 15% per year
    Time = 6 months

    A. $97.50
    B. $195
    C. $585
    Ⓓ none of these

THIRD-QUARTER TEST
(Chapters 9 through 12)

NAME _____

Choose the correct letter.

Sample:
Give the length.

A. 3 cm
B. 4 mm
C. 4 cm
D. none of these

First decide which answer is correct. Then find the problem number on your answer sheet and darken in the space for the correct answer. In the sample, c is the correct answer.

1. Give the length.

A. 30 mm
B. 32 mm
C. 35 mm
D. none of these

2. The length of a new pencil is about
A. 19 m
B. 19 km
C. 19 mm
D. 19 cm

3. 8 cm = ? mm
A. 80
B. 8
C. 800
D. 0.08

4. 750 m = ? km
A. 7.50
B. 0.750
C. 75
D. 7500

5. 16.4 m = ? cm
A. 1.64
B. 164
C. 1640
D. none of these

6. 1.5 L = ? mL
A. 15
B. 150
C. 1500
D. none of these

7. 432 mg = ? g
A. 43.2
B. 4.32
C. 4320
D. none of these

8. Give the length.

A. $1\frac{1}{2}$ in.
B. $1\frac{3}{4}$ in.
C. $1\frac{5}{8}$ in.
D. none of these

9. 9 ft = ? in.
A. 96
B. 108
C. 144
D. none of these

10. 8 yd 1 ft = ? ft
A. 72
B. 33
C. 25
D. none of these

© D. C. Heath and Company   S77   Page 1

THIRD-QUARTER TEST
(Chapters 9 through 12)

NAME _____

Choose the correct letter.

11. 8 pt = ? qt
A. 4
B. 16
C. 32
D. none of these

12. 96 oz = ? lb
A. 8
B. 12
C. 3
D. none of these

13. 2 T = ? lb
A. 1000
B. 2000
C. 4000
D. none of these

14. Add.   4 ft 9 in.
            +3 ft 7 in.
A. 8 ft 4 in.
B. 7 ft 4 in.
C. 8 ft 6 in.
D. none of these

15. Subtract.   4 gal
               −1 gal 3 qt
A. 3 gal 3 qt
B. 2 gal 1 qt
C. 3 gal 1 qt
D. none of these

16. Write as a fraction in lowest terms.
15:12 = ?
A. $\frac{12}{15}$
B. $\frac{15}{12}$
C. $\frac{5}{4}$
D. none of these

17. $\frac{6}{8}$ = ?
A. $\frac{4}{3}$
B. $\frac{2}{3}$
C. $\frac{7}{9}$
D. $\frac{9}{12}$

18. Solve. $\frac{n}{6} = \frac{10}{15}$
A. 4
B. 9
C. 25
D. none of these

19. Solve. $\frac{8}{3} = \frac{5}{n}$
A. $13\frac{1}{3}$
B. $4\frac{4}{5}$
C. $1\frac{7}{8}$
D. none of these

20. You type 216 words in 6 minutes. At that rate, how many words could you type in 8 minutes?
A. 288
B. 162
C. 324
D. none of these

21. You jog 2.4 miles in 18 minutes. At that rate, how many minutes would it take you to jog 4.0 miles?
A. 10.8
B. 30
C. 32
D. none of these

22. The triangles are similar. Find the length of n.
A. 4 m
B. 10 m
C. 9 m
D. none of these

23. The figures are similar. Find the length n.
A. 9.6 m
B. 8.4 m
C. 7.2 m
D. none of these

24. A flagpole casts a shadow of 12 meters. At the same time, a 2-meter post casts a shadow of 1 meter. What is the height of the flagpole?
A. 24 m
B. 6 m
C. 18 m
D. none of these

25. A tree is 9.6 meters tall. It casts a 24.0-meter shadow. How tall is a nearby building that casts a 45.0-meter shadow?
A. 5.12 m
B. 12.0 m
C. 18.0 m
D. none of these

© D. C. Heath and Company   S78   Page 2

THIRD-QUARTER TEST
(Chapters 9 through 12)

NAME _____

Choose the correct letter.

26. 80% = ?
A. $\frac{4}{5}$
B. $1\frac{1}{4}$
C. $\frac{3}{5}$
D. none of these

27. $66\frac{2}{3}$% = ?
A. $\frac{1}{3}$
B. $1\frac{1}{2}$
C. $\frac{2}{3}$
D. none of these

28. $\frac{5}{4}$ = ?
A. 80%
B. 125%
C. 150%
D. none of these

29. $\frac{1}{6}$ = ?
A. $12\frac{1}{2}$%
B. $18\frac{1}{3}$%
C. $33\frac{1}{3}$%
D. none of these

30. 3% = ?
A. 0.03
B. 0.3
C. 0.003
D. none of these

31. 15.6% = ?
A. 1.56
B. 1560
C. 0.156
D. none of these

32. 0.4 = ?
A. 4%
B. 40%
C. 0.04%
D. none of these

33. $1.83\frac{1}{3}$ = ?
A. $183\frac{1}{3}$%
B. $18.3\frac{1}{3}$%
C. $1.83\frac{1}{3}$%
D. none of these

34. Solve.   15% of 32 = n
A. 3.6
B. 4.2
C. 5.2
D. none of these

35. Solve. $16\frac{2}{3}$% of 72 = n
A. 12
B. 8
C. 9
D. none of these

36. Solve.   75% of n = 36
A. 27
B. 42
C. 48
D. none of these

37. Solve.   12.5% of n = 24
A. 3
B. 144
C. 196
D. none of these

38. The down payment is what percent of the total cost?
$21 DOWN
TOTAL COST $84
A. 20%
B. 25%
C. 30%
D. none of these

39. How much is the down payment?
20% DOWN
TOTAL COST $1236
A. $412.00
B. $309.00
C. $247.20
D. none of these

40. What is the total cost?
15% DOWN
$54 DOWN
A. $320
B. $360
C. $384
D. none of these

© D. C. Heath and Company   S79   Page 3

THIRD-QUARTER TEST
(Chapters 9 through 12)

NAME _____

Choose the correct letter.

41. A car salesperson is paid a 2% commission on all sales. What would be the commission for selling an $8460 car?
A. $144.60
B. $158.80
C. $169.20
D. none of these

42. A factory worker earns $7.25 per hour for a 40-hour week. $43 is withheld for federal income tax and $14.65 for Social Security. How much is his net pay?
A. $290
B. $232.35
C. $233.65
D. none of these

43. What is the sale price?
Reg. $48.60
25% off
A. $12.15
B. $38.88
C. $42.20
D. none of these

44. Give the unit cost rounded to the nearest cent.
ORANGES
5 pounds for $1.29
A. 25¢
B. 26¢
C. 27¢
D. none of these

45. You have a coupon that gives you $1.50 off on one record. What will you have to pay for 2 records that regularly sell for $5.97 each?
A. $10.44
B. $8.94
C. $11.94
D. none of these

46. A checking account has a balance of $492.26. A check of $49.35 is written and a deposit of $50 is made. What is the new balance?
A. $392.91
B. $493.91
C. $491.61
D. none of these

47. On January 31 you have a balance of $520 in your savings account. On February 1 you are paid $2.38 interest and make a withdrawal of $30. What is your new balance?
A. $487.65
B. $492.38
C. $547.62
D. none of these

48. Compute the interest.
Principal = $640
Rate = 1.5% per month
Time = 8 months
A. $9.60
B. $6.40
C. $76.80
D. none of these

49. Compute the interest.
Principal = $1460
Rate = 12% per year
Time = 9 months
A. $131.40
B. $116.80
C. $175.20
D. none of these

50. Your bank card statement shows that you owe the bank $340. At 1.5% per month, how much will the finance charge be for 1 month?
A. $61.20
B. $10.20
C. $5.10
D. none of these

© D. C. Heath and Company   S80   Page 4

THIRD-QUARTER TEST

The third-quarter test shown on these two pages is in standardized format so that the students can become accustomed to taking standardized tests.

292A

Use Copymaster S92 or Duplicating Master S92 to provide the students with an answer sheet in standardized test format.

Copymaster S107 has a quick-score answer key for the third-quarter test.

Answer Sheet for **QUARTERLY TESTS**
_____-Quarter Test (Chapters __—__)

NAME _____
DATE _____
SCORE _____

© D. C. Heath and Company   S92   Answer sheet—Quarterly Tests

Quick-Score Answer Key for **THIRD-QUARTER TEST** (Chapters 9–12)

Quick-Score Answer Key for **FOURTH-QUARTER TEST** (Chapters 13–17)

© D. C. Heath and Company   S107   Answer key—Quarterly Tests

The table below correlates test items with student text pages.

Test Item	Text Page	Test Item	Text Page	Test Item	Text Page	Test Item	Text Page
1	p. 198	14	p. 218	27	p. 248	40	p. 262
2	p. 200	15	p. 218	28	p. 250	41	p. 270
3	p. 202	16	p. 226	29	p. 250	42	p. 271
4	p. 202	17	p. 228	30	p. 252	43	p. 272
5	p. 202	18	p. 230	31	p. 252	44	p. 274
6	p. 204	19	p. 230	32	p. 253	45	p. 276
7	p. 206	20	p. 232	33	p. 253	46	p. 280
8	p. 210	21	p. 232	34	p. 256	47	p. 282
9	p. 212	22	p. 238	35	p. 258	48	p. 284
10	p. 212	23	p. 238	36	p. 260	49	p. 284
11	p. 214	24	p. 240	37	p. 260	50	p. 286
12	p. 216	25	p. 240	38	p. 262		
13	p. 216	26	p. 248	39	p. 262		

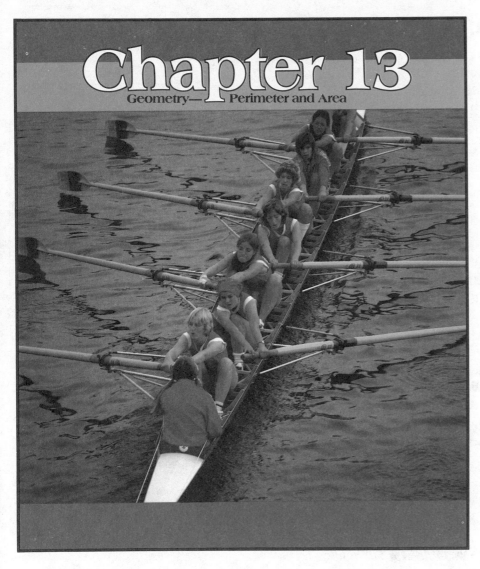

CHAPTER 13
Geometry—Perimeter, and Area

LESSON OBJECTIVES
To use a protractor to measure angles (*pages 294–295*)
To classify angles as acute, right, or obtuse (*pages 294–295*)
To use a protractor to draw angles having a given measurement (*pages 294–295*)
To identify perpendicular lines and parallel lines
(*pages 296–297*)
To classify polygons according to their sides and angles
(*pages 298–299*)
To compute the perimeter of a polygon, given the length of its sides (*pages 300–301*)
To compute the circumference of a circle, given its diameter or radius (*pages 302–303*)
To compute the areas of squares and other rectangles
(*pages 306–307*)
To compute the area of a parallelogram (*pages 308–309*)
To compute the area of a triangle (*pages 310–311*)
To compute the area of a circle (*pages 312–313*)

PROBLEM-SOLVING SKILLS
Estimating measurements (*pages 294, 295*)
Finding information in a drawing (*pages 296, 297, 300–303, 307–313*)
Using logical reasoning (*pages 297, 299*)
Reading a chart (*page 299*)
Making a drawing (*pages 299, 313*)
Using a formula (*pages 300–303, 306–313*)
Checking answers (*page 303*)
Finding information in an ad (*page 305*)
Using a drawing (*pages 305–307, 312–313*)
Choosing the correct operation (*page 307*)
Making a drawing to show an answer (*page 309*)
Selecting information from a computer drawing (*page 315*)

RESOURCES
* **VISUAL AIDS**
  Protractor from page 294 and decoder from page 295 (*Visual Aid 49, Copymaster S146*)
  Drawings from pages 296 and 297 (*Visual Aid 50, Copymaster S147*)
  Drawing from page 298 (*Visual Aid 51, Copymaster S148*)
  Drawing for problem 3 on page 305 (*Visual Aid 52, Copymaster S148*)
  Dot grid (*Visual Aid 26, Copymaster S129*)
* **WORKSHEETS 123–133** (*Copymasters S275–S285 or Duplicating Masters S275–S285*)

293

LESSON OBJECTIVES

To use a protractor to measure angles
To classify angles as acute, right, or obtuse
To use a protractor to draw angles having a given measurement

PROBLEM-SOLVING SKILL

Estimating measurements

STARTING THE LESSON

Draw these three angles on the chalkboard:

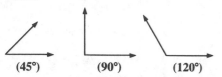

(45°)   (90°)   (120°)

Have the students estimate the degree measure of each angle. To determine who is the best estimator, have them add their three estimates. The student whose degree total is closest to 255° is the best estimator.

HERE'S HOW NOTE

A protractor is on **Visual Aid 49**. You may choose to use the visual aid when demonstrating how to use a protractor to measure and draw angles.

EXERCISE NOTE

The protractor decoder in exercise 26 is also on **Visual Aid 49**.

Measuring and classifying angles

Here's how *to use a* **protractor** *to measure an angle.*

Follow the steps to measure the angle.

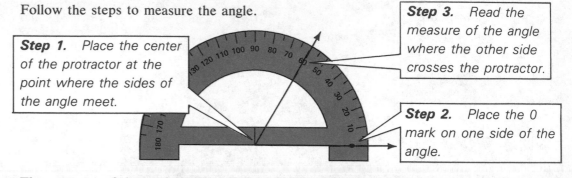

Step 1. *Place the center of the protractor at the point where the sides of the angle meet.*

Step 3. *Read the measure of the angle where the other side crosses the protractor.*

Step 2. *Place the 0 mark on one side of the angle.*

The measure of the angle is 60°.   Read "60°" as "sixty degrees."

A **B** **C**

1. An **acute** angle measures between 0° and 90°.
   Which angle (A, B, or C) is an acute angle? C

2. A **right** angle measures 90°.
   Which angle is a right angle? A

3. An **obtuse** angle measures between 90° and 180°.
   Which angle is an obtuse angle? B

Here's how *to draw a 50° angle.*

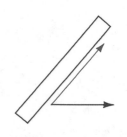

1. Draw one side.

2. Place the protractor as you would for measuring and make a mark at 50°.

3. Draw the other side.

EXERCISES

Measure each angle.

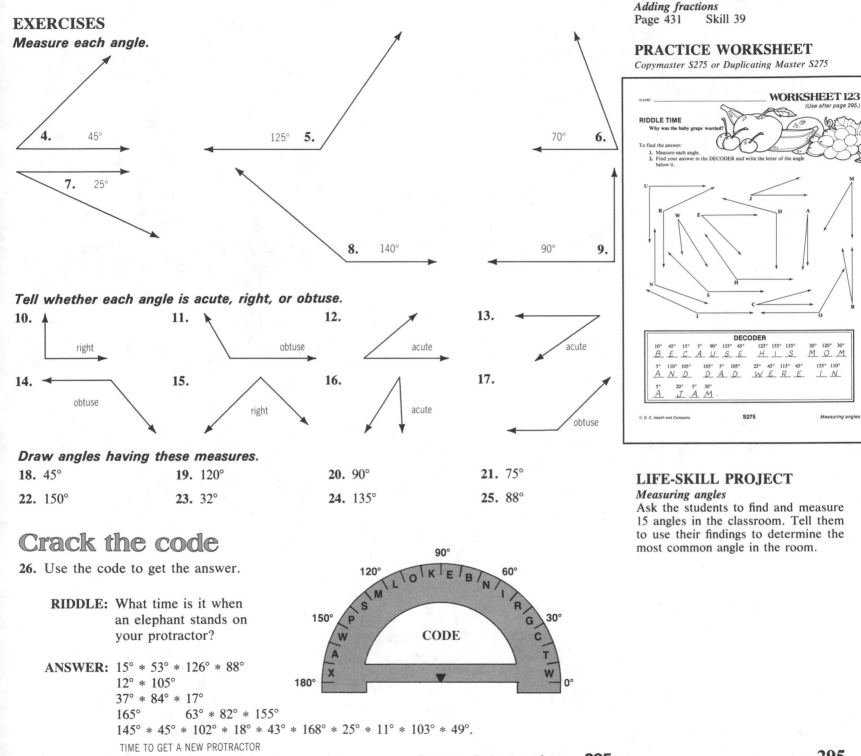

4. 45°

5. 125°

6. 70°

7. 25°

8. 140°

9. 90°

Tell whether each angle is acute, right, or obtuse.

10. right

11. obtuse

12. acute

13. acute

14. obtuse

15. right

16. acute

17. obtuse

Draw angles having these measures.

18. 45° **19.** 120° **20.** 90° **21.** 75°

22. 150° **23.** 32° **24.** 135° **25.** 88°

Crack the code

26. Use the code to get the answer.

RIDDLE: What time is it when
an elephant stands on
your protractor?

ANSWER: 15° * 53° * 126° * 88°
12° * 105°
37° * 84° * 17°
165°   63° * 82° * 155°
145° * 45° * 102° * 18° * 43° * 168° * 25° * 11° * 103° * 49°.

TIME TO GET A NEW PROTRACTOR

CODE

90°
120°   60°
150°   30°
180°   0°

REVIEW PRACTICE
Adding fractions
Page 431   Skill 39

PRACTICE WORKSHEET
Copymaster S275 or Duplicating Master S275

NAME _____   **WORKSHEET 123**
(Use after page 295.)

RIDDLE TIME
Why was the baby grape worried?

To find the answer:
1. Measure each angle.
2. Find your answer in the DECODER and write the letter of the angle below it.

U J M
R W E D A
N H B
S C O
I

DECODER
10°	45°	15°	5°	90°	135°	45°	125°	155°	135°	30°	120°	30°
B	E	C	A	U	S	E	H	I	S	M	O	M
5°	110°	105°	105°	5°	105°	25°	45°	115°	45°	155°	110°
A	N	D	D	A	D	W	E	R	E	I	N
5°	20°	5°	30°
A	J	A	M	.

© D. C. Heath and Company   S275   *Measuring angles*

LIFE-SKILL PROJECT
Measuring angles
Ask the students to find and measure
15 angles in the classroom. Tell them
to use their findings to determine the
most common angle in the room.

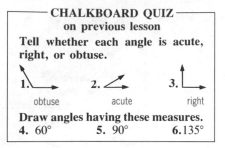
LESSON OBJECTIVE
To identify perpendicular lines and parallel lines

PROBLEM-SOLVING SKILLS
Finding information in a drawing
Using logical reasoning

STARTING THE LESSON
Write these sentences on the chalkboard:

Two straight streets that intersect to form right angles are EPDIPRENUCLRA.

Two straight streets that do not intersect (even if extended) are ALPERALL.

Before the students open their books, challenge them to unscramble the underlined letters so that each sentence makes sense. Then have them open their books and read the top of page 296 to see if they correctly unscrambled the letters.

EXERCISE NOTE
The drawings on page 296 and the drawing at the top of page 297 are also on **Visual Aid 50.** You may wish to use the visual aid when going over exercises 1–25.

Perpendicular and parallel lines

MAP MATH

Two straight streets that intersect to form right angles are **perpendicular.**

Two straight streets that do not intersect (even if extended) are **parallel.**

On the map,
L Street is perpendicular to V Street.
L Street is parallel to M Street.

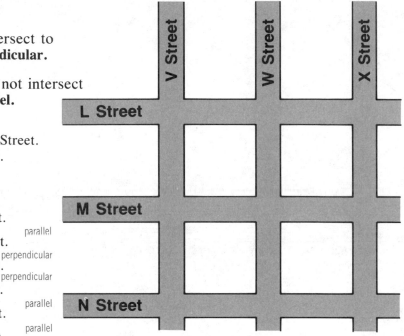

Parallel or perpendicular?

1. V Street is ⬚ to W Street.

2. W Street is ⬚ to M Street. parallel

3. N Street is ⬚ to X Street. perpendicular

4. L Street is ⬚ to N Street. perpendicular

5. W Street is ⬚ to X Street. parallel

6. L Street is ⬚ to W Street. parallel
perpendicular

EXERCISES
True or false?

7. Line s is parallel to line r.   True

8. Line r is perpendicular to line s. False

9. Line u is parallel to line t.   True

10. Line u is perpendicular to line r. True

11. Line v is perpendicular to line s. False

12. Line u is perpendicular to line s. True

13. Line s is parallel to line t.   False

14. There are more than 10 right angles in the drawing.   True

15. There are 4 acute angles in the drawing.   True

16. There are more than 4 obtuse angles in the drawing.   False

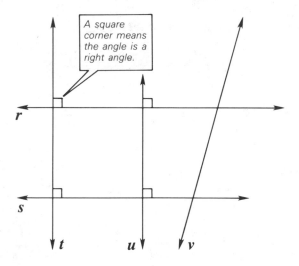

A square corner means the angle is a right angle.

296

True or false?

17. Lines *b* and *d* intersect. True

18. Lines *b* and *d* are perpendicular. True

19. Lines *f* and *g* intersect. False

20. Lines *c* and *f* are parallel. False

21. Lines *c* and *g* are perpendicular. True

22. Lines *d* and *e* are parallel. True

23. Lines *e* and *g* are perpendicular. False

24. Lines *c* and *d* are perpendicular. False

25. There are 16 right angles in the drawing. True

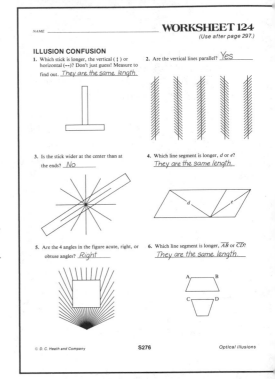

Make a drawing. Then answer the questions.

26. Draw 2 perpendicular lines. How many right angles can you find? 4

27. Draw 2 intersecting lines that are not perpendicular. How many acute angles can you find? 2

28. Draw 2 parallel lines. Now draw a line that intersects the 2 parallel lines but is not perpendicular to the parallel lines.
    a. How many right angles can you find? 0
    b. How many acute angles can you find? 4
    c. How many obtuse angles can you find? 4

Street wise Logical reasoning

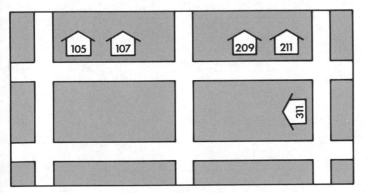

Clues:

- Paul lives east of Cindy.
- Darla lives west of Cindy.
- Paul lives between Cindy and Tim.
- Jan's street is perpendicular to Cindy's street.

Use the clues to answer the questions.

29. Who lives in house number 105? Darla

30. Who lives in house number 209? Paul

31. What is Cindy's house number? 107

32. What is Jan's house number? 311

REVIEW PRACTICE
Adding fractions
Page 431   Skill 40

PRACTICE WORKSHEET
Copymaster S276 or Duplicating Master S276

NAME _____ **WORKSHEET 124**
(Use after page 297.)

ILLUSION CONFUSION

1. Which stick is longer, the vertical (|) or horizontal (--)? Don't just guess! Measure to find out. *They are the same length.*

2. Are the vertical lines parallel? Yes

3. Is the stick wider at the center than at the ends? *No*

4. Which line segment is longer, *d* or *e*? *They are the same length.*

5. Are the 4 angles in the figure acute, right, or obtuse angles? *Right*

6. Which line segment is longer, $\overline{AB}$ or $\overline{CD}$? *They are the same length.*

© D. C. Heath and Company   S276   *Optical illusions*

CHALKBOARD CHALLENGE

Draw the capital letters of the alphabet so that as many as possible have all the lines either parallel or perpendicular.

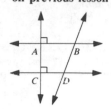

True or false?
1. Line *AB* is parallel to line *CD*.   True
2. Line *BD* is perpendicular to line *AB*.   False
3. Line *AC* is perpendicular to line *CD*.   True
4. Line *BD* is parallel to line *AC*.   False
5. Line *CD* is perpendicular to line *AC*.   True

LESSON OBJECTIVE
To classify polygons according to their sides and angles

PROBLEM-SOLVING SKILLS
Reading a chart
Using logical reasoning
Making a drawing

STARTING THE LESSON
The lot drawing shown at the top of page 298 is also on **Visual Aid 51**. Use the drawing and have the students name the lots described in questions 1–3. Then go over the *Here's how* and use the lot drawing to discuss question 4.

Polygons

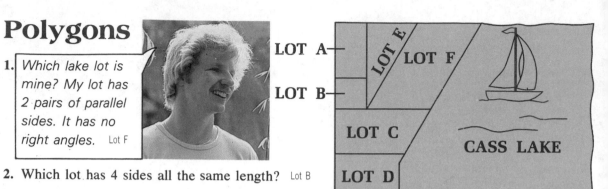

1. *Which lake lot is mine? My lot has 2 pairs of parallel sides. It has no right angles.*   Lot F

2. Which lot has 4 sides all the same length?   Lot B

3. Which lot has exactly 1 pair of parallel sides?   Lot C

Here's how *polygons (closed shapes with straight sides) are named.*

NAME OF POLYGON	DESCRIPTION	EXAMPLES
Triangle	3 sides	
Square	4 sides the same length 4 right angles	
Rectangle	4 sides 4 right angles	A square is also a rectangle.
Parallelogram	4 sides 2 pairs of parallel sides	A rectangle is also a parallelogram.
Trapezoid	4 sides Exactly 1 pair of parallel sides	
Pentagon	5 sides	
Hexagon	6 sides	

4. Use the map and the *Here's how* chart to answer these questions.
   a. Which lot is a square?   Lot B
   b. Which 2 lots are rectangles?   Lots A, B
   c. Which 3 lots are parallelograms?   Lots A, B, F
   d. Which lot is a triangle?   Lot E
   e. Which lot is a trapezoid?   Lot C
   f. Which lot is a pentagon?   Lot D

EXERCISES

Name these polygons. Some shapes have more than one name.

5. Square
Rectangle
Parallelogram

Hint: This polygon has 3 names.

6. Trapezoid

7. Parallelogram

8. Hexagon

9. Pentagon

10. Rectangle
Parallelogram

Hint: This polygon has 2 names.

11. Triangle

12. Square
Rectangle
Parallelogram

13. Hexagon

Use the clues. Draw and name each polygon.

14. Clues:
- This polygon has 4 sides.
- It has no right angles.
- It has 2 pairs of parallel sides.

Parallelogram

15. Clues:
- This polygon has 2 right angles.
- It has 4 sides.
- It has 1 acute angle.
- It has 1 obtuse angle.

Trapezoid

A lot of land

What is the price of each lake lot?

Hint: Find how many triangular lots were used to make each larger lot.

16. $? 50 ft
50 ft
$2000

17. $? 70.7 ft
100 ft
$4000

18. 70.7 ft
100 ft
$? 50 ft
$3000

19. 100 ft 100 ft
$?
141.4 ft
$4000

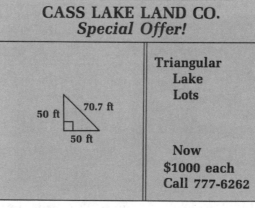

CASS LAKE LAND CO.
Special Offer!

Triangular
Lake
Lots

50 ft · 70.7 ft · 50 ft

Now
$1000 each
Call 777-6262

REVIEW PRACTICE
Adding mixed numbers
Page 432   Skill 41

PRACTICE WORKSHEET
Copymaster S277 or Duplicating Master S277

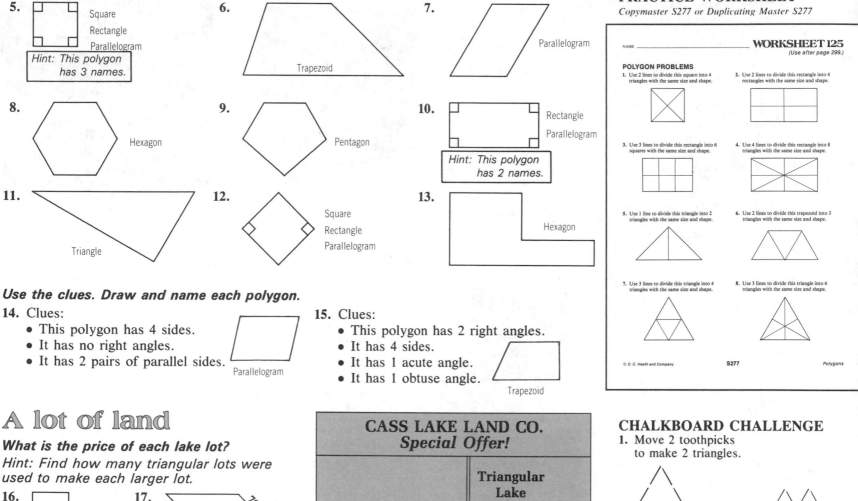

WORKSHEET 125
(Use after page 299.)

NAME _____

POLYGON PROBLEMS

1. Use 2 lines to divide this square into 4 triangles with the same size and shape.

2. Use 2 lines to divide this rectangle into 4 rectangles with the same size and shape.

3. Use 3 lines to divide this rectangle into 6 squares with the same size and shape.

4. Use 4 lines to divide this rectangle into 8 triangles with the same size and shape.

5. Use 1 line to divide this triangle into 2 triangles with the same size and shape.

6. Use 2 lines to divide this trapezoid into 3 triangles with the same size and shape.

7. Use 3 lines to divide this triangle into 4 triangles with the same size and shape.

8. Use 3 lines to divide this triangle into 6 triangles with the same size and shape.

© D. C. Heath and Company   S277   Polygons

CHALKBOARD CHALLENGE

1. Move 2 toothpicks to make 2 triangles.

2. Move 3 toothpicks to make 3 squares.

CHALKBOARD QUIZ
on previous lesson
Make a sketch of each polygon.
1. square   2. triangle
3. rectangle   4. hexagon
5. pentagon   6. trapezoid

LESSON OBJECTIVE
To compute the perimeter of a polygon, given the length of its sides

PROBLEM-SOLVING SKILLS
Finding information in a drawing
Using a formula

STARTING THE LESSON
Have the students look at the posters at the top of the page. Ask them which poster needed 96 centimeters of framing. (24 cm x 24 cm poster) Then go over the *Here's how* and discuss questions 1 and 2.

HERE'S HOW NOTE
After going over questions 1 and 2, let the students practice using the formulas on these squares and rectangles:

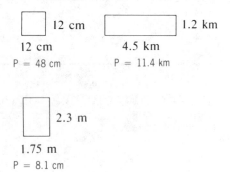

12 cm
12 cm
P = 48 cm

1.2 km
4.5 km
P = 11.4 km

2.3 m
1.75 m
P = 8.1 cm

Perimeter

FRAMED?

One of these posters needs 96 centimeters of framing. Which one is it?   The poster with cats

24 cm

24 cm

40 cm

32 cm

The **perimeter** of the figure is the distance around the figure.

Here's how *to use formulas to find the perimeters of squares and rectangles.*

Square

24 cm

24 cm

Rectangle

40 cm

32 cm

The perimeter (P) of a square is 4 times the length of one side (s).

FORMULA $P = 4 \times s$
$$P = 4 \times 24 \text{ cm}$$
$$= 96 \text{ cm}$$

The perimeter is 96 cm.

The perimeter (P) of a rectangle is 2 times the sum of the length (l) and the width (w).

FORMULA $P = 2 \times (l + w)$
$$P = 2 \times (40 \text{ cm} + 32 \text{ cm})$$
$$= 2 \times 72 \text{ cm}$$
$$= 144 \text{ cm}$$

The perimeter is 144 cm.

1. Look at the *Here's how*. What is the formula for the perimeter of a square? $P = 4 \times s$
What does the letter s stand for?   Length of a side

2. What is the formula for the perimeter of a rectangle? What does each letter $P = 2 \times (l + w)$
stand for? P = perimeter, l = length, w = width

EXERCISES

Find each perimeter.

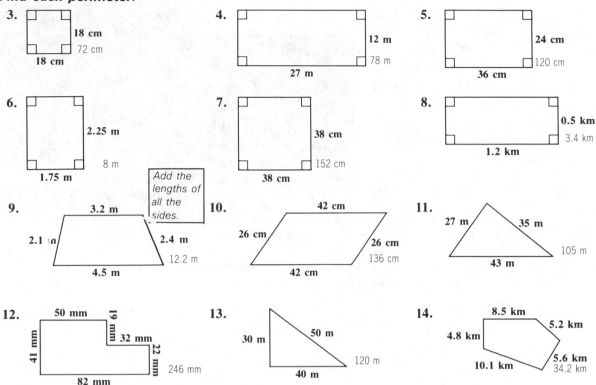

3. 18 cm, 72 cm, 18 cm

4. 12 m, 78 m, 27 m

5. 24 cm, 120 cm, 36 cm

6. 2.25 m, 8 m, 1.75 m

7. 38 cm, 152 cm, 38 cm

8. 0.5 km, 3.4 km, 1.2 km

Add the lengths of all the sides.

9. 3.2 m, 2.1 m, 2.4 m, 4.5 m, 12.2 m

10. 42 cm, 26 cm, 26 cm, 42 cm, 136 cm

11. 27 m, 35 m, 43 m, 105 m

12. 50 mm, 19 mm, 32 mm, 22 mm, 41 mm, 82 mm, 246 mm

13. 30 m, 50 m, 40 m, 120 m

14. 8.5 km, 5.2 km, 5.6 km, 10.1 km, 4.8 km, 34.2 km

Solve.

15. How many centimeters of wood framing are needed to frame a painting that is 65 centimeters long and 40 centimeters wide? 210 cm

16. A square photograph, 25 centimeters on each side, is to be framed. How many centimeters of framing are needed? 100 cm

17. How much fencing is needed to enclose a rectangular yard that is 15 meters by 24 meters? 78 m

18. A square pen is built. The pen is 15.5 meters on each side. How many meters of fencing are needed? 62 m

Triangle tangle

19. Find the triangle that has the same perimeter as triangle *AEI*. Triangle CGK

20. Find 5 triangles that have the same perimeter as triangle *ABL*. Triangles BCD, DEF, FGH, HIJ, JKL

21. Find the 2 parallelograms that have the same perimeter as parallelogram *LCFI*. Parallelograms ADGJ, BEHK

REVIEW PRACTICE
Subtracting fractions
Page 432   Skill 42

PRACTICE WORKSHEET
Copymaster S278 or Duplicating Master S278

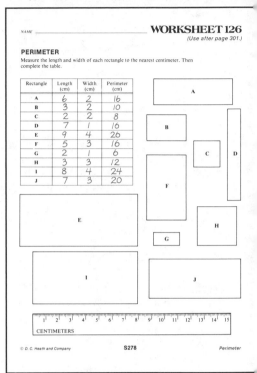

NAME _____   **WORKSHEET 126**
(Use after page 301.)

PERIMETER
Measure the length and width of each rectangle to the nearest centimeter. Then complete the table.

Rectangle	Length (cm)	Width (cm)	Perimeter (cm)
A	6	2	16
B	3	2	10
C	2	2	8
D	7	1	16
E	9	4	26
F	5	3	16
G	2	1	6
H	3	3	12
I	8	4	24
J	7	3	20

CENTIMETERS

© D. C. Heath and Company   S278   Perimeter

LIFE-SKILL PROJECT
Making measurements
Have the students find the perimeter of the following:

  their classroom
  a table top
  a student's desk top

In each case, they will have to decide on an appropriate unit of measurement.

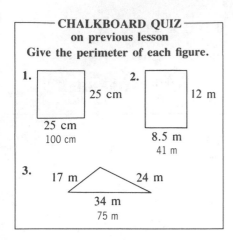

1. 25 cm / 25 cm
100 cm

2. 12 m / 8.5 m
41 m

3. 17 m 24 m 34 m
75 m

LESSON OBJECTIVE
To compute the circumference of a circle, given its diameter or radius

PROBLEM-SOLVING SKILLS
Finding information in a drawing
Using a formula
Checking answers

STARTING THE LESSON
Play 'What are the facts?' Have the students study the information at the top of page 302 for 30 seconds. Then tell them to close their books and answer these questions from memory:
- Which has the greater radius, the front or back wheel? (Front wheel)
- What is the radius of the front wheel? (32 inches)
- Which wheel has a diameter of 20 inches? (Back wheel)
- Is the diameter of the front wheel twice its radius? (Yes)

HERE'S HOW NOTE
After going over questions 1–4, have the students practice using the formula by finding the circumference of these circles.

2 yd — **12.56 yd**   6 ft — **18.84 ft**   14 in. — **43.96 in.**

Circumference

The radius of the front wheel is 32 inches, and the radius of the back wheel is 10 inches.

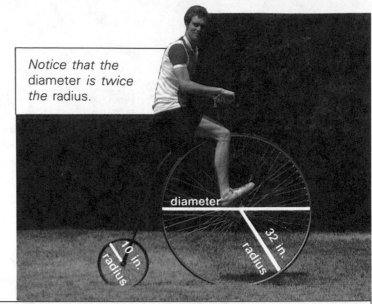

Notice that the diameter is twice the radius.

diameter   10 in. radius   32 in. radius

1. Which wheel has a diameter of 64 inches, the front or the back? Front

2. Make a guess! When the front wheel goes around once, will the bicycle travel more or less than 150 inches? More

Here's how *to use a formula to find the distance around a circle.*

The distance around a circle is called the **circumference**. The circumference of a circle is a little more than 3 times the length of its diameter.

To find the circumference (*C*), multiply π (read as "pi") by the diameter (*d*). We'll use 3.14 as a decimal approximation for π.

Front wheel

64 in.

≈ means "is approximately equal to."

FORMULA $C = \pi \times d$
$C \approx 3.14 \times 64$ in.
≈ 200.96 in.

3. Look at the *Here's how*. About how far does the bicycle travel when the front wheel goes around once? 200.96 in.

4. To compute the circumference of the back wheel, you would multiply 3.14 times what number? 20

EXERCISES
Find the circumference. Use 3.14 for π**.** *Here are scrambled answers for the next row of exercises:* 18.84 in.   31.4 in.   25.12 in.   12.56 in.

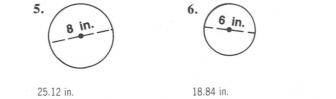

5. 8 in. — 25.12 in.

6. 6 in. — 18.84 in.

7. 4 in. — 12.56 in.

8. 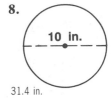 10 in. — 31.4 in.

302

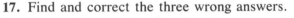

9. 5 yd
15.7 yd

10. 12 ft
37.68 ft

11. 2.5 ft
7.85 ft

12. 8 yd
25.12 yd

13. 1 ft | The diameter is 2 ft.
6.28 ft

14. 10 in.
62.8 in.

15. $1\frac{1}{2}$ ft
9.42 ft

16. 7 yd
43.96 yd

17. Find and correct the three wrong answers.

a. *Question:* What is the diameter of a wheel that has a radius of $1\frac{1}{2}$ feet?
Answer: The diameter is 3 feet.

(**b.**) *Question:* What is the radius of a circle that has a diameter of $6\frac{1}{2}$ feet?
Answer: The radius is 13 feet. $3\frac{1}{4}$ feet

(**c.**) *Question:* Which has the larger circumference, a circle with a diameter of 3 feet or a circle with a radius of 2 feet?
Answer: The circle with a diameter of 3 feet. The circle with a radius of 2 feet.

(**d.**) *Question:* What is the circumference of a wheel that has a radius of 26 inches?
Answer: Approximately 81.64 inches. 163.28 inches

e. *Question:* What do you get when you divide the circumference of a circle by π (3.14)?
Answer: You get the diameter of the circle.

Seeing is not believing

Are the red sides straight or curved? *Hint: Check with an edge of a paper.*

18.
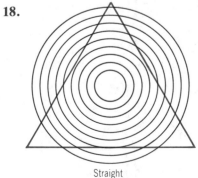
Straight

19.
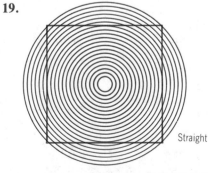
Straight

Geometry—Perimeter and Area **303**

PRACTICE WORKSHEET
Copymaster S279 or Duplicating Master S279

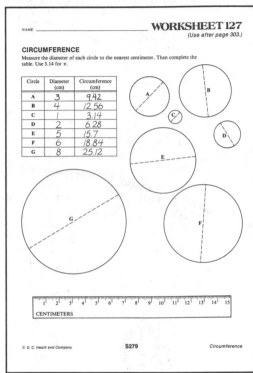

WORKSHEET 127
(Use after page 303.)

NAME _____

CIRCUMFERENCE
Measure the diameter of each circle to the nearest centimeter. Then complete the table. Use 3.14 for π.

Circle	Diameter (cm)	Circumference (cm)
A	3	9.42
B	4	12.56
C	1	3.14
D	2	6.28
E	5	15.7
F	6	18.84
G	8	25.12

© D. C. Heath and Company   S279   Circumference

LIFE-SKILL PROJECT
Using a calculator
Have the students determine how many revolutions the large and small wheels of the bicycle on page 302 must make to travel 1 mile. Let the students use calculators to shift the emphasis from the computation to the concept of circumference.

Large wheel: about 315
Small wheel: about 1009

303

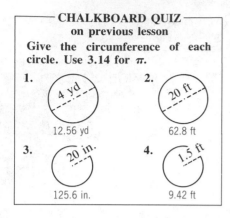
SKILLS REVIEWED
Changing a mixed number to a decimal
Adding and subtracting fractions
Multiplying and dividing fractions

PROBLEM-SOLVING SKILLS
Finding information in an ad
Using a drawing

STARTING THE LESSON
Cumulative Skill Practice
Write these four answers on the chalkboard:

$$6.75 \qquad 1\frac{3}{10} \qquad \frac{7}{24} \qquad 1\frac{2}{3}$$

Challenge the students to an answer hunt by saying, "Look for the four even-numbered exercises on page 304 that have these answers. You have five minutes to find as many of the exercises as you can." (Exercises 12, 36, 44, and 66.)

STARTING THE LESSON
Problem Solving
Have the students make a drawing to help answer each customer's question at the top of page 305. The drawing in problem 3 is also on **Visual Aid 52**. You may wish to use the visual aid and work through problem 3 before assigning the other problems.

Cumulative Skill Practice

Change to a decimal. *(page 146)*

1. $2\frac{1}{5}$ 2.2
2. $1\frac{1}{5}$ 1.2
3. $1\frac{4}{5}$ 1.8
4. $4\frac{1}{8}$ 4.125
5. $3\frac{3}{10}$ 3.3
6. $6\frac{1}{8}$ 6.125
7. $3\frac{1}{2}$ 3.5

8. $6\frac{3}{8}$ 6.375
9. $8\frac{1}{2}$ 8.5
10. $4\frac{5}{8}$ 4.625
11. $5\frac{1}{4}$ 5.25
12. $6\frac{3}{4}$ 6.75
13. $4\frac{3}{10}$ 4.3
14. $3\frac{1}{25}$ 3.0

15. $8\frac{9}{10}$ 8.9
16. $7\frac{2}{5}$ 7.4
17. $3\frac{7}{8}$ 3.875
18. $3\frac{2}{5}$ 3.4
19. $16\frac{3}{5}$ 16.6
20. $2\frac{1}{100}$ 2.01
21. $4\frac{3}{25}$ 4.1

Give the sum in simplest form. *(page 158)*

22. $\frac{3}{8} + \frac{1}{4}$ $\frac{5}{8}$
23. $\frac{3}{4} + \frac{1}{6}$ $\frac{11}{12}$
24. $\frac{1}{3} + \frac{1}{2}$ $\frac{5}{6}$
25. $\frac{3}{4} + \frac{2}{3}$ $1\frac{5}{12}$
26. $\frac{5}{8} + 4$ $4\frac{5}{8}$

27. $\frac{2}{3} + \frac{5}{9}$ $1\frac{2}{9}$
28. $\frac{1}{2} + \frac{4}{5}$ $1\frac{3}{10}$
29. $\frac{2}{3} + \frac{1}{6}$ $\frac{5}{6}$
30. $\frac{3}{5} + \frac{3}{4}$ $1\frac{7}{20}$
31. $3 + \frac{3}{10}$ $3\frac{3}{10}$

32. $\frac{1}{6} + \frac{3}{8}$ $\frac{13}{24}$
33. $\frac{7}{10} + \frac{1}{2}$ $1\frac{1}{5}$
34. $\frac{1}{4} + \frac{3}{10}$ $\frac{11}{20}$
35. $\frac{5}{8} + \frac{3}{4}$ $1\frac{3}{8}$
36. $\frac{7}{10} + \frac{3}{5}$ $1\frac{3}{10}$

Give the difference in simplest form. *(page 166)*

37. $\frac{5}{6} - \frac{1}{3}$ $\frac{1}{2}$
38. $\frac{5}{12} - \frac{1}{6}$ $\frac{1}{4}$
39. $\frac{5}{9} - \frac{1}{3}$ $\frac{2}{9}$
40. $\frac{7}{8} - \frac{3}{4}$ $\frac{1}{8}$
41. $\frac{7}{10} - \frac{2}{5}$ $\frac{3}{10}$

42. $\frac{8}{9} - \frac{5}{6}$ $\frac{1}{18}$
43. $\frac{5}{3} - \frac{3}{4}$ $\frac{11}{12}$
44. $\frac{2}{3} - \frac{3}{8}$ $\frac{7}{24}$
45. $\frac{9}{10} - \frac{3}{4}$ $\frac{3}{20}$
46. $3 - \frac{1}{2}$ $2\frac{1}{2}$

47. $\frac{9}{4} - \frac{5}{3}$ $\frac{7}{12}$
48. $\frac{4}{3} - \frac{3}{4}$ $\frac{7}{12}$
49. $1 - \frac{7}{8}$ $\frac{1}{8}$
50. $\frac{7}{6} - \frac{7}{8}$ $\frac{7}{24}$
51. $\frac{3}{2} - \frac{4}{3}$ $\frac{1}{6}$

Give the product in simplest form. *(page 178)*

52. $\frac{5}{8} \times \frac{2}{2}$ $\frac{5}{8}$
53. $\frac{1}{3} \times \frac{1}{3}$ $\frac{1}{9}$
54. $\frac{3}{8} \times \frac{4}{5}$ $\frac{3}{10}$
55. $\frac{3}{4} \times \frac{1}{2}$ $\frac{3}{8}$
56. $\frac{1}{4} \times 0$ 0

57. $\frac{1}{2} \times \frac{1}{3}$ $\frac{1}{6}$
58. $\frac{2}{5} \times \frac{5}{8}$ $\frac{1}{4}$
59. $\frac{2}{3} \times \frac{2}{3}$ $\frac{4}{9}$
60. $\frac{3}{8} \times \frac{1}{3}$ $\frac{1}{8}$
61. $\frac{3}{10} \times \frac{5}{6}$ $\frac{1}{4}$

62. $\frac{3}{4} \times \frac{5}{9}$ $\frac{5}{12}$
63. $\frac{4}{5} \times \frac{5}{3}$ $1\frac{1}{3}$
64. $\frac{7}{4} \times \frac{2}{7}$ $\frac{1}{2}$
65. $\frac{3}{2} \times 3$ $4\frac{1}{2}$
66. $5 \times \frac{1}{3}$ $1\frac{2}{3}$

Give the quotient in simplest form. *(page 188)*

67. $\frac{3}{4} \div \frac{1}{2}$ $1\frac{1}{2}$
68. $\frac{5}{9} \div \frac{5}{3}$ $\frac{1}{3}$
69. $\frac{2}{5} \div \frac{3}{5}$ $\frac{2}{3}$
70. $\frac{2}{3} \div \frac{1}{4}$ $2\frac{2}{3}$
71. $\frac{5}{6} \div \frac{5}{6}$ 1

72. $\frac{3}{8} \div 2$ $\frac{3}{16}$
73. $\frac{5}{8} \div \frac{3}{4}$ $\frac{5}{6}$
74. $\frac{5}{6} \div 3$ $\frac{5}{18}$
75. $\frac{4}{3} \div \frac{3}{4}$ $1\frac{7}{9}$
76. $0 \div \frac{2}{3}$ 0

77. $\frac{3}{4} \div \frac{6}{5}$ $\frac{5}{8}$
78. $\frac{7}{8} \div 4$ $\frac{7}{32}$
79. $3 \div \frac{3}{10}$ 10
80. $\frac{7}{8} \div \frac{4}{5}$ $1\frac{3}{32}$
81. $3 \div \frac{2}{3}$ $4\frac{1}{2}$

304

Problem solving

YOU'RE THE CLERK!

Use a drawing to help answer each customer's question.

1. Is 200 feet of fence enough to build a pen that is 60 feet long by 30 feet wide? **Yes**

2. How many feet of fence will I need to fence in my 120-foot by 75-foot yard? **390**

Use the weekend special prices. Find the total cost for each fencing project.

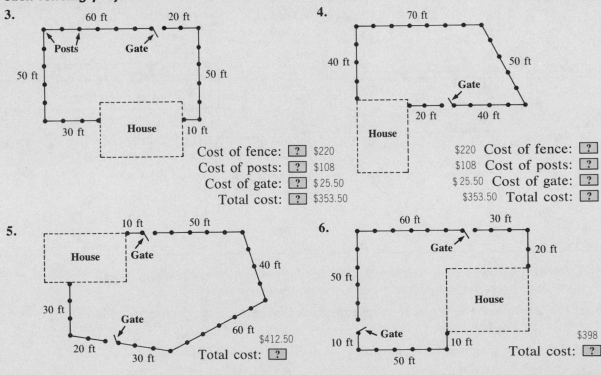

3.

60 ft   20 ft
Posts   Gate
50 ft   50 ft
30 ft   House   10 ft

Cost of fence: [?] $220
Cost of posts: [?] $108
Cost of gate: [?] $25.50
Total cost: [?] $353.50

4.

70 ft
40 ft   50 ft
Gate
House   20 ft   40 ft

$220 Cost of fence: [?]
$108 Cost of posts: [?]
$25.50 Cost of gate: [?]
$353.50 Total cost: [?]

5.

10 ft   50 ft
House   Gate
40 ft
30 ft   Gate
20 ft   30 ft   60 ft

$412.50 Total cost: [?]

6.

60 ft   30 ft
Gate   20 ft
50 ft   House
10 ft   Gate   10 ft
50 ft

$398 Total cost: [?]

Geometry—Perimeter and Area **305**

EXTRA PROBLEM SOLVING
Page 456   Odd exercises

PROBLEM-SOLVING WORKSHEET
Copymaster S280 or Duplicating Master S280

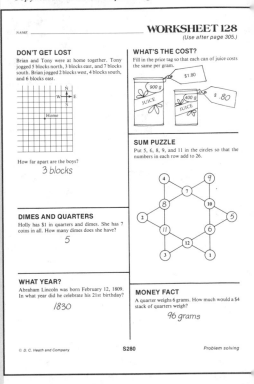

WORKSHEET 128
(Use after page 305.)

DON'T GET LOST
Brian and Tony were at home together. Tony jogged 5 blocks north, 3 blocks east, and 7 blocks south. Brian jogged 2 blocks east, 4 blocks south, and 6 blocks east.

How far apart are the boys? *3 blocks*

WHAT'S THE COST?
Fill in the price tag so that each can of juice costs the same per gram.
900 g JUICE $1.80
400 g JUICE $.80

SUM PUZZLE
Put 5, 6, 8, 9, and 11 in the circles so that the numbers in each row add to 26.

DIMES AND QUARTERS
Holly has $1 in quarters and dimes. She has 7 coins in all. How many dimes does she have? *5*

WHAT YEAR?
Abraham Lincoln was born February 12, 1809. In what year did he celebrate his 21st birthday? *1830*

MONEY FACT
A quarter weighs 6 grams. How much would a $4 stack of quarters weigh? *96 grams*

© D. C. Heath and Company   S280   Problem solving

CHALKBOARD CHALLENGE
Unscramble the letters of the geometry words.
1. ETAUC ENAGL   Acute angle
2. LLRAPRALE   Parallel
3. ERQSUA   Square
4. TEREPIMRE   Perimeter
5. UIARDS   Radius
6. ERUCICRMFEECN   Circumference

305

Area—squares and rectangles

The **area** of a region is the number of square units that it takes to cover the region.

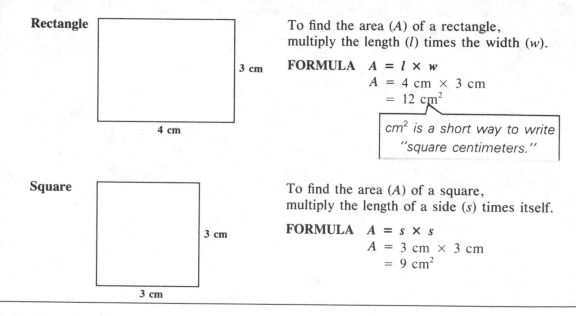

1 square centimeter

1. Count the squares. Which rectangle has an area of 12 square centimeters? A

2. Which rectangle has an area of 6 square centimeters? B

3. What is the area of square C? 9 square centimeters

Here's how *to use formulas to find the area of rectangles and squares.*

Rectangle

3 cm

4 cm

To find the area (A) of a rectangle, multiply the length (l) times the width (w).

FORMULA $A = l \times w$
$A = 4 \text{ cm} \times 3 \text{ cm}$
$= 12 \text{ cm}^2$

cm^2 is a short way to write "square centimeters."

Square

3 cm

3 cm

To find the area (A) of a square, multiply the length of a side (s) times itself.

FORMULA $A = s \times s$
$A = 3 \text{ cm} \times 3 \text{ cm}$
$= 9 \text{ cm}^2$

4. Look at the *Here's how*. What is the formula for the area of a rectangle? What does each letter stand for? $A = l \times w$, A = area, l = length, w = width

5. If the length and width of a rectangle are 10 centimeters and 5 centimeters, the area is 50 [?] centimeters. square

6. If the side of a square is 6 centimeters, its area is 36 square [?]. centimeters

306

EXERCISES

Find the area.

7.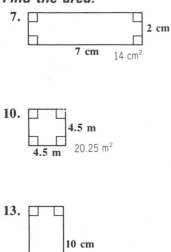
2 cm
7 cm
14 cm²

8.
8 m
8 m
64 m²

9.
12 km
20 km
240 km²

10.
4.5 m
4.5 m
20.25 m²

11.
14 cm
18.6 cm
260.4 cm²

12.
7 m
4.5 m
31.5 m²

13.
10 cm
4.2 cm
42 cm²

14.
0.8 km
0.8 km
0.64 km²

15.
0.4 m
1.5 m
0.6 m²

16. One of the squares above has a perimeter of 18 meters. Which one is it? Number 10

17. One of the rectangles above has a perimeter of 23 meters. Which one is it? Number 12

You decide!

First tell whether the problem is about perimeter or area. Then solve the problem.

18. How much fencing do I need to enclose a field that is 20 yards long and 15 yards wide? Perimeter, 70 yards

19. How many 1-foot-square tiles are needed to tile my 15-foot by 12-foot kitchen floor? Area, 180 tiles

20. How much sod is needed to cover a 20-yard by 40-yard lawn? Area, 800 yd²

21. How much molding is needed to go around a 25-foot by 15-foot ceiling? Perimeter, 80 feet

22. How much paint is needed to cover a floor that is 25 feet by 14 feet? A quart of paint covers about 50 square feet. Area, 7 quarts

23. How much does it cost to frame a square painting that is $2\frac{1}{2}$ feet on each side? Framing costs $.89 a foot. Perimeter, $8.90

REVIEW PRACTICE
Subtracting mixed numbers
Page 433   Skill 44

PRACTICE WORKSHEET
Copymaster S281 or Duplicating Master S281

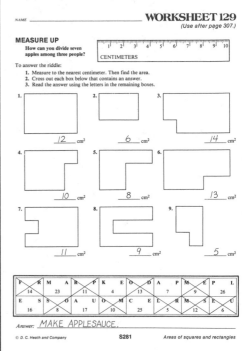

LIFE-SKILL PROJECT
Making measurements
Have the students compute the cost to carpet the classroom floor. Let them measure to find the classroom floor area. Then have them look at carpet ads in a newspaper. Tell them to pick out the carpet they want and determine how much it would cost to carpet the classroom.

CHALKBOARD QUIZ
on previous lesson
Find the area.

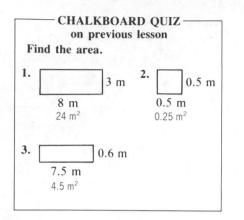

1. 3 m / 8 m / 24 m²
2. 0.5 m / 0.5 m / 0.25 m²
3. 0.6 m / 7.5 m / 4.5 m²

LESSON OBJECTIVE
To compute the area of a parallelogram

PROBLEM-SOLVING SKILLS
Finding information in a drawing
Using a formula
Making a drawing to show an answer

STARTING THE LESSON
Sketch these two shapes on the chalkboard:

Have the students show how the two shapes can be put together to form a parallelogram or a rectangle.

Then have the students count the squares to find the area of the parallelograms at the top of page 308. Some students may prefer to trace the two pieces of each figure, cut them out, form two rectangles, and then compute the areas.

EXERCISE NOTE
You may wish to use **Visual Aid 26** (dot grid) when going over the *Here's how* and questions 1–3.

Area—parallelograms

In each of these parallelograms, the **base** (b) is 4 centimeters and the **height** (h) is 3 centimeters.

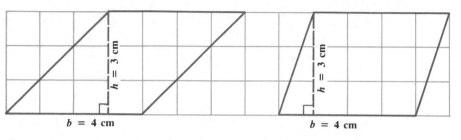

$h = 3$ cm $b = 4$ cm $h = 3$ cm $b = 4$ cm

Count the squares. Each parallelogram has an area of 12 square centimeters.

Here's how *to use a formula to find the area of a parallelogram.*

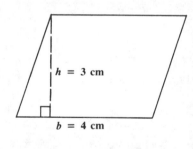

$h = 3$ cm

$b = 4$ cm

Notice that the height (h) is perpendicular to the base (b).

To find the area (A) of a parallelogram, multiply the base (b) times the height (h).

FORMULA $A = b \times h$
$A = 4$ cm $\times 3$ cm
$= 12$ cm²

The area of the parallelogram is 12 square centimeters.

1. Look at the *Here's how*. What is the formula for the area of a parallelogram? $A = b \times h$ What does each letter stand for? A = area, b = base, h = height

2. If the base and height of a parallelogram are 5 meters and 9 meters, the area is 45 square [?]. meters

EXERCISES
Find the area.

3.

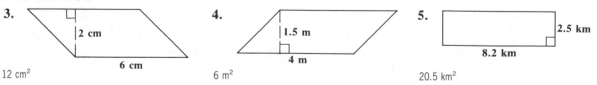

2 cm / 6 cm

12 cm²

4.

1.5 m / 4 m

6 m²

5.

2.5 km / 8.2 km

20.5 km²

6.

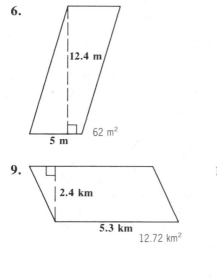

12.4 m

5 m   62 m²

7.

8 km   33.6 km²

4.2 km

8.

8.2 cm   27.88 cm²

3.4 cm

9.

2.4 km

5.3 km

12.72 km²

10.

60 cm

60 cm

3600 cm²

11.

0.5 m

1.5 m   0.75 m²

REVIEW PRACTICE
Subtracting mixed numbers
Page 434   Skill 45

PRACTICE WORKSHEET
Copymaster S282 or Duplicating Master S282

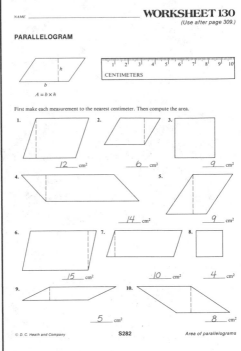

NAME _____   **WORKSHEET 130**
(Use after page 309.)

PARALLELOGRAM

h

b

CENTIMETERS

$A = b \times h$

First make each measurement to the nearest centimeter. Then compute the area.

1. *12* cm² 2. *6* cm² 3. *9* cm²

4. *14* cm² 5. *9* cm²

6. *15* cm² 7. *10* cm² 8. *4* cm²

9. *5* cm² 10. *8* cm²

© D. C. Heath and Company   S282   Area of parallelograms

Use the formula $A = b \times h$. Find the area of each parallelogram.

12. $b = 15$ cm
$h = 3$ cm 45 cm²

13. $b = 20$ cm
$h = 6.5$ cm 130 cm²

14. $b = 10$ m
$h = 4.4$ m 44 m²

15. $b = 2.1$ km
$h = 5$ km 10.5 km²

16. $b = 100$ m
$h = 65$ m 6500 m²

17. $b = 8.4$ km
$h = 2.2$ km 18.48 km²

18. $b = 6.1$ m
$h = 12$ m 73.2 m²

19. $b = 500$ m
$h = 35$ m 17,500 m²

20. $b = 85$ cm
$h = 25$ cm 2125 cm²

21. $b = 16$ cm
$h = 40$ cm 640 cm²

22. $b = 15$ km
$h = 13$ km 195 km²

23. $b = 68.3$ m
$h = 5.4$ m 368.82 m²

CHALKBOARD CHALLENGE
Construct a square, a rectangle, and a parallelogram that have a total area of 24 cm².

Pick up on these

Toothpicks were used to make this array of 9 small squares.

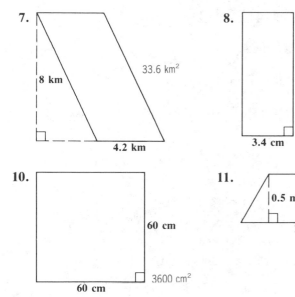

24. Draw a picture. Show how to remove 2 toothpicks to get 7 small squares.

25. Draw another picture. Show how to remove 4 toothpicks to get 5 small squares.

26. Show how to remove 4 toothpicks to get 6 small squares.

27. Show how to remove 8 toothpicks to get 5 small squares.

24.   25.   26.   27.   or

Geometry—Perimeter and Area **309**

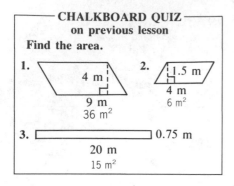
LESSON OBJECTIVE
To compute the area of a triangle

PROBLEM-SOLVING SKILLS
Finding information in a drawing
Using a formula

STARTING THE LESSON
Sketch this parallelogram on the chalkboard:

h = 3 in.
b = 4 in.

Before the students open their books, ask them to show how to cut the parallelogram in half to get two triangles that are the same shape and size. Then have the students turn to page 310 and compare their triangles with the triangles at the top of the page.

310

Area—triangles

CAN YOU CUT IT?

Think about cutting a parallelogram in half.

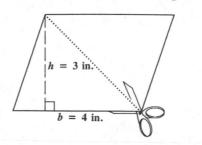
h = 3 in.
b = 4 in.

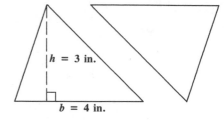
h = 3 in.
b = 4 in.

Two triangles are formed. The area of each triangle is half the area of the parallelogram.

1. The area of the parallelogram is 12 square [?]. inches

2. The area of each triangle is [?] square inches. 6

Here's how *to use a formula to find the area of a triangle.*

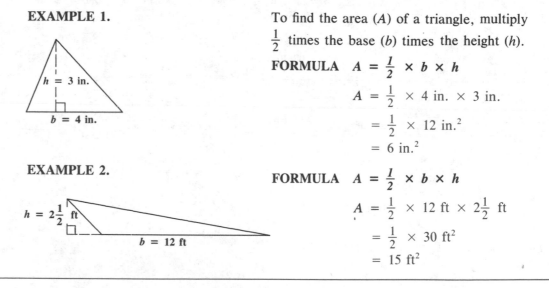

EXAMPLE 1.

h = 3 in.
b = 4 in.

To find the area (A) of a triangle, multiply $\frac{1}{2}$ times the base (b) times the height (h).

FORMULA $A = \frac{1}{2} \times b \times h$

$A = \frac{1}{2} \times 4 \text{ in.} \times 3 \text{ in.}$

$= \frac{1}{2} \times 12 \text{ in.}^2$

$= 6 \text{ in.}^2$

EXAMPLE 2.

$h = 2\frac{1}{2}$ ft
$b = 12$ ft

FORMULA $A = \frac{1}{2} \times b \times h$

$A = \frac{1}{2} \times 12 \text{ ft} \times 2\frac{1}{2} \text{ ft}$

$= \frac{1}{2} \times 30 \text{ ft}^2$

$= 15 \text{ ft}^2$

3. Look at the *Here's how*. What is the formula for the area of a triangle? What does each letter stand for? $A = \frac{1}{2} \times b \times h$, A = area, b = base, h = height

4. If the base and height of a triangle are 5 yards and 6 yards, the area is [?] square yards. 15

EXERCISES

Find the area. Use the formula $A = \frac{1}{2} \times b \times h$.

Here are scrambled answers for the next three exercises: 45 ft² 12 ft² 35 ft²

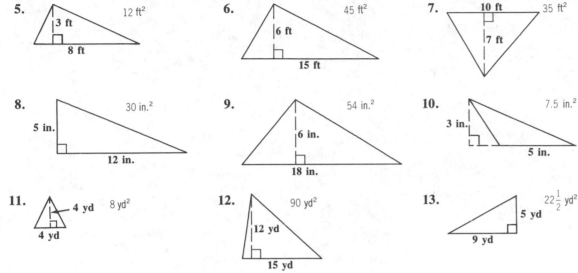

5. 12 ft²
3 ft
8 ft

6. 45 ft²
6 ft
15 ft

7. 10 ft
35 ft²
7 ft

8. 30 in.²
5 in.
12 in.

9. 54 in.²
6 in.
18 in.

10. 7.5 in.²
3 in.
5 in.

11. 4 yd   8 yd²
4 yd

12. 90 yd²
12 yd
15 yd

13. $22\frac{1}{2}$ yd²
5 yd
9 yd

Use $A = \frac{1}{2} \times b \times h$. Find the area of each triangle.

14.
$b = 9$ ft
$h = 4$ ft   18 ft²

15.
$b = 21$ ft
$h = 10$ ft   105 ft²

16.
$b = 40$ yd
$h = 7$ yd   140 yd²

17.
$b = 4$ in.
$h = 5$ in.   10 in.²

18.
$b = 20$ ft
$h = \frac{1}{2}$ ft   5 ft²

19.
$b = 10$ yd
$h = 2\frac{1}{2}$ yd $12\frac{1}{2}$ yd²

Crack the code

20. Use the code to get the answer.

RIDDLE: What is the easiest way to double your money?

ANSWER: 6 cm²* 2 cm²* 4 cm²* 5 cm²
12 cm²* 8cm²

Fold it.

|-1 cm-|

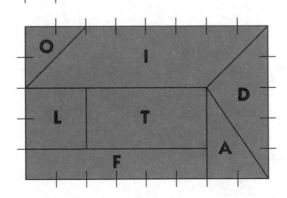

REVIEW PRACTICE
Multiplying fractions
Page 434   Skill 46

PRACTICE WORKSHEET
Copymaster S283 or Duplicating Master S283

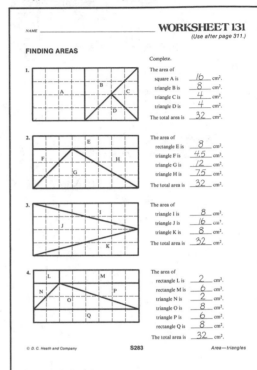

NAME _____ **WORKSHEET 131**
(Use after page 311.)

FINDING AREAS

Complete.

1.
The area of
square A is ___16___ cm².
triangle B is ___8___ cm².
triangle C is ___4___ cm².
triangle D is ___4___ cm².
The total area is ___32___ cm².

2.
The area of
rectangle E is ___8___ cm².
triangle F is ___4.5___ cm².
triangle G is ___12___ cm².
triangle H is ___7.5___ cm².
The total area is ___32___ cm².

3.
The area of
triangle I is ___8___ cm².
triangle J is ___16___ cm².
triangle K is ___8___ cm².
The total area is ___32___ cm².

4.
The area of
rectangle L is ___2___ cm².
rectangle M is ___6___ cm².
triangle N is ___2___ cm².
triangle O is ___8___ cm².
triangle P is ___6___ cm².
rectangle Q is ___8___ cm².
The total area is ___32___ cm².

© D. C. Heath and Company   S283   Area—triangles

LIFE-SKILL PROJECT

Making measurements
Have the students make tagboard cutouts of triangles. Have them use a ruler to make the necessary measurements and do the computation to find the area. Have other students find the area and compare answers. Because of the measurements involved, many of the answers will be close but not equal.

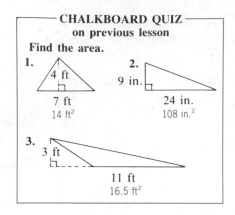
LESSON OBJECTIVE
To compute the area of a circle

PROBLEM-SOLVING SKILLS
Using a formula
Using a drawing

STARTING THE LESSON
Have the students take the Circle Quiz at the top of the page. Give the answers to quiz questions 1 and 2. Tell the students to study the *Here's how* and do exercise 4 to check their answer to quiz question 3.

HERE'S HOW NOTE
Let the students practice using the formula by finding the area of these circles.

2 ft
12.56 ft²

6 ft
113.04 ft²

10 ft
78.5 ft²

Area—circles

CIRCLE QUIZ

Choose the correct letter.

1. What caused these circles?
   a. Spaceships
   b. Sprinkler irrigation

2. What is the radius of each circle?
   a. 250 yards
   b. 500 yards

3. What is the area of each circle?
   a. Less than 1,000,000 yd²
   b. More than 1,000,000 yd²

1000 yd

Here's how *to use a formula to find the area of a circle.*

500 yd

To find the area (A) of a circle,
multiply π (about 3.14) times the radius (r)
times the radius.

FORMULA $A = \pi \times r \times r$
$A \approx 3.14 \times 500 \text{ yd} \times 500 \text{ yd}$
$\approx 3.14 \times 250,000 \text{ yd}^2$
$\approx 785,000 \text{ yd}^2$

4. Look at the *Here's how*. The area of the circle is approximately
   785,000 square [?]. yards

EXERCISES
Find the area. Use 3.14 for π.
Here are scrambled answers for the next row of exercises: 200.96 ft² 314 ft² 50.24 ft²

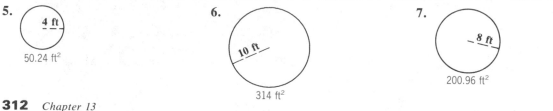

5. 4 ft
   50.24 ft²

6. 10 ft
   314 ft²

7. 8 ft
   200.96 ft²

8. 3 in.
28.26 in.²

9. 5 ft
78.5 ft²

10. 2 yd
12.56 yd²

11. 12 in.
Be careful! How long is the radius?
113.04 in.²

12. 2 yd
3.14 yd²

13. 5 ft
19.625 ft²

REVIEW PRACTICE
Fraction of a whole number
Page 435   Skill 47

PRACTICE WORKSHEET
Copymaster S284 or Duplicating Master S284

NAME _____

WORKSHEET 132
(Use after page 313.)

AREA FORMULAS

Rectangle: $A = l \times w$
Parallelogram: $A = b \times h$
Triangle: $A = \frac{1}{2} \times b \times h$
Circle: $A = \pi r^2$

CENTIMETERS

First make each necessary measurement to the nearest centimeter. Then compute the area. Use 3.14 for π.

1. ___12___ cm²
2. ___8___ cm²
3. ___10___ cm²
4. ___9___ cm²
5. ___9___ cm²
6. ___6___ cm²
7. ___45___ cm²
8. ___3.14___ cm²
9. ___12.56___ cm²

© D. C. Heath and Company   **S284**   *Using area formulas*

Use the area clues. Find the area of each red region.
Note that you can add and subtract areas.

14.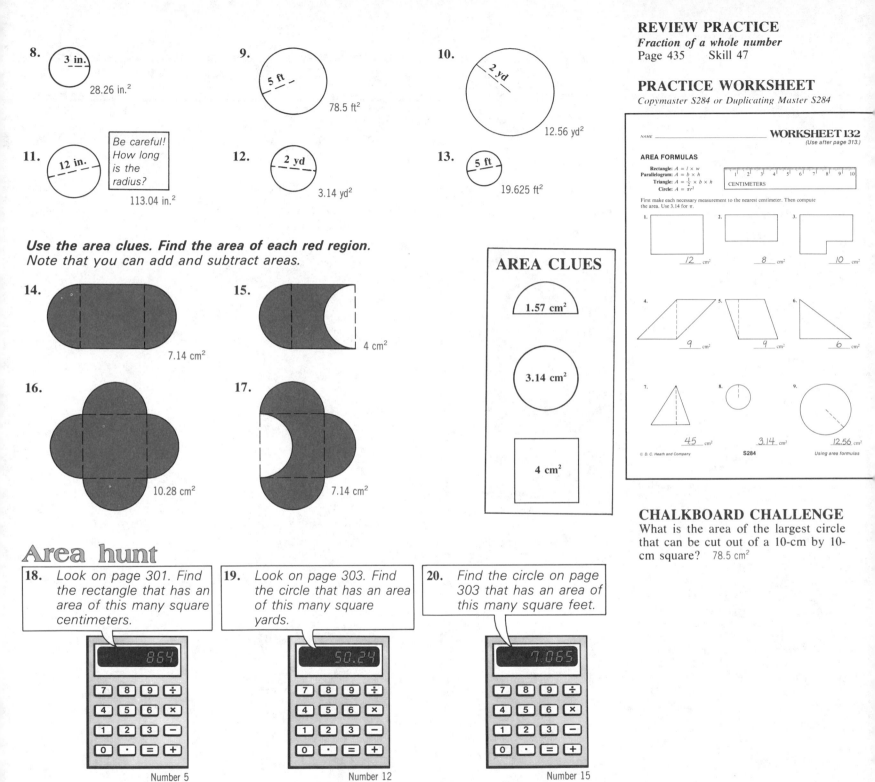
7.14 cm²

15.
4 cm²

16.
10.28 cm²

17.
7.14 cm²

AREA CLUES

1.57 cm²

3.14 cm²

4 cm²

CHALKBOARD CHALLENGE
What is the area of the largest circle that can be cut out of a 10-cm by 10-cm square? 78.5 cm²

Area hunt

18. *Look on page 301. Find the rectangle that has an area of this many square centimeters.*

864

Number 5

19. *Look on page 303. Find the circle that has an area of this many square yards.*

50.24

Number 12

20. *Find the circle on page 303 that has an area of this many square feet.*

7.065

Number 15

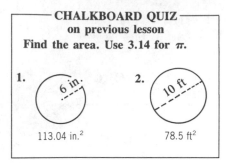
SKILLS REVIEWED
Making conversions between metric units of measure
Solving proportions
Changing a percent to a fraction
Changing a decimal to a percent
Solving percent problems

PROBLEM-SOLVING SKILL
Selecting information from a computer drawing

STARTING THE LESSON
Cumulative Skill Practice
Write these five answers on the chalkboard:

3.825   40 $\frac{1}{25}$ $62\frac{1}{2}\%$ 23

Challenge the students to an answer hunt by saying, "Look for the five even-numbered exercises on page 314 that have these answers. You have five minutes to find as many of the exercises as you can." (Exercises 4, 26, 44, 78, and 92)

STARTING THE LESSON
Problem Solving
Have the students read the paragraph at the top of the page. Then have the students close their books and sketch from memory a stick figure that shows the preferred angles for the wrist and elbow during a typical shot. Tell the students to compare their drawing with the stick figure at the top of the page.

Cumulative Skill Practice

Complete. *(page 202)*

1. 36 cm = _?_ m 0.36
2. 63 mm = _?_ cm 6.3
3. 24 km = _?_ m 24,000

4. 3825 m = _?_ km 3.825
5. 8.2 km = _?_ m 8200
6. 9.6 cm = _?_ mm 96

7. 52 cm = _?_ mm 520
8. 16 m = _?_ cm 1600
9. 2.4 m = _?_ cm 240

10. 225 km = _?_ m 225,000
11. 400 mm = _?_ m 0.4
12. 0.6 m = _?_ mm 600

Solve. *(page 230)*

13. $\frac{8}{9} = \frac{5}{n}$ $5\frac{5}{8}$
14. $\frac{9}{8} = \frac{n}{6}$ $6\frac{3}{4}$
15. $\frac{4}{n} = \frac{5}{9}$ $7\frac{1}{5}$
16. $\frac{7}{n} = \frac{5}{9}$ $12\frac{3}{5}$
17. $\frac{6}{8} = \frac{n}{4}$ 3

18. $\frac{n}{6} = \frac{8}{3}$ 16
19. $\frac{n}{5} = \frac{3}{5}$ 3
20. $\frac{n}{4} = \frac{5}{10}$ 2
21. $\frac{8}{4} = \frac{7}{n}$ $3\frac{1}{2}$
22. $\frac{n}{6} = \frac{3}{9}$ 2

23. $\frac{12}{n} = \frac{5}{8}$ $19\frac{1}{5}$
24. $\frac{15}{6} = \frac{10}{n}$ 4
25. $\frac{12}{16} = \frac{n}{4}$ 3
26. $\frac{n}{8} = \frac{10}{2}$ 40
27. $\frac{1}{2} = \frac{5}{n}$ 10

28. $\frac{9}{6} = \frac{12}{n}$ 8
29. $\frac{15}{2} = \frac{n}{6}$ 45
30. $\frac{8}{5} = \frac{n}{9}$ $14\frac{2}{5}$
31. $\frac{12}{n} = \frac{8}{20}$ 30
32. $\frac{13}{n} = \frac{5}{10}$ 26

Change to a fraction in simplest form. *(page 248)*

33. 20% $\frac{1}{5}$
34. 50% $\frac{1}{2}$
35. 25% $\frac{1}{4}$
36. 75% $\frac{3}{4}$
37. 30% $\frac{3}{10}$
38. 8% $\frac{2}{25}$

39. 16% $\frac{4}{25}$
40. 85% $\frac{17}{20}$
41. 48% $\frac{12}{25}$
42. 60% $\frac{3}{5}$
43. 72% $\frac{18}{25}$
44. 4% $\frac{1}{25}$

45. 120% $1\frac{1}{5}$
46. 125% $1\frac{1}{4}$
47. 250% $2\frac{1}{2}$
48. 175% $1\frac{3}{4}$
49. 290% $2\frac{9}{10}$
50. 135% $1\frac{7}{20}$

51. $33\frac{1}{3}\%$ $\frac{1}{3}$
52. $66\frac{2}{3}\%$ $\frac{2}{3}$
53. $12\frac{1}{2}\%$ $\frac{1}{8}$
54. $83\frac{1}{3}\%$ $\frac{5}{6}$
55. $62\frac{1}{2}\%$ $\frac{5}{8}$
56. $37\frac{1}{2}\%$ $\frac{3}{8}$

Change to a percent. *(page 253)*

57. 0.05 5%
58. 0.01 1%
59. 0.42 42%
60. 0.75 75%
61. 0.4 40%
62. 0.1 10%

63. 0.7 70%
64. 0.8 80%
65. 0.003 0.3%
66. 0.009 0.9%
67. 0.3 30%
68. 0.013 1.3%

69. 2.5 250%
70. 0.25 25%
71. 3.4 340%
72. 1.6 160%
73. 2.375 237.5%
74. 0.02 2%

75. $0.16\frac{2}{3}$ $16\frac{2}{3}\%$
76. $0.33\frac{1}{3}$ $33\frac{1}{3}\%$
77. $0.12\frac{1}{2}$ $12\frac{1}{2}\%$
78. $0.62\frac{1}{2}$ $62\frac{1}{2}\%$
79. $1.87\frac{1}{2}$ $187\frac{1}{2}\%$
80. $1.36\frac{1}{2}$ $136\frac{1}{2}\%$

Solve. *(page 260)*

81. 10% of n = 12 120
82. 30% of n = 15 50
83. 50% of n = 16 32

84. 20% of n = 18 90
85. 60% of n = 30 50
86. 6% of n = 9 150

87. 5% of n = 10 200
88. 75% of n = 45 60
89. 80% of n = 25 31.25

90. 120% of n = 75 62.5
91. 150% of n = 72 48
92. 200% of n = 46 23

314

Problem solving

COMPUTERS AND SPORTS

Coaches at the Olympic Training Center in Colorado Springs use computer-produced stick figures to help athletes analyze and improve their performance. The stick figure superimposed on the photo at the right can be used by basketball coaches. It shows the preferred angles for the wrist and elbow during a typical shot.

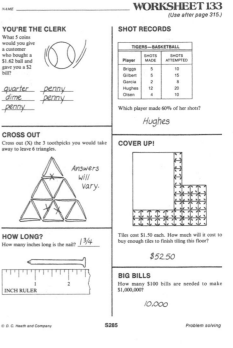

1. What is the elbow angle? 90°

2. Is the wrist angle about 45°? Yes

Study these computer-produced stick figures. Then match each of the coach's comments with the right player.

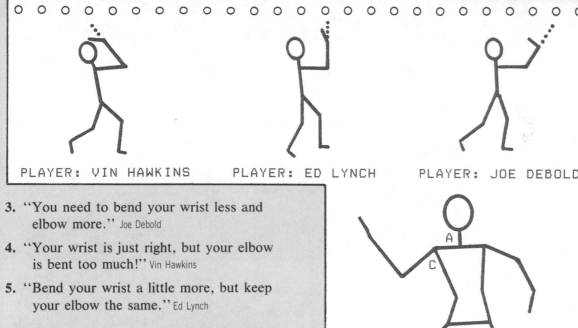

PLAYER: VIN HAWKINS   PLAYER: ED LYNCH   PLAYER: JOE DEBOLD

3. "You need to bend your wrist less and elbow more." Joe Debold

4. "Your wrist is just right, but your elbow is bent too much!" Vin Hawkins

5. "Bend your wrist a little more, but keep your elbow the same." Ed Lynch

Use the stick figure of this tennis player to complete the coach's statements.

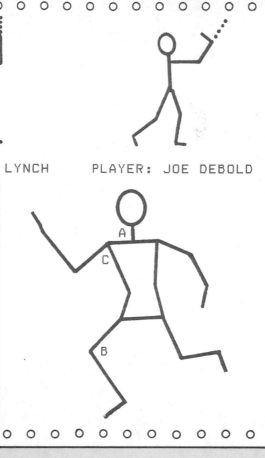

6. "Angle [?] in the figure is about 80°." C

7. "The [?] is bent at an angle of about 100°. It is labeled angle [?] in the figure." Knee, B

8. "The neck and shoulders form angle [?]. It is a(n) [?] angle, since it measures 90°." A, right

---

EXTRA PROBLEM SOLVING
Page 456   Even exercises

PROBLEM-SOLVING WORKSHEET
Copymaster S285 or Duplicating Master S285

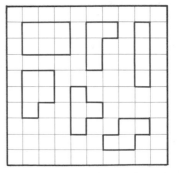

NAME _____

WORKSHEET 133
(Use after page 315.)

YOU'RE THE CLERK
What 5 coins would you give a customer who bought a $1.62 ball and gave you a $2 bill?

quarter   penny
dime   penny
penny

SHOT RECORDS

TIGERS—BASKETBALL		
Player	SHOTS MADE	SHOTS ATTEMPTED
Briggs	5	10
Gilbert	5	15
Garcia	2	8
Hughes	12	20
Olsen	4	10

Which player made 60% of her shots?

Hughes

CROSS OUT
Cross out (X) the 3 toothpicks you would take away to leave 6 triangles.

Answers will vary.

COVER UP!

Tiles cost $1.50 each. How much will it cost to buy enough tiles to finish tiling this floor?

$52.50

HOW LONG?
How many inches long is the nail? 1 3/4

INCH RULER

BIG BILLS
How many $100 bills are needed to make $1,000,000?

10,000

© D. C. Heath and Company   S285   Problem solving

CHALKBOARD CHALLENGE

Use graph paper or dot paper. (Dot paper can be made from **Visual Aid 26**.) Find six polygons of different shapes, each with a perimeter of 10 units. The length of each side must be a whole number.

Complete. *(pages 294, 296)*

1. A protractor is used to measure **angles**.
2. An acute angle measures between **0°** and 90°.
3. A right angle measures **90°**.
4. An obtuse angle measures between **90°** and 180°.
5. Angle **B** is an acute angle.
6. Angle **A** is an obtuse angle.
7. Angle **C** is a right angle.
8. Two lines that intersect to form **right** angles are perpendicular.
9. Two lines on a flat surface that do not intersect are **parallel**.
10. Line s is perpendicular to line **t**.
11. Line r is parallel to line **s**.
12. Line r is perpendicular to line **t**.

True or false? *(page 298)*

13. **True** A triangle has 3 sides.
14. **True** Both a square and a rectangle have 4 right angles.
15. **True** A rectangle has 4 sides and 4 right angles.
16. **False** The 4 sides of a rectangle are the same length.
17. **True** A square is also a rectangle.
18. **False** A rectangle is also a square.
19. **False** A parallelogram has 4 sides and exactly 1 pair of parallel sides.
20. **True** A rectangle is also a parallelogram.
21. **False** A parallelogram is also a rectangle.
22. **False** A trapezoid has 2 sides that are the same length.
23. **True** A trapezoid has exactly 1 pair of parallel sides.
24. **True** A pentagon has 5 sides.
25. **False** A hexagon has 8 sides.

ANSWERS
1. angles
2. 0°
3. 90°
4. 90°
5. B
6. A
7. C
8. right
9. parallel
10. t
11. s
12. t
13. True
14. True
15. True
16. False
17. True
18. False
19. False
20. True
21. False
22. False
23. True
24. True
25. False

© D. C. Heath and Company   S49   Page 1

Find the perimeter. *(page 300)*

26. **48 cm**
27. **72 cm**
28. **56 cm**
29. **36 cm**
30. **63.2 cm**
31. **16.4 cm**

Find the circumference. Use 3.14 as an approximation for π. *(page 302)*

32. **12.56 m**
33. **21.98 m**
34. **18.84 m**
35. **31.4 m**
36. **15.7 m**
37. **28.26 m**

Find the area. *(pages 306, 308, 310)*

38. **6.25 m²**
39. **7.2 m²**
40. **0.6 m²**
41. **13.5 m²**
42. **4.2 m²**
43. **11.04 m²**
44. **3.15 m²**
45. **3.22 m²**
46. **3.04 m²**

Find the area. Use 3.14 as an approximation for π. *(page 312)*

47. **28.26 cm²**
48. **78.5 cm²**
49. **50.24 cm²**
50. **113.04 cm²**

ANSWERS
26. 48 cm
27. 72 cm
28. 56 cm
29. 36 cm
30. 63.2 cm
31. 16.4 cm
32. 12.56 m
33. 21.98 m
34. 18.84 m
35. 31.4 m
36. 15.7 m
37. 28.26 m
38. 6.25 m²
39. 7.2 m²
40. 0.6 m²
41. 13.5 m²
42. 4.2 m²
43. 11.04 m²
44. 3.15 m²
45. 3.22 m²
46. 3.04 m²
47. 28.26 cm²
48. 78.5 cm²
49. 50.24 cm²
50. 113.04 cm²

© D. C. Heath and Company   S50   Page 2

Chapter REVIEW

Here are scrambled answers for the review exercises:

18	72	π	height	obtuse	perimeter	width
36	314	acute	hexagon	parallel	perpendicular	
50	628	base	multiply	parallelogram	trapezoid	

1. An [?] angle measures between 0° and 90°. An [?] angle measures between 90° and 180°. *(page 294)*

2. Line *r* is [?] to line *t*, and line *s* is [?] to line *t*. *(page 296)*

r
t
s

3. A rectangle is also a [?]. A [?] has exactly 1 pair of parallel sides. A [?] has 6 sides. *(page 298)*

4. The [?] of a figure is the distance around the figure. The perimeter of this rectangle is [?] cm. *(page 300)*

12 cm
24 cm

5. To find the circumference of a circle, you would [?] the diameter (*d*) by pi (π). The circumference of this circle is [?] ft. *(page 302)*

200 ft   π ≈ 3.14

6. To find the area of a rectangle, you would multiply the length (*l*) times the [?] (*w*). The area of this square is [?] cm². *(page 306)*

6 cm
6 cm

7. To find the area of a parallelogram, you would multiply the base (*b*) times the [?] (*h*). The area of this parallelogram is [?] cm². *(page 308)*

5 cm
10 cm

8. To find the area of a triangle, you would multiply $\frac{1}{2}$ times the [?] (*b*) times the height (*h*). The area of this triangle is [?] ft². *(page 310)*

4 ft
9 ft

9. To find the area of a circle, you would multiply [?] times the radius times the radius. The area of this circle is [?] ft². *(page 312)*

10 ft   π ≈ 3.14

1. acute, obtuse
4. perimeter, 72
7. height, 50
2. parallel, perpendicular
5. multiply, 628
8. base, 18
3. parallelogram, trapezoid, hexagon
6. width, 36
9. π, 314

Chapter TEST

Complete. *(pages 294, 296, 298)*

1. A [?] is used to measure angles. protractor

2. A right angle measures [?]. 90°

3. An acute angle measures between 0° and [?]. 90°

4. An obtuse angle measures between [?] and 180°. 90°

5. Two lines that intersect to form right angles are [?]. perpendicular

6. Two lines on a flat surface that do not intersect are [?]. parallel

7. A triangle has [?] sides. 3

8. A rectangle has 4 sides and 4 [?] angles. right

9. A parallelogram has 2 pairs of [?] sides. parallel

10. A trapezoid has exactly 1 pair of [?] sides. parallel

11. A pentagon has [?] sides. 5

12. A hexagon has [?] sides. 6

Find the perimeter. *(page 300)*

13. 6 cm, 6 cm 24 cm

14. 6 cm, 15 cm 42 cm

15. 13 cm, 5 cm, 12 cm 30 cm

Find the circumference. Use 3.14 as an approximation for π. *(page 302)*

16. 6 m 18.84 m

17. 8 m 25.12 m

18. 5 m 15.7 m

Find the area. *(pages 306, 308, 310)*

19. 3.5 m, 5.2 m 18.2 m²

20. 4.0 m, 4.0 m 16 m²

21. 4.0 m, 6.5 m 26 m²

22. 3.0 m, 2.2 m 6.6 m²

23. 2.0 m, 7.2 m 7.2 m²

24. 1.8 m, 1.6 m 1.44 m²

Find the area. Use 3.14 as an approximation for π. *(page 312)*

25. 10 cm 314 cm²

26. 12 cm 452.16 cm²

27. 12 cm 113.04 cm²

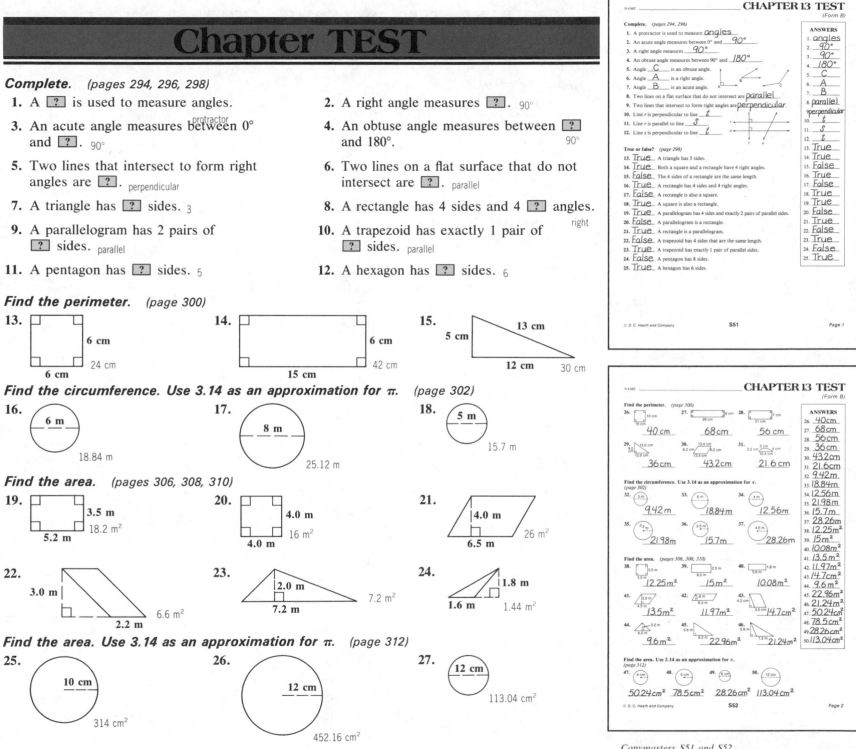

Use Copymaster S336 to provide the students with an answer sheet in standardized test format.

Cumulative TEST Standardized Format

Choose the correct letter.

Answers for Cumulative Test, Chapters 1–13

1. Ⓐ Ⓑ ● Ⓓ	2. ● Ⓑ Ⓒ Ⓓ	3. Ⓐ Ⓑ ● Ⓓ
4. Ⓐ Ⓑ ● Ⓓ	5. Ⓐ Ⓑ ● ●	6. Ⓐ ● Ⓒ Ⓓ
7. Ⓐ Ⓑ Ⓒ ●	8. ● Ⓑ Ⓒ Ⓓ	9. Ⓐ Ⓑ ● Ⓓ
10. ● Ⓑ Ⓒ Ⓓ	11. Ⓐ ● Ⓒ Ⓓ	12. Ⓐ Ⓑ ● Ⓓ

The table below correlates test items with student text pages.

Test Item	Page Taught	Skill Practice
1	146	p. 304, exercises 1–21
2	158	p. 304, exercises 22–36
3	164	p. 304, exercises 37–51
4	178	p. 304, exercises 52–66
5	188	p. 304, exercises 67–81
6	202	p. 314, exercises 1–12
7	230	p. 314, exercises 13–32
8	248	p. 314, exercises 33–56
9	253	p. 314, exercises 57–80
10	256	p. 314, exercises 81–92
11	272	
12	310	

318

1. Change to a decimal.

$5\frac{3}{4} = ?$

A. 0.75
B. 5.25
Ⓒ 5.75
D. none of these

2. Give the sum.

$\frac{5}{12} + \frac{7}{8}$

Ⓐ $1\frac{7}{24}$
B. $\frac{3}{5}$
C. $1\frac{1}{4}$
D. none of these

3. Give the difference.

$\frac{5}{6} - \frac{3}{4}$

A. 1
Ⓑ $\frac{1}{12}$
C. $\frac{1}{3}$
D. none of these

4. Give the product.

$\frac{5}{9} \times \frac{2}{3}$

A. $\frac{5}{6}$
B. $\frac{7}{27}$
Ⓒ $\frac{10}{27}$
D. none of these

5. Give the quotient.

$\frac{7}{8} \div \frac{1}{3}$

A. $\frac{7}{24}$
B. $2\frac{5}{16}$
C. $\frac{8}{21}$
Ⓓ none of these

6. 3475 m = ? km

A. 34.75
Ⓑ 3.475
C. 0.3475
D. none of these

7. Solve. $\frac{9}{n} = \frac{14}{5}$

A. 12
B. 11.25
C. 7.2
Ⓓ none of these

8. Change to a fraction.

$37\frac{1}{2}\% = ?$

Ⓐ $\frac{3}{8}$
B. $\frac{5}{8}$
C. $\frac{2}{5}$
D. none of these

9. Change to a percent.

$0.06 = ?$

A. 0.06%
B. 0.6%
Ⓒ 6%
D. none of these

10. Solve.

24% of n = 30

Ⓐ 125
B. 7.2
C. 22.8
D. none of these

11. A radio that regularly sells for $124 is on sale for 40% off. What is the sale price?

A. $49.60   Ⓑ $74.40
C. $173.60   D. none of these

12. Find the area.

6 ft
13 ft

A. 78 ft²   B. 9.5 ft²
Ⓒ 39 ft²   D. none of these

CHAPTER 14
Surface Area and Volume

LESSON OBJECTIVES
To classify space figures by their faces, corners, and edges
(*pages 320–321*)
To visualize how triangular, square, and rectangular faces are
used to build three-dimensional models (*pages 322–323*)
To compute the surface area of rectangular prisms and
cubes (*pages 324–325*)
To compute the volume of rectangular prisms and cubes
(*pages 328–329*)
To compute the volume of a cylinder (*pages 330–331*)
To find the volume of a pyramid or cone (*pages 332–333*)

PROBLEM-SOLVING SKILLS
Finding information in a drawing (*pages 320–321, 324–325, 328–333*)
Using logical reasoning (*page 321*)
Making geometric visualizations (*pages 321–323, 325, 329, 335*)
Selecting information from a display (*pages 322–323*)
Finding information in an ad (*page 327*)
Using a drawing to solve a problem (*page 327*)
Solving a multi-step problem (*page 327*)
Using a formula (*pages 328–333*)
Choosing the correct operation (*page 329*)
Choosing the correct formula (*page 331*)
Using a guess-and-check strategy (*page 333*)

RESOURCES
• **WORKSHEETS 134–141** (*Copymasters S286–S293 or Duplicating Masters S286–S293*)

LESSON OBJECTIVE
To classify space figures by their faces, corners, and edges

PROBLEM-SOLVING SKILLS
Finding information in a drawing
Using logical reasoning
Making geometric visualizations

STARTING THE LESSON
Have the students use the packages at the top of the page to answer questions 1–3. Then have them use the *Here's how* information to do exercise 4.

EXERCISE NOTE
Some students may have difficulty visualizing the cubes in exercises 15–23. Suggest that they draw each figure on graph paper, cut it out, and fold it into a cube.

Space figures
LOOK THEM OVER

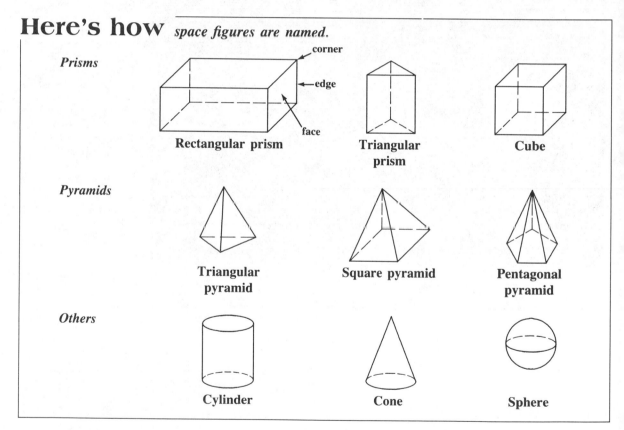

1. *Which package is mine? My package has 5 faces (sides), 6 corners, and 9 edges.* C

2. Which package has 6 square faces? B

3. Which package has 5 faces and 5 corners? D

Here's how *space figures are named.*

Prisms

Rectangular prism — corner, edge, face

Triangular prism

Cube

Pyramids

Triangular pyramid

Square pyramid

Pentagonal pyramid

Others

Cylinder

Cone

Sphere

4. Use the packages and the *Here's how* chart to answer the questions.
   a. Which package is a cube? B
   b. Which package is a cylinder? A
   c. Which package is a rectangular prism? E
   d. Which package is a square pyramid? D
   e. Which package is a triangular prism? C
   f. Which 3 packages are prisms? B,C,E

EXERCISES

Use the clues and the drawings on page 320. Name each space figure.

5. Clues: Cube
- This space figure is a prism.
- All its faces are squares.

6. Clues: Triangular pyramid
- This space figure is a pyramid.
- It has 4 corners.

7. Clues: Square pyramid
- This space figure has 5 faces.
- One of its faces is square.
- It has 8 edges.

8. Clues: Rectangular prism
- This space figure has 6 faces.
- None of its faces are square.
- It has 8 corners.

9. Clues: Pentagonal pyramid
- This space figure has 6 faces.
- One of its sides is a pentagon.

10. Clues: Triangular prism
- This space figure has 5 faces.
- It has 9 edges.

11. Clues: Cube
- This space figure has 8 corners.
- All its edges are the same length.

12. Clues: Cylinder
- This space figure has no corners.
- Two of its faces are circles.

13. Clues: Sphere
- This space figure has no corners.
- If you cut this figure using one straight cut, the shape that is formed is always a circle.

14. Clues: Cone
- Cut this space figure one way and the shape that is formed is a circle.
- Cut it another way and the shape that is formed is a triangle.

What's on top?

Each of these patterns can be folded to form a cube. If the red face is the bottom of the cube, which face is the top?

15. 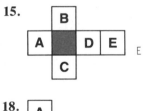 E

16. 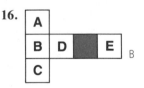 B

17. 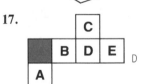 D

18. 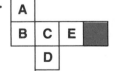 C

19. 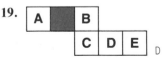 D

20. 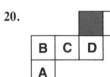 A

21. 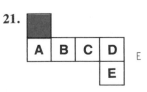 E

22. 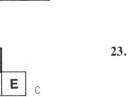 C

23. 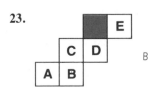 B

REVIEW PRACTICE
Multiplying mixed numbers
Page 435   Skill 48

PRACTICE WORKSHEET
Copymaster S286 or Duplicating Master S286

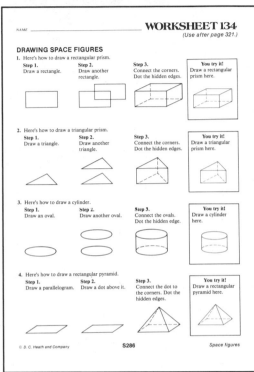

CHALKBOARD CHALLENGE
The six sides of a cube are lettered A through F. Here are three views of the cube:

1. Which letter is opposite side *A*? D
2. Which letter is opposite side *C*? F
3. Which letter is opposite side *B*? E

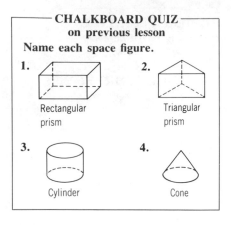
More on space figures

PIECES & PRICES

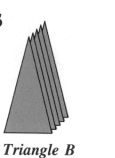

Square
25¢

Triangle A
11¢

Triangle B
24¢

Rectangle
50¢

LESSON OBJECTIVE
To visualize how triangular, square, and rectangular faces are used to build three-dimensional models

PROBLEM-SOLVING SKILLS
Selecting information from a display
Making geometric visualizations

STARTING THE LESSON
Sketch these shapes on the chalkboard:

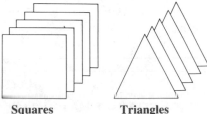

Squares   **Triangles**

Before discussing questions 1–4, ask the students to describe what space figures can be made with
• 6 square pieces. (Cube)
• 4 triangular pieces. (Triangular pyramid)
• 3 square pieces and 2 triangular pieces. (Triangular prism)

Here is a model that was made from some pieces that are shown above.

1. How many pieces were used to make the model? 5

2. **a.** Which piece was used for the top and bottom?
   b. What is the total cost of the top and bottom?
   a. Triangle A   **b.** 22¢

3. **a.** Which piece was used for the other faces? Square
   b. What is their total cost? 75¢

4. What is the total cost of the model? 97¢

EXERCISES
Find the total cost of each model.

5. $1.50

6. 44¢

7. $2.50

8. 69¢

9.  $1.21

10. 83¢

11. $1.72

12. $1.73

13.  97¢

14.  $1.97

15. 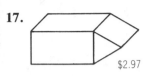 $1.69

16. 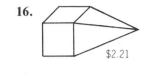 $2.21

17. 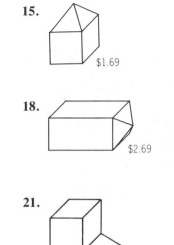 $2.97

18.  $2.69

19. $3.44

20. $3.50

21. 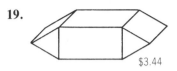 $2.97

22. $2.69

Solve.

23. Which 5 pieces would you use to make the least expensive prism? 3 squares
2 Triangle A's

24. Which pieces would you use to make the least expensive pyramid? 4 Triangle A's

25. Which pieces would you use to make the most expensive pyramid? 1 square, 4 Triangle B's

26. What is the price of the least expensive model that you can build that has 6 faces? *Hint: The answer is not $1.50.* 66¢

Name that product

Can you identify, just from the shape, what product is in each can?

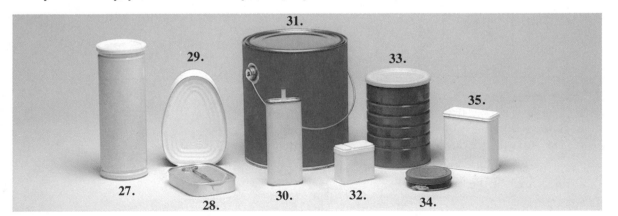

27. Tennis balls 28. Sardines 29. Ham 30. Oil
31. Paint 32. Spice 33. Coffee 34. Shoe polish 35. Adhesive bandages

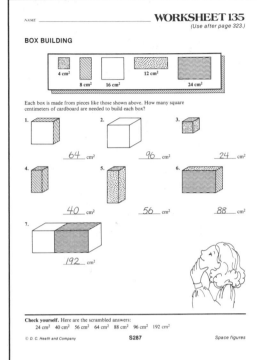

REVIEW PRACTICE
Fraction of a whole number
Page 436   Skill 49

PRACTICE WORKSHEET
Copymaster S287 or Duplicating Master S287

NAME _____ **WORKSHEET 135**
(Use after page 323.)

BOX BUILDING

4 cm² 8 cm² 16 cm² 12 cm² 24 cm²

Each box is made from pieces like those shown above. How many square centimeters of cardboard are needed to build each box?

1. *64* cm²   2. *96* cm²   3. *24* cm²
4. *40* cm²   5. *56* cm²   6. *88* cm²
7. *192* cm²

Check yourself. Here are the scrambled answers:
24 cm² 40 cm² 56 cm² 64 cm² 88 cm² 96 cm² 192 cm²

© D. C. Heath and Company   **S287**   *Space figures*

LIFE-SKILL PROJECT
Visualizing shapes
Have the students sketch the top, front, and side view of this solid.

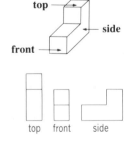

top   side   front

top   front   side

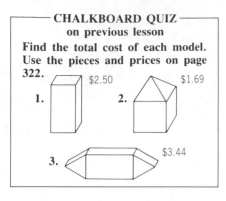

LESSON OBJECTIVE
To compute the surface area of rectangular prisms and cubes

PROBLEM-SOLVING SKILLS
Finding information in a drawing
Making geometric visualizations

STARTING THE LESSON
Have the students study the photo boxes
at the top of the page and answer question 1. Go over the *Here's how* and
then discuss questions 2–4.

Surface area— rectangular prisms and cubes

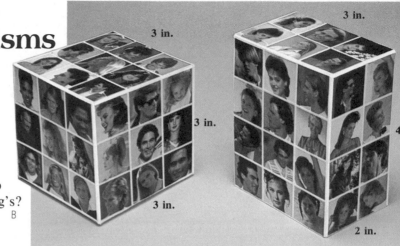

Photo box A   Photo box B

3 in.
3 in.
3 in.
3 in.
3 in.
2 in.

CAN YOU PICTURE IT?

1. Greg used 52 pictures to
cover the 6 faces of his photo
box. Which photo box is Greg's?
B

Here's how *to find the surface area of a rectangular prism.*

Think about unfolding **photo box B.** To find the surface area, compute the area
of each face by multiplying its length by its width. Then add all six areas.

```
              Top
            (2" × 3")

Left        Front       Right      Back
side        (3" × 4")   side       (3" × 4")
(2" × 4")               (2" × 4")

            Bottom
            (2" × 3")
```

Area of front .... 12 in.^{2}
         back .... 12 in.^{2}
         top.......... 6 in.^{2}
         bottom .... 6 in.^{2}
         left side ...... 8 in.^{2}
         right side ..... 8 in.^{2}
         Surface area = 52 in.^{2}

2. Look at the *Here's how.*
   a. The area of the front is the same as the area of the ☐?☐. back
   b. The area of the top is the same as the area of the ☐?☐. bottom
   c. The area of the left side is the same as the area of the ☐?☐ side. right

3. Look at photo box A. If the area of each face is 9 square inches, then the
surface area of the cube is ☐?☐ square inches. 54

4. Which photo box has the greater surface area? A

324

324 *Chapter 14*

EXERCISES

Find the surface area of each box.

5.
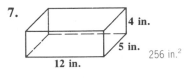
3 in.
6 in.
10 in.

front: _?_ in.² 30
back: _?_ in.² 30
top: _?_ in.² 60
bottom: _?_ in.² 60
left side: _?_ in.² 18
right side: _?_ in.² 18
Surface area = _?_ in.² 216

6.
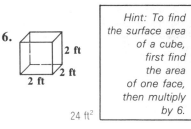
2 ft
2 ft
2 ft
24 ft²

> **Hint:** To find the surface area of a cube, first find the area of one face, then multiply by 6.

7.
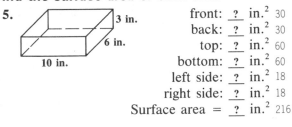
4 in.
5 in.
12 in.
256 in.²

8.
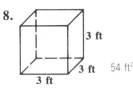
3 ft
3 ft
3 ft
54 ft²

9.
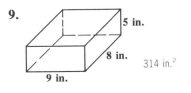
5 in.
8 in.
9 in.
314 in.²

10.
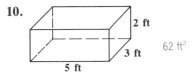
2 ft
3 ft
5 ft
62 ft²

11.
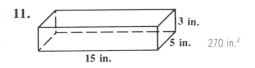
3 in.
5 in.
15 in.
270 in.²

12.
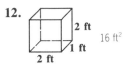
2 ft
1 ft
2 ft
16 ft²

Solve.

13. How many 1-inch-square pictures are needed to cover a photo box 5 inches long, 4 inches wide, and 6 inches tall? 148

14. How many 1-inch-square pictures are needed to cover a photo cube that is 5 inches on an edge? 150

Blockheads

15. This 3-inch photo cube is cut into 27 1-inch cubes. How many of the 1-inch cubes will have
  a. photos on 3 of the faces? 8
  b. photos on 2 of the faces? 12
  c. photos on 1 of the faces? 6
  d. no photos on any of the faces? 1

REVIEW PRACTICE
Dividing fractions
Page 436   Skill 50

PRACTICE WORKSHEET
Copymaster S288 or Duplicating Master S288

WORKSHEET 136
(Use after page 325.)

NAME _____

SURFACE AREA
Complete the table.

	FRONT FACE	BACK FACE	TOP FACE	BOTTOM FACE	RIGHT FACE	LEFT FACE	SURFACE AREA
1. (2 cm × 2 cm × 1 cm)	2 cm²	2 cm²	4 cm²	4 cm²	2 cm²	2 cm²	16 cm²
2. (3 cm × 2 cm × 2 cm)	6 cm²	6 cm²	6 cm²	6 cm²	4 cm²	4 cm²	32 cm²
3. (1 cm × 1 cm × 1 cm)	1 cm²	1 cm²	1 cm²	1 cm²	1 cm²	1 cm²	6 cm²
4. (2 cm × 2 cm × 1 cm)	4 cm²	4 cm²	2 cm²	2 cm²	2 cm²	2 cm²	16 cm²
5. (1.5 cm × 1 cm × 1 cm)	1.5 cm²	1.5 cm²	1.5 cm²	1.5 cm²	1 cm²	1 cm²	8 cm²
6. (1.5 cm × 2 cm × 1 cm)	3 cm²	3 cm²	1.5 cm²	1.5 cm²	2 cm²	2 cm²	13 cm²
7. (1.5 cm × 1.5 cm × 1.5 cm)	2.25 cm²	2.25 cm²	2.25 cm²	2.25 cm²	2.25 cm²	2.25 cm²	13.5 cm²

© D. C. Heath and Company   S288   Surface area of rectangular prisms and cubes

LIFE-SKILL PROJECT
Making measurements
Provide the students with boxes of varying sizes. Have the students measure the length, width, and height of each box to the nearest inch and then compute the surface area of each box.

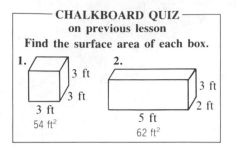
SKILLS REVIEWED
Multiplying and dividing decimals
Changing a fraction to a decimal
Subtracting mixed numbers
Dividing mixed numbers

PROBLEM-SOLVING SKILLS
Finding information in an ad
Using a drawing to solve a problem
Solving a multi-step problem

STARTING THE LESSON
Cumulative Skill Practice
Challenge the students to an estimation hunt by saying, "Find the five products in exercises 1–15 that are greater than 100." (Exercises 4, 8, 11, 12, and 14) Then have the students find the quotient in exercises 16–27 that is greater than 100. (Exercise 18)

STARTING THE LESSON
Problem Solving
Have the students use the sale ad at the top of page 327 to answer questions like these:
• How much does a square of shake shingles cost? ($89.90)
• How many squares of asphalt shingles are needed to cover 400 square feet? (4)
• Can you buy 10 squares of asphalt shingles for $500? (No)

Cumulative Skill Practice

Give the product. *(page 64)*

1. 5.1×0.4 2.04
2. 6.3×0.42 2.646
3. 0.59×0.8 0.4
4. 45×2.7 121.5
5. 0.82×6.2 5.084
6. 2.18×4.9 10.
7. 7.94×6 47.64
8. 52.6×9.1 478.66
9. 53.1×0.62 3
10. 6.59×12 79.08
11. 31.6×5.8 183.28
12. 207×1.5 310
13. 3.04×0.06 0.1824
14. 51.3×30.8 1580.04
15. 6.42×3.05 19.5

Give the quotient rounded to the nearest tenth. *(page 96)*

16. $17.4 \div 0.9$ 19.3
17. $4.65 \div 0.2$ 23.3
18. $6.47 \div 0.03$
19. $5.27 \div 1.6$ 3.3
20. $3.059 \div 2.1$ 1.5
21. $6.07 \div 0.35$
22. $16.083 \div 0.39$ 41.2
23. $4.003 \div 0.26$ 15.4
24. $7.03 \div 5.4$
25. $7.94 \div 6.5$ 1.2
26. $3.849 \div 5.7$ 0.7
27. $41 \div 3.2$ 12.8

Change to a decimal rounded to the nearest hundredth. *(page 146)*

28. $\frac{1}{3}$ 0.33
29. $\frac{1}{6}$ 0.17
30. $\frac{1}{9}$ 0.11
31. $\frac{2}{3}$ 0.67
32. $\frac{2}{9}$ 0.22
33. $\frac{5}{6}$ 0.83
34. $\frac{1}{8}$ 0.1

35. $\frac{1}{12}$ 0.08
36. $\frac{11}{6}$ 1.83
37. $\frac{5}{12}$ 0.42
38. $\frac{5}{3}$ 1.67
39. $\frac{5}{8}$ 0.63
40. $\frac{13}{6}$ 2.17
41. $\frac{20}{6}$ 3.

42. $\frac{4}{3}$ 1.33
43. $\frac{10}{9}$ 1.11
44. $\frac{3}{8}$ 0.38
45. $\frac{7}{3}$ 2.33
46. $\frac{7}{12}$ 0.58
47. $\frac{11}{3}$ 3.67
48. $\frac{10}{3}$ 3.

Subtract. Give the difference in simplest form. *(page 170)*

49. $3\frac{5}{6}$ $-1\frac{1}{6}$ $2\frac{2}{3}$
50. $5\frac{3}{4}$ $-3\frac{1}{4}$ $2\frac{1}{2}$
51. 7 $-2\frac{1}{2}$ $4\frac{1}{2}$
52. $8\frac{1}{3}$ $-3\frac{3}{8}$ $4\frac{23}{24}$
53. 6 $-4\frac{3}{4}$ $1\frac{1}{4}$
54. $9\frac{2}{5}$ $-1\frac{7}{10}$ $7\frac{}{}$

55. 10 $-5\frac{3}{4}$ $4\frac{1}{4}$
56. $12\frac{1}{3}$ $-8\frac{5}{6}$ $3\frac{1}{2}$
57. $15\frac{2}{5}$ $-4\frac{3}{4}$ $10\frac{13}{20}$
58. $16\frac{3}{4}$ $-11\frac{7}{8}$ $4\frac{7}{8}$
59. $22\frac{3}{10}$ $-18\frac{5}{6}$ $3\frac{7}{15}$
60. $25\frac{3}{4}$ $-5\frac{1}{2}$ 20

Give the quotient in simplest form. *(page 190)*

61. $1\frac{1}{3} \div 4$ $\frac{1}{3}$
62. $4\frac{1}{2} \div 2$ $2\frac{1}{4}$
63. $3 \div 1\frac{1}{2}$ 2
64. $4 \div 1\frac{1}{4}$ $3\frac{1}{5}$
65. $8 \div 1\frac{1}{2}$ $5\frac{1}{3}$

66. $2\frac{5}{6} \div 1\frac{1}{8}$ $2\frac{14}{27}$
67. $5\frac{7}{8} \div 4$ $1\frac{15}{32}$
68. $12\frac{1}{2} \div 2\frac{1}{2}$ 5
69. $6\frac{2}{3} \div 3\frac{1}{3}$ 2
70. $2\frac{1}{2} \div 3\frac{1}{2}$ $\frac{5}{7}$

Problem solving

YOU'RE THE ROOFER!

Use the newspaper ad to answer these customers' questions.

1. *How many square feet will a square of shingles cover?* 100

2. *Can I buy 6 squares of asphalt shingles for $350?* No

3. *Are 7 squares of shingles enough to shingle my house? My roof has an area of 720 square feet.* No

4. *My roof has an area of 900 square feet. How much will it cost to shingle my roof with shakes?* $809.10

Use the pictures to answer these questions.

15 ft.

30 ft.

5. a. What is the area of the roof? Remember: There are two parts to the roof. 900 ft²

b. How many squares of shingles will it take to cover the roof? 9

c. How much will it cost to shingle the roof with asphalt shingles? $539.10

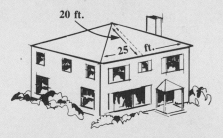

20 ft.

25 ft.

6. a. Each side of the roof is a triangle with a base of 25 feet and a height of 20 feet. What is the area of the roof? 1000 ft²

b. How many squares of shingles will it take to cover the roof? 10

c. How much will it cost to shingle the roof with shake shingles? $899

CHALKBOARD CHALLENGE

Unscramble the letters of these space figures.

1. EUCB   Cube

2. HPSREE   Sphere

3. MYPRADI   Pyramid

4. SRPIM   Prism

5. ELYCINDR   Cylinder

327

LESSON OBJECTIVE
To compute the volume of rectangular prisms and cubes

PROBLEM-SOLVING SKILLS
Finding information in a drawing
Using a formula
Choosing the correct operation
Making geometric visualizations

STARTING THE LESSON
Write these sentences on the chalkboard:

The amount that a space figure holds is called its <u>MOVLUE.</u> Volume is measured in <u>UICBC</u> units.

Before the students open their books, challenge them to unscramble the underlined letters so the sentences make sense. Then have them read the sentences at the top of page 328 to see if they correctly unscrambled the letters.

Next, discuss questions 1–6, using the drawings and the *Here's how.*

Volume—rectangular prisms and cubes

WHAT'S THE VOLUME?

The amount that a space figure holds is called its **volume.** Volume is measured in cubic units.

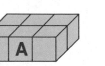 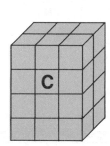

1 cubic centimeter

1. Count the cubes. Which prism has a volume of 6 cubic centimeters? A

2. Which prism has a volume of 8 cubic centimeters? B

3. What is the volume of prism C? 24 cubic centimeters

Here's how *to use a formula to find the volume of a prism.*

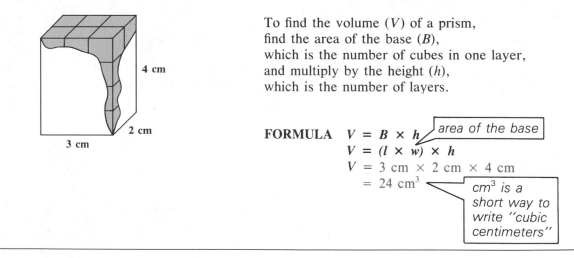

To find the volume (*V*) of a prism, find the area of the base (*B*), which is the number of cubes in one layer, and multiply by the height (*h*), which is the number of layers.

FORMULA $V = B \times h$ ← area of the base
$V = (l \times w) \times h$
$V = 3 \text{ cm} \times 2 \text{ cm} \times 4 \text{ cm}$
$= 24 \text{ cm}^3$ ← cm^3 is a short way to write "cubic centimeters"

4. Look at the *Here's how.* What is the formula for the volume of a rectangular prism? What does each letter stand for? $V = (l \times w) \times h$

V = volume
l = length
w = width
h = height

5. If the length, width, and height of a rectangular prism are 4 centimeters, 5 centimeters, and 6 centimeters, the volume is 120 ☐ centimeters. cubic

6. If the edge of a cube is 5 inches long, its volume is 125 cubic ☐. inches

328

EXERCISES

Use the formula $V = B \times h$. ***Find the volume.***

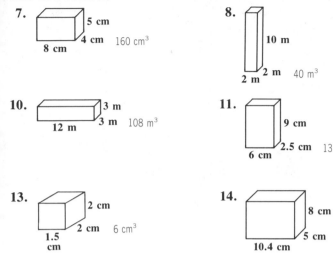

7. 5 cm, 4 cm, 8 cm 160 cm³

8. 10 m, 2 m, 2 m 40 m³

9. 10 cm, 7 cm, 10 cm 700 cm³

10. 3 m, 3 m, 12 m 108 m³

11. 9 cm, 2.5 cm, 6 cm 135 cm³

12. 3.5 cm, 5 cm, 15 cm 262.5 cm³

13. 2 cm, 2 cm, 1.5 cm 6 cm³

14. 8 cm, 5 cm, 10.4 cm 416 cm³

15. 3 m, 3 m, 3 m 27 m³

Solve.

16. Which box above has a surface area of 88 square meters? Number 8

17. Which box above has a surface area of 54 square meters? Number 15

Math on the job

Your job is to take an inventory of all the nails. There are three stacks of boxes.

18. a. How many boxes? 13
b. How many nails? 2600

19. a. How many boxes? 33
b. How many nails? 4950

20. a. How many boxes? 55
b. How many nails? 5500

200 NAILS IN EACH BOX

150 NAILS IN EACH BOX

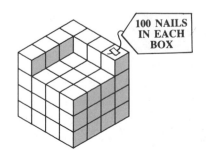

100 NAILS IN EACH BOX

Check your calculations. Your inventory should total 13,050 nails.

REVIEW PRACTICE
Dividing mixed numbers
Page 437   Skill 51

PRACTICE WORKSHEET
Copymaster S290 or Duplicating Master S290

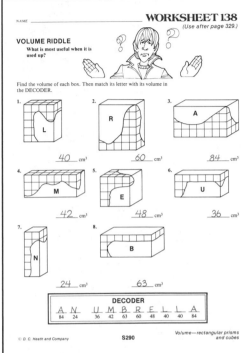

LIFE-SKILL PROJECT
Making measurements
Display a collection of rectangular boxes. Have the students measure the dimensions of each box to the nearest centimeter. Then have them compute the volume of each box.

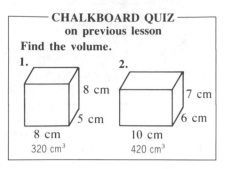
LESSON OBJECTIVE
To compute the volume of a cylinder

PROBLEM-SOLVING SKILLS
Finding information in a drawing
Using a formula
Choosing the correct formula

STARTING THE LESSON
Demonstrate the two ways to roll a sheet of paper to make cylinders like those shown at the top of the page. Ask students whether they think Cylinder A or Cylinder B has the greater volume. Then have the students go over the *Here's how* and answer questions 1–4.

Volume—cylinders

ROLL IT UP!

Here are two ways to roll a sheet of paper to make a cylinder.

Which cylinder do you think has the greater volume?

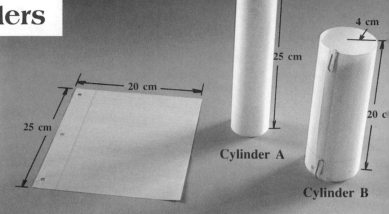

20 cm

25 cm

3 cm
25 cm
Cylinder A

4 cm
20 c
Cylinder B

Here's how *to use a formula to find the volume of a cylinder.*

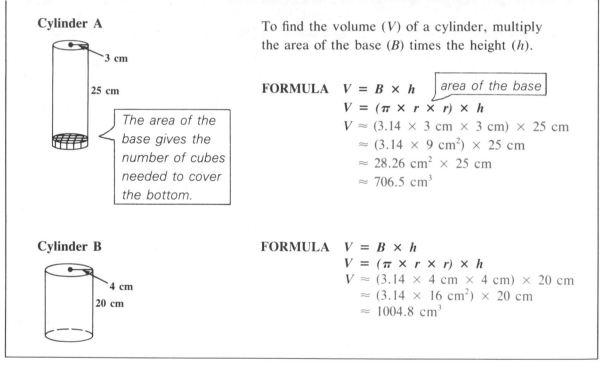

Cylinder A

3 cm

25 cm

The area of the base gives the number of cubes needed to cover the bottom.

To find the volume (V) of a cylinder, multiply the area of the base (B) times the height (h).

FORMULA $V = B \times h$ | area of the base |
$V = (\pi \times r \times r) \times h$
$V \approx (3.14 \times 3 \text{ cm} \times 3 \text{ cm}) \times 25 \text{ cm}$
$\approx (3.14 \times 9 \text{ cm}^2) \times 25 \text{ cm}$
$\approx 28.26 \text{ cm}^2 \times 25 \text{ cm}$
$\approx 706.5 \text{ cm}^3$

Cylinder B

4 cm
20 cm

FORMULA $V = B \times h$
$V = (\pi \times r \times r) \times h$
$V \approx (3.14 \times 4 \text{ cm} \times 4 \text{ cm}) \times 20 \text{ cm}$
$\approx (3.14 \times 16 \text{ cm}^2) \times 20 \text{ cm}$
$\approx 1004.8 \text{ cm}^3$

1. In the formula $V = (\pi \times r \times r) \times h$, what do the letters V, π, r, and h stand for?
   V = volume, π = 3.14, r = radius, h = height

2. Look at the *Here's how*. If the radius and height of a cylinder are 3 centimeters and 25 centimeters, the volume is approximately [?] cubic centimeters. 706.5

3. If the radius and height of a cylinder are 4 centimeters and 20 centimeters, the volume is approximately [?] cubic centimeters. 1004.8

4. Which has the greater volume, Cylinder A or Cylinder B? B

EXERCISES

The area of each base is given. Use V = B × h to find the volume.

5.

6 cm

28.56 cm²

171.36 cm³

6.

8 cm

7.6 cm²   60.8 cm³

7.

7 cm

78.5 cm²

549.5 cm³

The radius and height are given. Use V = π × r × r × h to find the volume. Use 3.14 as an approximation for π.

8.

2 cm

8 cm

100.48 cm³

9.

5 cm

6 cm

471 cm³

10.

6 cm

7 cm

791.28 cm³

11.

1 cm

8.5 cm

26.69 cm³

12.

2.5 cm

9 cm

176.625 cm³

13.

7 cm

7 cm

1077.02 cm³

You decide!

Is the question about perimeter, area, or volume?

14. *How much fencing is needed to fence a patio?* Perimeter

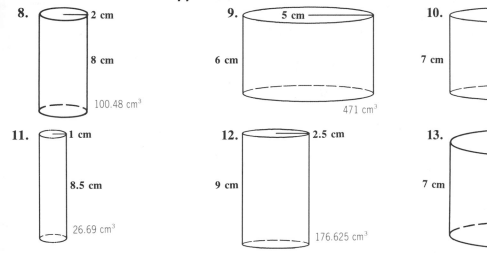

15. *How many flowers are needed to border a garden?* Perimeter

16. "How much paper is needed to gift-wrap a box?" Area

17. "How much space is needed to store a corn harvest?" Volume

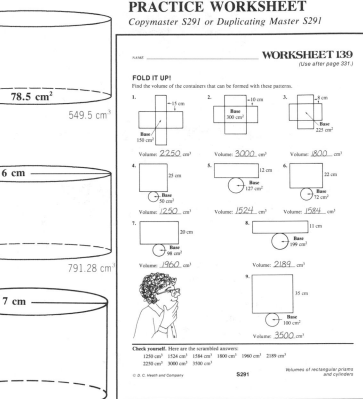

NAME _____   **WORKSHEET 139**
(Use after page 331.)

FOLD IT UP!
Find the volume of the containers that can be formed with these patterns.

1. ←15 cm   Base 150 cm²
Volume: 2250 cm³

2. ←10 cm   Base 300 cm²
Volume: 3000 cm³

3. 8 cm   Base 225 cm²
Volume: 1800 cm³

4. 25 cm   Base 50 cm²
Volume: 1250 cm³

5. 12 cm   Base 127 cm²
Volume: 1524 cm³

6. 22 cm   Base 72 cm²
Volume: 1584 cm³

7. 20 cm   Base 98 cm²
Volume: 1960 cm³

8. 11 cm   Base 199 cm²
Volume: 2189 cm³

9. 35 cm   Base 100 cm²
Volume: 3500 cm³

Check yourself. Here are the scrambled answers:
1250 cm³   1524 cm³   1584 cm³   1800 cm³   1960 cm³   2189 cm³
2250 cm³   3000 cm³   3500 cm³

© D. C. Heath and Company   S291   *Volumes of rectangular prisms and cylinders*

LIFE-SKILL PROJECT
Making measurements
Challenge the students to roll a sheet of paper to make a cylinder that has a volume of 500 cm³. Tell them to use paper clips to hold their cylinders in place. Let the students use calculators to shift the emphasis from computation to applying the formula.

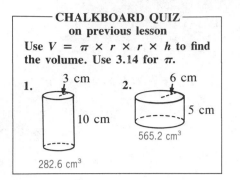
Volume—pyramids and cones

1. It takes 3 pyramids of sand to fill the prism. So, the volume of a pyramid is ? the volume of a prism having the same base and height. $\frac{1}{3}$

2. It takes 3 cones of sand to fill the cylinder. So, the volume of a cone is ? the volume of a cylinder having the same base and height. $\frac{1}{3}$

Here's how *to use a formula to find the volume of a pyramid or a cone.*

Pyramid

9 cm
8 cm
6 cm

Rectangular Base

The volume (V) of a pyramid is $\frac{1}{3}$ times the area of the base (B) times the height (h).

FORMULA $V = \frac{1}{3} \times B \times h$ [area of the base]

$V = \frac{1}{3} \times (l \times w) \times h$

$V = \frac{1}{3} \times 6\text{ cm} \times 8\text{ cm} \times 9\text{ cm}$

$= 144\text{ cm}^3$

Cone

10 cm
6 cm

The volume (V) of a cone is $\frac{1}{3}$ times the area of the base (B) times the height (h).

FORMULA $V = \frac{1}{3} \times B \times h$ [area of the base]

$V = \frac{1}{3} \times (\pi \times r \times r) \times h$

$V \approx \frac{1}{3} \times 3.14 \times 6\text{ cm} \times 6\text{ cm} \times 10\text{ cm}$

$\approx \frac{1}{3} \times 1130.4\text{ cm}^3$

$\approx 376.8\text{ cm}^3$

---

3. Look at the *Here's how*. If the area of the base of a pyramid is 48 square centimeters and the height is 9 centimeters, the volume is ? cubic centimeters. 144

4. If the radius and height of a cone are 6 centimeters and 10 centimeters, the volume is approximately 376.8 cubic ? . cm

EXERCISES

The area of each base is given. Use the formula $V = \frac{1}{3} \times B \times h$ **to find the volume.**

5.
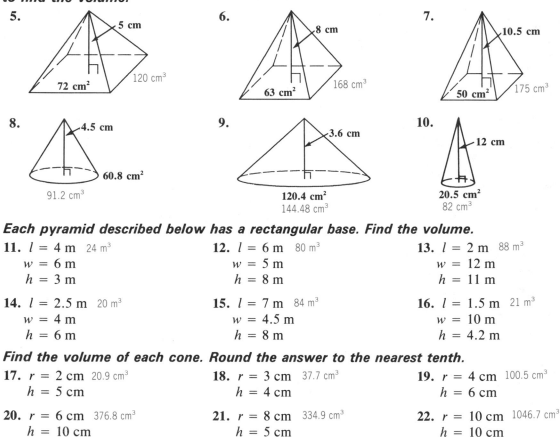
5 cm
72 cm² 120 cm³

6.
8 cm
63 cm² 168 cm³

7.
10.5 cm
50 cm² 175 cm³

8.
4.5 cm
60.8 cm²
91.2 cm³

9.
3.6 cm
120.4 cm²
144.48 cm³

10.
12 cm
20.5 cm²
82 cm³

Each pyramid described below has a rectangular base. Find the volume.

11. $l = 4$ m 24 m³
    $w = 6$ m
    $h = 3$ m

12. $l = 6$ m 80 m³
    $w = 5$ m
    $h = 8$ m

13. $l = 2$ m 88 m³
    $w = 12$ m
    $h = 11$ m

14. $l = 2.5$ m 20 m³
    $w = 4$ m
    $h = 6$ m

15. $l = 7$ m 84 m³
    $w = 4.5$ m
    $h = 8$ m

16. $l = 1.5$ m 21 m³
    $w = 10$ m
    $h = 4.2$ m

Find the volume of each cone. Round the answer to the nearest tenth.

17. $r = 2$ cm 20.9 cm³
    $h = 5$ cm

18. $r = 3$ cm 37.7 cm³
    $h = 4$ cm

19. $r = 4$ cm 100.5 cm³
    $h = 6$ cm

20. $r = 6$ cm 376.8 cm³
    $h = 10$ cm

21. $r = 8$ cm 334.9 cm³
    $h = 5$ cm

22. $r = 10$ cm 1046.7 cm³
    $h = 10$ cm

Volume hunt

23. What size cube would have a volume of this many cubic meters?

729
9-meter cube

24. What size cube would have a volume of this many cubic meters?
1728
12-meter cube

25. What size cube would have a volume of this many cubic meters?

3.375
1.5-meter cube

REVIEW PRACTICE
Changing a percent to a fraction
Page 438   Skill 53

PRACTICE WORKSHEET
Copymaster S292 or Duplicating Master S292

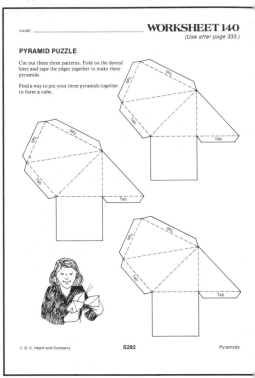

NAME _____ **WORKSHEET 140**
(Use after page 333.)

PYRAMID PUZZLE

Cut out these three patterns. Fold on the dotted lines and tape the edges together to make these pyramids.

Find a way to put your three pyramids together to form a cube.

© D. C. Heath and Company   S292   Pyramids

LIFE-SKILL PROJECT
Using library resources
Have the students use a book of world records to find the dimensions and volume of the world's largest pyramid. (This information can be found in the *Guinness Book of World Records.*)

The largest pyramid is the Quetzalcoatl near Mexico City. It is 177 feet tall, and its base covers an area of nearly 45 acres. Its total volume has been estimated at 4,300,000 yd³.

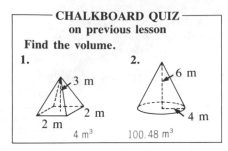
SKILLS REVIEWED
Making conversions between metric units of measure
Changing a percent to a decimal
Solving percent problems
Computing simple interest

PROBLEM-SOLVING SKILL
Making a geometric visualization

STARTING THE LESSON
Cumulative Skill Practice
Write these four answers on the chalkboard:

   0.275   12   25 $42

Challenge the students to an answer hunt by saying: "Look for the four even-numbered exercises on page 334 that have these answers. You have five minutes to find as many of the exercises as you can." (Exercises 8, 32, 46, and 58)

STARTING THE LESSON
Problem Solving
Have the students look at the space figures at the top of page 335. Ask, "Which space figure is a cone?" (Figure E) "Which space figure is a cylinder?" (Figure G) "Which space figure is a sphere?" (Figure A)

Cumulative Skill Practice

Complete. *(page 206)*

1. 5000 mg = _?_ g   5
2. 3452 mg = _?_ g   3.452
3. 845 mg = _?_ g   0.845
4. 2000 g = _?_ kg   2
5. 6428 g = _?_ kg   6.428
6. 425 g = _?_ kg   0.425
7. 6.3 kg = _?_ g   6300
8. 275 g = _?_ kg   0.275
9. 444 mg = _?_ g   0.444

Change to a decimal. *(page 252)*

10. 6% 0.06
11. 9% 0.09
12. 25% 0.25
13. 48% 0.48
14. 62% 0.62
15. 125% 1.25
16. 150% 1.50
17. 175% 1.75
18. 185% 1.85
19. 225% 2.25
20. 0.4% 0.004
21. 0.9% 0.009
22. 67.8% 0.678
23. 5.2% 0.052
24. 0.05% 0.000
25. $33\frac{1}{3}\%$ $0.33\frac{1}{3}$
26. $37\frac{1}{2}\%$ $0.37\frac{1}{2}$
27. $16\frac{2}{3}\%$ $0.16\frac{2}{3}$
28. $162\frac{1}{2}\%$ $1.62\frac{1}{2}$
29. $166\frac{2}{3}\%$ 1.6

Solve. *(page 258)*

30. 10% of 60 = n 6
31. 25% of 96 = n 24
32. 20% of 60 = n 12
33. 16% of 40 = n 6.4
34. 7% of 23.5 = n 1.645
35. 150% of 72 = n 108
36. 8.5% of 110 = n 9.35
37. 22.4% of 80 = n 17.92
38. 36.5% of 62.5 = n 22
39. $33\frac{1}{3}\%$ of 81 = n 27
40. $62\frac{1}{2}\%$ of 74 = n 46.25
41. $66\frac{2}{3}\%$ of 171 = n 114

Solve. *(page 260)*

42. 20% of n = 15   75
43. 10% of n = 16   160
44. 40% of n = 60   150
45. 6% of n = 24   400
46. 80% of n = 20   25
47. 12% of n = 3   25

Solve. Round each answer to the nearest tenth. *(page 260)*

48. 12.5% of n = 8.4   67.2
49. 8.5% of n = 11.2   131.8
50. 9.6% of n = 15   156.3
51. 1.4% of n = 2.6   185.7
52. 125% of n = 43   34.4
53. 132% of n = 7.5   5.7
54. 12.5% of n = 9   72
55. 100% of n = 56   56
56. 105% of n = 63   60

Compute the interest. Round to the nearest cent. *(page 284)*

57. Principal = $1000 $450
Rate = 15% per year
Time = 3 years

58. Principal = $700 $42
Rate = 12% per year
Time = 6 months

59. Principal = $100 $4.50
Rate = 1.5% per month
Time = 3 months

60. Principal = $350 $17.50
Rate = 1% per month
Time = 5 months

61. Principal = $900 $108
Rate = 16% per year
Time = 9 months

62. Principal = $250 $58.13
Rate = 15.5% per year
Time = 18 months

334

Problem solving

COMPUTER GRAPHICS A computer can be programmed to sketch a space figure. These sketches were generated by a computer:

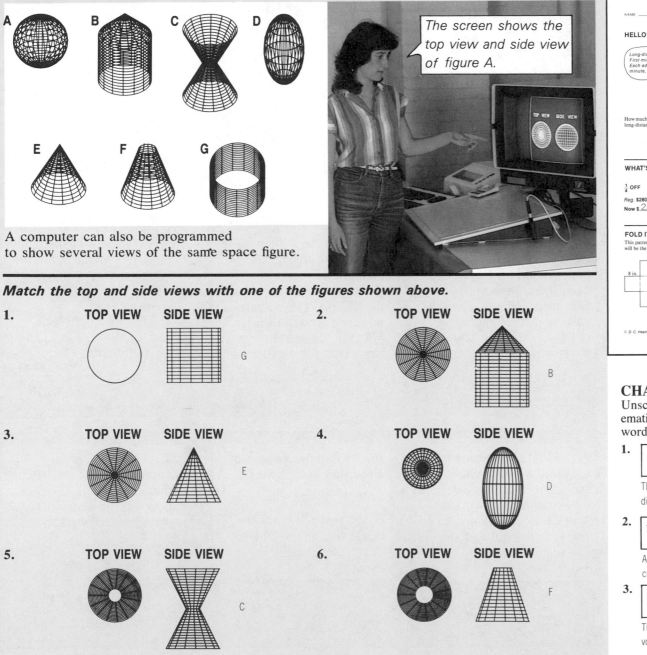

A
B
C
D

E
F
G

A computer can also be programmed to show several views of the same space figure.

The screen shows the top view and side view of figure A.

Match the top and side views with one of the figures shown above.

1. TOP VIEW   SIDE VIEW   G

2. TOP VIEW   SIDE VIEW   B

3. TOP VIEW   SIDE VIEW   E

4. TOP VIEW   SIDE VIEW   D

5. TOP VIEW   SIDE VIEW   C

6. TOP VIEW   SIDE VIEW   F

EXTRA PROBLEM SOLVING
Page 457   Even exercises

PROBLEM-SOLVING WORKSHEET
Copymaster S293 or Duplicating Master S293

NAME _____   **WORKSHEET 141**
(Use after page 335.)

HELLO!

Long-distance rate.
First minute, $.40
Each additional
minute, $.25

How much would it cost you to make an 8-minute long-distance call? $2.15

JOKES OR RIDDLES
Erika gave the clerk 3 coins and got back 2 coins.
Which book did she buy? *Jokes*

JOKES 60¢   RIDDLES 72¢

WHAT'S THE SALE PRICE?
¼ OFF
Reg. $280.00
Now $ 210

WHAT'S THE ANSWER?
Use the code to answer the riddle.
CODE

Riddle: Why did the baby pig eat so much?
Answer:
T O   M A K E
15° 42° 74° 2° 141° 36°
A   H O G   O F
8° 104° 47° 55° 43° 133°
H I M S E L F
109° 23° 73° 64° 38° 163° 135°

FOLD IT!
This pattern can be folded to make a box. What will be the volume of the box? *1280 in.³*
20 in.
8 in.
8 in.

© D. C. Heath and Company   S293   Problem solving

CHALKBOARD CHALLENGE
Unscramble these words to get a mathematical definition. Then write the math word that fits the definition.

1. DISTANCE A CIRCLE ACROSS THE CENTER THROUGH ITS

The distance across a circle through its center;
diameter

2. RECTANGULAR PRISM FACES ARE A SIX SQUARES WHOSE

A rectangular prism whose six faces are squares;
cube

3. OF SPACE A INSIDE MEASURE THE FIGURE THE SPACE

The measure of the space inside a space figure;
volume

Match each space figure with its name. *(page 320)*

a. cube
b. cone
c. sphere
d. square pyramid
e. cylinder
f. pentagonal pyramid
g. triangular prism
h. rectangular prism
i. triangular pyramid

ANSWERS
1. a
2. c
3. g
4. h
5. i
6. b
7. d
8. f
9. e
10. True
11. True
12. False
13. True
14. False
15. True
16. 12
17. 12
18. 24
19. 24
20. 18
21. 18
22. 108
23. 150
24. 64
25. 158

True or false? *(page 320)*
True 10. A cube has 6 faces.
True 11. A triangular pyramid has 4 corners.
False 12. A rectangular prism has exactly 6 edges.
True 13. A sphere has no corners.
False 14. A square pyramid has exactly 4 faces.
True 15. A cylinder has no corners and no edges.

Give each area. *(page 324)*
16. front: 12 ft²
17. back: 12 ft²
18. top: 24 ft²
19. bottom: 24 ft²
20. left side: 18 ft²
21. right side: 18 ft²
22. surface area: 108 ft²

Find each surface area. *(page 324)*
23. 150 ft²
24. 64 ft²
25. 158 ft²

© D. C. Heath and Company   S53   Page 1

True or false? *(pages 328, 330, 332)*
True 26. To find the volume of a prism, multiply the area of the base by the height.
False 27. A short way to write "cubic centimeter" is cm^2.
True 28. The formula $V = (l \times w) \times h$ is used to find the volume of a rectangular prism.
False 29. If the edge of a cube is 4 inches, then its volume is 16 in.³.
False 30. The formula $V = (\pi \times r) \times h$ is used to find the volume of a cylinder.
True 31. The formula $V = \frac{1}{3} \times (l \times w) \times h$ is used to find the volume of a pyramid with a rectangular base.
True 32. The formula $V = \frac{1}{3} \times (\pi \times r \times r) \times h$ is used to find the volume of a cone.

Find each volume. Use 3.14 as an approximation for π. Round the answer to the nearest hundredth. *(pages 328, 330, 332)*
33. 27 in.³
34. 64 in.³
35. 125 in.³
36. 112 in.³
37. 50 in.³
38. 96 in.³
39. 75.36 in.³
40. 141.3 in.³
41. 87.92 in.³
42. 21.33 in.³
43. 50 in.³
44. 84 in.³
45. 20.93 in.³
46. 37.68 in.³
47. 16.75 in.³
48. 169.56 in.³
49. 20 in.³
50. 25.12 in.³

ANSWERS
26. True
27. False
28. True
29. False
30. False
31. True
32. True
33. 27
34. 64
35. 125
36. 112
37. 50
38. 96
39. 75.36
40. 141.3
41. 87.92
42. 21.33
43. 50
44. 84
45. 20.93
46. 37.68
47. 16.75
48. 169.56
49. 20
50. 25.12

© D. C. Heath and Company   S54   Page 2

Chapter REVIEW

Here are scrambled answers for the review exercises:

12	125	add	cylinder	sphere
36	209	area	height	square pyramid
90	314	cone	rectangular prism	triangular prism

1. triangular prism   2. square pyramid   3. sphere   4. cylinder   5. rectangular prism

1. Figure A is called a ⬚.
2. Figure B is called a ⬚.
3. Figure C is called a ⬚.
4. Figure D is called a ⬚.
5. Figure E is called a ⬚. *(page 320)*

A   B   C   D   E

6. add, 90   7. height, 36   8. 125

6. To find the surface area of this figure, you would first compute the area of each face. Then you would ⬚ the six areas. The surface area of this figure is ⬚ in.² *(page 324)*

7. To find the volume of a rectangular prism, you multiply the length (*l*) times the width (*w*) times the ⬚ (*h*). The volume of this rectangular prism is ⬚ ft³. *(page 328)*

8. The volume of this cube is ⬚ ft³. *(page 328)*

9. area, 314   10. cone, 12   11. 209

9. To find the volume of a cylinder, you multiply the ⬚ of the base (*B*) times the height (*h*). Using 3.14 as an approximation for π, the volume of this cylinder is about ⬚ in.³ *(page 330)*

10. To find the volume of a pyramid or ⬚, you multiply $\frac{1}{3}$ times the area of the base (*B*) times the height (*h*). The volume of this pyramid is ⬚ in.³ *(page 332)*

11. Using 3.14 as an approximation for π, the volume of this cone is about ⬚ in.³ *(page 332)*

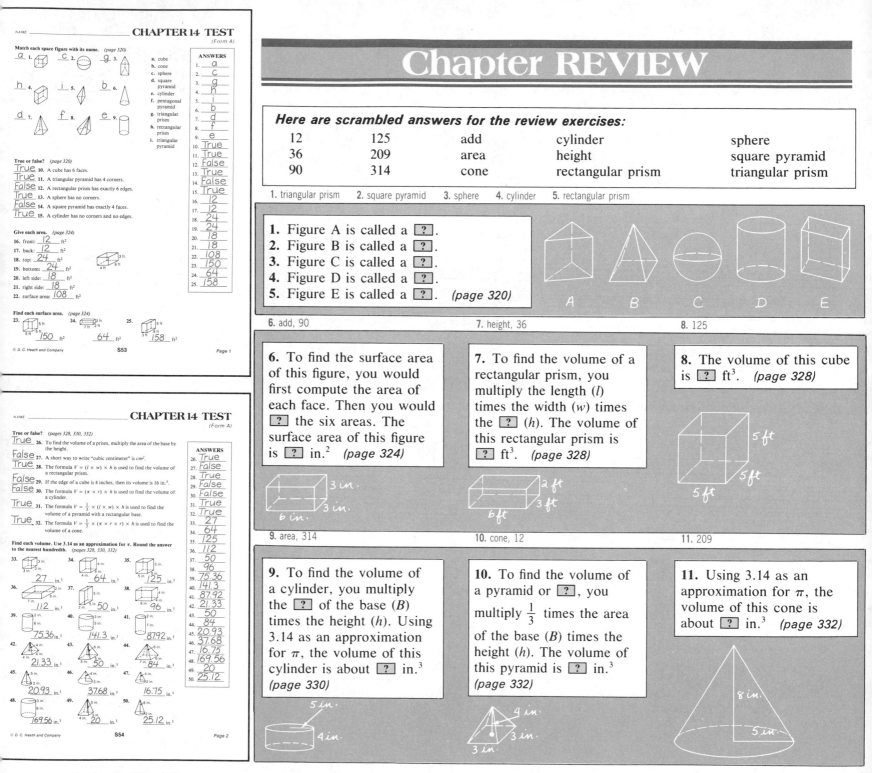

Chapter TEST

Match each space figure with its name. *(page 320)*

1. C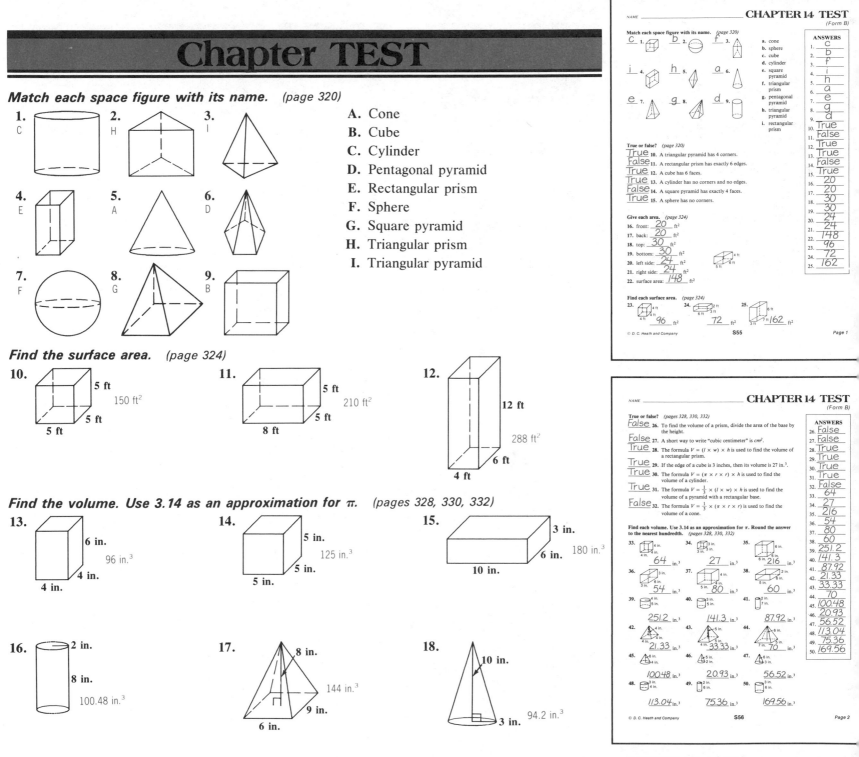
2. H
3. I

4. E
5. A
6. D

7. F
8. G
9. B

A. Cone
B. Cube
C. Cylinder
D. Pentagonal pyramid
E. Rectangular prism
F. Sphere
G. Square pyramid
H. Triangular prism
I. Triangular pyramid

Find the surface area. *(page 324)*

10. 5 ft, 5 ft, 5 ft — 150 ft²
11. 5 ft, 5 ft, 8 ft — 210 ft²
12. 12 ft, 6 ft, 4 ft — 288 ft²

Find the volume. Use 3.14 as an approximation for π. *(pages 328, 330, 332)*

13. 6 in., 4 in., 4 in. — 96 in.³
14. 5 in., 5 in., 5 in. — 125 in.³
15. 3 in., 6 in., 10 in. — 180 in.³

16. 2 in., 8 in. — 100.48 in.³
17. 8 in., 9 in., 6 in. — 144 in.³
18. 10 in., 3 in. — 94.2 in.³

CUMULATIVE TEST
(Chapters 1–14)

Use Copymaster S336 to provide the students with an answer sheet in standardized test format.

Cumulative TEST Standardized Format

Choose the correct letter.

Answers for Cumulative Test, Chapters 1–14

1. ⒶＢ C D 2. Ⓐ B Ⓒ D 3. A B Ⓒ D
4. Ⓐ B Ⓒ D 5. ＡＢ C D 6. Ⓐ B C D
7. Ⓐ B Ⓒ D 8. ＡＢ C D 9. A B Ⓒ D
10. Ⓐ B C Ⓓ 11. ＡＢ C D 12. Ⓐ B Ⓒ D

The table below correlates test items with student text pages.

Test Item	Page Taught	Skill Practice
1	64	p. 326, exercises 1–15
2	96	p. 326, exercises 16–27
3	146	p. 326, exercises 28–48
4	170	p. 326, exercises 49–60
5	190	p. 326, exercises 61–70
6	206	p. 334, exercises 1–9
7	252	p. 334, exercises 10–29
8	258	p. 334, exercises 30–41
9	260	p. 334, exercises 42–47
10	284	p. 334, exercises 57–62
11	308	
12	328	

1. Give the product.

29.04×1.09

A. 31.6536
B. 55.1760
C. 29.2506
D. none of these

2. Give the quotient rounded to the nearest tenth.

$64.08 \div 3.1$

A. 20.67   B. 20.6
C. 20.7   D. none of these

3. Change to a decimal rounded to the nearest hundredth.

$\frac{5}{12} = ?$

A. 2.40   B. 0.42
C. 0.41   D. none of these

4. Subtract. $4\frac{1}{3}$
$-2\frac{3}{4}$

A. $2\frac{5}{12}$ B. $2\frac{7}{12}$
C. $1\frac{7}{12}$ D. none of these

5. Give the quotient.

$3\frac{1}{4} \div 1\frac{1}{2}$

A. $2\frac{1}{6}$ B. $4\frac{7}{8}$
C. $\frac{6}{13}$ D. none of these

6. 525 mg = _?_ g

A. 5.25
B. 52.5
C. 5250
D. none of these

7. Change to a decimal.

$37\frac{1}{2}\% = ?$

A. 37.5
B. 3.75
C. 0.375
D. none of these

8. Solve.

$33\frac{1}{3}\%$ of $45 = n$

A. 15
B. 30
C. 135
D. none of these

9. Solve.

25% of $n = 17$

A. 4.25
B. 68
C. 12.75
D. none of these

10. Compute the interest.

Principal = $820
Rate = 14% per year
Time = 9 months

A. $114.80
B. $28.70
C. $1033.20
D. none of these

11. Find the area of this parallelogram.

6 ft
10 ft
12 ft

A. 72 ft²
B. 120 ft²
C. 44 ft²
D. none of these

12. Find the volume of this rectangular prism.

4 in.
5 in.
3 in.

A. 12 in.³
B. 35 in.³
C. 60 in.³
D. none of these

CHAPTER 15
Probability

LESSON OBJECTIVES
To find the total number of outcomes by using a tree diagram (*pages 340–341*)
To use a basic counting principle to determine the number of outcomes of a compound event (*pages 340–341*)
To compute the number of permutations (possible arrangements of things in a definite order) (*pages 342–343*)
To determine the probabilities of outcomes of simple events (*pages 344–345*)
To compute the probability of an outcome (*pages 346–347*)
To compute the probability of a compound outcome (*pages 350–351*)
To compute the odds of an outcome (*pages 352–353*)
To compute the expectation of an outcome (*pages 354–355*)

PROBLEM-SOLVING SKILLS
Drawing a tree diagram (*pages 340–341, 350–351*)
Selecting information from a display (*pages 342–347, 350–351, 354–355*)
Conducting an experiment and collecting data (*pages 344–345*)
Using a tree diagram (*pages 346–347*)
Reading an ad (*page 349*)
Choosing the correct operation (*pages 349, 357*)
Solving a multi-step problem (*pages 349, 357*)
Reading a chart (*page 352*)
Reading a blueprint (*page 357*)

RESOURCES
- **WORKSHEETS 142–150** (*Copymasters S294–S302 or Duplicating Masters S294–S302*)

339

LESSON OBJECTIVES

To find the total number of outcomes by using a tree diagram

To use a basic counting principle to determine the number of outcomes of a compound event

PROBLEM-SOLVING SKILL

Drawing a tree diagram

STARTING THE LESSON

Use questions 1–5 and the *Here's how* to introduce the terms *tree diagram* and *basic counting principle*. Go through the diagram and counting principle carefully so that the students see how they show 6 possible outfits.

HERE'S HOW **NOTE**

You may wish to use this additional chalkboard example before assigning exercises 6–12.

How many possible outcomes are there if you first flip a coin and then spin this spinner?

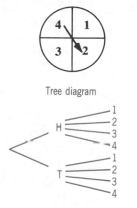

Tree diagram

Basic counting principle

Outcomes for flipping a coin	Outcomes for spinning a spinner	Total outcomes
2	× 4	= 8

A basic counting principle

DECISIONS, DECISIONS!

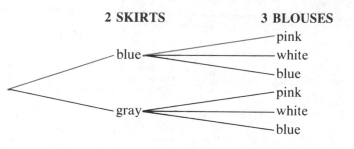

1. How many different outfits (a skirt and a blouse) can be made if the blue skirt is worn? 3

2. How many different outfits can be made if the gray skirt is worn? 3

3. How many different outfits are there in all? 6

Here's how *to show all the possible outfits with a* tree diagram.

2 SKIRTS   **3 BLOUSES**

blue —— pink
blue —— white
blue —— blue
gray —— pink
gray —— white
gray —— blue

The red "branch" represents a blue skirt and a pink blouse.
You can determine the number of outfits by counting the branches of the tree diagram.

4. Look at the *Here's how*. What outfit is represented by the top branch? Blue skirt, pink blouse
The bottom branch? Gray skirt, blue blouse

5. How many possible outfits are there? *Hint: Count the branches.* 6

Here's how *to use a* basic counting principle *to compute the total number of outfits.*

To compute the total number of ways that several decisions can be made, multiply the number of choices for each of the decisions.

Choices in First Decision (skirts)		Choices in Second Decision (blouses)		Total Choices (outfits)
2	×	3	=	6

340

EXERCISES

Solve.

6. **a.** How many choices of pants are there? How many choices of sweaters are there? 2, 4

   b. Draw a tree diagram to show all possible outfits.

   c. How many possible outfits are there? 8

   d. How many different outfits can be made if the black pants are worn? 4

   e. How many different outfits can be made if the red sweater is not worn? 6

7. You decide to wear a pair of corduroys and a sweater. How many outfits do you have if you have 4 pairs of corduroys and 5 sweaters? 20

8. How many outfits can you make from 3 pairs of pants, 4 shirts, and 2 sweaters if each outfit consists of pants, a shirt, and a sweater? 24

9. In an election of your class officers, 3 students are running for president, 3 for vice president, 2 for secretary, and 2 for treasurer. How many different combinations are possible? 36

10. You decide to buy a stereo system. You can choose from 5 amplifiers, 6 kinds of speakers, and 4 turntables. How many different systems are possible? 120

11. You are in Chicago and win a free trip to Waikiki Beach in Honolulu. The "map" shows the choices of ways to travel.

   a. How many ways can you travel from Chicago to Los Angeles? 3

   b. How many ways can you travel from Chicago to Honolulu? 6

   c. How many ways can you travel from Chicago to Waikiki Beach? 12

   d. How many choices would you have for making the round trip? 144

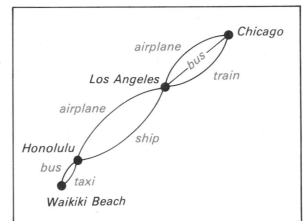

You're the detective!

12. A witness observed a speeding car leaving the scene of an accident. One digit and two letters on the license plate were covered with mud.

What is the greatest number of license plates that you would have to check to find the owner of the car? 6760

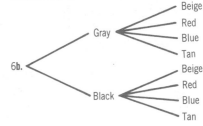

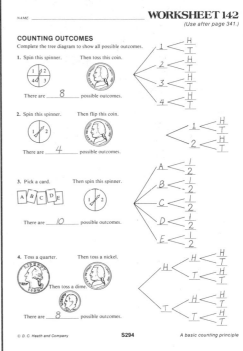

LIFE-SKILL PROJECT
Researching information
Have the students find out how many letters and numerals are combined to make license plates in their state. Then have them determine how many different license plates can be made.

Answers for page 341.

Permutations

Bob, Ann, and Mary had this photograph taken at an amusement park.

1. Who is on the left? The right? Who is in the middle?
   Bob, Mary, Ann
2. The letters BAM may be used to describe the order they were in when the photo was taken. Use the letters to list all possible orders. BAM, BMA, ABM, AMB, MAB, MBA
3. How many ways can the 3 people be arranged for the photograph? 6

An arrangement of things in a **definite order** is called a **permutation**.

Here's how *to compute the number of permutations (possible arrangements).*

Number of people to choose from for first position		Number left to choose from for second position		Number left to choose from for third position		Number of possible arrangements
↓		↓		↓		↓
3	×	2	×	1	=	6

4. Look at the *Here's how*. To compute the number of permutations (possible arrangements) of 3 things, you would multiply what three numbers? 3, 2, 1

5. Think about 4 people and a comic photo scene that requires 4 faces.
   a. How many people would there be to choose from for the first position? 4
   b. How many people would there be left to choose from for the second position? The third position? The fourth position? 3, 2, 1
   c. What four numbers would you multiply to compute the number of permutations (possible arrangements) of 4 things? 1, 2, 3, 4
   d. How many ways can the 4 people be arranged for the photograph? 24

EXERCISES

Solve.

6. Bob, Ann, and Mary decided to buy some ride tickets at the amusement park. How many ways could they line up to purchase their tickets? 6

7. Bob bought the tickets shown.
   a. For how many rides did he buy tickets? 5
   b. What was the average price of the tickets? $1.10
   c. In how many different orders could Bob take the 5 rides? 120

WHIP $1.15

INDY 500 $1.35

BOBSLED $1.25

SUBMARINE $.85

ROCKET SHIP $.90

8. Each bobsled seated 4 people in a row. In how many ways could 4 people be seated on a bobsled? 24

9. a. Ann decided to buy a sandwich and a drink for lunch. How many different lunches could she buy? 20

   b. Mary decided to buy a sandwich and a dessert for lunch. How many different lunches could she buy? 12

   c. Suppose that you wanted to buy a sandwich and a drink and that you decided not to order a fish sandwich. How many different lunches could you buy? 15

   d. How many different lunches could Bob order if he decided to order a sandwich, a drink, and a dessert? 60

   e. Bob ordered a cheeseburger, milk, and a dessert. He gave the clerk $5 and got $1.90 in change. What dessert did he order? Brownie

JOYLAND SNACK BAR

SANDWICHES	
Hamburger	$1.45
Cheeseburger	1.65
Hot Dog	1.30
Fish	1.45
DRINKS	
Coffee	.60
Cola	.65
Root Beer	.65
Lemonade	.75
Milk	.70
DESSERTS	
Ice Cream	.95
Brownie	.75
Apple Pie	1.30

Please be seated!

10. Each car on the Grand Canyon Railroad holds 10 people. Suppose that you and 9 of your friends were in one of the cars.
   a. How many ways could the group be seated? 3,628,800
   b. Suppose that the group could change the seating order every 5 seconds. How many seconds would it take for the group to sit in all possible orders? 18,144,000
   c. How many minutes would it take? How many hours? How many days? 302,400; 5040; 210

REVIEW PRACTICE
Changing a percent to a decimal
Page 439   Skill 55

PRACTICE WORKSHEET
Copymaster S295 or Duplicating Master S295

NAME _____   **WORKSHEET 143**
(Use after page 343.)

HOW MANY WAYS?
Fill in the blanks. Then multiply to find the total number of possible arrangements.

1. There are 8 teams competing for the top 3 places in the basketball standings. How many arrangements of the top 3 teams are possible?

first place	second place	third place		
8 choices	× 7 choices	× 6 choices	= 336	possible arrangements

2. Radio stations in the United States must have call letters that begin with either K or W. How many 4-letter sets of call letters are possible?

first letter	second letter	third letter	fourth letter		
2 choices	× 26 choices	× 26 choices	× 26 choices	= 35,152	possible arrangements

3. A drawing for a first and a second prize is to be made from a box containing 750 names. How many arrangements of first and second prize winners are possible?

first prize	second prize		
750 choices	× 749 choices	= 561,750	possible arrangements

4. There are 20 empty lockers. Five new students are to be assigned lockers. How many ways can they be assigned lockers?

first student locker choices	second student locker choices	third student locker choices	fourth student locker choices	fifth student locker choices		
20	× 19	× 18	× 17	× 16	= 1,860,480	possible arrangements

© D. C. Heath and Company   **S295**   *Permutations*

LIFE-SKILL PROJECT
Researching information
Have the students determine how many local telephone numbers the telephone company could assign using their present numbering system. Consider the number of different prefix numbers that are used, if that information is available.

Solve.
1. How many ways could 4 people line up to buy movie tickets? 24
2. How many ways could you buy a sandwich and a drink for lunch if there were 5 sandwich choices and 4 drink choices? 20

LESSON OBJECTIVE
To determine the probabilities of outcomes of simple events

PROBLEM-SOLVING SKILLS
Selecting information from a display
Conducting an experiment and collecting data

STARTING THE LESSON
Sketch this pattern on the chalkboard:

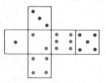

Tell the students that the pattern can be folded to make a die. Ask students to fill in the missing dots on the 3 blank faces. (Remind them that dots on opposite faces of a die add to 7.) Then go over questions 1 and 2, using the pattern on the chalkboard and the *Here's how.*

Probability

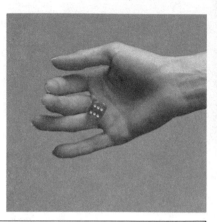

WHAT ARE YOUR CHANCES?

1. Suppose that you rolled the die. How many different outcomes would be possible? (How many different numbers could possibly land facing up?) 6

2. Would the possible outcomes be equally likely? (Would all numbers have the same chance of landing facing up?) Yes

Here's how *to find the probability (the chance) of a given outcome when all the outcomes are equally likely.*

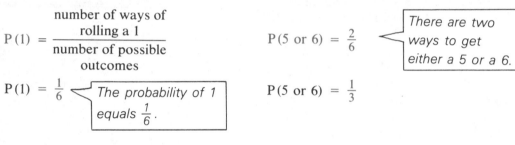

Probability of rolling a 1

$$P(1) = \frac{\text{number of ways of rolling a 1}}{\text{number of possible outcomes}}$$

$P(1) = \frac{1}{6}$ — *The probability of 1 equals $\frac{1}{6}$.*

Probability of rolling either a 5 or a 6

$P(5 \text{ or } 6) = \frac{2}{6}$ — *There are two ways to get either a 5 or a 6.*

$P(5 \text{ or } 6) = \frac{1}{3}$

3. Look at the *Here's how.* What is the probability of rolling a 1? $\frac{1}{6}$

4. What is the probability of rolling a 5 or a 6? $\frac{1}{3}$

EXERCISES

Give each probability as a fraction in simplest form.
Think about rolling a die.

5. $P(3)$ $\frac{1}{6}$

6. $P(6)$ $\frac{1}{6}$

7. $P(1 \text{ or } 2)$ $\frac{1}{3}$

8. $P(\text{even})$ $\frac{1}{2}$

9. $P(\text{odd})$ $\frac{1}{2}$

10. $P(1, 2, \text{ or } 3)$ $\frac{1}{2}$

11. $P(3 \text{ or less})$ $\frac{1}{2}$

12. $P(\text{greater than } 2)$ $\frac{2}{3}$

13. $P(\text{not } 1)$ $\frac{5}{6}$

14. $P(\text{not } 5)$ $\frac{5}{6}$

15. $P(7)$ 0

16. $P(6 \text{ or less})$ 1

17. Look at your answer to exercise 15.
What is the probability of an impossible outcome? 0

18. Look at your answer to exercise 16.
What is the probability of an outcome that is certain to occur? 1

Give each probability as a fraction in simplest form.

Think about spinning this spinner.

19. P(red) $\frac{1}{8}$ **20.** P(not red) $\frac{7}{8}$

21. P(blue) $\frac{1}{8}$ **22.** P(not blue) $\frac{7}{8}$

23. P(yellow) $\frac{1}{4}$ **24.** P(not yellow) $\frac{3}{4}$

25. P(green) $\frac{3}{8}$ **26.** P(not green) $\frac{5}{8}$

27. P(black) 0 **28.** P(not black) 1

29. P(brown or red) $\frac{1}{4}$ **30.** P(yellow or blue) $\frac{3}{8}$

31. P(yellow or green) $\frac{5}{8}$ **32.** P(red or green) $\frac{1}{2}$

33. P(blue or green) $\frac{1}{2}$ **34.** P(black or yellow) $\frac{1}{4}$

35. P(yellow, blue, or green) $\frac{3}{4}$

36. P(brown, blue, or red) $\frac{3}{8}$

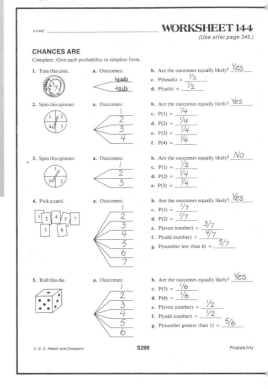

Think about shuffling these cards and then turning one of the cards face up.

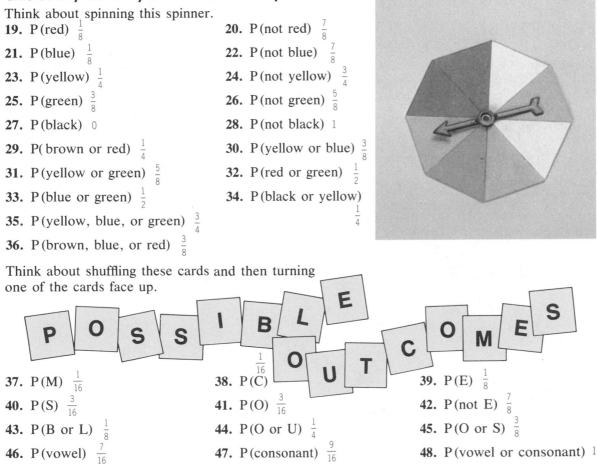

37. P(M) $\frac{1}{16}$ **38.** P(C) $\frac{1}{16}$ **39.** P(E) $\frac{1}{8}$

40. P(S) $\frac{3}{16}$ **41.** P(O) $\frac{3}{16}$ **42.** P(not E) $\frac{7}{8}$

43. P(B or L) $\frac{1}{8}$ **44.** P(O or U) $\frac{1}{4}$ **45.** P(O or S) $\frac{3}{8}$

46. P(vowel) $\frac{7}{16}$ **47.** P(consonant) $\frac{9}{16}$ **48.** P(vowel or consonant) 1

Tack toss

When you toss a thumbtack, there are two possible outcomes: landing point up or landing point down.

49. Do you think that the outcomes are equally likely? No

50. Toss a thumbtack 50 times and keep a record of the outcomes.

51. From the results of your experiment, do you think a thumbtack has a greater chance of landing point up or landing point down? Point down

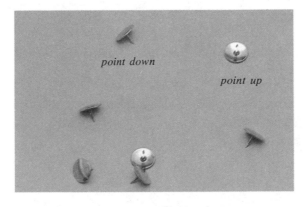

point down

point up

REVIEW PRACTICE
Changing a decimal to a percent
Page 439   Skill 56

PRACTICE WORKSHEET
Copymaster S296 or Duplicating Master S296

NAME _____   **WORKSHEET 144**
(Use after page 345.)

CHANCES ARE
Complete. Give each probability in simplest form.

1. Toss this coin. a. Outcomes: heads, tails b. Are the outcomes equally likely? Yes
   c. P(heads) = $\frac{1}{2}$
   d. P(tails) = $\frac{1}{2}$

2. Spin this spinner. a. Outcomes: 1 2 3 4 b. Are the outcomes equally likely? Yes
   c. P(1) = $\frac{1}{4}$
   d. P(2) = $\frac{1}{4}$
   e. P(3) = $\frac{1}{4}$
   f. P(4) = $\frac{1}{4}$

3. Spin this spinner. a. Outcomes: 1 2 3 b. Are the outcomes equally likely? No
   c. P(1) = $\frac{1}{2}$
   d. P(2) = $\frac{1}{4}$
   e. P(3) = $\frac{1}{4}$

4. Pick a card. a. Outcomes: 1 2 3 4 5 6 7 b. Are the outcomes equally likely? Yes
   c. P(1) = $\frac{1}{7}$
   d. P(2) = $\frac{1}{7}$
   e. P(even number) = $\frac{3}{7}$
   f. P(odd number) = $\frac{4}{7}$
   g. P(number less than 6) = $\frac{5}{7}$

5. Roll this die. a. Outcomes: 1 2 3 4 5 6 b. Are the outcomes equally likely? Yes
   c. P(5) = $\frac{1}{6}$
   d. P(6) = $\frac{1}{6}$
   e. P(even number) = $\frac{1}{2}$
   f. P(odd number) = $\frac{1}{2}$
   g. P(number greater than 1) = $\frac{5}{6}$

© D. C. Heath and Company   S296   Probability

LIFE-SKILL PROJECT
Collecting data
Have each student check 200 names in a telephone directory to determine how many of the people have the same first initial as the student's. Have the students use their findings to determine how likely it is that they will meet a stranger with the same first initial as theirs.

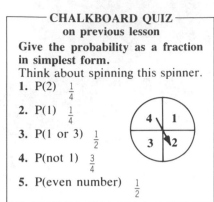
Sample spaces

FREE FRIES!

Each time you buy a hamburger or hot dog at BOB'S BURGER HOUSE, you get a card like the one shown. When you rub each square on your card, a picture of a hamburger is as likely to appear as a picture of a hot dog.

1. What is the prize for a winning card? A free order of fries

2. Is the card shown above a winning card? No

To find how many different kinds of cards are possible, you can list the **sample space** (all possible outcomes).

Here's how *to use a tree diagram to show the sample space.*

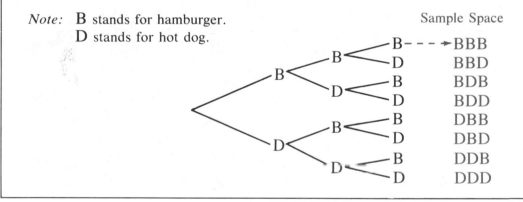

Note: B stands for hamburger.
D stands for hot dog.

	Sample Space
B	BBB
	BBD
	BDB
	BDD
	DBB
	DBD
	DDB
	DDD

3. Look at the *Here's how*. How many outcomes are in the sample space? 8

4. How many of the outcomes are winners (all of the pictures match)? 2

5. What is the probability (in simplest form) of getting a winning card? $\frac{1}{4}$

EXERCISES

Use the sample space above. Give each probability in simplest form.

What is the probability of getting a card having

6. exactly 1 hamburger? $\frac{3}{8}$

7. exactly 2 hamburgers? $\frac{3}{8}$

8. a hot dog in the first square? $\frac{1}{2}$

9. a hamburger in the middle square? $\frac{1}{2}$

10. What is the probability of getting a losing card? $\frac{3}{4}$

Solve.

11. a. One day BOB'S BURGER HOUSE gave away 296 cards. Suppose that one fourth of the cards were winning cards. How many orders of fries were given away? 74

b. It costs BOB'S BURGER HOUSE 23¢ to buy, prepare, and serve an order of fries. How much did the winning cards cost BOB'S? $17.02

12. a. Of the 296 hamburgers and hot dogs sold that day, 183 were hamburgers. If each hamburger sold for $1.35, how much money did BOB'S get from the sale of hamburgers? $247.05

b. How many hot dogs were sold? 113

c. If $107.35 was received from the sale of hot dogs, what was the price of each hot dog? $.95

If you buy an ice cream cone at BOB'S BURGER HOUSE you get one of the cards shown below. When you rub each square on your card, a vanilla, chocolate, or strawberry cone will appear. Each flavor is equally likely to appear.

13. Copy and complete the tree diagram to show the sample space.

Sample Space

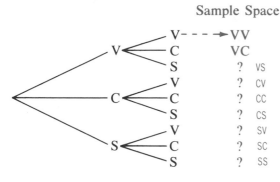

V - - - → VV
VC

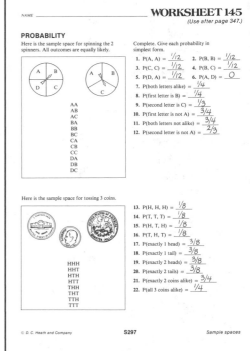

BOB'S-BURGER HOUSE
Rub each square.

If the two flavors match, you save 25¢ on your cone.

14. Use the sample space from exercise 13. Give each probability in simplest form.

a. P(exactly 1 vanilla) $\frac{4}{9}$
b. P(2 strawberry) $\frac{1}{9}$
c. P(no chocolate) $\frac{4}{9}$
d. P(winning) $\frac{1}{3}$
e. P(losing) $\frac{2}{3}$

15. a. During one day, 141 cones were sold. If one third of the cards were winners, how many cones were sold for 25¢ off the regular price? 47

b. The regular price for a cone is 75¢. How much money was received from cone sales that day? $94

Cone count

16. A certain ice-cream store sells 31 flavors. A customer decides to order a 3-dip cone. He first orders the flavor of the bottom dip, next orders the flavor of the middle dip, and last orders the flavor of the top dip. How many different such orders could he give? *Hint: He may order 3 scoops of the same flavor.* 29,791

REVIEW PRACTICE
Finding a percent of a number
Page 440   Skill 57

PRACTICE WORKSHEET
Copymaster S297 or Duplicating Master S297

NAME _____   **WORKSHEET 145**
(Use after page 347.)

PROBABILITY

Here is the sample space for spinning the 2 spinners. All outcomes are equally likely.

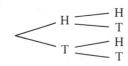

AA
AB
AC
BA
BB
BC
CA
CB
CC
DA
DB
DC

Complete. Give each probability in simplest form.

1. P(A, A) = 1/12   2. P(B, B) = 1/12
3. P(C, C) = 1/12   4. P(B, C) = 1/12
5. P(D, A) = 1/12   6. P(A, D) = 0
7. P(both letters alike) = 1/4
8. P(first letter is B) = 1/4
9. P(second letter is C) = 1/3
10. P(first letter is not A) = 3/4
11. P(both letters not alike) = 3/4
12. P(second letter is not A) = 2/3

Here is the sample space for tossing 3 coins.

HHH
HHT
HTH
HTT
THH
THT
TTH
TTT

13. P(H, H, H) = 1/8
14. P(T, T, T) = 1/8
15. P(H, T, H) = 1/8
16. P(T, H, T) = 1/8
17. P(exactly 1 head) = 3/8
18. P(exactly 1 tail) = 3/8
19. P(exactly 2 heads) = 3/8
20. P(exactly 2 tails) = 3/8
21. P(exactly 2 coins alike) = 3/4
22. P(all 3 coins alike) = 1/4

© D. C. Heath and Company   S297   Sample spaces

LIFE-SKILL PROJECT
Collecting data
Have the students toss two coins 80 times. Tell them to keep a tally of the number of times both coins turned up heads. Have them compare the results with the probability predicted by this tree diagram.

H ⟨ H
    T
T ⟨ H
    T

SKILLS REVIEWED
Rounding whole numbers
Multiplying and dividing decimals
Adding and subtracting fractions

PROBLEM-SOLVING SKILLS
Reading an ad
Choosing the correct operation
Solving a multi-step problem

STARTING THE LESSON
Cumulative Skill Practice
Write these answers on the chalkboard:

530,000   3158.92   82 $1\frac{1}{16}$ $\frac{1}{4}$

Challenge the students to an answer hunt by saying, "Look for the five even-numbered exercises on page 348 that have these answers. You have five minutes to find as many of the exercises as you can." (Exercises 16, 38, 44, 72, and 76)

STARTING THE LESSON
Problem Solving
Use the sale ad and ask questions like these:

• What is the regular price of a red oak? ($30)
• Which trees are on sale at a 25% discount? (Pin oak, sweet gum, and white birch)
• What is the cost of 2 pounds of grass seed? ($3.30)
• How much is the lawn tractor if you pay cash? ($900)

Cumulative Skill Practice

Round to the nearest ten thousand.   *(page 12)*

1. 12,750 10,000
2. 46,394 50,000
3. 75,008 80,000
4. 45,000 50,000
5. 59,981 60,0
6. 56,000 60,000
7. 94,999 90,000
8. 95,000 100,000
9. 97,074 100,000
10. 98,241 100
11. 386,381 390,000
12. 283,077 280,000
13. 439,500 440,000
14. 705,000 710,000
15. 164,138 160
16. 526,000 530,000
17. 664,990 660,000
18. 837,911 840,000
19. 895,000 900,000
20. 306,241 310

Give the product.   *(page 64)*

21. 4.6×0.7 3.22
22. 3.9×0.31 1.209
23. 0.65×0.6 0.390
24. 4.5×3.1 13.95
25. 52×2.6 135.2
26. 0.74×8.1 5.994
27. 5.13×1.4 7.182
28. 2.04×0.1 0.20
29. 8.72×16 139.52
30. 38.5×7.4 284.90
31. 56.3×0.75 42.225
32. 62.3×6.3 392.
33. 8.58×8 68.64
34. 23.3×5.6 130.48
35. 403×2.9 1168.7
36. 124×8.4 1041.
37. 2.01×0.08 0.1608
38. 52.3×60.4 3158.92
39. 5.92×22.9 135.568
40. 4.7×3.08 14.4

Give the quotient rounded to the nearest tenth.   *(page 96)*

41. $18.2 \div 0.6$ 30.3
42. $2.95 \div 0.2$ 14.8
43. $8.3 \div 0.03$ 276.7
44. $16.4 \div 0.2$ 82
45. $34.1 \div 0.5$ 68.2
46. $8.64 \div 0.07$ 123.4
47. $9.2 \div 0.08$ 115
48. $3.95 \div 0.03$ 13
49. $6.23 \div 1.4$ 4.5
50. $2.036 \div 3.1$ 0.7
51. $5.02 \div 0.35$ 14.3
52. $4.61 \div 0.21$ 22
53. $14.071 \div 0.33$ 42.6
54. $5.003 \div 0.54$ 9.3
55. $7.51 \div 8.2$ 0.9
56. $8.34 \div 2.4$ 3.5
57. $6.71 \div 8.03$ 0.8
58. $2759 \div 4.8$ 574.8
59. $37.7 \div 3.09$ 12.2
60. $46.3 \div 2.01$ 23

Give the sum in simplest form.   *(page 158)*

61. $\frac{2}{9} + \frac{4}{9}$ $\frac{2}{3}$
62. $\frac{1}{8} + \frac{3}{8}$ $\frac{1}{2}$
63. $\frac{1}{2} + \frac{1}{4}$ $\frac{3}{4}$
64. $\frac{1}{2} + \frac{1}{3}$ $\frac{5}{6}$
65. $\frac{3}{8} + \frac{1}{4}$ $\frac{5}{8}$
66. $\frac{1}{4} + \frac{1}{3}$ $\frac{7}{12}$
67. $\frac{2}{5} + \frac{1}{2}$ $\frac{9}{10}$
68. $\frac{1}{6} + \frac{1}{8}$ $\frac{7}{24}$
69. $\frac{1}{5} + \frac{3}{4}$ $\frac{19}{20}$
70. $\frac{1}{6} + \frac{4}{5}$ $\frac{29}{30}$
71. $\frac{3}{10} + \frac{3}{10}$ $\frac{3}{5}$
72. $\frac{5}{12} + \frac{3}{4}$ $1\frac{1}{6}$
73. $\frac{9}{16} + \frac{7}{8}$ $1\frac{7}{16}$
74. $\frac{4}{5} + \frac{3}{4}$ $1\frac{11}{20}$
75. $\frac{8}{15} + \frac{9}{10}$ $1\frac{13}{30}$

Give the difference in simplest form.   *(page 166)*

76. $\frac{1}{2} - \frac{1}{4}$ $\frac{1}{4}$
77. $\frac{2}{3} - \frac{1}{4}$ $\frac{5}{12}$
78. $\frac{1}{2} - \frac{1}{3}$ $\frac{1}{6}$
79. $\frac{2}{5} - \frac{1}{4}$ $\frac{3}{20}$
80. $\frac{3}{4} - \frac{2}{3}$ $\frac{1}{12}$
81. $\frac{2}{3} - \frac{1}{8}$ $\frac{13}{24}$
82. $\frac{1}{2} - \frac{2}{5}$ $\frac{1}{10}$
83. $\frac{7}{8} - \frac{3}{4}$ $\frac{1}{8}$
84. $\frac{4}{5} - \frac{3}{10}$ $\frac{1}{2}$
85. $\frac{3}{8} - \frac{1}{6}$ $\frac{5}{24}$
86. $3 - \frac{9}{10}$ $2\frac{1}{10}$
87. $\frac{11}{16} - \frac{1}{2}$ $\frac{3}{16}$
88. $\frac{11}{12} - \frac{5}{8}$ $\frac{7}{24}$
89. $\frac{7}{10} - \frac{1}{4}$ $\frac{9}{20}$
90. $\frac{9}{16} - \frac{3}{8}$ $\frac{3}{16}$

Problem solving

SPRING SPECIAL   ONLY $900

INSTALLMENT PLAN
$228 down payment
$65 per month for 12 months

SALE

SHADE TREES	Regular Price	THIS WEEK ONLY
Pin Oak $24		25% OFF
Red Oak $30		30% OFF
Sugar Maple $40		20% OFF
Sweet Gum $28		25% OFF
White Birch $36		25% OFF

Grass Seed .... $1.65 per lb
Fertilizer .... 10 lb for $9.60

You are the clerk. Answer each customer's question.

1. *What is the sale price of a white birch tree?* $27

2. *How much do I save by buying a pin oak on sale?* $6

3. "How much will 8 pounds of grass seed and 20 pounds of fertilizer cost?" $32.40

4. "How much do I save if I buy a sugar maple and a sweet gum on sale?" $15

5. "If I use 2 pounds of grass seed for every 600 square feet, how many pounds will I need to seed a square lawn that measures 60 feet on a side?" 12

6. "If I use 4 pounds of grass seed for every 1000 square feet, how much will it cost to seed a rectangular yard that is 50 feet by 80 feet?" $26.40

7. "What is the total cost of a red oak, a sweet gum, and a sugar maple on sale?" $74

8. "How much is the total installment cost for the lawn tractor?" $1008

9. "If I could borrow $900 at 12% per year for 1 year, would that be less expensive than buying the tractor on your installment plan?" No, the same

10. "If 10 pounds of fertilizer will cover 5000 square feet of lawn, how many pounds will I use to fertilize a lawn that is 50 feet by 70 feet?" 7

Probability **349**

EXTRA PROBLEM SOLVING
Page 458   Odd exercises

PROBLEM-SOLVING WORKSHEET
Copymaster S298 or Duplicating Master S298

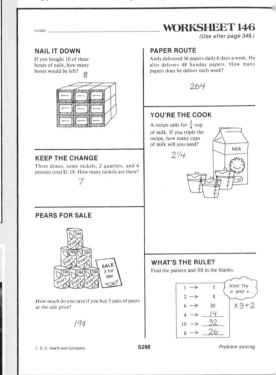

CHALKBOARD CHALLENGE
Find the number in exercises 1–20 on page 348 that fits the clues.

Clues:
• It is greater than 100,000.
• Rounded to the nearest hundred thousand, it is 300,000.
• Rounded to the nearest ten thousand, it is 310,000.

306,241 (Exercise 20)

CHALKBOARD QUIZ
on previous lesson
Solve. Use the sale ad on page 349.
1. How much do you save by buying a white birch on sale? $9
2. What is the total cost of a pin oak and a sugar maple on sale? $50

LESSON OBJECTIVE
To compute the probability of a compound outcome

PROBLEM-SOLVING SKILLS
Using a tree diagram
Selecting information from a display

STARTING THE LESSON
Before the students open their books, have them draw a tree diagram showing all possible outcomes of first rolling a die and then tossing a coin. Then have them compare their tree diagrams with the diagram shown at the top of page 350.

Discuss questions 1–5, using the sample space and the *Here's how*.

Probability— more than 1 event

The tree diagram shows all possible outcomes of a first event (rolling a die) followed by a second event (tossing a coin).

1. Think about the first event, rolling a die. What is the probability of rolling a 1? $\frac{1}{6}$

2. Think about the second event, tossing a coin. What is the probability of tossing heads (H)? $\frac{1}{2}$

3. Now look at the tree diagram. What is the probability of first rolling a 1 and then tossing heads (H)? $\frac{1}{12}$

Sample Space

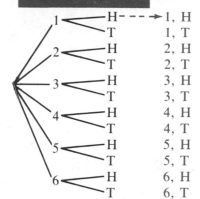

1	H - - - →	1, H
	T	1, T
2	H	2, H
	T	2, T
3	H	3, H
	T	3, T
4	H	4, H
	T	4, T
5	H	5, H
	T	5, T
6	H	6, H
	T	6, T

Here's how *to compute the probability of rolling a 1 and then tossing heads (H).*

Multiply the probability of the first outcome's occurring by the probability of the second outcome's occurring.

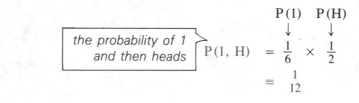

$$\text{the probability of 1 and then heads} \quad P(1, H) = \frac{1}{6} \times \frac{1}{2}$$
$$= \frac{1}{12}$$

4. Look at the *Here's how*. What is P(1)? What is P(H)? $\frac{1}{6}, \frac{1}{2}$

5. What is P(1, H)? $\frac{1}{12}$

EXERCISES
Give each probability as a fraction in simplest form.

Think about first rolling a die and then tossing a coin.

6. **a.** P(2) $\frac{1}{6}$
   b. P(T) $\frac{1}{2}$
   c. P(2, T) $\frac{1}{12}$

7. **a.** P(even number) $\frac{1}{2}$
   b. P(H) $\frac{1}{2}$
   c. P(even number, H) $\frac{1}{4}$

8. P(number less than 3, T) $\frac{1}{6}$

9. P(not 5, T) $\frac{5}{12}$

350

Think about first rolling the die and then spinning the spinner.

10. P(4, red) $\frac{1}{48}$

11. P(6, yellow) $\frac{1}{24}$

12. P(even number, yellow) $\frac{1}{8}$

13. P(not 6, blue) $\frac{5}{48}$

14. P(2, not yellow) $\frac{1}{8}$

15. P(not 1, not brown) $\frac{35}{48}$

16. P(number greater than 2, green) $\frac{1}{4}$

Think about spinning the above spinner once and then spinning it again.

17. P(red, red) $\frac{1}{64}$

18. P(yellow, yellow) $\frac{1}{16}$

19. P(green, green) $\frac{9}{64}$

20. P(brown, blue) $\frac{1}{64}$

21. P(red, yellow) $\frac{1}{32}$

22. P(yellow, green) $\frac{3}{32}$

23. P(not red, green) $\frac{21}{64}$

24. P(yellow, not yellow) $\frac{3}{16}$

25. P(not green, not blue) $\frac{35}{64}$

26. P(not green, not yellow) $\frac{15}{32}$

Think about placing the 6 marbles in a bag and thoroughly mixing them up. Suppose that, without looking, you picked out a first marble, **put it back into the bag,** and then picked out a second marble.

27. P(green, blue) $\frac{1}{18}$

28. P(orange, green) $\frac{1}{12}$

29. P(blue, red) 0

30. P(green, not orange) $\frac{1}{12}$

31. P(not orange, green) $\frac{1}{12}$

32. P(blue, not blue) $\frac{2}{9}$

Think about placing the 6 marbles in a bag and thoroughly mixing them up. Suppose that without looking, you picked out a first marble, **left it out of the bag,** and then picked out a second marble.

33. P(green, blue) $= \frac{1}{6} \times \frac{2}{5}$ — There are 2 blue marbles among the 5 remaining marbles.

$= ?$ $\frac{1}{15}$

34. P(orange, green) $\frac{1}{10}$

35. P(blue, orange) $\frac{1}{5}$

36. P(orange, orange) $\frac{1}{5}$

37. P(green, blue) $\frac{1}{15}$

38. P(blue, blue) $\frac{1}{15}$

39. P(green, green) 0

Seven up!

Think about tossing 2 dice.

40. How many ways can you get a sum of 7? 6

41. What is the probability of getting a sum of 7? $\frac{1}{6}$

REVIEW PRACTICE
Finding a percent of a number
Page 440   Skill 58

PRACTICE WORKSHEET
Copymaster S299 or Duplicating Master S299

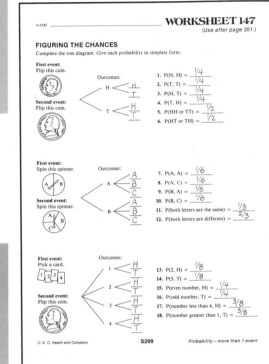

NAME _____ **WORKSHEET 147**
(Use after page 351.)

FIGURING THE CHANCES
Complete the tree diagram. Give each probability in simplest form.

First event:
Flip this coin.

Outcomes:

1. P(H, H) = $\frac{1}{4}$
2. P(T, T) = $\frac{1}{4}$
3. P(H, T) = $\frac{1}{4}$

Second event:
Flip this coin.

4. P(T, H) = $\frac{1}{4}$
5. P(HH or TT) = $\frac{1}{2}$
6. P(HT or TH) = $\frac{1}{2}$

First event:
Spin this spinner.

Outcomes:

7. P(A, A) = $\frac{1}{6}$
8. P(A, C) = $\frac{1}{6}$
9. P(B, A) = $\frac{1}{6}$
10. P(B, C) = $\frac{1}{6}$

Second event:
Spin this spinner.

11. P(both letters are the same) = $\frac{1}{3}$
12. P(both letters are different) = $\frac{2}{3}$

First event:
Pick a card.

13. P(2, H) = $\frac{1}{8}$
14. P(3, T) = $\frac{1}{8}$
15. P(even number, H) = $\frac{1}{4}$
16. P(odd number, T) = $\frac{1}{4}$
17. P(number less than 4, H) = $\frac{3}{8}$
18. P(number greater than 1, T) = $\frac{3}{8}$

Second event:
Flip this coin.

© D. C. Heath and Company   S299   Probability—more than 1 event

LIFE-SKILL PROJECT
Collecting data
Have the students toss two dice 72 times. Tell them to keep a tally of the number of times they get a sum of 7. Have them compare the results with the probability predicted by the 36 outcomes in this sample space.

(1, 1) (2, 1) (3, 1) (4, 1) (5, 1) (6, 1)
(1, 2) (2, 2) (3, 2) (4, 2) (5, 2) (6, 2)
(1, 3) (2, 3) (3, 3) (4, 3) (5, 3) (6, 3)
(1, 4) (2, 4) (3, 4) (4, 4) (5, 4) (6, 4)
(1, 5) (2, 5) (3, 5) (4, 5) (5, 5) (6, 5)
(1, 6) (2, 6) (3, 6) (4, 6) (5, 6) (6, 6)

351

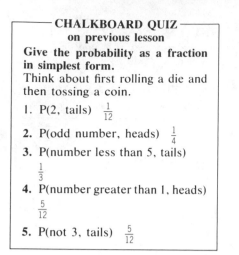
LESSON OBJECTIVE
To compute the odds of an outcome

PROBLEM-SOLVING SKILL
Reading a chart

STARTING THE LESSON
Discuss questions 1–5, using the chart and the *Here's how* example on page 352. Before assigning the exercises, let the students practice computing the odds in favor of getting

- an orange gumball. $\left(\frac{120}{600} \text{ or } \frac{1}{5}\right)$

- either a green or a yellow gumball. $\left(\frac{220}{600} \text{ or } \frac{11}{30}\right)$

EXERCISE NOTE
Tell the students to study the *Here's how* example on page 353 before attempting exercises 12–23.

Odds

The table shows the contents of the gum-ball machine.

COLOR	NUMBER OF GUM BALLS
Green	80
Blue	90
White	70
Yellow	140
Red	100
Orange	120

1. Suppose that the gum balls have been thoroughly mixed. Which color do you have the best chance of getting? The worst chance of getting? Yellow, White

2. How many gum balls are red? 100

3. How many gum balls are not red? 500

Here's how *to find the odds in favor of getting a red gum ball with your first penny.*

To find the **odds in favor of an outcome,** write the ratio of the number of ways the outcome can occur to the number of ways that the outcome cannot occur.

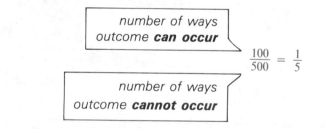

number of ways outcome **can occur**

number of ways outcome **cannot occur**

$\frac{100}{500} = \frac{1}{5}$

The odds in favor of getting a red gum ball are 1 to 5.

4. Look at the *Here's how*. What is the number of ways the outcome can occur? 100 Cannot occur? 500

5. What are the odds in favor of getting a red gum ball? $\frac{1}{5}$

EXERCISES
Give the odds as a fraction in lowest terms.
Think about putting your first penny into the gum-ball machine.

6. Odds in favor of getting a green $\frac{2}{13}$

7. Odds in favor of getting a blue $\frac{3}{17}$

8. Odds in favor of getting a white $\frac{7}{53}$

9. Odds in favor of getting a yellow $\frac{7}{23}$

10. Odds in favor of getting either a red or an orange $\frac{11}{19}$

11. Odds in favor of getting either a green or a white $\frac{1}{3}$

Here's how *to find the odds against getting a red gum ball with your first penny.*

To find the **odds against an outcome,** write the ratio of the number of ways that the outcome cannot occur to the number of ways that the outcome can occur.

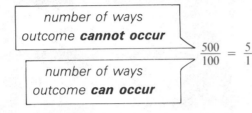

number of ways outcome **cannot occur**

number of ways outcome **can occur**

$\dfrac{500}{100} = \dfrac{5}{1}$

The odds against getting a red gum ball are 5 to 1.

Give the odds in lowest terms.

Think about putting your first penny into the gum-ball machine.

12. Odds against getting red $\dfrac{5}{1}$

13. Odds against getting blue $\dfrac{17}{3}$

14. Odds against getting white $\dfrac{53}{7}$

15. Odds against getting yellow $\dfrac{23}{7}$

16. Odds against getting either a blue or a white $\dfrac{11}{4}$

17. Odds against getting either a yellow or a red $\dfrac{3}{2}$

18. Suppose that your favorite color is yellow. What are the odds in favor of your getting your favorite color? The odds against? $\dfrac{7}{23}, \dfrac{23}{7}$

19. A friend likes either white or orange. What are the odds in favor of your friend's getting one of his favorite colors? The odds against? $\dfrac{19}{41}, \dfrac{41}{19}$

Solve.

20. Suppose that in another gum-ball machine the odds in favor of your getting your favorite color are 1 to 7. What would be the odds against your getting your favorite color? $\dfrac{7}{1}$

21. If the odds against getting a black gum ball are 11 to 3, what are the odds in favor of getting a black gum ball? $\dfrac{3}{11}$

Something to chew on!

22. The odds in favor of getting a red gum ball are 5 to 23. What is the probability of getting a red gum ball? $\dfrac{5}{28}$

23. The odds against getting a green gum ball are 25 to 3. What is the probability of getting a green gum ball? $\dfrac{3}{28}$

REVIEW PRACTICE

Finding the number when the percent is known
Page 441   Skill 59

PRACTICE WORKSHEET

Copymaster S300 or Duplicating Master S300

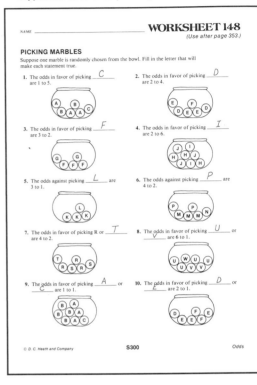

LIFE-SKILL PROJECT

Making predictions
Have each student pick a number from 1 to 10 and write it on a piece of paper. Collect the papers. Ask the students how often they think each number will appear in the stack of papers. Write the numbers 1–10 on the chalkboard and make a tally of the numbers the students picked. Compare the results with the predictions. Ask the students to account for the discrepancies. (Most of the students will pick one of the middle numbers in the range of 1–10.) Have the students use the results of the experiment to determine the odds that a person would pick 4, 5, or 6.

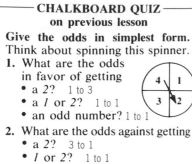
LESSON OBJECTIVE
To compute the expectation of an outcome

PROBLEM-SOLVING SKILL
Selecting information from a display

STARTING THE LESSON
Have the students read the introductory paragraph and answer questions 1–4. Then go over the *Here's how* and discuss questions 5–8.

Expectation

A set of triplets gave these childhood pictures to their school carnival committee. Each contestant is charged $2 to match the pictures with the names.

At the end of the carnival, each contestant who correctly matchs all three pictures wins an $8 calculator.

PLAY MATCH-UP!   BETH NANCY SUE

1. How much does it cost to play MATCH-UP? $2

2. How many ways can the pictures be matched with the names? 6

3. What is the probability of winning (matching all the pictures with the right names)? Assume that all matchings are equally likely. $\frac{1}{6}$

4. What is the value of the prize? $8

Here's how *to compute the* expectation *for a game of MATCH-UP.*

To find the expectation, multiply the probability of winning the prize times the value of the prize.

$$\text{Expectation} = \begin{array}{cc} P(\text{winning}) & \text{Value of Prize} \\ \frac{1}{6} & \times \quad \$8 \end{array} = \$1.33$$

The expectation for a game of MATCH-UP is $1.33

5. Look at the *Here's how*. What is the expectation for a game of MATCH-UP? $1.33

6. To decide whether such a game is a good deal for the player, you compare the cost of playing with the expectation. Is the expectation less than or greater than the cost of playing? Less than

7. If the expectation is less than the cost of playing, then such a game is a "bad deal" for the player. Is the game MATCH-UP a "bad deal" for the player? Yes

8. How much would the expectation have to be for the game to be considered a "good deal" for the player? Over $2

EXERCISES

Here is another game that was played at the school carnival. A player pays $1.50 to spin this wheel. If the wheel stops on yellow, the player wins a $4.00 movie ticket.

9. What is the probability (in simplest form) of winning? $\frac{1}{8}$

10. What is the value of the movie ticket? $4.00

11. How much is the expectation? $.50

12. How much does it cost to play? $1.50

13. Is the expectation less than or greater than the cost of playing the game? No

14. Is the game a good deal or a bad deal?
Bad deal

BUY A CHANCE ON A UNICYCLE WORTH $220!

A local merchant donated this unicycle to the school carnival. The carnival committee decided to sell 135 chances on it, at $2 each.

15. What is the cost of one chance? $2

16. If a person bought one chance, what would be that person's probability of winning? $\frac{1}{135}$

17. What is the value of the unicycle? $220

18. What is the expectation rounded to the nearest cent? $1.63

19. Is the expectation less than or greater than the cost of a chance? Less than

20. Is buying a chance a good deal or a bad deal? Bad deal

Which for what?

21. John bought 2 chances on the watch and 1 chance on the radio. He spent $4.00.
Sue bought 1 chance on the watch and 2 chances on the radio. She spent $3.50.
How much would one chance on each have cost? $2.50 (watch $1.50, radio $1.00)

REVIEW PRACTICE
Multiplying decimals
Page 420   Skill 18

PRACTICE WORKSHEET
Copymaster S301 or Duplicating Master S301

NAME _____   **WORKSHEET 149**
(Use after page 355.)

AND THE WINNER IS . . .
A hat contains these slips of paper:

1	2	3	4	5	6	7
8	9	10	11	12	13	14
15	16	17	18	19	20	
21	22	23	24	25	26	27

Without looking, someone draws a number from the hat.
Check (✓) the player who is most likely to win.

1. • A wins if the number is 8 or less.
    • B wins if the number is 20 or more.
    ✓ • C wins if both player A and player B lose.

2. • A wins if the number is a 1-digit number.
    ✓ • B wins if the number is a 2-digit number.
    • C wins if both player A and player B lose.

3. • A wins if the number is a multiple of 4.
    • B wins if the number is a multiple of 7.
    ✓ • C wins if both player A and player B lose.

4. ✓ • A wins if the number is a multiple of 3 or 5.
    • B wins if the number is a multiple of 7 or 8.
    • C wins if both player A and player B lose.

5. • A wins if the number is an even number.
    ✓ • B wins if the number is an odd number.
    • C wins if both player A and player B lose.

6. • A wins if the number has 2 even digits.
    • B wins if the number has 2 odd digits.
    ✓ • C wins if both player A and player B lose.

7. ✓ • A wins if the number is odd and less than 20.
    • B wins if the number is even and greater than 9.
    • C wins if both player A and player B lose.

8. ✓ • A wins if the tens digit is a 1.
    • B wins if the tens digit is a 2.
    • C wins if both player A and player B lose.

© D. C. Heath and Company   S301   *Most likely events*

LIFE-SKILL PROJECT
Making predictions
Ask the students which key on a typewriter will most often need to be replaced. Have the students use newspaper articles and make a frequency table of the number of times each letter appears. Since the letter *e* is the most commonly used letter, the *e* key will most likely need to be replaced first.

A player pays $2 to spin this spinner. If the pointer stops on an even number, the player wins $3.

1. What is the probability (in simplest form) of winning? $\frac{1}{2}$

2. How much is the expectation? $1.50

3. Is the game a good deal or a bad deal? Bad

SKILLS REVIEWED
Multiplying and dividing fractions
Solving proportions
Changing a fraction to a percent
Solving percent problems

PROBLEM-SOLVING SKILLS
Reading a blueprint
Choosing the correct operation
Solving a multi-step problem

STARTING THE LESSON
Cumulative Skill Practice
Challenge the students to an estimation hunt by saying, "Find the product in exercises 1–15 that is greater than 1." (Exercise 14) Have the students find the six quotients in exercises 16– 30 that are less than 1. (Exercises 18, 24, 26, 28, 29, and 30)

STARTING THE LESSON
Problem Solving
Help the students read the blueprint by asking questions such as these:
• Which room is 22 feet by 15 feet? (Living room)
• What are the dimensions of the garage? (10 feet by 15 feet)
• Which room has an area of 120 square feet? (Bedroom C)

Cumulative Skill Practice

Give the product in simplest form. *(page 178)*

1. $\frac{1}{2} \times \frac{1}{4}$ $\frac{1}{8}$
2. $\frac{1}{3} \times \frac{1}{3}$ $\frac{1}{9}$
3. $\frac{7}{8} \times \frac{4}{5}$ $\frac{7}{10}$
4. $\frac{3}{8} \times \frac{2}{3}$ $\frac{1}{4}$
5. $\frac{2}{5} \times \frac{2}{5}$ $\frac{4}{25}$

6. $\frac{9}{10} \times \frac{1}{3}$ $\frac{3}{10}$
7. $\frac{5}{6} \times \frac{3}{3}$ $\frac{5}{6}$
8. $\frac{4}{5} \times \frac{1}{2}$ $\frac{2}{5}$
9. $\frac{5}{6} \times \frac{0}{2}$ 0
10. $\frac{3}{8} \times \frac{3}{8}$ $\frac{9}{64}$

11. $\frac{5}{9} \times \frac{3}{10}$ $\frac{1}{6}$
12. $3 \times \frac{1}{3}$ 1
13. $\frac{0}{3} \times \frac{5}{6}$ 0
14. $\frac{3}{8} \times 4$ $1\frac{1}{2}$
15. $\frac{4}{4} \times \frac{7}{8}$ $\frac{7}{8}$

Give the quotient in simplest form. *(page 188)*

16. $3 \div \frac{1}{2}$ 6
17. $4 \div \frac{1}{3}$ 12
18. $\frac{1}{2} \div \frac{2}{3}$ $\frac{3}{4}$
19. $\frac{2}{3} \div \frac{1}{2}$ $1\frac{1}{3}$
20. $3 \div \frac{2}{3}$ $4\frac{1}{2}$

21. $\frac{2}{3} \div \frac{1}{2}$ $1\frac{1}{3}$
22. $\frac{3}{4} \div \frac{3}{8}$ 2
23. $\frac{3}{5} \div \frac{3}{8}$ $1\frac{3}{5}$
24. $\frac{3}{8} \div \frac{3}{4}$ $\frac{1}{2}$
25. $\frac{5}{8} \div \frac{1}{4}$ $2\frac{1}{2}$

26. $\frac{4}{5} \div 3$ $\frac{4}{15}$
27. $\frac{9}{10} \div \frac{3}{5}$ $1\frac{1}{2}$
28. $\frac{5}{16} \div \frac{3}{8}$ $\frac{5}{6}$
29. $\frac{2}{3} \div \frac{3}{4}$ $\frac{8}{9}$
30. $\frac{7}{12} \div \frac{5}{6}$ $\frac{7}{10}$

Solve. *(page 230)*

31. $\frac{5}{n} = \frac{2}{7}$ $17\frac{1}{2}$
32. $\frac{n}{3} = \frac{5}{2}$ $7\frac{1}{2}$
33. $\frac{1}{4} = \frac{n}{6}$ $1\frac{1}{2}$
34. $\frac{10}{n} = \frac{3}{5}$ $16\frac{2}{3}$
35. $\frac{3}{8} = \frac{n}{12}$ $4\frac{1}{2}$

36. $\frac{11}{n} = \frac{8}{21}$ $28\frac{7}{8}$
37. $\frac{3}{15} = \frac{5}{n}$ 25
38. $\frac{2}{3} = \frac{9}{n}$ $13\frac{1}{2}$
39. $\frac{n}{9} = \frac{5}{12}$ $3\frac{3}{4}$
40. $\frac{6}{15} = \frac{4}{n}$ 10

41. $\frac{n}{16} = \frac{13}{10}$ $20\frac{4}{5}$
42. $\frac{3}{16} = \frac{8}{n}$ $42\frac{2}{3}$
43. $\frac{15}{6} = \frac{n}{4}$ 10
44. $\frac{9}{n} = \frac{8}{5}$ $5\frac{5}{8}$
45. $\frac{9}{4} = \frac{18}{n}$ 8

Change to a percent. *(page 250)*

46. $\frac{1}{10}$ 10%
47. $\frac{2}{5}$ 40%
48. $\frac{1}{4}$ 25%
49. $\frac{1}{5}$ 20%
50. $\frac{1}{2}$ 50%
51. $\frac{1}{7}$ $14\frac{2}{7}$

52. $\frac{3}{4}$ 75%
53. $\frac{1}{3}$ $33\frac{1}{3}$%
54. 2 200%
55. $\frac{1}{6}$ $16\frac{2}{3}$%
56. $\frac{7}{8}$ $87\frac{1}{2}$%
57. $\frac{2}{9}$ 22

58. $\frac{3}{2}$ 150%
59. $\frac{4}{3}$ $133\frac{1}{3}$%
60. 3 300%
61. $\frac{7}{4}$ 175%
62. $\frac{9}{5}$ 180%
63. $\frac{1}{8}$ $12\frac{1}{2}$

Solve. *(page 258)*

64. 10% of 80 = n 8
65. 20% of 45 = n 9
66. 25% of 52 = n 13

67. 15% of 46 = n 6.9
68. 9% of 36.5 = n 3.285
69. 125% of 64 = n 80

70. 7.5% of 112 = n 8.4
71. 12.3% of 60 = n 7.38
72. 22.5% of 72.5 = n 16.

73. $62\frac{1}{2}$% of 62 = n 38.75
74. $33\frac{1}{3}$% of 126 = n 42
75. $66\frac{2}{3}$% of 159 = n 106

356

Problem solving

COMPUTERS AND ARCHITECTS

Computers are used to draw "blueprints" of an architect's design. The computer can be programmed to display a floor plan on a screen or printout.

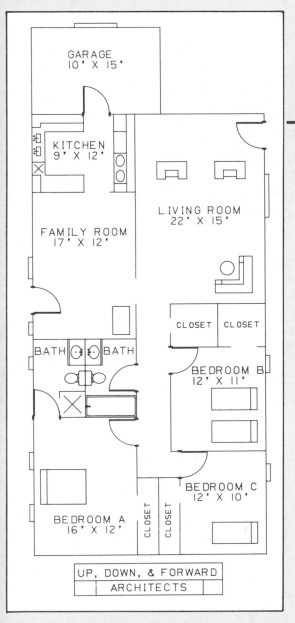

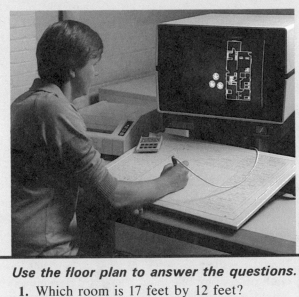

Use the floor plan to answer the questions.

1. Which room is 17 feet by 12 feet?
   Family Room
2. Which room is 16 feet by 12 feet?
   Bedroom A
3. What are the length and width of the living room? 22 feet by 15 feet
4. What are the dimensions of the kitchen?
   9 feet by 12 feet
5. Which room has an area of 132 square feet? Bedroom B
6. What is the area of the smallest bedroom?
   120 ft²
7. What is the area of the largest bedroom?
   192 ft²
8. Carpet costs $1.50 per square foot. How much will it cost to carpet bedroom B? *Hint: First find the area; then find the cost.* $198
9. At $1.75 per square foot, how much will it cost to carpet the living room? $577.50
10. A floor tile 1 foot by 1 foot costs $.49. How much will it cost to tile the family-room floor? $99.96
11. A contractor said this house could be built for $50 per square foot. Would you expect the cost to be more or less than $60,000?
    More

PROBLEM-SOLVING WORKSHEET
Copymaster S302 or Duplicating Master S302

NAME _____   **WORKSHEET 150**
(Use after page 357.)

ORANGES FOR SALE

ORANGES 4 for 75¢

How many oranges can you buy for $3?
16

FRACTION ACTION
Fill in the boxes to get the answer.

2   3   4   1

$\frac{3}{2} + \frac{7}{4} = 1\frac{3}{4}$

RADIO SALE

RADIO SHOP SALE 20% off

ACE ELECTRONICS SALE 30% off

Was $68.00 Now $47.60

Which store is selling this radio?
Ace Electronics

BE CAREFUL

Bridge closed to traffic over 10 tons

Could a truck weighing 500 pounds cross the bridge?
Yes

MULTIPLY IT
What is the largest whole number you can multiply by 300 and get an answer less than 401 × 12?
16

HOW OLD?
Maria's age is 3 times Barb's age. The sum of their ages is 48. How old is Barb?
12

© D. C. Heath and Company   S302   *Problem solving*

CHALKBOARD CHALLENGE
Unscramble the letters in these math words.

1. ERTE RADGIAM   Tree diagram
2. ITUEPRMTAON   Permutation
3. YIBRPOBALTI   Probability
4. MASPEL PSACE   Sample space
5. SDOD   Odds

357

NAME ________________ **CHAPTER 15 TEST**

(Form A)

Solve. *(pages 340, 342)*

The Ye Ol' Sandwich Shop sells 4 different sandwiches, 6 different drinks, and 3 different desserts. How many different orders could you place if you decided to buy

1. a sandwich and a drink? 24

2. a sandwich and a dessert? 12

3. a sandwich, a drink, and a dessert? 72

The Downtown Theater has 1 ticket window. In how many ways can

4. 2 people line up to buy tickets? 2

5. 3 people line up to buy tickets? 6

6. 4 people line up to buy tickets? 24

Think about spinning this spinner. Give each probability in simplest form. *(page 344)*

7. P(1) = 1/4

8. P(2) = 3/8

9. P(3) = 1/8

10. P(4) = 1/4

11. P(1 or 2) = 5/8 **12.** P(even) = 5/8

13. P(1 or 4) = 1/2 **14.** P(not 1) = 3/4

15. P(2 or 3) = 1/2 **16.** P(not 2) = 5/8

17. P(odd) = 3/8 **18.** P(not even) = 3/8

Below is a sample space for a family with 3 children. BGG stands for the oldest child being a boy, the middle child a girl, and the youngest a girl. Use the sample space to answer questions 19 through 25. *(page 346)*

19. How many outcomes are in the sample space? 8

Sample Space
BBB
BBG
BGB
BGG
GBB
GBG
GGB
GGG

What is the probability (in simplest form) that

20. the middle child is a boy? 1/2

21. the oldest child is a girl? 1/2

22. there are exactly 2 girls? 3/8

23. there is exactly 1 boy? 3/8

24. all are girls? 1/8

25. not all are girls? 7/8

ANSWERS	
1.	24
2.	12
3.	72
4.	2
5.	6
6.	24
7.	1/4
8.	3/8
9.	1/8
10.	1/4
11.	5/8
12.	5/8
13.	1/2
14.	3/4
15.	1/2
16.	5/8
17.	3/8
18.	3/8
19.	8
20.	1/2
21.	1/2
22.	3/8
23.	3/8
24.	1/8
25.	7/8

 S57 Page 1

NAME ________________ **CHAPTER 15 TEST**

(Form A)

Think about first picking a card and then rolling the die. Give each probability in simplest form. *(page 350)*

A B B C C C

26. P(A, 1) = 1/36 **27.** P(B, 4) = 1/18

28. P(C, 6) = 1/12 **29.** P(A, even number) = 1/12

30. P(B, odd number) = 1/6 **31.** P(C, even number) = 1/4

32. P(not A, 6) = 5/36 **33.** P(not B, 5) = 1/9

34. P(C, number greater than 4) = 1/6 **35.** P(B, number less than 5) = 2/9

36. P(A, not 2) = 5/36 **37.** P(not B, not even) = 1/3

38. P(not C, not greater than 3) = 1/4 **39.** P(not B, even) = 1/3

Think about spinning this spinner. Give each odds as a fraction in lowest terms. *(pages 352, 353)*

40. odds in favor of spinning 1 1/3

41. odds in favor of spinning 2 3/5

42. odds in favor of spinning 3 1/7

43. odds in favor of spinning 4 1/3

44. odds against spinning 1 3/1

45. odds against spinning 2 5/3

46. odds against spinning 3 7/1

47. odds against spinning 4 3/1

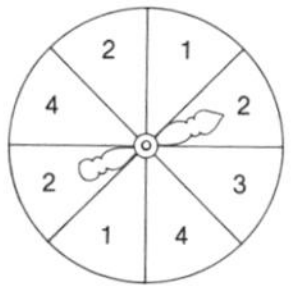

Solve. *(page 354)*

48. Suppose that you bought 1 of the 80 chances. What would be the probability of your winning the radio cassette player? 1/80

49. What would your expectation be? $1.20

50. Was buying a chance a "good deal"? No

ANSWERS	
26.	1/36
27.	1/18
28.	1/12
29.	1/12
30.	1/6
31.	1/4
32.	5/36
33.	1/9
34.	1/6
35.	2/9
36.	5/36
37.	1/3
38.	1/4
39.	1/3
40.	1/3
41.	3/5
42.	1/7
43.	1/3
44.	3/1
45.	5/3
46.	7/1
47.	3/1
48.	1/80
49.	$1.20
50.	No

 S58 Page 2

Chapter REVIEW

Here are scrambled answers for the review exercises:

$\frac{1}{12}$	$\frac{1}{3}$	5	18	permutation	sample
$\frac{3}{10}$	1	8	24	possible	value

1. A certain automobile is available in 3 different models, and each model comes in 6 different colors. If you decided to order such an automobile, you would have [?] choices. *(page 340)*

2. An arrangement of things in a definite order is called a [?]. Four students decide to go to lunch. They can line up in [?] different ways. *(page 342)*

3. If you roll a die, the probability of rolling a 2 is equal to

$$\frac{\text{number of ways of rolling a 2}}{\text{number of [?] outcomes}}$$

(page 344)

4. If you roll a die, the probability of rolling a number greater than 4 is [?]. *(page 344)*

5. A [?] space is the set of all possible outcomes. If you listed the sample space for tossing a coin 3 times, the sample space would have [?] outcomes. *(page 346)*

6. Think about first rolling a die and then tossing a coin. P(6, H) = [?]. *(page 350)*

7. Think about placing these marbles in a bag, thoroughly mixing them up, picking a marble, not replacing it, and then picking a second marble. P(red, blue) = [?]. *(page 350)*

8. Think about rolling a die. The odds in favor of rolling a 1 are [?] to [?]. *(page 352)*

9. You can find the expectation by multiplying the probability of winning a prize by the [?] of the prize. *(page 354)*

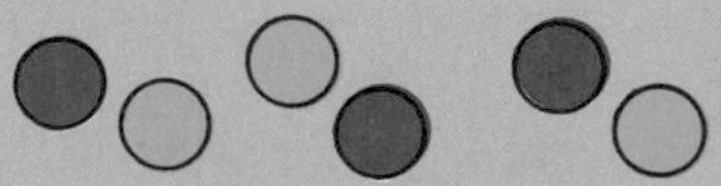

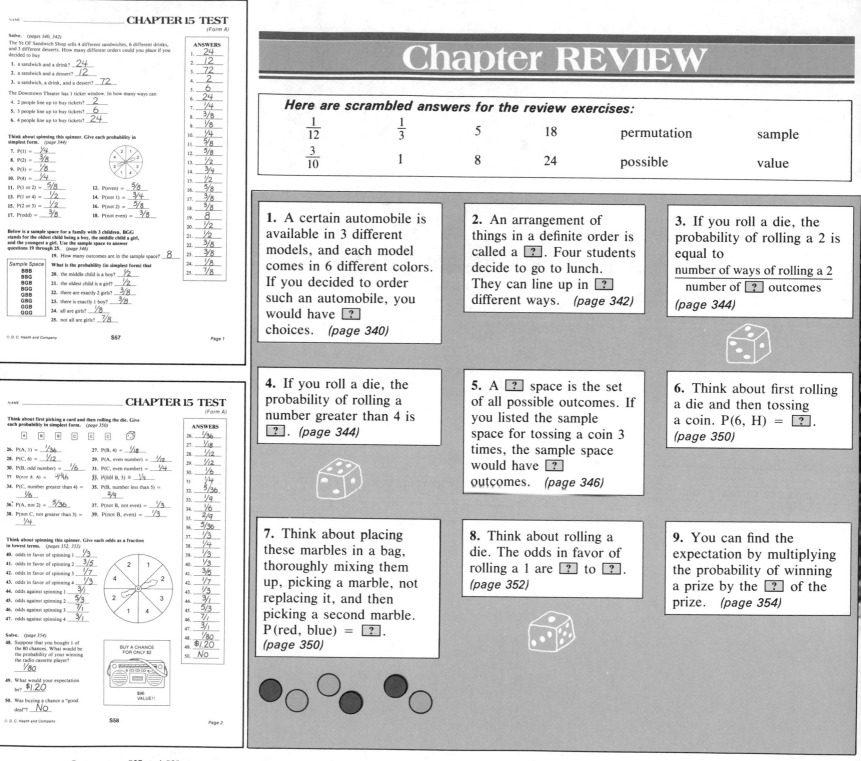

1. 18 2. permutation, 24 3. possible 4. $\frac{1}{3}$ 5. sample, 8 6. $\frac{1}{12}$ 7. $\frac{3}{10}$ 8. 1,5 9. value

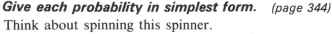

Solve. *(page 340, 342)*

1. You have 4 different colors of slacks and 6 different colors of shirts. How many different outfits can you make? 24

2. You and 5 friends decide to go to a movie. How many ways can you line up at the ticket office? 720

Give each probability in simplest form. *(page 344)*

Think about spinning this spinner.

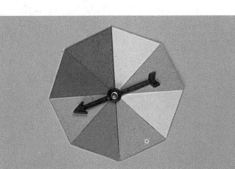

3. P(red) $\frac{1}{8}$ **4.** P(yellow) $\frac{1}{4}$

5. P(green) $\frac{3}{8}$ **6.** P(blue) $\frac{1}{8}$

7. P(red or brown) $\frac{1}{4}$ **8.** P(green or blue) $\frac{1}{2}$

9. P(not brown) $\frac{7}{8}$ **10.** P(not yellow) $\frac{3}{4}$

Solve. *(page 346)*

Think about a family with 3 children.

11. List the sample space for the children in the family. *Hint: Use GBB to represent a girl as the oldest, a boy as the "middle" child, and a boy as the youngest child.*
BBB, BBG, BGB, GB, B, B, G, G, GBG, G, G, B, GGG

12. a. What is the probability that in a family with 3 children, exactly 2 will be girls? $\frac{3}{8}$

b. What is the probability that in a family with 3 children, exactly 1 will be a girl? $\frac{3}{8}$

Give each probability in simplest form. *(page 350)*

Think about first flipping the coin and then tossing the die.

13. P(H, 3) $\frac{1}{12}$ **14.** P(T, 4) $\frac{1}{12}$

15. P(H, even number) $\frac{1}{4}$ **16.** P(T, number greater than 3) $\frac{1}{4}$

Give the odds as a fraction in lowest terms. *(pages 352, 353)*

Think about spinning the spinner shown above.

17. Odds in favor of spinning red $\frac{1}{7}$

18. Odds in favor of spinning green $\frac{3}{5}$

19. Odds against spinning blue $\frac{7}{1}$

20. Odds against spinning yellow $\frac{3}{1}$

Solve. *(page 354)*

21. a. Eighty chances were sold for $2 each. Suppose you bought a chance. What would be your expectation? $1.50

b. Is buying a chance on the binoculars a good deal? No

**BUY A CHANCE!
BINOCULARS
WORTH $120**

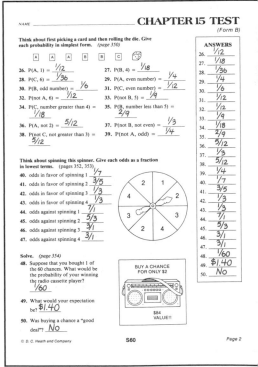

Use Copymaster S336 to provide the students with an answer sheet in standardized test format.

Cumulative TEST Standardized Format

Choose the correct letter.

Answers for Cumulative Test, Chapters 1–15

1. Ⓐ Ⓑ Ⓒ ● 2. Ⓐ ● Ⓒ Ⓓ 3. Ⓐ Ⓑ ● Ⓓ

4. ● Ⓑ Ⓒ Ⓓ 5. Ⓐ ● Ⓒ Ⓓ 6. Ⓐ Ⓑ ● Ⓓ

7. ● Ⓑ Ⓒ Ⓓ 8. ● Ⓑ Ⓒ Ⓓ 9. Ⓐ Ⓑ Ⓒ ●

10. Ⓐ ● Ⓒ Ⓓ 11. Ⓐ Ⓑ ● Ⓓ 12. Ⓐ ● Ⓒ Ⓓ

The table below correlates test items with student text pages.

Test Item	Page Taught	Skill Practice
1	12	p. 348, exercises 1–20
2	64	p. 348, exercises 21–40
3	96	p. 348, exercises 41–60
4	158	p. 348, exercises 61–75
5	166	p. 348, exercises 76–90
6	178	p. 356, exercises 1–15
7	188	p. 356, exercises 16–30
8	230	p. 356, exercises 31–45
9	250	p. 356, exercises 46–63
10	258	p. 356, exercises 64–75
11	302	
12	350	

1. 398,520 rounded to the nearest ten thousand is

A. 399,000
B. 390,000
C. 398,500
D. 400,000

2. Give the product.
52.4×2.07

A. 141.48
B. 108.468
C. 14.288
D. none of these

3. Give the quotient rounded to the nearest tenth.
$30.89 \div 3.7$

A. 8.35
B. 8.4
C. 8.3
D. none of these

4. Give the sum.
$\frac{7}{16} + \frac{5}{8}$

A. $1\frac{1}{16}$
B. $\frac{1}{2}$
C. $\frac{3}{4}$
D. none of these

5. Give the difference.
$\frac{5}{6} - \frac{2}{3}$

A. 1
B. $\frac{1}{6}$
C. $\frac{1}{2}$
D. none of these

6. Give the product.
$\frac{5}{12} \times \frac{3}{4}$

A. $\frac{5}{9}$
B. $1\frac{1}{4}$
C. $\frac{5}{16}$
D. none of these

7. Give the quotient.
$\frac{9}{10} \div \frac{3}{2}$

A. $\frac{3}{5}$
B. $1\frac{2}{3}$
C. $1\frac{7}{20}$
D. none of these

8. Solve.
$\frac{5}{8} = \frac{n}{6}$

A. 3.75
B. 9.6
C. 240
D. none of these

9. Change to a percent.
$\frac{3}{8} = ?$

A. $33\frac{1}{3}\%$
B. $38\frac{1}{2}\%$
C. $62\frac{1}{2}\%$
D. none of these

10. Solve.
32% of $18 = n$

A. 56.25
B. 5.76
C. 57.6
D. none of these

11. How many feet of fencing will it take to go around a circular garden that has a radius of 7 feet? Use 3.14 for π.

A. 21.98 B. 153.86
C. 43.96 D. none of these

12. If you toss a penny and a dime, what is the probability that both will land heads?

A. $\frac{1}{2}$ B. $\frac{1}{4}$
C. $\frac{1}{3}$ D. none of these

360

Chapter 16
Integers

CHAPTER 16
Integers

LESSON OBJECTIVES

To locate integers on a number line   (*pages 362–363*)
To compare integers   (*pages 362–363*)
To add integers   (*pages 364–365*)
To subtract integers   (*pages 366–367*)
To multiply integers   (*pages 370–371*)
To divide integers   (*pages 372–373*)
To give the coordinates of a point on a graph   (*pages 374–375*)
To draw the graph of an ordered pair of integers
   (*pages 374–375*)

PROBLEM-SOLVING SKILLS

Reading a map   (*pages 362–363*)
Finding information in a display   (*pages 364, 366, 370*)
Applying an addition model   (*pages 364–365*)
Applying a subtraction model   (*pages 366–367*)
Finding information in a price list   (*page 369*)
Choosing the correct operation   (*page 369*)
Solving a multi-step problem   (*page 369*)
Applying a multiplication model   (*pages 370–371*)
Discovering numerical relationships   (*page 372*)
Reading a graph   (*pages 374, 375*)
Interpreting directions correctly   (*page 374*)
Identifying differences in two photographs   (*page 377*)

RESOURCES

- **VISUAL AIDS**
  Number line from page 362   (*Visual Aid 53, Copymaster S149*)
  Models for positive and negative charges   (*Visual Aid 54, Copymaster S150*)
  Coordinate grid   (*Visual Aid 55, Copymaster S151*)
- **WORKSHEETS 151–158**   (*Copymasters S303–S310 or Duplicating Masters S303–S310*)

LESSON OBJECTIVES
To locate integers on a number line
To compare integers

PROBLEM-SOLVING SKILL
Reading a map

STARTING THE LESSON
Use the map at the top of the page and ask questions like these:
- Which city has a high temperature of positive 113 degrees? (Dallas)
- Which city has a low temperature of negative 24 degrees? (Duluth)
- How many cities have low temperatures below 20 degrees? (12)
- How many cities have high temperatures above Denver's high? (8)

Go over exercises 1–4, using the map and the *Here's how*. The number line in the *Here's how* is on **Visual Aid 53**.

Ordering and comparing integers

EXTREME TEMPERATURES OF SELECTED U.S. CITIES (1980)
Temperatures are given in degrees Fahrenheit

1. The low temperature for Seattle is 15 degrees above 0, which can be written as $^+15°$ ("positive fifteen degrees"). What is the low temperature for San Francisco? $^+31°$

2. The low temperature for Chicago is 8 degrees below 0, which can be written as $^-8°$ ("negative eight degrees"). What is the low temperature for Great Falls? $^-30°$

Here's how *to use the number line to compare two integers.*

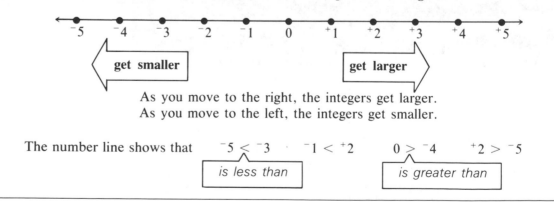

As you move to the right, the integers get larger.
As you move to the left, the integers get smaller.

The number line shows that $^-5 < ^-3$ $^-1 < ^+2$ $0 > ^-4$ $^+2 > ^-5$

| is less than |

| is greater than |

3. Look at the *Here's how*. Is $^-5$ less than or greater than $^-3$? Less than

4. Is 0 less than or greater than $^-4$? Greater than

EXERCISES

< or >?

5. $^+3$ ● $^+4$ <   6. $^+3$ ● $^-4$ >   7. $^-3$ ● $^+4$ <   8. $^-3$ ● $^-4$ >   9. $^-8$ ● $^+9$ <

10. $^+5$ ● $^-2$ >   11. $^-5$ ● $^+2$ <   12. $^-5$ ● $^-2$ <   13. $^+5$ ● $^+2$ >   14. $^-2$ ● 0 <

15. $^-10$ ● $^+6$ <   16. 0 ● $^+6$ <   17. 0 ● $^-6$ >   18. $^+10$ ● $^-6$ >   19. $^-4$ ● $^-8$ >

20. $^-7$ ● $^+9$ <   21. $^+7$ ● $^-9$ >   22. $^+7$ ● $^+9$ <   23. $^-7$ ● $^-9$ >   24. $^+7$ ● $^-4$ >

25. $^+8$ ● $^+11$ <   26. $^-12$ ● $^+10$ <   27. $^+15$ ● $^-19$ >   28. $^-20$ ● 0 <   29. 0 ● $^+15$ <

30. $^-21$ ● $^+12$ <   31. $^+24$ ● $^-27$ >   32. $^-32$ ● $^-25$ <   33. $^+30$ ● $^+25$ >   34. $^-30$ ● $^+8$ <

35. 0 ● $^-56$ >   36. $^-25$ ● $^+25$ <   37. $^-32$ ● $^+8$ <   38. $^-19$ ● 0 <   39. $^+32$ ● $^+23$ >

Complete.

40. All [?] integers are greater than 0. positive

41. All [?] integers are less than 0. negative

42. [?] is neither positive nor negative. 0

43. Zero is [?] than any negative integer. greater

44. A negative integer is [?] than any positive integer. less

45. A positive integer is [?] than any negative integer. greater

Solve. Use the information on page 362.

46. Which city has the highest high temperature? Phoenix

47. Which city has the lowest low temperature? Great Falls

48. Which city has the highest low temperature? Phoenix

49. Which city has the lowest high temperature? Seattle

50. List the low temperatures in order from least to greatest. (If two or more cities have the same low temperature, tell the number of cities with that low temperature.) $^-30$, $^-24$, $^-23$, $^-8$ (2 cities), $^-4$, $^-1$, $^+5$, $^+12$, $^+15$ (3 cities), $^+25$, $^+31$, $^+32$, $^+35$

51. List the high temperatures in order from least to greatest. (If two or more cities have the same high temperature, tell the number of cities with that high temperature.)

52. How many cities listed have low temperatures that are less than the low for Denver? 7

53. Which cities have high temperatures that are higher than the high for Washington, D.C.? Kansas City, Dallas, Phoenix

It was a record!

54. A record for extreme temperatures in a 24-hour period was set at Browning, Montana, in 1916. The high was 44°F. During the next 24 hours the temperature dropped 100 degrees. What was the low? $-56°F$

51. $^+87$, $^+89$, $^+95$ (2 cities), $^+97$, $^+98$, $^+100$ (2 cities), $^+101$ (2 cities), $^+102$ (2 cities), $^+103$, $^+106$, $^+113$, $^+115$

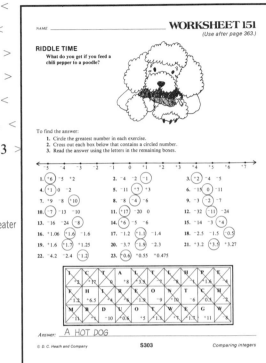

PRACTICE WORKSHEET
Copymaster S303 or Duplicating Master S303

CHALKBOARD CHALLENGE

These letters count $^-1$ point:
B, C, D, F, G, H, J, K, L, M, N, P, Q, R, S, T, V, W, X, Y, Z.

These letters count $^+2$ points:
A, E, I, O, U.

1. How many points for your first name?

2. How many points for your last name?

3. Whose last name in your class scores the most points?

LESSON OBJECTIVE
To add integers

PROBLEM-SOLVING SKILLS
Finding information in a display
Applying an addition model

STARTING THE LESSON
Have the students read the introductory paragraph. Go over exercises 1–5 and the *Here's how* examples. The positive-and negative-charges model is on **Visual Aid 54**.

EXERCISE NOTES
You may choose to have the students use their own models (from **Visual Aid 54**) to do exercises 6–35.

Adding integers

Imagine some small particles that have either a positive electrical charge or a negative electrical charge. The positive charges and negative charges are opposites. This means that when one positive charge and one negative charge are put together, the result is no charge, or a charge of 0.

1. Look at Example A. What is the charge when one positive charge and one negative charge are combined? 0

2. Look at Example B. What is the charge when three positive charges and one negative charge are combined? $^+2$

3. Look at Example C. What is the charge when two positive charges and five negative charges are combined? $^-3$

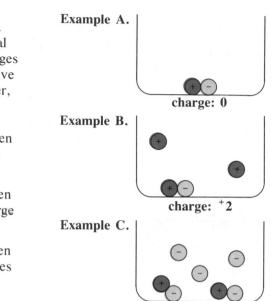

Example A.

charge: 0

Example B.

charge: $^+2$

Example C.

Here's how *to add integers by thinking about combining charges.*

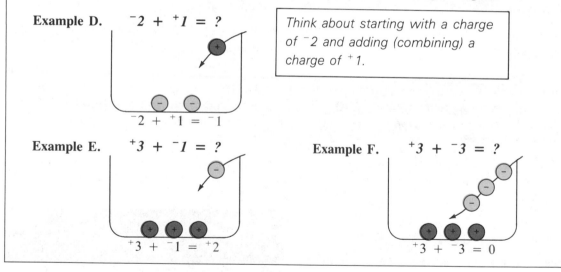

Example D. $^-2 + {}^+1 = ?$

Think about starting with a charge of $^-2$ and adding (combining) a charge of $^+1$.

$^-2 + {}^+1 = {}^-1$

Example E. $^+3 + {}^-1 = ?$

$^+3 + {}^-1 = {}^+2$

Example F. $^+3 + {}^-3 = ?$

$^+3 + {}^-3 = 0$

4. Look at the *Here's how*. What is the sum of $^-2$ and $^+1$? $^-1$
   What is the sum of $^+3$ and $^-1$? $^+2$

5. If the sum of the two numbers is 0, then one number is the **opposite** of the other. Look at Example F. Since the sum of the two numbers is 0, you know that the opposite of $^+3$ is what number? What is the opposite of $^-3$? $^-3, {}^+3$

364

EXERCISES

Give each sum.

Here are scrambled answers for the next row of exercises: 0 ⁺5 ⁺4 ⁺2 ⁻6

6. ⁺3 + ⁺2 ⁺5	**7.** ⁺4 + ⁻2 ⁺2	**8.** ⁻3 + ⁺3 0	**9.** ⁻1 + ⁻5 ⁻6	**10.** ⁺5 + ⁻1 ⁺4

11. ⁺6 + ⁻1 ⁺5   **12.** ⁻6 + ⁺1 ⁻5   **13.** ⁻6 + ⁻1 ⁻7   **14.** ⁺6 + ⁺1 ⁺7   **15.** ⁺6 + ⁻6 0

16. ⁻5 + ⁺4 ⁻1   **17.** ⁺5 + ⁺4 ⁺9   **18.** ⁻5 + ⁻4 ⁻9   **19.** ⁺5 + ⁻4 ⁺1   **20.** ⁺4 + ⁻9 ⁻5

21. ⁺7 + ⁻3 ⁺4   **22.** ⁻7 + ⁻3 ⁻10   **23.** ⁺7 + ⁺3 ⁺10   **24.** ⁻7 + ⁺3 ⁻4   **25.** ⁺5 + ⁻8 ⁻3

26. ⁺4 + ⁻4 0   **27.** ⁻5 + ⁺5 0   **28.** ⁺8 + ⁻8 0   **29.** ⁻9 + ⁺9 0   **30.** ⁻2 + ⁻2 ⁻4

31. ⁺7 + 0 ⁺7   **32.** ⁻6 + 0 ⁻6   **33.** 0 + ⁺5 ⁺5   **34.** 0 + 0 0   **35.** ⁻7 + ⁺7 0

36. ⁻12 + ⁻10 ⁻22   **37.** ⁺15 + ⁺18 ⁺33   **38.** ⁺17 + ⁻11 ⁺6   **39.** ⁻16 + ⁺19 ⁺3   **40.** ⁺13 + ⁻19 ⁻6

41. ⁻20 + ⁺12 ⁻8   **42.** ⁻24 + ⁻24 ⁻48   **43.** ⁺28 + ⁺21 ⁺49   **44.** ⁺26 + ⁻28 ⁻2   **45.** ⁻34 + ⁻11 ⁻45

46. ⁺30 + ⁻24 ⁺6   **47.** ⁺24 + ⁺30 ⁺54   **48.** ⁻36 + ⁺32 ⁻4   **49.** ⁻36 + ⁻32 ⁻68   **50.** ⁺46 + ⁻18 ⁺28

51. ⁻35 + 0 ⁻35   **52.** ⁻37 + ⁺37 0   **53.** ⁺39 + ⁻30 ⁺9   **54.** ⁻38 + ⁺34 ⁻4   **55.** ⁺25 + ⁻25 0

56. ⁻40 + ⁻48 ⁻88   **57.** ⁺40 + ⁻48 ⁻8   **58.** ⁻40 + ⁺48 ⁺8   **59.** ⁺40 + ⁺48 ⁺88   **60.** 0 + ⁻88 ⁻88

True or false?

61. The sum of two positive numbers is always positive. True

62. The sum of two negative numbers is always positive. False

63. The sum of a positive number and a negative number is always positive. False

64. The sum of a positive number and a negative number is always negative. False

65. The sum of a positive number and a negative number may be positive, may be negative, or may be 0. True

66. The sum of two opposites is 0. True

Magic squares

67. Add the numbers in each row, column, and diagonal. If the sums are the same, the square is a Magic Square. Is this a Magic Square? Yes. (The sum is ⁺6.)

⁺5	⁻2	⁺3
0	⁺2	⁺4
⁺1	⁺6	⁻1

68. Copy and complete this Magic Square.

⁺1

?	⁻6	?	⁻1
⁻4	⁻2	0	
⁻3	?	⁻5	

⁺2

Integers **365**

EXTRA PRACTICE
Page 442   Skill 61

PRACTICE WORKSHEET
Copymaster S304 or Duplicating Master S304

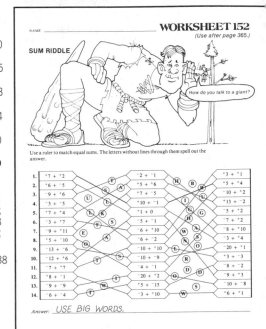

NAME _____

WORKSHEET 152
(Use after page 365.)

SUM RIDDLE

How do you talk to a giant?

Use a ruler to match equal sums. The letters without lines through them spell out the answer.

Answer: USE BIG WORDS.

© D. C. Heath and Company   S304   Adding integers

LIFE-SKILL PROJECT

Adding integers
Have the students mark two identical integer number lines from ⁻10 to ⁺10. To find the sum of ⁺4 and ⁻5, place 0 on Scale A over ⁺4 on Scale B. The sum appears on Scale B under ⁻5 on Scale A.

⁺4 + ⁻5 = ?

A
⁻6 ⁻5 ⁻4 ⁻3 ⁻2 ⁻1 0 ⁺1
⁻5 ⁻4 ⁻3 ⁻2 ⁻1 0 ⁺1 ⁺2 ⁺3 ⁺4 ⁺5
B
answer

Have the students use their slide rules to find these sums.

1. ⁺6 + ⁻9 ⁻3   **2.** ⁻6 + ⁺5 ⁻1
3. ⁻3 + ⁻2 ⁻5   **4.** ⁺8 + ⁻2 ⁺6
5. ⁺4 + ⁻3 ⁺1   **6.** ⁻1 + ⁻6 ⁻7

365

CHALKBOARD QUIZ
on previous lesson

Give each sum.

1. $^+6 + {}^-2$
   +4
2. $^-7 + {}^-3$
   −10
3. $^-7 + {}^+5$
   −2
4. $^+5 + {}^-5$
   0
5. $^-6 + 0$
   −6
6. $^-9 + {}^+10$
   +1
7. $^+14 + {}^-19$
   −5
8. $^-35 + {}^+12$
   −23
9. $^+20 + {}^-16$
   +4
10. $^-20 + {}^-16$
    −36

LESSON OBJECTIVE
To subtract integers

PROBLEM-SOLVING SKILLS
Finding information in a display
Applying a subtraction model

STARTING THE LESSON
Discuss questions 1–6 and the *Here's how* examples. The positive- and negative-charges model is on **Visual Aid 54**.

***HERE'S HOW* NOTE**
You may want to follow these steps in going over the examples.

Example A. $^-3 - {}^+2 = ?$

Do not have 2 ⊕ to take out.

Put in 2 ⊕⊖ pairs.

Take out 2 ⊕.

Example B. $^+2 - {}^-1 = ?$

No ⊖ to take out.

Put in 1 ⊕⊖ pair.

Take out 1 ⊖.

Example C. $^-2 - {}^-3 = ?$

Do not have 3 ⊖ to take out.

Put in 1 ⊕⊖ pair.

Take out 3 ⊖.

Subtracting integers

Look at the picture at the right to answer the following questions.

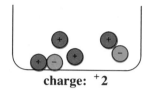

charge: $^+2$

1. What is the charge of the particles in the container? $_{+2}$

2. Suppose that you removed a charge of $^+1$. What would the charge be then? $_{+1}$

3. Suppose instead that you removed a charge of $^-2$. What would the charge be then? $_{+4}$

Here's how *to subtract integers by thinking about removing charges.*

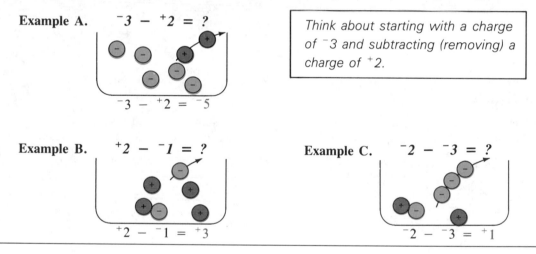

Example A. $^-3 - {}^+2 = ?$

$^-3 - {}^+2 = {}^-5$

Think about starting with a charge of $^-3$ and subtracting (removing) a charge of $^+2$.

Example B. $^+2 - {}^-1 = ?$

$^+2 - {}^-1 = {}^+3$

Example C. $^-2 - {}^-3 = ?$

$^-2 - {}^-3 = {}^+1$

4. Look at Example A in the *Here's how*. Adding a charge of $^-2$ would give the same result as subtracting a charge of $^+2$.

$$^-3 - {}^+2 = {}^-5$$
$$^-3 + \boxed{?} = {}^-5 \quad _{-2}$$

5. Look at Example B. Adding a charge of $^+1$ would give the same result as subtracting a charge of $^-1$.

$$^+2 - {}^-1 = {}^+3$$
$$^+2 + \boxed{?} = {}^+3 \quad _{+1}$$

6. Look at Example C.

$$^-2 - {}^-3 = {}^+1$$
$$^-2 + \boxed{?} = {}^+1 \quad _{+3}$$

Here's how *to subtract integers.*

To subtract an integer, add the opposite of the integer.

$$^+5 - {}^-4 = {}^+5 + {}^+4 \qquad {}^-6 - {}^+2 = {}^-6 + {}^-2 \qquad {}^+3 - {}^+7 = {}^+3 + {}^-7$$
$$= {}^+9 \qquad\qquad\qquad = {}^-8 \qquad\qquad\qquad = {}^-4$$

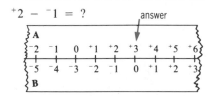

EXERCISES

7. The result of subtracting $^-4$ is the same as adding ? . $^+4$

8. The result of subtracting $^+2$ is the same as adding ? . $^-2$

9. To subtract $^+7$, you would add ? . $^-7$

10. To subtract $^-9$, you would add ? . $^+9$

Give each difference.

Here are scrambled answers for the next row of exercises: $^-3$ $^+10$ $^-8$ $^-15$ $^-4$

11. $^+7 - {}^-3$ $^+10$ 12. $^-9 - {}^-5$ $^-4$ 13. $^-2 - {}^+6$ $^-8$ 14. $^+4 - {}^+7$ $^-3$ 15. $^-10 - {}^+5$ $^-15$

16. $^-4 - {}^-9$ $^+5$ 17. $^+6 - {}^+2$ $^+4$ 18. $^-6 - {}^+6$ $^-12$ 19. $^+7 - 0$ $^+7$ 20. $0 - {}^+8$ $^-8$

21. $^+7 - {}^-5$ $^+12$ 22. $0 - {}^-6$ $^+6$ 23. $^+1 - {}^+9$ $^-8$ 24. $^-4 - {}^+4$ $^-8$ 25. $^-3 - {}^+4$ $^-7$

26. $^-6 - {}^+3$ $^-9$ 27. $^+6 - {}^+3$ $^+3$ 28. $^+6 - {}^-3$ $^+9$ 29. $^-6 - {}^-3$ $^-3$ 30. $^-9 - {}^+5$ $^-14$

31. $^+6 - 0$ $^+6$ 32. $0 - {}^+6$ $^-6$ 33. $^-7 - {}^+4$ $^-11$ 34. $^+4 - {}^+9$ $^-5$ 35. $^-11 - {}^-4$ $^-7$

36. $^-4 - {}^+9$ $^-13$ 37. $^-9 - {}^+4$ $^-13$ 38. $^+8 - {}^-3$ $^+11$ 39. $^+3 - {}^+8$ $^-5$ 40. $^-14 - {}^+8$ $^-22$

41. $^-10 - {}^+13$ $^-23$ 42. $^+11 - {}^-12$ $^+23$ 43. $^-14 - {}^-16$ $^+2$ 44. $^+12 - {}^+12$ 0 45. $^-21 - {}^-3$ $^-18$

46. $^+16 - {}^+18$ $^-2$ 47. $^+18 - {}^+16$ $^+2$ 48. $^-17 - {}^+11$ $^-28$ 49. $^+17 - {}^-11$ $^+28$ 50. $^-14 - {}^+18$ $^-32$

Give each sum or difference.

51. $^+10 + {}^+11$ $^+21$ 52. $^-12 - {}^+15$ $^-27$ 53. $^-16 - {}^-14$ $^-2$ 54. $^+18 + {}^-12$ $^+6$ 55. $^+13 - {}^+25$ $^-12$

56. $^-14 + 0$ $^-14$ 57. $0 + {}^+17$ $^+17$ 58. $^-11 + {}^-11$ $^-22$ 59. $^-11 - {}^-11$ 0 60. $^-30 + {}^-15$ $^-45$

61. $^+20 - {}^-16$ $^+36$ 62. $^-23 - {}^+23$ $^-46$ 63. $^+24 + {}^+16$ $^+40$ 64. $^-25 + {}^+25$ 0 65. $^-24 - {}^+18$ $^-42$

Add across. Subtract down.

Copy and complete these addition-subtraction boxes.

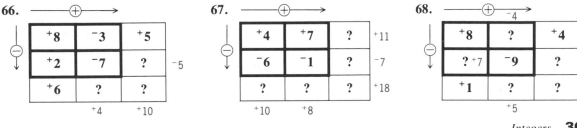

LIFE-SKILL PROJECT

Subtracting integers

Have the students use the integer slide rule described on page 365 to subtract. To find $^+2 - {}^-1$, place $^+2$ on Scale A over $^-1$ on Scale B. Find 0 on Scale B and read the answer on Scale A.

$^+2 - {}^-1 = ?$

Have the students use their slide rules to find these differences.

1. $^+3 - {}^-2$ $^+5$ 2. $^+3 - {}^+4$ $^-1$
3. $^-2 - {}^+3$ $^-5$ 4. $^-4 - {}^-2$ $^-2$
5. $^+5 - {}^-2$ $^+7$ 6. $^-3 - {}^-3$ 0

368

SKILLS REVIEWED
Multiplying and dividing by 10, 100, or 1000
Changing a fraction to a decimal
Adding mixed numbers
Multiplying mixed numbers

PROBLEM-SOLVING SKILLS
Finding information in a price list
Choosing the correct operation
Solving a multi-step problem

STARTING THE LESSON
Cumulative Skill Practice
Write these five answers on the chalkboard:

0.04   0.009   0.67 $5\frac{1}{2}$ 4

Challenge the students to an answer hunt by saying, "Look for the five even-numbered exercises on page 368 that have these answers. You have five minutes to find as many as you can." (Exercises 8, 24, 34, 46, and 58)

STARTING THE LESSON
Problem Solving
Use the pizza prices and ask questions like these:
- What is the cost of a medium pepperoni pizza? ($5.25)
- How much is a small sausage pizza with chili peppers? ($4.25)
- What kind of large pizza with green peppers can you buy for $7.25? (Pepperoni)

Cumulative Skill Practice

Give the product. *(page 68)*

1. 8.23×10 82.3
2. 8.23×100 823
3. 8.23×1000 8230
4. 45×1000 45,000
5. 45×10 450
6. 45×100 4500
7. 0.004×100 0.4
8. 0.004×10 0.04
9. 0.004×1000 4
10. 9.1×1000 9100
11. 9.1×10 91
12. 9.1×100 910

Give the quotient. *(page 92)*

13. $789.5 \div 10$ 78.95
14. $789.5 \div 100$ 7.895
15. $789.5 \div 1000$ 0.7
16. $297 \div 100$ 2.97
17. $297 \div 10$ 29.7
18. $297 \div 1000$ 0.297
19. $7.1 \div 100$ 0.071
20. $7.1 \div 10$ 0.71
21. $7.1 \div 1000$ 0.0071
22. $9 \div 10$ 0.9
23. $9 \div 100$ 0.09
24. $9 \div 1000$ 0.009

Change to a decimal rounded to the nearest hundredth. *(page 146)*

25. $\frac{1}{3}$ 0.33
26. $\frac{1}{6}$ 0.17
27. $\frac{1}{8}$ 0.13
28. $\frac{1}{12}$ 0.08
29. $\frac{5}{6}$ 0.83
30. $\frac{3}{8}$ 0.38
31. $\frac{7}{9}$ 0.78
32. $\frac{5}{12}$ 0.42
33. $\frac{11}{12}$ 0.92
34. $\frac{2}{3}$ 0.67
35. $\frac{1}{16}$ 0.06
36. $\frac{7}{8}$ 0.88
37. $\frac{9}{16}$ 0.56
38. $\frac{1}{11}$ 0.09
39. $\frac{5}{3}$ 1.67
40. $\frac{7}{6}$ 1.17
41. $\frac{5}{8}$ 0.63
42. $\frac{16}{9}$ 1.78
43. $\frac{4}{3}$ 1.33
44. $\frac{11}{8}$ 1.38
45. $\frac{13}{3}$ 4.33

Give the sum in simplest form. *(page 160)*

46. $2\frac{1}{2} + 3 = 5\frac{1}{2}$
47. $5 + 2\frac{2}{3} = 7\frac{2}{3}$
48. $1\frac{1}{4} + 2\frac{1}{2} = 3\frac{3}{4}$
49. $2\frac{1}{3} + 1\frac{1}{3} = 3\frac{2}{3}$
50. $3\frac{5}{8} + \frac{1}{4} = 3\frac{7}{8}$
51. $4\frac{2}{3} + 3\frac{1}{5} = 7\frac{13}{15}$
52. $5\frac{1}{2} + 4\frac{1}{3} = 9\frac{5}{6}$
53. $6\frac{2}{3} + 3\frac{1}{2} = 10\frac{1}{6}$
54. $5\frac{5}{8} + 1\frac{3}{4} = 7\frac{3}{8}$
55. $7\frac{5}{6} + 7\frac{2}{3} = 15\frac{1}{2}$
56. $9\frac{3}{4} + 8\frac{2}{5} = 18\frac{3}{20}$
57. $6\frac{1}{4} + 3\frac{1}{2} = 9\frac{3}{4}$

Give the product in simplest form. *(page 182)*

58. $3 \times 1\frac{1}{3}$ 4
59. $2 \times 2\frac{1}{2}$ 5
60. $1\frac{3}{4} \times 4$ 7
61. $3\frac{1}{3} \times 3$ 10
62. $1\frac{1}{3} \times 1\frac{1}{2}$ 2
63. $2\frac{1}{2} \times 2\frac{1}{3}$ $5\frac{5}{6}$
64. $3\frac{1}{2} \times 2\frac{1}{4}$ $7\frac{7}{8}$
65. $3\frac{1}{2} \times 2\frac{1}{2}$ $8\frac{3}{4}$
66. $1\frac{1}{6} \times 2\frac{3}{4}$ $3\frac{5}{24}$
67. $3\frac{1}{2} \times 1\frac{1}{4}$ $4\frac{3}{8}$
68. $1\frac{2}{3} \times 2\frac{1}{2}$ $4\frac{1}{6}$
69. $4\frac{1}{2} \times 2\frac{1}{3}$ $10\frac{1}{2}$

Problem solving

YOU'RE THE PIZZA MAKER!

THE PIZZA WITH PIZZAZZ!

	small 10-inch diameter	medium 12-inch diameter	large 14-inch diameter
CHEESE	$3.00	$4.50	$5.50
BACON	$3.60	$4.80	$6.25
PEPPERONI	$4.00	$5.25	$6.75
SAUSAGE	$3.75	$5.00	$6.50

Add 50¢ for each topping:
chili peppers
green peppers
mushrooms
onions

Use the information on the sign to answer these customers' questions.

1. How much will a large pepperoni pizza with mushrooms cost? $7.25

2. I have $10. Do I have enough to buy 2 small cheese pizzas and 1 small sausage pizza with onions? No

3. "What will 2 medium bacon and 3 large sausage pizzas cost?" $29.10

4. "We have $20. How much more will we need to buy 3 large pepperoni pizzas with green peppers and mushrooms?" $3.25

Solve.

5. On Wednesday, all large pizzas are 20% off. What would you charge a customer who orders a large bacon, a large cheese, and a small pepperoni pizza? $13.40

6. You get a special order for 18 medium pepperoni pizzas. It costs you $43.20 to make the pizzas. How much profit do you make? $51.30

7. You hire 2 part-time employees to work from 4:00 to 8:00 each day. If you pay each $4.50 an hour, how much does your part-time help cost per day? $36

8. You borrow $1150 for a pizza oven. How much interest will you have to pay if you borrow the money for 9 months at the yearly rate of 16%? $138

9. a. What is the area of a 10-inch pizza? Use 3.14 for π. 78.5 in.²

b. What is the price per square inch of a small cheese pizza? Give the answer to the nearest tenth of a cent. 3.8¢ or $.038

10. Which pizza is the better deal (costs less per square inch), a medium sausage or a large sausage? Large sausage

---

PROBLEM-SOLVING WORKSHEET
Copymaster S306 or Duplicating Master S306

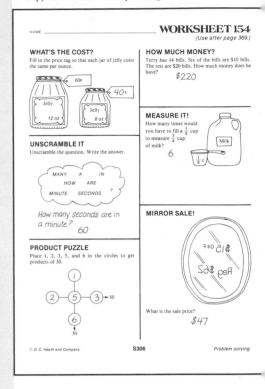

CHALKBOARD CHALLENGE
Unscramble the letters of these math words.

1. GTNIERE   Integer
2. VTGNEAIE EON   Negative one
3. VISIPOTE OWT   Positive two
4. ICAUSBTRTNO   Subtraction

LESSON OBJECTIVE
To multiply integers

PROBLEM-SOLVING SKILLS
Finding information from a display
Applying a multiplication model

STARTING THE LESSON
Go over questions 1–7 and the *Here's
how* examples. You may wish to use
Visual Aid 54 (positive- and negative-
charges model) to illustrate examples
A–D.

Multiplying integers

Look at the picture at the right to answer the
following questions.

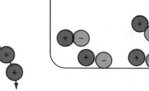

1. What is the charge of the particles in the container? 0

2. Suppose that you put in 2 sets of $^+2$ charges.
   What would the charge be then? $^+4$

Look again at the container with a charge of 0.

3. Suppose that you took out 2 sets of $^+2$ charges.
   What would the charge be then? $^-4$

4. What would the charge be if instead you put in 2 sets of $^-2$?
   $^-4$

5. What would the charge be if instead you took
   out 2 sets of $^-2$? $^+4$

Here's how *to multiply integers by thinking about putting in or*
taking out sets of charges.

To multiply, we will think of "putting charges in" as positive and
"taking charges out" as negative.

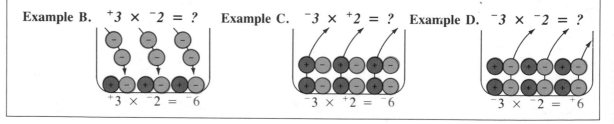

Example A. $^+3 \times {}^+2 = ?$

Start with a charge of 0
and put in 3 sets of $^+2$.

$^+3 \times {}^+2 = {}^+6$

Example B. $^+3 \times {}^-2 = ?$

$^+3 \times {}^-2 = {}^-6$

Example C. $^-3 \times {}^+2 = ?$

$^-3 \times {}^+2 = {}^-6$

Example D. $^-3 \times {}^-2 = ?$

$^-3 \times {}^-2 = {}^+6$

6. Look at the *Here's how*. In Examples A and D, we multiplied two integers with
   the same signs (both positive or both negative). Was the product positive or negative? Positive

7. In Examples B and C, we multiplied two integers with different signs. Was the product
   positive or negative? Negative

370

Here's how *to multiply integers.*

The product of two integers with the **same** signs is **positive.**

The product of two integers with **different** signs is **negative.**

The product of any integer and 0 is 0.

EXERCISES

Positive, negative, or zero?

8. The product of a positive integer and a positive integer is a ? integer. positive

9. The product of a positive integer and a negative integer is a ? integer. negative

10. The product of a negative integer and a negative integer is a ? integer. positive

11. The product of an integer and 0 is ? . 0

Give each product.

Here are scrambled answers for the next row of exercises: $^-12$ $^+8$ $^+9$ $^-12$ $^-10$

12. $^-2 \times {}^+5$ $^-10$ 13. $^+4 \times {}^+2$ $^+8$ 14. $^-3 \times {}^-3$ $^+9$ 15. $^+2 \times {}^-6$ $^-12$ 16. $^-3 \times {}^+4$ $^-12$

17. $^+3 \times {}^+5$ $^+15$ 18. $^+3 \times {}^-5$ $^-15$ 19. $^-3 \times {}^+5$ $^-15$ 20. $^-3 \times {}^-5$ $^+15$ 21. $^+1 \times {}^-8$ $^-8$

22. $^-6 \times {}^+4$ $^-24$ 23. $^+6 \times {}^+4$ $^+24$ 24. $^-6 \times {}^-4$ $^+24$ 25. $^+6 \times {}^-4$ $^-24$ 26. $^-4 \times {}^-7$ $^+28$

27. $^-6 \times 0$ 0 28. $0 \times {}^+4$ 0 29. $^+8 \times 0$ 0 30. 0×0 0 31. $0 \times {}^-3$ 0

32. $^-5 \times {}^+5$ $^-25$ 33. $^+7 \times {}^+6$ $^+42$ 34. $^-6 \times {}^-6$ $^+36$ 35. $^+5 \times {}^-9$ $^-45$ 36. $^-3 \times {}^+8$ $^-24$

37. $^-8 \times {}^-6$ $^+48$ 38. $^+9 \times {}^-6$ $^-54$ 39. $0 \times {}^+3$ 0 40. $^+9 \times {}^+5$ $^+45$ 41. $^+4 \times {}^+8$ $^+32$

42. $^+12 \times {}^+12$ $^+144$ 43. $^+12 \times {}^-12$ $^-144$ 44. $^-12 \times {}^+12$ $^-144$ 45. $^-12 \times {}^-12$ $^+144$ 46. $^-11 \times {}^-11$ $^+121$

47. $^-11 \times {}^+11$ $^-121$ 48. $^+15 \times 0$ 0 49. $^-16 \times {}^-14$ $^+224$ 50. $^+20 \times {}^-12$ $^-240$ 51. $^-4 \times {}^+8$ $^-32$

Build an expression

Use all the cards to build an expression for each of the following numbers.

52. $^-9$ $^+3 \times (^-2 + {}^-1)$

53. $^+5$ $^+3 + (^-1 \times {}^-2)$

54. $^-4$ $^-2 \times (^+3 + {}^-1)$

55. $^-7$ $^-1 + (^+3 \times {}^-2)$

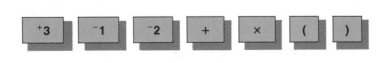

EXTRA PRACTICE
Page 443   Skill 63

PRACTICE WORKSHEET
Copymaster S307 or Duplicating Master S307

NAME _____

WORKSHEET 155
(Use after page 371.)

WHAT IS IT?

What occurs once in a minute, twice in a moment, and not once in a hundred years?

To find the answer:
1. Multiply.
2. Cross out each box below that contains an answer.
3. Read the answer using the letters in the remaining boxes.

Multiply.

1. $^-11 \times {}^+6$ $^-66$
2. $^+4 \times {}^-10$ $^-40$
3. $^-9 \times {}^-12$ $^+108$
4. $^+5 \times {}^-15$ $^-75$
5. $^-8 \times {}^+10$ $^-80$
6. $^-10 \times {}^+7$ $^-70$
7. $^-13 \times {}^-3$ $^+39$
8. $^+7 \times {}^-8$ $^-56$
9. $^-18 \times {}^+4$ $^-72$
10. $^+16 \times {}^-3$ $^-48$
11. $^+14 \times {}^+6$ $^+84$
12. $^-11 \times {}^-11$ $^+121$
13. $^-22 \times {}^+4$ $^-88$
14. $^+9 \times {}^-6$ $^-54$
15. $^-14 \times {}^+3$ $^-42$
16. $^+15 \times {}^-4$ $^-60$
17. $^-25 \times {}^-4$ $^+100$
18. $^+18 \times {}^+2$ $^+36$
19. $^-17 \times {}^-3$ $^+51$
20. $^-23 \times {}^+4$ $^-92$
21. $^-15 \times {}^-2$ $^+30$
22. $^-8 \times {}^-3$ $^+24$
23. $^+17 \times {}^-5$ $^-85$
24. $^-13 \times {}^-5$ $^+65$
25. $^-9 \times {}^-9$ $^+81$
26. $^-21 \times {}^+7$ $^-147$

Answer: THE LETTER M

© D. C. Heath and Company   S307   *Multiplying integers*

CHALKBOARD CHALLENGE

Multiply each number in this Magic Square by $^-2$ to get a new square.

$^+3$	$^-4$	$^+1$
$^-2$	0	$^+2$
$^-1$	$^+4$	$^-3$

$^-6$	$^+8$	$^-2$
$^+4$	0	$^-4$
$^+2$	$^-8$	$^+6$

Is your new square a Magic Square?

Yes

CHALKBOARD QUIZ
on previous lesson
Give each product.

1. $^-3 \times {}^+5$ $^-15$ 2. $^+6 \times {}^+2$ $^+12$
3. $^-4 \times {}^-4$ $^+16$ 4. $^+4 \times {}^-7$ $^-28$
5. $^-4 \times {}^+5$ $^-20$ 6. $^+7 \times {}^+9$ $^+63$
7. $^+3 \times {}^-8$ $^-24$ 8. $^-7 \times 0$ $\;0$
9. $^+9 \times {}^-6$ $^-54$ 10. $^-6 \times {}^-9$ $^+54$

LESSON OBJECTIVE
To divide integers

PROBLEM-SOLVING SKILL
Discovering numerical relationships

STARTING THE LESSON
Write this table on the chalkboard:

$\times$	$^+2$	$^+1$	0	$^-1$	$^-2$
$^+3$	$^+6$	$^+3$	0	$^-3$	$^-6$
$^-3$	$^-6$	$^-3$	0	$^+3$	$^+6$

Ask the students how they can use the integer multiplication table to find $^+6 \div {}^-2$. (To find $^+6 \div {}^-2$, find $^-2$ in the top row and go down to $^+6$. The number at the left of this row is the answer. $^+6 \div {}^-2 = {}^-3$.) Have the students use the table to find these quotients.

$^-6 \div {}^-2 = ?$
$^+6 \div {}^+2 = ?$
$^-6 \div {}^+2 = ?$

Dividing integers

1. What would you multiply by $^+3$ to get $^+18$? $^+6$

2. What would you multiply by $^-4$ to get $^+28$? $^-7$

3. What would you multiply by $^-9$ to get 0? 0

Here's how *to divide integers by finding a missing factor.*

Example A. $^+18 \div {}^+3 = ?$
$^+18 \div {}^+3 = {}^+6$
because
$^+3 \times {}^+6 = {}^+18$

Example B. $^+18 \div {}^-3 = ?$
$^+18 \div {}^-3 = {}^-6$
because
$^-3 \times {}^-6 = {}^+18$

Example C. $^-18 \div {}^+3 = ?$
$^-18 \div {}^+3 = {}^-6$
because
$^+3 \times {}^-6 = {}^-18$

Example D. $^-18 \div {}^-3 = ?$
$^-18 \div {}^-3 = {}^+6$
because
$^-3 \times {}^+6 = {}^-18$

4. Look at the *Here's how*. In Example A, we divided a positive integer by a positive integer. Was the quotient positive or negative? Positive

5. If you divide a positive integer by a negative integer, will the quotient be positive or negative? Negative

6. If you divide a negative integer by a positive integer, will the quotient be positive or negative? Negative

7. If you divide a negative integer by a negative integer, will the quotient be positive or negative? Positive

Here's how *to divide integers.*

The quotient of two integers with the **same** signs is **positive**.

The quotient of two integers with **different** signs is **negative**.

The quotient of 0 divided by any nonzero integer is 0.

EXERCISES

Give each quotient.
Here are scrambled answers for the next row of exercises: +8 +4 -10 -6 -8

8. +20 ÷ -2 = -10   9. +24 ÷ +3 = +8   10. -30 ÷ +5 = -6   11. -36 ÷ -9 = +4   12. -56 ÷ +7 = -8

13. +14 ÷ +2 = +7   14. +14 ÷ -2 = -7   15. -14 ÷ +2 = -7   16. -14 ÷ -2 = +7   17. +15 ÷ -5 = -3

18. +15 ÷ -3 = -5   19. -15 ÷ +3 = -5   20. -18 ÷ -6 = +3   21. +15 ÷ +3 = +5   22. -15 ÷ -3 = +5

23. +24 ÷ +6 = +4   24. +24 ÷ -6 = -4   25. +12 ÷ +6 = +2   26. -24 ÷ +6 = -4   27. -24 ÷ -6 = +4

28. -30 ÷ +6 = -5   29. 0 ÷ -6 = 0   30. +18 ÷ -6 = -3   31. -30 ÷ -5 = +6   32. +30 ÷ +5 = +6

33. +30 ÷ -5 = -6   34. 0 ÷ +8 = 0   35. -12 ÷ -4 = +3   36. +10 ÷ -2 = -5   37. -16 ÷ -4 = +4

38. -24 ÷ +8 = -3   39. +28 ÷ -4 = -7   40. +32 ÷ -8 = -4   41. +25 ÷ +5 = +5   42. -27 ÷ -3 = +9

43. -45 ÷ -5 = +9   44. +54 ÷ -6 = -9   45. +36 ÷ -6 = -6   46. -48 ÷ +8 = -6   47. +56 ÷ +7 = +8

48. +81 ÷ +9 = +9   49. 0 ÷ -12 = 0   50. +81 ÷ -9 = -9   51. -64 ÷ +8 = -8   52. +54 ÷ +9 = +6

53. -72 ÷ -9 = +8   54. +121 ÷ +11 = +11   55. +144 ÷ +12 = +12   56. +150 ÷ -10 = -15   57. -132 ÷ -12 = +11

58. +124 ÷ -4 = -31   59. -176 ÷ -16 = +11   60. -120 ÷ +20 = -6   61. +162 ÷ +18 = +9   62. -147 ÷ +21 = -7

Simplify.

Here are scrambled answers for the next row of exercises: -3 +4 +3 +12 +8

63. +6 + +2 = +8   64. +6 - +2 = +4   65. -6 ÷ +2 = -3   66. +6 × +2 = +12   67. +6 ÷ +2 = +3

68. +8 + -4 = +4   69. +8 - -4 = +12   70. -8 - +4 = -12   71. +8 × -4 = -32   72. +8 ÷ -4 = -2

73. -15 + +3 = -12   74. -15 - +3 = -18   75. +15 ÷ -3 = -5   76. -15 × +3 = -45   77. -15 ÷ +3 = -5

78. +8 + 0 = +8   79. +8 - 0 = +8   80. 0 × -8 = 0   81. +8 × 0 = 0   82. 0 ÷ +8 = 0

83. -24 + -6 = -30   84. -24 - -6 = -18   85. +24 + -6 = +18   86. -24 × -6 = +144   87. -24 ÷ -6 = +4

88. +18 + -9 = +9   89. +18 - -9 = +27   90. +18 ÷ +9 = +2   91. +18 × -9 = -162   92. +18 ÷ -9 = -2

93. -21 + +3 = -18   94. -21 - +3 = -24   95. +21 ÷ -3 = -7   96. -21 × +3 = -63   97. -21 ÷ +3 = -7

98. +20 + +5 = +25   99. +20 - +5 = +15   100. +20 × -5 = -100   101. +20 × +5 = +100   102. +20 ÷ +5 = +4

Multiply across. Divide down.

Copy and complete these multiplication-division boxes.

103.
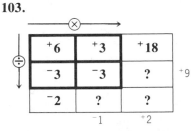

104.
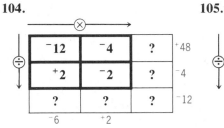

105.

⊗		
+24	? -6	-144
? -3	+2	? -6
-8	? -3	? +24

WORKSHEET 156
(Use after page 373.)

NAME _____

SKILL DRILL
Study these examples.

+21 ÷ +7 = +3   The quotient of two integers with the same sign is positive.
-21 ÷ -7 = +3

-21 ÷ +7 = -3   The quotient of two integers with different signs is negative.
+21 ÷ -7 = -3

Divide.

1. +32 ÷ -8 = -4   2. -72 ÷ -9 = +8   3. +24 ÷ -3 = -8
4. +45 ÷ +5 = +9   5. 0 ÷ +8 = 0   6. -27 ÷ -9 = +3
7. +81 ÷ +9 = +9   8. -100 ÷ -10 = +10   9. +84 ÷ -4 = -21
10. +32 ÷ +2 = -16   11. +120 ÷ -3 = -40   12. -65 ÷ +5 = -13
13. -24 ÷ +3 = -8   14. -32 ÷ -8 = +4   15. -49 ÷ -7 = +7
16. +27 ÷ +9 = +3   17. +55 ÷ -5 = -11   18. -81 ÷ -9 = +9
19. -84 ÷ +2 = -42   20. +120 ÷ +6 = -20   21. +16 ÷ -16 = -1
22. +72 ÷ -9 = -8   23. -36 ÷ -6 = +6   24. -150 ÷ +10 = -15
25. -84 ÷ +4 = -21   26. +49 ÷ -7 = -7   27. -45 ÷ +5 = +9
28. -32 ÷ +8 = -4   29. +56 ÷ +8 = +7   30. +66 ÷ -6 = -11
31. +65 ÷ -5 = -13   32. -120 ÷ +20 = -6   33. +100 ÷ -10 = -10
34. -120 ÷ -4 = +30   35. 0 ÷ +7 = 0   36. -32 ÷ +2 = -9
37. -81 ÷ +9 = -9   38. +120 ÷ -4 = -30   39. +150 ÷ -15 = -10
40. -77 ÷ -7 = +11   41. -65 ÷ -5 = +13   42. -72 ÷ -8 = +9
43. +45 ÷ -9 = -5   44. +22 ÷ +2 = +11   45. +84 ÷ -4 = -21
46. +240 ÷ -10 = -24   47. -27 ÷ +9 = -3   48. -56 ÷ -7 = +8
49. -33 ÷ +3 = -11   50. -39 ÷ -3 = +13   51. -75 ÷ +25 = -3
52. -42 ÷ -3 = +14   53. -80 ÷ -5 = +16   54. -60 ÷ +5 = -12

© D. C. Heath and Company   S308   Dividing integers

CHALKBOARD CHALLENGE

Find the END number.

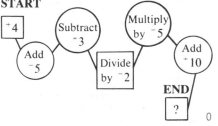

START   +4 → Add -5 → Subtract +3 → Divide by -2 → Multiply by -5 → Add +10 → END   ?   0

Answers for page 375. (34–57)

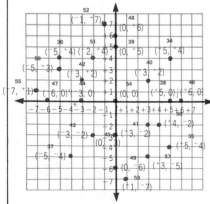

Graphing ordered pairs

Look at the picture on the right to
answer the following questions.

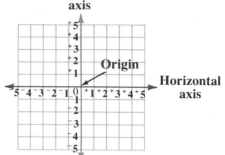

1. What is the red number line called?
   Horizontal axis

2. What is the blue number line called?
   Vertical axis

3. What is the point called where
   the two axes intersect? Origin

Here's how *to graph ordered pairs of integers.*

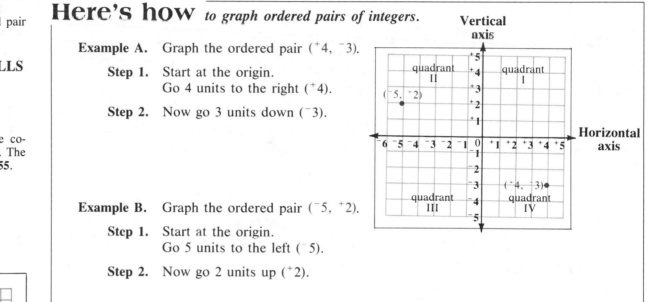

Example A. Graph the ordered pair ($^+4$, $^-3$).

   Step 1. Start at the origin.
              Go 4 units to the right ($^+4$).

   Step 2. Now go 3 units down ($^-3$).

Example B. Graph the ordered pair ($^-5$, $^+2$).

   Step 1. Start at the origin.
              Go 5 units to the left ($^-5$).

   Step 2. Now go 2 units up ($^+2$).

4. Look at the *Here's how*. Which ordered pair is graphed in quadrant II? ($^-5$, $^+2$)

5. Which ordered pair is graphed in quadrant IV? ($^+4$, $^-3$)

6. The ordered pair ($^+4$, $^+5$) would be graphed in quadrant ☐ . I

7. The ordered pair ($^-3$, $^-4$) would be graphed in quadrant ☐ . III

8. (0, $^+4$) would be graphed on the ☐ axis. Vertical

9. Where would the ordered pair (0, 0) be graphed? At the origin

EXERCISES

Give the ordered pair for each point.

10. A $(^+3, ^+3)$ 11. B $(^-3, ^+4)$ 12. C $(^-6, ^-4)$

13. D $(^+5, ^-7)$ 14. E $(^-4, ^-7)$ 15. F $(^-5, ^+7)$

16. G $(^+6, ^+7)$ 17. H $(^+3, ^-4)$ 18. I $(^+5, 0)$

19. J $(0, ^-7)$ 20. K $(^-6, 0)$ 21. L $(0, ^+6)$

22. M $(^+6, ^-3)$ 23. N $(^+5, ^+5)$ 24. P $(^+1, 0)$

25. Q $(^-4, ^-4)$ 26. R $(^+2, ^-2)$ 27. S $(^-6, ^+4)$

28. T $(^-7, ^-7)$ 29. U $(^-7, ^+6)$ 30. V $(^+3, ^+6)$

31. W $(^-7, ^-2)$ 32. X $(^+1, ^-5)$ 33. Y $(^-4, ^+2)$

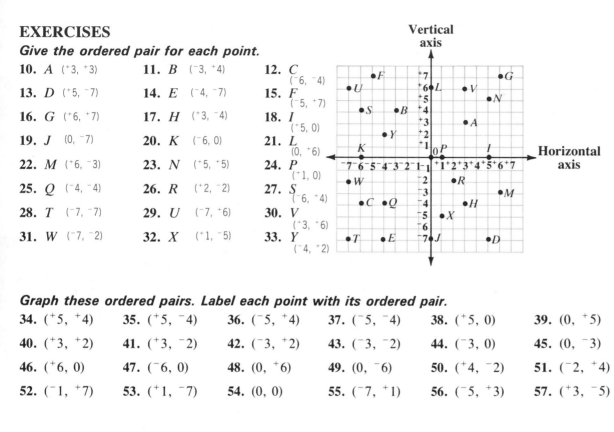

Graph these ordered pairs. Label each point with its ordered pair.

34. $(^+5, ^+4)$ 35. $(^+5, ^-4)$ 36. $(^-5, ^+4)$ 37. $(^-5, ^-4)$ 38. $(^+5, 0)$ 39. $(0, ^+5)$

40. $(^+3, ^+2)$ 41. $(^+3, ^-2)$ 42. $(^-3, ^+2)$ 43. $(^-3, ^-2)$ 44. $(^-3, 0)$ 45. $(0, ^-3)$

46. $(^+6, 0)$ 47. $(^-6, 0)$ 48. $(0, ^+6)$ 49. $(0, ^-6)$ 50. $(^+4, ^-2)$ 51. $(^-2, ^+4)$

52. $(^-1, ^+7)$ 53. $(^+1, ^-7)$ 54. $(0, 0)$ 55. $(^-7, ^+1)$ 56. $(^-5, ^+3)$ 57. $(^+3, ^-5)$

Triangle tricks

58. Copy the triangle on graph paper and give the ordered pairs for points A, B, and C. $(^+2, ^+2)$ $(^+4, ^+6)$ $(^+6, ^+2)$

59. Add $^+3$ to the second number of each ordered pair. Graph the new ordered pairs. Connect the points to make a new triangle.

60. Multiply the second number of each ordered pair (for points A, B, and C) by $^-1$. Graph the ordered pairs and draw the triangle.

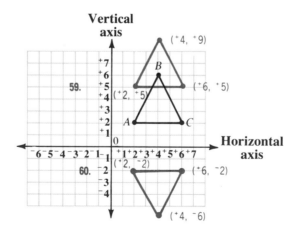

REVIEW PRACTICE
Dividing decimals
Page 425   Skill 28

PRACTICE WORKSHEET
Copymaster S309 or Duplicating Master S309

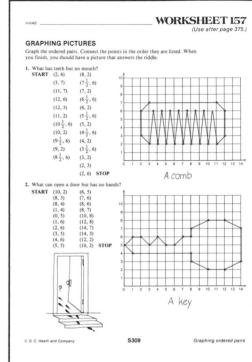

CHALKBOARD CHALLENGE
Graph each geometric figure by graphing the ordered pairs and connecting the points in the order given.

1. Hexagon
   (0, 0) (1, 3) (4, 3) (5, 0) (4, ⁻3) (1, ⁻3)
2. Rectangle
   (⁻1, 3) (3, ⁻1) (1, ⁻3) (⁻3, 1)
3. Octagon
   (1, 4) (3, 2) (3, 0) (1, ⁻2) (⁻1, ⁻2) (⁻3, 0) (⁻3, 2) (⁻1, 4)
4. Trapezoid
   (2, 4) (2, 0) (⁻2, ⁻2) (⁻4, 1)

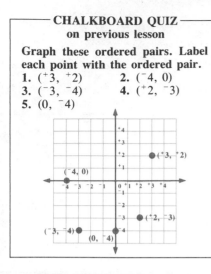

CHALKBOARD QUIZ
on previous lesson

CHALKBOARD QUIZ
on previous lesson

Graph these ordered pairs. Label each point with the ordered pair.
1. $(^+3, ^+2)$ 2. $(^-4, 0)$
3. $(^-3, ^-4)$ 4. $(^+2, ^-3)$
5. $(0, ^-4)$

SKILLS REVIEWED
Making conversions between metric units of length
Solving proportions
Changing a percent to a fraction
Solving a percent problem

PROBLEM-SOLVING SKILL
Identifying differences in two photographs

STARTING THE LESSON
Cumulative Skill Practice
Write these answers on the chalkboard:

1600   50 $\frac{1}{10}$ $1\frac{3}{4}$ 4

Challenge the students to an answer hunt by saying, "Look for the five even-numbered exercises on page 376 that have these answers. You have five minutes to find as many of the exercises as you can." (Exercises 8, 22, 28, 36, and 46)

STARTING THE LESSON
Problem Solving
Have the students look at the photos on page 377. Ask them to identify the city in the photos. (New York) Then ask "Which photo do you think shows the real New York skyline?" (The top photo) Have students read the introductory paragraphs and then work on question 1.

376

Complete. *(page 202)*

1. 49 cm = __?__ m 0.49
2. 58 mm = __?__ cm 5.8
3. 36 km = __?__ m 36,000

4. 2250 m = __?__ km 2.250
5. 9.6 km = __?__ m 9600
6. 7.4 cm = __?__ mm 74

7. 68 cm = __?__ mm 680
8. 16 m = __?__ cm 1600
9. 5.3 m = __?__ cm 530

10. 342 km = __?__ m 342,000
11. 700 mm = __?__ m 0.7
12. 0.8 m = __?__ mm 800

Solve. *(page 230)*

13. $\frac{n}{8} = \frac{3}{4}$ 6
14. $\frac{9}{n} = \frac{8}{5}$ $5\frac{5}{8}$
15. $\frac{16}{5} = \frac{n}{3}$ $9\frac{3}{5}$
16. $\frac{4}{12} = \frac{3}{n}$ 9
17. $\frac{5}{n} = \frac{10}{6}$ 3

18. $\frac{7}{n} = \frac{3}{5}$ $11\frac{2}{3}$
19. $\frac{n}{4} = \frac{13}{10}$ $5\frac{1}{5}$
20. $\frac{15}{8} = \frac{n}{6}$ $11\frac{1}{4}$
21. $\frac{2}{3} = \frac{11}{n}$ $16\frac{1}{2}$
22. $\frac{3}{5} = \frac{30}{n}$ 50

23. $\frac{3}{7} = \frac{12}{n}$ 28
24. $\frac{11}{6} = \frac{n}{12}$ 22
25. $\frac{n}{21} = \frac{11}{7}$ 33
26. $\frac{9}{n} = \frac{3}{4}$ 12
27. $\frac{8}{6} = \frac{2}{n}$ $1\frac{1}{2}$

Change to a fraction, whole number, or mixed number in simplest form. *(page 248)*

28. 10% $\frac{1}{10}$
29. 20% $\frac{1}{5}$
30. 25% $\frac{1}{4}$
31. 40% $\frac{2}{5}$
32. 50% $\frac{1}{2}$
33. 95% $\frac{19}{20}$

34. 80% $\frac{4}{5}$
35. 125% $1\frac{1}{4}$
36. 175% $1\frac{3}{4}$
37. 150% $1\frac{1}{2}$
38. 100% 1
39. 55% $\frac{11}{20}$

40. $12\frac{1}{2}$% $\frac{1}{8}$
41. $33\frac{1}{3}$% $\frac{1}{3}$
42. $37\frac{1}{2}$% $\frac{3}{8}$
43. $87\frac{1}{2}$% $\frac{7}{8}$
44. $166\frac{2}{3}$% $1\frac{2}{3}$
45. $66\frac{2}{3}$% $\frac{2}{3}$

Solve. *(page 258)*

46. 10% of 40 = n 4
47. 25% of 36 = n 9
48. 125% of 44 = n 55

49. 9% of 79 = n 7.11
50. 8.5% of 23 = n 1.955
51. 12.4% of 144 = n 17.8

52. 37.5% of 15.4 = n 5.775
53. 0.5% of 140 = n 0.7
54. 0.08% of 300 = n 0.24

55. $33\frac{1}{3}$% of 78 = n 26
56. $16\frac{2}{3}$% of 84 = n 14
57. $66\frac{2}{3}$% of 141 = n 94

Solve. *(page 260)*

58. 20% of n = 19 95
59. 25% of n = 23 92
60. 50% of n = 37 74

61. 8% of n = 24 300
62. 12% of n = 84 700
63. 40% of n = 28 70

64. 75% of n = 51 68
65. 125% of n = 75 60
66. 150% of n = 81 54

Solve. Round each answer to the nearest tenth. *(page 260)*

67. 18% of n = 37 205.6
68. 21% of n = 45 214.3
69. 35% of n = 29 82.9

70. 42% of n = 53 126.2
71. 12% of n = 25 208.3
72. 15% of n = 41 273.3

Problem solving

COMPUTERS AND PHOTOGRAPHY

Look at the two photographs. The top photograph was altered to produce the bottom photograph. This "trick" photography was performed by an image processor, a special machine that uses a large computer.

The computer divides the photograph into tiny squares called pixels. (If you take a close look at a television screen, you can see large pixels that make up a TV image.) Each of the pixels in the photograph is given a number. The numbers can then be rearranged to create a new photograph.

Use the two photographs to answer these questions.

1. Can you find seven ways that the bottom photograph differs from the top photograph? (*Hint: Look at each building identified by a letter.*)

2. What is the area of the original photograph? Give the answer to the nearest square inch. 9 in.²

3. There are more than 100,000 pixels in each square inch of the photograph. Does the photograph have more or less than 1 million pixels? Less

4. To change each square inch of the photograph, the computer used 360,000 bytes (parts) of its memory.
   a. How many bytes of the computer's memory were used to change the entire photograph? 3,240,000
   b. How many bytes of the computer's memory would be used to change an 8-inch by 10-inch photograph? 28,800,000

EXTRA PROBLEM SOLVING
Page 459   Even exercises

PROBLEM-SOLVING WORKSHEET
Copymaster S310 or Duplicating Master S310

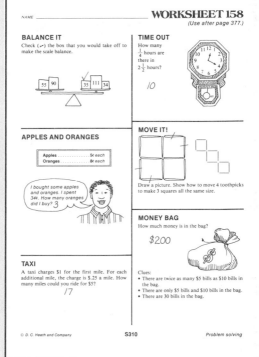

CHALKBOARD CHALLENGE
Find the missing number.

START ⁻6 → Add ⁺4 → Multiply by ⁻10 → Subtract ? (⁺10) → Divide by ⁻2 → END ⁻5

Answers for page 377.
1. a. Building A—Horizontal grids added
   b. Building B—Water tank removed
   c. Building C—Removed
   d. Building D—Removed
   e. Building E—Windows added
   f. Building F—Right tower removed
   g. Building F—Antenna moved from right to left tower

< or >? *(page 362)*

1. $^+7$ ⊘ $^+3$ 2. $^-4$ ⊘ $^+3$ 3. $^-5$ ⊘ $^-2$
4. $^+2$ ⊘ $^-8$ 5. 0 ⊘ $^-12$ 6. $^+16$ ⊘ 0
7. $^-15$ ⊘ $^-20$

Give each sum. *(page 364)*

8. $^+3 + ^+6 = +9$ 9. $^+3 + ^-6 = -3$
10. $^-3 + ^+6 = +3$ 11. $^-3 + ^-6 = -9$
12. $^+10 + ^+8 = +18$ 13. $^+10 + ^-8 = +2$
14. $^-10 + ^+8 = -2$ 15. $^-10 + ^-8 = -18$
16. $0 + ^-14 = -14$

Give each difference. *(pages 366, 367)*

17. $^+7 - ^+2 = +5$ 18. $^+7 - ^-2 = +9$
19. $^-7 - ^+2 = -9$ 20. $^-7 - ^-2 = -5$
21. $^+5 - ^+12 = -7$ 22. $^+5 - ^-12 = +17$
23. $^-5 - ^+12 = -17$ 24. $^-5 - ^-12 = +7$
25. $0 - ^-13 = +13$

ANSWERS
1. >
2. <
3. <
4. >
5. >
6. >
7. >
8. +9
9. -3
10. +3
11. -9
12. +18
13. +2
14. -2
15. -18
16. -14
17. +5
18. +9
19. -9
20. -5
21. -7
22. +17
23. -17
24. +7
25. +13

© D. C. Heath and Company   S61   Page 1

Give each product. *(pages 370, 371)*

26. $^+4 \times ^+6 = +24$ 27. $^+4 \times ^-6 = -24$
28. $^-4 \times ^+6 = -24$ 29. $^-4 \times ^-6 = +24$
30. $^+8 \times ^+5 = +40$ 31. $^+8 \times ^-5 = -40$
32. $^-8 \times ^+5 = -40$ 33. $^-8 \times ^-5 = +40$
34. $0 \times ^-6 = 0$

Give each quotient. *(page 372)*

35. $^+18 \div ^+6 = +3$ 36. $^+18 \div ^-6 = -3$
37. $^-18 \div ^+6 = -3$ 38. $^-18 \div ^-6 = +3$
39. $^+24 \div ^+3 = +8$ 40. $^+24 \div ^-3 = -8$
41. $^-24 \div ^+3 = -8$ 42. $^-24 \div ^-3 = +8$
43. $0 \div ^+10 = 0$

Give the ordered pair for each point. *(page 374)*

44. A $(^+3, ^+2)$
45. B $(^-3, ^+3)$
46. C $(^-4, ^-6)$
47. D $(^+3, ^-4)$
48. E $(^+1, 0)$
49. F $(0, ^+5)$
50. G $(0, ^-3)$

ANSWERS
26. +24
27. -24
28. -24
29. +24
30. +40
31. -40
32. -40
33. +40
34. 0
35. +3
36. -3
37. -3
38. +3
39. +8
40. -8
41. -8
42. +8
43. 0
44. (+3,+2)
45. (-3,+3)
46. (-4,-6)
47. (+3,-4)
48. (+1,0)
49. (0,+5)
50. (0,-3)

© D. C. Heath and Company   S62   Page 2

Chapter REVIEW

Here are scrambled answers for the review exercises:

$^-3$	$^+3$	different	less	opposite	right
$^-1$	$^+4$	down	negative	origin	same
0	add	greater	nonzero	positive	

1. As you move to the ☐ on this number line, the numbers get larger. *(page 362)*

2. The number line shows that negative 3 is ☐ than positive one. *(page 362)*

3. The number line also shows that zero is ☐ than negative two. *(page 362)*

4. The picture shows that $^-2 + ^+1 = $ ☐.
If the sum of two numbers is 0, then one number is the ☐ of the other.
The opposite of $^+3$ is ☐. *(page 364)*

5. The picture shows that $^+2 - ^-1 = $ ☐.
To subtract an integer, you ☐ the opposite of the integer. *(pages 366, 367)*

6. The picture shows that $^-2 \times ^-2 = $ ☐. *(page 370)*

$^-2 + ^+1$ $^+2 - ^-1$ $^-2 \times ^-2$

7. The product of two integers with the same signs is ☐.
The product of two integers with different signs is ☐.
The product of any integer and 0 is ☐. *(page 371)*

8. The quotient of two integers with the ☐ signs is positive.
The quotient of two integers with ☐ signs is negative.
The quotient of 0 divided by any ☐ integer is 0. *(page 372)*

9. To graph the ordered pair $(^+3, ^-2)$ you would start at the ☐ and go 3 units to the right $(^+3)$. Then you would go 2 units ☐ $(^-2)$. *(page 374)*

1. right   2. less   3. greater   4. $^-1$, opposite, $^-3$
5. $^+3$, add   6. $^+4$ 7. positive, negative, 0
8. same, different, nonzero   9. origin, down

Chapter TEST

< or >? *(page 362)*

1. $^+4$ ● $^+5$ <   2. $^+3$ ● $^-6$ >   3. $^-6$ ● $^+2$ <   4. $^-8$ ● $^-1$ <   5. $^-6$ ● $^+3$ <

6. $^+20$ ● $^-23$ >   7. $^-25$ ● $^-22$ <   8. $^-26$ ● $^+21$ <   9. $^+24$ ● $^-24$ >   10. $^-2$ ● 0 <

Give each sum. *(page 364)*

11. $^+6 + ^+2$ $_{+8}$ 12. $^+6 + ^-2$ $_{+4}$ 13. $0 + ^-2$ $_{-2}$ 14. $^-4 + ^-8$ $_{-12}$ 15. $^-4 + ^+8$ $_{+4}$

16. $^-5 + 0$ $_{-5}$ 17. $0 + ^+7$ $_{+7}$ 18. $0 + 0$ $_0$ 19. $^-9 + ^+9$ $_0$ 20. $^-9 + ^-9$ $_{-18}$

21. $^-7 + ^-10$ $_{-17}$ 22. $^+12 + ^-12$ $_0$ 23. $^+15 + ^+11$ $_{+26}$ 24. $^-18 + ^+16$ $_{-2}$ 25. $^-18 + ^-16$ $_{-34}$

Give each difference. *(pages 366, 367)*

26. $^+4 - ^+2$ $_{+2}$ 27. $^+4 - ^-2$ $_{+6}$ 28. $^-5 - ^+8$ $_{-13}$ 29. $^+5 - ^+8$ $_{-3}$ 30. $^-8 - 0$ $_{-8}$

31. $^+9 - 0$ $_{+9}$ 32. $0 - ^-7$ $_{+7}$ 33. $0 - 0$ $_0$ 34. $^+7 - ^-7$ $_{+14}$ 35. $^-6 - ^-3$ $_{-3}$

36. $^-12 - ^+10$ $_{-22}$ 37. $^-13 - ^-13$ $_0$ 38. $^+18 - ^-11$ $_{+29}$ 39. $^+15 - ^+19$ $_{-4}$ 40. $^+21 - ^-3$ $_{+24}$

Give each product. *(pages 370, 371)*

41. $^+3 \times ^+5$ $_{+15}$ 42. $^+3 \times ^-5$ $_{-15}$ 43. $^-7 \times ^-4$ $_{+28}$ 44. $^+7 \times ^+4$ $_{+28}$ 45. $^+7 \times ^-1$ $_{-7}$

46. $^-9 \times 0$ $_0$ 47. $0 \times ^+7$ $_0$ 48. 0×0 $_0$ 49. $^+6 \times ^-7$ $_{-42}$ 50. $^-4 \times ^-3$ $_{+12}$

51. $^-11 \times ^+8$ $_{-88}$ 52. $^-12 \times ^-12$ $_{+144}$ 53. $^+15 \times ^-6$ $_{-90}$ 54. $^+16 \times ^+10$ $_{+160}$ 55. $^-21 \times ^+10$ $_{-210}$

Give each quotient. *(page 372)*

56. $^+12 \div ^+3$ $_{+4}$ 57. $^+12 \div ^-3$ $_{-4}$ 58. $^-12 \div ^+3$ $_{-4}$ 59. $^+8 \div ^+1$ $_{+8}$ 60. $^+16 \div ^+2$ $_{+8}$

61. $^-16 \div ^+2$ $_{-8}$ 62. $0 \div ^-8$ $_0$ 63. $^-20 \div ^+5$ $_{-4}$ 64. $^+24 \div ^-6$ $_{-4}$ 65. $^-12 \div ^+6$ $_{-2}$

66. $^-32 \div ^-4$ $_{+8}$ 67. $^-36 \div ^+9$ $_{-4}$ 68. $^+45 \div ^+5$ $_{+9}$ 69. $^+54 \div ^-9$ $_{-6}$ 70. $^-63 \div ^-9$ $_{+7}$

Give the ordered pair for each point. *(page 374)*

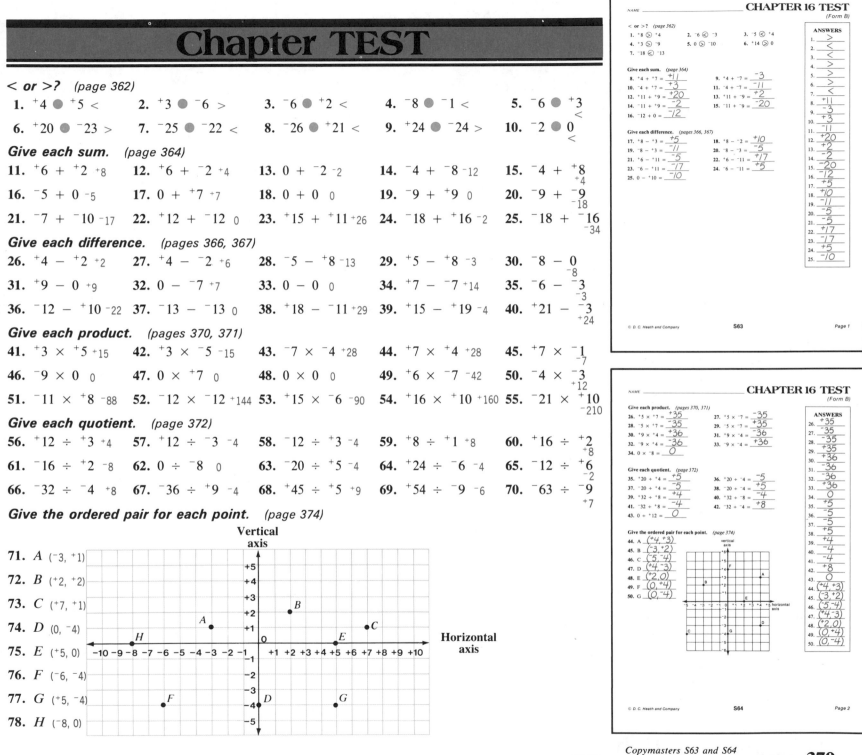

71. A $(^-3, ^+1)$

72. B $(^+2, ^+2)$

73. C $(^+7, ^+1)$

74. D $(0, ^-4)$

75. E $(^+5, 0)$

76. F $(^-6, ^-4)$

77. G $(^+5, ^-4)$

78. H $(^-8, 0)$

CHAPTER 16 TEST
(Form B)

NAME _____

< or >? *(page 362)*

1. $^+8$ ⊘ $^+4$ 2. $^-6$ ⊘ $^-3$ 3. $^-5$ ⊘ $^+4$
4. $^+3$ ⊘ $^-9$ 5. 0 ⊘ $^-10$ 6. $^+14$ ⊘ 0
7. $^-18$ ⊘ $^-13$

ANSWERS
1. >
2. <
3. <
4. >
5. >
6. >
7. <

Give each sum. *(page 364)*

8. $^+4 + ^+7 = $ +11   9. $^+4 + ^-7 = $ -3
10. $^-4 + ^+7 = $ +3   11. $^-4 + ^-7 = $ -11
12. $^+11 + ^+9 = $ +20   13. $^+11 + ^-9 = $ +2
14. $^-11 + ^+9 = $ -2   15. $^-11 + ^-9 = $ -20
16. $^-12 + 0 = $ -12

8. +11
9. -3
10. +3
11. -11
12. +20
13. +2
14. -2
15. -20
16. -12

Give each difference. *(pages 366, 367)*

17. $^+8 - ^+3 = $ +5   18. $^+8 - ^-3 = $ +10
19. $^-8 - ^+3 = $ -11   20. $^-8 - ^-3 = $ -5
21. $^+6 - ^+11 = $ -5   22. $^+6 - ^-11 = $ +17
23. $^-6 - ^+11 = $ -17   24. $^-6 - ^-11 = $ +5
25. $0 - ^+10 = $ -10

17. +5
18. +10
19. -11
20. -5
21. -5
22. +17
23. -17
24. +5
25. -10

© D. C. Heath and Company   S63   Page 1

CHAPTER 16 TEST
(Form B)

NAME _____

Give each product. *(pages 370, 371)*

26. $^+5 \times ^+7 = $ +35   27. $^+5 \times ^-7 = $ -35
28. $^-5 \times ^+7 = $ -35   29. $^-5 \times ^-7 = $ +35
30. $^+9 \times ^+4 = $ +36   31. $^+9 \times ^-4 = $ -36
32. $^-9 \times ^+4 = $ -36   33. $^-9 \times ^-4 = $ +36
34. $0 \times ^-8 = $ 0

Give each quotient. *(page 372)*

35. $^+20 \div ^+4 = $ +5   36. $^+20 \div ^-4 = $ -5
37. $^-20 \div ^+4 = $ -5   38. $^-20 \div ^-4 = $ +5
39. $^+32 \div ^+8 = $ +4   40. $^+32 \div ^-8 = $ -4
41. $^-32 \div ^+8 = $ -4   42. $^-32 \div ^-4 = $ +8
43. $0 \div ^+12 = $ 0

Give the ordered pair for each point. *(page 374)*

44. A $(^+4, ^+3)$
45. B $(^-3, ^+2)$
46. C $(^-5, ^-4)$
47. D $(^+4, ^-3)$
48. E $(^+2, 0)$
49. F $(0, ^+4)$
50. G $(0, ^-4)$

ANSWERS
26. +35
27. -35
28. -35
29. +35
30. +36
31. -36
32. -36
33. +36
34. 0
35. +5
36. -5
37. -5
38. +5
39. +4
40. -4
41. -4
42. +8
43. 0
44. $(^+4, ^+3)$
45. $(^-3, ^+2)$
46. $(^-5, ^-4)$
47. $(^+4, ^-3)$
48. $(^+2, 0)$
49. $(0, ^+4)$
50. $(0, ^-4)$

© D. C. Heath and Company   S64   Page 2

Use Copymaster S336 to provide the students with an answer sheet in standardized test format.

Cumulative TEST Standardized Format

Choose the correct letter.

Answers for Cumulative Test, Chapters 1–16

1. Ⓐ Ⓑ Ⓒ ●	2. Ⓐ ● Ⓒ Ⓓ	3. Ⓐ ● Ⓒ Ⓓ
4. Ⓐ Ⓑ ● Ⓓ	5. ● Ⓑ Ⓒ Ⓓ	6. Ⓐ ● Ⓒ Ⓓ
7. Ⓐ Ⓑ ● Ⓓ	8. Ⓐ Ⓑ Ⓒ ●	9. Ⓐ ● Ⓒ Ⓓ
10. ● Ⓑ Ⓒ Ⓓ	11. Ⓐ Ⓑ ● Ⓓ	12. Ⓐ Ⓑ ● Ⓓ

The table below correlates test items with student text pages.

Test Item	Page Taught	Skill Practice
1	68	p. 368, exercises 1–12
2	92	p. 368, exercises 13–24
3	146	p. 368, exercises 25–45
4	160	p. 368, exercises 46–57
5	182	p. 368, exercises 58–69
6	202	p. 376, exercises 1–12
7	230	p. 376, exercises 13–27
8	248	p. 376, exercises 28–45
9	258	p. 376, exercises 46–57
10	260	p. 376, exercises 58–66
11	324	
12	366	

1. Give the product.

2.408×100

A. 24.08
B. 0.02408
C. 2408
Ⓓ none of these

2. Give the quotient.

$78.95 \div 1000$

A. 78950
B. 0.7895
Ⓒ 0.07895
D. none of these

3. Change to a decimal rounded to the nearest hundredth.

$\frac{5}{6} = ?$

A. 0.17
Ⓑ 0.83
C. 0.67
D. none of these

4. Add. $3\frac{1}{2}$
$+2\frac{2}{3}$

A. $5\frac{3}{5}$ B. $5\frac{1}{6}$
Ⓒ $6\frac{1}{6}$ D. none of these

5. Give the product.

$2\frac{2}{3} \times 1\frac{3}{4}$

Ⓐ $4\frac{2}{3}$ B. $\frac{21}{32}$
C. $1\frac{11}{32}$ D. none of these

6. 345 cm = _?_ m

A. 34.5
Ⓑ 3.45
C. 345
D. none of these

7. Solve.

$\frac{n}{3} = \frac{11}{4}$

A. 3.5
B. 14.7
Ⓒ 8.25
D. none of these

8. Change to a fraction.

$37\frac{1}{2}\% = ?$

A. $\frac{1}{3}$
B. $\frac{5}{8}$
C. $\frac{2}{5}$
Ⓓ none of these

9. Solve.

25% of $24.5 = n$

A. 98
Ⓑ 6.125
C. 61.25
D. none of these

10. Solve.

40% of $n = 36$

Ⓐ 90
B. 14.4
C. 9.0
D. none of these

11. Find the surface area.

3 ft
4 ft
6 ft

A. 54 ft²   B. 72 ft²
Ⓒ 108 ft²   D. none of these

12. Give the difference.

$^{+}12 - {}^{-}10$

A. $^{+}2$
B. $^{-}2$
Ⓒ $^{+}22$
D. none of these

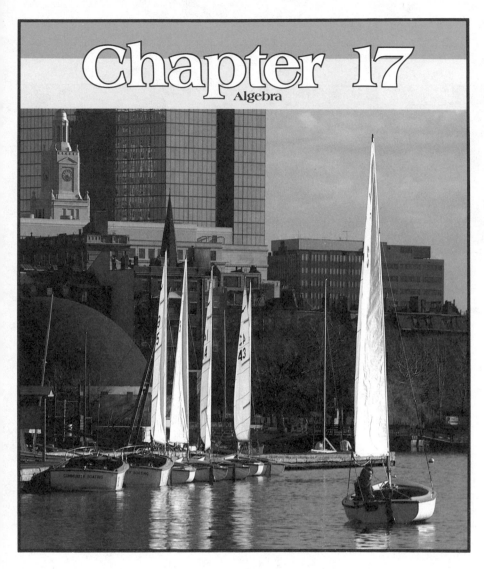

Chapter 17
Algebra

CHAPTER 17
Algebra

LESSON OBJECTIVES

PROBLEM-SOLVING SKILLS

RESOURCES

- **VISUAL AIDS**
  Balance scale   (*Visual Aid 56, Copymaster S152*)
- **WORKSHEETS 159–167**   (*Copymasters S311–S319 or Dupli-
  cating Masters S311–S319*)

LESSON OBJECTIVE
To write algebraic expressions for word phrases

PROBLEM-SOLVING SKILL
Interpreting and checking information

STARTING THE LESSON
Have the students read the age clues at the top of the page. Ask them who is the oldest (Craig) and who is the youngest (Chris). Then go over the phrases for the expressions on page 382.

Writing expressions

I'm **n** years old.

If you're **n** years old, then I'm **n + 2** years old.

I'm **n ÷ 2** years old.

I'm **2n** years old.

I'm **n − 2** years old.

Ann David Chris Craig Beth

Who's the oldest? Who's the youngest?

The letter **n** is a variable. It represents Ann's age in years.

Variables, numbers, and operation signs can be combined to form **mathematical expressions.** Look at the cards below. First a mathematical expression is given in red. Then several different word expressions are given for the mathematical expression.

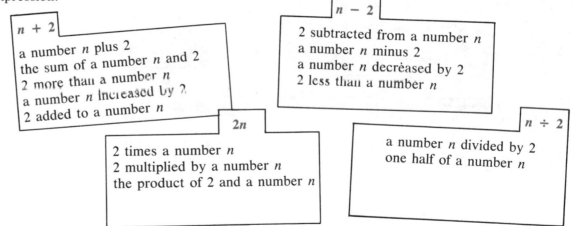

n + 2

a number n plus 2
the sum of a number n and 2
2 more than a number n
a number n increased by 2
2 added to a number n

n − 2

2 subtracted from a number n
a number n minus 2
a number n decreased by 2
2 less than a number n

2n

2 times a number n
2 multiplied by a number n
the product of 2 and a number n

n ÷ 2

a number n divided by 2
one half of a number n

Other examples:

Word Expression		Mathematical Expression
a number s increased by 6	⟶	$s + 6$
9 less than a number h	⟶	$h - 9$
4 times a number d	⟶	$4d$
one third of a number r	⟶	$r \div 3$ or $\frac{r}{3}$ or $\frac{1}{3}r$
5 times a number x, plus 4	⟶	$5x + 4$

EXERCISES

Write a mathematical expression for each word expression.

1. 5 more than a number n $n + 5$

2. 10 more than a number r $r + 10$

3. 11 times a number t $11t$

4. a number x minus 6 $x - 6$

5. the sum of a number y and 4 $y + 4$

6. a number b divided by 4 $b \div 4$ $(\frac{b}{4}, \frac{1}{4}b)$

7. 15 times a number c $15c$

8. a number t decreased by 4 $t - 4$

9. a number d increased by 6 $d + 6$

10. 15 less than a number x $x - 15$

11. 40 divided by a number s $40 \div s$ $(\frac{40}{s}, \frac{1}{40}s)$

12. the product of 2 and a number n $2n$

13. 3 times a number m, plus 2 $3m + 2$

14. 4 times a number c, minus 6 $4c - 6$

15. 6 multiplied by a number r, plus 8 $6r + 8$

16. a number e divided by 5, minus 3 $(e \div 5) - 3$ $(\frac{e}{5} - 3, \frac{1}{5}e - 3)$

Let n be the number of letters you wrote last year. Write a mathematical expression for the number of letters that is

17. 2 more than your number of letters. $n + 2$

18. 5 letters less than your number of letters. $n - 5$

19. one third the number of your letters. $\frac{1}{3}n$

20. your number of letters decreased by 8. $n - 8$

21. one fourth the number of your letters. $\frac{1}{4}n$

22. 4 less than your number of letters. $n - 4$

23. your number of letters increased by 3 letters. $n + 3$

24. your number of letters divided by 9. $n \div 9$ $(\frac{1}{9}n, \frac{n}{9})$

25. 4 times the number of your letters, plus 5 more letters. $4n + 5$

26. 3 times the number of your letters, plus 2 more letters. $3n + 2$

Who is it?

27. One of these people is not telling his/her true age. Who is it?   Beth
    Hint: Use the clues at the top of page 382.

I'm 22 years old.   I'm 24 years old.   I'm 11 years old.   I'm 44 years old.   I'm 18 years old.

Ann   David   Chris   Craig   Beth

REVIEW PRACTICE
Adding fractions
Page 431   Skill 40

PRACTICE WORKSHEET
Copymaster S311 or Duplicating Master S311

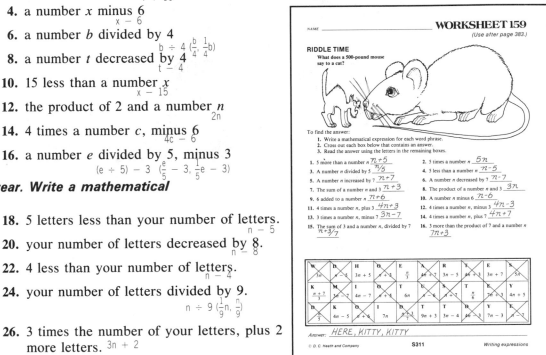

NAME _____   **WORKSHEET 159**
(Use after page 383.)

RIDDLE TIME
What does a 500-pound mouse
say to a cat?

To find the answer:
1. Write a mathematical expression for each word phrase.
2. Cross out each box below that contains an answer.
3. Read the answer using the letters in the remaining boxes.

1. 5 more than a number n $n + 5$
2. 5 times a number n $5n$
3. A number n divided by 5 $n/5$
4. 5 less than a number n $n - 5$
5. A number n increased by 7 $n + 7$
6. A number n decreased by 7 $n - 7$
7. The sum of a number n and 3 $n + 3$
8. The product of a number n and 3 $3n$
9. 6 added to a number n $n + 6$
10. A number n minus 6 $n - 6$
11. 4 times a number n, plus 3 $4n + 3$
12. 4 times a number n, minus 3 $4n - 3$
13. 3 times a number n, minus 7 $3n - 7$
14. 4 times a number n, plus 7 $4n + 7$
15. The sum of 3 and a number n, divided by 7 $n + 3/7$
16. 3 more than the product of 7 and a number n $7n + 3$

Answer: *HERE, KITTY, KITTY*

© D. C. Heath and Company   S311   Writing expressions

CHALKBOARD CHALLENGE
Follow the instructions for this number trick.

   Pick any number.
   Add 5.
   Multiply by 2.
   Subtract 4.
   Divide by 2.
   Subtract the number you picked.

Your answer is always 3.

CHALKBOARD QUIZ
on previous lesson

Write a mathematical expression for each word expression.

1. 3 more than a number n $n + 3$
2. a number n decreased by 10 $n - 10$
3. the product of a number n and 7 $7n$
4. the sum of a number n and 5 $n + 5$
5. a number n divided by 3, minus 2 $n \div 3 - 2$

LESSON OBJECTIVE
To substitute numbers for variables and then evaluate the resulting expression

PROBLEM-SOLVING SKILLS
Finding information in a display
Comparing prices
Choosing the correct operation

STARTING THE LESSON
Before going over exercises 1–4 and the *Here's how*, ask the students which rental plan they would choose if they planned to rent a car for 3 days and drive it 500 miles.

EXERCISE NOTE
Point out to the students that from now on in the textbook the raised plus sign for positive numbers will be omitted.

Evaluating expressions

WHAT DO YOU THINK?

Which is the cheapest plan?

JIFFY CAR RENTAL		
Plan A $.30 per mile	**Plan B** $40 per day	**Plan C** $10 per day plus $.20 per mile

1. Let d be the number of days and m be the number of miles. Which rental plan would cost $10d + .20m$ dollars? C

2. Which plan would cost $.30m$ dollars? A

3. What expression would you use for the cost of Plan B? 40d

Here's how *to evaluate mathematical expressions.*

What will it cost to rent a car for 3 days? I plan to drive it 500 miles.

To find the cost (in dollars) for each plan, substitute 3 for d and/or 500 for m in the expression and simplify.

Plan A. $.30m$
$.30 \times 500 = 150$ So Plan A would cost $150.

Plan B. $40d$
$40 \times 3 = 120$ So Plan B would cost $120.

Plan C. $10d + .20m$
$10 \times 3 + .20 \times 500$
$30 + 100 = 130$ So Plan C would cost $130.

4. Look at the *Here's how*. Which is the cheapest plan for renting a car for 3 days and 500 miles? B

EXERCISES

Evaluate each expression for n = 12.
Here are scrambled answers for the next row of exercises: 47 31 38 22 6

5. $n + 10$ 22   **6.** $3n - 5$ 31   **7.** $4n - 1$ 47   **8.** $n \div 2$ 6   **9.** $3n + 2$ 38

> From now on, let's agree not to write the raised plus sign when writing a positive number.

10. $2n + 1$ 25   **11.** $4 + n$ 16   **12.** $n - 11$ 1   **13.** $n + 12$ 24

14. $8n$ 96   **15.** $2n - 20$ 4   **16.** $n \div 12$ 1   **17.** $12n + 6$ 150

Evaluate each expression for r = 6 and s = 5.
Here are scrambled answers for the next row of exercises: 28 27 30 11 1

18. $r + s$ 11   **19.** $r - s$ 1   **20.** rs $\boxed{r \times s}$ 30   **21.** $2r + 3s$ 27   **22.** $rs - 2$ 28

23. $3r$ 18   **24.** $4s$ 20   **25.** $r \div 3$ 2   **26.** $\dfrac{10}{s}$ 2   **27.** $\dfrac{15}{s}$ 3

28. $r + s + 5$ 16   **29.** $2rs$ 60   **30.** $3r - 2s$ 8   **31.** $12s - r$ 54   **32.** $14r - 3$ 81

Evaluate each expression for a = 10 and b = ⁻2.
Here are scrambled answers for the next row of exercises: ⁻6 8 ⁻20 28 12

33. $a + b$ 8   **34.** ab ⁻20   **35.** $3a + b$ 28   **36.** $3b$ ⁻6   **37.** $a - b$ 12

38. $4a$ 40   **39.** $5a + 10$ 60   **40.** $b + a$ 8   **41.** $\dfrac{20}{a}$ 2   **42.** $ab - 5$ ⁻25

43. $10 \div b$ ⁻5   **44.** $ab + 20$ 0   **45.** $4a + 2b$ 36   **46.** $3ab$ ⁻60   **47.** $4ab - 8$ ⁻88

Solve. Use the car rental plans on page 384.

48. Using Plan A, how much would it cost to rent a car for 600 miles? $180

49. Using Plan B, how much would it cost to rent a car for 6 days? $240

50. Using Plan C, how much would it cost to rent a car for 4 days and drive it 1000 miles? $240

51. You want to rent a car for 5 days and drive it 2000 miles. Which is the cheapest plan for you? Plan B

Name the rental plan

52. Which rental plan did I use? It cost me $80 to rent a car for 2 days and 100 miles. Plan B

53. Which rental plan did I use? I paid $100 to rent a car for 4 days. I drove it 300 miles. Plan C

REVIEW PRACTICE
Subtracting fractions
Page 433   Skill 43

PRACTICE WORKSHEET
Copymaster S312 or Duplicating Master S312

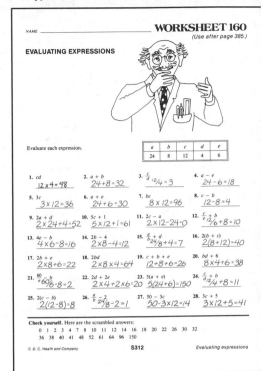

LIFE-SKILL PROJECT
Using a formula
The formula below gives the distance, *d*, that a car traveling 50 miles per hour would go in a certain time, *t*.

$$d = 50t$$

Have the students use the formula to find how far a car would go in these times:

1. 3 hours   150 miles
2. 2.5 hours   125 miles
3. 0.4 hour   20 miles
4. 2 days driving 7 hours each day   700 miles

LESSON OBJECTIVE
To solve addition equations

PROBLEM-SOLVING SKILL
Using equations to solve problems

STARTING THE LESSON
Use questions 1 and 2 and the *Here's how* to introduce solving addition equations by subtracting the same number from both sides. The balance-scale model is on **Visual Aid 56**.

Go over the examples in exercise 3 on the chalkboard to show the students the steps that they are expected to use. Be sure the students understand that they are learning a method that they will later use to solve more difficult equations. It is important for them to show their work.

Solving addition equations

A BALANCING ACT!

Each of the marbles weighs the same.

1. The marbles in the red box plus the 4 extra marbles weigh the same as how many marbles? 150

If we let m be the number of marbles in the red box, we can write the equation

$$m + 4 = 150$$

To **solve the equation** is to find the number that we can substitute for m to make the equation true.

Here's how *to solve an addition equation.*

Equation:	$m + 4 = 150$
Subtract 4 from both sides of the equation:	$m + 4 - 4 = 150 - 4$
Simplify both sides:	$m = 146$

Check the solution by substituting
146 for m in the equation $m + 4 = 150$: $146 + 4 = 150$ It checks!

2. Look at the *Here's how*. To find m, what number was subtracted from both sides of the equation? How many marbles are in the red box? 4, 146

3. Check these examples. Has each equation been solved correctly? Yes

a. $a + 7 = 20$
$a + 7 - 7 = 20 - 7$
$a = 13$

b. $b + 8 = 2$
$b + 8 - 8 = 2 - 8$
$b = {}^{-}6$

c. $c + 10 = {}^{-}6$
$c + 10 - 10 = {}^{-}6 - 10$
$c = {}^{-}16$

EXERCISES

Solve and check.
Here are scrambled answers for the next 2 rows of exercises:

2   13   ⁻14   25   ⁻1   22   ⁻10   ⁻21

4. $n + 16 = 38$ _22_

Hint: Subtract 16 from both sides.

5. $r + 10 = ⁻4$ _⁻14_

Hint: Subtract 10 from both sides.

6. $x + ⁻8 = 5$ _13_

Hint: Subtract ⁻8 from both sides.

7. $t + ⁻2 = ⁻3$ _⁻1_

Hint: Subtract ⁻2 from both sides.

8. $n + 28 = 30$ _2_
9. $y + ⁻20 = 5$ _25_
10. $x + ⁻15 = ⁻25$ _⁻10_
11. $z + 13 = ⁻8$ _⁻21_

12. $m + 9 = 19$ _10_
13. $r + ⁻6 = ⁻4$ _2_
14. $w + 7 = ⁻9$ _⁻16_
15. $m + 4 = 26$ _22_

16. $y + ⁻5 = ⁻1$ _4_
17. $d + ⁻15 = ⁻10$ _5_
18. $x + 18 = 25$ _7_
19. $y + ⁻5 = ⁻8$ _⁻3_

20. $27 + x = 68$ _41_
21. $42 + p = 40$ _⁻2_
22. $19 + s = 11$ _⁻8_
23. $g + 8 = ⁻7$ _⁻15_

24. $x + 4 = ⁻6$ _⁻10_
25. $m + ⁻11 = 40$ _51_
26. $t + 5 = ⁻7$ _⁻12_
27. $h + ⁻3 = ⁻3$ _0_

28. $g + ⁻8 = ⁻10$ _⁻2_
29. $s + ⁻3 = ⁻4$ _⁻1_
30. $r + 15 = ⁻50$ _⁻65_
31. $b + 4 = 10$ _6_

32. $m + ⁻8 = 50$ _58_
33. $x + 16 = 14$ _⁻2_
34. $g + ⁻20 = ⁻21$ _⁻1_
35. $n + 6 = 6$ _0_

36. $t + 97 = 80$ _⁻17_
37. $c + 46 = 58$ _12_
38. $x + 24 = 24$ _0_
39. $f + 21 = ⁻2$ _⁻23_

40. $a + 62 = 75$ _13_
41. $y + ⁻10 = ⁻10$ _0_
42. $k + 3 = ⁻32$ _⁻35_
43. $c + ⁻4 = 5$ _9_

44. $r + 15 = ⁻25$ _⁻40_
45. $k + 20 = 0$ _⁻20_
46. $c + ⁻46 = 0$ _46_
47. $p + 5 = ⁻8$ _⁻13_

48. $x + 16 = 9$ _⁻7_
49. $f + 17 = 17$ _0_
50. $d + ⁻18 = 4$ _22_
51. $k + 4 = 4$ _0_

52. $t + 12 = 15$ _3_
53. $r + ⁻9 = ⁻10$ _⁻1_
54. $6 + k = ⁻5$ _⁻11_
55. $a + 18 = ⁻15$ _⁻33_

56. $d + 0 = 9$ _9_
57. $w + 7 = 23$ _16_
58. $n + ⁻4 = ⁻9$ _⁻5_
59. $t + ⁻14 = 7$ _21_

60. $m + 6 = ⁻8$ _⁻14_
61. $q + ⁻9 = ⁻1$ _8_
62. $b + ⁻32 = 0$ _32_
63. $e + 10 = 3$ _⁻7_

64. $v + ⁻15 = 7$ _22_
65. $n + 18 = 18$ _0_
66. $s + 8 = ⁻2$ _⁻10_
67. $r + ⁻2 = ⁻21$ _⁻19_

68. $a + 24 = 0$ _⁻24_
69. $s + 9 = ⁻17$ _⁻26_
70. $p + 14 = ⁻5$ _⁻19_
71. $m + ⁻8 = 2$ _10_

72. $w + ⁻3 = ⁻9$ _⁻6_
73. $6 + y = ⁻2$ _⁻8_
74. $y + ⁻10 = 10$ _20_
75. $s + 14 = ⁻13$ _⁻27_

76. $t + 5 = 1$ _⁻4_
77. $c + 0 = ⁻7$ _⁻7_
78. $k + ⁻1 = 6$ _7_
79. $⁻20 + d = ⁻1$ _19_

REVIEW PRACTICE
Multiplying fractions
Page 434   Skill 46

PRACTICE WORKSHEET
Copymaster S313 or Duplicating Master S313

WORKSHEET 161
(Use after page 387.)

NAME _____

SKILL DRILL
Study these examples.

$n + 27 = 52$	$n + 83 = 80$
$n + 27 - 27 = 52 - 27$ ⟵ Subtract 27.	$n + 83 - 83 = 80 - 83$
$n = 25$ ⟵ Simplify.	$n = ⁻3$
Check: $25 + 27 = 52$	Check: $⁻3 + 83 = 80$

Solve and check.

1. $n + 39 = 60$
$n = 21$
$21 + 39 = 60$

2. $n + 51 = 60$
$n = 9$
$9 + 51 = 60$

3. $n + 47 = 60$
$n = 13$
$13 + 47 = 60$

4. $n + 28 = 53$
$n = 25$
$25 + 28 = 53$

5. $n + 52 = 97$
$n = 45$
$45 + 52 = 97$

6. $n + 45 = 74$
$n = 29$
$29 + 45 = 74$

7. $n + 53 = 105$
$n = 52$
$52 + 53 = 105$

8. $n + 38 = 95$
$n = 57$
$57 + 38 = 95$

9. $n + 29 = 52$
$n = 23$
$23 + 29 = 52$

10. $n + 26 = 103$
$n = 77$
$77 + 26 = 103$

11. $n + 18 = 0$
$n = ⁻18$
$⁻18 + 18 = 0$

12. $n + 59 = 60$
$n = 1$
$1 + 59 = 60$

13. $n + 38 = 38$
$n = 0$
$0 + 38 = 38$

14. $n + 43 = 91$
$n = 48$
$48 + 43 = 91$

15. $n + 48 = 8$
$n = ⁻40$
$⁻40 + 48 = 8$

16. $n + 92 = 108$
$n = 16$
$16 + 92 = 108$

17. $n + 70 = 102$
$n = 32$
$32 + 70 = 102$

18. $n + 47 = 40$
$n = ⁻7$
$⁻7 + 47 = 40$

Check yourself. Here are the scrambled answers:
⁻40 ⁻18 ⁻7 0 1 9 13 16 21 23 25 29 32 45 48 52
57 77

© D. C. Heath and Company   S313   Solving addition equations

CHALKBOARD CHALLENGE
Have the students see how many addition equations they can write that have a solution of 10. Here are some examples:
$$n + 9 = 19$$
$$n + 3\tfrac{1}{2} = 13\tfrac{1}{2}$$

Balance it!

Find the weight n that is needed to make each scale balance.

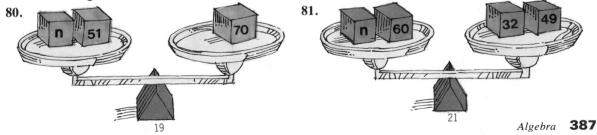

80. n 51 / 70 (19)

81. n 60 / 32 49 (21)

LESSON OBJECTIVE
To solve subtraction equations

PROBLEM-SOLVING SKILL
Choosing the correct equation

STARTING THE LESSON
Discuss questions 1–3, using the sale ad and the *Here's how* example. Then go over the examples in exercise 4. Be sure the students understand the technique of adding the same number to both sides of the equation.

Solving subtraction equations

1. What is the sale price of the cross-country ski package? $109

2. Is the regular price of the ski package more or less than $109? More

If we let r be the regular price (in dollars), we can write the equation

$$r - 55 = 109$$

and solve the equation to find the regular price.

X-COUNTRY SKI PACKAGE

$55 OFF THE REGULAR PRICE

NOW $109

Here's how *to solve a subtraction equation.*

Equation:	$r - 55 = 109$
Add 55 to both sides of the equation:	$r - 55 + 55 = 109 + 55$
Simplify both sides:	$r = 164$
Check:	$164 - 55 = 109$ It checks!

3. Look at the *Here's how*. To find r, what number was added to both sides of the equation? What is the regular price of the ski package? 55, $164

4. Check these examples. Has each equation been solved correctly? Yes

a. $a - 5 = 12$
$a - 5 + 5 = 12 + 5$
$a = 17$

b. $b - 6 = ⁻2$
$b - 6 + 6 = ⁻2 + 6$
$b = 4$

c. $c - ⁻4 = ⁻1$
$c - ⁻4 + ⁻4 = ⁻1 + ⁻4$
$c = ⁻5$

EXERCISES

Solve and check. *Here are scrambled answers for the next two rows of exercises:* 3 ⁻1 ⁻5 40 37 70 41 63

5. $n - 15 = 25$ 40

Hint: Add 15 to both sides.

6. $r - 46 = {}^-5$ 41

Hint: Add 46 to both sides.

7. $n - 10 = 60$ 70

Hint: Add 10 to both sides.

8. $p - {}^-3 = 6$ 3

Hint: Add ⁻3 to both sides.

9. $s - 19 = 18$ 37

10. $g - 5 = {}^-6$ ⁻1

11. $b - 35 = {}^-40$ ⁻5

12. $n - 25 = 38$ 63

13. $m - 23 = 49$ 72

14. $n - 42 = 76$ 118

15. $a - 65 = 61$ 126

16. $r - 24 = {}^-8$ 16

17. $x - 6 = 2$ 8

18. $d - 9 = {}^-1$ 8

19. $y - 20 = 7$ 27

20. $k - 125 = 0$ 125

21. $x - 18 = {}^-2$ 16

22. $b - 33 = 33$ 66

23. $s - 5 = {}^-5$ 0

24. $n - 2 = 5$ 7

25. $c - 61 = 62$ 123

26. $x - 2 = {}^-8$ ⁻6

27. $y - 17 = 20$ 37

28. $t - 14 = 2$ 16

29. $y - 17 = 14$ 31

30. $b - 3 = {}^-4$ ⁻1

31. $y - 20 = 1$ 21

32. $n - 4 = {}^-1$ 3

33. $p - 8 = {}^-3$ 5

34. $m - 8 = {}^-2$ 6

35. $t - 1 = 5$ 6

36. $x - 45 = 54$ 99

37. $c - {}^-7 = {}^-3$ ⁻10

38. $m - 100 = 0$ 100

39. $a - {}^-2 = 9$ 7

40. $y - 6 = {}^-11$ ⁻5

41. $c - {}^-4 = 10$ 6

42. $x - 12 = 6$ 18

43. $e - {}^-9 = 0$ 9

44. $t - 16 = {}^-8$ 8

45. $n - {}^-7 = 16$ 9

46. $z - 5 = 4$ 9

47. $d - {}^-8 = 0$ ⁻8

48. $w - 6 = 20$ 26

You decide!

Decide whether Equation A or B would be used to solve each problem. Then solve the problem.

| Equation A: | $n + 15 = 66$ |
| Equation B: | $n - 15 = 66$ |

49. *$15 off the regular price is $66. What is the regular price?* B, $81

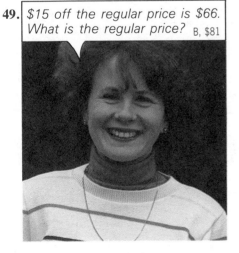

50. $15 more than the sale price is $66. What is the sale price? A, $51

51. The regular price decreased by $15 is $66. What is the regular price? B, $81

52. The sum of the sale price and a $15 discount is $66. What is the sale price? A, $51

53. Sarah gave her brother $15. She then had $66. How much money did Sarah have before she gave her brother the money? B, $81

54. James got paid $15. He then had $66. How much money did he have before he got paid? A, $51

REVIEW PRACTICE
Dividing fractions
Page 436   Skill 50

PRACTICE WORKSHEET
Copymaster S314 or Duplicating Master S314

NAME _____   **WORKSHEET 162**
(Use after page 389.)

RIDDLE TIME
Why is noon like the letter A?

To find the answer:
1. Solve each question.
2. Write its letter under its matching number in the DECODER.

1. $n - 15 = 38$	2. $n - 23 = 49$	3. $n - 71 = 90$	4. $n - 65 = 61$
$n - 15 + 15 = 38 + 15$	$n = 72$	$n = 161$	$n = 126$
$n = 53$ R	L	T	E
5. $n - 36 = 28$	6. $n - 62 = 55$	7. $n - 62 = 41$	8. $n - 33 = 26$
$n = 64$ I	$n = 117$ D	$n = 103$ F	$n = 59$ H
9. $n - 28 = 45$	10. $n - 15 = 69$	11. $n - 58 = 19$	12. $n - 30 = 53$
$n = 73$ E	$n = 84$ Y	$n = 77$ T	$n = 83$ O
13. $n - 39 = 61$	14. $n - 120 = 44$	15. $n - 27 = 23$	16. $n - 15 = 25$
$n = 100$ N	$n = 164$ E	$n = 50$ H	$n = 40$ I
17. $n - 42 = 112$	18. $n - 39 = 67$	19. $n - 53 = 42$	20. $n - 72 = 19$
$n = 154$ O	$n = 106$ D	$n = 95$ A	$n = 91$ B
21. $n - 31 = 27$	22. $n - 44 = 3$	23. $n - 100 = 1$	
$n = 58$ M	$n = 47$ D	$n = 101$ A	

| DECODER |
| 91 83 161 50   95 53 73   40 100   77 59 126 |
| B O T H   A R E   I N   T H E |
| 58 64 106 117 72 164 • 154 103   47 101 84 |
| M I D D L E   O F   D A Y . |

© D. C. Heath and Company   **S314**   Solving subtraction equations

LIFE-SKILL PROJECT
Writing and solving equations
Give the students a riddle such as this: "I am thinking of a number. If I subtract 7 from it, I get 2. What is the number?" Have the students write an equation and then solve it. Next, let the students make up equation riddles for others to solve.

SKILLS REVIEWED
Multiplying and dividing decimals
Adding and subtracting fractions
Multiplying fractions

PROBLEM-SOLVING SKILLS
Choosing the correct operations
Solving a multi-step problem

STARTING THE LESSON
Cumulative Skill Practice
Challenge the students to an estimation hunt by saying, "Find the six products in exercises 1–20 that are greater than 100." (Exercises 5, 10, 14, 15, 16, and 18) Then have the students find the two quotients in exercises 21–40 that are greater than 100. (Exercises 23 and 26)

STARTING THE LESSON
Problem Solving
Do exercises 1–4 on page 391 with the class. Assign the other exercises for independent work.

Cumulative Skill Practice

Give the product. *(page 64)*

1. 6.2×0.5 3.10
2. 8.4×0.61 5.124
3. 0.72×0.4 0.288
4. 6.2×0.83 5.1
5. 32×5.3 169.6
6. 0.79×5.3 4.187
7. 2.05×1.7 3.485
8. 3.01×1.5 4.51
9. 9.46×8 75.68
10. 47.1×6.2 292.02
11. 47.9×0.38 18.202
12. 48.6×0.11 5.3
13. 5.78×13 75.14
14. 33.4×4.7 156.98
15. 309×1.5 463.5
16. 403×1.8 725.
17. 2.09×0.03 0.0627
18. 35.3×20.5 723.65
19. 9.36×2.04 19.0944
20. 2.98×0.05 0.

Give the quotient rounded to the nearest tenth. *(page 96)*

21. $19.3 \div 0.9$ 21.4
22. $5.47 \div 0.2$ 27.4
23. $8.09 \div 0.03$ 269.7
24. $8.65 \div 0.2$ 43.
25. $15.7 \div 0.5$ 31.4
26. $8.43 \div 0.07$ 120.4
27. $5.405 \div 0.08$ 67.6
28. $3.09 \div 0.04$ 77.
29. $8.41 \div 1.7$ 4.9
30. $3.047 \div 2.9$ 1.1
31. $5.09 \div 0.35$ 14.5
32. $4.65 \div 0.21$ 22.
33. $15.085 \div 0.33$ 45.7
34. $8.001 \div 0.27$ 29.6
35. $5.05 \div 7.4$ 0.7
36. $5.006 \div 0.12$ 4
37. $5.92 \div 3.8$ 1.6
38. $7.397 \div 8.1$ 0.9
39. $38 \div 7.3$ 5.2
40. $46 \div 8.12$ 5.7

Give the sum in simplest form. *(page 158)*

41. $\frac{1}{2} + \frac{1}{4}$ $\frac{3}{4}$
42. $\frac{1}{4} + \frac{5}{8}$ $\frac{7}{8}$
43. $\frac{1}{5} + \frac{3}{10}$ $\frac{1}{2}$
44. $\frac{2}{3} + \frac{1}{3}$ 1
45. $\frac{1}{3} + \frac{2}{5}$ $\frac{11}{15}$
46. $\frac{3}{7} + \frac{4}{7}$
47. $\frac{1}{2} + \frac{5}{8}$ $1\frac{1}{8}$
48. $\frac{7}{8} + \frac{3}{5}$ $1\frac{19}{40}$
49. $\frac{1}{2} + \frac{3}{8}$ $\frac{7}{8}$
50. $\frac{7}{8} + 0$ $\frac{7}{8}$
51. $\frac{6}{11} + \frac{3}{11}$ $\frac{9}{11}$
52. $\frac{3}{5} + \frac{1}{2}$ $1\frac{1}{10}$
53. $\frac{1}{4} + \frac{3}{5}$ $\frac{17}{20}$
54. $\frac{2}{3} + \frac{3}{7}$ $1\frac{2}{21}$
55. $\frac{2}{3} + \frac{5}{6}$ $1\frac{1}{2}$
56. $\frac{2}{5} + \frac{3}{4}$ $1\frac{3}{20}$
57. $\frac{3}{5} + \frac{1}{3}$ $\frac{14}{15}$
58. $\frac{4}{9} + \frac{1}{3}$ $\frac{7}{9}$

Give the difference in simplest form. *(page 166)*

59. $\frac{3}{4} - \frac{1}{4}$ $\frac{1}{2}$
60. $\frac{3}{4} - \frac{1}{8}$ $\frac{5}{8}$
61. $\frac{1}{2} - \frac{1}{3}$ $\frac{1}{6}$
62. $\frac{5}{8} - \frac{1}{2}$ $\frac{1}{8}$
63. $\frac{6}{7} - \frac{1}{2}$ $\frac{5}{14}$
64. $\frac{1}{2} - \frac{1}{4}$ $\frac{1}{4}$
65. $\frac{3}{5} - \frac{1}{4}$ $\frac{7}{20}$
66. $\frac{3}{2} - \frac{2}{3}$ $\frac{5}{6}$
67. $\frac{3}{4} - \frac{1}{2}$ $\frac{1}{4}$
68. $\frac{9}{10} - \frac{1}{5}$ $\frac{7}{10}$
69. $\frac{4}{5} - \frac{1}{10}$ $\frac{7}{10}$
70. $\frac{2}{3} - \frac{1}{9}$ $\frac{5}{9}$
71. $\frac{2}{3} - \frac{5}{8}$ $\frac{1}{24}$
72. $\frac{7}{8} - \frac{3}{4}$ $\frac{1}{8}$
73. $\frac{4}{5} - \frac{3}{8}$ $\frac{17}{40}$
74. $\frac{5}{6} - \frac{1}{3}$ $\frac{1}{2}$
75. $\frac{9}{10} - \frac{1}{2}$ $\frac{2}{5}$
76. $\frac{3}{7} - \frac{1}{14}$ $\frac{5}{14}$

Give the product in simplest form. *(page 178)*

77. $\frac{1}{2} \times \frac{1}{3}$ $\frac{1}{6}$
78. $\frac{1}{2} \times \frac{1}{4}$ $\frac{1}{8}$
79. $\frac{1}{3} \times \frac{3}{5}$ $\frac{1}{5}$
80. $\frac{3}{4} \times \frac{2}{3}$ $\frac{1}{2}$
81. $\frac{2}{3} \times \frac{1}{5}$ $\frac{2}{15}$
82. $\frac{2}{7} \times \frac{1}{2}$ $\frac{1}{7}$
83. $\frac{3}{2} \times \frac{3}{4}$ $1\frac{1}{8}$
84. $\frac{5}{9} \times \frac{3}{8}$ $\frac{5}{24}$
85. $\frac{1}{2} \times \frac{2}{5}$ $\frac{1}{5}$
86. $2 \times \frac{7}{8}$ $1\frac{3}{4}$
87. $3 \times \frac{5}{9}$ $1\frac{2}{3}$
88. $\frac{3}{5} \times \frac{1}{4}$ $\frac{3}{20}$
89. $\frac{5}{2} \times \frac{3}{10}$ $\frac{3}{4}$
90. $\frac{1}{3} \times \frac{3}{8}$ $\frac{1}{8}$
91. $3 \times \frac{3}{4}$ $2\frac{1}{4}$
92. $\frac{1}{6} \times \frac{1}{6}$ $\frac{1}{36}$
93. $\frac{1}{7} \times \frac{1}{7}$ $\frac{1}{49}$
94. $\frac{5}{6} \times \frac{1}{2}$ $\frac{5}{12}$

390

Problem solving

Decide which operation sign (+, −, ×, ÷) should replace the question mark to give the correct equation. Then solve the equation.

1. One long-stemmed rose costs $2. What is the price (*p*) of 12 long-stemmed roses?

    2 ? 12 = *p*   ×, 24

2. Six carnations cost $4.50. What is the price (*p*) of one carnation?

    4.50 ? 6 = *p*   ÷, $.75

3. A dozen strawflowers cost $2.40. What is the price (*p*) of each flower?

    2.40 ? 12 = *p*   ÷, $.20

4. Five tulips cost $1.50. What is the price (*p*) of 3 tulips?

    (1.50 ? 5) ? 3 = *p*   ÷, ×, $.90

5. A customer bought 2 bunches of baby's breath at $.89 per bunch. How much change (*c*) should he get from a $10 bill?

    10 ? (2 ? .89) = *c*   −, ×, $8.22

Solve.

6. Mini carnations are priced at $3.89 per bunch. How much would you pay for 3 bunches of mini carnations? $11.67

7. A bunch of 15 daisies costs $3.45. What is the cost per daisy? $.23

8. A mixed bouquet costs $4.95. What is the cost of 2 mixed bouquets? $9.90

9. A customer bought 4 mixed bouquets at $4.95 each. How much change should she get from a $20 bill? $.20

10. Three dozen daffodils cost $9.60. What is the cost of 4 dozen daffodils? $12.80

11. Gladioli are selling at 3 for $2.37. How much would you expect to pay for 5 gladioli? $3.95

12. Marcia bought 3 dozen chrysanthemums at $10.50 per dozen and some fern for $1.25. How much did she spend in all? $32.75

13. Marty paid $3.30 for some sweetheart roses. If 3 sweetheart roses cost $1.65, how many did Marty buy? 6

Algebra **391**

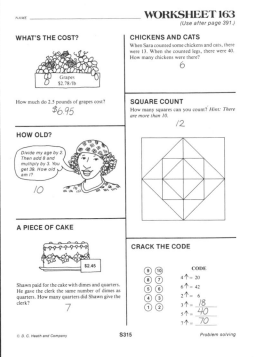

EXTRA PROBLEM SOLVING
Page 460   Odd exercises

PROBLEM-SOLVING WORKSHEET
Copymaster S315 or Duplicating Master S315

CHALKBOARD CHALLENGE

Unscramble the letters of these algebra words.

1. OSEXEPRSIN   Expression
2. TAVELUAE   Evaluate
3. IUQEATNO   Equation
4. TUSBTSIUTE   Substitute

Solve.
1. A customer bought 3 bunches of daisies at $2.29 per bunch. How much change should she get back from a $10 bill? $3.13
2. Roses are selling at 6 for $9. How much would you expect to pay for 4 roses? $6

LESSON OBJECTIVE
To solve multiplication equations

PROBLEM-SOLVING SKILL
Choosing the correct equation

STARTING THE LESSON
Discuss questions 1 and 2, using the balance-scale model and the *Here's how*. The balance-scale model is on **Visual Aid 56**. Go over the examples in exercise 3 before assigning the exercises on page 393.

Solving multiplication equations
ANOTHER BALANCING ACT!

Each box contains the same number of marbles.
1. Three times the number of marbles in 1 box weighs the same as how many marbles? 12

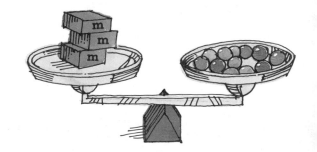

If we let m be the number of marbles in each box, we can write the equation

$$3m = 12$$

Here's how *to solve a multiplication equation.*

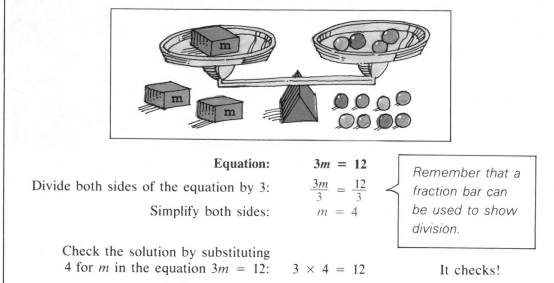

Equation:	$3m = 12$	
Divide both sides of the equation by 3:	$\dfrac{3m}{3} = \dfrac{12}{3}$	*Remember that a fraction bar can be used to show division.*
Simplify both sides:	$m = 4$	

Check the solution by substituting 4 for m in the equation $3m = 12$: $3 \times 4 = 12$ It checks!

2. Look at the *Here's how*. To find m, both sides of the equation were divided by what number? How many marbles are in each box? 3, 4

3. Check these examples. Has each equation been solved correctly? Yes

a. $5a = 60$
$$\frac{5a}{5} = \frac{60}{5}$$
$$a = 12$$

b. $3b = {}^-30$
$$\frac{3b}{3} = \frac{{}^-30}{3}$$
$$b = {}^-10$$

c. ${}^-2c = 14$
$$\frac{{}^-2c}{{}^-2} = \frac{14}{{}^-2}$$
$$c = {}^-7$$

EXERCISES

Solve and check.

Here are scrambled answers for the next row of exercises: ⁻7 5 6 ⁻3

4. $4n = 24$ 6

5. $⁻5t = 35$ ⁻7

6. $2r = ⁻6$ ⁻3

7. $⁻3x = ⁻15$
       5

| Hint: Divide both sides by 4. | Hint: Divide both sides by ⁻5. | Hint: Divide both sides by 2. | Hint: Divide both sides by ⁻3. |

8. $9n = 27$ 3

9. $⁻7n = 14$ ⁻2

10. $5s = 55$ 11

11. $3y = ⁻21$
        ⁻7

12. $4t = 48$ 12

13. $8w = 120$ 15

14. $⁻6n = 42$ ⁻7

15. $⁻2r = ⁻22$
        11

16. $9a = 108$ 12

17. $12n = 240$ 20

18. $⁻3x = 15$ ⁻5

19. $9y = ⁻27$
        ⁻3

20. $⁻2x = 6$ ⁻3

21. $30t = 30$ 1

22. $7x = ⁻21$ ⁻3

23. $⁻15a = 30$
        ⁻2

24. $⁻4s = 40$ ⁻10

25. $3s = 57$ 19

26. $6c = 66$ 11

27. $11n = 88$
        8

28. $⁻4c = ⁻40$ 10

29. $8n = ⁻16$ ⁻2

30. $⁻2x = ⁻2$ 1

31. $7n = 7$
        1

32. $⁻3b = ⁻33$ 11

33. $9y = 189$ 21

34. $25t = 100$ 4

35. $20n = ⁻60$
        ⁻3

36. $7h = ⁻77$ ⁻11

37. $⁻5s = ⁻5$ 1

38. $15t = 30$ 2

39. $25a = 0$
        0

40. $⁻15x = ⁻15$ 1

41. $12y = 132$ 11

42. $⁻20a = ⁻100$ 5

43. $25c = 175$
        7

44. $10w = 130$ 13

45. $⁻16r = 0$ 0

46. $14x = ⁻154$ ⁻11

47. $⁻9w = 270$
        ⁻30

48. $⁻8b = 168$ ⁻21

49. $11v = 165$ 15

50. $7r = ⁻84$ ⁻12

51. $⁻16n = 224$
        ⁻14

52. $30t = ⁻210$ ⁻7

53. $⁻15y = ⁻330$ 22

54. $32k = 0$ 0

55. $⁻24w = ⁻192$
        8

56. $⁻17x = 153$ ⁻9

57. $16c = ⁻272$ ⁻17

58. $15y = 15$ 1

59. $⁻26s = 0$
        0

You decide!

Decide whether Equation A, B, or C could be used to solve each problem. Then solve the problem.

| Equation A: $s + .99 = 1.65$ |
| Equation B: $3s = 5.28$ |
| Equation C: $2s = 1.14$ |

60. What is the price of a box of cereal? Clue: 3 boxes of cereal would cost $5.28. $1.76

61. What is the price of a can of soup? Clue: A can of soup and a jar of pickles cost a total of $1.65. A, $.66

62. What is the price of a can of juice? Clue: 2 cans of juice cost $.15 more than a jar of pickles. C, $.57

REVIEW PRACTICE
Solving Proportions
Page 437   Skill 52

PRACTICE WORKSHEET
Copymaster S316 or Duplicating Master S316

NAME _____

WORKSHEET 164
(Use after page 393.)

SKILL DRILL
Study these examples.

| $4n = 84$ | | $⁻5n = 60$ |
| $\frac{4n}{4} = \frac{84}{4}$ ◁ Divide by 4. ▷ $\frac{⁻5n}{⁻5} = \frac{60}{⁻5}$ |
| $n = 21$ Simplify. $n = ⁻12$ |
| Check: $4 \times 21 = 84$ Check: $⁻5 \times ⁻12 = 60$ |

Solve and check.

1. $8n = 120$
   $n = 15$
   $8 \times 15 = 120$

2. $7n = 91$
   $n = 13$
   $7 \times 13 = 91$

3. $9n = 108$
   $n = 12$
   $9 \times 12 = 108$

4. $3n = 51$
   $n = 17$
   $3 \times 17 = 51$

5. $6n = 84$
   $n = 14$
   $6 \times 14 = 84$

6. $5n = 135$
   $n = 27$
   $5 \times 27 = 135$

7. $⁻7n = 56$
   $n = ⁻8$
   $⁻7 \times ⁻8 = 56$

8. $8n = 88$
   $n = 11$
   $8 \times 11 = 88$

9. $6n = 180$
   $n = 30$
   $6 \times 30 = 180$

10. $4n = 76$
   $n = 19$
   $4 \times 19 = 76$

11. $⁻3n = 18$
   $n = ⁻6$
   $⁻3 \times ⁻6 = 18$

12. $5n = 245$
   $n = 49$
   $5 \times 49 = 245$

13. $15n = ⁻30$
   $n = ⁻2$
   $15 \times ⁻2 = ⁻30$

14. $4n = 228$
   $n = 57$
   $4 \times 57 = 228$

15. $8n = 0$
   $n = 0$
   $8 \times 0 = 0$

16. $3n = 84$
   $n = 28$
   $3 \times 28 = 84$

17. $⁻5n = 5$
   $n = ⁻1$
   $⁻5 \times ⁻1 = 5$

18. $9n = 198$
   $n = 22$
   $9 \times 22 = 198$

Check yourself. Here are the scrambled answers:
⁻8 ⁻6 ⁻2 ⁻1 0 11 12 13 14 15 17 19 22 27 28 30
49 57

© D. C. Heath and Company   **S316**   Solving multiplication equations

CHALKBOARD CHALLENGE

Write an equation. Solve your equation and check your solution.

1. n multiplied by 4 is 44. $4n = 44$
                                  $n = 11$

2. n increased by 15 is 9. $n + 15 = 9$
                                  $n = ⁻6$

3. n decreased by 8 is 2. $n − 8 = 2$
                                 $n = 10$

4. The sum of n and 5 is 1. $n + 5 = 1$
                                   $n = ⁻4$

5. The product of n and 3 is ⁻6. $3n = ⁻6$
                                        $n = ⁻2$

LESSON OBJECTIVE
To solve division equations

PROBLEM-SOLVING SKILL
Choosing the correct equation

STARTING THE LESSON
Discuss questions 1–3, using the travel ad and the *Here's how*. Go over the examples in exercise 4 before assigning the exercises on page 395.

Solving division equations

See your Holiday Travel Agent for your **Florida vacation.**

HAVE YOUR DAY   IN THE SUN

Pay no money now. Use our easy 12-month payment plan. Pay only $80 a month.

1. How many monthly payments are there? 12   **2.** How much is each monthly payment? $80

If we let t be the total cost (in dollars) of the Florida vacation,

we can write the equation $\frac{t}{12} = 80$

Here's how *to solve a division equation.*

Equation:	$\frac{t}{12} = 80$
Multiply both sides by 12:	$12 \times \frac{t}{12} = 12 \times 80$
Simplify both sides:	$t = 960$
Check:	$\frac{960}{12} = 80$ It checks!

3. Look at the *Here's how*. To find t, both sides of the equation were multiplied by what number? What is the total cost of the Florida vacation? 12, $960

4. Check these examples. Has each equation been solved correctly? Yes

a.　　$\frac{a}{4} = 20$

$4 \times \frac{a}{4} = 4 \times 20$

$a = 80$

b.　　$\frac{b}{^-2} = 16$

${}^-2 \times \frac{b}{^-2} = {}^-2 \times 16$

$b = {}^-32$

c.　　$\frac{c}{^-5} = {}^-4$

${}^-5 \times \frac{c}{^-5} = {}^-5 \times {}^-4$

$c = 20$

EXERCISES

Solve and check.
Here are scrambled answers for the next row of exercises: 10 ⁻18 ⁻12 64 35

5. $\dfrac{x}{2} = 32$ 64   **6.** $\dfrac{b}{-3} = 4$ ⁻12   **7.** $\dfrac{n}{6} = {}^-3$ ⁻18   **8.** $\dfrac{n}{-2} = {}^-5$ 10   **9.** $\dfrac{d}{7} = 5$ 35

10. $\dfrac{y}{5} = 3$ 15   **11.** $\dfrac{m}{9} = {}^-3$ ⁻27   **12.** $\dfrac{k}{10} = 15$ 150   **13.** $\dfrac{n}{5} = 12$ 60   **14.** $\dfrac{a}{20} = 2$ 40

15. $\dfrac{h}{15} = 3$ 45   **16.** $\dfrac{c}{-3} = {}^-4$ 12   **17.** $\dfrac{t}{12} = {}^-6$ ⁻72   **18.** $\dfrac{x}{10} = {}^-8$ ⁻80   **19.** $\dfrac{a}{2} = 15$ 30

20. $\dfrac{x}{4} = {}^-9$ ⁻36   **21.** $\dfrac{n}{7} = 9$ 63   **22.** $\dfrac{y}{100} = 5$ 500   **23.** $\dfrac{t}{-8} = {}^-1$ 8   **24.** $\dfrac{n}{50} = 6$ 300

25. $\dfrac{c}{-3} = {}^-40$ 120   **26.** $\dfrac{n}{30} = 4$ 120   **27.** $\dfrac{x}{4} = {}^-7$ ⁻28   **28.** $\dfrac{n}{-8} = {}^-2$ 16   **29.** $\dfrac{x}{4} = {}^-10$ ⁻40

30. $\dfrac{f}{15} = 8$ 120   **31.** $\dfrac{c}{-7} = 1$ ⁻7   **32.** $\dfrac{r}{5} = {}^-25$ ⁻125   **33.** $\dfrac{y}{-5} = {}^-2$ 10   **34.** $\dfrac{a}{4} = 300$ 1200

35. $\dfrac{x}{-9} = {}^-2$ 18   **36.** $\dfrac{b}{50} = 1$ 50   **37.** $\dfrac{a}{-8} = {}^-9$ 72   **38.** $\dfrac{n}{6} = 0$ 0   **39.** $\dfrac{x}{-9} = {}^-11$ 99

40. $\dfrac{t}{4} = {}^-5$ ⁻20   **41.** $\dfrac{r}{3} = 12$ 36   **42.** $\dfrac{b}{-10} = 10$ ⁻100   **43.** $\dfrac{n}{12} = {}^-3$ ⁻36   **44.** $\dfrac{c}{-7} = {}^-15$ 105

45. $\dfrac{k}{9} = 0$ 0   **46.** $\dfrac{y}{-6} = {}^-11$ 66   **47.** $\dfrac{w}{-5} = 20$ ⁻100   **48.** $\dfrac{s}{8} = 21$ 168   **49.** $\dfrac{m}{18} = {}^-13$ ⁻234

You decide!

Decide whether Equation A, B, C, or D could be used to solve each problem. Then solve the problem.

50. *I spent $450 for 5 nights' lodging at the resort. How much was it for 1 night's lodging?* A, $90

Equation A:	$5n = 450$
Equation B:	$\dfrac{n}{5} = 450$
Equation C:	$n + 50 = 450$
Equation D:	$n - 50 = 450$

51. Karen spent $50 more for her trip than Alan did. She spent $450. How much did Alan spend? C, $400

52. After spending $50 at the ski resort, Brian had $450 left. How much money did he have to start with? D, $500

53. A vacation cottage at the ocean rents for $450 a week. How much rent is paid in 5 weeks? B, $2250

REVIEW PRACTICE
Finding a percent of a number
Page 440   Skill 57

PRACTICE WORKSHEET
Copymaster S317 or Duplicating Master S317

NAME _____   **WORKSHEET 165**
(Use after page 395.)

If all the cars in the United States were pink, what would we have?

To find the answer:
1. Solve each equation.
2. Cross out each box below that contains an answer.
3. Read the answer using the letters in the remaining boxes.

1. $\frac{n}{5} = 13$	2. $\frac{n}{8} = 6$	3. $\frac{n}{15} = 3$	4. $\frac{n}{20} = 7$
$5 \times \frac{n}{5} = 13 \times 5$ $n = 65$	$n = 48$	$n = 45$	$n = 140$
5. $\frac{n}{4} = 13$	6. $\frac{n}{7} = 12$	7. $\frac{n}{9} = 11$	8. $\frac{n}{5} = 15$
$n = 52$	$n = 84$	$n = 99$	$n = 75$
9. $\frac{n}{2} = {}^-6$	10. $\frac{n}{7} = 10$	11. $\frac{n}{12} = 12$	12. $\frac{n}{-7} = 3$
$n = {}^-12$	$n = 70$	$n = 144$	$n = {}^-21$
13. $\frac{n}{4} = 25$	14. $\frac{n}{5} = 32$	15. $\frac{n}{3} = {}^-15$	16. $\frac{n}{7} = 0$
$n = 100$	$n = 160$	$n = {}^-45$	$n = 0$
17. $\frac{n}{6} = 30$	18. $\frac{n}{4} = 19$	19. $\frac{n}{14} = 1$	20. $\frac{n}{-3} = {}^-3$
$n = {}^-180$	$n = 76$	$n = 14$	$n = 9$
21. $\frac{n}{25} = 8$	22. $\frac{n}{8} = 12$		
$n = 200$	$n = 96$		

B	M	I	O	S	A	N	T	L	O	L	R	P	C	I	Y	N	C
64	⁻180	21	65	75	36	0	45	70	45	70	19	100	81	76	110	140	
K	L	C	E	A	R	V	N	A	A	T	T	E	I	A	V	O	N
64	12	16	200	⁻20	130	44	8	9	49	160	21	52	14	52	⁻10	144	64	50

Answer: ___A PINK CARNATION___

© D. C. Heath and Company   **S317**   *Solving division equations*

LIFE-SKILL PROJECT

Using a calculator
Have the students use a calculator to solve these equations.

1. $465n = 2418$ 5.2

2. $\dfrac{n}{7.8} = 23.5$ 183.3

3. $n + 9.12 = 275.6$ 266.48

4. $4.6n = 33.35$ 7.25

5. $n - 0.265 = 31.28$ 31.545

Let the students write equations for others to solve with a calculator.

LESSON OBJECTIVE
To solve two-step equations

PROBLEM-SOLVING SKILL
Choosing the correct equation

STARTING THE LESSON
Have the students read the ad at the top of the page. Go over the *Here's how* and then discuss questions 1 and 2. Work through exercise 3 with the class. Be sure that the students understand the steps in each of the examples.

Solving two-step equations

To find the number of reprints he can get for $20, solve this two-step equation:

cost of
1 reprint

$$\underset{\substack{\uparrow \\ \text{number} \\ \text{of} \\ \text{reprints}}}{3r} \quad + \quad \underset{\substack{\uparrow \\ \text{handling} \\ \text{charge}}}{2} \quad = \quad \underset{\substack{\uparrow \\ \text{total} \\ \text{cost}}}{20}$$

How many reprints can I get for $20?

SPECIAL DEAL

8″ × 10″
Color Reprints

$3 each plus
$2 handling charge

Here's how *to solve a two-step equation.*

To solve the equation, get an equation with only the variable r on one side of the equal sign.

Equation: $3r + 2 = 20$

First subtract 2 from both sides: $3r + 2 - 2 = 20 - 2$

Then divide both sides by 3: $\frac{3r}{3} = \frac{18}{3}$

$$r = 6$$

Check: $3 \times 6 + 2 = 20$ It checks!

1. Look at the *Here's how*. To find r, first subtract ⬚?⬚ from both sides of the equation and then divide both sides by ⬚?⬚. 2, 3

2. Check the solution. How many reprints can be bought for $20? $6

3. Check these examples. Has each two-step equation been solved correctly? Yes

a. $2a + 4 = 26$
$2a + 4 - 4 = 26 - 4$
$2a = 22$
$\frac{2a}{2} = \frac{22}{2}$
$a = 11$

b. $4b - 3 = 21$
$4b - 3 + 3 = 21 + 3$
$4b = 24$
$\frac{4b}{4} = \frac{24}{4}$
$b = 6$

c. $\frac{c}{2} + 7 = 18$
$\frac{c}{2} + 7 - 7 = 18 - 7$
$\frac{c}{2} = 11$
$2 \times \frac{c}{2} = 2 \times 11$
$c = 22$

EXERCISES

Copy and finish solving each equation. Check your solution.

4. $2y + 8 = 14$

$2y + 8 - 8 = 14 - ?$ 8

$2y = ?$ 6

$y = ?$ 3

5. $5t - 7 = 28$

$5t - 7 + 7 = 28 + ?$ 7

$5t = ?$ 35

$t = ?$ 7

6. $\frac{n}{3} + 6 = 12$

$\frac{n}{3} + 6 - 6 = 12 - ?$ 6

$\frac{n}{3} = ?$ 6

$n = ?$ 18

Solve and check.
Here are scrambled answers for the next two rows of exercises: 17   9   4   11   5   2   6   7

7. $4x + 3 = 27$ 6

8. $2n + 5 = 39$ 17

9. $4t + 8 = 28$ 5

10. $3m - 2 = 25$ 9

11. $6y - 4 = 20$ 4

12. $6k - 3 = 39$ 7

13. $2y + 10 = 32$ 11

14. $8y - 2 = 14$ 2

15. $6a + 4 = 28$ 4

16. $3y - 5 = 7$ 4

17. $5t + 7 = 52$ 9

18. $5c - 2 = 33$ 7

19. $\frac{m}{3} + 7 = 9$ 6

20. $\frac{n}{2} + 2 = 5$ 6

21. $\frac{t}{7} + 4 = 6$ 14

22. $\frac{d}{3} - 4 = 5$ 27

23. $\frac{n}{3} + 20 = 21$ 3

24. $5n + {}^-3 = 7$ 2

25. $\frac{t}{6} - 9 = {}^-3$ 36

26. $6a - 12 = 30$ 7

27. $\frac{c}{{}^-3} + 7 = {}^-8$ 45

28. ${}^-7x + 4 = 32$ ⁻4

29. $\frac{y}{{}^-4} - {}^-2 = 10$ ⁻32

30. $9a - 4 = 23$ 3

31. $\frac{d}{9} + 9 = 0$ ⁻81

32. $8r + {}^-5 = 11$ 2

33. ${}^-10y + 6 = {}^-14$ 2

34. $\frac{s}{{}^-7} - 3 = 8$ ⁻77

35. ${}^-4x + 8 = 0$ 2

36. $\frac{n}{{}^-4} + {}^-6 = 1$ ⁻28

37. $12s - {}^-3 = {}^-9$ ⁻1

38. $\frac{n}{7} + {}^-5 = 0$ 35

Mystery numbers

Decide whether Equation A, B, C, or D would be used to solve each problem. Then solve the problem.

39. I'm thinking of a number. If I multiply it by 6 and then subtract 3, I get 33. What's my number?   B, 6

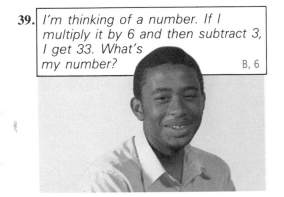

Equation A:	$6y + 3 = 33$
Equation B:	$6y - 3 = 33$
Equation C:	$\frac{y}{6} + 3 = 33$
Equation D:	$\frac{y}{6} - 3 = 33$

40. If you multiply a number by 6 and then add 3, you get 33. What is the number?   A, 5

41. A number divided by 6 and then decreased by 3 is 33. What is the number?   D, 216

42. If you divide a number by 6 and then add 3, you get 33. What is the number?   C, 180

REVIEW PRACTICE
Finding a percent of a number
Page 440   Skill 58

PRACTICE WORKSHEET
Copymaster S318 or Duplicating Master S318

NAME _____   **WORKSHEET 166**
(Use after page 397.)

SKILL DRILL
Solve.

1. $6n + 8 = 50$
$6n + 8 - 8 = 50 - 8$
$6n = 42$
$\frac{6n}{6} = 42$
$n = 7$

2. $12n - 4 = 68$ $n = 6$

3. $5n + 15 = 60$ $n = 9$

4. $9n - 16 = 92$ $n = 12$

5. $3n + 13 = 46$ $n = 11$

6. $7n + 5 = 110$ $n = 15$

7. $13n + 14 = 40$ $n = 2$

8. $4n - 30 = 46$ $n = 19$

9. $15n + 15 = 30$ $n = 1$

10. $\frac{n}{4} + 11 = 31$
$\frac{n}{4} + 11 - 11 = 31 - 11$
$\frac{n}{4} = 20$
$4 \times \frac{n}{4} = 20 \times 4$
$n = 80$

11. $\frac{n}{3} - 5 = 2$ $n = 21$

12. $\frac{n}{2} - 8 = 7$ $n = 30$

13. $\frac{n}{3} + 16 = 33$ $n = 51$

14. $\frac{n}{5} + 6 = 13$ $n = 35$

15. $\frac{n}{2} - 8 = 6$ $n = 28$

16. $\frac{n}{5} + 2 = 10$ $n = 40$

17. $\frac{n}{7} - 3 = 8$ $n = 77$

18. $\frac{n}{4} - 3 = 2$ $n = 20$

Check yourself. Here are the scrambled answers:
1   2   6   7   9   11   12   15   19   20   21   28   30   35   40   51   77   80

© D. C. Heath and Company   S318   Solving two-step equations

LIFE-SKILL PROJECT
Writing and solving equations
Have the students write true equations—
for example,

$$4 \times 9 - 7 = 29$$

Then have them erase one of the numbers and replace it with a letter. For example, from the equation above they might write one of these equations:

$$4n - 7 = 29 \qquad 4 \times 9 - n = 29$$

Ask them to solve each other's equations.

SKILLS REVIEWED

Solving percent problems
Computing simple interest
Adding integers

PROBLEM-SOLVING SKILLS

Following computer commands
Making a geometric visualization

STARTING THE LESSON

Cumulative Skill Practice
Write these four answers on the chalkboard: 12   180 $31.50   ⁻13
Challenge the students to an answer hunt by saying, "Look for the four even-numbered exercises on page 398 that have these answers. You have five minutes to find as many as you can." (Exercises 20, 34, 52, and 62)

STARTING THE LESSON

Problem Solving
Give each of the students a piece of graph paper and have them follow these directions: "Put your pencil on a point in the middle of your paper. Turn your pencil to the left. Go forward 1 unit. Make a 90° turn to the right. Go forward 4 units. Make a 90° turn to the right. Go forward 4 units. Make a 90° turn to the right. Go forward 1 unit." Then have the students each compare their drawings with the drawing in Screen E on page 399.

Have the students read the information at the top of the page and answer these questions:
• What computer language is being described? (Logo)
• What is the triangular printer called? (The "turtle")
• What angle did the turtle rotate in Screen 6? (45°)

Cumulative Skill Practice

Give the quotient in simplest form. *(page 188)*

1. $\frac{1}{2} \div \frac{1}{4}$ 2
2. $\frac{1}{6} \div \frac{1}{2}$ $\frac{1}{3}$
3. $\frac{3}{5} \div \frac{3}{2}$ $\frac{2}{5}$
4. $\frac{3}{4} \div \frac{2}{3}$ $1\frac{1}{8}$
5. $\frac{2}{3} \div 2$ $\frac{1}{3}$
6. $\frac{4}{5} \div \frac{1}{2}$ $1\frac{3}{5}$

7. $\frac{3}{5} \div \frac{3}{8}$ $1\frac{3}{5}$
8. $0 \div \frac{2}{3}$ 0
9. $\frac{9}{10} \div \frac{4}{5}$ $1\frac{1}{8}$
10. $\frac{5}{8} \div 2$ $\frac{5}{16}$
11. $\frac{2}{5} \div 5$ $\frac{2}{25}$
12. $4 \div \frac{1}{8}$ 32

13. $2 \div \frac{7}{8}$ $2\frac{2}{7}$
14. $\frac{9}{10} \div \frac{3}{2}$ $\frac{3}{5}$
15. $3 \div \frac{3}{4}$ 4
16. $\frac{5}{4} \div \frac{5}{2}$ $\frac{1}{2}$
17. $\frac{5}{6} \div \frac{1}{3}$ $2\frac{1}{2}$
18. $\frac{3}{7} \div \frac{6}{7}$ $\frac{1}{2}$

Solve. *(page 258)*

19. 10% of 70 = n 7
20. 25% of 48 = n 12
21. 40% of 65 = n 26

22. 14% of 58 = n 8.12
23. 8% of 36.5 = n 2.92
24. 125% of 52 = n 65

25. 6.5% of 147 = n 9.555
26. 13.2% of 60 = n 7.92
27. 22.6% of 34.7 = n 7.8422

28. $16\frac{2}{3}$% of 78 = n 13
29. $66\frac{2}{3}$% of 81 = n 54
30. $62\frac{1}{2}$% of 120 = n 75

31. 16.4% of 8.2 = n 1.3448
32. 9.6% of 59.3 = n 5.6928
33. 8.9% of 238.3 = n 21.2087

Solve. *(page 260)*

34. 10% of n = 18 180
35. 20% of n = 20 100
36. 25% of n = 16 64

37. 50% of n = 26 52
38. 75% of n = 60 80
39. 150% of n = 90 60

40. 6% of n = 21 350
41. 60% of n = 51 85
42. 15% of n = 30 200

Solve. Round each number to the nearest tenth. *(page 260)*

43. 3.5% of n = 8 228.6
44. 8.4% of n = 10 119.0
45. 6.2% of n = 11 177.4

46. 9.5% of n = 12 126.3
47. 32.4% of n = 12.4 38.3
48. 16.8% of n = 9.7 57.7

Compute the interest. *(page 284)*

49. Principal = $1000 $480
Rate = 12% per year
Time = 4 years

50. Principal = $900 $45
Rate = 15% per year
Time = 4 months

51. Principal = $150 $6.75
Rate = 1.5% per month
Time = 3 months

52. Principal = $450 $31.50
Rate = 1% per month
Time = 7 months

53. Principal = $800 $84
Rate = 14% per year
Time = 9 months

54. Principal = $500 $101.25
Rate = 13.5% per year
Time = 18 months

Give the sum. *(page 364)*

55. ⁺4 + ⁺6 ⁺10
56. ⁺4 + ⁻6 ⁻2
57. ⁻4 + ⁺6 ⁺2
58. ⁻4 + ⁻6 ⁻10
59. ⁻6 + 0 ⁻6

60. 0 + ⁺9 ⁺9
61. 0 + ⁻9 ⁻9
62. ⁻6 + ⁻7 ⁻13
63. 0 + 0 0
64. ⁻7 + ⁺7 0

Problem solving

LOGO—A COMPUTER LANGUAGE

Logo is a popular **computer language** that allows students to use a computer as a tool in learning, playing, and exploring. Many students learn Logo by starting with "turtle graphics." The "turtle" is a small triangular printer on the computer screen that responds to commands. Study these examples.

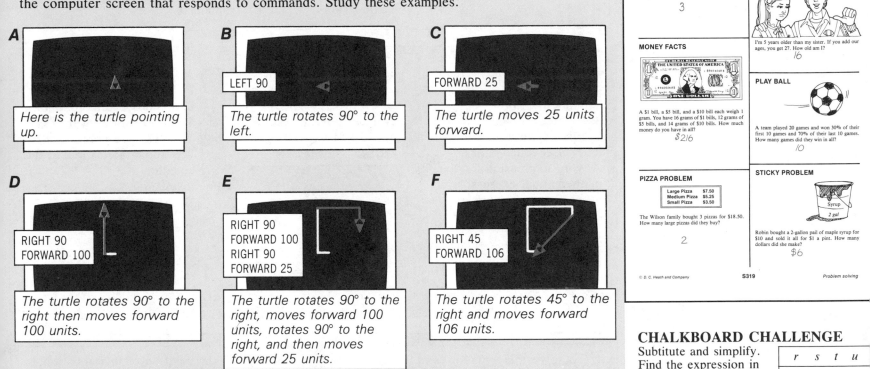

A
Here is the turtle pointing up.

B
LEFT 90
The turtle rotates 90° to the left.

C
FORWARD 25
The turtle moves 25 units forward.

D
RIGHT 90
FORWARD 100
The turtle rotates 90° to the right then moves forward 100 units.

E
RIGHT 90
FORWARD 100
RIGHT 90
FORWARD 25
The turtle rotates 90° to the right, moves forward 100 units, rotates 90° to the right, and then moves forward 25 units.

F
RIGHT 45
FORWARD 106
The turtle rotates 45° to the right and moves forward 106 units.

**Match each of the turtle graphics with its set of Logo commands.
Assume that the turtle starts pointing up.**

1. a
2. b
3. c

a. FORWARD 60
LEFT 72
FORWARD 60
LEFT 72
FORWARD 60
LEFT 72
FORWARD 60
LEFT 72
FORWARD 60
LEFT 72
END

b. FORWARD 100
LEFT 144
FORWARD 100
LEFT 144
FORWARD 100
LEFT 144
FORWARD 100
LEFT 144
FORWARD 100
LEFT 144
END

c. FORWARD 60
LEFT 120
FORWARD 60
LEFT 120
FORWARD 60
END

EXTRA PROBLEM SOLVING
Page 460   Even exercises

PROBLEM-SOLVING
WORKSHEET
Copymaster S319 or Duplicating Master S319

NAME _____
WORKSHEET 167
(Use after page 399.)

NICKELS AND DIMES
Three dimes, some nickels, and 2 quarters total 95¢. How many nickels are there?
3

HOW OLD?
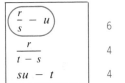
I'm 5 years older than my sister. If you add our ages, you get 27. How old am I?
16

MONEY FACTS
THE UNITED STATES OF AMERICA
ONE DOLLAR
A $1 bill, a $5 bill, and a $10 bill each weigh 1 gram. You have 16 grams of $1 bills, 12 grams of $5 bills, and 14 grams of $10 bills. How much money do you have in all?
$216

PLAY BALL
A team played 20 games and won 30% of their first 10 games and 70% of their last 10 games. How many games did they win in all?
10

PIZZA PROBLEM

Large Pizza	$7.50
Medium Pizza	$5.25
Small Pizza	$3.50

The Wilson family bought 3 pizzas for $18.50. How many large pizzas did they buy?
2

STICKY PROBLEM
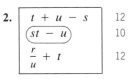
Syrup
2 gal
Robin bought a 2-gallon pail of maple syrup for $10 and sold it all for $1 a pint. How many dollars did she make?
$6

© D. C. Heath and Company   S319   *Problem solving*

CHALKBOARD CHALLENGE

Subtitute and simplify. Find the expression in each group whose value does not belong.

r	s	t	u
24	2	8	6

1.
$\dfrac{r}{s} - u$ 6

$\dfrac{r}{t - s}$ 4

$su - t$ 4

2.
$t + u - s$ 12

$st - u$ 10

$\dfrac{r}{u} + t$ 12

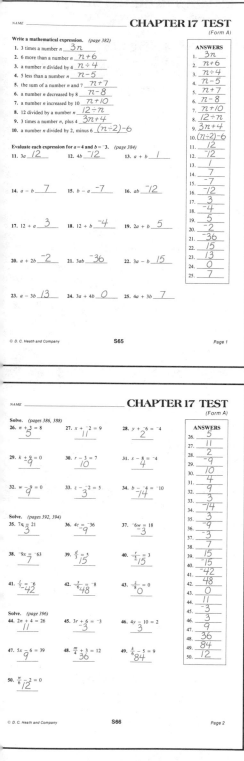

Chapter REVIEW

Here are scrambled answers for the review exercises:

$^-2$	5	add	more	variable
$^-7$	35	divide	multiply	
3	48	expressions	simplified	

1. expressions, variable, more   2. 48, 35   3. 5, simplified, $^-7$

1. Variables, numbers, and operation signs can be combined to form mathematical ☐. In this expression, the letter n is called a ☐. A word expression for this mathematical expression is 6 ☐ than a number n. *(page 382)*

$$n + 6$$

2. If you evaluate this expression for $a = 6$ and $b = 9$, you get ☐. If you evaluate this expression for $a = 3$ and $b = 10$, you get ☐. *(page 384)*

$$5a + 2b$$

3. To solve the equation, ☐ was subtracted from both sides of the equation. Then both sides were ☐. To check the solution, ☐ was substituted for x in the equation $x + 5 = ^-2$. *(page 386)*

$$x + 5 = ^-2$$
$$x + 5 - 5 = ^-2 - 5$$
$$x = ^-7$$
$$\text{Check: } ^-7 + 5 = ^-2$$

4. $^-2$ 5. divide

4. To solve this equation, you would first add ☐ to both sides of the equation and then simplify both sides. *(page 388)*

$$c - ^-2 = 7$$

5. To find the solution of this equation, you would ☐ both sides by 9 and then simplify both sides. *(page 392)*

$$9d = ^-45$$

6. multiply   7. add, 3

6. To find the solution of this equation, you would ☐ both sides by $^-4$ and then simplify both sides. *(page 394)*

$$\frac{t}{^-4} = 7$$

7. To solve this equation, you would first ☐ 4 to both sides and then divide by ☐. *(page 396)*

$$3y - 4 = 14$$

Chapter TEST

Write a mathematical expression. *(page 382)*

1. 7 more than a number n n + 7

2. 11 times a number n 11n

3. the sum of a number n and 3 n + 3

4. a number n divided by 6 $n \div 6$ $(\frac{n}{6}, \frac{1}{6}n)$

5. 12 times a number n 12n

6. 8 less than a number n n − 8

7. 2 more than 4 times a number n 4n + 2

8. a number n divided by 5, minus 6 $\frac{n}{5} - 6$

Evaluate each expression for a = 2 and b = ⁻3. *(page 384)*

9. $a + b$ ⁻1

10. $a - b$ 5

11. $b - a$ ⁻5

12. ab ⁻6

13. ^-5ab 30

14. $4a$ 8

15. $ab + 10$ 4

16. $16 \div a$ 8

17. $3ab$ ⁻18

18. ^-8ab 48

19. $2a + b$ 1

20. $a + 4b$ ⁻10

21. $4a + 3b$ ⁻1

22. $3a + 4b$ ⁻6

23. $4a + 5b + 6$ ⁻1

Solve and check. *(pages 386, 388)*

24. $n + 7 = 4$ ⁻3

25. $x + 9 = ^-3$ ⁻12

26. $a + 6 = 6$ 0

27. $y + 8 = 8$ 0

28. $r + 9 = 5$ ⁻4

29. $l - 12 = 7$ 19

30. $12 + v = ^-1$ ⁻13

31. $m - 9 = ^-8$ 1

32. $a - 3 = 6$ 9

33. $c - 7 = ^-2$ 5

34. $y - 5 = 5$ 10

35. $n - 8 = 16$ 24

36. $x - 8 = 0$ 8

37. $h - 11 = 3$ 14

38. $t - 15 = ^-10$ 5

39. $6 + r = 12$ 6

Solve and check. *(pages 392, 394)*

40. $6n = 42$ 7

41. $5c = ^-35$ ⁻7

42. $8d = 24$ 3

43. $^-9x = 81$ ⁻9

44. $9y = ^-27$ ⁻3

45. $^-7x = 49$ ⁻7

46. $6k = 54$ 9

47. $6m = 42$ 7

48. $^-5g = 55$ ⁻11

49. $10w = 40$ 4

50. $^-12t = ^-60$ 5

51. $^-3h = ^-33$ 11

52. $\frac{x}{3} = 6$ 18

53. $\frac{y}{^-4} = 9$ ⁻36

54. $\frac{j}{3} = ^-10$ ⁻30

55. $\frac{f}{4} = 20$ 80

56. $\frac{r}{^-5} = 7$ ⁻35

57. $\frac{t}{9} = 11$ 99

58. $\frac{d}{7} = ^-6$ ⁻42

59. $\frac{y}{8} = ^-64$ ⁻512

60. $\frac{s}{3} = 12$ 36

61. $\frac{v}{^-6} = 8$ ⁻48

62. $\frac{y}{^-10} = ^-20$ 200

63. $\frac{x}{^-30} = ^-90$ 2700

Solve and check. *(page 396)*

64. $3n + 6 = 30$ 8

65. $4k + 2 = 34$ 8

66. $7j + 3 = 52$ 7

67. $7m + 2 = 51$ 7

68. $5x - 6 = 34$ 8

69. $6r - 8 = 46$ 9

70. $9t - 10 = 44$ 6

71. $12a - 3 = 45$ 4

72. $\frac{x}{3} + 2 = 6$ 12

73. $\frac{n}{4} + 3 = 9$ 24

74. $\frac{c}{7} - 6 = 0$ 42

75. $\frac{r}{4} - 8 = 12$ 80

NAME _____

CHAPTER 17 TEST
(Form B)

Write a mathematical expression. *(page 382)*

	ANSWERS
1. 4 times a number n 4n	1. 4n
2. 7 more than a number n n+7	2. n+7
3. a number n divided by 6 n÷6	3. n÷6
4. 1 less than a number n n−1	4. n−1
5. the sum of a number n and 9 n+9	5. n+9
6. a number n decreased by 5 n−5	6. n−5
7. a number n increased by 12 n+12	7. n+12
8. 10 divided by a number 10÷n	8. 10÷n
9. 4 times a number n, plus 3 4n+3	9. 4n+3
10. a number n divided by 6, minus 2 (n÷6)−2	10. (n÷6)−2

Evaluate each expression for $a = ^-4$ and $b = 3$. *(page 384)*

			ANSWERS
11. 3a ⁻12	12. 4b 12	13. a + b ⁻1	11. ⁻12
			12. 12
			13. ⁻1
14. a − b ⁻7	15. b − a 7	16. ab ⁻12	14. ⁻7
			15. 7
			16. ⁻12
17. 12 + a ⁻3	18. 12 + b 4	19. 2a + b ⁻5	17. ⁻3
			18. 4
			19. ⁻5
20. a + 2b 2	21. 3ab ⁻36	22. 3a − b ⁻15	20. 2
			21. ⁻36
			22. ⁻15
23. a − 3b ⁻13	24. 3a + 4b 0	25. 4a + 3b ⁻7	23. ⁻13
			24. 0
			25. ⁻7

© D. C. Heath and Company   S67   Page 1

NAME _____

CHAPTER 17 TEST
(Form B)

Solve. *(pages 386, 388)*

			ANSWERS
26. n + 7 = 11 4	27. x + ⁻5 = 7 12	28. y + ⁻3 = ⁻2 1	26. 4
			27. 12
			28. 1
29. k + 6 = 0 ⁻6	30. r − 4 = 8 12	31. s − 6 = ⁻2 4	29. ⁻6
			30. 12
			31. 4
32. w − 5 = 0 5	33. z − ⁻6 = 4 ⁻2	34. b − ⁻3 = ⁻12 ⁻15	32. 5
			33. ⁻2
			34. ⁻15

Solve. *(pages 392, 394)*

			ANSWERS
35. 5n = 35 7	36. 3c = ⁻27 ⁻9	37. ⁻8w = 24 ⁻3	35. 7
			36. ⁻9
			37. ⁻3
38. ⁻9x = ⁻54 6	39. $\frac{d}{4}$ = 6 24	40. $\frac{t}{^-3}$ = 4 ⁻12	38. 6
			39. 24
			40. ⁻12
41. $\frac{l}{6}$ = ⁻8 ⁻48	42. $\frac{s}{^-7}$ = ⁻7 49	43. $\frac{z}{^-9}$ = 0 0	41. ⁻48
			42. 49
			43. 0

Solve. *(page 396)*

			ANSWERS
44. 2n + 4 = 24 10	45. 3r + 6 = ⁻6 ⁻4	46. 4y − 10 = 6 4	44. 10
			45. ⁻4
			46. 4
47. 5k − 4 = 26 6	48. $\frac{m}{3}$ + 7 = 13 18	49. $\frac{k}{6}$ − 3 = 8 66	47. 6
			48. 18
			49. 66
50. $\frac{w}{7}$ − 3 = 0 21			50. 21

© D. C. Heath and Company   S68   Page 2

Use Copymaster S336 to provide the students with an answer sheet in standardized test format.

Cumulative TEST Standardized Format

Choose the correct letter.

Answers for Cumulative Test,
Chapters 1–17

1. Ⓐ ● Ⓒ Ⓓ	2. ● Ⓑ Ⓒ Ⓓ	3. Ⓐ Ⓑ ● Ⓓ
4. Ⓐ Ⓑ ● Ⓓ	5. ● Ⓑ Ⓒ Ⓓ	6. Ⓐ ● Ⓒ Ⓓ
7. Ⓐ ● Ⓒ Ⓓ	8. ● Ⓑ Ⓒ Ⓓ	9. Ⓐ Ⓑ Ⓒ ●
10. ● Ⓑ Ⓒ Ⓓ	11. Ⓐ Ⓑ ● Ⓓ	12. Ⓐ ● Ⓒ Ⓓ

The table below correlates test items with student text pages.

Test Item	Page Taught	Skill Practice
1	64	p. 390, exercises 1–20
2	96	p. 390, exercises 21–40
3	158	p. 390, exercises 41–58
4	166	p. 390, exercises 59–76
5	178	p. 390, exercises 77–94
6	188	p. 398, exercises 1–18
7	258	p. 398, exercises 19–33
8	260	p. 398, exercises 34–42
9	284	p. 398, exercises 49–54
10	364	p. 398, exercises 55–64
11	332	
12	396	

1. Give the product.

0.26×0.031

A. 0.0806
Ⓑ 0.00806
C. 0.00104
D. none of these

2. Give the quotient rounded to the nearest tenth.

$17.43 \div 2.9$

Ⓐ 6.0
B. 6.1
C. 0.61
D. none of these

3. Give the sum.

$\frac{4}{9} + \frac{5}{6}$

A. $\frac{3}{5}$
B. 1
Ⓒ $1\frac{5}{18}$
D. none of these

4. Give the difference.

$\frac{7}{8} - \frac{2}{3}$

A. 1   B. $\frac{5}{8}$
Ⓒ $\frac{5}{24}$ D. none of these

5. Give the product.

$\frac{4}{5} \times \frac{3}{2}$

Ⓐ $1\frac{1}{5}$ B. $\frac{8}{15}$
C. $1\frac{7}{8}$ D. none of these

6. Give the quotient.

$\frac{5}{6} \div \frac{2}{3}$

A. $\frac{5}{9}$ Ⓑ $1\frac{1}{4}$
C. $\frac{4}{5}$ D. none of these

7. Solve.

$66\frac{2}{3}\%$ of $42 = n$

A. 63
Ⓑ 28
C. 14
D. none of these

8. Solve.

20% of $n = 15$

Ⓐ 75
B. 3
C. 150
D. none of these

9. Compute the interest.

Principal = $720
Rate = 12% per year
Time = 4 months

A. $86.40
B. $43.20
C. $1036.80
Ⓓ none of these

10. Give the sum.

$^-9 + {}^+7$

Ⓐ $^-2$
B. $^+2$
C. $^-16$
D. $^+16$

11. Find the volume of this cone. Use 3.14 for π.

A. 62.8 in.^{3}
B. 282.6 in.^{3}
Ⓒ 94.2 in.^{3}
D. none of these

10 in.
3 in.

12. Solve.

$2b + 8 = 32$

A. 20
Ⓑ 12
C. 24
D. none of these

FOURTH-QUARTER TEST

The fourth-quarter test shown on these two pages is in standardized format so that the students can become accustomed to taking standardized tests.

Copymaster S81 or Duplicating Master S81

NAME _____ **FOURTH-QUARTER TEST**
(Chapters 13 through 17)

Choose the correct letter.
Sample:
A right angle measures

A. 45°
B. 90°
C. 180°
D. none of these

Ⓐ Ⓑ Ⓒ Ⓓ

First decide which answer is correct. Then find the problem number on your answer sheet and darken in the space for the correct answer. In the sample, B is the correct answer.

1. An obtuse angle measures between 90° and ? .
A. 120°
B. 160°
C. 180°
D. none of these

2. Two lines that intersect to form right angles are
A. acute
B. parallel
C. perpendicular
D. none of these

3. Line r is parallel to line
A. s
B. t
C. u
D. none of these

4. A square is also a
A. triangle
B. rectangle
C. trapezoid
D. none of these

5. A 4-sided figure that has exactly 1 pair of parallel sides is called a
A. parallelogram
B. trapezoid
C. pentagon
D. hexagon

6. Find the perimeter.
A. 106.08 cm
B. 22.4 cm
C. 38.0 cm
D. none of these
15.6 cm, 6.8 cm

7. Find the circumference. Use 3.14 as an approximation for π.
A. 7.065 m
B. 15.896 m
C. 14.175 m
D. none of these
4.5 m

8. Find the area.
A. 50 cm²
B. 72 cm²
C. 144 cm²
D. none of these
9 cm, 16 cm

9. Find the area.
A. 120.4 cm²
B. 65.1 cm²
C. 130.2 cm²
D. none of these
10.5 cm, 12.4 cm

10. Find the area.
A. 7.065 m²
B. 28.25 m²
C. 9.42 m²
D. none of these
1.5 m

© D. C. Heath and Company   **S81**   Page 1

Copymaster S82 or Duplicating Master S82

NAME _____ **FOURTH-QUARTER TEST**
(Chapters 13 through 17)

Choose the correct letter.
11. This space figure is called a
A. cube
B. square pyramid
C. rectangular prism
D. none of these

12. This space figure is called a
A. cone
B. cylinder
C. square pyramid
D. none of these

13. A cube has exactly ? corners.
A. 8
B. 6
C. 4
D. none of these

14. A square pyramid has exactly ? faces.
A. 4
B. 5
C. 6
D. none of these

15. Find the surface area.
A. 9 ft²
B. 27 ft²
C. 54 ft²
D. none of these
3 ft, 3 ft

16. Find the surface area.
A. 48 ft²
B. 44 ft²
C. 80 ft²
D. none of these
6 ft, 2 ft

17. Find the volume.
A. 768 in.³
B. 28 in.³
C. 512 in.³
D. none of these
8 in., 12 in., 8 in.

18. Find the volume. Use 3.14 as an approximation for π.
A. 345.4 in.³
B. 172.7 in.³
C. 863.5 in.³
D. none of these
5 in., 11 in.

19. Find the volume.
A. 288 in.³
B. 96 in.³
C. 144 in.³
D. none of these
8 in., 6 in., 6 in.

20. Find the volume. Use 3.14 as an approximation for π.
A. 942 in.³
B. 188.4 in.³
C. 314 in.³
D. none of these
12 in., 5 in.

21. Suppose that there are 6 kinds of ice cream and 4 kinds of topping. How many different ice cream-and-topping orders could you place?
A. 10
B. 6
C. 4
D. none of these

22. In how many ways can 4 people line up at a drinking fountain?
A. 4
B. 10
C. 24
D. none of these

23. Think about spinning this spinner.
P(1 or 3) = ?
A. $\frac{1}{8}$
B. $\frac{1}{4}$
C. $\frac{3}{8}$
P(3) = ?
A. $\frac{5}{8}$
B. $\frac{1}{2}$
C. $\frac{3}{8}$
D. none of these

24. Think about spinning the spinner shown in exercise 23.
P(1 or 3) = ?
A. $\frac{5}{8}$
B. $\frac{1}{2}$
C. $\frac{3}{8}$
D. none of these

25. Think about tossing 3 pennies. What is the probability that all will land heads?
A. $\frac{1}{4}$
B. $\frac{1}{2}$
C. $\frac{1}{8}$
D. none of these

© D. C. Heath and Company   **S82**   Page 2

Copymaster S83 or Duplicating Master S83

NAME _____ **FOURTH-QUARTER TEST**
(Chapters 13 through 17)

Choose the correct letter.
26. Think about rolling the die and then spinning the spinner.
P(4, B) = ?
A. $\frac{13}{24}$
B. $\frac{1}{48}$
C. $\frac{1}{16}$
D. none of these

27. Think about rolling the die and spinning the spinner in exercise 26.
P(even, not C) = ?
A. $\frac{9}{24}$
B. $\frac{1}{8}$
C. $\frac{1}{4}$
D. none of these

28. Think about picking a card. What are the odds in favor of picking A?
A. $\frac{2}{5}$
B. $\frac{2}{3}$
C. $\frac{3}{5}$
D. none of these

29. Think about picking one of the cards shown in exercise 28. What are the odds against picking C?
A. $\frac{1}{5}$
B. $\frac{4}{5}$
C. $\frac{4}{1}$
D. none of these

30. You buy a $1 chance on an $80 radio. What would your expectation be if 200 chances were sold?
A. $1.00
B. $.80
C. $.40
D. none of these

31. $^+2 < $?
A. $^-3$
B. 0
C. $^-6$
D. $^+6$

32. $^+3 + ^-9 = $?
A. $^+12$
B. $^-12$
C. $^+6$
D. $^-6$

33. $^-7 + ^+7 = $?
A. 0
B. $^+14$
C. $^-14$
D. $^+7$

34. $^-2 - ^-5 = $?
A. $^-7$
B. $^+7$
C. $^+3$
D. $^-3$

35. $0 - ^+6 = $?
A. $^-6$
B. $^+6$
C. 0
D. $^-12$

36. $^+7 \times ^-3 = $?
A. $^-28$
B. $^-21$
C. $^+21$
D. none of these

37. $^-8 \times ^-4 = $?
A. $^-32$
B. $^-24$
C. $^+32$
D. none of these

38. $^-36 \div ^+4 = $?
A. $^-9$
B. $^-8$
C. $^+9$
D. none of these

39. $^-48 \div ^-12 = $?
A. $^-3$
B. $^+3$
C. $^-4$
D. none of these

40. Give the ordered pair for point X.
A. $(^-2, ^+1)$
B. $(^+1, ^-2)$
C. $(^-1, ^+2)$
D. $(^+2, ^-1)$

© D. C. Heath and Company   **S83**   Page 3

Copymaster S84 or Duplicating Master S84

NAME _____ **FOURTH-QUARTER TEST**
(Chapters 13 through 17)

Choose the correct letter.
41. An expression for 12 less than a number n is
A. $n + 12$
B. $12 - n$
C. $n \div 12$
D. $n - 12$

42. An expression for 3 times a number n plus 5 is
A. $5n + 3$
B. $5n - 3$
C. $3n + 5$
D. $3n - 5$

43. Evaluate the expression
$a - b$
for $a = ^-6$ and $b = 3$.
A. $^-9$
B. 9
C. $^-3$
D. 3

44. Evaluate the expression
$3a + 2b$
for $a = ^-6$ and $b = 3$.
A. $^-12$
B. $^-3$
C. 3
D. 12

45. Solve. $n + ^-8 = ^-3$
A. $^-5$
B. 5
C. 11
D. $^-11$

46. Solve. $n - 6 = ^-8$
A. $^-14$
B. 14
C. $^-2$
D. 2

47. Solve. $5n = ^-35$
A. $^-7$
B. 7
C. $^-9$
D. none of these

48. Solve. $\frac{n}{8} = 40$
A. $^-320$
B. 5
C. $^-5$
D. none of these

49. Solve. $3n + 4 = ^-11$
A. $^-5$
B. $^-5$
C. 4
D. none of these

50. Solve. $\frac{n}{6} - 3 = 0$
A. $^-18$
B. 18
C. 12
D. none of these

© D. C. Heath and Company   **S84**   Page 4

Use Copymaster S92 or Duplicating Master S92 to provide the students with an answer sheet in standardized test format.

Copymaster S107 has a quick-score answer key for the fourth-quarter test.

Answer Sheet for **QUARTERLY TESTS**
_____-Quarter Test (Chapters __—__)

NAME _____
DATE _____
SCORE _____

page 1

1. Ⓐ Ⓑ Ⓒ Ⓓ
2. Ⓐ Ⓑ Ⓒ Ⓓ   3. Ⓐ Ⓑ Ⓒ Ⓓ   4. Ⓐ Ⓑ Ⓒ Ⓓ
5. Ⓐ Ⓑ Ⓒ Ⓓ   6. Ⓐ Ⓑ Ⓒ Ⓓ   7. Ⓐ Ⓑ Ⓒ Ⓓ
8. Ⓐ Ⓑ Ⓒ Ⓓ   9. Ⓐ Ⓑ Ⓒ Ⓓ   10. Ⓐ Ⓑ Ⓒ Ⓓ

page 2

11. Ⓐ Ⓑ Ⓒ Ⓓ   12. Ⓐ Ⓑ Ⓒ Ⓓ   13. Ⓐ Ⓑ Ⓒ Ⓓ
14. Ⓐ Ⓑ Ⓒ Ⓓ   15. Ⓐ Ⓑ Ⓒ Ⓓ   16. Ⓐ Ⓑ Ⓒ Ⓓ
17. Ⓐ Ⓑ Ⓒ Ⓓ   18. Ⓐ Ⓑ Ⓒ Ⓓ   19. Ⓐ Ⓑ Ⓒ Ⓓ
20. Ⓐ Ⓑ Ⓒ Ⓓ   21. Ⓐ Ⓑ Ⓒ Ⓓ   22. Ⓐ Ⓑ Ⓒ Ⓓ
23. Ⓐ Ⓑ Ⓒ Ⓓ   24. Ⓐ Ⓑ Ⓒ Ⓓ   25. Ⓐ Ⓑ Ⓒ Ⓓ

page 3

26. Ⓐ Ⓑ Ⓒ Ⓓ   27. Ⓐ Ⓑ Ⓒ Ⓓ   28. Ⓐ Ⓑ Ⓒ Ⓓ
29. Ⓐ Ⓑ Ⓒ Ⓓ   30. Ⓐ Ⓑ Ⓒ Ⓓ   31. Ⓐ Ⓑ Ⓒ Ⓓ
32. Ⓐ Ⓑ Ⓒ Ⓓ   33. Ⓐ Ⓑ Ⓒ Ⓓ   34. Ⓐ Ⓑ Ⓒ Ⓓ
35. Ⓐ Ⓑ Ⓒ Ⓓ   36. Ⓐ Ⓑ Ⓒ Ⓓ   37. Ⓐ Ⓑ Ⓒ Ⓓ
38. Ⓐ Ⓑ Ⓒ Ⓓ   39. Ⓐ Ⓑ Ⓒ Ⓓ   40. Ⓐ Ⓑ Ⓒ Ⓓ

page 4

41. Ⓐ Ⓑ Ⓒ Ⓓ   42. Ⓐ Ⓑ Ⓒ Ⓓ   43. Ⓐ Ⓑ Ⓒ Ⓓ
44. Ⓐ Ⓑ Ⓒ Ⓓ   45. Ⓐ Ⓑ Ⓒ Ⓓ   46. Ⓐ Ⓑ Ⓒ Ⓓ
47. Ⓐ Ⓑ Ⓒ Ⓓ   48. Ⓐ Ⓑ Ⓒ Ⓓ   49. Ⓐ Ⓑ Ⓒ Ⓓ
50. Ⓐ Ⓑ Ⓒ Ⓓ

© D. C. Heath and Company   **S92**   Answer sheet—Quarterly Tests

Quick-Score Answer Key for **THIRD-QUARTER TEST** (Chapters 9–12)

Quick-Score Answer Key for **FOURTH-QUARTER TEST** (Chapters 13–17)

© D. C. Heath and Company   **S107**   Answer key—Quarterly Tests

The table below correlates test items with student text pages.

Test Item	Text Page	Test Item	Text Page	Test Item	Text Page	Test Item	Text Page
1	p. 294	14	p. 320	27	p. 350	40	p. 374
2	p. 296	15	p. 324	28	p. 352	41	p. 382
3	p. 296	16	p. 324	29	p. 353	42	p. 382
4	p. 298	17	p. 328	30	p. 354	43	p. 384
5	p. 298	18	p. 330	31	p. 362	44	p. 384
6	p. 300	19	p. 332	32	p. 364	45	p. 386
7	p. 302	20	p. 332	33	p. 364	46	p. 388
8	p. 308	21	p. 340	34	p. 366	47	p. 392
9	p. 310	22	p. 342	35	p. 366	48	p. 394
10	p. 312	23	p. 344	36	p. 371	49	p. 396
11	p. 320	24	p. 344	37	p. 371	50	p. 396
12	p. 320	25	p. 350	38	p. 372		
13	p. 320	26	p. 350	39	p. 372		

NAME _____ **FINAL TEST**

Choose the correct letter.
Sample:
75,000 is
A. 75 million
B. 750 thousand
c. 75 thousand
D. none of these

Ⓐ Ⓑ ● Ⓓ

First decide which answer is correct. Then find the problem number on your answer sheet and darken in the space for the correct answer. In the sample, c is the correct answer.

1. 34,008,000 is
Ⓐ 34 million, 8 thousand
B. 34 billion, 8 million
c. 34 million, 80 thousand
D. none of these

2. Add.   86,253
        +19,478
A. 95,621
B. 95,731
Ⓒ 105,731
D. none of these

3. 29,642 rounded to the nearest thousand is
A. 29,600
B. 29,000
Ⓒ 30,000
D. none of these

4. 9.061 is
Ⓐ 9 and 61 hundredths
B. 9 and 61 thousandths
C. 9 and 61 ten-thousandths
D. none of these

5. 7.085 rounded to the nearest hundredth is
A. 7.1
B. 7.08
C. 7.0
Ⓓ none of these

6. 4.03 + 6.4 + 9.59 = ?
Ⓐ 20.02
B. 14.26
c. 19.92
D. none of these

7. [$5.97] [$1.49]
The total cost of 2 large records and 1 small record is
A. $7.46
B. $8.95
Ⓒ $13.43
D. none of these

8. 47,089 > ?
A. 48,088
B. 47,098
C. 47,100
Ⓓ none of these

9. Subtract. 68,301
            −15,476
A. 52,835
Ⓑ 52,825
c. 53,175
D. none of these

10. 0.054 < ?
Ⓐ 0.54
B. 0.045
c. 0.05
D. none of these

© D. C. Heath and Company   **S85**   Page 1

NAME _____ **FINAL TEST**

Choose the correct letter.

11. 9.4 − 2.835 = ?
Ⓐ 6.565
B. 7.435
c. 6.575
D. none of these

12. You had $10. You bought 2 rolls of film for $2.69 each. How much money did you have then?
A. $7.31
Ⓑ $4.62
c. $5.38
D. none of these

13. Multiply.   374
              × 6
A. 1824
B. 2044
Ⓒ 2244
D. none of these

14. Multiply.   638
              ×204
A. 129,022
B. 129,152
c. 15,312
Ⓓ none of these

15. 1.03 × 0.02 = ?
Ⓐ 0.0206
B. 0.206
c. 2.06
D. none of these

16. 12 − (2.25 × 1.04) = ?
A. 10.14
B. 10.34
Ⓒ 9.66
D. none of these

17. 4.36 × 1000 = ?
A. 436
Ⓑ 4360
C. 43,600
D. none of these

18. CHEESE
How much would 1.5 pounds of cheese cost?
A. $5.30   Ⓑ $5.52
c. $4.52   D. none of these

19. Divide. 8)1640
A. 25
Ⓑ 205
C. 2005
D. none of these

20. Round the quotient to the nearest whole number.
157)38,296
A. 243   Ⓑ 244
c. 245   D. none of these

21. 4 × 6 + 8 ÷ 2 = ?
A. 16
Ⓑ 28
C. 40
D. none of these

22. 8.7 ÷ 100 = ?
A. 870
B. 0.87
Ⓒ 0.087
D. none of these

23. 0.835 ÷ 0.05 = ?
A. 1.67
B. 0.167
c. 0.0167
Ⓓ none of these

24. Round the quotient to the nearest tenth.
26.5 ÷ 0.36 = ?
Ⓐ 73.6
B. 7.36
c. 73.7
D. none of these

25. You bought 4 packages of notebook paper. You gave the clerk $10 and got $4.44 back in change. How much did each package cost?
A. $5.56   B. $1.11
Ⓒ $1.39   D. none of these

© D. C. Heath and Company   **S86**   Page 2

NAME _____ **FINAL TEST**

Choose the correct letter.

26. Cassette Tapes in Collection
How many tapes does Jack have?
A. 10
Ⓑ 11
C. 12
D. none of these

27. Beth's Weekly Earnings
How much did Beth earn during week 2?
A. $8
B. $17
C. $18
Ⓓ none of these

28. Number of Stamps in Collection
Each ■ stands for 24 stamps.
How many stamps does Jon have?
A. 54
B. 120
C. 125
D. none of these

29. The mean of 35, 47, 43, 47, 50, 39, and 47 is
Ⓐ 44
B. 47
C. 43
D. none of these

30. The median of 58, 59, 63, 61, and 54 is
A. 60
B. 58
C. 61
Ⓓ none of these

31. The mode of 222, 228, 219, 218, and 218 is
A. 219
B. 221
Ⓒ 218
D. none of these

32. 18/24 written in lowest terms is
A. 9/12   B. 2/3
C. 6/8   Ⓓ none of these

33. 5/8 < ?
A. 2/3   B. 1/2
c. 3/5   D. 3/7

34. 5 3/4 = ?
A. 20/4   B. 21/4
Ⓒ 23/4   D. none of these

35. 18/8 written in simplest form is
A. 9/4   B. 2 2/8
Ⓒ 2 1/4   D. none of these

36. 2 5/8 = ?
A. 0.625
Ⓑ 2.625
C. 2.65
D. none of these

37. 1.125 = ?
A. 1 1/4   B. 1 3/8
Ⓒ 1 1/8   D. none of these

38. 2/3 + 3/5 = ?
A. 1/3
B. 5/8
c. 2/5
Ⓓ none of these

39. Add. 3 3/4 + 1 2/3 = ?
A. 4 5/12
B. 4 5/7
Ⓒ 5 5/12
D. none of these

40. 5/12 − 3/8 = ?
Ⓐ 1/24
B. 1/2
c. 1/3
D. none of these

© D. C. Heath and Company   **S87**   Page 3

NAME _____ **FINAL TEST**

Choose the correct letter.

41. Subtract.   5 2/3
              −2 1/6
Ⓐ 3 1/2
B. 2 1/2
c. 3 1/3
D. none of these

42. Subtract.   4 3/8
              −2 3/4
A. 2 3/8
B. 2 1/8
Ⓒ 1 5/8
D. none of these

43. A chili recipe calls for 3 pounds of beef. You have 1 3/4 pounds of beef. How many more pounds do you need?
A. 4 3/4   B. 3/4
Ⓒ 1 1/4   D. none of these

44. 3/4 × 5/6 = ?
A. 1/3   B. 1 1/4
Ⓒ 5/8   D. none of these

45. 5/6 of 30 = ?
A. 5
Ⓑ 25
C. 24
D. none of these

46. 1 2/3 × 2 1/2 = ?
A. 6 2/3   B. 1 1/15
C. 15/16   Ⓓ none of these

47. 2 3/4 ft = ? in.
A. 21
B. 27
C. 30
Ⓓ none of these

48. 2/3 ÷ 4/5 = ?
Ⓐ 5/6   B. 1 1/5
C. 8/15   D. none of these

49. 3 3/4 ÷ 1 1/3 = ?
A. 5   Ⓑ 2 13/16
c. 16/45   D. none of these

50. You jogged at the rate of 6 3/4 miles in 1 1/2 hours. How many miles per hour did you average?
A. 10 1/8   Ⓑ 4 1/2
c. 4 3/4   D. none of these

51. The width of a piece of notebook paper is about
A. 21 m
B. 21 km
C. 21 mm
Ⓓ 21 cm

52. 86 m = ? km
A. 860
B. 8600
C. 0.86
Ⓓ 0.086

53. 5.2 L = ? mL
A. 52
B. 520
Ⓒ 5200
D. none of these

54. 5 yd 1 ft = ? ft
Ⓐ 16
B. 11
c. 61
D. none of these

55. 3 T = ? lb
Ⓐ 6000
B. 2000
c. 3000
D. none of these

© D. C. Heath and Company   **S88**   Page 4

FINAL TEST

The final test shown on these two pages is in standardized format so that the students can become accustomed to taking standardized tests.

FINAL TEST

NAME _____

Choose the correct letter.

56. Add. 5 ft 9 in.
+3 ft 6 in.
A. 9 ft 3 in.
B. 9 ft 5 in.
C. 8 ft 3 in.
D. none of these

57. Subtract. 5 gal
−2 gal 3 qt
A. 3 gal 3 qt
B. 3 gal 1 qt
C. 2 gal 1 qt
D. none of these

58. Write as a fraction in lowest terms.
12:18
A. $\frac{2}{3}$ B. $\frac{3}{2}$
C. $\frac{6}{4}$
D. none of these

59. Solve. $\frac{n}{8} = \frac{9}{24}$
A. 6
B. 3
C. 16
D. none of these

60. Solve. $\frac{4}{5} = \frac{n}{6}$
A. $7\frac{1}{2}$ B. $4\frac{4}{5}$
C. $3\frac{1}{3}$ D. none of these

61. You read 642 words in 3 minutes. At that rate, how many words could you read in 7 minutes?
A. 1498   B. 1284
C. 1298   D. none of these

62. The figures are similar. Find the length n.
A. 13.5
B. 20
C. 24
D. none of these

63. A tower casts a shadow of 60 meters. At the same time, an 8-meter flagpole casts a shadow of 10 meters. How high is the tower?
A. 50 m   B. 36 m
C. 44 m   D. none of these

64. 120% = ?
A. $\frac{5}{6}$
B. $1\frac{1}{3}$
C. $1\frac{1}{4}$
D. none of these

65. $\frac{2}{3}$ = ?
A. $16\frac{2}{3}$%   B. $66\frac{2}{3}$%
C. $66\frac{2}{3}$%   D. none of these

66. 9.05% = ?
A. 9.0f
B. 90.5
C. 0.0905
D. none of these

67. Solve. $33\frac{1}{3}$% of 57 = n
A. 10
B. 18
C. 17
D. none of these

68. Solve. 37.5% of n = 24
A. 18
B. 15
C. 12
D. none of these

69. You earn $6.85 an hour for a 40-hour week. $39 is withheld for federal income tax and $12.44 for Social Security. How much is your net pay?
A. $247.94   B. $325.94
C. $222.06   D. none of these

70. What is the sale price?
A. $48.60
B. $16.20
C. $43.20
D. none of these

FINAL TEST

NAME _____

Choose the correct letter.

71. Give the unit cost rounded to the nearest cent.
BANANAS
3 pounds for $.95
A. $.31   B. $.32
C. $.33
D. none of these

72. A checking account has a balance of $407.26. A check for $38.75 is written and a deposit of $90 is made. What is the new balance?
A. $278.51   B. $356.01
C. $536.01   D. none of these

73. Compute the interest.
Principal = $720
Rate = 12% per year
Time = 9 months
A. $64.80   B. $86.40
C. $57.60   D. none of these

74. An acute angle is between 0° and
A. 45°
B. 90°
C. 180°
D. none of these

75. Line l is perpendicular to line
A. m
B. n
C. o
D. none of these

76. Find the circumference. π ≈ 3.14
A. 8.635 m
B. 17.27 m
C. 23.75 m
D. none of these

77. Find the area.
A. 80 cm²
B. 160 cm²
C. 40 cm²
D. none of these

78. Find the area. π ≈ 3.14
A. 7.85 m²
B. 19.625 m²
C. 15.7 m²
D. none of these

79. This space figure is called a
A. square pyramid
B. cylinder
C. cone
D. none of these

80. A rectangular prism has exactly ? faces.
A. 4
B. 6
C. 8
D. none of these

81. Find the surface area.
A. 88 ft²
B. 116 ft²
C. 128 ft²
D. none of these

82. Find the volume. π ≈ 3.14
A. 942 in.³
B. 188.4 in.³
C. 376.8 in.³
D. none of these

83. Find the volume.
A. 576 in.³
B. 96 in.³
C. 129 in.³
D. none of these

84. In how many ways can you stack 5 books in a locker?
A. 120
B. 24
C. 15
D. none of these

85. Think about spinning this spinner.
P(A or B) = ?
A. $\frac{3}{4}$ B. $\frac{1}{4}$
C. $\frac{5}{8}$ D. none of these

FINAL TEST

NAME _____

Choose the correct letter.

86. Think about rolling the die and then spinning the spinner.
P(3, B) = ?
A. $\frac{1}{24}$
B. $\frac{1}{12}$
C. $\frac{13}{24}$
D. none of these

87. Think about rolling the die and spinning the spinner shown in exercise 86.
P(odd, not C) = ?
A. $\frac{3}{8}$
B. $\frac{1}{4}$
C. $\frac{1}{2}$
D. none of these

88. Think about picking a card. What are the odds in favor of picking 2?
A. $\frac{1}{2}$
B. $\frac{2}{1}$
C. $\frac{1}{3}$
D. none of these

89. Think about picking one of the cards shown in exercise 88. What are the odds against picking 3?
A. $\frac{1}{6}$ B. $\frac{6}{1}$
C. $\frac{5}{1}$ D. none of these

90. ⁻9 + ⁺6 = ?
A. ⁺3
B. ⁻3
C. ⁺15
D. none of these

91. ⁺6 − ⁻4 = ?
A. ⁺10
B. ⁻10
C. ⁺2
D. none of these

92. ⁻3 × ⁻4 = ?
A. ⁻7
B. ⁻12
C. ⁺12
D. none of these

93. ⁺18 ÷ ⁻6 = ?
A. ⁺3
B. ⁻3
C. ⁺24
D. none of these

94. Give the ordered pair for point X.
A. (⁻1, ⁻2)
B. (⁻1, ⁺2)
C. (⁻2, ⁻1)
D. (⁻2, ⁺1)

95. An expression for 4 times a number n, minus 3 is
A. 3n − 4   B. 3n + 4
C. 4n + 3   D. 4n − 3

96. Evaluate the expression 2a − b for a = 6 and b = ⁻2.
A. ⁻10   B. 10
C. 14   D. 2

97. Solve. n − 3 = ⁻2
A. ⁻5   B. ⁻6
C. ⁺1   D. none of these

98. Solve. $\frac{n}{-3}$ = 18
A. ⁻6   B. 6
C. ⁻54   D. none of these

99. Solve. 4n − 2 = 26
A. 6   B. ⁻6
C. ⁻7   D. none of these

100. Solve. $\frac{n}{6}$ − 12 = 0
A. 72   B. 12
C. ⁻36   D. none of these

Answer Sheet for FINAL TEST

NAME _____
DATE _____
SCORE _____

page 1

1. Ⓐ Ⓑ Ⓒ Ⓓ
2. Ⓐ Ⓑ Ⓒ Ⓓ   3. Ⓐ Ⓑ Ⓒ Ⓓ   4. Ⓐ Ⓑ Ⓒ Ⓓ
5. Ⓐ Ⓑ Ⓒ Ⓓ   6. Ⓐ Ⓑ Ⓒ Ⓓ   7. Ⓐ Ⓑ Ⓒ Ⓓ
8. Ⓐ Ⓑ Ⓒ Ⓓ   9. Ⓐ Ⓑ Ⓒ Ⓓ   10. Ⓐ Ⓑ Ⓒ Ⓓ

page 2

11. Ⓐ Ⓑ Ⓒ Ⓓ   12. Ⓐ Ⓑ Ⓒ Ⓓ   13. Ⓐ Ⓑ Ⓒ Ⓓ
14. Ⓐ Ⓑ Ⓒ Ⓓ   15. Ⓐ Ⓑ Ⓒ Ⓓ   16. Ⓐ Ⓑ Ⓒ Ⓓ
17. Ⓐ Ⓑ Ⓒ Ⓓ   18. Ⓐ Ⓑ Ⓒ Ⓓ   19. Ⓐ Ⓑ Ⓒ Ⓓ
20. Ⓐ Ⓑ Ⓒ Ⓓ   21. Ⓐ Ⓑ Ⓒ Ⓓ   22. Ⓐ Ⓑ Ⓒ Ⓓ
23. Ⓐ Ⓑ Ⓒ Ⓓ   24. Ⓐ Ⓑ Ⓒ Ⓓ   25. Ⓐ Ⓑ Ⓒ Ⓓ

page 3

26. Ⓐ Ⓑ Ⓒ Ⓓ   27. Ⓐ Ⓑ Ⓒ Ⓓ   28. Ⓐ Ⓑ Ⓒ Ⓓ
29. Ⓐ Ⓑ Ⓒ Ⓓ   30. Ⓐ Ⓑ Ⓒ Ⓓ   31. Ⓐ Ⓑ Ⓒ Ⓓ
32. Ⓐ Ⓑ Ⓒ Ⓓ   33. Ⓐ Ⓑ Ⓒ Ⓓ   34. Ⓐ Ⓑ Ⓒ Ⓓ
35. Ⓐ Ⓑ Ⓒ Ⓓ   36. Ⓐ Ⓑ Ⓒ Ⓓ   37. Ⓐ Ⓑ Ⓒ Ⓓ
38. Ⓐ Ⓑ Ⓒ Ⓓ   39. Ⓐ Ⓑ Ⓒ Ⓓ   40. Ⓐ Ⓑ Ⓒ Ⓓ

page 4

41. Ⓐ Ⓑ Ⓒ Ⓓ   42. Ⓐ Ⓑ Ⓒ Ⓓ   43. Ⓐ Ⓑ Ⓒ Ⓓ
44. Ⓐ Ⓑ Ⓒ Ⓓ   45. Ⓐ Ⓑ Ⓒ Ⓓ   46. Ⓐ Ⓑ Ⓒ Ⓓ
47. Ⓐ Ⓑ Ⓒ Ⓓ   48. Ⓐ Ⓑ Ⓒ Ⓓ   49. Ⓐ Ⓑ Ⓒ Ⓓ
50. Ⓐ Ⓑ Ⓒ Ⓓ   51. Ⓐ Ⓑ Ⓒ Ⓓ   52. Ⓐ Ⓑ Ⓒ Ⓓ
53. Ⓐ Ⓑ Ⓒ Ⓓ   54. Ⓐ Ⓑ Ⓒ Ⓓ   55. Ⓐ Ⓑ Ⓒ Ⓓ

page 5

56. Ⓐ Ⓑ Ⓒ Ⓓ   57. Ⓐ Ⓑ Ⓒ Ⓓ   58. Ⓐ Ⓑ Ⓒ Ⓓ
59. Ⓐ Ⓑ Ⓒ Ⓓ   60. Ⓐ Ⓑ Ⓒ Ⓓ   61. Ⓐ Ⓑ Ⓒ Ⓓ
62. Ⓐ Ⓑ Ⓒ Ⓓ   63. Ⓐ Ⓑ Ⓒ Ⓓ   64. Ⓐ Ⓑ Ⓒ Ⓓ
65. Ⓐ Ⓑ Ⓒ Ⓓ   66. Ⓐ Ⓑ Ⓒ Ⓓ   67. Ⓐ Ⓑ Ⓒ Ⓓ
68. Ⓐ Ⓑ Ⓒ Ⓓ   69. Ⓐ Ⓑ Ⓒ Ⓓ   70. Ⓐ Ⓑ Ⓒ Ⓓ

page 6

71. Ⓐ Ⓑ Ⓒ Ⓓ   72. Ⓐ Ⓑ Ⓒ Ⓓ   73. Ⓐ Ⓑ Ⓒ Ⓓ
74. Ⓐ Ⓑ Ⓒ Ⓓ   75. Ⓐ Ⓑ Ⓒ Ⓓ   76. Ⓐ Ⓑ Ⓒ Ⓓ
77. Ⓐ Ⓑ Ⓒ Ⓓ   78. Ⓐ Ⓑ Ⓒ Ⓓ   79. Ⓐ Ⓑ Ⓒ Ⓓ
80. Ⓐ Ⓑ Ⓒ Ⓓ   81. Ⓐ Ⓑ Ⓒ Ⓓ   82. Ⓐ Ⓑ Ⓒ Ⓓ
83. Ⓐ Ⓑ Ⓒ Ⓓ   84. Ⓐ Ⓑ Ⓒ Ⓓ   85. Ⓐ Ⓑ Ⓒ Ⓓ

page 7

86. Ⓐ Ⓑ Ⓒ Ⓓ   87. Ⓐ Ⓑ Ⓒ Ⓓ   88. Ⓐ Ⓑ Ⓒ Ⓓ
89. Ⓐ Ⓑ Ⓒ Ⓓ   90. Ⓐ Ⓑ Ⓒ Ⓓ   91. Ⓐ Ⓑ Ⓒ Ⓓ
92. Ⓐ Ⓑ Ⓒ Ⓓ   93. Ⓐ Ⓑ Ⓒ Ⓓ   94. Ⓐ Ⓑ Ⓒ Ⓓ
95. Ⓐ Ⓑ Ⓒ Ⓓ   96. Ⓐ Ⓑ Ⓒ Ⓓ   97. Ⓐ Ⓑ Ⓒ Ⓓ
98. Ⓐ Ⓑ Ⓒ Ⓓ   99. Ⓐ Ⓑ Ⓒ Ⓓ   100. Ⓐ Ⓑ Ⓒ Ⓓ

Quick-Score Answer Key for FINAL TEST

page 1

1. ● Ⓑ Ⓒ Ⓓ
2. Ⓐ Ⓑ ● Ⓓ   3. Ⓐ Ⓑ ● Ⓓ   4. Ⓐ ● Ⓒ Ⓓ
5. Ⓐ ● Ⓒ Ⓓ   6. Ⓐ ● Ⓒ Ⓓ   7. Ⓐ Ⓑ Ⓒ ●
8. Ⓐ Ⓑ Ⓒ ●   9. ● Ⓑ Ⓒ Ⓓ   10. ● Ⓑ Ⓒ Ⓓ

page 2

11. ● Ⓑ Ⓒ Ⓓ   12. Ⓐ ● Ⓒ Ⓓ   13. Ⓐ ● Ⓒ Ⓓ
14. Ⓐ Ⓑ Ⓒ ●   15. Ⓐ ● Ⓒ Ⓓ   16. Ⓐ ● Ⓒ Ⓓ
17. Ⓐ ● Ⓒ Ⓓ   18. Ⓐ Ⓑ ● Ⓓ   19. Ⓐ Ⓑ ● Ⓓ
20. Ⓐ ● Ⓒ Ⓓ   21. Ⓐ Ⓑ ● Ⓓ   22. Ⓐ ● Ⓒ Ⓓ
23. Ⓐ ● Ⓒ Ⓓ   24. ● Ⓑ Ⓒ Ⓓ   25. Ⓐ ● Ⓒ Ⓓ

page 3

26. ● Ⓑ Ⓒ Ⓓ   27. Ⓐ ● Ⓒ Ⓓ   28. Ⓐ ● Ⓒ Ⓓ
29. ● Ⓑ Ⓒ Ⓓ   30. Ⓐ Ⓑ ● Ⓓ   31. Ⓐ ● Ⓒ Ⓓ
32. Ⓐ ● Ⓒ Ⓓ   33. Ⓐ ● Ⓒ Ⓓ   34. Ⓐ ● Ⓒ Ⓓ
35. Ⓐ ● Ⓒ Ⓓ   36. Ⓐ ● Ⓒ Ⓓ   37. Ⓐ ● Ⓒ Ⓓ
38. Ⓐ ● Ⓒ Ⓓ   39. Ⓐ Ⓑ ● Ⓓ   40. ● Ⓑ Ⓒ Ⓓ

page 4

41. ● Ⓑ Ⓒ Ⓓ   42. Ⓐ ● Ⓒ Ⓓ   43. Ⓐ Ⓑ ● Ⓓ
44. Ⓐ ● Ⓒ Ⓓ   45. Ⓐ ● Ⓒ Ⓓ   46. Ⓐ Ⓑ ● Ⓓ
47. Ⓐ ● Ⓒ Ⓓ   48. Ⓐ Ⓑ ● Ⓓ   49. Ⓐ Ⓑ ● Ⓓ
50. ● Ⓑ Ⓒ Ⓓ   51. Ⓐ Ⓑ Ⓒ ●   52. Ⓐ Ⓑ ● Ⓓ
53. Ⓐ ● Ⓒ Ⓓ   54. ● Ⓑ Ⓒ Ⓓ   55. ● Ⓑ Ⓒ Ⓓ

page 5

56. ● Ⓑ Ⓒ Ⓓ   57. Ⓐ ● Ⓒ Ⓓ   58. Ⓐ Ⓑ Ⓒ ●
59. Ⓐ ● Ⓒ Ⓓ   60. Ⓐ Ⓑ Ⓒ ●   61. Ⓐ Ⓑ ● Ⓓ
62. Ⓐ ● Ⓒ Ⓓ   63. Ⓐ Ⓑ ● Ⓓ   64. Ⓐ Ⓑ ● Ⓓ
65. Ⓐ Ⓑ ● Ⓓ   66. Ⓐ Ⓑ ● Ⓓ   67. Ⓐ Ⓑ ● Ⓓ
68. Ⓐ Ⓑ ● Ⓓ   69. Ⓐ Ⓑ ● Ⓓ   70. ● Ⓑ Ⓒ Ⓓ

page 6

71. ● Ⓑ Ⓒ Ⓓ   72. Ⓐ ● Ⓒ Ⓓ   73. Ⓐ ● Ⓒ Ⓓ
74. Ⓐ ● Ⓒ Ⓓ   75. Ⓐ ● Ⓒ Ⓓ   76. Ⓐ ● Ⓒ Ⓓ
77. ● Ⓑ Ⓒ Ⓓ   78. Ⓐ ● Ⓒ Ⓓ   79. Ⓐ Ⓑ ● Ⓓ
80. Ⓐ ● Ⓒ Ⓓ   81. Ⓐ ● Ⓒ Ⓓ   82. Ⓐ Ⓑ ● Ⓓ
83. Ⓐ Ⓑ ● Ⓓ   84. Ⓐ ● Ⓒ Ⓓ   85. ● Ⓑ Ⓒ Ⓓ

page 7

86. Ⓐ Ⓑ Ⓒ ●   87. ● Ⓑ Ⓒ Ⓓ   88. Ⓐ Ⓑ ● Ⓓ
89. Ⓐ Ⓑ ● Ⓓ   90. Ⓐ ● Ⓒ Ⓓ   91. Ⓐ ● Ⓒ Ⓓ
92. Ⓐ Ⓑ ● Ⓓ   93. Ⓐ ● Ⓒ Ⓓ   94. Ⓐ Ⓑ ● Ⓓ
95. Ⓐ Ⓑ ● Ⓓ   96. Ⓐ ● Ⓒ Ⓓ   97. Ⓐ Ⓑ ● Ⓓ
98. Ⓐ Ⓑ ● Ⓓ   99. Ⓐ ● Ⓒ Ⓓ   100. ● Ⓑ Ⓒ Ⓓ

Use Copymaster S93 or Duplicating Master S93 to provide the students with an answer sheet in standardized format.

Copymaster S108 has a quick-score answer key for the final test.

402D

SKILL TEST
EXTRA PRACTICE
EXTRA PROBLEM SOLVING

SKILL TEST

Pages 404–411

This test will help you find out which skills you know well and which skills you need to practice more.

EXTRA PRACTICE

Pages 412–443

These practice sets cover the skills tested on the SKILL TEST. Each set practices one skill. The skills are presented in the same order as they are in the book. Page references will help you and your teacher decide when to use them.

EXTRA PROBLEM SOLVING

Pages 444–460

These lessons provide additional opportunities to apply what you learn in the book to situations you will encounter in everyday life.

MINIMUM COMPETENCY
This Skill Test may be used to help students prepare for **minimum competency tests**. If a student responds incorrectly to two or more items on a particular skill, assign the corresponding Extra Practice set.

SKILL	TEST ITEMS				EXTRA PRACTICE
1 Adding whole numbers *page 6*	78 +35 113	396 +672 1068	56 37 +92 185	406 328 78 +281 1093	*page 412*
2 Adding whole numbers *page 8*	7549 + 4261 11,810 496 + 3081 + 2566 6143		80,665 + 24,364 105,029 26,245 + 6518 + 276 33,039		*page 412*
3 Rounding whole numbers *page 12*	Round to the nearest ten. 63 60 Round to the nearest hundred. 446 400	123 130 967 1000	682 680 2809 2800	598 600 650 700	*page 413*
4 Rounding decimals *page 20*	Round to the nearest tenth. 1.38 1.4 Round to the nearest hundredth. 18.342 18.34	2.50 2.5 0.375 0.38	63.05 63.1 0.496 0.50	36.95 37.0 8.640 8.64	*page 413*
5 Adding decimals *page 22*	3.8 +2.3 6.1	5.62 +2.94 8.56	7.46 2.18 +6.53 16.17	4.71 0.39 9.24 +1.68 16.02	*page 414*
6 Adding decimals *page 24*	2.34 + 1.7 4.04 8.04 + 7 + 9.6 24.64		5.62 + 2.94 8.56 0.483 + 1.56 + 4.4 6.443		*page 414*
7 Comparing whole numbers *page 32*	< or >? 743 ● 734 > 42,382 ● 42,328 >		3321 ● 3400 < 599,999 ● 600,000 <		*page 415*
8 Subtracting whole numbers *page 34*	89 −37 52	90 −41 49	763 −280 483	846 −198 648	*page 415*

SKILL TEST

	SKILL		TEST ITEMS		EXTRA PRACTICE
9	**Subtracting whole numbers** *page 36*	70 − 37 *33* 802 − 378 *424* 500 − 142 *358*	80 − 19 *61* 600 − 374 *226* 300 − 62 *238*	900 − 514 *386* 4500 − 3492 *1008* 3800 − 1452 *2348*	*page 416*
10	**Subtracting whole numbers** *page 38*	50,341 − 28,220 *22,121*	83,510 − 27,496 *56,014*	573,017 − 77,480 *495,537* 800,356 − 366,082 *434,274*	*page 416*
11	**Comparing decimals** *page 42*	< or >? 3.57 ● 3.75 *<* 0.345 ● 0.3366 *>*	4.2 ● 3.21 *>* 0.4 ● 4.0 *<*	0.2 ● 0.19 *>* 0.031 ● 0.13 *<*	*page 417*
12	**Subtracting decimals** *page 44*	43.6 − 6.4 *37.2*	9.15 − 2.08 *7.07*	6.02 − 3.96 *2.06* 14.00 − 0.65 *13.35*	*page 417*
13	**Subtracting decimals** *page 46*	5 − 2.7 *2.3* 4.23 − 2.849 *1.381*	7 − 2.4 *4.6* 13 − 6.7 *6.3*	25.3 − 6 *19.3* 16.2 − 3.571 *12.629*	*page 418*
14	**Multiplying by multiples of 10, 100, 1000** *page 54*	35 × 100 *3500* 78 × 1000 *78,000* 92 × 10 *920*	40 × 60 *2400* 70 × 500 *35,000* 90 × 60 *5400*	324 × 10 *3240* 500 × 600 *300,000* 300 × 40 *12,000*	*page 418*
15	**Multiplying whole numbers** *page 56*	42 × 3 *126*	426 × 8 *3408*	608 × 6 *3648* 4815 × 7 *33,705*	*page 419*
16	**Multiplying whole numbers** *page 58*	58 × 35 *2030*	304 × 62 *18,848*	879 × 28 *24,612* 2836 × 81 *229,716*	*page 419*
17	**Multiplying whole numbers** *page 60*	248 × 112 *27,776*	644 × 306 *197,064*	1320 × 638 *842,160* 4801 × 709 *3,403,909*	*page 420*

SKILL TEST

	SKILL	TEST ITEMS			EXTRA PRACTICE
18	**Multiplying decimals** *page 64*	5.4×0.36 1.944 6.05×0.39 2.3595	6.3×1.2 7.56 2.04×1.6 3.264	34×0.88 29.92 8.25×2.06 16.995	*page 420*
19	**Simplifying expressions** *page 66*	$12 - (2.8 + 7.4)$ 1.8 $(23.97 \times 1.6) + 17.4$ 55.752		$5.6 \times (9.9 - 3.8)$ 34.16 $5 - (3.07 \times 0.44)$ 3.6492	*page 421*
20	**Multiplying decimals by 10, 100, 1000** *page 68*	0.93×100 93 5.28×1000 5280 3.8×10 38	0.3×10 3 4.1×1000 4100 5.22×100 522	4.7×10 47 0.004×100 0.4 0.03×1000 30	*page 421*
21	**Dividing whole numbers** *page 76*	$4\overline{)96}$ 24 $8\overline{)784}$ 98	$5\overline{)85}$ 17 $3\overline{)678}$ 226	$6\overline{)384}$ 64 $7\overline{)833}$ 119	*page 422*
22	**Dividing whole numbers** *page 78*	$618 \div 6$ 103 $8514 \div 9$ 946	$104 \div 2$ 52 $404 \div 4$ 101	$1505 \div 5$ 301 $7595 \div 7$ 1085	*page 422*
23	**Dividing whole numbers** *page 80*	$12\overline{)5842}$ 468 R10 $52\overline{)45,388}$ 872 R44	$25\overline{)5750}$ 230 $50\overline{)7500}$ 150	$26\overline{)4097}$ 157 R15 $78\overline{)60,411}$ 774 R39	*page 423*
24	**Dividing whole numbers** *page 84*	Round each quotient to the nearest whole number. $125\overline{)83,772}$ 670 $372\overline{)386,945}$ 1040	$101\overline{)68,204}$ 675 $400\overline{)682,140}$ 1705	$245\overline{)89,447}$ 365 $466\overline{)631,100}$ 1354	*page 423*
25	**Simplifying expressions** *page 86*	$12 - 8 + 4$ 8 $24 \times (12 - 2)$ 240		$18 \div 6 \times 2$ 6 $16 + 3 \times 4 \div 2$ 22	*page 424*
26	**Dividing decimals** *page 88*	Round each quotient to the nearest hundredth. $8\overline{)12.17}$ 1.52 $24\overline{)6.335}$ 0.26	$3\overline{)6.34}$ 2.11 $25\overline{)7.873}$ 0.31	$9\overline{)27.62}$ 3.07 $44\overline{)1.6238}$ 0.04	*page 424*

406

SKILL TEST

SKILL	TEST ITEMS	EXTRA PRACTICE
27 **Dividing decimals by 10, 100, 1000** *page 92*	$9.45 \div 10$ 0.945 $8.3 \div 10$ 0.83 $450.5 \div 100$ 4.505 $53.5 \div 1000$ 0.0535 $6.94 \div 1000$ 0.00694 $0.84 \div 100$ 0.0084	*page 425*
28 **Dividing decimals** *page 94*	$0.6\overline{)2.04}$ 3.4 $0.4\overline{)1.64}$ 4.1 $0.04\overline{)0.0644}$ 1.61 $0.18\overline{)0.1206}$ 0.67 $0.21\overline{)4.221}$ 20.1 $5.3\overline{)0.3233}$ 0.061	*page 425*
29 **Dividing decimals** *page 96*	Round each quotient to the nearest tenth. $0.3\overline{)1.7}$ 5.7 $0.2\overline{)3.7}$ 18.5 $0.06\overline{)0.574}$ 9.6 $2.6\overline{)3.79}$ 1.5 $1.3\overline{)6.21}$ 4.8 $0.82\overline{)0.097}$ 0.1	*page 426*
30 **Finding equivalent fractions** *page 126*	$\frac{1}{4} = \frac{?}{8}$ 2 $\frac{3}{9} = \frac{?}{3}$ 1 $\frac{8}{12} = \frac{?}{6}$ 4 $\frac{5}{8} = \frac{?}{24}$ 15 $\frac{1}{3} = \frac{?}{9}$ 3 $\frac{4}{8} = \frac{?}{2}$ 1 $\frac{4}{5} = \frac{?}{10}$ 8 $\frac{5}{12} = \frac{?}{24}$ 10	*page 426*
31 **Writing fractions in lowest terms** *page 128*	$\frac{3}{12} = ?$ $\frac{1}{4}$ $\frac{15}{20} = ?$ $\frac{3}{4}$ $\frac{9}{6} = ?$ $\frac{3}{2}$ $\frac{18}{10} = ?$ $\frac{9}{5}$ $\frac{2}{6} = ?$ $\frac{1}{3}$ $\frac{3}{9} = ?$ $\frac{1}{3}$ $\frac{8}{7} = ?$ $\frac{8}{7}$ $\frac{15}{10} = ?$ $\frac{3}{2}$	*page 427*
32 **Find the least common denominator** *page 130*	Find the least common denominator. $\frac{1}{3}$ $\frac{1}{2}$ 6 $\frac{1}{4}$ $\frac{3}{4}$ 4 $\frac{3}{4}$ $\frac{5}{6}$ 12 $\frac{5}{6}$ $\frac{5}{8}$ 24	*page 427*
33 **Comparing fractions** *page 132*	< or >? $\frac{4}{5} \bullet \frac{3}{5}$ > $\frac{1}{4} \bullet \frac{3}{8}$ < $\frac{3}{4} \bullet \frac{2}{3}$ > $\frac{5}{6} \bullet \frac{7}{8}$ <	*page 428*
34 **Writing whole and mixed numbers as fractions** *page 136*	Change to fourths. $2 = ?$ $\frac{8}{4}$ $4 = ?$ $\frac{16}{4}$ $6 = ?$ $\frac{24}{4}$ $3 = ?$ $\frac{12}{4}$ Change to a fraction. $1\frac{1}{4} = ?$ $\frac{5}{4}$ $1\frac{2}{3} = ?$ $\frac{5}{3}$ $2\frac{3}{4} = ?$ $\frac{11}{4}$ $3\frac{5}{6} = ?$ $\frac{23}{6}$	*page 428*

SKILL TEST

	SKILL	TEST ITEMS	EXTRA PRACTICE
35	**Writing fractions as whole or mixed numbers** *page 138*	Change to a whole number. $\frac{8}{2} = ?$ 4 $\quad\frac{9}{3} = ?$ 3 $\quad\frac{16}{4} = ?$ 4 $\quad\frac{18}{6} = ?$ 3 Change to a mixed number. $\frac{4}{3} = ?$ $1\frac{1}{3}$ $\quad\frac{5}{2} = ?$ $2\frac{1}{2}$ $\quad\frac{13}{5} = ?$ $2\frac{3}{5}$ $\quad\frac{11}{4} = ?$ $2\frac{3}{4}$	*page 429*
36	**Writing fractions and mixed numbers in simplest form** *page 140*	Write in simplest form. $\frac{6}{9} = ?$ $\frac{2}{3}$ $\quad 3\frac{2}{4} = ?$ $3\frac{1}{2}$ $\quad\frac{15}{3} = ?$ 5 $\quad\frac{14}{6} = ?$ $2\frac{1}{3}$	*page 429*
37	**Writing fractions and mixed numbers as decimals** *page 146*	Change to a decimal. $\frac{2}{5} = ?$ 0.4 $\quad\frac{3}{2} = ?$ 1.5 $\quad 1\frac{3}{4} = ?$ 1.75 $\quad 2\frac{3}{8} = ?$ 2.375 Change to a decimal rounded to the nearest hundredth. $\frac{1}{3} = ?$ 0.33 $\quad\frac{5}{6} = ?$ 0.83 $\quad\frac{10}{9} = ?$ 1.11 $\quad\frac{20}{3} = ?$ 6.67	*page 430*
38	**Writing decimals as fractions or mixed numbers** *page 148*	Change to a fraction in simplest form. $0.4 = ?$ $\frac{2}{5}$ $\quad 0.75 = ?$ $\frac{3}{4}$ $\quad 0.375 = ?$ $\frac{3}{8}$ $\quad 0.36 = ?$ $\frac{9}{25}$ Change to a mixed number in simplest form. $1.25 - ?$ $1\frac{1}{4}$ $\quad 3.5 - ?$ $3\frac{1}{2}$ $\quad 1.625 = ?$ $1\frac{5}{8}$ $\quad 2.08 = ?$ $2\frac{2}{25}$	*page 430*
39	**Adding fractions** *page 156*	Give the sum in simplest form. $\frac{1}{8} + \frac{3}{8}$ $\frac{1}{2}$ $\quad\frac{1}{3} + \frac{2}{3}$ 1 $\quad\frac{4}{5} + \frac{3}{5}$ $1\frac{2}{5}$ $\quad\frac{7}{16} + \frac{5}{16}$ $\frac{3}{4}$	*page 431*
40	**Adding fractions** *page 158*	Give each sum in simplest form. $\frac{1}{6} + \frac{1}{3}$ $\frac{1}{2}$ $\quad\frac{1}{3} + \frac{1}{2}$ $\frac{5}{6}$ $\quad\frac{5}{6} + \frac{3}{4}$ $1\frac{7}{12}$ $\quad\frac{9}{16} + \frac{5}{8}$ $1\frac{3}{16}$	*page 431*

SKILL TEST

SKILL	TEST ITEMS	EXTRA PRACTICE

41 **Adding mixed numbers** *page 160*

Give the sum in simplest form.   *page 432*

$$3\tfrac{1}{4} \atop +2\tfrac{1}{2}$$ $5\tfrac{3}{4}$ $$4\tfrac{3}{4} \atop +3\tfrac{1}{8}$$ $7\tfrac{7}{8}$ $$2\tfrac{2}{3} \atop +2\tfrac{1}{2}$$ $5\tfrac{1}{6}$ $$4\tfrac{1}{4} \atop +3\tfrac{7}{8}$$ $8\tfrac{1}{8}$

42 **Subtracting fractions** *page 164*

Give the difference in simplest form.   *page 432*

$\tfrac{4}{5} - \tfrac{1}{5}$ $\tfrac{3}{5}$ $\tfrac{3}{4} - \tfrac{1}{4}$ $\tfrac{1}{2}$ $\tfrac{5}{6} - \tfrac{1}{6}$ $\tfrac{2}{3}$ $\tfrac{11}{8} - \tfrac{5}{8}$ $\tfrac{3}{4}$

43 **Subtracting fractions** *page 166*

Give the difference in simplest form.   *page 433*

$\tfrac{3}{4} - \tfrac{1}{2}$ $\tfrac{1}{4}$ $\tfrac{5}{8} - \tfrac{1}{3}$ $\tfrac{7}{24}$ $\tfrac{5}{6} - \tfrac{1}{4}$ $\tfrac{7}{12}$ $\tfrac{7}{6} - \tfrac{5}{9}$ $\tfrac{11}{18}$

44 **Subtracting mixed numbers** *page 168*

Give the difference in simplest form.   *page 433*

$$4\tfrac{3}{4} \atop -2\tfrac{1}{2}$$ $2\tfrac{1}{4}$ $$5\tfrac{3}{5} \atop -1\tfrac{1}{3}$$ $4\tfrac{4}{15}$ $$6\tfrac{2}{3} \atop -4\tfrac{1}{6}$$ $2\tfrac{1}{2}$ $$4\tfrac{7}{8} \atop -3\tfrac{5}{16}$$ $1\tfrac{9}{16}$

45 **Subtracting mixed numbers** *page 170*

Give the difference in simplest form.   *page 434*

$$4\tfrac{1}{8} \atop -1\tfrac{3}{8}$$ $2\tfrac{3}{4}$ $$6 \atop -2\tfrac{1}{2}$$ $3\tfrac{1}{2}$ $$8\tfrac{1}{4} \atop -3\tfrac{2}{3}$$ $4\tfrac{7}{12}$ $$5\tfrac{1}{4} \atop -4\tfrac{2}{5}$$ $\tfrac{17}{20}$

46 **Multiplying fractions** *page 178*

Give the product in simplest form.   *page 434*

$\tfrac{1}{2} \times \tfrac{1}{3}$ $\tfrac{1}{6}$ $\tfrac{2}{3} \times \tfrac{3}{4}$ $\tfrac{1}{2}$ $3 \times \tfrac{3}{4}$ $2\tfrac{1}{4}$ $\tfrac{5}{6} \times \tfrac{6}{5}$ 1

47 **Finding a fraction of a number** *page 180*

    page 435

$\tfrac{1}{2}$ of $24 = ?$ 12 $\tfrac{1}{3}$ of $18 = ?$ 6 $\tfrac{2}{3}$ of $42 = ?$ 28

$\tfrac{3}{5}$ of $60 = ?$ 36 $\tfrac{2}{7}$ of $21 = ?$ 6 $\tfrac{3}{4}$ of $72 = ?$ 54

SKILL TEST

	SKILL	TEST ITEMS	EXTRA PRACTICE
48	**Multiplying mixed numbers** *page 182*	Give the product in simplest form. $1\frac{1}{4} \times 1\frac{1}{2}\,1\frac{7}{8}$ $2 \times 2\frac{1}{2}\,5$ $1\frac{2}{3} \times 1\frac{3}{4}\,2\frac{11}{12}$ $3\frac{1}{5} \times 2\frac{3}{8}\,7\frac{3}{5}$	*page 435*
49	**Finding a fraction of a number** *pages 184, 185*	$1\frac{2}{3}$ h = __?__ min 100 $2\frac{1}{2}$ ft = __?__ in. 30 $2\frac{2}{3}$ yd = __?__ ft 8 $1\frac{3}{4}$ gal = __?__ qt 7	*page 436*
50	**Dividing fractions** *page 188*	Give the quotient in simplest form. $\frac{2}{3} \div 4\,\frac{1}{6}$ $\frac{3}{4} \div \frac{3}{2}\,\frac{1}{2}$ $\frac{4}{9} \div \frac{1}{3}\,1\frac{1}{3}$ $\frac{5}{2} \div \frac{3}{4}\,3\frac{1}{3}$	*page 436*
51	**Dividing mixed numbers** *page 190*	Give the quotient in simplest form. $3 \div 2\frac{1}{3}\,1\frac{2}{7}$ $3\frac{2}{3} \div 1\frac{1}{2}\,2\frac{4}{9}$ $4\frac{3}{4} \div 2\,2\frac{3}{8}$ $4\frac{1}{5} \div 2\frac{5}{8}\,1\frac{3}{5}$	*page 437*
52	**Solving proportions** *page 230*	$\frac{12}{n} = \frac{1}{4}\,48$ $\frac{n}{8} = \frac{4}{5}\,6\frac{2}{5}$ $\frac{2}{3} = \frac{3}{n}\,4\frac{1}{2}$ $\frac{7}{10} = \frac{n}{8}\,5\frac{3}{5}$	*page 437*
53	**Writing percents as fractions or mixed numbers** *page 248*	Change to a fraction or mixed number in simplest form. $25\% = ?\,\frac{1}{4}$ $150\% = ?\,1\frac{1}{2}$ $33\frac{1}{3}\% = ?\,\frac{1}{3}$ $62\frac{1}{2}\% = ?\,\frac{5}{8}$	*page 438*
54	**Writing fractions as percents** *page 250*	Change to a percent. $\frac{3}{5} = ?\,60\%$ $\frac{3}{2} = ?\,150\%$ $\frac{1}{6} = ?\,16\frac{2}{3}\%$ $\frac{2}{3} = ?\,66\frac{2}{3}\%$	*page 438*
55	**Writing percents as decimals** *page 252*	Change to a decimal. $8\% = ?\,0.08$ $32\% = ?\,0.32$ $37.5\% = ?\,0.375$ $5.6\% = ?\,0.056$	*page 439*

SKILL TEST

SKILL	TEST ITEMS	EXTRA PRACTICE

56 **Writing decimals as percents** *page 253*

Change to a percent.

$0.05 = ?$ 5% $0.9 = ?$ 90% $1.375 = ?$ 137.5% $0.12\frac{1}{2} = ?$ $12\frac{1}{2}\%$

page 439

---

57 **Finding a percent of a number** *page 256*

25% of $44 = n$ 11 9% of $37 = n$ 3.33 *page 440*

6.5% of $38 = n$ 2.47 0.5% of $60 = n$ 0.3

---

58 **Finding a percent of a number** *page 258*

$33\frac{1}{3}\%$ of $81 = n$ 27 $12\frac{1}{2}\%$ of $48 = n$ 6 *page 440*

$66\frac{2}{3}\%$ of $96 = n$ 64 $16\frac{2}{3}\%$ of $72 = n$ 12

---

59 **Finding the number when a percent is given** *page 260*

20% of $n = 16$ 80 75% of $n = 48$ 64 *page 441*

Round each answer to the nearest tenth.

8.5% of $n = 12.5$ 147.1 32.2% of $n = 34.6$ 107.5

---

60 **Comparing integers** *page 362*

$<$ or $>$?

$^-3 \bullet ^-2$ < $^+9 \bullet 0$ > $^+12 \bullet ^+11$ > $^+10 \bullet ^-13$ >

page 441

---

61 **Adding integers** *page 364*

$^+4 + ^+7$ $^+9 + ^-3$ $^-8 + ^+8$ $^-12 + ^-15$ *page 442*

$^+11$ $^+6$ 0 $^-27$

---

62 **Subtracting integers** *pages 366, 367*

$^-7 - ^+3$ $^+8 - ^-9$ $^+14 - ^+14$ $^-16 - ^-20$ *page 442*

$^-10$ $^+17$ 0 $^+4$

---

63 **Multiplying integers** *pages 370, 371*

$^+6 \times ^-7$ $^+8 \times ^+3$ $^-5 \times ^+9$ $^-7 \times 0$ *page 443*

$^-42$ $^+24$ $^-45$ 0

---

64 **Dividing integers** *page 372*

$^-24 \div ^+8$ $^+54 \div ^-9$ $^-45 \div ^-5$ $^+72 \div ^+8$ *page 443*

$^-3$ $^-6$ $^+9$ $^+9$

EXTRA PRACTICE

SKILL 1 *(Use after page 6.)*

Here's how

Add ones and regroup.

```
   1
  96
 284
+163
   3
```

Add tens and regroup.

```
   1
 ₂96
 284
₊163
  43
```

Add hundreds.

```
   1
 ₂96
 284
₊163
 543
```

Add.

1. 84 +15 = 99	**2.** 50 +38 = 88	**3.** 63 +28 = 91	**4.** 65 +27 = 92
5. 29 +48 = 77	**6.** 47 +27 = 74	**7.** 68 +68 = 136	**8.** 93 +49 = 142
9. 356 + 82 = 438	**10.** 483 + 56 = 539	**11.** 297 +240 = 537	**12.** 839 +374 = 1213
13. 74 29 +38 = 141	**14.** 82 30 +56 = 168	**15.** 534 217 + 92 = 843	**16.** 611 309 +200 = 1120
17. 516 86 129 +202 = 933	**18.** 892 114 63 + 29 = 1098	**19.** 331 75 209 +113 = 728	**20.** 455 333 86 +264 = 1138

SKILL 2 *(Use after page 8.)*

Here's how

245 + 92 + 3916 = ?

Line up the digits that are in the same place.

```
  245
   92
+3916
```

Add.

```
 1 1
  245
 ₁ 92
+3916
 4253
```

Give the sum.

1. 6438 + 8310 14,748
2. 5832 + 694 6526
3. 966 + 2947 3913
4. 3370 + 1938 5308
5. 34,006 + 8825 42,831
6. 4721 + 76,082 80,803
7. 12,500 + 38,926 51,426
8. 38,842 + 27,111 65,953
9. 493 + 3493 + 977 4963
10. 8218 + 739 + 1005 9962
11. 182 + 4200 + 3628 8010
12. 7467 + 941 + 604 9012
13. 593 + 444 + 1660 2697
14. 2741 + 8009 + 476 11,226
15. 4850 + 1188 + 2055 8093
16. 1748 + 2966 + 1826 6540
17. 54,388 + 2112 + 599 57,099
18. 4368 + 829 + 12,477 17,674
19. 29,006 + 2704 + 1822 33,532
20. 2864 + 31,000 + 8002 41,866
21. 458 + 359 + 1642 + 28 2487
22. 56 + 2516 + 929 + 311 3812

SKILL 3 *(Use after page 12.)*

Here's how ___

Round 45,359 to the nearest hundred.

Rounding to this place
↓
45,359
↑

When the next digit to the right is 5 or greater, round up.

45,359 rounds to 45,400.

Round to the nearest ten.

1. 74   70 | **2.** 37   40 | **3.** 42   40 | **4.** 75   80

5. 183   180 | **6.** 366   370 | **7.** 805   810 | **8.** 411   410

9. 4336   4340 | **10.** 3721   3720 | **11.** 3605   3610 | **12.** 2398   2400

Round to the nearest hundred.

13. 276   300 | **14.** 550   600 | **15.** 743   700 | **16.** 849   800

17. 3408   3400 | **18.** 3423   3400 | **19.** 6660   6700 | **20.** 8050   8100

21. 20,305   20,300 | **22.** 32,780   32,800 | **23.** 42,912   42,900 | **24.** 62,950   63,000

Round to the nearest thousand.

25. 4841   5000 | **26.** 6851   7000 | **27.** 9310   9000 | **28.** 6500   7000

29. 35,431   35,000 | **30.** 42,573   43,000 | **31.** 719,527   720,000 | **32.** 273,500   274,000

Round to the nearest ten thousand.

33. 24,146   20,000 | **34.** 52,700   50,000 | **35.** 56,913   60,000 | **36.** 49,430   50,000

37. 92,604   90,000 | **38.** 28,911   30,000 | **39.** 249,300   250,000 | **40.** 613,812   610,000

SKILL 4 *(Use after page 20.)*

Here's how ___

Round 36.417 to the nearest tenth.

Rounding to this place
↓
36.417
↑

When the next digit to the right is 5 or greater, round up.

36.417 rounds to 36.4.

Round to the nearest whole number.

1. 16.6   17 | **2.** 38.3   38 | **3.** 92.4   92 | **4.** 35.5   36

5. 51.27   51 | **6.** 38.93   39 | **7.** 0.025   0 | **8.** 20.19   20

9. 327.04   327 | **10.** 118.40   118 | **11.** 0.500   1 | **12.** 12.099   12

Round to the nearest tenth.

13. 403.38   403.4 | **14.** 26.10   26.1 | **15.** 5.25   5.3 | **16.** 3.95   4.0

17. 21.39   21.4 | **18.** 24.188   24.2 | **19.** 22.06   22.1 | **20.** 7.472   7.5

21. 204.29   204.3 | **22.** 444.484   444.5 | **23.** 0.0592   0.1 | **24.** 0.95   1.0

Round to the nearest hundredth.

25. 22.317   22.32 | **26.** 56.208   56.21 | **27.** 5.531   5.53 | **28.** 54.325   54.33

29. 71.594   71.59 | **30.** 6.30196   6.30 | **31.** 0.0518   0.05 | **32.** 1.065   1.07

33. 0.0946   0.09 | **34.** 11.269   11.27 | **35.** 3.9421   3.94 | **36.** 0.097   0.10

37. 42.3381   42.34 | **38.** 28.095   28.10 | **39.** 0.6422   0.64 | **40.** 1.4920   1.49

Here's how

Add hundredths and regroup.

$$\begin{array}{r} 1 \\ 4.74 \\ +2.38 \\ \hline 2 \end{array}$$

Add tenths and regroup.

$$\begin{array}{r} 1\ 1 \\ 4.74 \\ +2.38 \\ \hline .12 \end{array}$$

Add ones.

$$\begin{array}{r} 1\ 1 \\ 4.74 \\ +2.38 \\ \hline 7.12 \end{array}$$

SKILL 5 (Use after page 22.)

Add.

1.
$$\begin{array}{r} 5.1 \\ +2.3 \\ \hline 7.4 \end{array}$$

2.
$$\begin{array}{r} 6.3 \\ +1.6 \\ \hline 7.9 \end{array}$$

3.
$$\begin{array}{r} 4.8 \\ +4.0 \\ \hline 8.8 \end{array}$$

4.
$$\begin{array}{r} 9.7 \\ +0.2 \\ \hline 9.9 \end{array}$$

5.
$$\begin{array}{r} 5.9 \\ +2.6 \\ \hline 8.5 \end{array}$$

6.
$$\begin{array}{r} 7.7 \\ +1.8 \\ \hline 9.5 \end{array}$$

7.
$$\begin{array}{r} 8.6 \\ +2.5 \\ \hline 11.1 \end{array}$$

8.
$$\begin{array}{r} 4.2 \\ +6.6 \\ \hline 10.8 \end{array}$$

9.
$$\begin{array}{r} 6.06 \\ +2.75 \\ \hline 8.81 \end{array}$$

10.
$$\begin{array}{r} 5.55 \\ +4.88 \\ \hline 10.43 \end{array}$$

11.
$$\begin{array}{r} 6.73 \\ +0.95 \\ \hline 7.68 \end{array}$$

12.
$$\begin{array}{r} 8.33 \\ +1.78 \\ \hline 10.11 \end{array}$$

13.
$$\begin{array}{r} 22.68 \\ +\ 8.66 \\ \hline 31.34 \end{array}$$

14.
$$\begin{array}{r} 18.93 \\ +\ 9.22 \\ \hline 28.15 \end{array}$$

15.
$$\begin{array}{r} 11.06 \\ +10.47 \\ \hline 21.53 \end{array}$$

16.
$$\begin{array}{r} 32.55 \\ +13.78 \\ \hline 46.33 \end{array}$$

17.
$$\begin{array}{r} 8.4 \\ 0.6 \\ +7.5 \\ \hline 16.5 \end{array}$$

18.
$$\begin{array}{r} 9.6 \\ 3.5 \\ +0.4 \\ \hline 13.5 \end{array}$$

19.
$$\begin{array}{r} 8.59 \\ 2.22 \\ +1.47 \\ \hline 12.28 \end{array}$$

20.
$$\begin{array}{r} 5.07 \\ 3.06 \\ +2.81 \\ \hline 10.94 \end{array}$$

21.
$$\begin{array}{r} 21.74 \\ 12.08 \\ 32.68 \\ +12.12 \\ \hline 78.62 \end{array}$$

22.
$$\begin{array}{r} 35.06 \\ 31.88 \\ 19.75 \\ +10.74 \\ \hline 97.43 \end{array}$$

23.
$$\begin{array}{r} 8.59 \\ 19.23 \\ 25.75 \\ +\ 9.09 \\ \hline 62.66 \end{array}$$

24.
$$\begin{array}{r} 46.66 \\ 7.42 \\ 31.66 \\ +\ 7.00 \\ \hline 92.74 \end{array}$$

Here's how

$3 + 2.51 + 8.6 = ?$

Line up the decimal points.

$$\begin{array}{r} 3 \\ 2.51 \\ +8.6 \\ \hline \end{array}$$

Add.

$$\begin{array}{r} 1 \\ 3 \\ 2.51 \\ +8.6 \\ \hline 14.11 \end{array}$$

SKILL 6 (Use after page 24.)

Give the sum.

1. $4.64 + 3.08$ 7.72

2. $7.564 + 3.806$ 11.37

3. $6.3521 + 0.5821$ 6.9342

4. $721.6 + 38.4$ 760

5. $2.35 + 4.829$ 7.179

6. $5.008 + 3.62$ 8.628

7. $43.6 + 27.48$ 71.08

8. $10.88 + 9.3$ 20.18

9. $5.6 + 3.04 + 2.7$ 11.34

10. $2.64 + 5.7 + 8.8$ 17.14

11. $4.20 + 9.2 + 3.65$ 17.05

12. $6.1 + 2.22 + 6.83$ 15.15

13. $2.641 + 0.75 + 3.58$ 6.971

14. $5.34 + 0.756 + 2.84$ 8.936

15. $9.3645 + 2.055 + 0.221$ 11.6405

16. $8.471 + 0.4911 + 3.300$ 1

17. $7.4 + 4.611 + 8.5$ 20.511

18. $15.966 + 8.4 + 4.8$ 29.166

19. $32 + 3.4 + 2.08$ 37.48

20. $5.7 + 41 + 6.63$ 53.33

414

SKILL 7 *(Use after page 32.)*

Here's how

> 54,375 ● 54,491
> Start at the left and compare digits that are in the same place.
>
> ──is less than──
>
> 54,375   54,491
>
> So
>
>   54,375 < 54,491

< or >?

1. 93 ● 90   >
2. 74 ● 79   <
3. 376 ● 388   <
4. 200 ● 186   >
5. 565 ● 566   <
6. 496 ● 490   >
7. 567 ● 576   <
8. 699 ● 700   <
9. 950 ● 1000   <
10. 1503 ● 999   >
11. 875 ● 1100   <
12. 1224 ● 899   >
13. 3721 ● 3615   >
14. 6732 ● 6655   >
15. 8472 ● 8427   >
16. 3818 ● 3811   >
17. 57,352 ● 58,410   <
18. 29,435 ● 29,400   >
19. 88,642 ● 89,000   <
20. 49,462 ● 50,362   <
21. 74,000 ● 73,999   >
22. 53,078 ● 53,780   <
23. 480,000 ● 479,000   >
24. 799,999 ● 800,000   <

SKILL 8 *(Use after page 34.)*

Here's how

> Regroup and subtract ones.
>
> $$\begin{array}{r} 5 \\ 5\,6\,{}^{1}4 \\ -2\,9\,7 \\ \hline 7 \end{array}$$
>
> Regroup and subtract tens.
>
> $$\begin{array}{r} 4\ 15 \\ \cancel{5}\,\cancel{6}\,{}^{1}4 \\ -2\,9\,7 \\ \hline 6\ 7 \end{array}$$
>
> Subtract hundreds.
>
> $$\begin{array}{r} 4\ 15 \\ \cancel{5}\,\cancel{6}\,{}^{1}4 \\ -2\,9\,7 \\ \hline 2\ 6\ 7 \end{array}$$

Subtract.

#		#		#		#	
1.	82 − 21 = 61	2.	75 − 33 = 42	3.	94 − 40 = 54	4.	88 − 65 = 23
5.	91 − 24 = 67	6.	80 − 54 = 26	7.	52 − 19 = 33	8.	46 − 27 = 19
9.	462 − 36 = 426	10.	350 − 18 = 332	11.	274 − 59 = 215	12.	783 − 47 = 736
13.	832 − 258 = 574	14.	856 − 193 = 663	15.	470 − 295 = 175	16.	673 − 488 = 185
17.	629 − 274 = 355	18.	900 − 366 = 534	19.	531 − 295 = 236	20.	842 − 416 = 426
21.	631 − 289 = 342	22.	497 − 179 = 318	23.	469 − 293 = 176	24.	259 − 140 = 119

SKILL 9 *(Use after page 36.)*

Here's how

No tens! Regroup 1 hundred for 10 tens.

$$\begin{array}{r} {}^{2}\\ 8\;\cancel{3}\,{}^{1}0\;5\\ -4\;0\;7\;8\\ \hline \end{array}$$

Regroup 1 ten for 10 ones.

$$\begin{array}{r} {}^{2}\quad{}^{9}\\ 8\;\cancel{3}\;{}^{1}\cancel{0}\,{}^{1}5\\ -4\;0\;7\;8\\ \hline \end{array}$$

Subtract.

$$\begin{array}{r} {}^{2}\quad{}^{9}\\ 8\;\cancel{3}\;{}^{1}\cancel{0}\,{}^{1}5\\ -4\;0\;7\;8\\ \hline 4\;2\;2\;7 \end{array}$$

Give the difference.

1. 828 − 411 417
2. 594 − 221 373
3. 710 − 463 247
4. 824 − 258 566
5. 504 − 356 148
6. 701 − 588 113
7. 806 − 529 277
8. 903 − 165 738
9. 800 − 361 439
10. 400 − 249 151
11. 700 − 318 382
12. 600 − 233 367
13. 800 − 444 356
14. 500 − 381 119
15. 4916 − 2854 2062
16. 5874 − 2222 3652
17. 3406 − 2153 1253
18. 7112 − 4338 2774
19. 2502 − 458 2044
20. 3701 − 229 3472
21. 5205 − 1286 3919
22. 6101 − 2255 3846
23. 3111 − 2478 633
24. 9055 − 3861 5194

SKILL 10 *(Use after page 38.)*

Here's how

Subtract.

$$\begin{array}{r} 5\,0,4\,5\,3\\ -4\,6,4\,7\,3\\ \hline 0 \end{array}$$

Regroup and subtract.

$$\begin{array}{r} {}^{3}\\ 5\,0,\,\cancel{4}\,{}^{1}5\,3\\ -4\,6,\,4\,7\,3\\ \hline 8\,0 \end{array}$$

Regroup twice and subtract.

$$\begin{array}{r} {}^{4}\quad{}^{9}\;{}^{13}\\ \cancel{5}\;{}^{1}\cancel{0},\cancel{4}\,{}^{1}5\,3\\ -4\;6,\,4\,7\,3\\ \hline 3,9\,8\,0 \end{array}$$

Subtract.

1. 5831 − 2127 = 3704
2. 6427 − 3408 = 3019
3. 5377 − 1724 = 3653
4. 8212 − 3001 = 5211
5. 6811 − 2366 = 4445
6. 3422 − 1830 = 1592
7. 5136 − 2209 = 2927
8. 4725 − 3546 = 1179
9. 7038 − 4152 = 2886
10. 3206 − 1137 = 2069
11. 5013 − 2963 = 2050
12. 8607 − 4359 = 4248
13. 9003 − 2814 = 6189
14. 4006 − 1759 = 2247
15. 7000 − 3644 = 3356
16. 4000 − 1842 = 2158
17. 42,583 − 8,077 = 34,506
18. 29,531 − 6,499 = 23,032
19. 56,031 − 23,740 = 32,291
20. 38,205 − 13,418 = 24,787
21. 38,003 − 27,584 = 10,419
22. 51,009 − 29,446 = 21,563
23. 345,729 − 158,362 = 187,367
24. 841,371 − 158,492 = 682,879

SKILL 11 *(Use after page 42.)*

Here's how

82.64 ● 82.39

Start at the left and compare digits that are in the same place.

┌── is greater than ──┐
82.64   82.39

So

82.64 > 82.39

< or >?

1. 0.3 ● 0.8 <
2. 0.6 ● 0.1 >
3. 0.04 ● 0.03 >
4. 0.06 ● 0.07 <
5. 0.004 ● 0.002 >
6. 0.008 ● 0.009 <
7. 15.5 ● 15.0 >
8. 8.43 ● 8.34 >
9. 0.57 ● 0.5 >
10. 0.007 ● 0.06 <
11. 0.6 ● 0.07 >
12. 9.73 ● 9.37 >
13. 42.89 ● 42.9 <
14. 5.1 ● 4.99 >
15. 4.352 ● 43.52 <
16. 0.625 ● 1.2 <
17. 3.08 ● 3.008 >
18. 0.715 ● 0.72 <
19. 51.86 ● 51.87 <
20. 33.78 ● 31.88 >

SKILL 12 *(Use after page 44.)*

Here's how

Regroup and subtract hundredths.

$$\begin{array}{r} {\scriptstyle 1} \\ 6.\overset{\scriptstyle 1}{\cancel{2}}4 \\ -1.47 \\ \hline 7 \end{array}$$

Regroup and subtract tenths.

$$\begin{array}{r} {\scriptstyle 5\ \ 11} \\ \cancel{6}.\overset{\scriptstyle 1}{\cancel{2}}4 \\ -1.47 \\ \hline .77 \end{array}$$

Subtract ones.

$$\begin{array}{r} {\scriptstyle 5\ \ 11} \\ \cancel{6}.\overset{\scriptstyle 1}{\cancel{2}}4 \\ -1.47 \\ \hline 4.77 \end{array}$$

Subtract.

1. 8.5 − 0.4 = 8.1
2. 7.4 − 3.2 = 4.2
3. 6.3 − 1.5 = 4.8
4. 5.2 − 3.3 = 1.9
5. 47.3 − 9.2 = 38.1
6. 58.4 − 6.6 = 51.8
7. 60.2 − 7.1 = 53.1
8. 71.5 − 8.4 = 63.1
9. 5.12 − 0.58 = 4.54
10. 6.93 − 0.95 = 5.98
11. 8.44 − 2.86 = 5.58
12. 7.43 − 1.66 = 5.77
13. 8.11 − 2.88 = 5.23
14. 7.23 − 3.45 = 3.78
15. 5.46 − 0.67 = 4.79
16. 9.71 − 4.86 = 4.85
17. 39.3 − 22.3 = 17.0
18. 42.1 − 34.7 = 7.4
19. 53.2 − 52.9 = 0.3
20. 74.5 − 15.8 = 58.7
21. 112.3 − 24.6 = 87.7
22. 15.53 − 8.66 = 6.87
23. 321.6 − 21.8 = 299.8
24. 25.34 − 7.65 = 17.69
25. 43.56 − 29.38 = 14.18
26. 38.44 − 10.74 = 27.70
27. 284.3 − 147.9 = 136.4
28. 583.5 − 265.3 = 318.2

SKILL 13 *(Use after page 46.)*

Here's how

20 − 14.38 = ?

Line up the decimal points. Write the zeros.

```
  2 0 . 0 0
− 1 4 . 3 8
```

Regroup.

```
    1   9   9
  2  ⁰0 . ⁰0 ¹0
 − 1  4 . 3   8
```

Subtract.

```
    1   9   9
  2  ⁰0 . ⁰0 ¹0
 − 1  4 . 3   8
   ───────────
      5 . 6   2
```

Give the difference.

1. 9 − 3.2 5.8
2. 8 − 4.6 3.4
3. 15 − 7.2 7.8
4. 23 − 8.6 14.4
5. 18.01 − 9.45 8.56
6. 14.05 − 7.75 6.30
7. 9.4 − 6.73 2.67
8. 8.5 − 4.55 3.95
9. 8.3 − 6 2.3
10. 7.4 − 2 5.4
11. 10.3 − 8.4 1.9
12. 30.1 − 9.7 20.4
13. 7 − 3.44 3.56
14. 8 − 6.45 1.55
15. 8.23 − 0.749 7.481
16. 6.729 − 0.88 5.849
17. 8.5 − 3.692 4.808
18. 5.1 − 0.651 4.449
19. 42 − 8.2 33.8
20. 34 − 9.5 24.5
21. 81.64 − 33 48.64
22. 63.89 − 18 45.89
23. 100 − 44.63 55.37
24. 200 − 53.87 146.13
25. 102 − 9.4 92.6
26. 105 − 49.7 55.3

SKILL 14 *(Use after page 54.)*

Here's how

30 × 200 = ?

Multiply 3 × 2.

30 × 200 = 6

Copy all the zeros.

30 × 200 = 6000

Give the product.

1. 9 × 10 90
2. 6 × 100 600
3. 5 × 1000 5000
4. 3 × 100 300
5. 8 × 20 160
6. 8 × 200 1600
7. 12 × 10 120
8. 15 × 1000 15,000
9. 20 × 30 600
10. 80 × 300 24,000
11. 3 × 800 2400
12. 20 × 40 800
13. 30 × 2000 60,000
14. 40 × 400 16,000
15. 50 × 100 5000
16. 50 × 1000 50,000
17. 40 × 200 8000
18. 20 × 3000 60,000
19. 30 × 20 600
20. 40 × 300 12,000
21. 400 × 30 12,000
22. 145 × 100 14,500
23. 256 × 1000 256,000
24. 100 × 300 30,000

SKILL 15 (Use after page 56.)

Here's how

Multiply ones.

$$\begin{array}{r} 564 \\ \times\ \ 2 \\ \hline 8 \end{array}$$

Multiply tens and regroup.

$$\begin{array}{r} 1\ \ \ \\ 564 \\ \times\ \ 2 \\ \hline 28 \end{array}$$

Multiply hundreds and add.

$$\begin{array}{r} 1\ \ \ \\ 564 \\ \times\ \ 2 \\ \hline 1128 \end{array}$$

Multiply.

1. $\begin{array}{r} 23 \\ \times\ 3 \\ \hline 69 \end{array}$
2. $\begin{array}{r} 12 \\ \times\ 4 \\ \hline 48 \end{array}$
3. $\begin{array}{r} 44 \\ \times\ 2 \\ \hline 88 \end{array}$
4. $\begin{array}{r} 11 \\ \times\ 6 \\ \hline 66 \end{array}$

5. $\begin{array}{r} 56 \\ \times\ 5 \\ \hline 280 \end{array}$
6. $\begin{array}{r} 70 \\ \times\ 7 \\ \hline 490 \end{array}$
7. $\begin{array}{r} 39 \\ \times\ 9 \\ \hline 351 \end{array}$
8. $\begin{array}{r} 82 \\ \times\ 4 \\ \hline 328 \end{array}$

9. $\begin{array}{r} 142 \\ \times\ \ 3 \\ \hline 426 \end{array}$
10. $\begin{array}{r} 481 \\ \times\ \ 6 \\ \hline 2886 \end{array}$
11. $\begin{array}{r} 330 \\ \times\ \ 2 \\ \hline 660 \end{array}$
12. $\begin{array}{r} 511 \\ \times\ \ 5 \\ \hline 2555 \end{array}$

13. $\begin{array}{r} 309 \\ \times\ \ 8 \\ \hline 2472 \end{array}$
14. $\begin{array}{r} 622 \\ \times\ \ 7 \\ \hline 4354 \end{array}$
15. $\begin{array}{r} 711 \\ \times\ \ 4 \\ \hline 2844 \end{array}$
16. $\begin{array}{r} 961 \\ \times\ \ 9 \\ \hline 8649 \end{array}$

17. $\begin{array}{r} 446 \\ \times\ \ 6 \\ \hline 2676 \end{array}$
18. $\begin{array}{r} 705 \\ \times\ \ 5 \\ \hline 3525 \end{array}$
19. $\begin{array}{r} 512 \\ \times\ \ 4 \\ \hline 2048 \end{array}$
20. $\begin{array}{r} 878 \\ \times\ \ 6 \\ \hline 5268 \end{array}$

21. $\begin{array}{r} 2103 \\ \times\ \ \ 2 \\ \hline 4206 \end{array}$
22. $\begin{array}{r} 3854 \\ \times\ \ \ 4 \\ \hline 15{,}416 \end{array}$
23. $\begin{array}{r} 6007 \\ \times\ \ \ 6 \\ \hline 36{,}042 \end{array}$
24. $\begin{array}{r} 8615 \\ \times\ \ \ 3 \\ \hline 25{,}845 \end{array}$

SKILL 16 (Use after page 58.)

Here's how

Multiply by 3.

$$\begin{array}{r} 145 \\ \times\ 23 \\ \hline 435 \end{array}$$

Multiply by 20.

$$\begin{array}{r} 145 \\ \times\ 23 \\ \hline 435 \\ 2900 \end{array}$$

Add.

$$\begin{array}{r} 145 \\ \times\ 23 \\ \hline 435 \\ 2900 \\ \hline 3335 \end{array}$$

Multiply.

1. $\begin{array}{r} 34 \\ \times 12 \\ \hline 408 \end{array}$
2. $\begin{array}{r} 26 \\ \times 20 \\ \hline 520 \end{array}$
3. $\begin{array}{r} 40 \\ \times 41 \\ \hline 1640 \end{array}$
4. $\begin{array}{r} 51 \\ \times 33 \\ \hline 1683 \end{array}$

5. $\begin{array}{r} 75 \\ \times 18 \\ \hline 1350 \end{array}$
6. $\begin{array}{r} 84 \\ \times 25 \\ \hline 2100 \end{array}$
7. $\begin{array}{r} 59 \\ \times 36 \\ \hline 2124 \end{array}$
8. $\begin{array}{r} 47 \\ \times 29 \\ \hline 1363 \end{array}$

9. $\begin{array}{r} 43 \\ \times 55 \\ \hline 2365 \end{array}$
10. $\begin{array}{r} 50 \\ \times 62 \\ \hline 3100 \end{array}$
11. $\begin{array}{r} 78 \\ \times 18 \\ \hline 1404 \end{array}$
12. $\begin{array}{r} 95 \\ \times 77 \\ \hline 7315 \end{array}$

13. $\begin{array}{r} 125 \\ \times\ 31 \\ \hline 3875 \end{array}$
14. $\begin{array}{r} 236 \\ \times\ 22 \\ \hline 5192 \end{array}$
15. $\begin{array}{r} 304 \\ \times\ 58 \\ \hline 17{,}632 \end{array}$
16. $\begin{array}{r} 411 \\ \times\ 70 \\ \hline 28{,}770 \end{array}$

17. $\begin{array}{r} 638 \\ \times\ 63 \\ \hline 40{,}194 \end{array}$
18. $\begin{array}{r} 905 \\ \times\ 85 \\ \hline 76{,}925 \end{array}$
19. $\begin{array}{r} 731 \\ \times\ 17 \\ \hline 12{,}427 \end{array}$
20. $\begin{array}{r} 592 \\ \times\ 46 \\ \hline 27{,}232 \end{array}$

21. $\begin{array}{r} 3015 \\ \times\ \ 33 \\ \hline 99{,}495 \end{array}$
22. $\begin{array}{r} 4628 \\ \times\ \ 60 \\ \hline 277{,}680 \end{array}$
23. $\begin{array}{r} 5911 \\ \times\ \ 45 \\ \hline 265{,}995 \end{array}$
24. $\begin{array}{r} 6408 \\ \times\ \ 28 \\ \hline 179{,}424 \end{array}$

Extra Practice **419**

Here's how

Start each product directly below the digit you are multiplying by.

```
    3 5 8
  × 2 3 9
    3 2 2 2
  1 0 7 4
  7 1 6
  8 5,5 6 2
```

SKILL 17 *(Use after page 60.)*

Multiply.

1. 456
    ×122
    55,632

2. 311
    ×232
    72,152

3. 506
    ×456
    230,736

4. 811
    ×348
    282,228

5. 630
    ×505
    318,150

6. 910
    ×644
    586,040

7. 713
    ×309
    220,317

8. 298
    ×400
    119,200

9. 542
    ×550
    298,100

10. 491
    ×389
    190,999

11. 670
    ×507
    339,690

12. 384
    ×229
    87,936

13. 2043
    × 150
    306,450

14. 4951
    × 238
    1,178,338

15. 6004
    × 356
    2,137,424

16. 5101
    × 474
    2,417,874

Here's how

3.08 × 4.2 = ?

Multiply as whole numbers.

```
    3.0 8
  ×   4.2
    6 1 6
  1 2 3 2
  1 2 9 3 6
```

Count the digits to the right of the decimal points.

```
    3.0 8    3
  × 4.2
    6 1 6
  1 2 3 2
  1 2 9 3 6
```

Count off the same number of digits in the product.

SKILL 18 *(Use after page 64.)*

Give the product.

1. 4.2 × 12 50.4
2. 3.8 × 10 38
3. 2.6 × 2.6 6.76
4. 5.9 × 8.7 51.33
5. 4.06 × 0.8 3.248
6. 2.05 × 5.5 11.275
7. 0.94 × 0.34 0.3196
8. 0.95 × 0.55 0.5225
9. 58 × 0.25 14.5
10. 74 × 0.78 57.72
11. 221 × 4.6 1016.6
12. 360 × 8.2 2952
13. 3.62 × 0.95 3.439
14. 2.88 × 0.47 1.3536
15. 6.16 × 7.5 46.2
16. 2.09 × 0.8 1.672
17. 5.4 × 0.06 0.324
18. 8.8 × 0.07 0.616
19. 6.25 × 0.56 3.5
20. 8.65 × 0.44 3.806
21. 30.5 × 20.2 616.1
22. 56.7 × 18.4 1043.28
23. 55.5 × 21.6 1198.8
24. 63.2 × 8.94 565.008
25. 300 × 4.8 1440
26. 600 × 0.52 312
27. 2.54 × 2.54 6.4516
28. 3.08 × 3.08 9.4864
29. 298 × 16.1 4797.8
30. 315 × 22.5 7087.5

SKILL 19 *(Use after page 66.)*

Here's how

2.8 + (0.2 × 0.3) = ?

Work inside the grouping symbols first.

First multiply.

$$\begin{array}{r} 0.2 \\ \times 0.3 \\ \hline 0.06 \end{array}$$

Then add.

$$\begin{array}{r} 0.2 \\ \times 0.3 \\ \hline 0.06 \\ + 2.8 \\ \hline 2.86 \end{array}$$

Simplify.

1. 4.1 + (0.2 × 0.3) 4.16
2. 12 − (4.3 + 2.8) 4.9
3. 5.2 × (6.1 + 3.8) 51.48
4. (8.2 × 0.7) + 4.11 9.85
5. (0.5 × 0.04) + 2.49 2.51
6. 8 − (0.3 × 0.06) 7.982
7. (5.3 − 1.4) × 0.08 0.312
8. (9.22 + 4.1) − 1.82 11.5
9. (23 − 15.5) × 2.1 15.75
10. (17.9 + 8.4) + 0.9 27.2
11. 18.3 + (8.6 + 7.7) 34.6
12. (11.34 − 6.91) − 2.08 2.35
13. 14.37 − (6.02 − 3.11) 11.46
14. (7.4 × 2.3) × 1.7 28.934
15. 3.5 × (9.1 − 2.03) 24.745
16. (3.5 × 9.1) − 2.03 29.82
17. 4.2 × (3.1 × 6) 78.12
18. (4.2 × 3.1) × 6 78.12
19. 6.01 + (2.5 + 3.7) 12.21
20. (6.01 + 2.5) + 3.7 12.21
21. 22 − (6.6 + 1.9) 13.5
22. (22 − 6.6) + 1.9 17.3
23. 12 + (4.5 × 0.5) 14.25
24. (12 + 4.5) × 0.5 8.25
25. 10 − (2.4 × 0.06) 9.856
26. (10 − 2.4) × 0.06 0.456

SKILL 20 *(Use after page 68.)*

Here's how

Multiplying by 10 moves the decimal point 1 place to the right.

2.47 × 10 = 24.7

Multiplying by 100 moves the decimal point 2 places to the right.

2.47 × 100 = 247

Give the product.

1. 42 × 10 420
2. 38 × 100 3800
3. 65 × 100 6500
4. 125 × 100 12,500
5. 8.2 × 10 82
6. 0.05 × 1000 50
7. 4.7 × 100 470
8. 2.95 × 10 29.5
9. 220 × 1000 220,000
10. 300 × 10 3000
11. 9.55 × 100 955
12. 8.74 × 1000 8740
13. 0.005 × 10 0.05
14. 0.002 × 100 0.2
15. 8.4 × 1000 8400
16. 7.2 × 100 720
17. 6.9 × 10 69
18. 3.74 × 100 374
19. 3.96 × 1000 3960
20. 6.66 × 10 66.6
21. 4.798 × 100 479.8
22. 4.798 × 10 47.98
23. 2.655 × 1000 2655
24. 148 × 100 14,800

SKILL 21 *(Use after page 76.)*

Here's how

Not enough hundreds.
Think 42 tens.

$$8\overline{)424}$$

Divide tens and
subtract.

$$\begin{array}{r} 5 \\ 8\overline{)424} \\ -40 \\ \hline 2 \end{array}$$

Think 24 ones.

$$\begin{array}{r} 5 \\ 8\overline{)424} \\ -40 \\ \hline 24 \end{array}$$

Divide ones. Subtract.

$$\begin{array}{r} 53 \\ 8\overline{)424} \\ -40 \\ \hline 24 \\ -24 \\ \hline 0 \end{array}$$

Divide.

1. $3\overline{)96}$ — 32
2. $4\overline{)84}$ — 21
3. $2\overline{)62}$ — 31
4. $3\overline{)63}$ — 21
5. $6\overline{)96}$ — 16
6. $8\overline{)88}$ — 11
7. $7\overline{)84}$ — 12
8. $9\overline{)99}$ — 11
9. $4\overline{)76}$ — 19
10. $5\overline{)90}$ — 18
11. $3\overline{)81}$ — 27
12. $6\overline{)84}$ — 14
13. $5\overline{)135}$ — 27
14. $7\overline{)245}$ — 35
15. $8\overline{)504}$ — 63
16. $4\overline{)352}$ — 88
17. $6\overline{)816}$ — 136
18. $4\overline{)588}$ — 147
19. $9\overline{)369}$ — 41
20. $5\overline{)295}$ — 59
21. $8\overline{)464}$ — 58
22. $3\overline{)207}$ — 69
23. $5\overline{)635}$ — 127
24. $6\overline{)450}$ — 75
25. $2\overline{)934}$ — 467
26. $9\overline{)513}$ — 57
27. $4\overline{)728}$ — 182
28. $7\overline{)812}$ — 116
29. $5\overline{)485}$ — 97
30. $6\overline{)558}$ — 93
31. $9\overline{)342}$ — 38
32. $8\overline{)952}$ — 119
33. $7\overline{)917}$ — 131
34. $4\overline{)696}$ — 174
35. $3\overline{)741}$ — 247
36. $6\overline{)498}$ — 83
37. $8\overline{)920}$ — 115
38. $2\overline{)584}$ — 292
39. $6\overline{)696}$ — 116
40. $5\overline{)950}$ — 190
41. $3\overline{)933}$ — 311
42. $5\overline{)675}$ — 135
43. $2\overline{)388}$ — 194
44. $7\overline{)819}$ — 117
45. $2\overline{)198}$ — 99
46. $5\overline{)695}$ — 139
47. $3\overline{)981}$ — 327
48. $6\overline{)366}$ — 61
49. $3\overline{)258}$ — 86
50. $4\overline{)508}$ — 127
51. $9\overline{)729}$ — 81
52. $4\overline{)896}$ — 224

SKILL 22 *(Use after page 78.)*

Here's how

Don't forget to write
this zero!

$$\begin{array}{r} 109 \\ 4\overline{)436} \\ -4 \\ \hline 36 \\ -36 \\ \hline 0 \end{array}$$

Divide.

1. $428 \div 4$ 107
2. $198 \div 9$ 22
3. $624 \div 6$ 104
4. $742 \div 7$ 106
5. $485 \div 5$ 97
6. $840 \div 8$ 105
7. $735 \div 7$ 105
8. $900 \div 3$ 300
9. $615 \div 5$ 123
10. $582 \div 6$ 97
11. $422 \div 2$ 211
12. $636 \div 6$ 106
13. $2016 \div 4$ 504
14. $5688 \div 8$ 711
15. $9396 \div 9$ 1044
16. $8330 \div 7$ 1190
17. $4656 \div 6$ 776
18. $4000 \div 8$ 500
19. $2945 \div 5$ 589
20. $3804 \div 4$ 951
21. $6210 \div 9$ 690

SKILL 23 (Use after page 80.)

Here's how

Think about dividing 39 by 4. So try 9.

$$48 \quad 48\overline{)3999}$$

$$\times 9$$
$$\overline{432} \quad 432 \text{ is too big!}$$

Try 8.
$$48 \qquad 8$$
$$\times 8 \quad 48\overline{)3999}$$
$$\overline{384} \quad -384$$
$$\qquad\qquad \overline{15}$$

Think about dividing 15 by 4. So try 3.

$$\qquad\qquad\quad 83 \text{ R15}$$
$$48 \quad 48\overline{)3999}$$
$$\times 3 \quad -384$$
$$\overline{144} \quad \overline{159}$$
$$\qquad\quad -144$$
$$\qquad\qquad \overline{15}$$

Divide.

1. $12\overline{)2946}$ 245 R6
2. $32\overline{)9375}$ 292 R31
3. $25\overline{)8611}$ 344 R11
4. $30\overline{)4789}$ 159 R19
5. $42\overline{)7194}$ 171 R12
6. $18\overline{)6978}$ 387 R12
7. $43\overline{)2589}$ 60 R9
8. $50\overline{)8526}$ 170 R26
9. $61\overline{)3810}$ 62 R28
10. $70\overline{)4490}$ 64 R10
11. $81\overline{)6351}$ 78 R33
12. $49\overline{)8555}$ 174 R29
13. $64\overline{)5773}$ 90 R13
14. $38\overline{)6310}$ 166 R2
15. $31\overline{)6000}$ 193 R17
16. $60\overline{)7008}$ 116 R48
17. $75\overline{)9362}$ 124 R62
18. $53\overline{)4867}$ 91 R44
19. $46\overline{)7351}$ 159 R37
20. $68\overline{)8022}$ 117 R66
21. $99\overline{)3366}$ 34
22. $25\overline{)4875}$ 195
23. $35\overline{)8610}$ 246
24. $60\overline{)8614}$ 143 R34
25. $91\overline{)6235}$ 68 R47
26. $35\overline{)6842}$ 195 R17
27. $43\overline{)9286}$ 215 R41
28. $61\overline{)8642}$ 141 R41
29. $32\overline{)6192}$ 193 R16
30. $60\overline{)7815}$ 130 R15
31. $18\overline{)73,202}$ 4066 R14
32. $35\overline{)20,496}$ 585 R21
33. $26\overline{)34,571}$ 1329 R17
34. $83\overline{)62,440}$ 752 R24
35. $80\overline{)70,709}$ 883 R69
36. $44\overline{)82,522}$ 1875 R22

SKILL 24 (Use after page 84.)

Here's how

Divide. Write a zero in the tenths place and carry out the division to that place.

$$\qquad\qquad 42.8$$
$$124\overline{)5309}.0$$
$$\quad -496$$
$$\quad \overline{349}$$
$$\quad -248$$
$$\quad \overline{1010}$$
$$\quad -992$$
$$\quad \overline{18}$$

Divide.

1. $125\overline{)38,500}$ 308
2. $150\overline{)67,800}$ 452
3. $212\overline{)91,372}$ 431
4. $318\overline{)57,558}$ 181
5. $222\overline{)49,506}$ 223
6. $300\overline{)56,100}$ 187
7. $360\overline{)91,080}$ 253
8. $436\overline{)57,988}$ 133
9. $278\overline{)82,288}$ 296

Divide. Round the quotient to the nearest whole number.

10. $516\overline{)81,088}$ 157
11. $406\overline{)73,849}$ 182
12. $616\overline{)47,321}$ 77
13. $700\overline{)46,831}$ 67
14. $688\overline{)91,156}$ 132
15. $927\overline{)55,780}$ 60
16. $250\overline{)465,890}$ 1864
17. $400\overline{)965,421}$ 2414
18. $536\overline{)571,903}$ 1067
19. $348\overline{)691,483}$ 1987
20. $198\overline{)485,579}$ 2452
21. $822\overline{)936,004}$ 1139

Here's how

$6 + 8 \times (4 - 2) = ?$

First, work within the grouping symbols.

$6 + 8 \times 2$

Next, do the multiplication and division.

$6 + 16$

Last, do the addition and subtraction.

22

SKILL 25 *(Use after page 86.)*

Simplify.

1. $6 \div 3 \times 2$ 4
2. $12 - 8 + 4$ 8
3. $5 + 2 \times 5 - 1$ 14
4. $5 \times 2 + 10 \div 2$ 15
5. $5 + (3 + 9) \div 6$ 7
6. $(4 + 5) \times 2 - 8$ 10
7. $12 \div 4 - 1$ 2
8. $8 \times 5 - 3$ 37
9. $24 - 4 \div 4$ 23
10. $30 - 12 - 6$ 12
11. $10 + 16 \div 4$ 14
12. $18 + 6 \div 3$ 20
13. $48 \div 8 \times 2$ 12
14. $35 + 12 - 10$ 37
15. $18 - 6 + 6$ 18
16. $20 - 9 + 5$ 16
17. $(12 + 18) \div 6$ 5
18. $34 \times (8 - 3)$ 170
19. $16 + 8 \div 4 + 4$ 22
20. $(16 + 8) \div 4 + 4$ 10
21. $16 + 8 \div (4 + 4)$ 17
22. $20 + 12 \times 4 - 1$ 67

Here's how

Divide.

$$\begin{array}{r} 0.56 \\ 23 \overline{)12.99} \\ -11\ 5 \\ \hline 1\ 49 \\ -1\ 38 \\ \hline 11 \end{array}$$

Write a zero and carry out the division another place.

$$\begin{array}{r} 0.564 \\ 23 \overline{)12.990} \\ -11\ 5 \\ \hline 1\ 49 \\ -1\ 38 \\ \hline 110 \\ -92 \\ \hline 18 \end{array}$$

SKILL 26 *(Use after page 88.)*

Divide.

1. $5 \overline{)8.1}$ 1.62
2. $7 \overline{)25.9}$ 3.7
3. $8 \overline{)4.32}$ 0.54
4. $2 \overline{)0.938}$ 0.469
5. $9 \overline{)67.5}$ 7.5
6. $7 \overline{)0.847}$ 0.121
7. $12 \overline{)1.44}$ 0.12
8. $23 \overline{)7.13}$ 0.31
9. $36 \overline{)1.008}$ 0.028
10. $47 \overline{)0.2491}$ 0.0053
11. $42 \overline{)16.212}$ 0.386
12. $65 \overline{)352.95}$ 5.43

Divide. Round the quotient to the nearest hundredth.

13. $3 \overline{)2.5}$ 0.83
14. $6 \overline{)0.32}$ 0.05
15. $9 \overline{)0.53}$ 0.06
16. $25 \overline{)56.92}$ 2.28
17. $14 \overline{)7.34}$ 0.52
18. $49 \overline{)8.91}$ 0.18
19. $39 \overline{)0.62}$ 0.02
20. $53 \overline{)0.834}$ 0.02
21. $26 \overline{)2.96}$ 0.11
22. $57 \overline{)0.952}$ 0.02
23. $48 \overline{)6.501}$ 0.14
24. $32 \overline{)7.319}$ 0.23
25. $71 \overline{)23.61}$ 0.33
26. $42 \overline{)3.114}$ 0.07
27. $29 \overline{)0.8113}$ 0.03
28. $83 \overline{)72.9}$ 0.88
29. $94 \overline{)89.1}$ 0.95
30. $85 \overline{)5.347}$ 0.06

SKILL 27 *(Use after page 92.)*

Here's how

Dividing by 10 moves the decimal point 1 place to the left.

5.2 ÷ 10 = 0.52

Dividing by 100 moves the decimal point 2 places to the left.

5.2 ÷ 100 = 0.052

Give the quotient.

1. 34.2 ÷ 10   3.42
2. 34.2 ÷ 100   0.342
3. 458 ÷ 100   4.58
4. 458 ÷ 1000   0.458
5. 252.5 ÷ 100   2.525
6. 252.5 ÷ 10   25.25
7. 80 ÷ 10   8
8. 80 ÷ 100   0.80
9. 23.94 ÷ 10   2.394
10. 23.94 ÷ 100   0.2394
11. 2.8 ÷ 10   0.28
12. 2.8 ÷ 100   0.028
13. 2.8 ÷ 1000   0.0028
14. 9.05 ÷ 10   0.905
15. 9.05 ÷ 100   0.0905
16. 9.05 ÷ 1000   0.00905
17. 325 ÷ 100   3.25
18. 325 ÷ 10   32.5
19. 325 ÷ 1000   0.325
20. 9 ÷ 10   0.9
21. 9 ÷ 1000   0.009
22. 9 ÷ 100   0.09
23. 26.7 ÷ 100   0.267
24. 26.7 ÷ 1000   0.0267
25. 26.7 ÷ 10   2.67
26. 42.059 ÷ 100   0.42059
27. 42.059 ÷ 10   4.2059
28. 42.059 ÷ 1000   0.042059

SKILL 28 *(Use after page 94.)*

Here's how

$$0.42 \overline{)\, 0.5670}$$

Move both decimal points two places to the right.

$$0.42 \overline{)\, 0.56.70}$$

Divide.

$$\begin{array}{r} 1.35 \\ 0.42 \overline{)\, 0.56.70} \\ -42 \\ \hline 147 \\ -126 \\ \hline 210 \\ -210 \\ \hline 0 \end{array}$$

Divide.

1. $0.7 \overline{)\, 38.36}$ 54.8
2. $0.6 \overline{)\, 2.634}$ 4.39
3. $0.9 \overline{)\, 5.067}$ 5.63
4. $0.08 \overline{)\, 4.584}$ 57.3
5. $0.03 \overline{)\, 1.473}$ 49.1
6. $0.005 \overline{)\, 3.605}$ 721
7. $0.004 \overline{)\, 0.2656}$ 66.4
8. $0.3 \overline{)\, 96.30}$ 321
9. $0.04 \overline{)\, 6.400}$ 160.
10. $0.6 \overline{)\, 350.4}$ 584
11. $0.07 \overline{)\, 0.0644}$ 0.92
12. $0.9 \overline{)\, 0.963}$ 1.07
13. $0.005 \overline{)\, 8.6055}$ 1721.1
14. $0.08 \overline{)\, 0.0152}$ 0.19
15. $0.4 \overline{)\, 2.208}$ 5.52
16. $0.002 \overline{)\, 0.5978}$ 298.9
17. $0.03 \overline{)\, 2.0172}$ 67.24
18. $0.7 \overline{)\, 8.407}$ 12.01
19. $1.2 \overline{)\, 0.144}$ 0.12
20. $0.15 \overline{)\, 0.6075}$ 4.05
21. $2.3 \overline{)\, 28.52}$ 12.4
22. $0.45 \overline{)\, 1.3995}$ 3.11
23. $2.4 \overline{)\, 1.2912}$ 0.538
24. $0.37 \overline{)\, 0.22274}$ 0.602
25. $6.7 \overline{)\, 29.011}$ 4.33
26. $5.3 \overline{)\, 19.292}$ 3.64
27. $0.86 \overline{)\, 0.38442}$ 0.447

Here's how

Write a 0 in the dividend to place the decimal point.

$$0.06.\overline{)16.30.}$$

Divide.

$$\begin{array}{r} 271.66 \\ 0.06.\overline{)16.30.00} \\ -12 \\ \hline 43 \\ -42 \\ \hline 10 \\ -6 \\ \hline 40 \\ -36 \\ \hline 40 \\ -36 \\ \hline 4 \end{array}$$

SKILL 29 (Use after page 96.)

Divide.

1. $0.5\overline{)6.1}$ 12.2
2. $0.2\overline{)8.7}$ 43.5
3. $0.4\overline{)0.42}$ 1.05

4. $0.08\overline{)0.052}$ 0.65
5. $0.06\overline{)0.033}$ 0.55
6. $0.05\overline{)0.17}$ 3.4

7. $0.6\overline{)1.05}$ 1.75
8. $0.4\overline{)3.1}$ 7.75
9. $0.2\overline{)1.033}$ 5.165

10. $0.05\overline{)0.4}$ 8
11. $0.6\overline{)3}$ 5
12. $0.4\overline{)9}$ 22.5

13. $1.2\overline{)7.8}$ 6.5
14. $3.1\overline{)124}$ 40
15. $0.25\overline{)17.5}$ 70

16. $0.42\overline{)159.6}$ 380
17. $0.049\overline{)401.8}$ 8200
18. $0.066\overline{)48.84}$ 740

Divide. Round each quotient to the nearest tenth.

19. $0.3\overline{)1.7}$ 5.7
20. $0.6\overline{)1.02}$ 1.7
21. $1.3\overline{)4.0}$ 3.1

22. $2.5\overline{)9.1}$ 3.6
23. $3.7\overline{)0.99}$ 0.3
24. $7.1\overline{)52.8}$ 7.4

25. $4.3\overline{)0.271}$ 0.1
26. $0.55\overline{)0.382}$ 0.7
27. $0.67\overline{)1.092}$ 1.6

28. $0.59\overline{)0.377}$ 0.6
29. $6.1\overline{)7.055}$ 1.2
30. $5.2\overline{)8.033}$ 1.5

Here's how

$$\frac{2}{5} = \frac{?}{15}$$

Multiply numerator and denominator by 3.

$$\boxed{\times 3}$$
$$\frac{2}{5} = \frac{6}{15}$$
$$\boxed{\times 3}$$

$$\frac{12}{20} = \frac{?}{5}$$

Divide numerator and denominator by 4.

$$\boxed{\div 4}$$
$$\frac{12}{20} = \frac{3}{5}$$
$$\boxed{\div 4}$$

SKILL 30 (Use after page 126.)

Complete.

1. $\frac{1}{2} = \frac{?}{4}$ 2
2. $\frac{1}{3} = \frac{?}{6}$ 2
3. $\frac{1}{4} = \frac{?}{12}$ 3
4. $\frac{2}{3} = \frac{?}{6}$ 4

5. $\frac{6}{8} = \frac{?}{4}$ 3
6. $\frac{9}{24} = \frac{?}{8}$ 3
7. $\frac{9}{6} = \frac{?}{2}$ 3
8. $\frac{3}{9} = \frac{?}{3}$ 1

9. $\frac{1}{4} = \frac{?}{20}$ 5
10. $\frac{1}{2} = \frac{?}{6}$ 3
11. $\frac{1}{5} = \frac{?}{10}$ 2
12. $\frac{4}{5} = \frac{?}{15}$ 12

13. $\frac{8}{12} = \frac{?}{3}$ 2
14. $\frac{25}{10} = \frac{?}{2}$ 5
15. $\frac{4}{16} = \frac{?}{4}$ 1
16. $\frac{6}{9} = \frac{?}{3}$ 2

17. $\frac{1}{3} = \frac{?}{15}$ 5
18. $\frac{1}{6} = \frac{?}{18}$ 3
19. $\frac{5}{8} = \frac{?}{16}$ 10
20. $\frac{3}{4} = \frac{?}{16}$ 12

21. $\frac{4}{24} = \frac{?}{6}$ 1
22. $\frac{12}{10} = \frac{?}{5}$ 6
23. $\frac{5}{10} = \frac{?}{2}$ 1
24. $\frac{4}{20} = \frac{?}{5}$ 1

25. $\frac{5}{2} = \frac{?}{10}$ 25
26. $\frac{1}{4} = \frac{?}{8}$ 2
27. $\frac{3}{2} = \frac{?}{10}$ 15
28. $\frac{3}{5} = \frac{?}{20}$ 12

29. $\frac{6}{12} = \frac{?}{2}$ 1
30. $\frac{30}{18} = \frac{?}{3}$ 5
31. $\frac{10}{15} = \frac{?}{3}$ 2
32. $\frac{4}{12} = \frac{?}{3}$ 1

SKILL 31 *(Use after page 128.)*

Here's how

To write a fraction in lowest terms, divide both terms by their greatest common divisor.

$$\frac{12}{18} = \frac{2}{3}$$
$\div 6$ (top) $\div 6$ (bottom)

Write in lowest terms.

1. $\frac{3}{6}$ $\frac{1}{2}$
2. $\frac{3}{9}$ $\frac{1}{3}$
3. $\frac{2}{8}$ $\frac{1}{4}$
4. $\frac{6}{9}$ $\frac{2}{3}$
5. $\frac{9}{6}$ $\frac{3}{2}$
6. $\frac{14}{16}$ $\frac{7}{8}$
7. $\frac{9}{12}$ $\frac{3}{4}$
8. $\frac{10}{12}$ $\frac{5}{6}$
9. $\frac{8}{10}$ $\frac{4}{5}$
10. $\frac{5}{15}$ $\frac{1}{3}$
11. $\frac{6}{4}$ $\frac{3}{2}$
12. $\frac{7}{14}$ $\frac{1}{2}$
13. $\frac{8}{16}$ $\frac{1}{2}$
14. $\frac{15}{6}$ $\frac{5}{2}$
15. $\frac{2}{10}$ $\frac{1}{5}$
16. $\frac{16}{12}$ $\frac{4}{3}$
17. $\frac{21}{6}$ $\frac{7}{2}$
18. $\frac{4}{8}$ $\frac{1}{2}$
19. $\frac{6}{16}$ $\frac{3}{8}$
20. $\frac{4}{12}$ $\frac{1}{3}$
21. $\frac{3}{12}$ $\frac{1}{4}$
22. $\frac{4}{6}$ $\frac{2}{3}$
23. $\frac{3}{18}$ $\frac{1}{6}$
24. $\frac{15}{18}$ $\frac{5}{6}$
25. $\frac{10}{6}$ $\frac{5}{3}$
26. $\frac{15}{20}$ $\frac{3}{4}$
27. $\frac{5}{10}$ $\frac{1}{2}$
28. $\frac{10}{15}$ $\frac{2}{3}$
29. $\frac{6}{12}$ $\frac{1}{2}$
30. $\frac{4}{20}$ $\frac{1}{5}$
31. $\frac{18}{24}$ $\frac{3}{4}$
32. $\frac{6}{18}$ $\frac{1}{3}$

SKILL 32 *(Use after page 130.)*

Here's how

To find the least common denominator of two fractions, find the least common multiple of the denominators.

$\frac{2}{3}$ $\frac{3}{4}$

3, 6, 9, (12), 15   4, 8, (12), 16, 20

The least common denominator is 12.

Find the least common denominator.

1. $\frac{1}{6}$ $\frac{1}{5}$ 30
2. $\frac{3}{4}$ $\frac{1}{2}$ 4
3. $\frac{1}{5}$ $\frac{2}{9}$ 45
4. $\frac{3}{7}$ $\frac{1}{6}$ 42
5. $\frac{1}{10}$ $\frac{2}{5}$ 10
6. $\frac{3}{20}$ $\frac{1}{10}$ 20
7. $\frac{1}{4}$ $\frac{1}{6}$ 12
8. $\frac{1}{2}$ $\frac{3}{7}$ 14
9. $\frac{5}{6}$ $\frac{3}{8}$ 24
10. $\frac{1}{6}$ $\frac{1}{8}$ 24
11. $\frac{1}{8}$ $\frac{4}{3}$ 24
12. $\frac{1}{10}$ $\frac{3}{4}$ 20
13. $\frac{7}{8}$ $\frac{1}{12}$ 24
14. $\frac{1}{6}$ $\frac{3}{4}$ 12
15. $\frac{1}{5}$ $\frac{3}{7}$ 35
16. $\frac{1}{3}$ $\frac{5}{6}$ 6
17. $\frac{2}{5}$ $\frac{1}{4}$ 20
18. $\frac{1}{10}$ $\frac{4}{5}$ 10
19. $\frac{5}{9}$ $\frac{1}{2}$ 18
20. $\frac{1}{4}$ $\frac{3}{5}$ 20
21. $\frac{3}{10}$ $\frac{1}{4}$ 20
22. $\frac{1}{6}$ $\frac{4}{5}$ 30
23. $\frac{7}{6}$ $\frac{5}{9}$ 18
24. $\frac{3}{8}$ $\frac{1}{9}$ 72
25. $\frac{5}{6}$ $\frac{1}{15}$ 30
26. $\frac{1}{7}$ $\frac{1}{3}$ 21
27. $\frac{2}{5}$ $\frac{1}{8}$ 40
28. $\frac{1}{12}$ $\frac{2}{3}$ 12
29. $\frac{1}{4}$ $\frac{1}{7}$ 28
30. $\frac{1}{9}$ $\frac{2}{3}$ 9
31. $\frac{1}{3}$ $\frac{2}{9}$ 9
32. $\frac{3}{8}$ $\frac{1}{7}$ 56

Here's how

Find the least common denominator.

$$\frac{2}{3} \bullet \frac{3}{4}$$

$$12$$

Change to equivalent fractions.

$$\frac{8}{12}\left.\frac{2}{3} \bullet \frac{3}{4}\right.\frac{9}{12}$$

Compare.

$$\frac{2}{3} < \frac{3}{4}$$

SKILL 33 *(Use after page 132.)*

< or >?

1. $\frac{1}{4} \bullet \frac{3}{4}$ <   2. $\frac{3}{5} \bullet \frac{2}{5}$ >   3. $\frac{3}{7} \bullet \frac{4}{7}$ <   4. $\frac{0}{8} \bullet \frac{5}{8}$ <

5. $\frac{5}{4} \bullet \frac{4}{4}$ >   2 6. $\frac{7}{5} \bullet \frac{9}{5}$ <   7. $\frac{5}{8} \bullet \frac{7}{8}$ <   8. $\frac{7}{3} \bullet \frac{5}{3}$ >

9. $\frac{2}{3} \bullet \frac{5}{6}$ <   10. $\frac{5}{4} \bullet \frac{3}{2}$ <   11. $\frac{2}{7} \bullet \frac{1}{3}$ <   12. $\frac{3}{4} \bullet \frac{3}{8}$ >

13. $\frac{1}{8} \bullet \frac{1}{6}$ <   14. $\frac{3}{8} \bullet \frac{1}{4}$ >   15. $\frac{3}{10} \bullet \frac{1}{3}$ <   16. $\frac{1}{4} \bullet \frac{2}{5}$ <

17. $\frac{1}{4} \bullet \frac{1}{3}$ <   18. $\frac{2}{9} \bullet \frac{3}{4}$ <   19. $\frac{2}{3} \bullet \frac{3}{4}$ <   20. $\frac{5}{8} \bullet \frac{4}{7}$ >

21. $\frac{3}{5} \bullet \frac{3}{7}$ 22. $\frac{3}{4} \bullet \frac{5}{6}$ <   23. $\frac{8}{11} \bullet \frac{7}{8}$ >   24. $\frac{1}{3} \bullet \frac{5}{12}$ <

25. $\frac{7}{8} \bullet \frac{5}{6}$ >   26. $\frac{2}{3} \bullet \frac{7}{10}$ <   27. $\frac{7}{9} \bullet \frac{2}{3}$ >   28. $\frac{9}{2} \bullet \frac{9}{4}$ >

Here's how

$$4 = \frac{?}{3}$$

Write the whole number over 1 and multiply both numerator and denominator by 3.

$$\frac{4}{1} = \frac{12}{3}$$

$$2\frac{3}{4} = ?$$

To change a mixed number to a fraction, multiply the denominator by the whole number and add the numerator.

$$2\frac{3}{4} = \frac{11}{4}$$

SKILL 34 *(Use after page 136.)*

Change to thirds.

1. $2\ \frac{6}{3}$ 2. $1\ \frac{3}{3}$ 3. $4\ \frac{12}{3}$ 4. $5\ \frac{15}{3}$

5. $3\ \frac{9}{3}$ 6. $8\ \frac{24}{3}$ 7. $10\ \frac{30}{3}$ 8. $6\ \frac{18}{3}$

Change to fourths.

9. $3\ \frac{12}{4}$ 10. $1\ \frac{4}{4}$ 11. $4\ \frac{16}{4}$ 12. $2\ \frac{8}{4}$

13. $7\ \frac{28}{4}$ 14. $9\ \frac{36}{4}$ 15. $10\ \frac{40}{4}$ 16. $8\ \frac{32}{4}$

Change to a fraction.

17. $1\frac{1}{3}\ \frac{4}{3}$ 18. $2\frac{1}{4}\ \frac{9}{4}$ 19. $2\frac{1}{2}\ \frac{5}{2}$ 20. $1\frac{1}{5}\ \frac{6}{5}$

21. $1\frac{2}{3}\ \frac{5}{3}$ 22. $2\frac{1}{3}\ \frac{7}{3}$ 23. $1\frac{1}{4}\ \frac{5}{4}$ 24. $3\frac{1}{4}\ \frac{13}{4}$

25. $1\frac{1}{2}\ \frac{3}{2}$ 26. $2\frac{7}{8}\ \frac{23}{8}$ 27. $3\frac{3}{8}\ \frac{27}{8}$ 28. $2\frac{5}{6}\ \frac{17}{6}$

29. $5\frac{1}{4}\ \frac{21}{4}$ 30. $2\frac{2}{3}\ \frac{8}{3}$ 31. $3\frac{1}{2}\ \frac{7}{2}$ 32. $4\frac{5}{8}\ \frac{37}{8}$

33. $4\frac{4}{5}\ \frac{24}{5}$ 34. $3\frac{1}{3}\ \frac{10}{3}$ 35. $5\frac{3}{10}\ \frac{53}{10}$ 36. $4\frac{1}{5}\ \frac{21}{5}$

SKILL 35 *(Use after page 138.)*

Here's how

To change a fraction to a whole number or mixed number, divide the numerator by the denominator.

$$\frac{18}{3} = 6$$

$$\frac{19}{4} = 4\frac{3}{4}$$

$$4\overline{)19} \quad \begin{array}{r} 4 \\ -16 \\ \hline 3 \end{array}$$

There are 3 fourths left over.

Change to a whole number.

1. $\frac{4}{2}$ 2

2. $\frac{40}{5}$ 8

3. $\frac{10}{2}$ 5

4. $\frac{9}{3}$ 3

5. $\frac{25}{5}$ 5

6. $\frac{8}{2}$ 4

7. $\frac{32}{4}$ 8

8. $\frac{30}{3}$ 10

9. $\frac{18}{3}$ 6

10. $\frac{35}{5}$ 7

11. $\frac{16}{4}$ 4

12. $\frac{50}{5}$ 10

Change to a mixed number.

13. $\frac{3}{2}$ $1\frac{1}{2}$

14. $\frac{5}{4}$ $1\frac{1}{4}$

15. $\frac{5}{3}$ $1\frac{2}{3}$

16. $\frac{9}{2}$ $4\frac{1}{2}$

17. $\frac{11}{4}$ $2\frac{3}{4}$

18. $\frac{4}{3}$ $1\frac{1}{3}$

19. $\frac{13}{5}$ $2\frac{3}{5}$

20. $\frac{7}{6}$ $1\frac{1}{6}$

21. $\frac{16}{3}$ $5\frac{1}{3}$

22. $\frac{13}{10}$ $1\frac{3}{10}$

23. $\frac{5}{2}$ $2\frac{1}{2}$

24. $\frac{8}{3}$ $2\frac{2}{3}$

25. $\frac{23}{10}$ $2\frac{3}{10}$

26. $\frac{9}{5}$ $1\frac{4}{5}$

27. $\frac{13}{12}$ $1\frac{1}{12}$

28. $\frac{19}{6}$ $3\frac{1}{6}$

29. $\frac{7}{2}$ $3\frac{1}{2}$

30. $\frac{11}{3}$ $3\frac{2}{3}$

31. $\frac{19}{4}$ $4\frac{3}{4}$

32. $\frac{18}{5}$ $3\frac{3}{5}$

SKILL 36 *(Use after page 140.)*

Here's how

simplest form
↓

$$\frac{6}{9} = \frac{2}{3}$$

simplest form
↓

$$3\frac{4}{6} = 3\frac{2}{3}$$

simplest form
↓

$$\frac{18}{3} = 6$$

simplest form
↓

$$\frac{14}{4} = 3\frac{2}{4} = 3\frac{1}{2}$$

Write in simplest form.

1. $\frac{8}{2}$ 4

2. $\frac{6}{9}$ $\frac{2}{3}$

3. $\frac{10}{15}$ $\frac{2}{3}$

4. $\frac{15}{5}$ 3

5. $\frac{10}{12}$ $\frac{5}{6}$

6. $\frac{6}{15}$ $\frac{2}{5}$

7. $\frac{4}{3}$ $1\frac{1}{3}$

8. $\frac{4}{24}$ $\frac{1}{6}$

9. $\frac{9}{2}$ $4\frac{1}{2}$

10. $1\frac{8}{12}$ $1\frac{2}{3}$

11. $1\frac{3}{6}$ $1\frac{1}{2}$

12. $2\frac{4}{6}$ $2\frac{2}{3}$

13. $1\frac{2}{4}$ $1\frac{1}{2}$

14. $\frac{10}{2}$ 5

15. $\frac{11}{3}$ $3\frac{2}{3}$

16. $3\frac{6}{16}$ $3\frac{3}{8}$

17. $\frac{23}{4}$ $5\frac{3}{4}$

18. $4\frac{4}{10}$ $4\frac{2}{5}$

19. $5\frac{9}{24}$ $5\frac{3}{8}$

20. $\frac{20}{24}$ $\frac{5}{6}$

21. $\frac{36}{6}$ 6

22. $\frac{17}{2}$ $8\frac{1}{2}$

23. $\frac{25}{5}$ 5

24. $\frac{13}{3}$ $4\frac{1}{3}$

25. $\frac{18}{5}$ $3\frac{3}{5}$

26. $\frac{24}{3}$ 8

27. $\frac{12}{15}$ $\frac{4}{5}$

28. $\frac{9}{12}$ $\frac{3}{4}$

29. $6\frac{10}{12}$ $6\frac{5}{6}$

30. $\frac{19}{4}$ $4\frac{3}{4}$

31. $8\frac{12}{16}$ $8\frac{3}{4}$

32. $\frac{17}{5}$ $3\frac{2}{5}$

SKILL 37 *(Use after page 146.)*

Here's how

To change a fraction to a decimal, divide the numerator by the denominator.

$$\frac{5}{8} = ?$$

$$\begin{array}{r} 0.625 \\ 8\overline{)5.000} \\ -4\,8 \\ \hline 20 \\ -16 \\ \hline 40 \\ -40 \\ \hline 0 \end{array}$$

$$\frac{5}{8} = 0.625$$

$$1\frac{5}{8} = ?$$

$$1\frac{5}{8} = 1.625$$

Change to a decimal.

1. $\frac{1}{4}$ 0.25
2. $\frac{3}{4}$ 0.75
3. $\frac{1}{5}$ 0.2
4. $\frac{1}{2}$ 0.5

5. $\frac{9}{10}$ 0.9
6. $\frac{2}{5}$ 0.4
7. $\frac{7}{10}$ 0.7
8. $\frac{4}{5}$ 0.8

9. $\frac{1}{8}$ 0.125
10. $\frac{3}{10}$ 0.3
11. $\frac{7}{4}$ 1.75
12. $\frac{9}{8}$ 1.125

13. $\frac{9}{2}$ 4.5
14. $\frac{3}{8}$ 0.375
15. $\frac{3}{5}$ 0.6
16. $\frac{7}{8}$ 0.875

17. $\frac{9}{4}$ 2.25
18. $\frac{11}{2}$ 5.5
19. $\frac{1}{16}$ 0.0625
20. $\frac{11}{8}$ 1.37

21. $\frac{5}{16}$ 0.3125
22. $\frac{3}{2}$ 1.5
23. $\frac{8}{5}$ 1.6
24. $\frac{13}{5}$ 2.6

25. $2\frac{1}{2}$ 2.5
26. $3\frac{3}{4}$ 3.75
27. $3\frac{4}{5}$ 3.8
28. $2\frac{7}{8}$ 2.87

Change to a decimal rounded to the nearest hundredth.

29. $\frac{1}{9}$ 0.11
30. $\frac{1}{3}$ 0.33
31. $\frac{4}{3}$ 1.33
32. $\frac{1}{6}$ 0.17

33. $\frac{11}{6}$ 1.83
34. $\frac{3}{16}$ 0.19
35. $\frac{5}{6}$ 0.83
36. $\frac{5}{3}$ 1.67

37. $\frac{7}{9}$ 0.78
38. $\frac{17}{6}$ 2.83
39. $\frac{9}{16}$ 0.56
40. $\frac{21}{16}$ 1.31

SKILL 38 *(Use after page 148.)*

Here's how

Write as a fraction in simplest form.

$$0.75 = \frac{75}{100} = \frac{3}{4}$$

Write as a mixed number in simplest form.

$$3.4 = 3\frac{4}{10} = 3\frac{2}{5}$$

Change to a fraction in simplest form.

1. 0.4 $\frac{2}{5}$
2. 0.8 $\frac{4}{5}$
3. 0.6 $\frac{3}{5}$
4. 0.1 $\frac{1}{10}$

5. 0.9 $\frac{9}{10}$
6. 0.5 $\frac{1}{2}$
7. 0.3 $\frac{3}{10}$
8. 0.2 $\frac{1}{5}$

9. 0.25 $\frac{1}{4}$
10. 0.75 $\frac{3}{4}$
11. 0.15 $\frac{3}{20}$
12. 0.45 $\frac{9}{20}$

13. 0.375 $\frac{3}{8}$
14. 0.625 $\frac{5}{8}$
15. 0.875 $\frac{7}{8}$
16. 0.125 $\frac{1}{8}$

Change to a mixed number in simplest form.

17. 1.2 $1\frac{1}{5}$
18. 2.3 $2\frac{3}{10}$
19. 1.6 $1\frac{3}{5}$
20. 3.8 $3\frac{4}{5}$

21. 2.4 $2\frac{2}{5}$
22. 7.7 $7\frac{7}{10}$
23. 4.5 $4\frac{1}{2}$
24. 5.9 $5\frac{9}{1}$

25. 3.25 $3\frac{1}{4}$
26. 1.75 $1\frac{3}{4}$
27. 2.12 $2\frac{3}{25}$
28. 4.48 $4\frac{12}{25}$

29. 4.625 $4\frac{5}{8}$
30. 6.875 $6\frac{7}{8}$
31. 2.125 $2\frac{1}{8}$
32. 5.375 5

SKILL 39 *(Use after page 156.)*

Here's how

Add the numerators and use the common denominators.

$$\frac{3}{8} + \frac{1}{8} = \frac{4}{8}$$

Write in simplest form.

$$\frac{3}{8} + \frac{1}{8} = \frac{4}{8}$$
$$= \frac{1}{2}$$

Give the sum in simplest form.

1. $\frac{1}{4} + \frac{1}{4}$ $\frac{1}{2}$
2. $\frac{1}{5} + \frac{2}{5}$ $\frac{3}{5}$
3. $\frac{1}{4} + \frac{3}{4}$ 1
4. $\frac{1}{6} + \frac{1}{6}$ $\frac{1}{3}$

5. $\frac{1}{9} + \frac{1}{9}$ $\frac{2}{9}$
6. $\frac{2}{7} + \frac{2}{7}$ $\frac{4}{7}$
7. $\frac{2}{9} + \frac{1}{9}$ $\frac{1}{3}$
8. $\frac{1}{8} + \frac{3}{8}$ $\frac{1}{2}$

9. $\frac{5}{8} + \frac{5}{8}$ $1\frac{1}{4}$
10. $\frac{4}{9} + \frac{4}{9}$ $\frac{8}{9}$
11. $\frac{3}{10} + \frac{3}{10}$ $\frac{3}{5}$
12. $\frac{2}{5} + \frac{3}{5}$ 1

13. $\frac{1}{6} + \frac{5}{6}$ 1
14. $\frac{3}{4} + \frac{3}{4}$ $1\frac{1}{2}$
15. $\frac{1}{8} + \frac{1}{8}$ $\frac{1}{4}$
16. $\frac{7}{10} + \frac{3}{10}$ 1

17. $\frac{7}{12} + \frac{5}{12}$ 1
18. $\frac{2}{9} + \frac{2}{9}$ $\frac{4}{9}$
19. $\frac{4}{5} + \frac{1}{5}$ 1
20. $\frac{3}{8} + \frac{3}{8}$ $\frac{3}{4}$

21. $\frac{1}{5} + \frac{1}{5}$ $\frac{2}{5}$
22. $\frac{5}{7} + \frac{1}{7}$ $\frac{6}{7}$
23. $\frac{5}{16} + \frac{3}{16}$ $\frac{1}{2}$
24. $\frac{3}{7} + \frac{4}{7}$ 1

25. $\frac{5}{12} + \frac{1}{12}$ $\frac{1}{2}$
26. $\frac{9}{16} + \frac{5}{16}$ $\frac{7}{8}$
27. $\frac{2}{5} + \frac{2}{5}$ $\frac{4}{5}$
28. $\frac{9}{16} + \frac{9}{16}$ $1\frac{1}{8}$

29. $\frac{3}{5} + \frac{3}{5}$ $1\frac{1}{5}$
30. $\frac{5}{9} + \frac{3}{9}$ $\frac{8}{9}$
31. $\frac{3}{8} + \frac{5}{8}$ 1
32. $\frac{5}{9} + \frac{1}{9}$ $\frac{2}{3}$

SKILL 40 *(Use after page 158.)*

Here's how

Change to equivalent fractions with common denominators.

$$\frac{2}{3} + \frac{3}{4} = \frac{8}{12} + \frac{9}{12}$$

Add. Write in simplest form.

$$\frac{2}{3} + \frac{3}{4} = \frac{8}{12} + \frac{9}{12}$$
$$= \frac{17}{12}$$
$$= 1\frac{5}{12}$$

Give the sum in simplest form.

1. $\frac{1}{2} + \frac{1}{4}$ $\frac{3}{4}$
2. $\frac{1}{6} + \frac{2}{3}$ $\frac{5}{6}$
3. $\frac{3}{8} + \frac{1}{4}$ $\frac{5}{8}$
4. $\frac{1}{2} + \frac{3}{8}$ $\frac{7}{8}$

5. $\frac{1}{3} + \frac{1}{6}$ $\frac{1}{2}$
6. $\frac{2}{5} + \frac{3}{10}$ $\frac{7}{10}$
7. $\frac{1}{5} + \frac{3}{10}$ $\frac{1}{2}$
8. $\frac{1}{3} + \frac{1}{4}$ $\frac{7}{12}$

9. $\frac{1}{3} + \frac{3}{7}$ $\frac{16}{21}$
10. $\frac{5}{9} + \frac{1}{6}$ $\frac{13}{18}$
11. $\frac{1}{8} + \frac{3}{4}$ $\frac{7}{8}$
12. $\frac{2}{5} + \frac{1}{4}$ $\frac{13}{20}$

13. $\frac{2}{3} + \frac{1}{9}$ $\frac{7}{9}$
14. $\frac{1}{3} + \frac{1}{2}$ $\frac{5}{6}$
15. $\frac{2}{3} + \frac{1}{8}$ $\frac{19}{24}$
16. $\frac{1}{2} + \frac{1}{6}$ $\frac{2}{3}$

17. $\frac{3}{8} + \frac{1}{6}$ $\frac{13}{24}$
18. $\frac{1}{3} + \frac{2}{5}$ $\frac{11}{15}$
19. $\frac{1}{3} + \frac{5}{8}$ $\frac{23}{24}$
20. $\frac{1}{8} + \frac{1}{6}$ $\frac{7}{24}$

21. $\frac{3}{4} + \frac{1}{2}$ $1\frac{1}{4}$
22. $\frac{1}{6} + \frac{2}{9}$ $\frac{7}{18}$
23. $\frac{5}{16} + \frac{1}{8}$ $\frac{7}{16}$
24. $\frac{1}{4} + \frac{2}{3}$ $\frac{11}{12}$

25. $\frac{5}{12} + \frac{1}{4}$ $\frac{2}{3}$
26. $\frac{2}{3} + \frac{11}{12}$ $1\frac{7}{12}$
27. $\frac{3}{7} + \frac{1}{2}$ $\frac{13}{14}$
28. $\frac{7}{8} + \frac{5}{16}$ $1\frac{3}{16}$

29. $\frac{2}{9} + \frac{2}{3}$ $\frac{8}{9}$
30. $\frac{1}{6} + \frac{4}{9}$ $\frac{11}{18}$
31. $\frac{1}{2} + \frac{2}{5}$ $\frac{9}{10}$
32. $\frac{9}{16} + \frac{1}{8}$ $\frac{11}{16}$

Here's how

Write equivalent fractions with common denominators.

$$3\frac{2}{3} = 3\frac{8}{12}$$
$$+2\frac{3}{4} = +2\frac{9}{12}$$

Add the fractions. Add the whole numbers. Write in simplest form.

$$3\frac{2}{3} = 3\frac{8}{12}$$
$$+2\frac{3}{4} = +2\frac{9}{12}$$
$$5\frac{17}{12} = 6\frac{5}{12}$$

SKILL 41 *(Use after page 160.)*

Give the sum in simplest form.

1. $2\frac{1}{4}$ $+3\frac{1}{2}$ $5\frac{3}{4}$
2. $3\frac{1}{8}$ $+3\frac{3}{4}$ $6\frac{7}{8}$
3. $1\frac{3}{8}$ $+4\frac{1}{4}$ $5\frac{5}{8}$
4. $5\frac{1}{3}$ $+2\frac{1}{4}$ $7\frac{7}{12}$

5. $8\frac{5}{9}$ $+2\frac{1}{6}$ $10\frac{13}{18}$
6. $9\frac{1}{4}$ $+3\frac{2}{5}$ $12\frac{13}{20}$
7. $6\frac{1}{9}$ $+8\frac{2}{3}$ $14\frac{7}{9}$
8. $4\frac{1}{6}$ $+5\frac{1}{2}$ $9\frac{2}{3}$

9. $7\frac{3}{8}$ $+4\frac{1}{6}$ $11\frac{13}{24}$
10. $8\frac{1}{6}$ $+5\frac{2}{3}$ $13\frac{5}{6}$
11. $9\frac{1}{2}$ $+9\frac{3}{8}$ $18\frac{7}{8}$
12. $7\frac{1}{3}$ $+7\frac{1}{2}$ $14\frac{5}{6}$

13. $6\frac{11}{12}$ $+8\frac{2}{3}$ $15\frac{7}{12}$
14. $5\frac{1}{3}$ $+5\frac{2}{5}$ $10\frac{11}{15}$
15. $7\frac{1}{8}$ $+8\frac{5}{16}$ $15\frac{7}{16}$
16. $6\frac{2}{3}$ $+9\frac{1}{4}$ $15\frac{11}{12}$

17. $9\frac{2}{5}$ $+3\frac{3}{10}$ $12\frac{7}{10}$
18. $6\frac{1}{6}$ $+7\frac{1}{3}$ $13\frac{1}{2}$
19. $8\frac{1}{4}$ $+6\frac{5}{12}$ $14\frac{2}{3}$
20. $5\frac{1}{6}$ $+9\frac{2}{9}$ $14\frac{7}{18}$

Here's how

Subtract the numerators and use the common denominator.

$$\frac{5}{8} - \frac{1}{8} = \frac{4}{8}$$

Write in simplest form.

$$\frac{5}{8} - \frac{1}{8} = \frac{4}{8}$$
$$= \frac{1}{2}$$

SKILL 42 *(Use after page 164.)*

Give the difference in simplest form.

1. $\frac{3}{4} - \frac{1}{4}$ $\frac{1}{2}$
2. $\frac{1}{3} - \frac{1}{3}$ 0
3. $\frac{3}{2} - \frac{1}{2}$ 1
4. $\frac{4}{3} - \frac{1}{3}$ 1

5. $\frac{4}{5} - \frac{1}{5}$ $\frac{3}{5}$
6. $\frac{5}{6} - \frac{1}{6}$ $\frac{2}{3}$
7. $\frac{5}{4} - \frac{3}{4}$ $\frac{1}{2}$
8. $\frac{1}{6} - \frac{1}{6}$ 0

9. $\frac{5}{3} - \frac{2}{3}$ 1
10. $\frac{5}{8} - \frac{1}{8}$ $\frac{1}{2}$
11. $\frac{4}{5} - \frac{2}{5}$ $\frac{2}{5}$
12. $\frac{7}{3} - \frac{3}{3}$ $1\frac{1}{3}$

13. $\frac{3}{8} - \frac{3}{8}$ 0
14. $\frac{7}{4} - \frac{3}{4}$ 1
15. $\frac{5}{2} - \frac{1}{2}$ 2
16. $\frac{5}{8} - \frac{3}{8}$ $\frac{1}{4}$

17. $\frac{2}{3} - \frac{0}{3}$ $\frac{2}{3}$
18. $\frac{3}{5} - \frac{1}{5}$ $\frac{2}{5}$
19. $\frac{7}{6} - \frac{3}{6}$ $\frac{2}{3}$
20. $\frac{7}{2} - \frac{1}{2}$ 3

21. $\frac{9}{4} - \frac{3}{4}$ $1\frac{1}{2}$
22. $\frac{5}{6} - \frac{0}{6}$ $\frac{5}{6}$
23. $\frac{5}{5} - \frac{3}{5}$ $\frac{2}{5}$
24. $\frac{7}{8} - \frac{3}{8}$ $\frac{1}{2}$

25. $\frac{9}{10} - \frac{1}{10}$ $\frac{4}{5}$
26. $\frac{9}{2} - \frac{3}{2}$ 3
27. $\frac{11}{4} - \frac{7}{4}$ 1
28. $\frac{11}{6} - \frac{5}{6}$ 1

SKILL 43 *(Use after page 166.)*

Here's how

Write equivalent fractions with common denominators.

$$\frac{2}{3} - \frac{1}{6} = \frac{4}{6} - \frac{1}{6}$$

Subtract. Write in simplest form.

$$\frac{2}{3} - \frac{1}{6} = \frac{4}{6} - \frac{1}{6}$$
$$= \frac{3}{6}$$
$$= \frac{1}{2}$$

Give the difference in simplest form.

1. $\frac{1}{3} - \frac{1}{4}$ $\frac{1}{12}$
2. $\frac{1}{2} - \frac{1}{4}$ $\frac{1}{4}$
3. $\frac{3}{4} - \frac{1}{2}$ $\frac{1}{4}$
4. $\frac{5}{8} - \frac{1}{4}$ $\frac{3}{8}$

5. $\frac{3}{4} - \frac{0}{2}$ $\frac{3}{4}$
6. $\frac{2}{3} - \frac{1}{2}$ $\frac{1}{6}$
7. $\frac{1}{4} - \frac{1}{8}$ $\frac{1}{8}$
8. $\frac{1}{3} - \frac{1}{8}$ $\frac{5}{24}$

9. $\frac{3}{4} - \frac{3}{8}$ $\frac{3}{8}$
10. $\frac{7}{8} - \frac{2}{3}$ $\frac{5}{24}$
11. $\frac{1}{2} - \frac{1}{3}$ $\frac{1}{6}$
12. $\frac{2}{3} - \frac{5}{8}$ $\frac{1}{24}$

13. $\frac{5}{9} - \frac{1}{6}$ $\frac{7}{18}$
14. $\frac{1}{3} - \frac{1}{6}$ $\frac{1}{6}$
15. $\frac{5}{8} - \frac{2}{5}$ $\frac{9}{40}$
16. $\frac{7}{10} - \frac{2}{5}$ $\frac{3}{10}$

17. $\frac{1}{2} - \frac{3}{8}$ $\frac{1}{8}$
18. $\frac{9}{10} - \frac{2}{3}$ $\frac{7}{30}$
19. $\frac{3}{4} - \frac{2}{3}$ $\frac{1}{12}$
20. $\frac{2}{3} - \frac{2}{5}$ $\frac{4}{15}$

21. $\frac{11}{12} - \frac{3}{8}$ $\frac{13}{24}$
22. $\frac{2}{3} - \frac{1}{4}$ $\frac{5}{12}$
23. $\frac{1}{2} - \frac{5}{12}$ $\frac{1}{12}$
24. $\frac{7}{12} - \frac{3}{8}$ $\frac{5}{24}$

25. $\frac{5}{6} - \frac{5}{9}$ $\frac{5}{18}$
26. $\frac{7}{8} - \frac{5}{16}$ $\frac{9}{16}$
27. $\frac{8}{9} - \frac{5}{6}$ $\frac{1}{18}$
28. $\frac{3}{4} - \frac{7}{12}$ $\frac{1}{6}$

29. $\frac{1}{2} - \frac{7}{16}$ $\frac{1}{16}$
30. $\frac{1}{4} - \frac{3}{16}$ $\frac{1}{16}$
31. $\frac{11}{12} - \frac{5}{6}$ $\frac{1}{12}$
32. $\frac{11}{16} - \frac{3}{8}$ $\frac{5}{16}$

SKILL 44 *(Use after page 168.)*

Here's how

Write equivalent fractions with common denominators.

$$8\frac{5}{6} = 8\frac{10}{12}$$
$$-2\frac{1}{12} = -2\frac{1}{12}$$

Subtract the fractions. Subtract the whole numbers. Write in simplest form.

$$8\frac{5}{6} = 8\frac{10}{12}$$
$$-2\frac{1}{12} = -2\frac{1}{12}$$
$$6\frac{9}{12} = 6\frac{3}{4}$$

Give the difference in simplest form.

1. $3\frac{5}{8}$ $-2\frac{1}{4}$ $1\frac{3}{8}$
2. $6\frac{3}{4}$ $-4\frac{3}{8}$ $2\frac{3}{8}$
3. $4\frac{1}{2}$ $-2\frac{1}{4}$ $2\frac{1}{4}$
4. $5\frac{5}{9}$ $-3\frac{1}{6}$ $2\frac{7}{18}$

5. $8\frac{1}{3}$ $-4\frac{1}{6}$ $4\frac{1}{6}$
6. $5\frac{3}{4}$ $-1\frac{1}{2}$ $4\frac{1}{4}$
7. $9\frac{5}{8}$ $-3\frac{2}{5}$ $6\frac{9}{40}$
8. $5\frac{7}{8}$ $-3\frac{2}{3}$ $2\frac{5}{24}$

9. $7\frac{2}{3}$ $-6\frac{5}{8}$ $1\frac{1}{24}$
10. $5\frac{7}{10}$ $-1\frac{2}{5}$ $4\frac{3}{10}$
11. $6\frac{3}{4}$ $-1\frac{1}{8}$ $5\frac{5}{8}$
12. $9\frac{2}{3}$ $-3\frac{1}{2}$ $6\frac{1}{6}$

13. $6\frac{1}{3}$ $-4\frac{1}{4}$ $2\frac{1}{12}$
14. $5\frac{1}{3}$ $-3\frac{1}{8}$ $2\frac{5}{24}$
15. $7\frac{1}{2}$ $-2\frac{3}{8}$ $5\frac{1}{8}$
16. $3\frac{9}{10}$ $-1\frac{2}{3}$ $2\frac{7}{30}$

SKILL 45 *(Use after page 170.)*

(Use after page 170.)

Here's how

Change to a common denominator.

$$5\tfrac{1}{3} = 5\tfrac{2}{6}$$
$$-2\tfrac{1}{2} = -2\tfrac{3}{6}$$

Regroup.

$$5\tfrac{1}{3} = 5\tfrac{2}{6} = 4\tfrac{8}{6}$$
$$-2\tfrac{1}{2} = -2\tfrac{3}{6} = -2\tfrac{3}{6}$$

Subtract.

$$5\tfrac{1}{3} = 5\tfrac{2}{6} = 4\tfrac{8}{6}$$
$$-2\tfrac{1}{2} = -2\tfrac{3}{6} = -2\tfrac{3}{6}$$
$$2\tfrac{5}{6}$$

Give the difference in simplest form.

1. $4\tfrac{1}{2} - 3\tfrac{3}{4}$ $\tfrac{3}{4}$
2. $5\tfrac{5}{8} - 1\tfrac{3}{4}$ $3\tfrac{7}{8}$
3. $7\tfrac{3}{4} - 4\tfrac{1}{2}$ $3\tfrac{1}{4}$
4. $8\tfrac{2}{5} - 2\tfrac{1}{2}$ $5\tfrac{9}{10}$

5. $9\tfrac{1}{3} - 6\tfrac{3}{4}$ $2\tfrac{7}{12}$
6. $6\tfrac{1}{4} - 1\tfrac{3}{8}$ $4\tfrac{7}{8}$
7. $8\tfrac{1}{8} - 3\tfrac{1}{3}$ $4\tfrac{19}{24}$
8. $5\tfrac{2}{3} - 4\tfrac{7}{8}$ $\tfrac{19}{24}$

9. $7\tfrac{3}{8} - 2\tfrac{2}{3}$ $4\tfrac{17}{24}$
10. $8\tfrac{5}{9} - 3\tfrac{1}{6}$ $5\tfrac{7}{18}$
11. $6\tfrac{1}{6} - 4\tfrac{1}{3}$ $1\tfrac{5}{6}$
12. $4\tfrac{3}{8} - 2\tfrac{1}{2}$ $1\tfrac{7}{8}$

13. $6\tfrac{2}{3} - 5\tfrac{3}{4}$ $\tfrac{11}{12}$
14. $8\tfrac{2}{5} - 3\tfrac{2}{3}$ $4\tfrac{11}{15}$
15. $7\tfrac{1}{4} - 6\tfrac{2}{3}$ $\tfrac{7}{12}$
16. $5\tfrac{5}{12} - 2\tfrac{1}{2}$ $2\tfrac{11}{12}$

17. $9\tfrac{5}{9} - 4\tfrac{5}{6}$ $4\tfrac{13}{18}$
18. $7\tfrac{5}{16} - 2\tfrac{7}{8}$ $4\tfrac{7}{16}$
19. $6\tfrac{7}{16} - 3\tfrac{1}{2}$ $2\tfrac{15}{16}$
20. $8\tfrac{3}{10} - 4\tfrac{4}{5}$ $3\tfrac{1}{2}$

SKILL 46 *(Use after page 178.)*

(Use after page 178.)

Here's how

Multiply numerators and denominators.

$$\tfrac{3}{4} \times \tfrac{4}{5} = \tfrac{12}{20}$$

Write in simplest form.

$$\tfrac{3}{4} \times \tfrac{4}{5} = \tfrac{12}{20}$$
$$= \tfrac{3}{5}$$

Give the product in simplest form.

1. $\tfrac{1}{2} \times \tfrac{1}{3}$ $\tfrac{1}{6}$
2. $\tfrac{3}{4} \times \tfrac{1}{4}$ $\tfrac{3}{16}$
3. $\tfrac{2}{3} \times \tfrac{4}{5}$ $\tfrac{8}{15}$
4. $\tfrac{3}{8} \times 2$ $\tfrac{3}{4}$

5. $3 \times \tfrac{1}{5}$ $\tfrac{3}{5}$
6. $\tfrac{1}{2} \times \tfrac{1}{4}$ $\tfrac{1}{8}$
7. $\tfrac{4}{3} \times \tfrac{3}{2}$ 2
8. $\tfrac{3}{4} \times \tfrac{16}{3}$ 4

9. $\tfrac{1}{3} \times \tfrac{3}{8}$ $\tfrac{1}{8}$
10. $\tfrac{7}{4} \times \tfrac{4}{3}$ $2\tfrac{1}{3}$
11. $\tfrac{1}{3} \times \tfrac{4}{5}$ $\tfrac{4}{15}$
12. $\tfrac{1}{2} \times \tfrac{4}{9}$ $\tfrac{2}{9}$

13. $\tfrac{5}{8} \times \tfrac{4}{5}$ $\tfrac{1}{2}$
14. $\tfrac{1}{4} \times \tfrac{8}{5}$ $\tfrac{2}{5}$
15. $\tfrac{3}{2} \times \tfrac{2}{3}$ 1
16. $5 \times \tfrac{4}{5}$ 4

17. $\tfrac{5}{6} \times \tfrac{6}{5}$ 1
18. $\tfrac{1}{2} \times \tfrac{2}{3}$ $\tfrac{1}{3}$
19. $\tfrac{3}{8} \times \tfrac{4}{3}$ $\tfrac{1}{2}$
20. $\tfrac{2}{3} \times 9$ 6

21. $\tfrac{1}{3} \times 6$ 2
22. $\tfrac{5}{8} \times \tfrac{4}{5}$ $\tfrac{1}{2}$
23. $\tfrac{1}{2} \times \tfrac{4}{5}$ $\tfrac{2}{5}$
24. $3 \times \tfrac{8}{3}$ 8

SKILL 47 *(Use after page 180.)*

Complete.

1. $\frac{1}{4}$ of 12 = ?   3

2. $\frac{1}{2}$ of 18 = ?   9

3. $\frac{1}{3}$ of 24 = ?   8

4. $\frac{1}{5}$ of 30 = ?   6

5. $\frac{1}{8}$ of 72 = ?   9

6. $\frac{1}{6}$ of 42 = ?   7

7. $\frac{2}{3}$ of 18 = ?   12

8. $\frac{3}{4}$ of 20 = ?   15

9. $\frac{2}{5}$ of 10 = ?   4

10. $\frac{3}{8}$ of 32 = ?   12

11. $\frac{2}{3}$ of 24 = ?   16

12. $\frac{5}{6}$ of 30 = ?   25

13. $\frac{3}{4}$ of 32 = ?   24

14. $\frac{5}{8}$ of 40 = ?   25

15. $\frac{2}{5}$ of 40 = ?   16

16. $\frac{3}{5}$ of 25 = ?   15

17. $\frac{5}{6}$ of 42 = ?   35

18. $\frac{2}{3}$ of 36 = ?   24

19. $\frac{9}{10}$ of 90 = ?   81

20. $\frac{2}{3}$ of 21 = ?   14

21. $\frac{4}{5}$ of 45 = ?   36

22. $\frac{3}{4}$ of 36 = ?   27

23. $\frac{7}{10}$ of 40 = ?   28

24. $\frac{7}{8}$ of 56 = ?   49

SKILL 48 *(Use after page 182.)*

Give the product in simplest form.

1. $2 \times 1\frac{1}{2}$ 3

2. $1\frac{1}{2} \times 1\frac{1}{3}$ 2

3. $2\frac{2}{3} \times 1\frac{1}{4}$ $3\frac{1}{3}$

4. $1\frac{3}{4} \times 1\frac{3}{4}$ $3\frac{1}{16}$

5. $3 \times 2\frac{1}{3}$ 7

6. $2\frac{1}{3} \times 2$ $4\frac{2}{3}$

7. $2\frac{2}{5} \times 3$ $7\frac{1}{5}$

8. $1\frac{5}{6} \times 2\frac{1}{3}$ $4\frac{5}{18}$

9. $3\frac{1}{4} \times 3\frac{1}{4}$ $10\frac{9}{16}$

10. $4\frac{1}{6} \times 2\frac{1}{3}$ $9\frac{13}{18}$

11. $2\frac{2}{3} \times 2\frac{1}{2}$ $6\frac{2}{3}$

12. $3 \times 4\frac{1}{2}$ $13\frac{1}{2}$

13. $2 \times 1\frac{2}{3}$ $3\frac{1}{3}$

14. $1\frac{1}{2} \times 2\frac{1}{2}$ $3\frac{3}{4}$

15. $3\frac{3}{4} \times 2$ $7\frac{1}{2}$

16. $1\frac{3}{8} \times 2\frac{1}{2}$ $3\frac{7}{16}$

17. $3\frac{3}{4} \times 3\frac{1}{8}$ $11\frac{23}{32}$

18. $1\frac{5}{8} \times 1\frac{5}{8}$ $2\frac{41}{64}$

19. $1\frac{1}{2} \times 1\frac{3}{4}$ $2\frac{5}{8}$

20. $2 \times 2\frac{3}{4}$ $5\frac{1}{2}$

21. $2\frac{2}{3} \times 1\frac{3}{4}$ $4\frac{2}{3}$

22. $4\frac{1}{2} \times 2\frac{3}{8}$ $10\frac{11}{16}$

23. $1\frac{5}{8} \times 6$ $9\frac{3}{4}$

24. $6\frac{3}{4} \times 3\frac{3}{8}$ $22\frac{25}{32}$

Here's how

$2\frac{3}{4}$ days = __?__ h

Find the hours in 2 days and $\frac{3}{4}$ of a day.

$2\frac{3}{4}$ days = 48 h + 18 h

Add.

$2\frac{3}{4}$ days = 48 h + 18 h
   = 66 h

SKILL 49 *(Use after page 185.)*

Complete.

1. $1\frac{1}{2}$ days = __?__ h 36

2. $1\frac{1}{4}$ h = __?__ min 75

3. $1\frac{3}{4}$ h = __?__ min 105

4. $2\frac{1}{2}$ min = __?__ sec 150

5. $2\frac{1}{4}$ min = __?__ sec 135

6. $2\frac{1}{3}$ days = __?__ h 56

7. $1\frac{2}{3}$ yd = __?__ ft 5

8. $1\frac{3}{4}$ ft = __?__ in. 21

9. $1\frac{1}{2}$ yd = __?__ in. 54

10. $2\frac{2}{3}$ ft = __?__ in. 32

11. $4\frac{1}{3}$ yd = __?__ ft 13

12. $1\frac{3}{4}$ yd = __?__ in. 63

13. $1\frac{1}{4}$ gal = __?__ qt 5

14. $2\frac{1}{2}$ qt = __?__ pt 5

15. $3\frac{1}{2}$ pt = __?__ c 7

16. $3\frac{1}{2}$ qt = __?__ pt 7

Here's how

To divide by a fraction, multiply by its reciprocal.

$\frac{5}{4} \div \frac{3}{2} = \frac{5}{4} \times \frac{2}{3}$
   $= \frac{10}{12}$

Write in simplest form.

$\frac{5}{4} \div \frac{3}{2} = \frac{5}{4} \times \frac{2}{3}$
   $= \frac{10}{12}$
   $= \frac{5}{6}$

SKILL 50 *(Use after page 188.)*

Give the quotient in lowest terms.

1. $\frac{3}{4} \div \frac{1}{4}$ 3

2. $\frac{2}{3} \div \frac{1}{3}$ 2

3. $\frac{1}{2} \div \frac{1}{3}$ $1\frac{1}{2}$

4. $\frac{3}{5} \div \frac{1}{5}$ 3

5. $\frac{4}{5} \div 3$ $\frac{4}{15}$

6. $\frac{7}{8} \div \frac{7}{8}$ 1

7. $\frac{5}{6} \div \frac{2}{3}$ $1\frac{1}{4}$

8. $\frac{2}{3} \div \frac{1}{2}$ $1\frac{1}{3}$

9. $\frac{3}{10} \div \frac{4}{5}$ $\frac{3}{8}$

10. $\frac{3}{4} \div \frac{3}{2}$ $\frac{1}{2}$

11. $6 \div \frac{3}{4}$ 8

12. $\frac{5}{8} \div 3$ $\frac{5}{24}$

13. $\frac{5}{6} \div \frac{5}{8}$ $1\frac{1}{3}$

14. $\frac{5}{8} \div \frac{2}{3}$ $\frac{15}{16}$

15. $\frac{2}{3} \div \frac{4}{5}$ $\frac{5}{6}$

16. $\frac{7}{10} \div \frac{1}{5}$ $3\frac{1}{2}$

17. $\frac{2}{3} \div \frac{5}{6}$ $\frac{4}{5}$

18. $\frac{3}{5} \div \frac{6}{1}$ $\frac{1}{10}$

19. $9 \div \frac{4}{3}$ $6\frac{3}{4}$

20. $\frac{1}{2} \div \frac{5}{8}$ $\frac{4}{5}$

21. $\frac{5}{3} \div \frac{3}{2}$ $1\frac{1}{9}$

22. $\frac{1}{2} \div \frac{5}{4}$ $\frac{2}{5}$

23. $\frac{3}{4} \div \frac{3}{8}$ 2

24. $\frac{7}{4} \div \frac{2}{5}$ $4\frac{3}{8}$

25. $6 \div \frac{2}{3}$ 9

26. $\frac{5}{9} \div \frac{2}{3}$ $\frac{5}{6}$

27. $\frac{5}{8} \div \frac{3}{4}$ $\frac{5}{6}$

28. $\frac{3}{5} \div \frac{5}{4}$ $\frac{12}{25}$

29. $\frac{3}{4} \div \frac{5}{8}$ $1\frac{1}{5}$

30. $\frac{9}{4} \div \frac{6}{5}$ $1\frac{7}{8}$

31. $\frac{9}{10} \div \frac{5}{4}$ $\frac{18}{25}$

32. $\frac{8}{3} \div \frac{5}{6}$ $3\frac{1}{5}$

SKILL 51 (Use after page 190.)

Give the quotient in simplest form.

1. $5 \div 2\frac{1}{2}$ 2

2. $2\frac{1}{2} \div 1\frac{1}{4}$ 2

3. $5 \div 1\frac{1}{4}$ 4

4. $3\frac{1}{2} \div 2$ $1\frac{3}{4}$

5. $10 \div 3\frac{1}{3}$ 3

6. $5\frac{1}{4} \div 3$ $1\frac{3}{4}$

7. $4\frac{1}{6} \div 5$ $\frac{5}{6}$

8. $4\frac{3}{4} \div 2$ $2\frac{3}{8}$

9. $2\frac{1}{3} \div 1\frac{1}{4}$ $1\frac{13}{15}$

10. $2\frac{1}{2} \div 2\frac{1}{2}$ 1

11. $7\frac{1}{2} \div 2\frac{1}{2}$ 3

12. $6\frac{3}{4} \div 3\frac{1}{2}$ $1\frac{13}{14}$

13. $3\frac{1}{2} \div 1\frac{3}{4}$ 2

14. $2\frac{7}{8} \div 3\frac{1}{4}$ $\frac{23}{26}$

15. $4\frac{5}{8} \div 2\frac{2}{3}$ $1\frac{47}{64}$

16. $3\frac{5}{6} \div 2\frac{1}{3}$ $1\frac{9}{14}$

17. $5 \div 1\frac{1}{4}$ 4

18. $5\frac{3}{4} \div 2\frac{2}{3}$ $2\frac{5}{32}$

19. $6\frac{2}{3} \div 5\frac{1}{3}$ $1\frac{1}{4}$

20. $4\frac{7}{8} \div 6\frac{1}{4}$ $\frac{39}{50}$

21. $2\frac{3}{4} \div 5\frac{2}{3}$ $\frac{33}{68}$

22. $10 \div 3\frac{1}{3}$ 3

23. $4\frac{1}{4} \div 3\frac{1}{8}$ $1\frac{9}{25}$

24. $3\frac{1}{2} \div 1\frac{3}{4}$ 2

SKILL 52 (Use after page 230.)

Solve.

1. $\frac{n}{6} = \frac{11}{4}$ $16\frac{1}{2}$

2. $\frac{8}{n} = \frac{2}{9}$ 36

3. $\frac{9}{8} = \frac{n}{7}$ $7\frac{7}{8}$

4. $\frac{10}{7} = \frac{4}{n}$ $2\frac{4}{5}$

5. $\frac{5}{n} = \frac{2}{9}$ $22\frac{1}{2}$

6. $\frac{n}{13} = \frac{6}{5}$ $15\frac{3}{5}$

7. $\frac{7}{4} = \frac{n}{6}$ $10\frac{1}{2}$

8. $\frac{5}{8} = \frac{3}{n}$ $4\frac{4}{5}$

9. $\frac{3}{7} = \frac{9}{n}$ 21

10. $\frac{18}{n} = \frac{6}{5}$ 15

11. $\frac{n}{21} = \frac{6}{7}$ 18

12. $\frac{n}{6} = \frac{15}{8}$ $11\frac{1}{4}$

13. $\frac{9}{n} = \frac{3}{13}$ 39

14. $\frac{18}{n} = \frac{9}{16}$ 32

15. $\frac{6}{11} = \frac{24}{n}$ 44

16. $\frac{5}{7} = \frac{9}{n}$ $12\frac{3}{5}$

17. $\frac{n}{7} = \frac{11}{4}$ $19\frac{1}{4}$

18. $\frac{6}{n} = \frac{8}{3}$ $2\frac{1}{4}$

19. $\frac{19}{2} = \frac{n}{5}$ $47\frac{1}{2}$

20. $\frac{10}{13} = \frac{16}{n}$ $20\frac{4}{5}$

21. $\frac{9}{n} = \frac{2}{15}$ $67\frac{1}{2}$

22. $\frac{n}{9} = \frac{4}{3}$ 12

23. $\frac{6}{15} = \frac{30}{n}$ 75

24. $\frac{11}{4} = \frac{n}{8}$ 22

25. $\frac{n}{4} = \frac{6}{8}$ 3

26. $\frac{1}{n} = \frac{7}{21}$ 3

27. $\frac{6}{9} = \frac{n}{3}$ 2

28. $\frac{6}{10} = \frac{18}{n}$ 30

29. $\frac{5}{15} = \frac{3}{n}$ 9

30. $\frac{10}{3} = \frac{n}{12}$ 40

31. $\frac{7}{n} = \frac{10}{9}$ $6\frac{3}{10}$

32. $\frac{n}{8} = \frac{7}{4}$ 14

Here's how

Write the percent as a fraction with a denominator of 100. Write the fraction in simplest form.

$$25\% = \frac{25}{100} = \frac{1}{4}$$

$$33\frac{1}{3}\% = \frac{33\frac{1}{3}}{100}$$

$$= 33\frac{1}{3} \div 100$$

$$= \frac{100}{3} \times \frac{1}{100}$$

$$= \frac{100}{300}$$

$$= \frac{1}{3}$$

SKILL 53 *(Use after page 248.)*

Change to a fraction in simplest form.

1. 10% $\frac{1}{10}$ 2. 15% $\frac{3}{20}$ 3. 40% $\frac{2}{5}$ 4. 50% $\frac{1}{2}$

5. 90% $\frac{9}{10}$ 6. 60% $\frac{3}{5}$ 7. 25% $\frac{1}{4}$ 8. 75% $\frac{3}{4}$

9. 20% $\frac{1}{5}$ 10. 30% $\frac{3}{10}$ 11. 45% $\frac{9}{20}$ 12. 85% $\frac{17}{20}$

13. 80% $\frac{4}{5}$ 14. 40% $\frac{2}{5}$ 15. 48% $\frac{12}{25}$ 16. 96% $\frac{24}{25}$

17. 18% $\frac{9}{50}$ 18. 24% $\frac{6}{25}$ 19. 72% $\frac{18}{25}$ 20. 84% $\frac{21}{25}$

21. 150% $1\frac{1}{2}$ 22. 125% $1\frac{1}{4}$ 23. 175% $1\frac{3}{4}$ 24. 120% $1\frac{1}{5}$

25. 180% $1\frac{4}{5}$ 26. 250% $2\frac{1}{2}$ 27. 275% $2\frac{3}{4}$ 28. 225% $2\frac{1}{4}$

29. 160% $1\frac{3}{5}$ 30. 200% 2   31. 300% 3   32. 320% $3\frac{1}{5}$

33. $33\frac{1}{3}\%$ $\frac{1}{3}$ 34. $66\frac{2}{3}\%$ $\frac{2}{3}$ 35. $37\frac{1}{2}\%$ $\frac{3}{8}$ 36. $16\frac{2}{3}\%$ $\frac{1}{6}$

37. $87\frac{1}{2}\%$ $\frac{7}{8}$ 38. $81\frac{1}{4}\%$ $\frac{13}{16}$ 39. $162\frac{1}{2}\%$ $1\frac{5}{8}$ 40. $118\frac{3}{4}\%$ 1

Here's how

Change to an equivalent fraction with a denominator of 100. Write as a percent.

$$\frac{1}{2} = \frac{50}{100} = 50\%$$

Solve a proportion.

$$\frac{1}{6} = \frac{n}{100}$$

$$6n = 100$$

$$n = 16\frac{2}{3}$$

$$\text{So } \frac{1}{6} = \frac{16\frac{2}{3}}{100} = 16\frac{2}{3}\%$$

SKILL 54 *(Use after page 250.)*

Change to a percent.

1. $\frac{1}{5}$ 20%   2. $\frac{1}{4}$ 25%   3. $\frac{1}{2}$ 50%   4. $\frac{4}{5}$ 80%

5. $\frac{3}{4}$ 75%   6. $\frac{1}{3}$ $33\frac{1}{3}\%$ 7. $\frac{2}{5}$ 40%   8. $\frac{2}{3}$ $66\frac{2}{3}\%$

9. $\frac{1}{8}$ $12\frac{1}{2}\%$ 10. $\frac{3}{5}$ 60%   11. $\frac{3}{8}$ $37\frac{1}{2}\%$ 12. $\frac{3}{2}$ 150%

13. $\frac{6}{5}$ 120%   14. $\frac{1}{6}$ $16\frac{2}{3}\%$ 15. $\frac{5}{4}$ 125%   16. $\frac{7}{5}$ 140%

17. $\frac{1}{10}$ 10%   18. $\frac{8}{5}$ 160%   19. $\frac{3}{10}$ 30%   20. $\frac{1}{12}$ $8\frac{1}{3}\%$

21. $\frac{5}{2}$ 250%   22. 3 300%   23. $\frac{7}{4}$ 175%   24. $\frac{1}{20}$ 5%

25. $\frac{5}{8}$ $62\frac{1}{2}\%$ 26. $\frac{7}{10}$ 70%   27. $\frac{11}{8}$ $137\frac{1}{2}\%$ 28. $\frac{7}{3}$ $233\frac{1}{3}$

29. $\frac{5}{12}$ $41\frac{2}{3}\%$ 30. $\frac{5}{3}$ $166\frac{2}{3}\%$ 31. 2 200%   32. $\frac{7}{12}$ $58\frac{1}{3}$

SKILL 55 *(Use after page 252.)*

(Use after page 252.)

Here's how

To change a percent to a decimal, move the decimal point two places to the left and remove the percent sign.

$3\% = 0.03$

$17\% = 0.17$

$15.2\% = 0.152$

$66\frac{2}{3}\% = 0.66\frac{2}{3}$

$112\% = 1.12$

Change to a decimal.

1. 25% 0.25
2. 20% 0.20
3. 45% 0.45
4. 82% 0.82
5. 34% 0.34
6. 65% 0.65
7. 80% 0.80
8. 56% 0.56
9. 75% 0.75
10. 12% 0.12
11. 81% 0.81
12. 62% 0.62
13. 5% 0.05
14. 8% 0.08
15. 2% 0.02
16. 4% 0.04
17. 1% 0.01
18. 3% 0.03
19. 7% 0.07
20. 6% 0.06
21. 150% 1.50
22. 125% 1.25
23. 173% 1.73
24. 225% 2.25
25. 160% 1.60
26. 250% 2.50
27. 300% 3
28. 500% 5
29. 28.5% 0.285
30. 16.2% 0.162
31. 34.6% 0.346
32. 56.8% 0.568
33. 47.2% 0.472
34. 93.9% 0.939
35. 60.5% 0.605
36. 85.2% 0.852
37. $33\frac{1}{3}\%$ $0.33\frac{1}{3}$
38. $87\frac{1}{2}\%$ $0.87\frac{1}{2}$
39. $16\frac{2}{3}\%$ $0.16\frac{2}{3}$
40. $37\frac{1}{2}\%$ $0.37\frac{1}{2}$

SKILL 56 *(Use after page 253.)*

(Use after page 253.)

Here's how

To change a decimal to a percent, move the decimal point two places to the right and write the percent sign.

$0.5 = 50\%$

$0.125 = 12.5\%$

$0.87\frac{1}{2} = 87\frac{1}{2}\%$

$1.475 = 147.5\%$

Change to a percent.

1. 0.04 4%
2. 0.07 7%
3. 0.02 2%
4. 0.06 6%
5. 0.08 8%
6. 0.01 1%
7. 0.05 5%
8. 0.03 3%
9. 0.09 9%
10. 0.56 56%
11. 0.49 49%
12. 0.66 66%
13. 0.71 71%
14. 0.11 11%
15. 0.98 98%
16. 0.38 38%
17. 0.5 50%
18. 0.4 40%
19. 0.3 30%
20. 0.8 80%
21. 0.2 20%
22. 0.6 60%
23. 0.1 10%
24. 0.9 90%
25. 2.25 225%
26. 1.58 158%
27. 1.55 155%
28. 2.75 275%
29. 3.46 346%
30. 8.25 825%
31. 7.52 752%
32. 5.37 537%
33. $0.12\frac{1}{2}$ $12\frac{1}{2}\%$
34. $0.33\frac{1}{3}$ $33\frac{1}{3}\%$
35. $0.62\frac{1}{2}$ $62\frac{1}{2}\%$
36. $0.16\frac{2}{3}$ $16\frac{2}{3}\%$
37. $1.37\frac{1}{2}$ $137\frac{1}{2}\%$
38. $1.66\frac{2}{3}$ $166\frac{2}{3}\%$
39. $2.33\frac{1}{3}$ $233\frac{1}{3}\%$
40. $2.83\frac{1}{3}$ $283\frac{1}{3}\%$

SKILL 57 (Use after page 256.)

Here's how

First change the percent to a fraction or decimal. Then multiply.

$$75\% \text{ of } 36 = \frac{3}{4} \times 36$$
$$= 27$$

$$6.5\% \text{ of } 9 = 0.065 \times 9$$
$$= 0.585$$

Solve.

1. 50% of 28 = n 14
2. 25% of 24 = n 6
3. 40% of 60 = n 24
4. 20% of 45 = n 9
5. 80% of 40 = n 32
6. 10% of 50 = n 5
7. 75% of 48 = n 36
8. 25% of 64 = n 16
9. 100% of 56 = n 56
10. 150% of 18 = n 27
11. 125% of 40 = n 50
12. 250% of 72 = n 180
13. 14% of 26 = n 3.64
14. 23% of 75 = n 17.25
15. 56% of 29 = n 16.24
16. 41% of 83 = n 34.03
17. 5.4% of 60 = n 3.24
18. 6.5% of 47 = n 3.055
19. 0.25% of 160 = n 0.4
20. 0.6% of 314 = n 1.884

SKILL 58 (Use after page 258.)

Here's how

Change to a fraction or decimal and multiply.

$$20\% \text{ of } 45 = \frac{1}{5} \times 45$$
$$= 9$$

$$8.2\% \text{ of } 6 = 0.082 \times 6$$
$$= 0.492$$

Solve a proportion.

$$16\frac{2}{3}\% \text{ of } 72 = n$$

$$\frac{16\frac{2}{3}}{100} = \frac{n}{72}$$

$$100n = 16\frac{2}{3} \times 72$$

$$= \frac{50}{3} \times 72$$

$$= 1200$$

$$n = 12$$

Solve.

1. 25% of 116 = n 29
2. 60% of 60 = n 36
3. 100% of 73 = n 73
4. 75% of 12 = n 9
5. 20% of 95 = n 19
6. $87\frac{1}{2}$% of 88 = n 77
7. 8.2% of 50 = n 4.1
8. 6.5% of 35 = n 2.275
9. 2.25% of 304 = n 6.04
10. $37\frac{1}{2}$% of 104 = n 39
11. $62\frac{1}{2}$% of 72 = n 45
12. 3.45% of 156 = n 5.382
13. 7.5% of 56 = n 4.2
14. $33\frac{1}{3}$% of 81 = n 27
15. 0.36% of 100 = n 0.36
16. 0.25% of 200 = n 0.5
17. $66\frac{2}{3}$% of 63 = n 42
18. $8\frac{1}{3}$% of 96 = n 8
19. 0.5% of 38 = n 0.19
20. $16\frac{2}{3}$% of 48 = n 8

440

SKILL 59 *(Use after page 260.)*

Here's how

60% of n = 27

Solve a proportion.

$$\boxed{\frac{part}{whole}}\ \frac{60}{100} = \frac{27}{n}\ \boxed{\frac{part}{whole}}$$

$$60n = 2700$$
$$n = 45$$

Solve.

1. 25% of n = 14   56
2. 50% of n = 19   38
3. 75% of n = 33   44
4. 60% of n = 48   80
5. 80% of n = 64   80
6. 40% of n = 46   115
7. 10% of n = 16   160
8. 5% of n = 120   2400
9. 30% of n = 57   190
10. 20% of n = 65   325

Solve. Round each answer to the nearest tenth.

11. 8.5% of n = 6   70.6
12. 7.5% of n = 11   146.7
13. 20.5% of n = 16.2   79.0
14. 14.2% of n = 37   260.6
15. 34.6% of n = 18.5   53.5
16. 42.8% of n = 10.3   24.1
17. 1.8% of n = 2.4   133.3
18. 4.7% of n = 2.9   61.7
19. 125% of n = 17.6   14.1
20. 250% of n = 31.3   12.5

SKILL 60 *(Use after page 362.)*

Here's how

-2 -1 0 +1 +2

⟵ smaller   larger ⟶

0 < +2
+1 < +2
+2 > -1
+2 > 0
-2 < -1

< or >?

1. +5 ● +8   <
2. +5 ● -8   >
3. -5 ● -8   >
4. -6 ● +1   <
5. +6 ● -1   >
6. +6 ● +1   >
7. 0 ● -5   >
8. 0 ● +5   <
9. -7 ● 0   <
10. +9 ● -4   >
11. -9 ● +4   <
12. +9 ● +4   >
13. -7 ● -2   <
14. -8 ● +3   <
15. 0 ● +6   <
16. +9 ● +4   >
17. -6 ● +6   <
18. -3 ● -5   >
19. -11 ● +10   <
20. +16 ● -17   >
21. +15 ● +17   <
22. 0 ● -12   >
23. +15 ● -15   >
24. -19 ● -13   <
25. -16 ● +11   <
26. -19 ● -18   <
27. +14 ● +17   <
28. -22 ● +22   <
29. -26 ● -21   <
30. +23 ● +24   <
31. +27 ● -20   >
32. -29 ● +23   <
33. -28 ● -26   <
34. 0 ● +32   <
35. -36 ● 0   <
36. +37 ● -31   >

Here's how

$^+2 + {}^-3 = {}^-1$

$^-1 + {}^+2 = {}^+1$

SKILL 61 *(Use after page 364.)*

Give the sum.

1. $^+3 + {}^+2$ +5
2. $^+3 + {}^-2$ +1
3. $^-3 + {}^-2$ -5
4. $^-1 + {}^+5$ +4
5. $^-1 + {}^-5$ -6
6. $^+1 + {}^-5$ -4
7. $0 + {}^-8$ -8
8. $0 + {}^+8$ +8
9. $^-6 + 0$ -6
10. $^+4 + {}^-4$ 0
11. $^-4 + {}^+4$ 0
12. $^+4 + {}^+4$ +8
13. $^+7 + {}^-3$ +4
14. $^-7 + {}^+3$ -4
15. $^-7 + {}^-3$ -10
16. $^-6 + {}^+9$ +3
17. $^+6 + {}^-9$ -3
18. $^-6 + {}^-9$ -15
19. $^+10 + {}^+12$ +22
20. $^+11 + {}^-11$ 0
21. $^-17 + {}^+14$ -3
22. $^-19 + {}^-13$ -32
23. $^+18 + {}^-19$ -1
24. $^-16 + {}^+11$ -5
25. $^+15 + {}^+14$ +29
26. $^-18 + {}^-12$ -30
27. $^-11 + {}^+19$ +8
28. $^+17 + {}^-17$ 0
29. $^-19 + {}^+14$ -5
30. $^+12 + {}^+15$ +27
31. $^-20 + {}^-20$ -40
32. $^-21 + {}^+25$ +4
33. $^+27 + 22$ +5
34. $^-31 + {}^+31$ 0
35. $0 + {}^+34$ +34
36. $^-32 + {}^-36$ -68

Here's how

To subtract an integer, add the opposite of the integer.

$^+5 - {}^+2 = {}^+5 + {}^-2$
$\qquad = {}^+3$

$^-5 - {}^+2 = {}^-5 + {}^-2$
$\qquad = {}^-7$

$^+5 - {}^-2 = {}^+5 + {}^+2$
$\qquad = {}^+7$

$^-5 - {}^-2 = {}^-5 + {}^+2$
$\qquad = {}^-3$

SKILL 62 *(Use after page 367.)*

Give the difference.

1. $^+4 - {}^-6$ +10
2. $^-4 - {}^+6$ -10
3. $^+4 - {}^+6$ -2
4. $^-7 - {}^-3$ -4
5. $^+7 - {}^-3$ +10
6. $^-7 - {}^+3$ -10
7. $^+8 - {}^+1$ +7
8. $^-8 - {}^+1$ -9
9. $^+8 - {}^-1$ +9
10. $^-7 - 0$ -7
11. $0 - {}^+7$ -7
12. $0 - {}^-7$ +7
13. $^+5 - {}^+9$ -4
14. $^+5 - {}^-9$ +14
15. $^-5 - {}^+9$ -14
16. $^-5 - {}^-5$ 0
17. $^+5 - {}^+5$ 0
18. $^-5 - {}^+5$ -10
19. $^+12 - {}^-11$ +23
20. $^-13 - {}^+16$ -29
21. $^-14 - {}^-14$ 0
22. $^-16 - {}^+19$ -35
23. $^+18 - {}^+11$ +7
24. $^+19 - {}^+14$ +5
25. $^+17 - {}^-10$ +27
26. $^-10 - {}^+17$ -27
27. $^-16 - {}^-16$ 0
28. $^+11 - {}^+15$ -4
29. $^-15 - {}^+18$ -33
30. $^+17 - {}^-14$ +31
31. $^-23 - {}^-27$ +4
32. $^+25 - {}^+25$ 0
33. $^-28 - {}^+24$ -52
34. $0 - {}^-34$ +34
35. $^-36 - {}^+32$ -68
36. $^+33 - {}^-38$ +71

SKILL 63 *(Use after page 371.)*

The product of two integers with the same signs is positive.

$$^+2 \times ^+3 = ^+6$$
$$^-4 \times ^-5 = ^+20$$

The product of two integers with different signs is negative.

$$^+6 \times ^-3 = ^-18$$
$$^-5 \times ^+6 = ^-30$$

The product of any integer and 0 is 0.

$$^+7 \times 0 = 0$$
$$0 \times ^-4 = 0$$

Give the product.

1. $^+3 \times ^+4$ $^+12$
2. $^+3 \times ^-4$ $^-12$
3. $^-3 \times ^-4$ $^+12$
4. $^-6 \times ^+5$ $^-30$
5. $^+6 \times ^+5$ $^+30$
6. $^+6 \times ^-5$ $^-30$
7. $^-5 \times ^+7$ $^-35$
8. $^-5 \times ^-7$ $^+35$
9. $^+5 \times ^+7$ $^+35$
10. $^+2 \times ^-6$ $^-12$
11. $^-6 \times ^+2$ $^-12$
12. $^-6 \times ^-2$ $^+12$
13. $^+7 \times 0$ 0
14. $^-7 \times 0$ 0
15. 0×0 0
16. $^-9 \times ^-8$ $^+72$
17. $^+8 \times ^-8$ $^-64$
18. $^-6 \times ^+5$ $^-30$
19. $^+4 \times ^+6$ $^+24$
20. $^-5 \times ^+5$ $^-25$
21. $^+6 \times ^-6$ $^-36$
22. $^-5 \times ^-9$ $^+45$
23. $^+7 \times ^-8$ $^-56$
24. $^-8 \times ^+7$ $^-56$
25. $^+9 \times ^+7$ $^+63$
26. $^-7 \times ^-7$ $^+49$
27. $0 \times ^+8$ 0
28. $^+10 \times ^-6$ $^-60$
29. $^-10 \times ^+6$ $^-60$
30. $^+10 \times ^+6$ $^+60$
31. $^-11 \times ^-11$ $^+121$
32. $^+11 \times ^-11$ $^-121$
33. $^+11 \times ^+11$ $^+121$
34. $^-13 \times ^+14$ $^-182$
35. $^+18 \times ^+15$ $^+270$
36. $^-19 \times ^-13$ $^+247$

SKILL 64 *(Use after page 372.)*

The quotient of two integers with the same signs is positive.

$$^+12 \div ^+6 = ^+2$$
$$^-21 \div ^-7 = ^+3$$

The quotient of two integers with different signs is negative.

$$^+20 \div ^-4 = ^-5$$
$$^-32 \div ^+8 = ^-4$$

The quotient of 0 divided by any non-zero integer is 0.

$$0 \div ^-6 = 0$$
$$0 \div ^+7 = 0$$

Give the quotient.

1. $^+12 \div ^+3$ $^+4$
2. $^+12 \div ^-3$ $^-4$
3. $^-12 \div ^-3$ $^+4$
4. $^-8 \div ^+2$ $^-4$
5. $^+8 \div ^+2$ $^+4$
6. $^+8 \div ^-2$ $^-4$
7. $^-16 \div ^+4$ $^-4$
8. $^-16 \div ^-4$ $^+4$
9. $^+16 \div ^-4$ $^-4$
10. $^-18 \div ^+6$ $^-3$
11. $^+18 \div ^+6$ $^+3$
12. $^+18 \div ^-6$ $^-3$
13. $^-25 \div ^+5$ $^-5$
14. $^-25 \div ^-5$ $^+5$
15. $^+25 \div ^-5$ $^-5$
16. $0 \div ^+4$ 0
17. $0 \div ^-4$ 0
18. $0 \div ^-9$ 0
19. $^+49 \div ^-7$ $^-7$
20. $^-42 \div ^+6$ $^-7$
21. $^-45 \div ^-5$ $^+9$
22. $^+36 \div ^+6$ $^+6$
23. $^-32 \div ^+8$ $^-4$
24. $^+35 \div ^-7$ $^-5$
25. $^-36 \div ^-9$ $^+4$
26. $^+54 \div ^+6$ $^+9$
27. $^-64 \div ^+8$ $^-8$
28. $^+72 \div ^-9$ $^-8$
29. $^-81 \div ^-9$ $^+9$
30. $^+63 \div ^-7$ $^-9$
31. $^-70 \div ^+10$ $^-7$
32. $^+90 \div ^+10$ $^+9$
33. $^-60 \div ^-10$ $^+6$
34. $^-132 \div ^+12$ $^-11$
35. $^+182 \div ^-13$ $^-14$
36. $^+224 \div ^+16$ $^+14$

EXTRA PROBLEM SOLVING

SET 1 *(Use after Chapter 1.)*

BOWLER	Scores		
	GAME 1	GAME 2	GAME 3
Robin	126	146	132
Jenny	125	163	140
Amy	113	123	145
Sarah	138	151	124

Use the bowling scores to solve these problems.

1. Who had a score of 138 in Game 1? Sarah

2. Who had the high score in Game 2? Jenny

3. What was Robin's high score? 146

4. What was Sarah's high score? 151

5. What was Jenny's low score? 125

6. In Game 1, who scored 12 more than Robin? Sarah

7. Whose high score was 27 more than her low score? Sarah's

8. What was Sarah's total score for her first two games? 289

9. What was Amy's total score for her last two games? 268

10. Who had a total score of 289 for her first two games? Sarah

11. Who scored 38 more in her second game than in her first game? Jenny

12. In Game 3, did Sarah bowl better than Robin? No

13. In Game 3, did Sarah and Amy together bowl better than Robin and Jenny? No

14. Who had the lowest total score for all three games? Amy

15. Who had the highest total score for all three games? Jenny

SET 2 *(Use after Chapter 2.)*

TOWN DINER

SANDWICHES		SOUP OF THE DAY	DRINK	
Hamburger	$1.10	$.85	Milk	$.55
Hot Dog	.90		Orange Juice	.70
Chili Dog	1.40		Apple Juice	.60

Use the menu prices to answer each question.

1. What is the price of a hot dog? $.90

2. Is $2 enough money to buy a chili dog and apple juice? Yes

3. How many hamburgers can you buy for $5? 4

4. Can you buy a hot dog, bowl of soup, and milk for less than $2? No

Solve.

5. Emily gave the cashier $5 and got $3.90 in change. She had a ? for lunch.
   hamburger

6. Renée spent $1.45. She bought a bowl of soup and ? . apple juice

7. Joel spent $2.10. He bought a chili dog and ? . orange juice

8. Jeff's order cost $2.80. He had a chili dog, soup, and ? . milk

9. Heather spent $1.60. She bought a ? and ? . hot dog, orange juice

10. Amy spent $1.70. She had a ? and ? . hamburger, apple juice

11. Brian gave the cashier $2 and got a nickel in change. He had a ? and ? .
    hamburger, soup
    or
    chili dog, milk

12. Kevin ordered a ? and ? . He got $3.25 change from a five-dollar bill.
    hot dog, soup

SET 3 *(Use after Chapter 3.)*

FIRST-CLASS STAMP FACTS

Before 1885, the first-class letter rate (cost for the first ounce) depended on distance traveled. On July 1, 1885, the national rate became 2 cents. Since then the rate has been changed several times. The following list shows these changes.

Date	Rate
November 3, 1917	3 cents
July 1, 1919	2 cents
July 6, 1932	3 cents
August 1, 1958	4 cents
January 7, 1963	5 cents
May 16, 1971	8 cents
March 2, 1974	10 cents
December 11, 1975	13 cents
May 29, 1978	15 cents
March 22, 1981	18 cents
November 1, 1981	20 cents

Use the information in the article to solve these problems.

1. What was the first-class letter rate on July 2, 1919? 2 cents

2. What was the first-class letter rate in 1976? 13 cents

3. On what date did the first-class letter rate increase from 13 cents to 15 cents? May 29, 1978

4. On what date was there a decrease in the first-class letter rate? July 1, 1919

5. How much more was the first-class letter rate on January 20, 1973, than on January 20, 1963? 3 cents

6. How much was the increase in the first-class letter rate from November 10, 1977, to November 10, 1981? 7 cents

7. What was the total cost of postage for mailing 15 one-ounce letters on July 5, 1971? $1.20

8. After July 5, 1932, a roll of 50 stamps cost $1.50. How much did a similar roll of 50 stamps cost 40 years later? $4.00

9. How much more did it cost to mail a Father's Day card in 1975 than it did in 1915? *Hint: Father's Day is always in June.* 8 cents

10. How much more did it cost to mail 24 Valentine cards in 1980 than it did in 1950? *Hint: Valentine's Day is February 14.* $2.88

SET 4 *(Use after Chapter 4.)*

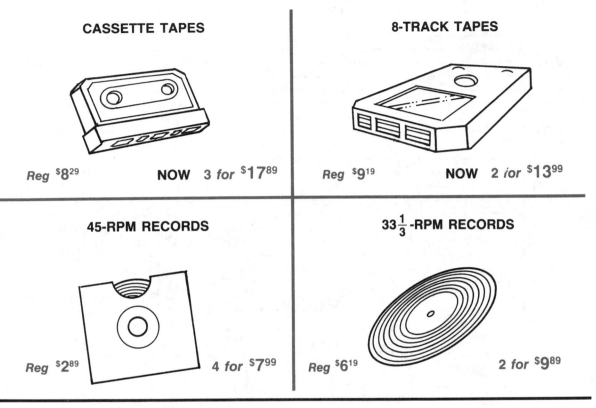

CASSETTE TAPES

Reg $8²⁹   **NOW** 3 *for* $17⁸⁹

8-TRACK TAPES

Reg $9¹⁹   **NOW** 2 *for* $13⁹⁹

45-RPM RECORDS

Reg $2⁸⁹   4 *for* $7⁹⁹

33⅓-RPM RECORDS

Reg $6¹⁹   2 *for* $9⁸⁹

Use the ad to solve these problems.

1. What was the regular price of the cassette tapes? $8.29

2. How many cassette tapes can you buy on sale for about $18?   3

3. How many 33⅓-RPM records can you buy on sale for about $20?   4

4. Is $15 enough money to buy eight 45-RPM records at the sale price?   No

5. Alison spent about $5. She bought one ? on sale.   33⅓-RPM record

6. Greg spent about $7. He bought one ? on sale.   8-track tape

7. Ted spent about $4. He bought two ? on sale.   45-RPM records

8. Mike spent about $12. He bought two ? on sale.   cassette tapes

9. How much would you save if you bought 3 cassette tapes on sale? $6.98

10. Can you save more than $1.50 if you buy four 45-RPM records on sale?   Yes

11. If you pay the sale price, how much would a dozen cassette tapes cost? $71.56

12. How much would you have to pay for two 8-track tapes and four 33⅓-RPM records on sale? $33.77

SET 5 *(Use after Chapter 5.)*

PRICE INCREASES

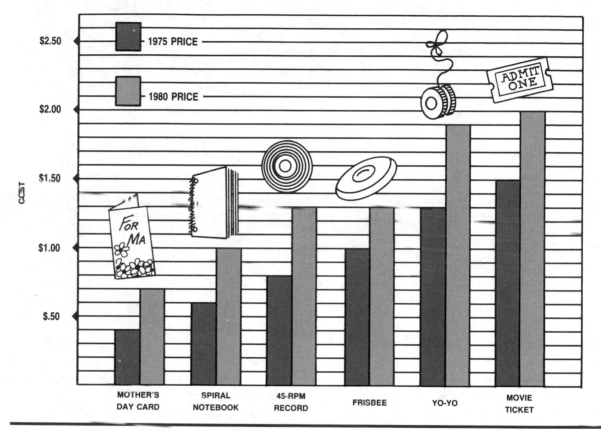

COST

$2.50 — 1975 PRICE

$2.00 — 1980 PRICE

$1.50

$1.00

$.50

MOTHER'S DAY CARD   SPIRAL NOTEBOOK   45-RPM RECORD   FRISBEE   YO-YO   MOVIE TICKET

Use the bar graph to solve these problems.

1. Which of the items cost $.60 in 1975?
   Spiral notebook

2. Which of the items cost $1.90 in 1980?
   Yo-yo

3. What was the cost of a Frisbee in 1975?
   $1.00

4. Which item cost $.60 more in 1980 than it did in 1975? Yo-yo

5. Which items cost $.30 less in 1975 than they did in 1980? Mother's Day card, Frisbee

6. Which had the greater increase in price from 1975 to 1980, a 45 RPM record or a Frisbee? 45-RPM record

7. In which year could you have bought 4 movie tickets for $6.00? 1975

8. In which year could you have paid for 2 yo-yos with a $5 bill and received $1.20 in change? 1980

9. In 1975, would $5.00 have been enough money to buy 3 movie tickets, a 45-RPM record, and a yo-yo? No

10. In which year could you have bought a Frisbee, a 45-RPM record, and a Mother's Day card for $2.20? 1975

SET 6 *(Use after Chapter 6.)*

Here is a schedule for direct-dial telephone rates for calls made from Des Moines, Iowa, to other cities in the United States.

FROM DES MOINES TO	8 A.M.–5 P.M. Monday through Friday		5 P.M.–11 P.M. Sunday through Friday		11 P.M.–8 A.M. Every night 8 A.M.–11 P.M. Saturday 8 A.M.–5 P.M. Sunday	
	First Minute	Each Additional Minute	First Minute	Each Additional Minute	First Minute	Each Additional Minute
Atlanta	**$.66**	**$.46**	**$.42**	**$.30**	**$.26**	**$.19**
Boston	.68	.48	.43	.31	.26	.19
Chicago	.64	.44	.41	.29	.25	.18
Minneapolis	.62	.42	.39	.28	.24	.17
Omaha	.59	.40	.37	.27	.23	.16

Use the rate-schedule information to solve these problems.

1. Sandy called her sister in Atlanta. She called at 3 P.M. on Wednesday. They talked for 5 minutes.

  a. What was the cost for the first minute of their call? $.66

  b. What was the cost for the next 4 minutes? $1.84

  c. What was the total cost of their 5-minute call? $2.50

3. Kari called her brother in Boston. She called at 9 A.M. on Saturday. They talked for 11 minutes. What was the cost? $2.16

5. Mr. Bix called his son in Omaha at 1:30 P.M. on Monday. The charge was $1.79. How many minutes did they talk? 4

2. David called his grandfather in Chicago. He called at 5:45 P.M. on Tuesday. They talked for 8 minutes.

  a. What was the cost for the first minute? $.41

  b. What was the cost for the next 7 minutes? $2.03

  c. What was the total cost? $2.44

4. Robin called her friend in Minneapolis on Sunday. They talked from 9:10 A.M. to 9:17 A.M. What was the cost? $1.26

6. A 20-minute call to Atlanta on a weekday before 5 P.M. costs $9.40. How much money can you save if you wait until after 5 P.M. to make the call? $3.28

SET 7 *(Use after Chapter 7.)*

SAVE TRADING STAMPS
REDEEM STAMPS FOR FREE GIFTS

Pocket Radio $5\frac{1}{2}$ books   Binoculars $9\frac{1}{2}$ books   Calculator $7\frac{1}{4}$ books

Flashlight $2\frac{3}{4}$ books   Spincast Reel $3\frac{1}{4}$ books   Camera 6 books

Use the information in the ad to solve these problems.

1. How many books of trading stamps do you need to get a calculator? $7\frac{1}{4}$

2. Which item can you get for $9\frac{1}{2}$ books of trading stamps? Binoculars

3. How many books of trading stamps do you need to get a Spincast reel and binoculars? $12\frac{3}{4}$

4. Charlene has $3\frac{1}{4}$ books of trading stamps. How many more books does she need to get a pocket radio? $2\frac{1}{4}$

5. If Sidney saves $\frac{1}{4}$ book of stamps each month, how many months will it take him to get a flashlight? 11

6. Randy saved $3\frac{1}{2}$ books of trading stamps and his sister saved $2\frac{1}{4}$ books. How many more books do they need to get a calculator? $1\frac{1}{2}$

7. Gina saved 12 books of trading stamps. Does she have enough stamps to get a Spincast reel, a flashlight, and a pocket radio? Yes

8. If you have $4\frac{1}{4}$ books of trading stamps, how many more books do you need to get a camera? $1\frac{3}{4}$

9. It takes 1600 stamps to fill a trading-stamp book. Ted has 1200 stamps. What fraction of a book has he filled? $\frac{3}{4}$

10. Rita has saved 4000 stamps. How many more stamps does she need to save in order to get a camera? (Remember—It takes 1600 stamps to fill a book.) 5600

TICKET PRICES

Ferris Wheel	$.85
Roller Coaster	.75
Loop-the-Loop	.65
Dizzy Swing	.60

Use the ticket prices to solve these problems.

1. How much would 4 Ferris-wheel tickets cost? $3.40

2. Is $5 enough money to buy 8 roller-coaster tickets? No

3. How much would you spend for 3 loop-the-loop tickets and 2 roller-coaster tickets? $3.45

4. Marcia spent $5.20 on Ferris-wheel tickets and dizzy-swing tickets. She had 3 rides on the dizzy swing. How many rides did she have on the Ferris wheel? 4

5. Wendy bought 5 roller-coaster tickets. She gave the clerk $10. How much change did she get? $6.25

6. Craig has $5. How many loop-the-loop tickets can he buy? 7

7. Dan bought 4 roller-coaster tickets. Melinda bought 5 loop-the-loop tickets. How much more did Melinda pay for her tickets than Dan? $.25

8. Juan had $9. He spent $\frac{1}{3}$ of his money on dizzy-swing tickets. How many dizzy-swing tickets did he buy? 5

9. Anita had $6.80. She spent $\frac{1}{2}$ of her money for Ferris-wheel tickets. How many rides did she have on the Ferris wheel? 4

10. Lenny had $6. He spent $\frac{3}{4}$ of his money on roller-coaster tickets. How many rides did he have on the roller coaster? 6

SET 9 *(Use after Chapter 9.)*

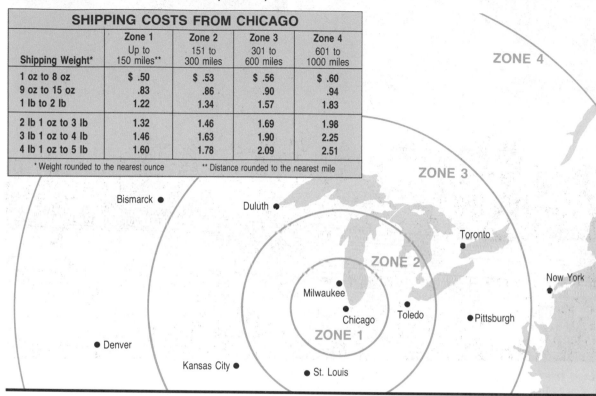

SHIPPING COSTS FROM CHICAGO				
Shipping Weight*	**Zone 1** Up to 150 miles**	**Zone 2** 151 to 300 miles	**Zone 3** 301 to 600 miles	**Zone 4** 601 to 1000 miles
1 oz to 8 oz	$ .50	$ .53	$ .56	$ .60
9 oz to 15 oz	.83	.86	.90	.94
1 lb to 2 lb	1.22	1.34	1.57	1.83
2 lb 1 oz to 3 lb	1.32	1.46	1.69	1.98
3 lb 1 oz to 4 lb	1.46	1.63	1.90	2.25
4 lb 1 oz to 5 lb	1.60	1.78	2.09	2.51

* Weight rounded to the nearest ounce   ** Distance rounded to the nearest mile

Use the map and the shipping information to solve these problems.

1. How much does it cost to ship a 10-ounce package to zone 4? $.94

2. What is the cost to ship a 4-pound package 800 miles? $2.25

3. How much does it cost to ship a 40-ounce package 500 miles? (Remember: 16 ounces = 1 pound.) $1.69

4. How much does it cost to ship a 12-ounce package from Chicago to St. Louis? $.86

5. It cost Cindy $1.90 to ship a $3\frac{1}{2}$-pound package from Chicago to her sister. Does Cindy's sister live in Duluth or Toledo? Duluth

6. How much would it cost Bob to ship a 4-pound 10-ounce package from Chicago to Bismarck? $2.51

7. What is the total cost to ship a 2-pound package and a 1-pound 6-ounce package from Chicago to Milwaukee? $2.44

8. How much more does it cost to ship a 5-pound package from Chicago to New York than from Chicago to Kansas City? $.42

9. Can you ship a 20-ounce package from Chicago to Pittsburgh for less than $1.50? No

10. What is the total cost to ship a 3-pound package from Chicago to Denver and a 4-pound 2-ounce package from Chicago to Toronto? $4.07

SET 10 *(Use after Chapter 10.)*

DRIVING COSTS UP

The average cost of driving a car took an upturn this year, according to a recent study conducted by a national car-rental agency.

Operating costs for compact cars increased from 28.6 cents per mile to 32.7 cents per mile. The costs for mid-size cars increased from 34.6 cents to 38.5 cents per mile, and the costs per mile for full-size cars leaped from 37.3 cents to 43.8 cents.

Use the information in the article to solve these problems.

1. Which size car costs 32.7 cents per mile to operate this year? Compact

2. Which size car costs more than 40 cents per mile to operate? Full-size

3. Which size car had an operating-cost increase of 6.5 cents per mile? Full-size

4. Which size car had an operating-cost increase of 4.1 cents per mile? Compact

5. What was the operating-cost increase for mid-size cars? 3.9 cents per mile

6. According to the study, how much does it cost to drive a compact car 200 miles? $65.40

7. How much does it cost to drive a mid-size car 200 miles? $77.00

8. How much does it cost to drive a full-size car 200 miles? $87.60

9. How much more does it cost to drive a mid-size car on a 400-mile trip this year than last year? $15.60

10. How much money could you save by driving a compact car on a 500-mile trip rather than a full-size car? $55.50

SET 11 *(Use after Chapter 11.)*

SUPER SPECIALS

Telescope

Sale Price
$135.00

Digital Watch

SAVE
$7.77

Now $39.99

Calculator

SALE
$8.80
Reg $10.99

Headphones
25% off
regular price

SALE
PRICE $12.45

Pocket Radio

$33.99
Reg $44.00

Use the information in the ad to solve these problems.

1. What is the regular price of the calculator? $10.99

2. What is the sale price of the pocket radio? $33.99

3. What is the regular price of the digital watch? $47.76

4. Jill bought the telescope at the sale price and saved $19.99. What is the regular price of the telescope? $154.99

5. How much money will you save if you buy the calculator at the sale price instead of the regular price? $2.19

6. How much money can be saved by buying the pocket radio at the sale price? $10.89

7. Greg is paid $3 an hour. How many hours would he need to work to earn enough money to buy a telescope? 45

8. Pepe earns $1.10 an hour baby-sitting and always saves half of his money. How many hours of sitting will it take him to save enough money to buy a calculator? 16

9. Shelly and her two friends bought a pocket radio at the sale price. If they share the cost equally, how much will Shelly pay? $11.33

10. Joel says that the regular price of the headphones was $18.80. Brad said that the regular price was $16.60. Who is correct, Joel or Brad? Brad

SET 12 *(Use after Chapter 12.)*

RENTAL CHARGES		
ITEM	HOURLY RATE	DAILY RATE
Drill	$1.25	$ 8.00
Disk Sander	1.50	9.00
Chain Saw	4.50	25.00
Rug Shampooer	2.50	12.00
Circular Saw	2.75	15.00
Power Rake	3.25	20.00
Metal Detector	1.75	10.00

Use the rental charges to solve these problems.

1. Which item can you rent for $4.50 per hour? Chain saw

2. What is the hourly rate to rent a power rake? $3.25

3. Which item can you rent for $15.00 per day? Circular saw

4. What is the daily rate to rent a disk sander? $9.00

5. What is the cost of renting a drill for 5 hours? $6.25

6. How much does it cost to rent a circular saw for 4 hours? $11.00

7. Ray rented a disk sander and rug shampooer for 3.5 hours. What was the total rental cost? $14.00

8. If you rent a chain saw for 8 hours, how much cheaper is it to pay the daily rate rather than the hourly rate? $11.00

9. Fran rented a metal detector at 10:00 A.M. and returned it at 3:00 P.M. If she paid the hourly rate, what was the rental charge? $8.75

10. Tony rented a rug shampooer for 8 hours. How much did he save by paying the daily rate rather than the hourly rate? $8.00

11. Sonia paid a deposit of $5.00 on a circular saw. How much more did she owe if she returned the saw 3 hours later and was charged at the hourly rate? $3.25

12. Nancy paid a deposit of $10.00 on a power rake. She returned the rake 4 hours later. Based on the hourly rate, how much more did she owe? $3.00

SET 13 (Use after Chapter 13.)

In the scorebook each X represents a field goal made during the game and is worth 2 points.

Each o represents a successful free throw and is worth 1 point.

Each ● represents a missed free throw.

Team East		Team West	
Player	Points	Player	Points
Benson, K.	X O ● ● ● X	Dietz, R.	X X X X ●
Evans, E.	X X ● X X ●	Gibson, C.	X ● O X X
Fuller, M.	● X ●	Hauser, T.	X X X ● ● X O O
Lufkin, J.	X X O	McBride, K.	X ● ● X X O
Patton, R.	X X X ● O	Moody, L.	X U X X ● ● ● ● O
Sneller, S.	X X X X ● ● ● O	Voss, D.	O O X ● ● ●

Use the score-book information to solve these problems.

1. Which player on the East team made 4 field goals and 1 free throw? S. Sneller

2. Which West player scored a total of 9 points? T. Hauser

3. Who was the highest scorer for East? S. Sneller

4. Who was the high scorer for West? T. Hauser

5. How many points did Sneller score? 9

6. How many more points did Dietz score than Gibson? 1

7. Which player made 100% of his free throws? J. Lufkin

8. Which two players for West made 50% of their free throws? C. Gibson, D. Voss

9. How many of the East players made less than 50% of their free throws? 4

10. Benson attempted a total of 8 field goals. What percent of his field goals did he make? 25%

11. Hauser attempted a total of 10 field goals. What percent of his field goals did he make? 40%

12. Which team's players made an average of 3 field goals? West

13. How many points did East score? 36

14. Which team won the game? West

SET 14 (Use after Chapter 14.)

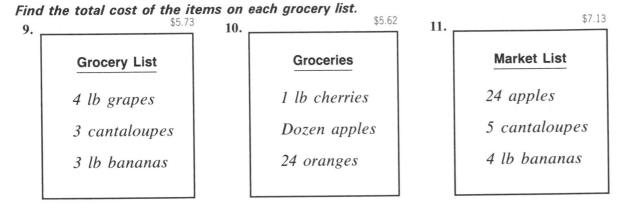

WEEKEND SPECIALS

Bananas	....	$.20/lb
Oranges	....	6 for $.96
Grapes	....	$.69/lb
Cantaloupe	.....	$.79 each
Cherries	....	3 lb / $1.77
Apples	....	$1.19/dozen

Use the grocery ad to solve these problems. Round answers to the nearest cent.

1. What is the cost of 2 pounds of grapes? $1.38

2. What is the cost of 5 cantaloupes? $3.95

3. Can you buy 3 cantaloupes for $2? No

4. How many pounds of bananas can you buy for $1? 5

5. How much would $\frac{1}{2}$ dozen apples cost? $.60

6. What is the cost of a dozen oranges? $1.92

7. If you gave the cashier $5 for 2.5 pounds of grapes, how much change would you get? $3.27

8. If you wanted to buy only 2 pounds of cherries, how much would they cost? *Hint: What is the cost of 1 pound of cherries?* $1.18

Find the total cost of the items on each grocery list.

9. $5.73

Grocery List
4 lb grapes
3 cantaloupes
3 lb bananas

10. $5.62

Groceries
1 lb cherries
Dozen apples
24 oranges

11. $7.13

Market List
24 apples
5 cantaloupes
4 lb bananas

SET 15 *(Use after Chapter 15.)*

NOVELTY ITEMS

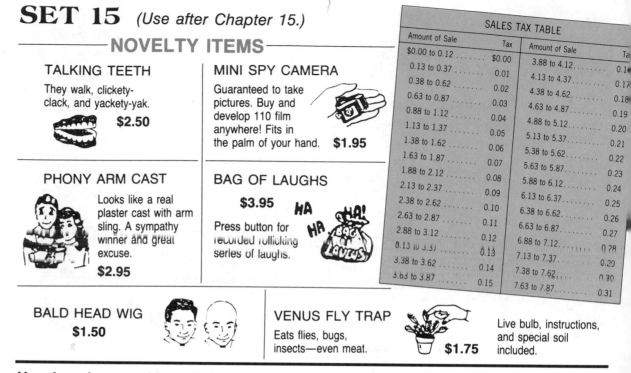

TALKING TEETH

They walk, clickety-clack, and yackety-yak.

$2.50

MINI SPY CAMERA

Guaranteed to take pictures. Buy and develop 110 film anywhere! Fits in the palm of your hand. **$1.95**

PHONY ARM CAST

Looks like a real plaster cast with arm sling. A sympathy winner and great excuse.

$2.95

BAG OF LAUGHS

$3.95

Press button for recorded rollicking series of laughs.

SALES TAX TABLE

Amount of Sale	Tax	Amount of Sale	Tax
$0.00 to 0.12	$0.00	3.88 to 4.12	0.16
0.13 to 0.37	0.01	4.13 to 4.37	0.17
0.38 to 0.62	0.02	4.38 to 4.62	0.18
0.63 to 0.87	0.03	4.63 to 4.87	0.19
0.88 to 1.12	0.04	4.88 to 5.12	0.20
1.13 to 1.37	0.05	5.13 to 5.37	0.21
1.38 to 1.62	0.06	5.38 to 5.62	0.22
1.63 to 1.87	0.07	5.63 to 5.87	0.23
1.88 to 2.12	0.08	5.88 to 6.12	0.24
2.13 to 2.37	0.09	6.13 to 6.37	0.25
2.38 to 2.62	0.10	6.38 to 6.62	0.26
2.63 to 2.87	0.11	6.63 to 6.87	0.27
2.88 to 3.12	0.12	6.88 to 7.12	0.28
3.13 to 3.37	0.13	7.13 to 7.37	0.29
3.38 to 3.62	0.14	7.38 to 7.62	0.30
3.63 to 3.87	0.15	7.63 to 7.87	0.31

BALD HEAD WIG
$1.50

VENUS FLY TRAP

Eats flies, bugs, insects—even meat. **$1.75**

Live bulb, instructions, and special soil included.

Use the sales tax table to find the sales tax on each item.

1. Talking Teeth $.10

2. Mini Spy Camera $.08

3. Phony Arm Cast $.12

4. Bag of Laughs $.16

5. Bald Head Wig $.06

6. Venus Fly Trap $.07

Solve.

7. Scott bought a Phony Arm Cast and a Bag of Laughs.
  a. What was the total cost of the items? $6.90
  b. What was the sales tax on the total? $.28
  c. What was the total cost including the sales tax? $7.18

8. Daphne bought a Mini Spy Camera, a Venus Fly Trap, and Talking Teeth.
  a. What was the total cost of the three items? $6.20
  b. What was the sales tax on the total? $.25
  c. What was the total cost including the sales tax? $6.45

9. What is the total cost, including the sales tax, for a Phony Arm Cast and a Bald Head Wig? $4.63

10. If you have $5.90, do you have enough money to buy a Bag of Laughs and a Venus Fly Trap? *Hint: Don't forget the sales tax.* No

11. Cristy bought two novelty items. The sales tax was $.13. What two items did she buy? Bald head wig, Venus fly trap

12. The sales tax on the two novelty items Brad bought was $.28. What two items did he buy? Phony arm cast, Bag of laughs

SET 16 (Use after Chapter 16.)

DOWNTOWN
PARKING

$1.00 for the first hour
or less

$ .50 for each additional
hour or part of an hour

Use the parking-rate information to solve these problems.

1. How much does it cost to park a car for the first hour? $1.00

2. What is the parking rate for the first two hours? $1.50

3. How much does it cost to park a car for 8 hours? $4.50

4. How much does it cost to park a car from 11:00 A.M. to 4:00 P.M.? $3.00

5. Marty said it would cost $.50 to park a car for one-half hour. Lynn said it would cost $1.00. Who is correct, Marty or Lynn? Lynn

6. Maria parked her car from 1:30 P.M. to 4:15 P.M. How much did she pay for parking? $2.00

7. Mr. Friendly paid $2.50. Did he park his car for more than 3 hours? Yes

8. What is the maximum number of hours that you can park for $6.00? 11

9. Ms. Wilson paid $4.50. Did she park her car for less than 10 hours? Yes

10. Brian parked his car for 12 hours. He gave the parking attendant $10.00. How much change did Brian get? $3.50

11. Mrs. VerMeer gave the attendant $10.00 and got $2.50 in change. How many hours of parking did she pay for? 14

12. Andy, Jan, Phil, and Brian parked their jeep for 7 hours. They shared the parking cost equally. How much was Andy's share of the parking cost? $1.00

SET 17 (Use after Chapter 17.)

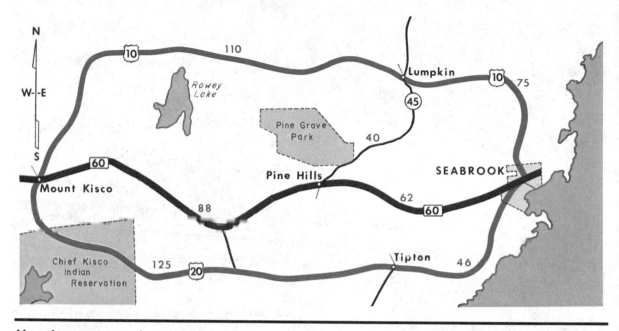

Use the map to solve these problems.

1. Which city is 125 miles from Mount Kisco? Tipton

2. Highway 10 goes through which three cities? Mount Kisco, Lumpkin, Seabrook

3. Which highway from Mount Kisco to Seabrook is 14 miles shorter than Highway 10? Highway 20

4. Sharon drove from Mount Kisco to Seabrook. Before the trip her car's odometer showed 17,685 miles. After the trip the odometer showed 17,856 miles. Which highway did she take? Highway 20

5. How many miles per gallon is a car averaging if it takes 5 gallons of gasoline to drive from Lumpkin to Mount Kisco on Highway 10? 22

6. At a speed of 50 miles per hour, how many hours would it take to get from Tipton to Mount Kisco on Highway 20? $2\frac{1}{2}$

7. How fast (miles per hour) should a driver travel on Highway 10 to get from Lumpkin to Seabrook in 1 hour 30 minutes? 50 miles per hour

8. You are traveling east on Highway 60. How far are you from Pine Hills if you have traveled 50% of the distance from Mount Kisco to Seabrook? 13 miles

9. You are traveling east on Highway 60. Your speed is 50 miles per hour. How many hours is the trip from Mount Kisco to Seabrook? 3

10. If gasoline costs $1.39 per gallon and your car averages 30 miles per gallon, how much will the gasoline cost for your trip on Highway 60 from Mount Kisco to Seabrook? $6.95

GLOSSARY

acute angle An angle that measures between 0° and 90°.

A.M. A symbol used for times after 12:00 midnight and before 12:00 noon.

angle A figure formed by two rays with the same endpoint.

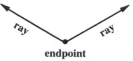

area The number of unit squares that it takes to cover a region.

average The sum of the numbers divided by the number of numbers.

axes Two perpendicular lines used as a reference for graphing ordered pairs.

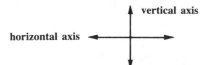

balance The amount of money remaining in an account.

budget A plan for using your money.

Celsius temperature scale (°C) The metric temperature scale, in which 0°C is the freezing point of water and 100°C is the boiling point of water.

centimeter A metric unit of length.
1 centimeter = 0.01 meter.

checking account An account in which money is deposited and held until the bank is told to pay a certain amount by means of a check.

circle A curved plane figure with all points a given distance from the center.

circumference The distance around a circle.

commission The part of the total sales that goes to the salesperson.

common denominator A common denominator for $\frac{1}{2}$ and $\frac{1}{3}$ is 6 because $\frac{1}{2} = \frac{3}{6}$ and $\frac{1}{3} = \frac{2}{6}$. A common denominator is a common multiple of the denominators of two fractions.

common divisor 2 is a common divisor of 4 and 6 because it is a divisor of both 4 and 6.

common multiple 30 is a common multiple of 5 and 6 because it is a multiple of both 5 and 6.

compound interest Interest that is added to the principal at regular intervals. This makes the principal grow and earn more and more interest.

computer language A set of symbols and terms used to tell a computer what to do.

computer program A list of instructions to a computer telling it what to do and when to do it.

cone A space figure with one flat face (known as the base) that is a circle and with one other face that is curved.

corresponding sides Sides of similar figures that are proportional.

cross products The cross products for the ratios below are 2×10 and 5×4. Two ratios are equal if their cross products are equal.

$$\frac{2}{5} = \frac{4}{10} \text{ because } 2 \times 10 = 5 \times 4$$

cube A rectangular prism whose six faces are squares.

Customary System The system of measurement that uses foot, quart, pound, and Fahrenheit temperature.

cylinder A space figure that has two circular bases that are the same size and are in parallel planes. It has one curved face.

data Pieces of information.

decimal A number such as 3.86 or 0.4 that is written using a decimal point and place value.

decimeter A metric unit of length.
    1 decimeter = 0.1 meter.

deductions The amount of money withheld from a person's pay.

degree A unit for measuring angles. This is a 1° (1-degree) angle.

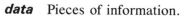

dekameter A metric unit of length.
    1 dekameter = 10 meters.

denominator In the fraction $\frac{2}{3}$, the denominator is 3.

deposit A sum of money put into a checking or savings account.

diameter The distance across a circle through its center. The length of the diameter is twice the length of the radius.

difference The answer to a subtraction problem.

digits The basic symbols used to write numerals. In our system, the digits are 0, 1, 2, 3, 4, 5, 6, 7, 8, and 9.

discount An amount subtracted from the regular price of an item.

dividend The number that is divided.

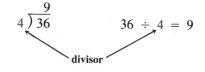

divisor The number that one divides by.

$$4 \overline{)\ 36}^{\ 9} \qquad 36 \div 4 = 9$$
    divisor

down payment The first amount paid when buying on an installment plan.

equal ratios Ratios that indicate the same rate or comparison. The cross product of equal ratios are equal.

equation A sentence with an equal sign such as $3 \times 9 = 27$ or $8 + x = 10$.

equivalent fractions Fractions that name the same number. $\frac{1}{2}$, $\frac{2}{4}$, and $\frac{3}{6}$ are equivalent fractions.

estimate To use rounded numbers to check whether an answer is correct. To estimate $47 + 32$, you would add $50 + 30$. The sum should be about 80.

462

evaluate an expression To replace a variable in an expression with one of its values and then complete the indicated arithmetic.

even number Zero and multiples of 2.

expectation The probability of winning times the value of the prize.

Fahrenheit temperature scale (°F) The customary temperature scale, in which 32°F is the freezing point of water, and 212°F is the boiling point of water.

finance charge Buying an item on an installment plan costs more than paying cash. The difference is called the finance charge.

formula A general way of expressing a relationship using symbols.

$A = l \times w$

fraction A numeral for part of a group or for part of a region. $\frac{1}{2}$, $\frac{4}{6}$, and $\frac{6}{5}$ are fractions.

frequency table A table showing the number of times different events or responses occur.

gram A metric unit of weight (mass).
1 gram = 0.001 kilogram.

graph A picture used to show numerical information. It can be a bar graph, a picture graph, a circle graph, or a line graph.

greatest common divisor The greatest number that is a divisor of each of two or more numbers.

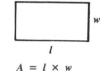

4 is the greatest common divisor of 8 and 12.

gross pay Total pay before deductions.

hectometer A metric unit of length.
1 hectometer = 100 meters.

hexagon A polygon with six sides.

indirect measurement A measurement that is computed from other measurements rather than measured directly.

installment plan A way of buying expensive items. You pay part of the cost (the down payment) when you get the item and then agree to pay a certain amount each month for a certain number of months.

integers The numbers . . . , $^-5$, $^-4$, $^-3$, $^-2$, $^-1$, 0, $^+1$, $^+2$, $^+3$, $^+4$, $^+5$, . . .

interest The amount a borrower pays for using the money.

intersecting lines Lines that meet at only one point.

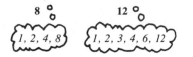

invert To reverse in position. When $\frac{3}{4}$ is inverted, you get $\frac{4}{3}$.

kilogram A metric unit of weight.
1 kilogram = 1000 grams.

kilometer A metric unit of length.
1 kilometer = 1000 meters.

least common denominator The least (smallest) common multiple of two or more numbers. The least common multiple of 6 and 15 is 30.

liter A metric unit of liquid volume.

loan Money that is borrowed for a fixed period of time at a set rate of interest.

long word-name The name for a standard numeral written in words. The long word-name for 6,100,087 is six million, one hundred thousand, eighty-seven.

lower terms To write a fraction in lower terms, divide the numerator and denominator by a common divisor.

lowest terms A fraction is in lowest terms if the greatest common factor of the numerator and denominator is 1.

mainframe computer A large machine costing several hundred thousand dollars. It requires a large staff of operators and programmers. It must be kept in a specially constructed building.

mass The measure of the quantity of matter an object contains.

mean The average of all the numbers.

median If there is an odd number of numbers, the median is the number in the middle. If there is an even number of numbers, the median is the average of the two numbers in the middle.

memory A computer device capable of storing information temporarily or permanently.

meter A metric unit of length.
   1 meter = 100 centimeters.

metric system An international system of measurement that uses meter, liter, gram, and Celsius temperature.

milligram A metric unit of weight (mass).
   1 milligram = 0.001 gram.

milliliter A metric unit of liquid volume.
   1 milliliter = 0.001 liter.

millimeter A metric unit of length.
   1 millimeter = 0.001 meter.

mixed number A number that has a whole-number part and a fraction part. $2\frac{3}{4}$ is a mixed number.

mode The number that occurs most often.

multiple A product. 4, 8, 12, 16, 20, and so on, are multiples of 4.

negative number A number that is less than 0.

net pay Pay after deductions; "take-home" pay.

numerator In the fraction $\frac{2}{3}$, the numerator is 2.

obtuse angle An angle that measures between 90° and 180°.

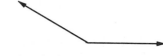

odd number A whole number that is not divisible by 2. The numbers 1, 3, 5, 7, 9, 11, and so on, are odd.

odds The ratio of the number of ways that an outcome can occur to the number of ways that the outcome cannot occur

operation Addition, subtraction, multiplication, and division are examples of operations.

opposites Two numbers are opposites if their sum is 0.

$$^-3 + {}^+3 = 0$$

opposites

ordered pair A pair of numbers that give the location of a point on a grid.

origin The point where axes intersect.

outcome   A possible result.

parallel lines   Lines in a plane that do not intersect.

parallelogram   A polygon with four sides and two pairs of parallel sides.

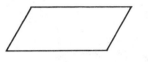

passbook   A book issued by a bank when a person opens a savings account. It is used by the bank to record deposits, withdrawals, and interest.

pentagon   A polygon with five sides.

percent (%)   *Percent* means "per hundred." 5% (5 percent) equals $\frac{5}{100}$.

perimeter   The distance around a figure; the sum of the lengths of the sides.

The perimeter is 9 cm.

permutation   An arrangement of things in a definite order.

perpendicular lines   Two lines that intersect to form right angles.

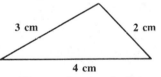

pi   The number that is the ratio of the circumference of a circle to its diameter. It is represented by the Greek letter π and is approximately equal to 3.14.

P.M.   A symbol used for times after 12:00 noon and before 12:00 midnight.

polygon   A closed plane figure made up of segments.

polygons   not polygons

positive number   A number greater than 0.

principal   An amount of money borrowed.

prism   A space figure that has two bases that are the same size and shape and are in parallel planes. The other faces are all rectangles.

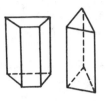

probability   The ratio of the number of favorable outcomes to the total number of outcomes.

probability of picking black $= \frac{3}{5}$

product   The answer to a multiplication problem.

proportion   An equation stating that two ratios are equal.

$$\frac{5}{8} = \frac{30}{48}$$

protractor   An instrument used to measure angles.

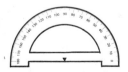

pyramid   A solid figure with a face (known as the base) that is any polygon and with all other faces, which are triangles, sharing a common vertex.

← common vertex

quadrant The regions into which the plane is separated by the horizontal and vertical axes.

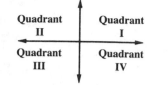

quotient The answer to a division problem.

radius The distance from the center of a circle to the circle. The radius is equal to one half the diameter.

range The difference between the least and greatest numbers.

rate A comparison by division of two quantities.

$$\frac{87 \text{ kilometers}}{2 \text{ hours}}$$

ratio A comparison of two quantities by division. Below, the ratio of squares to circles is 4 to 2, 4:2, or $\frac{4}{2}$.

reciprocal Two numbers are reciprocals when their product is 1.

$$\frac{3}{4} \times \frac{4}{3} = 1$$

reciprocals

rectangle A polygon with four sides and four right angles.

rectangular prism A prism whose six faces are rectangles.

regular price The price of an item before a discount is subtracted.

remainder In a division problem, the number that is "left over." When it is added to the product of the divisor and quotient, the sum is the dividend.

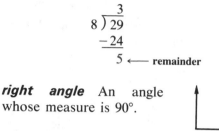

right angle An angle whose measure is 90°.

round a number To replace a number by another one that is easier to use. You round a number to the nearest ten by choosing the nearest multiple of 10. (5 is rounded up.)

$$13 \rightarrow 10 \qquad 27 \rightarrow 30 \qquad 45 \rightarrow 50$$

You round a number to the nearest hundred by choosing the nearest multiple of 100.

$$487 \rightarrow 500 \qquad 1238 \rightarrow 1200 \qquad 550 \rightarrow 600$$

salary Wages paid on a regular basis.

sale price The price of an item after a discount is subtracted.

sample space The set of all possible outcomes of an event.

savings account A bank account in which money is deposited or withdrawn. The money earns interest.

scale drawing A drawing of an object such that the ratio of a unit of length on the drawing to a unit of length on the object is fixed.

segment A part of a line that has two endpoints.

short word-name   The name for a standard numeral written using both words and numerals. The short word name for 6,100,087 is 6 million, 100 thousand, 87.

side of an angle   One of the rays that make up an angle.

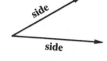

side of a plane figure   One of the segments that make up a figure.

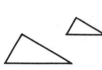

similar figures   Two figures that have the same shape.

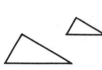

simple interest   Interest that is computed by using the formula $I = prt$, where p is principal, r is rate, and t is time.

simplest form   A fraction or mixed number is in simplest form if the fraction or fraction-part of the mixed number is less than 1 and in lowest terms.

software   Computer programs.

solution   A number that makes an equation true.

solve   To find all the numbers that make an equation true.

sphere   A round space figure shaped like a basketball. All points on a sphere are the same distance from the center.

square   A polygon with 4 sides the same length and 4 right angles.

standard numeral   The standard numeral for 3 billion, 24 million, 65 is 3,024,000,065.

statistics   A branch of mathematics that studies numerical facts as a basis for drawing general conclusions and making predictions.

substitute   To replace a variable with a numeral.

$$7a + 3$$
$$7 \cdot 6 + 3$$

sum   The answer to an addition problem.

surface area   The sum of the areas of all the surfaces of a solid figure.

trapezoid   A polygon with 4 sides and exactly 1 pair of parallel sides.

tree diagram   A diagram that shows all the possible outcomes of an event.

triangle   A polygon with three sides.

triangular prism   A prism with two triangular faces in parallel planes.

unit price   The cost per unit (weight, volume, etc.) of an item.

variable   A symbol—usually a letter—that holds the place for a number.

$$8x + 19 = 23$$

volume   The amount that a space figure holds.

whole number   Any of the numbers 0, 1, 2, 3, 4, and so on.

withdrawal   A sum of money taken out of a checking or savings account.

withholdings   An amount deducted from a person's pay for the payment of taxes.

SYMBOLS

<	is less than	$a{:}b$	the ratio of a to b
>	is greater than	%	percent
=	is equal to	°	degree
≠	is not equal to	π	pi
≈	is approximately equal to	P(2)	the probability of the outcome 2
'	foot/feet	$^{+}5$	positive 5
"	inch/inches	$^{-}5$	negative 5

FORMULAS

Perimeter of a square	$P = 4 \times s$
Perimeter of a rectangle	$P = 2 \times (l + w)$
Circumference of a circle	$C = \pi \times d$
Area of a rectangle	$A = l \times w$
Area of a square	$A = s \times s$
Area of a parallelogram	$A = b \times h$
Area of a triangle	$A = \frac{1}{2} \times b \times h$
Area of a circle	$A = \pi \times r \times r$
Volume of a prism	$V = B \times h$
Volume of a rectangular prism	$V = l \times w \times h$
Volume of a cylinder	$V = (\pi \times r \times r) \times h$
Volume of a pyramid	$V = \frac{1}{3} \times B \times h$
Volume of a cone	$V = \frac{1}{3} \times (\pi \times r \times r) \times h$
Interest	$I = p \times r \times t$

INDEX

472

2 3 4 5 6 7 8 9 0